Edgar M Williams
Mar. 1993

Integrated Continuous-Time Filters

Integrated Continuous-Time Filters
Principles, Design, and Applications

Edited by

Y. P. Tsividis
National Technical University of Athens

J. O. Voorman
Philips Research Laboratories

A Selected Reprint Volume
IEEE Circuits and Systems Society, *Sponsor*

The Institute of Electrical and Electronics Engineers, Inc., New York

This book may be purchased at a discount from the publisher when ordered in bulk quantities. For more information contact:

IEEE PRESS Marketing
Attn: Special Sales
PO Box 1331
445 Hoes Lane
Piscataway, NJ 08855-1331
Fax: (908) 981-8062

Printed in the United States of America

10 9 8 7 6 5 4 3 2 1

ISBN 0-7803-0425-X

IEEE Order Number: PC0321-0

Library of Congress Cataloging-in-Publication Data

Integrated continuous-time filters / [edited by] Yannis P. Tsividis, J. O. Voorman.
    p.   cm.
    Includes bibliographical references and index.
    ISBN 0-7803-0425-X
    1 Electric filters. I. Tsividis, Yannis. II. Voorman, J. O.
TK7872.F5I55 1993
621.3815'324—dc20
                                                          92-53216
                                                            CIP

Contents

Preface

AMONG several electronic filter types, continuous-time filters were the first to be invented and the last to be established in integrated form on a massive scale. Thus, we saw digital and switched-capacitor filters (both discrete-time types) develop and mature in integrated form, while researchers attempting to place continuous-time filters on chips were still tackling severe issues related to precision, noise, and signal swing. Nevertheless, today integrated continuous-time filters are a reality, having finally reached the stage of commercial exploitation in such products as TVs, VCRs, disk drive electronics, line equalizers for computer networks, and telephony circuits, to name a few. The recent excitement in industry and academia about this form of integrated filters prompted us to assemble this volume.

This volume is one of three on continuous-time filters published by IEEE Press, with one volume appearing about every ten years. The first volume, *Active Inductorless Filters*, edited by S. K. Mitra in 1971, and the second, *Modern Active Filter Design*, edited by R. Schaumann, M. A. Soderstrand, and K. R. Laker in 1981, dealt almost exclusively with "active" filters assembled from discrete components. A large amount of work, which took place mostly since the publication of the second volume, led to the successful integration of continuous-time filters and their incorporation into large integrated systems implemented in VLSI technology. The present volume puts together key papers describing such work.

In light of the numerous high-quality papers on many aspects of integrated continuous-time filters, we had to make choices. To provide a concise volume, we decided to focus on papers that emphasize real integrated implementations of complete filters. Thus, with the exception of some studies on automatic tuning, practically every paper in this volume reports on results from fabricated chips. The very few exceptions are papers that complete or expand on material of other companion papers that do report on chips. Our emphasis on complete filter chip implementation meant that two categories of valuable papers had to be excluded: those dealing with network-theoretic aspects and those dealing with the design of active elements (operational amplifiers and transconductors). Nevertheless, several issues from these two excluded categories are considered both in the papers we did include, and, of course, in the references.

Even among the papers reporting on real chips, the selection was difficult. We tried to include papers that describe time-enduring or promising techniques, or at least contain considerations of value to the design of successful chips. We tried to have all major filter types represented. Still, not every high-quality paper that met the above criteria could be included because of space limitations, IEEE Press editorial policy, visual appearance, reviewers' suggestions, and the need of these editors to compromise with each other. We apologize to our colleagues whose good work could not be included.

This volume contains 64 papers and is divided into seven parts. Part 1 is an overview of the field and includes original material unique to this volume. Part 2 deals with integrated filters most closely resembling classic active filters, namely MOSFET-C circuits that use operational amplifiers, capacitors, and MOS transistors implementing resistors. Original material is also included in Part 2. Parts 3 and 4 concentrate on filters using transconductors instead of resistors. The filters described in Part 3 use only transconductors and capacitors, while those in Part 4 use operational amplifiers in addition. In Part 5 we have included papers reporting on several other types of integrated filters, namely active R, distributed, NIC, and true active RC and passive filters which can, in some cases, be advantageously integrated. Part 6 is devoted to the study of on-chip automatic tuning of filters and to the related subject of adaptivity; it augments on related discussions in many of the papers elsewhere in the volume. Finally, the use of integrated filters is illustrated in Part 7, which contains papers on representative applications and application studies, including an original paper. In all, over 15% of the pages contain original material written specifically for this volume and not published elsewhere.

We hope this book will be useful as a reference for practicing engineers and researchers and as material accompanying industrial courses on the subject. It can also serve as a companion book for senior-year and graduate courses, supplementing a main text on discrete-component filter design. We hope the volume will be a good starting point for newcomers, some of whom will eventually make further advances in this exciting field.

We want to thank A. van Bezooijen, N. Ramalho, R. Schaumann, G. J. Smolka, U. Riedle, U. Greje, B. Jahn, F. Parzefall, W. Veit, and H. Werker, who wrote original material for this volume and V. Gopinathan, J. Khoury, D. Rich, R. Schaumann, E. Seevinck, K.-S. Tan, and G. Temes for their valuable comments on the original material and on the proposed list of publications and book format. We also want to thank IEEE Press Executive Editor Dudley Kay who, through all communication channels known to man (mostly electronic mail), kept after us and helped us produce what we hope is a concise, focused and useful book.

Y. Tsividis
J. Voorman

Part 1
Overview

THIS part is an overview of integrated continuous-time filters. The tutorial paper by Schaumann was written specifically for this volume, and will probably be especially appreciated by newcomers; it explains why integrated continuous-time filters are needed and how they are designed, gives examples of various types of such filters, and discusses their tuning by automatic means. The next paper, by Voorman, discusses the same issues at a more advanced level and in much more detail. It also has been written specifically for this volume, and includes original material. Although this is the longest paper in the volume, it is nevertheless dense because of the large amount of information it contains. Hence it may not be easy reading for newcomers, who may want to defer reading it until they have read other papers in the volume; this paper can then really help put things together, in addition to providing much extra information. Useful general introductions to integrated continuous-time filters can also be found in the beginning of other, more specialized papers in this volume.

Although the overview papers in this part summarize relevant topics from classical filter theory and design, much more detailed discussions can be found in textbooks (see, for example, [1–4]). An in-depth review of classical results on active filters, covering the period up to the early 1970s, can be found elsewhere [5]; many of these results are, or may become in the future, relevant in the context of fully integrated filters.

References

[1] G. C. Temes and J. W. LaPatra, *Introduction to Circuit Synthesis and Design*, New York: McGraw-Hill, 1977.

[2] A. S. Sedra and P. O. Brackett, *Filter Theory and Design*: *Active and Passive*, Chesterfield, Ohio: Weber Systems Inc., 1978.

[3] R. R. Schaumann, M. Ghausi, and K. R. Laker, *Design of Analog Filters*, Englewood Cliffs, NJ: Prentice-Hall, 1990.

[4] M. Herpy and J.C. Berka, *Active RC Filter Design*, Amsterdam: Elsevier, 1986.

[5] W. E. Heinlein and W. H. Holmes, *Active Filters for Integrated Circuits*: *Fundamentals and Design Methods*, New York: Springer-Verlag, 1974.

Continuous-Time Integrated Filters—
A Tutorial[1]

ROLF SCHAUMANN

DEPARTMENT OF ELECTRICAL ENGINEERING

PORTLAND STATE UNIVERSITY

P.O. BOX 751, PORTLAND, OR 97207-0751, USA

Abstract—This paper summarizes the fundamental concepts and methods used for designing continuous-time (CT) signal-processing circuits (i.e., filters) in fully integrated form. The resulting filter structures can be integrated together with other parts of the system on the same chip and are compatible with any desired IC technology. The two main design procedures are the promising MOSFET-C approach that is closely based on classical active *RC* concepts, and the currently dominant transconductance-C method, which uses only capacitors and transconductors for the implementation of monolithic CT filters. The critically important problem of automatic tuning against fabrication tolerances and component drifts during operation is discussed in detail.

1. INTRODUCTION

ALL modern communication systems and most measuring equipment contain various types of electrical filters that the designer has to realize in an appropriate technology. In general, a filter is a two-port circuit designed to process the magnitude and/or phase of an input signal in some prescribed way in order to generate a desired output signal. For example, the filter may transmit (pass) the desired frequency components in the spectrum of an input signal with little or no change, and reject (stop) the remaining components interfering with the signal processing task at hand. In this sense, *passbands* (PB) and *stopbands* (SB) can be defined as illustrated in Fig. 1 for a lowpass and a bandpass characteristic. The literature contains many well-defined techniques and computer programs to help the designer find the appropriate transfer function that a filter must realize to satisfy the required behavior [2–6].

Once the filter's transfer function is obtained, implementation methods must be found that are compatible with the technology selected for the design of the total system. In some situations, dictated by such factors as power consumption, frequency range, signal level, or production numbers, discrete (passive or active) filter realizations may be the appropriate choice. In many circumstances, however, the goal will be to realize as much as possible of the total system, fully integrated in microelectronic form, so that naturally the question arises whether the filters can be implemented in the same technology.

In many signal processing situations, filters must interface with the real world where the input and output signals take on continuous values as functions of the continuous variable time; that is, they are *continuous-time* (CT) signals. Because it is the performance of the total system that is relevant and not just that of the intrinsic filter, the designer may have to consider whether it might not be preferable to implement the entire system in the CT domain rather than as a digital or sampled-data system. Although at least at low frequencies, the latter methods have the advantages of being able to attain very high accuracy and little or no parameter drifts, they entail a number of peripheral problems connected with analog-to-digital (A/D) and digital-to-analog (D/A) conversion, sample-and-hold, switching, antialiasing, and reconstruction circuitry. For the implementation of digital and sampled-data switched-capacitor filters, the reader is urged to consult the literature [6–12]. In this paper, only

---

[1] The paper is a revised and updated version of [1] and was written especially for this volume.

Reprinted from *IEE Proceedings,* vol. 136, Pt. G, pp. 184–190, Aug. 1989.

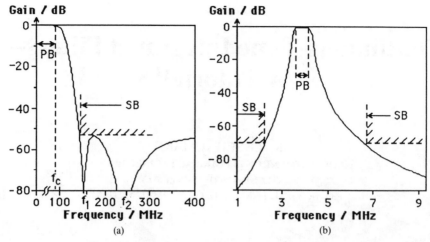

Fig. 1. (a) fifth-order elliptic lowpass and (b) eight-order Chebyshev bandpass characteristics.

those cases are considered where the signals must be CT in nature.

2. IMPLEMENTATION METHODS

Traditionally, the implementation of CT filters has relied on discrete designs. Well-defined procedures exist for deriving passive *LC* networks or active *RC* circuits from a given transfer function [2, 3, 6]. If, however, a microelectronic realization with full integration is the goal, inductors usually are not used because there is no practical method for realizing high-quality inductors on an integrated circuit (IC) chip. Thus, to realize the required complex natural frequencies, the designer of an IC filter is forced to use active devices. As is well known, active filters can realize complex poles by using gain, for example, an operational amplifier (op amp) or an operational transconductance amplifier (OTA) embedded in an *RC* feedback network [2, 3, 6, 13–18].

Consider, for example, a fully differential transconductor whose simplified model[2] and the circuit symbol employed in this paper are shown in Fig.

2. Many realizations of such cells exist in CMOS [9, 18, 19–24, 26, 27, 29, 35–37, 48, 49, 57, 59], bipolar, or in BiCMOS technologies, and even in GaAs [20–38, 47, 51]. Because op amps and OTAs are electronic circuits, it becomes apparent that the problem of monolithic filter design is solved in principle—all active devices and any necessary capacitors and resistors can be integrated together on one silicon chip. Although this conclusion is correct, three other factors that are peculiar to integrated CT filters and perhaps are not immediately obvious must be addressed. The first concerns probably the most formidable obstacle to achieving commercially practical designs—integrated filters must be *electronically tunable* [6, 39]. Because of its importance, this topic is discussed separately elsewhere in this paper. The second factor deals with the economics of practical implementations of active filters—in discrete designs, the cost of acquiring and stocking components usually necessitate designing the filter with a minimum number of active devices, such as one or possibly two op amps per pole pair, and using the smallest number of different (if possible, all identical) capacitors. In integrated realizations, capacitors are determined by processing mask dimensions and the number of different capacitor values is unimportant as long as the spread is not excessive. Furthermore, active devices frequently occupy less chip area than passive elements so it is often preferable to use active elements. In particular, for the problem at hand (i.e., integrated CT filters), frequency parameters are set by *RC* products or, equivalently, by C/g_m ratios [see Equation (2a)] and

[2] The linear OTA model in Fig. 2(a) is valid for signals in the linear range of the respective electronic implementation. The model also shows the dominant parasitics, the input and output capacitors, and conductors c_i, g_i, and c_o, g_o, respectively. Although their effects and those of transconductance phase errors, modeled as $g_m(j\omega)e^{j\Phi(\omega)}$ [6, 19, 20, 38] are neglected in this tutorial paper, the designer is well advised to investigate their effects carefully when designing monolithic filters at high frequencies and with large quality factors, Q_i. The most troublesome effects are that phase errors tend to increase Q_i above the design values, whereas g_i and g_o cause Q_i to decrease.

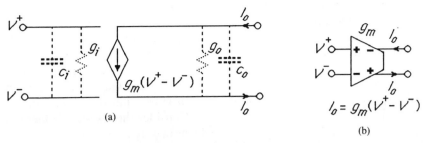

Fig. 2. Fully differential transconductor. (a) Small-signal model with the main parasitic components shown in dashed form; (b) circuit symbol.

the dimensionless quality factors are determined by ratios of like components [see Equation (2b)]. Also, as was pointed out earlier, gain is needed to realize complex poles. Recalling further that the function of resistance can be obtained from transconductors[3] leads to the important conclusion that capacitors and transconductors $(C - g_m)$ form a minimal irreducible set of elements necessary for the realization of integrated CT filters. Finally, the third factor pertains to the fact that filters usually have to share an integrated circuit with other, possibly switched or digital systems, so that the AC ground lines (power supply and ground wires) are likely to contain switching transients and are generally noisy. Measuring the analog signals relative to AC ground, therefore, results in designs with poor signal-to-noise ratio and low power supply rejection. The situation is remedied in practice by building the continuous-time filter in fully differential, balanced form where the signals are referred to each other as $V = V^+ - V^-$ as shown in Fig. 2. An additional advantage of this arrangement is that the signal range is doubled (for an added 6 dB of signal-to-noise ratio) and that the even-order harmonics of the in principle nonlin-

ear operation of the transconductors cancel. The examples in this paper are, therefore, drawn as fully differential designs.

The transconductor model and the symbol in Fig. 2 are used in the circuit in Fig. 3. By writing node equations at the nodes labeled V_{LP} and V_{BP} and observing that the left transconductor g_{m2} implements a resistor of value $1/g_{m2}$, the reader can verify that the circuit realizes the second-order bandpass and lowpass functions.

$$H_{BP}(s) = \frac{V_{BP}}{V_i}$$
$$= \frac{sC_2 g_{m1}}{C_1 C_2 s^2 + s C_2 g_{m2} + g_{m1} g_{m2}}$$
$$= \frac{sM\omega_o/Q_o}{s^2 + s\omega_o/Q_o + \omega_o^2} \quad (1a)$$

$$H_{LP}(s) = \frac{V_{LP}}{V_i}$$
$$= \frac{g_{m1} g_{m2}}{C_1 C_2 s^2 + s C_2 g_{m2} + g_{m1} g_{m2}}$$
$$= \frac{\omega_o^2}{s^2 + s\omega_o/Q_o + \omega_o^2} \quad (1b)$$

[3] Note that an inverting transconductor g_m with its output connected to its input simulates a grounded resistor of value $1/g_m$. See the left OTA g_{m2} in Fig. 3.

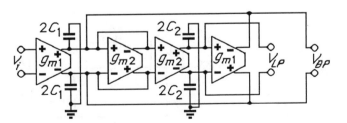

Fig. 3. Second-order active $g_m - C$ filter with lowpass and bandpass outputs.

The right hand sides of Equation (1) were written in a form that shows explicitly the relevant filter parameters: the midband gain M of the bandpass, the pole frequency ω_o, and the pole quality factor Q_o. In particular,

$$\omega_o = \sqrt{\frac{g_{m1}g_{m2}}{C_1C_2}} \qquad (2a)$$

and

$$Q_o = \sqrt{\frac{g_{m1}C_1}{g_{m2}C_2}} \qquad (2b)$$

so that, evidently, the functions can have complex poles provided that the coefficient $C_2 g_{m2}$ is less than $4C_1 g_{m1}$ or, using the more common nomenclature [2, 3, 6], provided that Q_o is larger than $\frac{1}{2}$. By connecting four such circuits in cascade to obtain the product of four functions of the form of Equation (1a), the designer can implement the eighth-order Chebyshev bandpass function required for the specifications in Fig. 1(b) without the use of inductors and, it is pointed out, without using resistors but only grounded capacitors and transconductors.

The structure in Fig. 3 is one of many possible $g_m - C$ circuits [6] that can realize a second-order transfer function, specifically, two conjugate complex poles. Generally, for any given topology, the user can implement an arbitrary first- or second-order numerator polynomial (i.e., arbitrary transmission zeros) without destroying the poles by feeding the input signal voltage V_i forward into any node(s) lifted off ground (see [47] for an example) and/or by feeding a current proportional to V_i into any floating node(s). The resulting second-order or biquadratic sections are then connected in cascade to realize the desired high-order transfer function. Detailed discussions of this approach, along with experimental results, can be found in [43, 47, 60]. Apart from its modularity, the main advantage of the cascade approach is its generality: a cascade structure can realize a transfer function with arbitrary zero locations, whereas the simulations of lossless LC ladders discussed next are restricted to $j\omega$ – axis transmission zeros. The main reason for using ladder simulations is the generally lower sensitivity to component tolerances of this topology [2, 3, 6].

The popular ladder simulation method for filter design is best illustrated with the help of an example. Consider the classical ladder structure in Fig. 4, which can realize the fifth-order elliptic lowpass characteristic of the form

$$H_{ell}(s) = \frac{(s^2 + \omega_1^2)(s^2 + \omega_2^2)}{(s + a)(s^2 + bs + c)(s^2 + ds + e)}$$

A plot of such a function is shown in Fig. 1(a). The two transmission zeros f_1 and f_2 in Fig. 1(a) are obtained when L_4, C_4, and L_2, C_2, respectively, resonate. Two methods are available to simulate the ladder. The first and most intuitive method replaces the inductors L_2 and L_4 by capacitively loaded gyrators[4] [2, 3, 6] as is shown in Fig. 5(a). (The two transconductors in the dashed box form a gyrator.) Note that all transconductors are identical and that all capacitors except C_2 and C_4 could be grounded; for example, instead of connecting $C_1/2$ between nodes A and B in Fig. 5(a), a capacitor of value C_1 could be connected from both nodes A and B to ground. This approach was taken in Fig. 5(b), which is an illustration of the operational simulation to be described next.

The second method recognizes that the inductors and the grounded capacitors in Fig. 4 perform the function of integration. Note that the operation of the circuit Fig. 4 is described by

$$I_1 = \frac{V_i - V_1}{R} \qquad I_{L2} = \frac{V_1 - V_3}{sL_2} \qquad I_{L4} = \frac{V_3 - V_5}{sL_4}$$

$$(3a)$$

[4] A gyrator is a two-port circuit whose input impedance is inversely proportional to the load impedance: $Z_{in} = r^2/Z_{load}$; if $Z_{load} = 1/(sC)$, $Z_{in} = sr^2C$ realizes an inductor of value $L = r^2C$; for the $g_m - C$ circuits of concern here one obtains $L = C/g_m^2$. Because the inductors in Fig. 4 are floating, two gyrators are needed to realize each inductor.

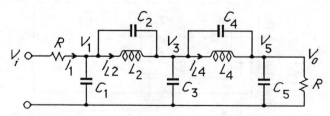

Fig. 4. Fifth-order elliptic LC lowpass filter.

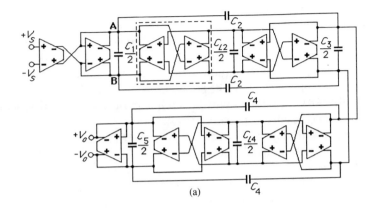

(a)

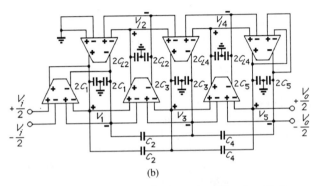

(b)

Fig. 5. Transconductor-C realizations of a fifth-order elliptic lowpass function. The circuits are active simulations of the LC-ladder in Fig. 4, including source and load resistors [6, 18, 29, 33, 38]. All g_m-cells are identical. (a) Ladder simulation by the element replacement method. Note that the floating inductors require two gyrators for implementation. (b) Operational simulation by the signal-flow graph method.

$$V_1 = \frac{I_1 - [I_{L2} + sC_2(V_1 - V_3)]}{sC_1} \quad (3b)$$

$$V_3 = \frac{I_{L2} - I_{L4} + sC_2(V_1 - V_3) - sC_4(V_3 - V_5)]}{sC_3}$$

$$(3c)$$

$$V_5 = V_o = \frac{I_{L4} + sC_4(V_3 - V_5)}{sC_5 + 1/R} \quad (3d)$$

and that $1/s$ corresponds to integration in the Laplace domain. The currents through C_2 and C_4 are realized directly by connecting these capacitors to the corresponding nodes. An integrator is implemented simply by loading a transconductor with a capacitor C to realize ideally[5]

$$V_{\text{out}} = \frac{g_m}{sC} V_{\text{in}} \quad (4)$$

Evidently, V_{out} is the integral of V_{in}, with an integration time constant given by C/g_m. Going through Equations (3) of the LC circuit of Fig. 4 step-by-step and implementing them by lossless or lossy integrators results in the configuration in Fig. 5(b). Note that in both realizations in Fig. 5, the OTA at the input performs a voltage-to-current conversion (V_i to I_1) and that the last OTA implements

---

[5] Note that in practice, g_o and c_o of the OTA as modeled in Fig. 2a are in parallel with the integrator capacitor to yield, instead of (4), $V_{\text{out}} = g_m/[s(C + c_o) + g_o]V_{\text{in}}$. If C is large enough c_o can be absorbed in C, but g_o causes the integrator to be lossy and gives rise to Q-errors.

the load resistor; the second OTA in Fig. 5(a) realizes the source resistor, whereas in Fig. 5(b) an implementation of the source resistor is avoided by sending the current l_1 directly into the integrating node (the capacitor $2C_1$) as suggested by Equation 3(b). Also note that circuit complexity in Fig. 5(b) was kept low by resorting to OTAs with dual inputs. This trick can always be used and results in possible savings of power consumption and chip area when two OTAs share a common output node. In such cases only the linearized input stages of the OTA must be duplicated but bias, output, and common-mode rejection circuitry can be shared [40, 47]. For instance, the circuit in Fig. 5(a) can be simplified to the one shown in Fig. 6[6]

We note again that all transconductors in Figs. 5 and 6 are identical[7] so that a single optimized g_m-cell (an analog gate) can be used throughout the filter chip for an especially simple IC design process, analogous to that of a gate array [63, 72]. It can also be shown [41, 42] that the filters can be designed with only grounded capacitors. Apart from being simpler to realize in most IC technologies, grounded capacitors are less affected by parasitics because the capacitor from the bottom plate to the substrate is shorted out. However, the designer should keep in mind that this advantage is obtained at the cost of additional active devices (i.e., increased power consumption and chip area) and more parasitics.

Although the $g_m - C$ approach appears to be the preferred technique for high-frequency IC CT filter design [17–20, 25–29, 33, 36, 38–51, 61], it should be mentioned that several very or reasonably successful IC CT filters have been reported in the literature that are based on different, often more standard op

amp–based active filter techniques [30–32], [52–57]. The most successful among those is the MOSFET-C method, which replaces the resistors used in standard active RC designs by MOSFET devices biased in the triode (ohmic) region. The resulting "resistor" is, of course, nonlinear because of the MOSFET's nonlinear i-v characteristics; its linear part equals

$$R(V_C) = \frac{1}{\mu C_{ox} W/L (V_C - V_T)} \tag{5}$$

where the device parameters μ, C_{ox}, W, L, and V_T have their usual meaning and the gate bias voltage V_C is used for control or tuning. In the MOSFET-C method, the even-order nonlinearities can be shown to be eliminated by carefully balanced circuit design where all signals are measured strictly differentially [52–55].

As an example, note that the lossy active RC integrator in Fig. 7(a) realizes

$$V_o = -\frac{G}{sC_F + G_F} V_a - \frac{sC}{sC_F + G_F} V_b \tag{6}$$

Replacing the resistors by MOSFETs biased in the triode region (with aspect ratios W/L appropriately chosen to realize R and R_F and converting the structure to balanced form to eliminate the nonlinear performance leads to the circuit in Fig. 7(b) with voltage-variable resistors given by Equation (5), so that loss and time constants can be electronically tuned. If higher-order filters are constructed in this fashion from differential, fully balanced integrator modules, the even-order nonlinearities are eliminated [23, 52–54]. Odd-order nonlinearities are usually small enough to be negligible.

First- and second-order sections [58] can be developed from the integrator structure in Fig. 7(b) as is indicated in Fig. 8. Combining the inputs $V_a = V_b = V_i$ and adding two further cross-coupled feed-in capacitors leads to the first-order circuit in Fig. 8(a) realizing

$$\frac{V_o}{V_i} = \frac{G_1 + s(C_1 - C_2)}{G_2 + sC_F} \tag{7a}$$

---

[6] Because V_s is applied to both inputs of the first OTA, its output current equals twice that of Fig. 5a: $l_1 = 2g_m V_s$. This results in an automatic 6 dB gain to compensate the inherent 6 dB loss of the prototype LC ladder caused by the $R/(2R)$ voltage division at DC.

[7] This is generally true in $g_m - C$ ladder simulations; the only exception occurs for those LC-ladders that require unequal terminating resistors, such as even-order Chebyshev filters; in that case, one of the transconductors will also be different.

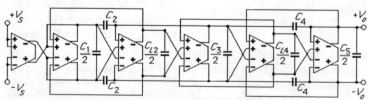

Fig. 6. The LC ladder simulation of Fig. 5(a) with dual input OTAs.

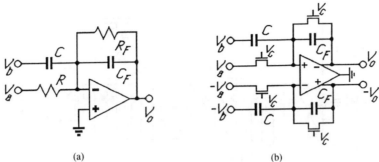

Fig. 7. (a) Op amp *RC* integrator. (b) Fully balanced MOS-
FET-*C* equivalent.

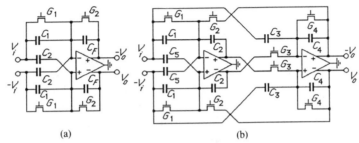

Fig. 8. General (a) first- and (b) second-order MOSFET-*C*
sections. The MOSFETs are labeled by the conductance
values they are to implement.

Similarly, combining two such integrators with appropriate signs and elements in a loop results in the general second-order section in Fig. 8(b) whose operation is described by

$$\frac{V_o}{V_i} = \frac{G_1G_3 + s(C_1 - C_5) + s^2C_2C_3}{G_2G_3 + sC_2G_4 + s^2C_2C_4} \quad (7b)$$

Note that the circuits can realize zeros anywhere on the real axis or in the *s*-plane, respectively, depending on the choice of element values. Consequently, these sections can be used to implement arbitrary high-order transfer functions in a cascade topology.

With MOSFET-*C* integrators available it stands to reason that simulations of *LC*-ladders can be obtained in much the same way as was done for the $g_m - C$ approach described before [52–54]. Starting from Equation (3), this process is illustrated in Fig. 9, which shows the MOSFET-*C* implementation of the fifth-order elliptic filter of Fig. 4 by the signal-flow graph method. The aspect ratio of each MOSFET is adjusted to realize the corresponding resistor of a standard active *RC* implementation [6], and all MOSFET gates are controlled by the same control voltage V_C for tuning purposes. Programmable filter coefficients can be achieved by implementing resis-

tors as arrays of MOSFETs connected in parallel, and with each MOSFET's gate connected either to V_C or to a voltage that turns the device off (i.e., no separate switches are required for opening some of the parallel branches).

An often-cited advantage of the MOSFET-*C* technique is the reduced sensitivity to parasitic capacitors, whereas the $g_m - C$ approach must carefully account for parasitics by predistortion (see footnote 5). Note from Figs. 7(b), 8 and 9 that all capacitors and the MOSFET resistors are connected to voltage-driven or to virtual ground nodes so that parasitic capacitors to ground are of no consequences as long as amplifiers with sufficiently high gain and wide bandwidth are used. Fortunately, such amplifiers are being developed [56] so that MOSFET-*C* circuits promise to become increasingly attractive in the future.

3. THE TUNING PROBLEM IN CONTINUOUS-TIME
INTEGRATED FILTERS

In order to obtain accurate filter performance, such as the small passband ripple or the exact location of the transmission zeros in Fig. 1(a), accurate, low-

9

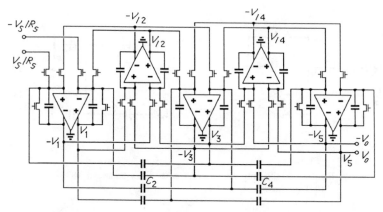

Fig. 9. Operational simulation of the *LC* ladder of Fig. 4 with MOSFET-*C* integrators.

tolerance component values are required. As frequency parameters of active filters are set by *RC*-products or C/g_m-ratios, very accurate absolute values of resistors, transconductors, and capacitors must be realized and maintained during operation. Since these are not normally available or are too expensive, filters must be turned to their desired performance by adjusting element values. Clearly, in fully integrated filters where all components are on a silicon chip, tuning in the usual sense is not economical or even possible, in particular because the electronic components must be expected to vary during operation because of environmental effects, such as temperature changes, humidity, or aging. Furthermore, although IC processing is very reliable in realizing accurate ratios of like components on a chip[8], the processing tolerances of absolute values of *R*s, g_ms and *C*s must be expected to be of the order

---

[8] Dimensionless filter parameters, such as gain or quality factors {see Equation (2b)}, are determined by ratios of like components but the realization of frequency parameters requires accurate absolute values of elements {see Equation (2a)}.

of 20 to 50 percent. In many applications, tolerances of this magnitude are far too large for an untuned filter to perform within specifications.

Since manual tuning is not a viable proposition but some tuning is quite unavoidable, an automatic tuning scheme must be designed onto the chip as part of the total CT filter system. To appreciate the difficulty of this task, the reader should understand that, fundamentally, tuning implies *measuring* filter performance, *comparing* it with a standard, *calculating* the error, and *applying* a correction to the system to reduce the error. From reviewing the literature [6, 26, 29–32, 39, 43, 48, 49, 52–54, 57, 60, 64–66] it appears that an accurate reference frequency (e.g., a system clock) (V_{REF} in Fig. 10) has been agreed upon as the most reliable and convenient standard. From the filter's response to the signal at this known frequency, any mistuning is detected and the appropriate corrections are applied via a suitable control circuit.

A block diagram of this scheme is shown in Fig. 10, which should help elucidate the principle of the

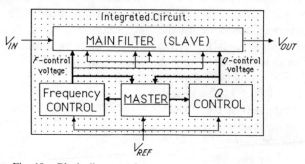

Fig. 10. Block diagram of master–slave control system for integrated CT filters.

operation without having to examine the actual circuitry. The main filter (the 'slave') performs the required signal processing task; the master filter consists of any subsection of the slave's circuitry (up to a full duplicate of the slave) of sufficient complexity to model the slave's behavior that is relevant for tuning. To avoid any crosstalk or intermodulation between the main information carrying signal and the reference signal, the latter is applied to the master filter and matching and tracking properties of master and slave are used to tune the slave (i.e., the main filter). Tuning is accomplished by applying the correction signal simultaneously to both master and slave. The system contains a frequency control block that detects frequency errors in the master's response to the reference signal V_{REF} and generates a frequency (F) control voltage that is applied to the master in a closed-loop control scheme such that any detected errors are minimized.[9] Since master and slave are on the same chip and the master is constructed specifically to provide an accurate model of the slave, the errors of the slave filter can be assumed to match and track those of the master. Consequently, the F-control voltage is applied at one or more locations of the slave, as appropriate, and can be expected to correct any frequency errors in the main filter.

The purpose of the additional block in Fig. 10, labelled "Q-Control," is to tune the shape of the transfer characteristic. Once the frequency parameters are correct as tuned by the frequency control loop, the transfer function shape is determined only by the pole quality factors Q_i. Q, as a ratio of two frequencies, is a dimensionless number and as such is determined by a ratio of like components {resistor, capacitor, or g_m ratio, see Equation (2b)}. Indeed, Q is realizable quite accurately in an IC design at fairly low frequencies and moderate values of Q [6, 26, 29–32, 47–49, 52–55]; for high-frequency, high-Q designs, however, Q is found to be a very strong function of parasitic elements and phase shifts [6, 29, 38, 43, 60, 62, 71] so that it is unreasonable to expect Q to be correct without tuning. Therefore, including for generality a Q-control block[10] permits tuning of the filter's bandwidth automatically by a

scheme that is completely analogous to the F-control method, as illustrated in Fig. 10.

With few exceptions [47, 50, 51, 66–68, 70] all currently proposed automatic tuning schemes follow the approach of Fig. 10. The actual implementation is, naturally, very circuit-specific; it depends on such items as the technology used, the type of circuit, and the kind of tunable elements available. The new concepts proposed in [67] and [68] are especially interesting; they use adaptive techniques to tune all poles and zeros of a filter function for, theoretically, very high accuracy. Whereas the master-slave scheme is based on the premise that the filter must operate continuously, the methods proposed in [66–68] assume that the signal can be switched off occasionally to permit tuning in a signal-free environment, thereby alleviating serious matching, noise, and crosstalk problems. (See observations (c) below). A few observations concerning the still-prevalent master-slave control methods that the designer of such systems should keep in mind are:

(a) A key assumption in the operation is that master and slave are matched in their behavior and track; therefore, the whole scheme can be only as accurate as the achievable matching of circuit components across a silicon chip. Experience has shown that frequency parameters are not very sensitive to parasitic effects so that matching does not appear to be a problem; Q, however, turns out to be extremely sensitive to parasitics and to small phase errors in the feedback loops so that great care must be taken when modelling the slave's behavior by a master circuit. Quite apart from the tuning scheme or the filter's implementation method, this problem becomes particularly critical in high-frequency and high-Q designs where phase errors as small as a fraction of a degree can cause serious deviations and even oscillations.

(b) Because filter control is to be completely automatic, the important filter parameters must depend on electronically variable components. (In the $g_m - C$ approach discussed above, the transconductors are tunable by changing bias voltages or currents. Similarly, in the MOSFET-C approach, the MOSFET resistors are tuned by varying the gate voltages.) When selecting a filter structure, the designer of the IC filter chip must consider at the outset whether the contemplated circuit is tunable,

---

[9] In the designs reported to date, frequency control blocks built around some type of phase-locked loop scheme, using a multiplier or an EXOR gate as phase detector, have been found most successful [25, 26, 28–32, 43, 48, 49, 52–54, 60, 65].

[10] Because magnitude errors can be shown in most cases to be proportional to errors in quality factor [6], the Q-control block is normally implemented around an amplitude-locking scheme [6, 43, 60, 64].

that is, whether an observed error can be related dominantly to a certain component value. Also, if possible, the selection of the filter topology should be such that parasitic components do not create additional critical frequencies (poles or zeros) because their effects generally can not be removed by tuning. An *LC* ladder is such a topology because every circuit node is loaded by a design capacitor that can absorb parasitics without increasing the order of the transfer function (see Figs. 5 and 6).

(c) The IC contains not only the information signal of interest but also the reference signal; moreover, quite often there are digital signals that may be needed for switching, time sharing, or multiplexing the filter and/or control circuitry, or that may arise in other parts of the IC chip. The utmost care must be taken to keep these extraneous signals from the main filtering path where they would otherwise interfere with the signal processing job, introduce intermodulation distortion, or−at least−cause the signal-to-noise ratio to deteriorate. (Noise here means not only random, such as thermal, noise but also the presence of any unwanted signals.)

Conclusions

Recent work on the problems associated with monolithic implementations of CT filters has proven increasingly successful in overcoming many of the design difficulties by making use of the intrinsic advantages of IC technology, such as "cheap gain" and good matching and tracking between "electrically like" components. Indeed, continuous-time IC filters have become a commercial reality [47, 57]. Although CMOS designs have been emphasized in this paper, it should be recognized that IC filter design procedures can be applied equally well to other technologies [25, 28, 30−34, 36, 38, 47, 51, 60−62, 69]; for example, it presents clearly no fundamental problem to implement the transconductances in the circuits of Fig. 5 or the op amps in Fig. 9 with silicon-bipolar [38, 47], BiCMOS [56], or even GaAs [33, 34, 36] devices. The design processes implement the circuitry either with only transconductance elements and capacitors or with op amps, capacitors, and MOSFET "resistors." It was shown that, at least in some (quite general) cases, the $g_m - C$ procedure can be further adapted to the simplest IC design, layout, and processing requirements by making all transconductors identical and using only grounded capacitors. With the development of suitable software, the design of continuous-time IC filters can thereby be reduced to a level similar to that of digital gate arrays, with transconductors serving as analog gate cells [63, 72]. As in any analog design, attention must be paid to layout and wiring parasitics but the available experimental chips indicate that these effects are not overwhelming [63].

The requirement of automatic electronic tuning, unavoidable in any critical design, was explained via a generic block diagram. Indeed, the development of reliable automatic control (tuning) techniques combined with a guaranteed tunable filter is of foremost importance for the development of commercially useful integrated CT high-Q filters. As the implementation details of tuning loops depend on the overall realization selected for the whole filter system, tuning can be discussed only for specific circuit examples. They are left to the papers contained in this volume. An additional point that cannot be overemphasized is noise immunity: utmost care must be taken in design and layout of the filter chip to prevent the various peripheral switching and control signals, arising from the tuning circuitry as well as power supply noise, from coupling into the main signal processing circuit where they may cause distortion, intermodulation, and, at least, result in a reduced signal-to-noise ratio. Problems with parasitic signal injection and power supply rejection, as well as with nonlinearities, are generally reduced in fully differential (balanced) designs. For increasing frequencies, the design problems become much more severe because parasitic elements not only result in changed component values and increased filter order that place a greater burden on the tuning scheme but parasitic effects also increase the likelihood of coupling stray signals into the main filter.

Acknowledgments

The author would like to acknowledge the contributions of his past and present students, in particular Chii-Fa Chiou, Chin-Sup Park, Mehmet Ali Tan, Geert de Veirman, Pan Wu, and Adam Wyszynski—whose research provided many solutions to IC CT filter problems. Some of the work reported in this paper was supported by the National Science Foundation under grants No. 82-15001 and

MIP 91-21360. Support of the Tektronix Foundation during 1990 to 1992 is gratefully acknowledged.

REFERENCES

[1] R. Schaumann, "The design of continuous-time fully integrated filters: A review," *IEE Proceedings*, Part G, vol. 136, pp. 184–190, Aug. 1989.

[2] A. S. Sedra and P. O. Brackett, *Filter Theory and Design: Active and Passive*, Beaverton, OR: Matrix Publishers, 1978.

[3] G. C. Temes and J. W. LaPatra, *Introduction to Circuit Synthesis and Design*, New York: McGraw-Hill, 1977.

[4] S/FILSYN Software for Filter Analysis and Design. DGS Associates, 1353 Sarita Way, Santa Clara, CA 95051.

[5] C. Ouslis, M. Snelgrove, and A. S. Sedra, "A filter designer's filter design aid: filtorX," *Proc. Int. Symp. Circuits Syst.*, pp. 376–379, 1991.

[6] R. Schaumann, M. S. Ghausi, and K. R. Laker, *Design of Analog Filters: Passive, Active RC and Switched Capacitor*, Englewood Cliffs, NJ: Prentice-Hall, 1990.

[7] L. R. Rabiner and B. Gold, *Theory and Application of Digital Signal Processing*, Englewood Cliffs, NJ: Prentice-Hall, 1975.

[8] N. K. Bose, *Digital Filters—Theory and Applications*, New York: Elsevier Science Publisher, 1985.

[9] R. Gregorian and G. C. Temes, *Analog MOS Integrated Circuits for Signal Processing*, New York: J. Wiley & Sons, 1986.

[10] A. S. Sedra, "Switched-Capacitor Filter Synthesis Techniques," in *Design of MOS VLSI Circuits for Telecommunications*, Y. Tsividis and P. Antognetti, Eds., Englewood Cliffs, NJ: Prentice-Hall, 1985.

[11] P. R. Gray and R. Castello, "Performance Limitations in Switched-Capacitor Filters," in *Design of MOS VLSI Circuits for Telecommunications*, Y. Tsividis and P. Antognetti; Eds., Englewood Cliffs, NJ: Prentice-Hall, 1985.

[12] T. C. Choi et al., "High-frequency switched-capacitor filters for telecommunications applications," *IEEE J. Solid-State Circuits*, vol. SC-18, pp. 652–664, 1983.

[13] G. Daryanani, *Principles of Active Network Synthesis and Design*, New York: J. Wiley, and Sons, 1976.

[14] W. Heinlein and H. Holmes, *Active Filters for Integrated Circuits*, Germany: Oldenburg, Verlag, 1974.

[15] K. R. Laker, R. Schaumann, and M. S. Ghausi, "Multiple-loop feedback topologies for the design of low-sensitivity active filters," *IEEE Trans. Circuits Syst.*, vol. CAS-26, pp. 1–21, 1979.

[16] R. Schaumann, M. A. Soderstrand, and K. R. Laker, *Modern Active Filter Design*, Piscataway, NJ: IEEE Press, 1981.

[17] R. L. Geiger and E. Sánchez-Sinencio, "Active filter design using operational transconductance amplifiers; Tutorial," *IEEE Circuits and Devices Mag.*, vol. 1, 20–32, 1985.

[18] A. C. M. De Queiroz, L. P. Calôba, and E. Sánchez-Sinencio, "Signal flow graph OTA-C integrated filters," *Proc. Int. Symp. Circuits Syst.*, pp. 2165–2168, 1988.

[19] A. Wyszynski and R. Schaumann, "Highly linear VHF fully-balanced CMOS OTA," submitted for publication.

[20] H. Névarez-Lozano, J. A. Hill, and E. Sánchez-Sinencio, "Frequency limitations of continuous-time OTA-C filters," *Proc. Int. Symp. Circuits Syst.*, pp. 2169–2172, 1988.

[21] C. S. Park and R. Schaumann, "A high-frequency CMOS linear transconductance element," *IEEE Trans. Circuits Syst.*, vol. CAS-33, pp. 1132–1138, 1986.

[22] A. Nedungadi and T. R. Viswanathan, "Design of linear CMOS transconductance elements," *IEEE Trans. Circuits Syst.*, vol. CAS-31, pp. 891–894, 1985.

[23] Y. Tsividis, Z. Czarnul, and S. C. Fang, "MOS transconductors and integrators with high linearity," *Electron. Lett.*, vol. 22, pp. 245–246, 619, 1986.

[24] K. D. Peterson and R. L. Geiger, "CMOS OTA structures with improved linearity," *Proc. 27th Midwest Symp. Circuits Syst.*, pp. 63–66, 1984.

[25] K. W. Moulding, J. R. Quartly, P. J. Rankin, R. S. Thompson, and G. A. Wilson, "Gyrator video filter IC with automatic tuning," *IEEE J. Solid-State Circuits*, vol. SC-15, pp. 963–967, 1980.

[26] H. Khorramabadi and P. R. Gray, "High-frequency CMOS continuous-time filters," *IEEE J. Solid-State Circuits*, vol. SC-19, pp. 939–948, 1984.

[27] E. Seevinck, "Design and application of integrated analog interface filters," *Proc. Int. Symp. Circuits Syst.*, pp. 1923–1926, 1988.

[28] J. O. Voorman, W. H. A. Brüls, and P. J. Barth, "Integration of analog filters in a bipolar process," *IEEE J. Solid-State Circuits*, vol. SC-17, pp. 713–722, 1982.

[29] F. Krummenacher and N. Joehl, "A 4-MHz CMOS continuous-time filter with on-chip automatic tuning," *IEEE J. Solid-State Circuits*, vol. SC-23, 750–758, 1988.

[30] K. Miura, et al., "VCR signal processing LSIs with self-adjusted integrated filters," *Proc. Bipolar Circ. Techn. Meeting (BTCM)*, pp. 85–86, 1986.

[31] K. S. Tan and P. R. Gray, "Fully integrated analog filters using bipolar-JFET technology," *IEEE J. Solid-State Circuits*, vol. SC-13, pp. 814–824, 1978.

[32] K. Fukahori, "A bipolar voltage-controlled tunable filter," *IEEE J. Solid-State Circuits*, vol. SC-16, pp. 729–737, 1981.

[33] P. Wu and R. Schaumann, "A high-frequency GaAs transconductance circuit and its applications," *Proc. IEEE Int. Symp. Circuits Syst.*, pp. 3081–3084, May 1990.

[34] P. Visocchi, J. Taylor, A. Betts, and D. Haigh, "Novel tunable GaAs MESFET OTA-C integrator suitable for high-precision filtering applications," *Electron. Lett.*, vol. 27, pp. 1671–1673, 1991.

[35] S. Szczepanski, R. Schaumann, and P. Wu, "A linear transconductor based on cross-coupled CMOS pairs," *Electron. Lett.*, vol. 27, no. 9, pp. 783–785, 1991.

[36] P. Wu and R. Schaumann, "Design considerations for CMOS and GaAs OTAs: Frequency response, linearity, tuning, and common-mode feedback," *J. Analog Integrated Circuits and Signal Processing*, vol. 1, no. 3, pp. 247–268, 1991.

[37] B. Nauta and E. Seevinck, "Linear CMOS transconductance element for VHF filters," *Electron. Lett.*, vol. 25, pp. 488–450, 1989.

[38] A. Wyszynski, R. Schaumann, S. Szczepanski, and P. Van Halen, "Design of a 2.7 GHz linear OTA in bipolar transistor-array technology with lateral PNPs," *IEEE Int. Symp. Circuits Syst.*, pp. 2844–2847, May 1992.

[39] R. Schaumann and M. A. Tan, "The problem of on-chip automatic tuning in continuous time integrated filters," *Proc. IEEE Int. Symp. Circuits Syst.*, pp. 106–109, May 1989.

[40] A. Wyszynski and R. Schaumann, "Using multiple-input transconductors to reduce the number of components in OTA-C filter design," *Electron. Lett.*, vol. 28, no. 3, pp. 217–220, 1992.

[41] M. A. Tan and R. Schaumann, "Design of a general bi-

quadratic filter section with only transconductances and grounded capacitors," *IEEE Trans. Circuits Syst.*, vol. CAS-35, no. 4, pp. 478–480, April 1988.

[42] M. A. Tan and R. Schaumann, "Simulating general-parameter *LC*-ladder filters for monolithic realizations with only transconductance elements and grounded capacitors," *IEEE Trans. Circuits Syst.*, vol. CAS-36, no. 2, pp. 299–307, February 1989.

[43] C. S. Park and R. Schaumann, "Design of a 4 MHz Analog integrated CMOS Transconductance-*C* Bandpass Filter," *IEEE J. Solid-State Circuits*, vol. SC-23, no. 4, pp. 987–996, 1988.

[44] H. S. Malvar, "Electronically controlled active-*C* filter and equalizers with operational transconductance amplifiers," *IEEE Trans. Circuits Syst.*, vol. CAS-31, pp. 645–649, 1984.

[45] M. A. Tan and R. Schaumann, "Generation of transconductance—grounded capacitor filters by signal-flow-graph methods for VLSI implementation," *Electron. Lett.*, vol. 23, no. 20, pp. 1093–1094, 1987.

[46] M. A. Tan and R. Schaumann, "Generation of transconductance—grounded capacitor filters by signal-flow graph simulation of *LC*-ladders," *Proc. Int. Symp. Circuits Syst.*, pp. 2407–2410, June 1988.

[47] G. A. De Veirman and R. G. Yamasaki, "Design of a bipolar 10-MHz continuous-time 0.05° equiripple linear phase filter," *IEEE J. Solid-State Circuits*, vol. SC-27, pp. 324–331, March 1992.

[48] J. M. Khoury, "Design of a 15 MHz CMOS continuous-time filter with on-chip tuning," *IEEE J. Solid State-Circuits*, vol. SC-26, pp. 1988–1997, 1991.

[49] V. Gopinathan, Y. P. Tsividis, K. S. Tan, and R. Hester, "Design considerations for continuous-time filters and implementation of an antialiasing filter for digital video," *IEEE J. Solid-State Circuits*, vol. SC-25, pp. 1368–1378, 1990.

[50] K. H. Loh, D. L. Hiser, W. J. Adams, and R. L. Geiger, "A versatile digitally controlled continuous-time filter structure with wide-range and fine resolution capability," *IEEE Trans. Circuits Syst.*, vol. CAS-39, pp. 265–276, 1992.

[51] C. A. Laber and P. R. Gray, "A 20 MHz 6th-order BiCMOS programmable filter using parasitic insensitive integrators," *Symposium on VLSI Circuits*, Digest of Technical Papers, pp. 104–105, 1992.

[52] M. Banu and Y. Tsividis, "Fully integrated active RC filters in MOS technology," *IEEE J. Solid-State Circuits*, vol. SC-18, pp. 644–651, 1983.

[53] M. Banu and Y. Tsividis, "An elliptic continuous-time CMOS filter with on-chip automatic tuning," *IEEE J. Solid-State Circuits*, vol. SC-20, pp. 1114–1121, 1985.

[54] Y. Tsividis, M. Banu and J. Khoury, "Continuous-time MOSFET-*C* filters in VLSI," *IEEE Trans. Circuits Syst.*, vol. CAS-33, pp. 125–140, 1986.

[55] J. M. Khoury and Y. P. Tsividis, "Analysis and compensation of high-frequency effects in integrated MOSFET-*C* continuous time filters," *IEEE Trans. Circuits Syst.*, vol. CAS-34, pp. 862–875, 1987.

[56] A. van Bezooijen, N. Ramalho, and J. O. Voorman, "Balanced integrator filters for video frequencies," *ESSCIRC*, pp. 1–4, 1991.

[57] G. J. Smolka, et al., "A low noise trunk interface circuit," Digest, *ESSCIRC*, pp. 257–260, 1992.

[58] J. O. Voorman, "Balanced integrator-filter arrangement," US Patent 4,926,135, 1990.

[59] J. Silva-Martinez, M. S. J. Steyaert, and W. Sansen, "A large-signal very low-distortion transconductor for high-frequency," *IEEE J. Solid-State Circuits*, vol. SC-27, pp. 93–1001, 1992.

[60] C.-F. Chiou and R. Schaumann, "Design and performance of a fully integrated bipolar 10.7 MHz analog bandpass filter," *IEEE Trans. Circuits Syst.*, vol. CAS-33, pp. 116–124, 1986.

[61] B. Nauta, "A CMOS transconductance-*C* filter for very high frequencies," *IEEE J. Solid-State Circuits*, vol. SC-27, pp. 142–153, 1992.

[62] H. Hagiwara, et al., "A monolithic video frequency filter using NIC based gyrators," *IEEE J. Solid-State Circuits*, vol. SC-23, pp. 175–182, 1988.

[63] W. R. Daasch, M. Wedlake, R. Schaumann, and P. Wu, "Automation of the IC layout of continuous-time transconductance-capacitor filters," *Intern. J. Circ. Theory Applic.*, vol. 20, no. 3, pp. 267–282, 1992.

[64] M. A. Tan, "Design and automatic tuning of fully integrated transconductance-grounded capacitor filters," Ph.D. Thesis University of Minnesota, 1988.

[65] D. Senderowicz, D. A. Hodges, and P. R. Gray, "An NMOS integrated vector-locked loop," *Proc. Int. Symp. Circuits Syst.*, pp. 1164–1167, 1982.

[66] Y. Tsividis, "Self-tuned filters," *Electron. Lett.*, vol. 17, no. 12, pp. 406–407, 1981.

[67] K. A. Kozma, D. A. Johns, and A. S. Sedra, "Automatic tuning of continuous-time filters using an adaptive tuning technique," *IEEE Trans. Circuits Syst.*, vol. CAS-38, pp. 1241–1248, 1991.

[68] T. Kwan and K. Martin, "An adaptive analog continuous-time CMOS biquadratic filter," *IEEE J. Solid-State Circuits*, vol. SC-26, pp. 859–867, 1991.

[69] S. Tagaki, T. Anzai and T. Yanagisawa, "A differential input/output integrator without pnp transistors and its application to leapfrog filter synthesis," *Proc. Int. Symp. Circuits Syst.*, pp. 2855–2858, 1988.

[70] J. Silva-Martinez, M. Steyaert, and W. Sansen, "A novel approach for the automatic tuning of continuous-time filters," *Proc. Int. Symp. Circuits Syst.*, pp. 1452–1455, 1991.

[71] L. T. Bruton and A. I. A. Salama, "Frequency limitations of coupled biquadratic active ladder structures," *IEEE J. Solid-State Circuits*, vol. SC-9, pp. 70–72, 1974.

[72] R. Schaumann and W. R. Daasch, "Design and design automation of continuous-time fully integrated transconductance-*C* filters," *Frequenz*, vol. 46, pp. 117–123, March/April 1992.

CONTINUOUS–TIME ANALOG INTEGRATED FILTERS[1]

J. O. VOORMAN

PHILIPS RESEARCH LABORATORIES

P.O. BOX 80.000

5600 JA EINDHOVEN

THE NETHERLANDS

Abstract—A survey is given of continuous-time analog filters for very large scale integration (VLSI). The most important design methods, filter elements on silicon (bipolar, MOS and biMOS), circuit principles, and application areas are reviewed. New understanding, methods, and results have been added. Filter requirements, design yardsticks, control methods, matched oscillators, refined filter design methods, special filter types, and considerations on limits of performance are part of the survey.

1. INTRODUCTION

Information processing is being conducted more and more frequently by digital means. The transmission of analog as well as digital information is and will remain an analog issue. Between the analog outside world and the digital processors there are interfaces. These are of mixed types (Fig. 1). Buffer circuits, analog-to-digital (A/D) and digital-to-analog (D/A) converters, coder/decoder combinations (codecs), modulator/demodulator combinations (modems), line interfaces, receivers, and transmitters are examples of interfaces.

The transition to VLSI involves "shrinking" the digital processors as well as the analog pre- and post-processors (interfaces). The trend is to combine all parts on one chip. Digital and analog on one chip can be done in bipolar processes as well as in MOS processes, but biCMOS processes are optimum for the combination.

Many analog processors are chips with integrated amplifiers, modulators, oscillators, and so on, often with external selectivity (e.g., external resistors, capacitors, coils, transformers, crystal, crystal filter, SAW filter, etc.). The versatility of the analog processors is due to the fact that different external components (component values) can be chosen.

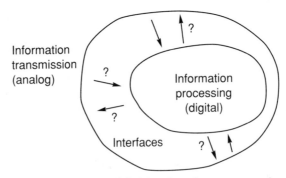

Fig. 1. Mixed analog/digital interfaces between an analog outside world and a digital processor. Processors and interfaces are put on one chip—we go to VLSI.

Chips with integrated selectivity often have fixed filters. With the integration of the external components, the versatility is lost. This can be overcome by using controllable or programmable integrated circuits. VLSI requires (digitally) programmable analog processors (BUS-controlled analog processors). Variability and programmability are important features for integrated filters.

Digital filters are found in the digital processors. Analog circuits, including filters, are found in the interfaces to the analog outside world. Sampled-signal filters (e.g., CCD filters, switched capacitor filters, switched-current filters) are found in between. Where the analog/sampled-signal/digital divisions are located depends on

- costs (chip area),
- power consumption, and
- performance,

Some examples can be given (see Fig. 2). Antialiasing filters are analog. Noise-shaping filters can be analog, of the sampled-signal type, or be digital. Receiver selectivity are mainly analog. For narrow-

[1] This survey is a revised and extended version of a previous survey [1]. Many new topics, methods, and results have been included.

band applications, switched-capacitor filters generally are somewhat more accurate than continuous-time filters. Image processing is digital. Analog is preferred for high frequencies and low power. Interference across neighboring circuits is low for analog filters. For low frequencies, digital processing (with time-sharing) often provides the best solution.

VLSI means using simple circuits and methods. Design time should be as short as possible and the probability of a first design being correct should be very high. Even a complex filter takes up only a small part of the chip. Implementation of VLSI generally means the use of lower supply voltages (i.e., from 18 V and 12 V to 5 V, 3 V, and even lower). VLSI also means lower bias currents per transistor and crosstalk problems to and from neighboring circuits. In particular, the crosstalk from huge digital signal processors with pulsed bias currents is a matter of concern. Filter circuits should be robust against interference.

This paper deals with analog integrated filters. We start with the most useful design methods for active filters, consider filter requirements, introduce yardsticks, provide a survey of filter elements and circuits

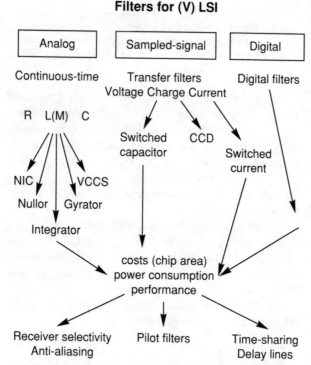

Filters for (V) LSI

Fig. 2. Analog filters, sampled-signal filters, and digital filters—each has particular advantages and disadvantages. The choice is made after considering cost (chip area), power consumption, and performance.

on silicon (with examples of application), show the effects of balancing, consider control (tuning) methods and the design of oscillators using the same techniques (matched oscillators), and conclude by considering refined design techniques (polyphase filters, etc.) in relation to design limitations and the challenges facing future design.

2. *RC*-ACTIVE FILTERS

Conventional analog filters are made from resistors, inductors, capacitors, and transformers (or mutual inductances): R-L-C-T filters. Coils and transformers are the most expensive of these elements. Whereas resistors and capacitors are common elements in integrated circuits, coils are not. The main limitation is the resistivity of the windings (aluminium interconnect) of the coils, yielding high losses (see Fig. 3). Only in the near GHz region and higher can LC resonance circuits and filters be integrated; see for example [2]. At these high frequencies, it is even better, for noise and power consumption, to undamp a lossy LC resonance circuit, by using electronic circuits than it is to use RC-active filters.

Assuming that coils (and mutual inductances) cannot be integrated, one could try to use passive R-C filters. Using Laguerre function expansions, [3] (see Fig. 4), it can be shown that any physical impulse response (causal, with finite energy), that is any physical filter function, can be arbitrarily closely approximated using passive RC filters (apart from a constant gain factor). Thus, useful filters can be made. However, in many other cases the requirements will lead to complex networks of high order and to a high insertion loss.

Using active elements in addition to resistors and capacitors, poles can be shifted off the real axis and a similar complexity can be retained, as in the case of LC filters. We arrive at RC-active filters.

3. METHODS FOR THE DESIGN OF *RC*-ACTIVE FILTERS

In integrated circuits, *active* implies the use of transistors. In network theory and in filter theory, transistors are not considered to be elements (as R, L, C and ideal transformer). Network theory "idealizes" the transistor. Two idealizations are:

- the voltage-controlled current source (VCCS) or transconductor: a two-port with zero input

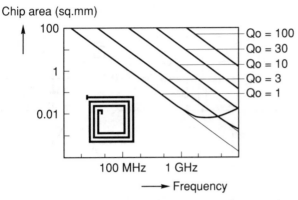

Chip area (sq.mm)

Qo = 100
Qo = 30
Qo = 10
Qo = 3
Qo = 1

100 MHz   1 GHz

⟶ Frequency

Fig. 3. Coils can be integrated using planar (aluminium) interconnect. Ohmic losses limit the application. The figure shows a typical example of chip area needed for an integrated LC resonance circuit as a function of resonance frequency for different values of Q_o (quality factor at resonance).

Roughly,

$$L = 10^{-6} d.n^2,$$

where $L[H]$ is the inductance, $d[m]$ is the average diameter and n is the number of windings. The ohmic resistance of the interconnect is the main cause of loss. A best compromise between losses and inductor value is obtained when the outer diameter is some 2.4 times the inner diameter. In that case,

$$L = 6.10^{-8} AL^{3/2}/p^2,$$

where AL [m^2] is the area of the inductor and $p[m]$ is the pitch of the windings. Let the width of the interconnect be $p/2$, the resistivity 0.03 Ohm/square. The series resistance R[Ohm] of the windings can be shown to be

$$R = 0.05 \, AL/p^2.$$

Adding a capacitor, an LC resonance circuit is made. The capacitance $C[F]$ can be expressed in the capacitor area AC[m^2]. Using a typical capacitor density of 1 $nF/$mm^2,

$$C = 10^{-3} AC.$$

Conversely, in terms of $\omega_o = 1/\sqrt{LC}$ and $Q_o = \omega_o.L/R$, we have

$$AL = 1.8 \, 10^{10} Q_o^2/f_o^2, \qquad AC = 1.8 \, 10^{-7} p^2 f_o/Q_o^3,$$
$$A = AL + AC.$$

The figure shows the areas (for a pitch of 3 μm). The thin lines (visible only in the lower right-hand edge) indicate the area of the coil (which is independent of the pitch) and the thick ones that of the resonance circuit. For example, on a chip area of 1 mm^2 at 1 GHz a quality factor Q_o of roughly 10 can be obtained.

current, whose output current is proportional to the input voltage, and
- the nullor (also ideal operational amplifier): a two-port element with zero input voltage and zero input current [4] (see Fig. 5).

Laguerre filter

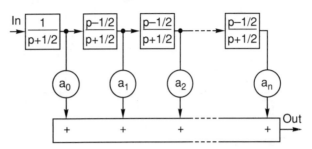

Fig. 4. Laguerre filter. Any physical impulse response (causal, with finite energy) can be expanded in a series of Laguerre functions. The Laplace transform of the expansion has the form

$$H(p) = \sum_{k=0}^{+\infty} a_k \frac{1}{p + 1/2} \left(\frac{p - 1/2}{p + 1/2} \right)^k.$$

What a Fourier series is for periodic waveforms, a Laguerre series is for causal waveforms. The Laguerre series can be implemented as a Laguerre filter. An impulse at the input yields orthogonal impulse responses at the taps. Depending on the tapweights, any physical impulse response can be approximated arbitrarily well. On the other hand, the transfer function of a passive RC filter has all (simple) poles on the negative real frequency axis (and it has no positive real zeroes). Apart from a constant gain factor, an arbitrarily close approximation to the Laguerre series and hence to any physical impulse response can be made by employing a cluster of distinct poles on the negative real axis.

The transconductor is a resistive element. The nullor is dimensionless. Electronics uses combinations of transistors to make better approximations to the idealizations.

3.1. Straightforward design of RC-amplifier filters

Simple RC-nullor filter types, which are in common use, are

- Sallen and Key filters (Fig. 6): they are derived from a passive RC lowpass ladder filter by the inclusion of an amplifier with finite voltage gain (for design tables, see [5]).
- cascade of second-order sections (Fig. 7): the transfer function is written as a product of first- and second-order transfer functions and is implemented as a cascade connection of simple first- and second-order filters (for design tables, see [6], for example).

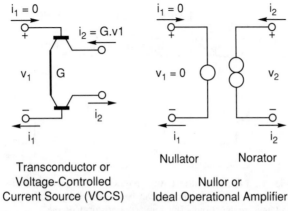

Transconductor or
Voltage-Controlled
Current Source (VCCS)

Nullor or
Ideal Operational Amplifier

Fig. 5. Two useful idealizations of the transistor: the transconductor or voltage-controlled current source (VCCS) and the ideal operational amplifier or nullor. The transconductor symbol represents the equations: $i_1 = 0$, $i_2 = G.v_1$. The symbol is not usual, but it is particularly convenient for complex circuits.

The nullor consists of a pair of 1-ports: the nullator ($i_1 = 0$, $v_1 = 0$) and the norator (i_2, v_2 are determined by feedback).

3.2. Tolerances

The high sensitivity of the filter characteristics (e.g., attenuation) of the RC-active filters to tolerances on the element values, in particular for

Sallen and Key filter

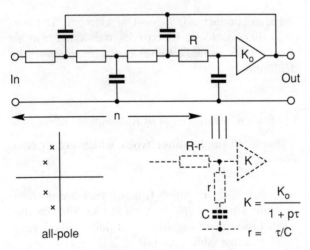

Fig. 6. Sallen and Key type filters. The addition of an amplifier (with finite voltage gain) to a passive RC lowpass ladder filter shifts the poles of the transfer function away from the negative real frequency axis. Simple all-pole filters of orders $n = 2$ to 5 can be made. A simple compensation is shown for the first-order roll-off with frequency of the amplifier gain.

Cascade design

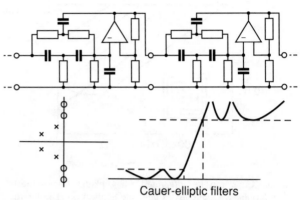

Cauer-elliptic filters

Fig. 7. Cascade of second-order sections. Factorization of the transfer function in factors with real poles (and zeroes) and complex conjugate pole pairs (and zero pairs) opens the way for implementation as a cascade of simple second-order filter sections. In some cases, first- and third-order sections are used in addition. For example, Cauer-elliptic types of filter can be made.

higher-order Sallen and Key filters and for filters using negative immittance converters[2] and, to a lesser extent for cascade designs of simple first- and second-order filter sections, has led designers facing more stringent requirements to return to the classical filters. The properties of the classical LC filters were appreciated as never before [7, 8] (see, Fig. 8).

Nowadays, LC lossless ladders between resistive terminations are simulated in many ways, maintaining the low sensitivity to tolerances. Figure 9 contains some Monte-Carlo statistical analyses showing the effects (for a higher-order Sallen-and-Key filter, a cascade design, an LC filter and two modern RC-active simulations of LC filters). Today, the LC filter simulation technique is applied not only to continuous-time RC-active filters but also to switched-capacitor filters and even to digital filters.

For RC-active filters, which simulate LC filters, we mention the following design approaches:

- (gyrator-C) transconductor-C approaches (see Figs. 10 to 17),
- super-capacitor or frequency dependent negative conductance (FDNC) types of approach (see Figs. 18 and 19), and

[2] A negative immittance converter (NIC) is a two-port with equations: $v_1 = v_2$, $i_1 = i_2$ or $v_1 = -v_2$, $i_1 = -i_2$. It owes its name to the property that it converts an impedance Z to $-Z$. In the 1950s and 1960s it was extensively studied to undamp resistive losses of RC-active filters. The compensations (subtractions) caused problems with tolerances.

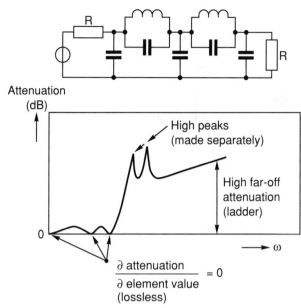

Attenuation
(dB)

High peaks
(made separately)

High far-off
attenuation
(ladder)

0

$$\frac{\partial \text{ attenuation}}{\partial \text{ element value}} = 0$$
(lossless)

ω

Fig. 8. Lossless ladders between resistive terminations show important properties: zero first-order sensitivity at attenuation zeroes, high attenuation peaks in the stop band, and high far-off attenuation (addition of attenuations of all ladder sections). The above properties reduce the requirements for the tolerances of the filter elements. This should be preserved in *RC*-active design methods.

- signal-flow graph approaches (see Figs. 20 to 25).

3.3. Gyrator methods: transconductor-C filters

Gyrator-capacitor combinations can simulate inductances (see Fig. 10). The gyrator, defined by Tellegen [9], by itself is not an element in integrated circuits. It can be put together from transistors and resistors and be made in various ways.

One way is to implement the two voltage-to-current relations of the gyrator by transconductors. Two transconductors are used for one gyrator (Fig. 11). In addition, one transconductor is used for a resistor. From *R-L-C* filters via the gyrator concept we arrive at transconductor-C filters.

In Fig. 12 an example is shown of the transformation of a fifth-order high-pass filter. All transconductors are one-sided grounded. This is important to be able to guarantee latch-up freedom[3] of the circuits.

[3] Latch-up, from a network theory viewpoint, comes into the picture where transconductors are implemented as electronic circuits from resistors and transistors. The circuits behave well only if they are properly biased. An incorrectly designed circuit may go into a wrong biasing state and may be latched in it. The condition that in a filter all transconductors are one-sided grounded makes it far easier to prove (with certain requirements to the transconductor) that there can be only one (the correct) DC biasing state. Only in that case the designer can be certain that the circuit will always behave as a transconductor.

An *LC* lowpass filter has floating coils. Each floating coil can be simulated using a floating gyrator and a capacitor. However, in order to arrive at grounded transconductors, we apply a transformation that has been devised by Holt and Taylor [10]. A floating coil is replaced by two grounded gyrators and a capacitor. The grounded gyrators are, in turn, replaced by pairs of grounded transconductors. Almost all transconductors are combined in pairs to reduce the complexity. For the result, see Fig. 13. For more details of the design method, see [11, 12].

In Fig. 14 we show some "lossless" all-pass sections [11]. The all-pass sections are nonreciprocal and have no *LC* counterpart. Their constant-resistance character permits them to be inserted in any filter in front of the load resistor.

We have introduced transconductor-*C* filters via the gyrator concept. Alternatively, one may first combine a transconductor and a capacitor to an integrator and use the integrator as an element for filter design [13]. Corresponding design methods use signal-flow-graph or state-variable representations, see below and [14].

3.4. Balanced transconductor-C filters

So far we have considered transconductor-*C* filters with all-grounded transconductors. Balancing of the filters is more integration-friendly. A corresponding transformation has been depicted in Fig. 15. With a lower total capacitance we can arrive at a signal-to-noise ratio improved by 3 dB (for roughly the same supply voltage and supply current).

Going to balanced transconductor filters means that, in principle, each earthed transconductor is transformed into a pair of balanced transconductors. Usually, in the electronic implementation, parts of the two transconductor circuits of the pair are combined. Therefore, and for convenience of drawing, we have introduced a symbol for the combination: a "full" balanced transconductor. A fifth-order, low-pass filter uses five full balanced transconductors (see Fig. 16). In some cases, in a resonance circuit, for example, "half" balanced transconductors are required (Fig. 17).

3.5. "Lossless" RC-amplifier filters

Thusfar, we have made the gyrator of transconductors. We have implemented the equations: $i_1 = G_1 v_2$, $i_2 = -G_2 v_1$. Strictly speaking, they are the equations of a positive immittance inverter (PII). An impedance Z across port 2 is inverted to an admit-

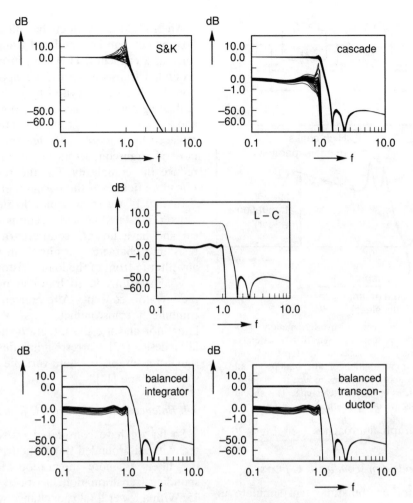

Fig. 9. Tolerances. Resistive and capacitive elements show tolerances. In the figure all tolerances were given a normal distribution (spread 1%). Five examples have been considered. The first is a 5th-order Chebyshev Sallen and Key filter (passband ripple: 0.5 dB) and the others are 5th-order Cauer-elliptic filters (passband ripple: 0.28 dB, stopband rejection: > 50 dB). Each figure shows the results of 25 Monte-Carlo statistical analyses of the voltage transfer function. In four of the five cases, to show more detail, an inset has been made with the passband on a different scale. The large deviations of the Sallen and Key filter (*top left*), the lower but still high deviations of the cascade design (*top right*) and the excellent properties of the *LC* filter (in the center) are obvious. Two modern (lossless *LC* ladder filter simulating) *RC*-active filter types show results with a similarly low passband ripple.

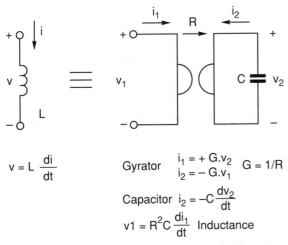

$$v = L \frac{di}{dt}$$

Gyrator $\begin{aligned}i_1 &= + G.v_2 \\ i_2 &= - G.v_1\end{aligned}$ $G = 1/R$

Capacitor $i_2 = -C\dfrac{dv_2}{dt}$

$v1 = R^2C\dfrac{di_1}{dt}$ Inductance

Fig. 10. A coil cannot be integrated. Interchanging voltage and current for a capacitor yields the equation for an inductance. The corresponding voltage-to-current conversions are the equations of a gyrator. A coil is simulated using a capacitor and a gyrator.

tance $Y = G_1 G_2 Z$ at port 1. We have a gyrator only when $G_1 = G_2$.

Instead of using transconductors, the gyrator or positive immittance inverter equations can also be implemented using nullors and resistors. The following possibilities exist:

- 1 nullor, 6 resistors [15]: this circuit is lossless by compensation,

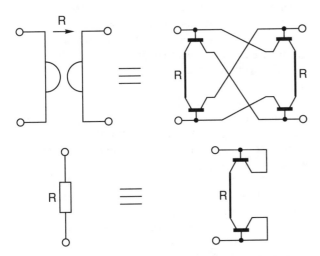

Fig. 11. Transconductor-C filters. Starting from the classical RLC filters, coils are eliminated using gyrators. We arrive at RC-gyrator filters. The gyrator and the resistor can be made with transconductors. We arrive at transconductor-C filters. Transconductors as well as capacitors can be integrated.

High-pass

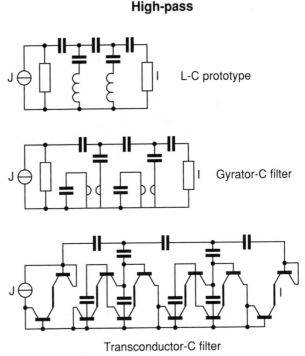

L-C prototype

Gyrator-C filter

Transconductor-C filter

Fig. 12. Simulation of inductances: highpass filter. Starting from an LC prototype filter, in an intermediate step, all inductances are replaced by gyrator-capacitor combinations, which in turn are implemented using transconductors. We arrive at a highpass transconductor-capacitor filter.

- 2 nullors, 4 resistors (12 possibilities): lossless, independent of element values,
- 3 nullors, 2 resistors (20 possibilities): lossless, independent of element values, (see also [16] and [17]).

3.6. Super-capacitor methods

Here we consider the use of circuits with 2 nullors and 4 resistors, of which some are of particular interest. In the high-pass filter in Fig. 18, all inductors (grounded) are simulated by (R operational amplifier) gyrators (with 2 nullors and 4 resistors) and capacitors. The losses of the gyrator circuit can be made largely independent of the first-order frequency roll-off (gain-bandwidth product) of the operational amplifiers [18].

Lowpass filters require an extra transformation, the Bruton transformation [19], to get all electronic components connected to ground with one side (Fig. 19). The transformation makes the capacitors into "super-capacitors". Matching the op amps can provide compensation for the phase effects of the first-order frequency roll-off of the two amplifiers [18]. An alternative name for a super-capacitor is fre-

Low-pass

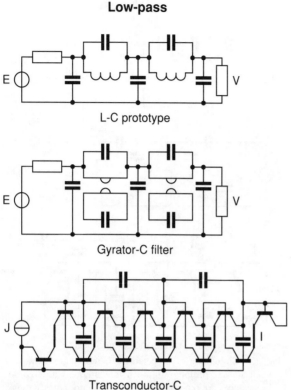

L-C prototype

Gyrator-C filter

Transconductor-C

Fig. 13. Simulation of inductances: lowpass filter. Starting from an *LC* prototype filter, all inductances are replaced by gyrator-capacitor combinations. Transconfigurations (floating gyrators to grounded gyrators, then to transconductors and combining pairs of transconductors) yield an equivalent transconductor-capacitor circuit with a minimum number of all input-grounded transconductors.

All-pass
constant resistance

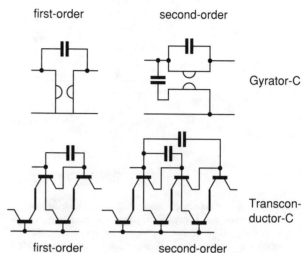

first-order   second-order

Gyrator-C

Transcon-
ductor-C

first-order   second-order

Fig. 14. Gyrator and transconductor methods: allpass filters. The first- and second-order gyrator-type allpass sections (in the upper part of the figure) have no *LC* counterpart. They show a delay in one direction and zero delay in the opposite direction (nonreciprocal). The transconductor-capacitor equivalents (lower part of the figure) have input-grounded transconductors. The sections can be inserted in any filter in front of the load resistor (they are constant-resistance allpass sections). Because the circuits are lossless between resistive terminations, they show low tolerances on the gain characteristic (zero first-order gain sensitivities over the entire passband).

quency dependent negative conductance (FDNC). Similarly, we can speak of a "super inductor" or frequency dependent negative resistor (FDNR). Second-order allpass sections [20, 21] and an alternative design method for bandpass filters [22] are discussed in the literature.

3.7. Signal-flow-graph filters

Transconductor methods transform inductors to capacitors and vice versa. Integrator methods see the capacitor as an integrator of current and the inductor as an integrator of voltage (Fig. 20). In an *LC* resonance circuit the capacitor current is integrated to the capacitor voltage. The capacitor voltage is also the inductor voltage, which in turn is integrated to the inductor current. The inductor current is the negative of the capacitor current. We observe a closed loop: integration—integration—inversion.

Similarly, starting from an *LC* prototype filter, the network equations and the descriptive equations for the elements can be implemented in a signal-flow graph (SFG). For a simple example see Fig. 21. In the signal-flow graph we have elementary operations: additions, subtractions and integrations. The underlying equations to signal-flow graphs can be formulated as state-variable equations [14]. Subsequently, the signal-flow graph is implemented (as in analog computers) using operational amplifier integrators and inverters [4].

Fig. 21 is the classic example of an all-pole *LC* lowpass filter. Figure 22 shows a more sophisticated example of a lowpass filter with transmission zeroes at finite frequencies. To implement a transmission zero, two extra capacitors are used.

---

[4] In principle, the integrators can be designed to ensure that the phase errors of the negative and positive integrators cancel [18]. However, as one of the reviewers of this manuscript remarked, in this case the active compensation generally yields problems with stability.

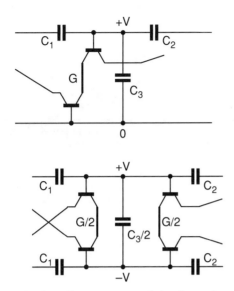

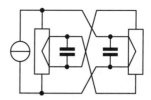

Fig. 17. Balanced transconductors. A resonance circuit uses two "half" balanced transconductors.

High-pass filter

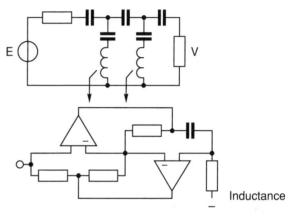

Inductance

Fig. 15. Balancing. The upper part of the figure shows a typical part of a transconductor-C filter (with grounded transconductor). The corresponding balanced arrangement has been depicted in the lower part of the figure. The same (and opposite) currents are made. Capacitors C_1 and C_2 are used twice, whereas C_3 has been halved. In many cases C_1, $C_2 \ll C_3$ (for all-pole filters $C_1 = C_2 = 0$) and then the total capacitance is significantly reduced. Signal voltages are 6 dB higher. Noise voltages are 3 dB higher. The signal-to-noise ratio is improved by 3 dB. The total supply current and the supply voltage can be the same.

Fig. 18. High-pass filter with R-operational amplifier gyrators. The LC prototype filter has grounded inductors. A grounded inductance can be simulated by an electronic circuit with 2 operational amplifiers and 4 resistors (a gyrator) and a capacitor. The dissipation factor (or loss angle) of the inductance can be made zero (to a first order) independent of the high-frequency roll-off (gain-bandwidth product) of the amplifiers.

Instead of using integrators as elementary circuits, blocks with resonance circuits can be used (see Fig. 23). Thus, bandpass filters can be implemented. The method also yields an alternative for the implementation of finite-frequency transmission zeroes.

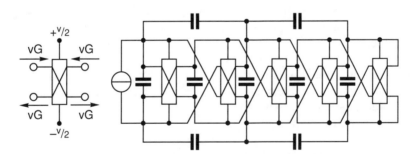

Fig. 16. Balanced transconductors. The left part of the figure defines a full balanced transconductor. In theory, full balanced transconductors can be seen as two separate transconductors, either connected back-to-back or cross-coupled. In practice, parts of the circuitry of the two transconductors are in common. The right-hand part of the figure shows a fifth-order lowpass filter with five "full" balanced transconductors. The upper and lower capacitors implement transmission zeroes.

Low-pass

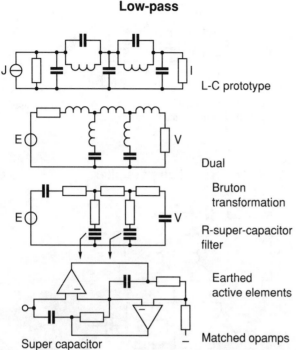

L-C prototype

Dual

Bruton transformation

R-super-capacitor filter

Earthed active elements

Super capacitor

Matched opamps

Fig. 19. Lowpass filter with super-capacitors. An *LC* low-pass filter has floating coils. Taking the dual and multiplication of all admittances by the complex frequency *p* (Bruton transformation) leaves the voltage transfer function invariant. Inductors are transformed to resistors, resistors to capacitors, and capacitors to super-capacitors. All super-capacitors are connected to ground. They can be made with combinations of 2 operational amplifiers, 3 resistors, and 2 capacitors. High-frequency roll-off phase-error effects can compensate when matched amplifiers are used. We should point out that some filter nodes have no DC path to earth, yet they have to fix the DC bias of electronic circuits. The inclusion of extra resistive and/or inductive elements can solve the problem.

Although the transconductor and integrator methods lead to different circuits, they are not fundamentally different. They are just two ways of looking at the same problem. If one wishes, gyrators can be indicated in the signal-flow graph filters and the integrators in transconductor-*C* filters; they can also be designed using the alternative method.

3.8. Balanced integrator filters (using balanced amplifiers)

MOSFET-*C* balanced integrator filters were first proposed by Banu and Tsividis [23, 24]. The transformation from unbalanced to balanced is depicted in Fig. 24. For the same supply voltage and supply current the signal-to-noise ratio can be improved by 3dB. Alternatively, for the same signal-to-noise ra-

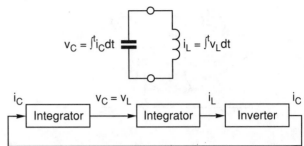

Fig. 20. Integrator filters. A capacitor integrates current. An inductor integrates voltage. The equations of an *LC* resonance circuit are depicted in the integrator-integrator-inverter scheme. Similarly, *LC* filters can be converted to arrangements with integrators and inverters (and adders and subtractors). From the lower part of the figure we see that the loop-gain decreases with frequency (near resonance the loop-gain approximates 1). If we had made a closed loop of differentiators instead of integrators, we would have implemented the same resonance circuit, but the loop-gain would increase strongly at high frequencies. In practice, the latter leads to instable circuits. For this same reason, we use transconductor filters and not transresistor filters.

low-pass all pole filter

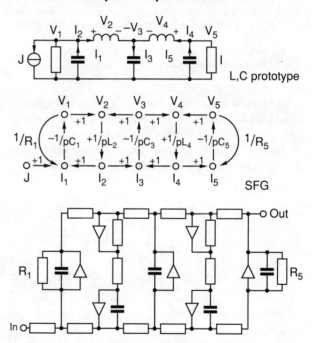

Circuit with negative and positive integrators

Fig. 21. Signal-flow graph filter (all-pole lowpass filter). A leapfrog-type signal-flow graph is derived from the *LC* prototype lowpass filter. It uses additions, subtractions, and integrations as operations. The corresponding integrator circuit is shown in the lower part of the figure. The first, third, and fifth integrators, which are directed upward, are common negative summing integrators. The second and fourth integrators, which are directed downward, are positive integrators (or integrator-inverter combinations).

24

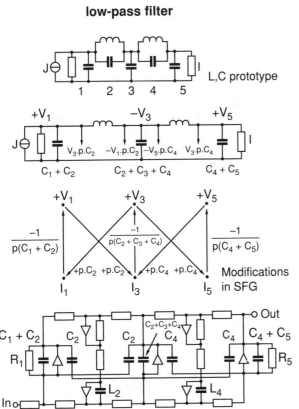

low-pass filter

L,C prototype

Modifications in SFG

Arrangement with negative and positive integrators

Fig. 22. Signal-flow graph filter (lowpass filter). Transmission zeroes (at finite frequencies) can be included in the design procedure by replacing the floating capacitances by earthed ones and pairs of earthed transcapacitances. We again arrive at a circuit with inductive series branches and capacitive shunt branches and the signal-flow graph can be derived (only those parts that have been modified relative to the all-pole case have been indicated). The implementation with integrators (needing 4 extra capacitors) has been depicted in the lowest part of the figure.

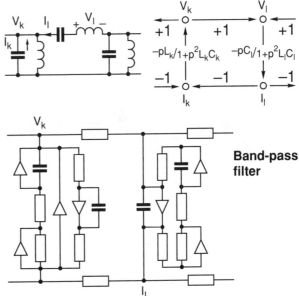

Band-pass filter

Fig. 23. Signal-flow graph method (for bandpass filters). From the *LC* prototype filter (*top left*) we again derive a leapfrog-type signal-flow graph (*top right*). The integrations have been replaced by immittance functions of *LC* resonance circuits. The integrators are replaced by electronic resonators (see bottom part of the figure). A similar method can be used to implement transmission zeroes (at finite frequencies) of a lowpass filter. This permits an independent tuning of the transmission zeroes (for variable and programmable filters).

tio, the capacitor values can be halved (the impedance level is doubled).

A fifth-order balanced-integrator lowpass filter arrangement is depicted in Fig. 25. It has no inverters; inversions have simply been implemented by cross-couplings, thus saving on bias current and chip area. Balanced amplifier circuits need not be more complex than common op amp circuits. Balanced amplifiers can be seen as common op amps, where the differential-to-single-ended converting output stage has been omitted [25].

Lossless balanced integrator allpass sections do not exist. For allpass sections we apply canonic filter sections. Balanced integrator canonic filter sections exist for any order of the filter function [25]. More-

over, they can implement any filter function without having subtractions in the coefficients, which is important for tolerances—compare with [26]. A second-order section is depicted in Fig. 26. Finally, we observe that any transfer function can be made from 4 pairs of passive *RC* admittances and a single balanced amplifier [25].

4. INTEGRATION: YARDSTICKS AND DESIGN ESTIMATIONS

The cost of common (external) resistors and capacitors for *RC*-active filters is roughly a factor 10 lower than the cost of 1 mm^2 of silicon. Many examples of integrated filter proposals in literature are more expensive than their nonintegrated counterparts. In some cases, analog filters are integrated to reduce size (irrespective of the cost).

To make filter integration worthwhile in terms of cost (which is by far the main factor for industry that counts), integrated filters should be made on a small chip area. Capacitors should not be significantly

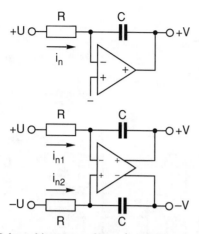

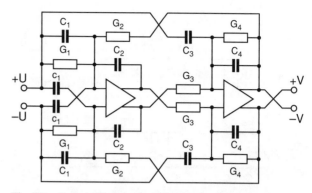

Fig. 26. Canonic filter section. The transfer function is

$$\frac{V}{U} = \frac{G_1.G_2 + p(C_1 - c_1)G_3 + p^2 C_2.C_3}{G_2.G_3 + p.C_2.G_4 + p^2 C_2.C_4}.$$

Any second-order transfer function can be implemented. If we choose either $C_1 = 0$ and/or $c_1 = 0$ there are no subtractions in the coefficients. In the case of a lowpass filter (all-pole) $C_1 = c_1 = C_3 = 0$, for a high-pass filter $G_1 = 0$, $C_1 = c_1 = 0$, in the case of a transmission zero at finite frequencies $C_1 = c_1 = 0$ and in the case of an allpass we may choose $G_1 = G_2$, $G_3 = G_4$, $C_1 = 0$, $c_1 = C2$ and $C_3 = C_4$. Canonic filter sections (in practice of second and third order) are used for cascade designs of filter transfer functions, in particular for allpass sections (for group-delay equalization and short delay lines).

Fig. 24. Balanced-integrator filters (using amplifiers). The transformation from unbalanced to balanced, at first glance, seems to require a doubling of the total capacitance. However, the single-ended signal voltage is the same. The noise currents can be written as $i_{n1} = (i_{n1} + i_{n2})/2 + (i_{n1} - i_{n2})/2$ and $i_{n2} = (i_{n1} + i_{n2})/2 - (i_{n1} - i_{n2})/2$. Because of the low common-mode gain, the common-mode part of the noise currents $(i_{n1} + i_{n2})/2$ has no influence. The differential-mode parts: $(i_{n1} - i_{n2})/2$ yield a 3 dB lower noise than in the single-ended case. We arrive at a 3 dB-increased signal-to-noise ratio, which fully agrees with a factor-two-larger total capacitance. This higher signal-to-noise ratio can be obtained with the same supply voltage and roughly the same supply current. Furthermore, in balanced-integrator filters, inverters are replaced by cross-couplings (not noisy, need no supply current). This further reduces the supply power consumption for the filters relative to the single-ended circuits.

larger than 0.1 mm^2; that is, their value should not be larger than 50-100 pF.

In many cases only the electronic elements (amplifiers, for example) are integrated and the filter resistors and capacitors are left outside the chip. For a Sallen-and-Key filter, only a few pins are needed. The user of the integrated circuit can still modify the filter characteristic. Also, in integrated circuits one often sees *RC*-amplifier filters integrated as such (with fixed integrated resistors and capacitors). Design methods are simple and the filter elements can be highly linear, but tuning is not possible (except for switching to different element values [27]). In cases where one can cope with tolerances on cut-off frequencies of the order of magnitude of $\pm 30\%$ (due to nonnominal processing, temperature influences, aging, etc.) this method is a good one. For example, Sallen-and-Key filters are often integrated. Below, we shall mainly consider the integration of filters, the cut-off frequencies of which can be tuned (i.e., scaled in frequency).

In practice, we design integrated filters with capacitor values in the range between 0.1 pF to 10 pF. For special cases (e.g., for low frequencies and where a high dynamic range is required) we go to somewhat higher values. This also means that the impedance level of integrated filters is high, much higher than for filters with external elements. Common impedance levels are 1-10 MOhm for an audio filter and 5-50 kOhm for a video filter.

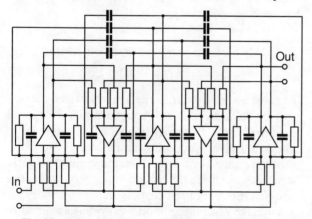

Fig. 25. Balanced-integrator lowpass filter. The fifth-order filter needs five balanced amplifiers. Inverters have been replaced by cross-couplings. The capacitors at the top of the figure implement finite-frequency transmission zeroes.

4.1. Initial design estimations

The designer of a filter will start by choosing a circuit technique (using his knowledge of the requirements and based upon experience). The circuit technique fixes the maximum signal voltages that can be handled by the filter elements (depending on compression, distortion and/or intermodulation requirements). In many cases the signals at the output of a filter are kept lower because of signal enhancement inside the filter (resonance effects). Knowing the maximum and/or nominal signal voltages and the requirements for the signal-to-noise ratio, the maximum noise voltage level is fixed. The latter determines the maximum impedance level of the filter.

For a bandpass filter we take the noise of a resonance circuit of the same bandwidth (see Fig. 27) and [28]. From the noise level the minimum capacitor value is fixed (resistor values follow, knowing the center frequency). An excess noise factor F accounts for extra noise from the electronic circuitry, which adds to the noise of the gyrator and integrator resistors.

Based upon experience, a simple and useful yardstick for the noise in an nth-order lowpass filter is n times the noise of a filter resistor over the passband (see Fig. 28). Generally, the low-frequency noise from the filter resistors is lower but electronics (for example, bias current sources) as well as resonance effects increase the noise. The noise determines the maximum resistance level. Capacitor values follow from the time constants (RC products), which are related to the bandwidth of the filter (see Fig. 28).

Knowing the order of magnitude of the resistor and capacitor values, the chip area is estimated, mainly by accounting for

- the electronic circuits, for which we take a value of the order of magnitude of 0.1 mm^2 per filter order (including resistive elements) and
- the total capacitance (using the capacitor density of the IC process, for example 1 nF/mm^2).

From the maximum signal voltage and the resistance level, the maximum signal current is obtained. This signal current has to be handled by the transconductors and/or by the output stages of the amplifiers. This fixes the minimum bias current.

The bias current (per filter order) should be larger than one or two times the peak value of the signal current (depending on the design). We apply a safety margin of some 3 dB (for linearity margins, auxiliary circuitry, etc.). Because in practice more than one filter element is incident to a node, we multiply the bias current by a factor 2 to obtain an average value, see (Fig. 28).

As a first example, we consider a Cauer-elliptic lowpass filter for video frequencies (bandwidth: 5 MHz, order: 5, supply voltage: 5 V, S_{max}/noise (and S_{max}/distortion) ratios: 60 dB). Because of accuracy requirements, balanced integrator filters will be used for the implementation. In view of the distortion requirements we admit a maximum signal voltage within the filter (on the circuits) of 0.5 V (RMS), and because of internal enhancement, at the filter output 0.2 V (RMS). The noise voltage should be lower than 0.2 mV (RMS). With $F = 2$ we obtain as maximum resistance level: 50 kOhm, a typical capacitor value: 0.6 pF, $C_{tot} = 3$ pF, chip area: 0.5 mm^2, bias current: 0.3 mA (dissipation: 1.5 mW).

As a second example, we consider a part of a 10 MHz FM IF (frequency modulation, intermediate frequency) bandpass filter: a pair of resonance circuits ($n = 4$, bandwidth: 300 kHz, supply voltage: 5 V, S_{max}/noise (S_{max}/distortion) ratios of 80 dB). Severe power-efficiency requirements lead us to opt for balanced transconductor circuits: $V_s(max) = 2$ V (RMS) differentially, $V_n = 0.2$ mV (RMS), $Q_o = 33$, $F = 2$, hence $C(min) = 13$ pF, $R_{max} = 1200$ Ohm, $C_{tot} = 53$ pF, chip area: 0.5 mm^2 ($C_{sq} = 500$ pF/mm^2), bias current: 40 mA, supply power consumption: 200 mW. Although the above dissipation is lower than any value that has been reported in literature, it is too high for most applications. A solution is to modify the system and go to a lower intermediate frequency.

Thus, rough estimates (orders of magnitude) are obtained. They give an indication of where problems may arise during later, more detailed design efforts.

5. FILTER ELEMENTS ON SILICON

The main problems of integrating analog filters are that:

- coils cannot be integrated (below GHz frequencies),
- common integrated resistors have large temperature coefficients, and
- integrated elements show high initial tolerances (deviations of the mean value from the design value).

A solution to the first problem is that coils are replaced by capacitors and active circuits. Matching

27

Noise

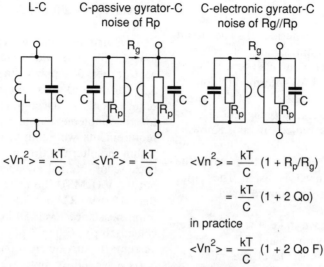

L-C   C-passive gyrator-C   C-electronic gyrator-C
noise of Rp   noise of Rg//Rp

$$\langle Vn^2 \rangle = \frac{kT}{C} \qquad \langle Vn^2 \rangle = \frac{kT}{C} \qquad \langle Vn^2 \rangle = \frac{kT}{C}(1 + R_p/R_g)$$

$$= \frac{kT}{C}(1 + 2Qo)$$

in practice

$$\langle Vn^2 \rangle = \frac{kT}{C}(1 + 2Qo\ F)$$

Fig. 27. Noise of a "symmetric" gyrator resonance circuit. We follow a simple derivation credited to J. S. Visser. For a passive *LC* resonance circuit (*left part of the figure*) the wide-band noise voltage is given by the expression

$$\langle V_n^2 \rangle = \frac{k.T}{C}.$$

The same expression applies to a resonance circuit with a passive gyrator (i.e., passive implementation with noiseless gyration resistances—*see center of the figure*). The noise can be thought to be noise from the loss resistances (R_p). The corresponding noise currents are given by the equation

$$\langle I_n^2 \rangle = 4.k.T/R_p.df$$

An electronic gyrator (*right-hand part of the figure*) has, in addition, the noise of the gyration resistors. The corresponding noise sources can be drawn across the gyrator ports. In fact, they add to the noise of the loss resistances, according to

$$\langle I_n^2 \rangle = 4.k.T/R_p.df + 4.k.T/R_g.df.$$

The total squared noise currents have increased by a factor $1 + R_p/R_g = 1 + 2.Q_o$. The introduction of an excess noise factor F yields as multiplication factor: $1 + 2.Q_o.F$. Hence,

$$\langle V_n^2 \rangle = \frac{k.T}{C}(1 + 2.Q_o.F).$$

$F = 1$ in the case that the gyration resistors are noisy as common resistors. The excess noise factor can account for the fact that the gyration resistors can be the bipolar-diode type (making $F = 0.5$) and/or for noise of bias current sources (making F higher).

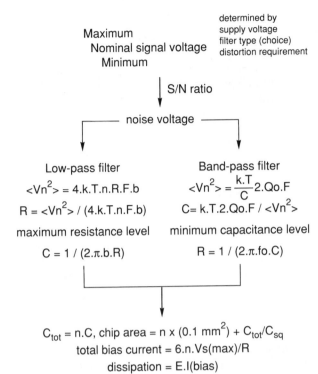

First estimates

Maximum
Nominal signal voltage
Minimum

determined by
supply voltage
filter type (choice)
distortion requirement

↓ S/N ratio

── noise voltage ──

Low-pass filter

$<V_n^2> = 4.k.T.n.R.F.b$

$R = <V_n^2> / (4.k.T.n.F.b)$

maximum resistance level

$C = 1 / (2.\pi.b.R)$

Band-pass filter

$<V_n^2> = \dfrac{k.T}{C}2.Q_o.F$

$C = k.T.2.Q_o.F / <V_n^2>$

minimum capacitance level

$R = 1 / (2.\pi.f_o.C)$

$C_{tot} = n.C$, chip area $= n \times (0.1 \text{ mm}^2) + C_{tot}/C_{sq}$

total bias current $= 6.n.V_s(max)/R$

dissipation $= E.I(bias)$

Fig. 28. At the start of a filter design, rough estimates are made to get a first impression of what can be made. Typical steps in the estimation procedure are indicated in the figure. Given the supply voltage, the *IC* process and S/N ratio (or S/D ratio), a type of filter circuit is chosen. Subsequently, signal voltage, noise voltage, maximum resistor value and minimum capacitor value, chip area, bias current, and power consumption are estimated roughly. For the noise of a lowpass filter we simply take the noise of *n* resistors and for a bandpass filter we take the noise of a corresponding resonance circuit. Notation: $k.T = 4 \cdot 10^{-21}$, $\pi = 3.14$, *n*: filter order, *b*: bandwidth, f_o: center frequency, Q_o: equivalent quality factor ($Q_o = f_o/b$), V_s: signal voltage, V_n: noise voltage, *F*: excess noise factor ($F = 2$, typically), *R*: (typical) resistor value, *C*: (typical) capacitor value, C_{sq}: capacitor density for the *IC* process, *E*: supply voltage.

elements on a chip means that, in principle, the shape of the filter will be correct. The filter needs only a tuning (a frequency scaling). This can be done either by trimming resistor and/or capacitor values or by using electrically variable resistances or capacitances.

In integrated circuits the resistor and the capacitor are elements of filter design whereas the transistor is not. Combinations of transistors and/or resistors are used instead. Simple high-performance combinations are optimum for VLSI. Elements and components are combined to form filters. We mention the following:

● elements:
    inductive
    —not on silicon (below GHz frequencies),
    capacitive
    —junction capacitor,
    —dielectric capacitor,
    resistive
    —metal-film resistor,
    —diffused/implanted resistor,
    —transistor (trans)conductance,
● components:
    nullor (op amp, balanced amplifier),
    VCCS (transconductor),
    gyrator (pair of transconductors),
    NIC (negative immittance converter),
    integrator,
    resonance circuit, oscillator,
● filters:
    lowpass, highpass, bandpass (bandstop) filter,
    allpass filter, (tapped) delay line.

5.1. Capacitors

Junction capacitors are present in all processes, gate-oxide capacitors are present in all MOS processes (in some cases also on top of a low-ohmic area). In standard digital MOS processes, MOS transistors are used as capacitors: in strips to reduce the series resistance and in balanced arrangements to improve the linearity. In more sophisticated IC processes, we have capacitors between layers of interconnect (also used for switched-capacitor filters). The dielectric is either silicon oxide, silicon nitride, or aluminum oxide. Large dielectric capacitors (oxide-nitride sandwich) can be made on monolithic low-ohmic silicon [11] (see also Fig. 29). Advanced etching techniques (U-groove) can significantly increase the effective area of capacitors (trench capacitors) [29]. Common densities for dielectric capacitors range from 500 pF/mm² to 2000 pF/mm². Junction capacitors can have a higher density, for example up to 4000 pF/mm² and their variability can be of practical importance. However, reliability problems and nonlinear effects limit their application. Aluminum oxide is used as a dielectric in GaAs processes [30]. Silicon oxide has lower leakage currents and a lower temperature coefficient compared with silicon nitride. Silicon nitride is less sensitive to electrical damage. The oxide/nitride combination has the advantages of both. The presence of silicon

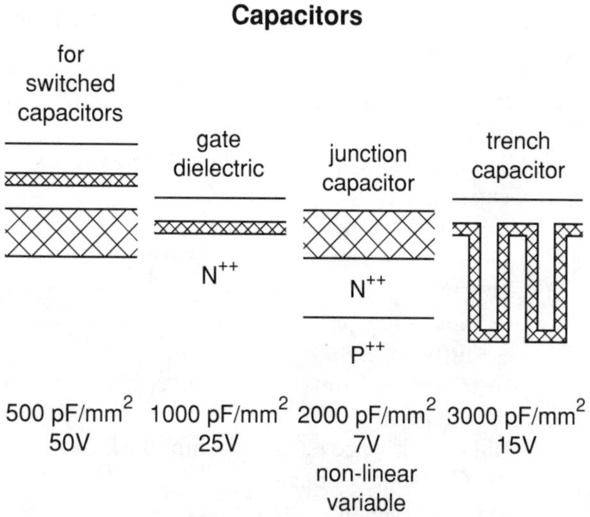

Capacitors

for switched capacitors

gate dielectric

junction capacitor

trench capacitor

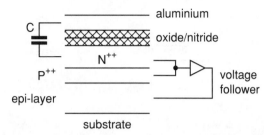

500 pF/mm^2	1000 pF/mm^2	2000 pF/mm^2	3000 pF/mm^2
50V	25V	7V	15V
		non-linear	
		variable	

Fig. 29. Capacitor types. From *left to right*, capacitor between two layers of interconnect (as commonly used for switched-capacitor filters), capacitor between one interconnect layer and a (low-ohmic) diffusion, a junction capacitor (between 2 low-ohmic diffusions), a trench type capacitor (as has been made for application in memories). Some typical values of capacitor densities and breakdown voltages have been indicated.

Bootstrapping

Fig. 30. Bootstrapping of stray capacitors. In some cases the influence of stray capacitances can be eliminated by keeping the layer below the lower terminal at the same (signal) voltage. In the figure, the N^{++} layer and the P^{++} layer are short-circuited and form the lower terminal of the capacitor. The stray capacitor to the epitaxial layer is not felt because the signal voltage across it is kept to almost zero. The capacitive stray current from the epitaxial layer to the substrate is provided by the amplifier (not by the filter). Often, several filter capacitors are incident to a node. In that case, one voltage follower suffices for bootstrapping the corresponding stray capacitors.

in the silicon oxide increases the dielectric constant [31]. Different capacitor types may be combined as a sandwich and connected in parallel to increase the capacitance per mm^2. A junction capacitor below a gate-oxide capacitor and a capacitor between two layers of interconnect can be shunted to arrive at a density of over 5 nF/mm^2.

Initial tolerances (deviation of the mean capacitor value from the design value) are of the order of magnitude of $\pm 10\%$. Trimming is possible (e.g., laser trimming, zener zapping) but is seldom applied —capacitor ratios are used instead. Matching is important. Matching accuracy can be significantly better than 1% [32, 33]. Temperature coefficients can be of the order of 100 ppm/K and lower. Dielectric capacitors can have a low voltage dependence ($< 0.1\%/V$). Depletion layers in diffused monolithic or in polysilicon electrodes may be the cause of increased voltage dependence. Depletion layers may also be applied to create voltage-variable capacitors [34]. The ratio of the stray capacitance (to lower layers) to the desired capacitance is of the order of magnitude of 5 to 25%. The percentage is almost invariant for capacitors on field oxide. It depends on the capacitor size (and bias) for capacitors on diffusions. Constructing larger capacitors from combinations of unit capacitors can improve

the accuracy. Lower doping and thinner field oxides in modern processes shift the preference for capacitors on field oxide to capacitors on silicon (with a silicon lower plate). In some cases the influence of parasitic capacitors can be largely reduced by bootstrapping, see Fig. 30 and [11].

5.2. Resistive elements

Resistors of various types are used:

- metal-film resistors,
- diffused resistors (monolithic or polysilicon), and
- transistor (trans)conductances.

In the case of metal film resistors with a low temperature coefficient and on-chip trimming, the designer can rely upon the absolute resistor value. The technique has been used for single-substrate hybrid-integrated filters [35]. The technology is an expensive addition to IC processes. It is used for some analog-to-digital converters.

In other cases the designer must rely upon matching rather than on absolute values. Typical (locally obtainable) spreads are for implanted resistors: 0.2% and for diffused resistors: 0.4%. One should observe that in order to avoid loss of yield, we have to design with 3 or 4 times the spread values. Dynamic matching of element values [36] can improve the above values by some orders of magnitude at the cost of circuit complexity. Trimming (using electric currents) of heavily doped polysilicon resistors can yield similar extreme matching accuracies [37].

Parasitic capacitances can be eliminated by bootstrapping. Nonlinearity owing to modulation of the width of diffused resistors can be reduced by distributed bootstrapping [38].

The (trans)conductances of bipolar and field-effect transistors also are used as resistive elements. They are used as resistors as well as in transconductor-type arrangements. The feature of the transconductor (voltage-controlled current source (VCCS)) of having separate voltage input and current output is extensively used in filters.

The transconductance of a bipolar transistor: $qI_c/(kT)$, where I_c is the collector current, is a physical quantity (no geometrical parameters are involved). Generally, the above expression or, equivalently, the exponential relationship between collector current and base-emitter voltage, is accurate over at least four decades of collector current (large tuning range). The MOS transistor can be used in saturation (in transconductors) as well as in the triode region. The MOS transistor resistors can handle an order of magnitude higher signal voltages than bipolar transistors for the same distortion. Filters using MOS transistor resistors can be made at a higher impedance level (for the same signal-to-noise ratio) and require lower capacitor values. On the other hand, the control range is smaller (in general, less than one decade) and the (trans)conductance is geometry dependent.

Transistor (trans)conductances are variable and their linearity is not as good as that of fixed resistors. Remedies include antimetric excitation of symmetric arrangements (i.e., balanced filters), whereby all even-order harmonics are cancelled and the use of more sophisticated transistor combinations.

6. CIRCUIT EXAMPLES

In the examples that follow, principles are given rather than detailed transistor circuits, which can be found in the references. Transconductors, integrators, and resonators are circuits that can be seen as building blocks, which can be combined to implement all kinds of filter. Below, we start the discussion with bipolar circuits and go to biCMOS and CMOS circuits. Single-ended circuits are considered before their balanced counterparts. This order, to some extent corresponds with history.

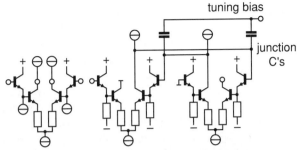

Fig. 31. Junction-capacitor-gyrator combination. *Left*, transconductor having a fixed value. *Right*, resonance circuit. Tuning is provided by a variable bias voltage across the junction capacitors. The reference for the tuning is a frequency, to which a master resonance circuit is locked (frequency-locked loop). The filter capacitors (slaves) get the same bias voltage. The method is used for video resonance circuits and short analog luminance delay lines.

The first example uses fixed resistive elements (transconductors) and variable (junction) capacitors (Fig. 31). The combination has been used for resonance circuits and short analog delay lines in the MHz region (video frequencies [39–41]).

In the next examples fixed capacitors have been combined with variable resistive elements. In particular, fixed resistive elements have been made variable using multipliers [42]. For an example, see Fig. 32 and [11]. Alternative implementations have been presented [43–45], the first two being single-ended and the last a balanced arrangement. The noise of the circuits is mainly from the multiplier. In *LC* filters losses of the elements are expressed in a dissipation factor or loss-angle (unwanted additional phase-shift). In electronic filters phase-shifts in the

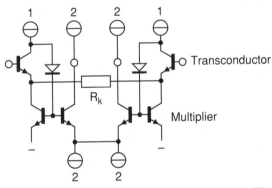

Fig. 32. Transconductor-multiplier combination. The transconductor value is controlled by multiplication of the signal current by a ratio of bias currents in the lower bipolar multiplier ring. In this case, the reference is a reference resistor (external, see tuning methods). One adjustment is needed to tune the filter (or filters).

31

stages play the same role. Generally, they increase with frequency. Phase-shifts of cascaded stages add. This means that the circuits with multipliers are not the best ones for high frequencies, in particular when PNP transistors are used in the signal path (in almost all IC processes PNP transistors have much lower cut-off frequencies than NPN transistors and give correspondingly higher phase-shifts).

Smaller phase-shifts can be obtained in arrangements where long-tailed pair type transconductors are linearized. Combinations of nonlinear elements are used to arrive at more linear circuits. For the simplest example, see Fig. 33 [46]. The simplicity and versatility of the circuits are advantages. The small signal voltages are a disadvantage. Somewhat higher signal voltages can be handled by putting diodes in series or using combinations of more than two long-tailed pairs [47].

A different linearization method is shown in Fig. 34. The circuit can handle twice the signal voltage of the former circuit and can easily be extended with more stages see [48]. A particularly interesting feature is that the circuits can be used in class A/B (i.e., output bias current increasing with increasing signal current). In the case of low signals, we have low DC offset and low noise. For an application, see [49].

Figure 35 shows another circuit in a bipolar IC process [50]. It is an integrator with a transconductor of junction field-effect transistors (which can handle

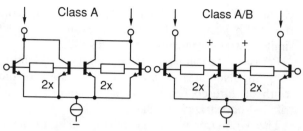

Fig. 34. Linearized transconductors with bipolar transistors. The circuits have a low input impedance and can be operated from (balanced) amplifiers. The circuit on the left is equivalent to the circuit in the former figure, but it can handle a factor of two higher signal voltages (for the same distortion). The numbers of transistors and resistors in the resistor string can be extended to permit handling of larger signals (in practice, to 1 V). The collector currents of all inner transistors should be drawn half from the left and half from the right side. In the circuit on the right, the inner currents are thrown away. The difference between the output currents remains the same and we operate the transconductor in class A/B. At near zero input signals the bias current and noise are low.

higher signal voltages than a bipolar transistor stage). The circuit can be seen as an intermediate step between analog-computer–type circuits and modern fully balanced integrator circuits.

Balanced integrator circuits (see Fig. 36, and [23, 24]) are simpler than their unbalanced counterparts, partly because inverters are not needed (cross-couplings are used instead) and partly because the amplifiers can be simpler [25, 51]. Signals and biasing are properly separated: signals are differential, biasing is common-mode. Antimetric excitation of balanced circuits automatically yields cancellation of even-order harmonic distortion. As in most integrator circuits with operational amplifiers, all filter nodes are either inputs to amplifiers (virtual ground)

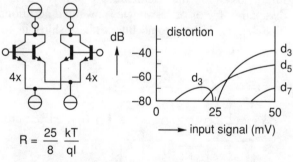

$$R = \frac{25}{8} \frac{kT}{qI}$$

Fig. 33. A combination of two long-tailed pairs is the simplest example of a linearized transconductor of bipolar transistors. The two tangent hyperbolic characteristics of the long-tailed pairs have been shifted using emitter ratios. The ratio $1 : (2 + \sqrt{3}) = 1 : 3.732\ldots$ yields a maximally flat characteristic. The more practical ratio 1:4 gives some over-compensation (and the nonmonotonic distortion behavior). The circuit is employed in all kinds of transconductor-capacitor filters, in particular at low supply voltages (1 V) and up to high frequencies (10 MHz). For a temperature-independent transconductance, the tuning bias current has to be proportional to the absolute temperature.

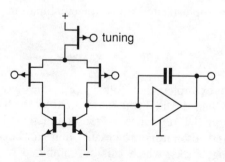

Fig. 35. A junction FET variable transconductor in an integrator arrangement in bipolar technology. Application of field-effect transistors is an alternative way to increase the voltage handling capability of the circuits. The integrator has an inverting and a noninverting input and has been employed in signal-flow graph filters.

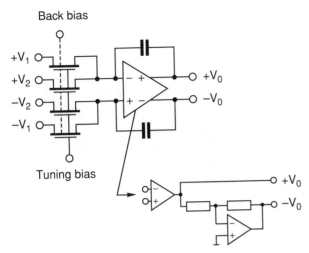

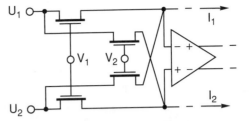

MOS equation: $Id = b (Vg - Vth - \frac{Vs + Vd}{2}) (Vd - Vs)$

$I_1 - I_2 = b (U_1 - U_2) (V_1 - V_2)$

Fig. 38. A quad of MOS resistors, with all sources at the same voltage, gives a particularly simple equation for the voltage-to-current conversion. The arrangement can be used in balanced and unbalanced linear and nonlinear applications.

Fig. 36. Balanced integrator with MOS-transistor resistors operating in the triode region. It has two voltage inputs and integrates the weighted sum. The conductance values and, hence, the inverses of the time constants, are linearly controlled by the gate voltage. The more detailed diagram of the amplifier shows the function of the balanced amplifier rather than a realistic implementation.

or outputs of amplifiers (low ohmic). Strays at the filter nodes barely influence the filter performance. The balanced integrator filters are very accurate.

It is astonishing that with nonlinear resistors, a perfectly linear integrator can be made. That this is true can be shown using simple (nonlinear) MOS transistor equations (Fig. 37). Once this is known, it is not so surprising, that, in practice, signal-to-distor-

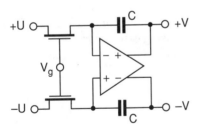

simple MOS equation: $Id = b (Vg - Vth - \frac{Vs + Vd}{2}) (Vd - Vs)$

non-linear

integrator equation: $b (Vg - Vth) U + \frac{d}{dt} C V = 0$

linear

Fig. 37. Nonlinear resistors can yield a perfectly linear integrator. The MOS resistors are nonlinear. Input voltages are balanced. The balanced amplifier is assumed to be ideal—zero input current, zero input voltage differentially (not common-mode) and balanced output voltage. Using simple nonlinear equations for the MOS transistors, a perfectly linear equation is derived for the integrator.

tion ratios of 60 dB can be obtained for signal voltages of the order of magnitude of 1 V.

Double balancing by adding cross-coupled MOS transistors (see Fig. 38 [52]) yields a particularly simple equation independent of the balancing of input signals and independent of the threshold voltage of the MOS transistors. The arrangement shows a natural high-frequency phase-error compensation. The principle is used for balanced and unbalanced [53, 54] linear applications and is a basis for the design of balanced multipliers (and squarers) for the control of oscillators and for adaptive filters.

Taking into account body effects for the MOS transistor, the simple equation still holds true for double balanced circuits. In practice, however, the double balancing is not very effective in further improving the linearity. Distortion levels of better than 70 dB for, say, 1 V signals are hard to obtain. The main limiting phenomena are unbalance due to mismatch (for details on mismatch of MOS transistors, see [55]), mobility nonconstancy, and thermal feedback. Thermal feedback is the nonlinear effect that the resistor value varies with its temperature, which depends on the signal (dissipation). Nonlinear body effects can, in some cases, give surprising improvements (see for example [56]).

In addition to the DC-bias we can apply half the signal voltage to the gate [57]. This can balance the resistor in unbalanced applications (see [58], [1], and Fig. 39). In balanced applications the linearity is improved and we obtain full circuit compatibility with multipliers in double balanced arrangements [25].

A problem is that in standard CMOS the gate tuning voltage is preferably higher than the positive

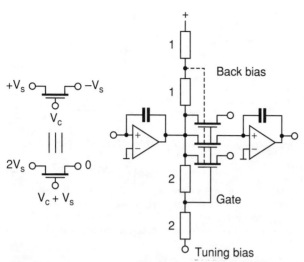

Fig. 39. In unbalanced applications, the excitation of the MOS transistors can be balanced by putting half the signal voltage on gate (and back-gate) in addition to the bias voltages. In balanced circuits the method further reduces the distortion.

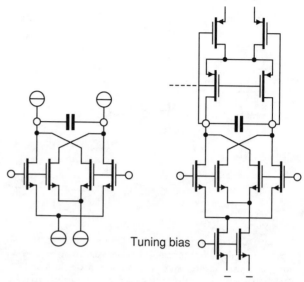

Fig. 40. Balanced CMOS transconductor integrator. The transconductor is a long-tailed pair. In the figure it has been linearized using a cross-coupled pair (with half the W/L ratio and some 15% of the total bias current). The transconductance tunes linearly with the bias voltage. The PMOS current sources have been implemented as a balanced load circuit. The integrator has been used for band-pass filters (a set of capacitively coupled, fully balanced resonance circuits).

supply voltage (or lower than the negative supply voltage). In biCMOS the bipolar part often permits the use of higher voltages, which can solve this problem. Moreover, bipolar balanced amplifiers can be simple (because of the high transconductance of the bipolar transistors). Balanced integrators can also be made by replacing the MOS-transistor resistors with transconductors or with fixed resistors and junction capacitors [25].

Let us return to transconductors, but this time in MOS. The MOS long-tailed pair is the counterpart of the bipolar long-tailed pair. It can be used with and without linearization (see Fig. 40 [59]). The figure shows an example of a balanced transconductor integrator. In practice, maximum signal voltages can be employed of up to several 100 mV (differentially). This is an order of magnitude larger than for the bipolar circuits and leads to lower currents, a higher impedance level, and smaller filter capacitors (for a given signal-to-noise ratio).

In balanced filters signal handling is differential and biasing is common-mode. For stability, the common-mode gain should be low. A simple common-mode feedback is shown in Fig. 41 in a gyrator resonance circuit. The common mode control part has been indicated in dashed lines. In this circuit all signal-carrying nodes are filter nodes. Capacitive strays at the nodes can be part of the filter capacitors. The circuit can be used up to relatively high frequencies.

Larger signal voltages can be handled when the long-tailed pairs are degenerated using MOS-transistor resistors, (see Fig. 42). The upper circuit [60] (applied in [61–63]) uses a bias voltage for tuning and the lower circuit (see [64–66]) bias currents. The transconductors have internal signal-carrying nodes (giving extra phase-shifts).

The quadratic characteristic of an MOS transistor in saturation is fully exploited in the transconductor circuits in [67] and in Fig. 43 [68]. In the latter circuit the transconductance is controlled by offset voltages, either as indicated in the figure or between the sources of the outer and inner pair of transistors. A particularly simple grounded linear resistor (not directly a transconductor) is shown in Fig. 44 [69].

CMOS digital gate-type circuits are also used as resistive elements (see Fig. 45). We refer to [70, 71] for unbalanced circuits and to [72, 73] for balanced circuits and a solution to keep the common-mode gain low. The balanced circuits are good for linearity and high frequencies.

In the next few examples, the MOS transistors (in the triode region) have no signal voltage across the channel (V_d-V_s is a bias voltage), see Fig. 46. Unlike

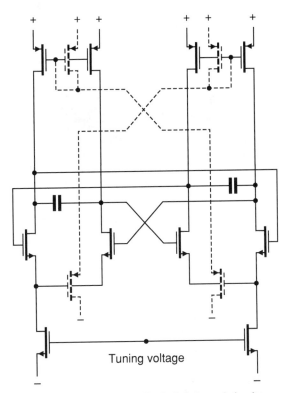

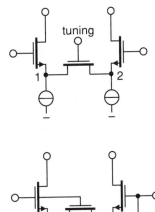

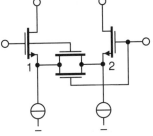

Fig. 42. Linearized transconductors. The input transistors are used as source followers. The transistors in the center are resistors. Capacitive strays at internal nodes 1 and 2 yield excess phase-shifts. The circuits show a good linearity, but they are not the best for high frequencies. The upper circuit uses a tuning bias voltage, and the lower circuit employs bias currents for tuning.

Fig. 41. Common-mode feedback. In balanced circuits, common-mode control circuitry provides biasing. The common-mode gain should be low in order not to excite common mode–type free oscillations. In the figure we have two NMOS long-tailed pair transconductors forming a gyrator and with the capacitors forming a resonance circuit. NMOS current sources provide the biasing and the tuning. PMOS load circuits are high-ohmic for differential signals and low-ohmic for common-mode biasing. The common mode feedback, taken from common-mode points of "next" transconductors, has been drawn in dashed lines. This simple common-mode control method can be applied not only to resonance circuits but to filters in general.

plex filter elements. For some modern examples, see [78, 79].

Above, we have surveyed a part of the abundance of different circuit principles and ways in which they have been worked out. For example, the use of

all the previous circuits, the single-ended version is linear by itself. Linearity does not depend upon the canceling of harmonics. Furthermore, the gate-source voltage can be relatively high (low sensitivity to tolerances on the threshold voltages). The circuit in Fig. 47 [74] uses quad NMOS transistors and a balanced amplifier. The common-mode gain is zero when the drain-source voltages of the upper and lower transistors are equal. Transconductor versions can be found in [75–77].

NIC circuits by themselves are no longer considered to be very useful as filter elements (because of problems with tolerances). However, in electronics they play a part for the undamping of cables (bidirectional loss compensation), undamping of lossy coils (resonance circuits) and also within more com-

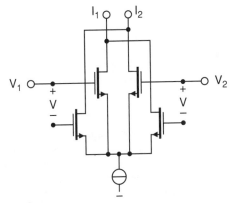

MOS transistor: $Id = K (Vgs - Vth)^2$

$I_1 - I_2 = 2 K V (V_1 - V_2)$

Fig. 43. Linear transconductor based upon the quadratic characteristic of the MOS transistor in saturation. The transconductor value is linearly controlled by the offset voltages V. The bias current has no effect on the transconductance; it determines the current handling capacity.

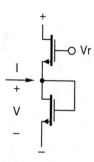

MOS equation: $Id = K(Vgs - Vth)^2$

$$I = K(Vr - Vth)(2V - Vr)$$

Fig. 44. Grounded linear resistor of two MOS transistors in saturation. The simple circuit can be used in transconductors and in filters.

depletion MOS (see [80] for an example) has not been considered. All circuits have their advantages and disadvantages. Simple applications can be implemented in many ways. More demanding applications require an accurate choice of circuit type.

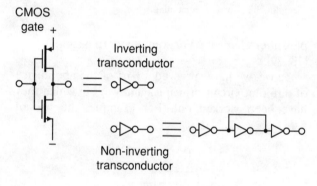

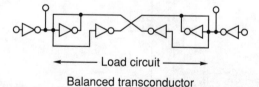

Fig. 45. CMOS-gate type circuits as transconductors. Single-ended: one gate is an inverting transconductor and three gates constitute a noninverting transconductor, combinations of inverting and noninverting transconductors, often of a somewhat more complex type, are used to design analog filters. Balanced: just two gates (the outer ones) are needed as transconductors. A load circuit (of four gates in the center) reduces the common-mode gain. For a better understanding, the load circuit can also be drawn in terms of four current mirrors. The transconductors have a good linearity, but a relatively poor output impedance (Early effect). All nodes can be filter nodes (strays can be included in filter capacitors). The control voltage is the supply voltage.

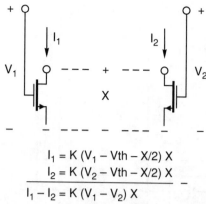

$$I_1 = K(V_1 - Vth - X/2)X$$
$$I_2 = K(V_2 - Vth - X/2)X$$
$$\overline{I_1 - I_2 = K(V_1 - V_2)X}$$

Fig. 46. Constant drain-source-voltage methods. The MOS transistor is used in the triode region. The two stages together yield a simple equation. The tuning is linear with the control voltage X. The transconductance of each stage (single-ended) is already linear. This means that in cases of mismatch, even-order distortion is not strongly coming up. The principle is particularly promising when a low signal distortion is of primary concern.

Requirements in respect of high linearity, small chip area (i.e., low cost), high (or very low) frequencies, low dissipation, very linear tuning, low supply voltage, and others limit the number of possibilities for specific applications. Usually, the choice of the IC

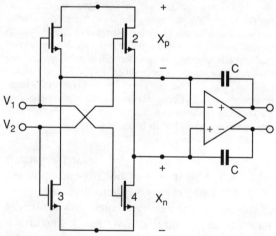

$$I_1 = K(V_1 - Vth - Xp/2)Xp$$
$$I_2 = K(V_2 - Vth - Xp/2)Xp$$
$$I_3 = K(V_2 - Vth + Xn/2)Xn$$
$$I_4 = K(V_1 - Vth + Xn/2)Xn$$

Fig. 47. Quad NMOS (or PMOS) balanced integrator. The MOS transistors are used in the triode region. Differentially: $I_1 - I_2 - I_3 + I_4 = K(V_1 - V_2)(X_p + X_n)$. The expression shows the linearity for signals and control. The common-mode gain is zero if $X_p = X_n$. The DC-level shift between input and output of the transconductor requires an opposite DC-level shift in the amplifier.

36

process (bipolar, CMOS or biCMOS) is not fixed by the filters (filters are only a minor part of the integrated circuit). This further restricts the set of filter types (if not yet empty) that can be employed. In the case of the threshold voltages of standard digital CMOS, several circuits do not fit within the standard digital (or lower) supply voltage. In high-performance biCMOS processes, all combinations can be made and compared.

7. TUNING

The tuning of integrated filters can remedy two effects:

- it may correct time constants in the filter(s) (frequency control), and
- it may provide a correction for excess phase-shifts (Q-control).

Q-control methods typically correct for phase-shifts owing to finite cut-off frequencies of circuits, capacitive strays, and those caused by finite output resistances (Early effect). Q-control may lead to complex control schemes [76]. In many cases it can be cost effectively eliminated by using modified or different filter circuits. Problems can arise, in particular for narrow-band filters at high frequencies. However, one should be aware that these filters also have problems with respect to obtaining a useful signal-to-noise ratio for an acceptable supply power consumption. This may be an extra reason to modify the system design and reduce the filter requirements.

Without frequency control the gain and phase of the filters will have the correct shape (on a logarithmic frequency scale) because of accurate matching of filter elements on a chip. The filter will be de-tuned, possibly by tens of percents (owing to non-nominal processing, temperature effects, etc.). The use of variable filter elements enables us to correct for the detuning.

Frequency control methods are (see also Fig. 48):
- without reference (large tolerance region),
- with a reference resistor (one adjustment),
- with a reference frequency:
  PLL, FLL, etc. (master-slave technique),
  clock oscillator (matched to filter),
  master = slave (time multiplex),
  signal = reference.

In IC processes the gap voltage (of silicon) is an accurate voltage reference. A similar reference for

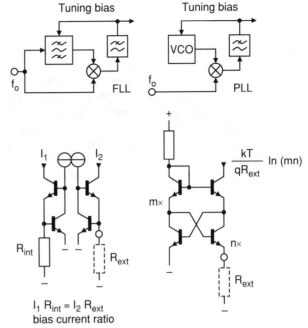

Fig. 48. Examples of filter tuning. *Top left*, a master resonance circuit is locked to a reference frequency using a frequency-locked loop (FLL). The tuning bias is also applied to the filter elements (slaves). *Top right*, a master oscillator is synchronized using a phase-locked loop (PLL). *Bottom left*, all integrated filter resistors R_k are multiplied by the ratio of two bias currents, $I_1/I_2 = R_{ext}/R_{int}$. The effective resistance $(R_k/R_{int})R_{ext}$ is the ratio of 2 integrated resistors (constant factor) multiplied by the reference resistor. *Bottom right*, the stabilizer provides a temperature-proportional bias current (to control linearized bipolar transconductors).

frequencies is not known. Without a reference we have to take into account wide tolerance limits, in practice of the order of magnitude of $\pm 20\%$ and variations with temperature (and aging). Many filters, in particular antialiasing filters, are designed with these wide tolerances. In some cases we can obtain tighter limits. For example, MOS transistors have an effective conductance

$$G_{eff} :: \frac{W}{L} C_{ox} \mu (V_{GS} - V_{th}) \qquad (1)$$

(in saturation as well as in the triode region). In time constants (G_{eff}/C ratios) the oxide capacitance (oxide thickness) can cancel out (assuming that the capacitors have the MOS gate-oxide as a dielectric). The mobility (and a voltage) are left. The mobility is not very promising as a reference (for details on the modeling of the mobility, see [82]).

In some cases we rely upon the invariability of the

37

capacitors and we use an external resistor as a reference. It is adjusted once (for all filters and oscillators on the chip). It can be used either in a temperature-proportional bias-current stabilizer (PTAT), or to generate a pair of bias currents for multiplier control [11], or as a direct reference to a master transconductor in a feedback circuit. The methods are simple and are interference-free.

With a phase-locked loop or a frequency-locked loop (and other methods) a master (oscillator, resonance circuit, etc.) can be locked to a reference frequency. The control voltage (or current) is also applied to the filter(s) (the slaves). Mismatch between master and slaves limits the accuracy to values that are generally not better than 1%.

In many cases, filter(s) are used in a system that already has a clock oscillator, for example, a relaxation oscillator, which may be locked to a crystal. In that case, the simplest procedure can be to redesign the clock oscillator with the same technique used for the filter(s) (for examples see [25]). The natural matching of clock oscillator and filter can even improve the performance of the system.

In cases where a filter has to be active periodically, the pauses can be used to tune the filter (for example, during the field fly-back of a video signal). Time-multiplex of the same circuit can yield very accurate tuning results. In other cases the signal itself (for example, time-averaged) can be the reference.

Filter parts or filter coefficients can also be tuned to obtain filter properties that vary with the signals in the filter. This brings us to adaptive filters. An example is a continuous-time adaptive equalizer for Teletext signals [83].

8. SOME SPECIAL SUBJECTS

A short review will be given on some special subjects:

- matched oscillators:
  independent amplitude and frequency control, carrier-to-noise ratio,
- design optimization:
  dynamic range optimization,
- complex filters (or polyphase filters):
  frequency translation,
  image-free filters, and
- performance limitations.

8.1. Matched oscillators

Van der Pol oscillators show a dependence between amplitude and frequency control. In the case of a gyrator (or conjunctor) oscillator, the controls can be independent [84]. A "symmetric" gyrator oscillator has the descriptive equations (including noise currents i_{n1} and i_{n2}) (see Fig. 49):

$$C\frac{dv_1}{dt} + g.v_1 + G.v_2 = i_{n1},$$

$$C\frac{dv_2}{dt} + g.v_2 - G.v_1 = i_{n2}. \qquad (2)$$

The conductances g and G are controlled. A resonance circuit of balanced integrators (using amplifiers) is described by a similar pair of equations as the gyrator (or transconductor-C) circuit, see for example [25]. Insertion of: $v_1 = a.\cos(\phi)$ and $v_2 = a.\sin(\phi)$ with $a = a(t)$ and $\phi = \phi(t)$ in the (noise-free) equations yields a separation of variables:

$$\frac{d(\phi)}{dt} = \frac{G(t)}{C}, \qquad \frac{da}{dt} = -\frac{g(a)}{C}a. \qquad (3)$$

The left-hand expression shows that the instantaneous frequency is controlled by the gyration conductance. We have an ideal frequency modulator. If in the right-hand equation the loss conductance g is a function of just the signal amplitude, the equation independently governs the amplitude control. One should observe that the signal amplitude can be derived from the sum of the squares of the signal voltages v_1 and v_2 (see Fig. 49). Apparently, we

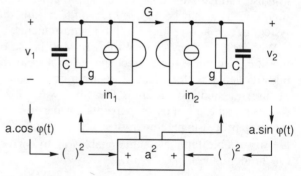

Fig. 49. Oscillator. We start from a gyrator resonance circuit (*top part of the figure*) or a (balanced) integrator resonance circuit with equal capacitors C and loss conductances g. The value of the loss conductances g can be positive as well as negative. Near oscillation or oscillating the voltages v_1 and v_2 are 90 degrees phase-shifted sinewaves with almost equal amplitudes. Two squarers and an adder provide the square of the signal amplitude, which, compared with the correct value controls the damping (undamping) of the resonance circuit via control of the conductances g. Thus, the signal amplitude is stabilized. Amplitude control and frequency control are independent. A simple expression has been derived for the carrier-to-noise ratio of the oscillator.

have a quadrature sinewave oscillator with independent amplitude and frequency control.

A straightforward noise analysis can be performed. To this end, we insert in the descriptive equations: $v_1 = a.\cos(\phi) + v_{n1}$, $v_2 = a.\sin(\phi) + v_{n2}$. Hence,

$$C\frac{dv_{n1}}{dt} + g.v_{n1} + G.v_{n2} = i_{n1}$$

$$C\frac{dv_{n2}}{dt} + g.v_{n2} - G.v_{n1} = i_{n2} \qquad (4)$$

Introducing complex functions,

$$j.\omega.C.V_{n1} + g.V_{n1} + G.V_{n2} = I_{n1},$$

$$j.\omega.C.V_{n2} + g.V_{n2} - G.V_{n1} = I_{n2}. \qquad (5)$$

With $g = 0$,

$$V_{n1} = \frac{j.\omega.C.I_{n1} - G.I_{n2}}{G^2 - \omega^2 C^2}, \quad V_{n2} = \frac{G.I_{n1} + j.\omega.C.I_{n2}}{G^2 - \omega^2 C^2} \qquad (6)$$

The noise sources are independent.

$$\langle i_{n1}^2 \rangle = \langle i_{n2}^2 \rangle = 4.k.T.G.F.df, \qquad (7)$$

where F is an excess noise factor. Writing $R = 1/G$ and $G/C = 2\pi.f_o$, we derive

$$\langle v_{n1}^2 \rangle = \langle v_{n2}^2 \rangle = \frac{1 + (f/f_o)^2}{\left(1 - (f/f_o)^2\right)^2} 4.k.T.R.F.df. \qquad (8)$$

An oscillator is often specified in terms of carrier-to-noise ratio (the power of the carrier divided by the noise in a band of 1 Hz near the carrier: distance df ($df \ll f_o$).

$$C/N = \frac{a^2}{4.k.T.R.F}\left(\frac{df}{f_0}\right)^2, \qquad \text{approx.} \qquad (9)$$

Alternatively, we may replace ϕ by $\phi + \phi_n$ (and a by $a + a_n$), from which we derive the noise on the instantaneous frequency

$$\left\langle \left(\frac{1}{\omega_o}\frac{d\phi_n}{dt}\right)^2 \right\rangle = 4.k.T.R.df/a^2. \qquad (10)$$

The noise on the instantaneous frequency proves to be independent of the frequency.

For a triangular-wave equivalent to the sinewave quadrature oscillator, see [85]. For a different survey on oscillators, see [86].

8.2. Design optimization: noise and dissipation

Step 1. Generally, we start the design of a filter circuit from a prototype *LC* filter or better from a prototype gyrator-*C* filter or integrator filter. This prototype has resulted from discussions with system design people (we may have done the system design ourselves). This prototype (with ideal filter elements) should not only satisfy the specifications, but there should be a firm idea of feasibility and/or optimality when designed as part of an integrated circuit. At this stage it is important to know the IC process for the implementation and to have chosen the best electronic circuits for the implementation of the filter elements. Generally, resistor (transconductor) values are all equal or have simple ratios (to be made as series and/or shunt circuits). Capacitor values are still free but, preferably, all capacitors should be of the same order of magnitude. If this is not the case, it may be necessary to choose a different filter architecture.

Step 2. The signal voltages and/or currents in all filter elements are analyzed (as a function of frequency). This shows to what extent the electronic elements are equally near to overload at realistic input signals. If one (or some) elements are overloaded while others are far from overload, local impedance scalings (within the filter) often can improve the signal-handling capacity of the filter. Similarly, if one (or some) of the elements is still far from overload when all others are overloaded, it is not well used (low signal levels relative to the noise level). Again, simple local scaling of impedance levels can improve the design.

Step 3. The next step is that the design is analyzed with electronic circuits (transistor circuits). We still use unit resistors (unit transconductors). The capacitors may be designed using unit capacitors (possibly with small additions). Imperfections are analyzed. The effects of process variations are estimated. Statistical analyses and/or best and worst case analyses are performed. Stability is analyzed to detail—latch-up (starting-up), small-signal stability, the circuits are excited with large pulses: differential mode as well as common mode (if applicable). Noise and distortion analyses are performed. The layout is designed and verified against the schematic. The last step before mask making is chip finishing.

At the end of Step 2 we have arrived at a filter with all resistor values and all capacitor values of the same order of magnitude and all electronic elements almost equally well used. The better these goals have been approximated, the better the filter noise and dissipation estimates below apply. The estimates should be seen as the best that can be obtained.

In a passive RLC filter, the noise originates from the dissipative elements: the terminating resistors and filter losses. The filter noise at a node with impedance Z is:

$$\langle v_n^2 \rangle = 4 \, k.T \, \mathrm{Re}\{Z\} df. \qquad (11)$$

In an RC-active "simulation of the passive filter" we have the same noise sources. In addition, we introduce noise (for example) of gyrators, which in fact convert the magnetic energy in the LC filter to electric energy in the electronic filter.

The noise analysis below follows ideas of Fettweis [87], and, partly, [88] and [17]. We start from a prototype LC ladder filter between resistive terminations. Each inductor is implemented as a gyrator and a capacitor. The noise of the electronic inductors is represented by a series noise voltage source (see Fig. 50),

$$\langle v_{n_L}^2 \rangle = 4 \, k.T \, F \left(1 + \left(\frac{\omega.L}{R_g} \right)^2 \right) R_g \, df, \quad (12)$$

where F is an excess noise factor. For the analysis below we apply a sinewave excitation at the "output port" of the filter. The terminating resistance is R_o. The available signal power is P_o. According to [87] the noise contribution at the filter output of electronic inductor L_k can be written as,

$$\langle V_{n_k}^2 \rangle = \langle V_{n_{Lk}}^2 \rangle \frac{R_o.W_{m_k}}{2.L_k.P_o} \qquad (13)$$

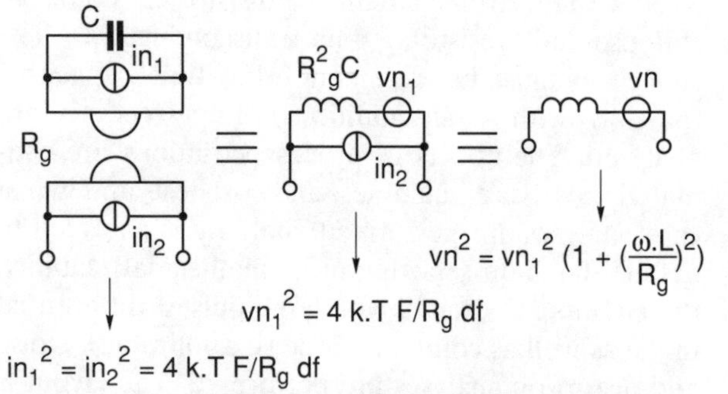

Fig. 50. Noise of an electronic coil. The left-hand part of the figure shows a simplified gyrator noise model—it assumes noisy gyrator resistors with an excess noise factor F. Going to the right we arrive at noisy coils. The noise can be placed in a single noise source: either a series noise voltage source (as in the far right-hand side of the figure) or a shunt noise current source. The noise spectrum is frequency dependent.

where W_{m_k} is the average magnetic energy which is stored in inductor L_k (corresponding to the excitation P_o). Hence,

$$\langle V_{n_k}^2 \rangle = 4 \, k.T.F \left(\frac{R_{g_k}}{\omega.L_k} + \frac{\omega.L_k}{R_{g_k}} \right) \frac{\omega.W_{m_k}}{2.P_o} R_o \, df.$$

$$\overset{\longleftarrow \theta_k \longrightarrow}{} \qquad (14)$$

Summation yields the total noise of the electronic inductors.

$$\langle V_n^2 \rangle = 4 \, k.T.F. \, \theta \frac{\omega.W_m}{2.P_o} R_o.df, \qquad (15)$$

where $\theta \geq 2$ is an average weighting factor and W_m is the total magnetic energy. According to Dicke and Poschenrieder the total magnetic energy is directly related to the group-delay of the filter (in this case from output to input, see [87]),

$$2.W_m/P_o = \tau_{1,2} \qquad (16)$$

We arrive at,

$$\langle V_n^2 \rangle = k.T.F. \, \theta.\omega.\tau_{1,2} R_o \, df. \qquad (17)$$

For a lossless LC ladder between resistive terminations, the group-delay is the same in both directions.

The minimum noise from the electronic inductors (seen at the filter output) is

$$\langle V_n^2 \rangle = 2.k.T.F.\omega.\tau.R_o.df, \qquad (18)$$

where F is an excess noise factor, τ is the group delay of the filter and R_o is the terminating resistance at the filter output. The derivation shows the relationship between noise and stored magnetic energy (which has to be converted to electric energy). It also shows that the noise spectrum has a strong relationship with the group-delay of the filter. $1/f$-noise may be included in the excess noise factor.

On the other hand, the magnetic energy has to be handled by the gyrators (in transconductor or in integrator form). Let the efficiency of the gyrators be η (ratio of signal power that can be handled and dissipation for a "symmetric" resonance circuit). The supply power consumption P of all gyrators together satisfies (see [87])

$$P > \omega.W_m/\eta = \omega.\tau S/\eta \qquad (19)$$

where τ is the group-delay of the filter and S is the signal power as delivered to the load (in-band: half the available power at the input).

The latter is a useful lower limit for the power consumption of the filter expressed in its group-delay, the signal power as delivered to the load resistor, and the efficiency of the gyrators. The lower limit is independent of the implementation. In practice, the efficiency η is of the order of magnitude of 1%. Recent detailed estimates for balanced integrator filters can be found in [89].

8.3. Complex filters (polyphase filters)

Let us consider a filter with impulse response $h(t)$. Because $h(t)$ is a real function,

$$H(-j.\omega) = H^*(j.\omega), \qquad (20)$$

where $H(j.\omega)$ is the spectrum of $h(t)$ and the asterisk denotes a complex conjugation. The real part and the magnitude of $H(j.\omega)$ show even symmetry and the imaginary part and the phase show odd symmetry for positive and negative frequencies. Further, RLC filters lead to transfer functions, which are ratios of polynomials with real coefficients.

If we could use imaginary conductances $\pm j.G$ for filter design, the coefficients of the transfer functions could be complex and the above symmetry relations would not necessarily apply. In fact, with imaginary conductances in addition to the common lossless filter elements, any transfer function with complex coefficients can be designed. Asymmetric filters can be made, for example, with a passband for positive frequencies and a stopband for the same negative frequencies (image rejection).

Next let us assume that we have two identical filters with common filter elements as well as imaginary conductances. The filters are excited with signals in quadrature (as we can derive from a pair of mixers—see Fig. 51). Any voltage V_k in filter 1 corresponds with a voltage $j.V_k$ in filter 2. When we connect a gyrator (gyration conductance G_k) between the two voltages, the admittance in the gyrator (seen from filter 1) is: $G_k.(j.V_k)/V_k = j.G_k$. Seen from filter 2 the admittance is $-V_k.G_k/(j.V_k) = j.G_k$, as well. We implement imaginary conductances. The antireciprocal couplings by transconductor-type gyrators can be replaced equally well by antireciprocal couplings between balanced integrators.

A particularly interesting example is the case that we start from a pair of lowpass filters with (trans)conductors, capacitors and with or without imaginary conductances. We replace all capacitive admittances $j.\omega.C_k$ by $j(\omega - \omega_o)C_k = j.\omega.C_k - j(\omega_o.C_k)$. We obtain a translation of the filter(s) along the frequency axis. By putting imaginary con-

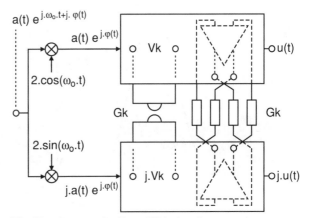

Fig. 51. Asymmetric filter. With imaginary conductances, asymmetric filters can be made. In the figure we apply a modulated signal to two demodulators in quadrature. We assume that the resulting spectra around $2.\omega_o$ are rejected by the filters (they can further be neglected). The low-frequency parts of the input signals to the filters are in quadrature. If the filters, possibly with imaginary conductances, are identical and have no coupling between them, any voltage V_k in the upper filter corresponds with a voltage $j.V_k$ in the lower filter. The pairs of corresponding imaginary conductances are made using antireciprocal couplings between the filters, using gyrators either of transconductor type or of balanced-integrator type (*far right-hand side of the figure*).

ductances $j.\omega_o.C_k$ in parallel to all capacitors (and imaginary resistances in series with all inductors), we obtain a true shift of the filter along the frequency axis. Unlike the common lowpass-to-bandpass transformation

$$p \to p + \omega_0^2/p, \quad \omega \to \omega - \omega_0^2/\omega \qquad (21)$$

the frequency translation $\omega \to \omega - \omega_0$ does not distort the gain and the group-delay characteristic (Fig. 52).

We thus can make seemingly asymmetric filters. They are a kind of polyphase filter [90]. For more details, see [17] and [91].

8.4. Limits of performance

Integrated filters should achieve a specified performance for minimum costs and minimum supply power. Costs include design and production costs. Design cost are influenced by simplicity of the circuits, simplicity of interfacing, usefulness for more than one application, electromagnetic compatibility, and so on. Production costs are influenced by process complexity, chip area, functional yield, etc. Design costs are very important for small production

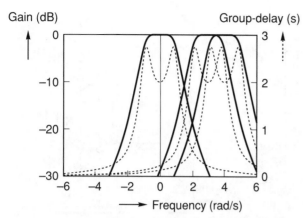

Fig. 52. Frequency shift. By employing antireciprocal couplings between a pair of identical filters with input signals in quadrature, imaginary conductances are made. They can be used to implement a frequency shift: $\omega \to \omega - \omega_o$. The figure shows third-order Butterworth lowpass filter characteristics, which have been shifted. The results are bandpass filters without an image at negative frequencies. The shapes of gain and group-delay (in dashes) are preserved.

series. Production costs are of primary importance in the case of mass production.

Lower limits have been indicated for the supply-power consumption of integrated filters. Methods to further reduce the average supply-power consumption are:

- control of the supply current proportional to the (instantaneous) signal level (as implemented in the adaptive gyrator [17]), and
- class-B or class A/B operation.

These methods are not widely used in practice. This is due to disadvantages such as increased circuit complexity, higher signal distortion, and signal-dependent supply currents causing crosstalk via supply lines.

Common supply voltages are 18 V, 12 V, 5 V, 3 V and lower, for example, multiples of 0.9 V (minimum values) for battery operation. The lower the supply voltage is and the less sophisticated the IC process, the more restricted is the set of circuit types that can be applied. The lowest supply voltages call for bipolar circuits (see [1] and [47]) and in some cases for CMOS with reduced threshold voltages.

At lower supply voltages it is increasingly difficult to design filters for a high signal-handling capacity. A useful yardstick for the signal-handling capacity is the intermodulation-free dynamic range (IMFDR), which is the signal range above the noise where the distortion remains below the noise. An IMFDR = 60 dB means that S/N ratio and S/D ratio both can be

60 dB. For practical applications it proves to be difficult to arrive at IMFDR values of 70 dB and higher in cases of tunable integrated filters. For comparison, compact-disc type signals and in receivers, upwards of 90 dB is needed.

At low frequencies (say, 10 Hz and lower), large time constants (RC products) have to be implemented. The requirement of a small chip area calls for small capacitors (not larger than 200 pF) and, hence, nonrealistic resistor values (100 MOhm). Electronic multiplication techniques, similar to the Miller effect, are applied. An example is shown in Fig. 53. With two resistors of 100 kOhm and a resistor of 1 kOhm, an effective resistance of 10 MOhm is achieved. In general, the amount of electronic time-constant multiplication is limited by DC-offset enhancement and/or capacitor leakage. Low-frequency filters are of importance for the integration of control loops, DC fixation [92], and for AC-coupling between circuits.

The approach in Fig. 53 shows a further interesting aspect. In the case that R_3/R_2 and R_2/R_1 are significantly larger than 1, the noise factor of the effective resistance is lower than 1 or, equivalently, we have a low noise temperature for the equivalent resistance: electronic cooling. This effect can be implemented in various ways. However, electronic cooling costs supply power.

Circuits without signal-voltage–carrying nodes, other than filter nodes, can be accurately used up to high frequencies (hundreds of MHz) [25, 73]. Power

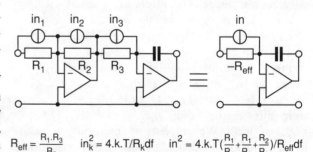

$$R_{eff} = \frac{R_1 \cdot R_3}{R_2} \qquad in_k^2 = 4.k.T/R_k df \qquad in^2 = 4.k.T\left(\frac{R_1}{R_2} + \frac{R_1}{R_3} + \frac{R_2}{R_3}\right)/R_{eff} df$$

$$\underbrace{\qquad\qquad\qquad}_{\text{noise factor}}$$

Fig. 53. Time-constant multiplication. If R_1, $R_3 \gg R_2$ the effective integrator resistance is larger than $R_1 + R_2 + R_3$. For example, with $R_1 = R_3 = 100$ kOhm and $R_2 = 1$ kOhm an effective resistance of 10 MOhm is made.

Electronic cooling. If $R_3 \gg R_2 \gg R_1$, the noise factor of the effective integrator resistor can be lower than 1 (the resistance seems to have a low noise temperature). For example, with $R_3 = 100$ kOhm, $R_2 = 10$ kOhm, $R_1 = 1$ kOhm the effective resistance is 10 kOhm. The noise factor is 0.21 (noise temperature 60 K).

consumption is one of the main limiting factors. It will often be better not just to replace an existing passive filter by its active counterpart, but to reconsider the system (filtering can sometimes be transformed to lower frequencies). System modifications may reduce the dissipation and the accuracy requirements.

In applications for higher frequencies, one should avoid slow PNP and PMOS transistors in the signal paths. A minor phase-shift can be as important as the dissipation factor of a capacitor. Also, delay in resistive elements can degrade the filter characteristics. The influence of uniform delay in transconductors in transconductor-C filters is shown in Fig. 54. The gain enhancement proves to be proportional to the group-delay of the filter. Compensation is possible by adding small resistors in series with the filter capacitors. In balanced-integrator filters, compensation of the first-order roll-off with frequency of high-transconductance balanced amplifiers can be carried out in a similar way [25]. One should be aware that the compensations may lead to instability.

Together with a higher density on the chips, crosstalk and interference problems increase. In particular, sensitive analog circuits cannot be put near large-swing digital or switched-capacitor circuits. Balancing is important and shielding methods are being studied, but digital circuits are also being developed with lower levels of interference. In spite of all this, crosstalk problems within the VLSI chip via supply lines and substrate and also capacitive and magnetic couplings between IC-pins are becoming more and more problematic.

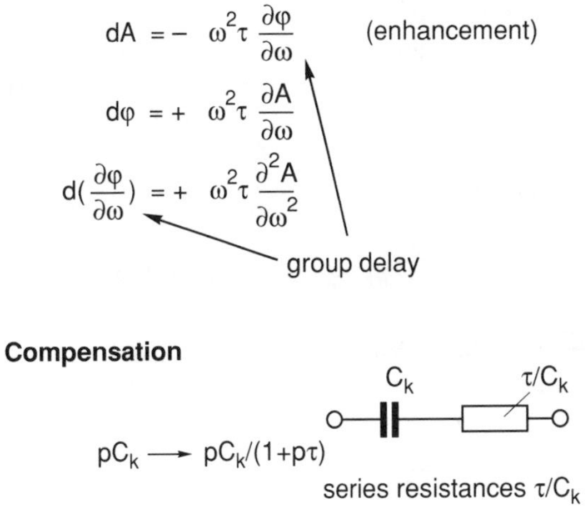

9. CONCLUSION

We have considered elements and circuits for continuous-time analog filters for bipolar, CMOS and biCMOS IC processes (including tuning of time constants). We have surveyed filter design methods. We have not considered filter approximation and synthesis and we have only touched upon design problems concerning latch-up, overflow-limit-cycle oscillations, and stability at high frequencies. Nor have distributed RC structures been included in the survey. Design strategies, governed by yardsticks (for example, in respect of noise and supply-power consumption), form a key issue. Matched oscillators, image-free complex filters, as well as performance limitations have been discussed as special subjects.

$$dA = -\ \omega^2\tau\ \frac{\partial\varphi}{\partial\omega} \qquad \text{(enhancement)}$$

$$d\varphi = +\ \omega^2\tau\ \frac{\partial A}{\partial\omega}$$

$$d\left(\frac{\partial\varphi}{\partial\omega}\right) = +\ \omega^2\tau\ \frac{\partial^2 A}{\partial\omega^2}$$

group delay

Compensation

$$pC_k \longrightarrow pC_k/(1+p\tau)$$

series resistances τ/C_k

Fig. 54. Effects of uniform transconductor delay. We consider a dimensionless filter function $F(p)$ (for example, a voltage transfer ratio). The filter has as elements G_k and C_k. Uniform transconductor delay means: $G_k \to G_k/(1 + p.\tau)$. This is equivalent to multiplication of all capacitive admittances by the factor $1 + p.\tau$, that is: $p.C_k \to p(1 + p.\tau)C_k$. We have the frequency transformation: $p \to p(1 + p.\tau)$.

$$dF(p) = \frac{dF(p)}{dp}dp + \ldots = \frac{dF(p)}{dp}p^2\tau + \ldots.$$

Everywhere $F(p)$ is analytic $dF(p)/dp = dF(p)/d(j.\omega)$. Hence, for $p = j.\omega$,

$$dF(j.\omega) = j\frac{dF(j.\omega)}{d\omega}\omega^2\tau + \ldots.$$

Let $F(j.\omega)$ be the (negative of the) natural logarithm of a transfer function. $F = -\ln(H) = A + j.\phi$: the real part A is the attenuation (in Neper) and the imaginary part ϕ is the phase in radians. Insertion in the above expression and taking real and imaginary parts yields two of the relationships in the figure. The third can be derived in a similar way. One of the effects of transconductor delay is an enhancement of the gain proportional to the square of the frequency and to the group-delay of the filter. Uniform transconductor delay effects can be compensated by dividing all capacitive admittances by the factor $1 + p.\tau$ (addition of resistances in series with the capacitors).

We conclude by stating that:

- continuous-time analog filters are needed in the interfaces between integrated digital processors and the analog outside world
- design methods (including approximation and synthesis and also electronic circuit design) of analog filters in VLSI are manifold but stabilizing
- the use in real applications is proceeding to more and more optimum solutions (the latter has not yet run its course).

The challenges to designers are to achieve higher signal-to-noise ratios at lower supply voltages, higher frequencies, larger time constants (for control loops), further improved accuracy (for standard cells and simplified filter design) and, in particular, to devise more sophisticated applications.

ACKNOWLEDGMENT

Herewith I thank Yannis Tsividis for his many helpful suggestions to improve the manuscript and also one of the reviewers, who has given some particulary valuable remarks.

REFERENCES

[1] J. O. Voorman, "Analog integrated filters or continuous-time filters for LSI and VLSI," *Revue de Physique Appliquée*, vol. 22, pp. 3–14, 1987.

[2] N. M. Nguyen and R. G. Meyer, "Si IC-compatible inductors and *LC* passive filters," *IEEE J. Solid-State Circuits*, vol. SC-25, pp. 1028–1031, 1990.

[3] G. Salomonsson, "Linear network synthesis with Laguerre polynomials," *Ericsson Technics*, vol. 2, pp. 83–109, 1971.

[4] H. J. Carlin, "Singular network elements," *IEEE Trans. on Circuit Theory*, vol. CT-11, pp. 67–72, 1964.

[5] D. Blom, H. W. Hanneman, and J. O. Voorman, "Some inductorless filters," *Philips Technical Review*, vol. 33, pp. 294–308, 1973.

[6] R. J. Sluyter, "Design tables for *RC* active Cauer filters," *J. Appl. Sci. Eng. A*, vol. 3, pp. 1–14, 1978.

[7] H. J. Orchard, "Inductorless filters," *Electron. Lett.*, vol. 2, pp. 224–225, 1966.

[8] G. C. Temes and H. J. Orchard, "First-order sensitivity and worst-case analysis of doubly terminated reactance two-ports," *IEEE Trans. on Circuit Theory*, vol. CT-20, pp. 567–571, 1973.

[9] B. D. H. Tellegen, "The gyrator, a new electric network element," *Philips Research Reports*, vol. 3, pp. 81–101, 1948.

[10] A. G. J. Holt and J. Taylor, "Method of replacing ungrounded inductors by grounded gyrators," *Electron. Lett.*, vol. 1, p. 105, 1965.

[11] J. O. Voorman, W. H. A. Brüls, and P. J. Barth, "Integration of analog filters in a bipolar process," *IEEE J. Solid-State Circuits*, vol. SC-17, pp. 713–722, 1982.

[12] P. Kwa, "Homogeneous gyrator-chain networks," *Electron. Lett.*, vol. 21, pp. 1080–1081, 1985.

[13] A. C. M. de Queiroz, L. P. Caloba, and E. Sanchez-Sinencio, "Signal-flow-graph OTA-C integrated filters," *Proc. ISCAS*, pp. 2165–2168, 1988.

[14] W. Heinlein and H. Holmes, "Active filters for integrated circuits," München: Oldenbourg, Ch. 8, 1974.

[15] H. J. Orchard and A. N. Wilson, "New active-gyrator circuit," *Electron. Lett.*, vol. 10, pp. 261–262, 1974.

[16] V. M. Pauker, "Equivalent networks with nullors for positive immittance inverters," *IEEE Trans. on Circuit Theory*, vol. CT-17, pp. 642–645, 1970.

[17] J. O. Voorman, "The gyrator as a monolithic circuit in electronic systems," Thesis, University of Nijmegen, 1977.

[18] L. T. Bruton, "Multiple amplifier *RC*-active filter design with emphasis on GIC realizations," *IEEE Trans. Circuits Syst.*, vol. CAS-25, pp. 830–845, 1978.

[19] L. T. Bruton, "Network transfer functions using the concept of frequency-dependent negative resistance," *IEEE Trans. on Circuit Theory*, vol. CT-16, pp. 406–408, 1969.

[20] T. Deliyannis, "*RC* active allpass sections," *Electron Lett.*, vol. 5, pp. 59–60, 1969.

[21] G. Wilson, "An *RC*-active allpass section with reduced magnitude response error," *IEEE Trans. Circuits Syst.*, vol. CAS-26, pp. 144-148, 1979.

[22] H. J. Orchard and D. F. Sheahan, "Inductorless bandpass filters," *IEEE J. Solid-State Circuits*, vol. SC-5, pp. 108—118, 1970.

[23] M. Banu and Y. Tsividis, "Fully integrated active *RC* filters in MOS technology," *IEEE J. Solid-State Circuits*, vol. SC-18, pp. 644–651, 1983.

[24] Y. Tsividis, M. Banu, and M. Khoury, "Continuous-time MOSFET-*C* filters in VLSI," *IEEE J. Solid-State Circuits*, vol. SC-21, pp. 15–30, 1986.

[25] J. O. Voorman, A. van Bezooijen, and N. Ramalho, "On balanced integrator filters," in *Integrated Continuous-Time Filters: Principles, Design, and Applications*, Y. P. Tsividis and J. O. Voorman, Eds., Piscataway, NJ: IEEE PRESS, 1993.

[26] P. V. Ananda Mohan, "New structures for MOSFET-*C* filters," *Proc. IEEE*, vol. 75, pp. 957–960, 1987.

[27] A. M. Durham, W. Redman-White, and J. B. Hughes, "Low-distortion VLSI compatible self-tuned continuous-time monolithic filters," *Proc. ISCAS*, pp. 1448–1451, 1991.

[28] D. Blom and J. O. Voorman, "Noise and dissipation of electronic gyrators," *Philips Research Reports*, vol. 26, pp. 103–113, 1971.

[29] T. Fukano, T. Ito, T. Hisatsugu, and H. Ishikawa, "Ultra sharp trench capacitors formed by peripheral etching," *Extended Abstracts of the 16th Conference on Solid-State Devices and Materials*, Kobe, pp. 471-474, 1984.

[30] M. Binet, "Capacitors made by anodisation of aluminium for wideband GaAs IC's," *Electron. Lett.*, vol. 18, pp. 197–198, 1982.

[31] S. K.-C. Lai, D. J. Dimaria, and F. F. Fang, "Silicon-rich SiO$_2$ and thermal SiO$_2$ dual dielectric for yield improvement and high capacitance," *IEEE Trans. on Electron Devices*, vol. ED-30, pp. 894–897, 1983.

[32] J. L. McCreary, "Matching properties and voltage and temperature dependence of MOS capacitors," *IEEE J. Solid-State Circuits*, vol. SC-16, pp. 608–616, 1981.

[33] J-B. Shyu, G. C. Temes, and F. Krummenacher, "Random error effects in matched MOS capacitors and current sources," *IEEE J. Solid-State Circuits*, vol. SC-19, pp. 948–955, 1984.

[34] A. B. Bhattacharyya and H. Wallinga, "An area-variable MOS varicap and its application in programmable tap weighting of CCD transversal filters," *IEEE Trans. on Electron Devices*, vol. ED-29, pp. 827–833, 1982.

[35] R. A. Friedenson, R. W. Daniels, R. J. Dow, and P. H. McDonald, "*RC* active filters for the *D*3 channel bank," *Bell Syst. Tech. J.*, vol. 54, pp. 507–529, 1975.

[36] R. J. van de Plassche and D. Goedhart, "A monolithic 14-bit D/A converter," *IEEE J. Solid-State Circuits*, vol. SC-14, pp. 552–556, 1979.

[37] K. Kato, T. Ono, and Y. Amemiya, "A monolithic 14 bit D/A converter fabricated with a new trimming technique

(DOT)," *IEEE J. Solid-State Circuits*, vol. SC-19, pp. 802–807, 1984.

[38] Y. Amemiya and K. Kato, "Compensation for voltage dependence of diffused feedback resistors in operational amplifiers," *IEEE J. Solid-State Circuits*, vol. SC-14, pp. 1118–1120, 1979.

[39] K. W. Moulding and G. A. Wilson, "A fully integrated five-gyrator filter at video frequencies," *IEEE J. Solid-State Circuits*, vol. SC-13, pp. 303–307, 1978.

[40] K. W. Moulding, J. R. Quartly, P. J. Rankin, R. S. Thompson, and G. A. Wilson, "Gyrator video filter *IC* with automatic tuning," *IEEE J. Solid-State Circuits*, vol. SC-15, 963–967, 1980.

[41] K. W. Moulding and P. J. Rankin, "Experience with high frequency gyrator filters including a new video delay-line *IC*," *Proc. ECCTD*, Stuttgart, pp. 105–107, 1983.

[42] L. T. Bruton, "Electronically tunable active filters," *IEEE Trans. on Circuit Theory*, vol. CT-19. pp. 299–301, 1972.

[43] K. Fukahori, "A bipolar voltage-controlled tunable filter," *IEEE J. Solid-State Circuits*, vol. SC-16, pp. 729–737, 1981.

[44] T. Fukuda, K. Nishitani, F. Yamaguchi, K. Abe, and T. Narabu, "New video signal-processing LSI's for 8mm VCR's," *IEEE Trans. Consumer Electron.*, vol. CE-34, pp. 543–551, 1988.

[45] G. A. De Veirman and R. G. Yamasaki, "Fully-integrated 5 to 15 MHz programmable bipolar Bessel lowpass filter," *Proc. ISCAS*, pp. 1155–1158, 1990.

[46] J. O. Voorman, W. H. A. Brüls, and P. J. Barth, "Bipolar integration of analog gyrator and Laguerre type filters (transconductor-capacitor filters)," *Proc. ECCTD*, Stuttgart, pp. 108–110, 1983.

[47] H. Tanimoto, M. Koyama, and Y. Yoshida, "Realization of a 1-V active filter using a linearization technique employing plurality of emitter-coupled pairs," *IEEE J. Solid-State Circuits*, vol. SC-26, pp. 937–945, 1991.

[48] J. O. Voorman, "Transconductance amplifier," US Patent 4,723,110, 1988.

[49] C. L. Perry, "An integrated continuous-time bipolar transconductance-capacitor filter," *IEEE J. Solid-State Circuits*, vol. SC-24, pp. 732–735, 1989.

[50] K-S Tan and P. R. Gray, "Fully integrated analog filters using bipolar-JFET technology," *IEEE J. Solid-State Circuits*, vol. SC-13, pp. 814–821, 1978.

[51] M. Banu, J. M. Khoury, and Y. Tsividis, "Fully differential operational amplifiers with accurate output balancing," *IEEE J. Solid-State Circuits*, vol. SC-23, pp. 1410–1414, 1988.

[52] Z. Czarnul, "Modification of Banu-Tsividis continuous-time integrator structure," *IEEE Trans. Circuits Syst.*, vol. CAS-33, pp. 714–716, 1986.

[53] Z. Czarnul, "Novel MOS resistive circuit for synthesis of fully integrated continuous-time filters," *IEEE Trans. Circuits Syst.*, vol. CAS-33, pp. 718–721, 1986.

[54] M. Ismail, S. V. Smith, and R. G. Beale, "A new MOSFET-*C* universal filter structure for VLSI," *IEEE J. Solid-State Circuits*, vol. SC-23, pp. 183–194, 1988.

[55] M. J. M. Pelgrom, A. C. J. Duinmaijer, and A. P. G. Welbers, "Matching properties of MOS transistors," *IEEE J. Solid-State Circuits*, vol. SC-24, pp. 1433–1440, 1989.

[56] W. R. Patterson and F. S. Shoucair, "Harmonic suppression in unbalanced analogue MOSFET circuit topologies using body signals," *Electron. Lett.*, vol. 25, pp. 1737–1739, 1989.

[57] A. Bilotti, "Operation of the MOS transistor as a variable resistor," *Proc. IEEE*, vol. 54, pp. 1093–1094, 1966.

[58] M. Banu and Y. Tsividis, "Fully integrated active *RC* filters," *Proc. ISCAS*, pp. 602–605, 1983.

[59] H. Khorramabadi and P. R. Gray, "High-frequency CMOS continuous-time filters," *IEEE J. Solid-State Circuits*, vol. SC-19, pp. 939–948, 1984.

[60] Y. Tsividis, Z. Czarnul, and S. C. Fang, "MOS transconductors and integrators with high linearity," *Electron. Lett.*, vol. 22, pp. 245–246, 1986.

[61] A. Kaiser, "A micropower CMOS continuous-time lowpass filter," *IEEE J. Solid-State Circuits*, vol. SC-24, pp. 736–743, 1989.

[62] V. Gopinathan, Y. P. Tsividis, K. Tan, and R. K. Hester, "Design considerations for high-frequency continuous-time filters and implementation of an antialiasing filter for digital video," *IEEE J. Solid-State Circuits*, vol. SC-25, pp. 1368–1378, 1990.

[63] J. Khoury, "Design of a 15-MHz CMOS continuous-time filter with on-chip tuning," *IEEE J. Solid-State Circuits*, vol. SC-26, pp. 1988–1997, 1991.

[64] F. Krummenacher and N. Joehl, "A 4-MHz CMOS continuous-time filter with on-chip automatic tuning," *IEEE J. Solid-State Circuits*, vol. SC-23, pp. 750–758, 1988.

[65] F. Krummenacher, "Design considerations in high-frequency CMOS transconductance amplifier capacitor (TAC) filters," *Proc. ISCAS*, pp. 100–105, 1989.

[66] M. Steyaert, J. Silva-Martinez, and W. Sansen, "High-performance OTA-*RC* continuous-time filters with full CMOS low distortion floating resistors," *Digest ESSCIRC*, pp. 5–8, 1991.

[67] T. L. Viswanathan, "CMOS transconductance element," *Proc. IEEE*, vol. 74, pp. 222–224, 1986.

[68] Z. Wang and W. Guggenbühl, "A voltage-controllable linear MOS transconductor using bias offset technique," *IEEE J. Solid-State Circuits*, vol. SC-25, pp. 315–317, 1990.

[69] K. Bult and H. Wallinga, "A CMOS analog continuous-time delay-line with adaptive delay-time control," *IEEE J. Solid-State Circuits*, vol. SC-23, pp. 759–766, 1988.

[70] C.-S. Park and R. Schaumann, "A high-frequency CMOS linear transconductance element," *IEEE Trans. on Circuits Syst.*, vol. CAS-33, pp. 1132–1138, 1986.

[71] C.-S. Park and R. Schaumann, "Design of a 4-MHz analog integrated CMOS transconductance-C bandpass filter," *IEEE J. Solid-State Circuits*, vol. SC-23, pp. 987–996, 1988.

[72] B. Nauta and E. Seevinck, "Linear CMOS transconductance element for VHF filters," *Electron. Lett.*, vol. 25, pp. 448–450, 1989.

[73] B. Nauta, "CMOS VHF transconductance-C lowpass filter," *Electron. Lett.*, vol. 26, pp. 421–422, 1990.

[74] P. J. Ryan and D. G. Haigh, "Novel fully differential MOS transconductor for integrated continuous-time filters," *Electron. Lett.*, vol. 23, pp. 742–743, 1987.

[75] J. L. Pennock, "CMOS triode transconductor for continuous-time active integrated filters," *Electron. Lett.*, vol. 21, pp. 817–818, 1985.

[76] J. L. Pennock, P. Frith, and R. G. Barker, "CMOS triode transconductor continuous-time filters," *Proc. Custom. Int. Circ. Conf.*, pp. 378–381, 1986.

[77] R. Castello, F. Montecchi, R. Alini, and A. Baschirotto, "A very linear BiCMOS transconductor for high-frequency filtering applications," *Proc. ISCAS*, pp. 1364–1367, 1990.

[78] S. Tagaki, H. Nitta, J. Koyama, M. Furihata, N. Fujii, M. Nagata, and T. Yaganisawa, "100-MHz monolithic low-pass filters with transmission zeroes using NIC integrators," *IEEE J. Solid-State Circuits*, vol. SC-26, pp. 669–671, 1991.

[79] G. A. De Veirman and R. G. Yamasaki, "Monolithic 10–30 MHz tunable Bessel lowpass filter," *Proc. ISCAS*, pp. 1444–1447, 1991.

[80] J. N. Babanezhad and G. C. Temes, "A linear NMOS depletion resistor and its application in an integrated amplifier," *IEEE J. Solid-State Circuits*, vol. SC-19, pp. 932–938, 1984.

[81] R. Schaumann and M. A. Tan, "The problem of on-chip automatic tuning in continuous-time integrated filters," *Proc. ISCAS*, pp. 106–109, 1989.

[82] Y. P. Tsividis, "Operation and modelling of the MOS transistor," New York: McGraw-Hill, 1987.

[83] J. O. Voorman, P. J. Snijder, P. J. Barth, and J. S. Vromans, "A one-chip automatic equalizer for echo reduction in Teletext," *IEEE Trans. Consumer Electron.*, vol. CE-27, pp. 512–529, 1981.

[84] J. O. Voorman, "Ideal frequency modulator," *Electron. Lett.*, vol. 10, pp. 387–388, 1974.

[85] B. Z. Kaplan and Y. Tatrash, "New method for generating precise triangular waves and square waves," *Electron. Lett.*, vol. 13, pp. 71–73, 1977.

[86] A. Rodriguez-Vazquez, B. Linares-Barranco, J. L. Huertas, and E. Sanchez-Sinencio, "On the design of voltage-controlled sinusoidal oscillators using OTA's," *IEEE Trans. Circuits Syst.*, vol. CAS-37, pp. 198–211, 1990.

[87] A. Fettweis, "On noise performance of capacitor-gyrator filters," *Circuit Theory and Applications*, vol. 2, pp. 181–186, 1974.

[88] J. O. Voorman and D. Blom, "Noise in gyrator-capacitor filters," *Philips Research Reports*, vol. 26, pp. 114–133, 1971.

[89] G. Groenewold, "The design of high dynamic range continuous-time integratable filters," *IEEE Trans. Circuits Syst.*, vol. CAS-38, pp. 838–852, 1991.

[90] M. J. Gingell, "Single sideband modulation using sequence asymmetric polyphase networks," *Elect. Comm.*, vol. 48, pp. 21–25, 1973.

[91] J. O. Voorman, "Asymmetric polyphase filter," US Patent 4,914,408, 1990.

[92] R. J. Wiegerink, E. Seevinck, and W. de Jager, "Offset cancelling circuit," *IEEE J. Solid-State Circuits*, vol. 24, pp. 651–658, 1989.

Part 2
Mosfet-C Filters
Using Operational Amplifiers

Section 2-A   Principles and Overview

MOSFET-C filters consist of MOS transistors, capacitors, and active elements that are usually operational amplifiers. The MOS transistors serve the function of voltage-controlled resistors and are adjusted by an on-chip automatic tuning system. The topologies used are such that the effects of MOS transistor nonlinearities are accurately and reliably cancelled out within each building block. Attractive features of MOSFET-C filters are their insensitivity to parasitics, their modularity and amenability to standard cell design, and their strong relation to well-understood, integrator-based active *RC* filters.

This section introduces MOSFET-C filters. Paper 2-A.1 is a tutorial that provides the basics. The topologies covered can be thought of as balanced extensions of classical topologies using active-*RC*, single-ended integrators. Overall filter performance is critically dependent on integrator performance [1]. A larger class of circuits is possible by taking full advantage of the balanced nature of MOSFET-C filters and the availability of pairs of signals of opposite polarity [2]*. This, as well as the basics covered in the first paper, are expanded on and extended in Paper 2-A.2 by Voorman, van Bezooijen and Ramalho. This paper has been written specifically for this volume. The paper also covers new techniques that have allowed operation of MOSFET-C filters in the video frequency range.

In the MOSFET-C circuits described in this volume, the "resistor" nonlinearities are not cancelled individually but rather within each building block (integrator) as a whole. A different approach, not covered here because of space limitations, is to use individually linearized, voltage-controlled resistors akin to those used for many years in voltage-controlled amplifiers and AGC circuits [3] but without parasitic control paths [4–11] and preferably floating [4, 5, 7, 9–11], to allow flexibility in choosing the filter topology. MOS resistors can be further linearized through the use of body signals [6, 12, 13]. We should note that although the name "MOSFET-C" implies the use of MOS transistors, the techniques described here and in the references can be used with certain other types of transistors; perhaps

a more appropriate name would have been "transistor-C," in which "transistor" replaces "*R*" in the classic "*RC*" filters. For example, a voltage-controlled resistor in GaAs technology, which may be considered for filter implementation, is described elsewhere [14]. MOSFET-C filters using negative immittance converters (NICs) are also described elsewhere [15].

*We note, by the way, an error in [2]: in Fig. 1c of that paper, the filter outputs should be taken at the outputs of the second operational amplifier.

References

[1] W. J. A. De Heij, E. Seevinck and K. Hoen, "Practical formulation of the relation between filter specification and the requirements for integrator circuits," *IEEE Trans. Circuits Syst.*, vol. 36, no. 8, pp. 1124–1128, August 1989.

[2] P. V. Ananda Mohan,"New structures of MOSFET-C filters," *Proc. IEEE*, vol. 75, pp. 957–960, July 1987.

[3] A. Bilotti, "Operation of a MOS transistor as a variable resistor," *Proc. IEEE*, vol. 54, pp. 1093–1094, August 1966.

[4] M. Banu and Y. Tsividis, "Floating voltage-controlled resistors in CMOS technology," *Electron. Lett.*, vol. 18, pp. 678–679, July 22, 1982.

[5] K. Nagaraj, "New CMOS floating voltage-controlled resistor," *Electron. Lett.*, vol. 22, pp. 667–668, June 5, 1986.

[6] P. M. VanPeteghem and G. L. Rice, "New CMOS resistor implementation for linear IC applications," *Electron. Lett.*, vol. 24, no. 5, pp 288–290, March 3, 1988.

[7] S. P. Singh, J. V. Hanson and J. Vlach, "A new floating resistor for CMOS technology," *IEEE Trans. Circuits Syst.*, vol. 136, pp. 1217–1220, 1989.

[8] G. Wilson and P. K. Chan, "Novel voltage-controlled grounded resistor," *Electron. Lett.*, vol. 25, no. 25, pp. 1725–1726, Dec. 7, 1989.

[9] J. Silva-Martinez, M. Steyaert and W. Sansen, "Very linear CMOS floating resistor," *Electron. Lett.*, vol. 26, pp. 1610–1611, September 13, 1990.

[10] Z. Wang, "Novel electronically-controlled floating resistors using MOS transistors operating in saturation," *Electron. Lett.*, vol. 27, pp. 188–189, January 1991.

[11] M. Steyaert, J. Silva-Martinez, and W. Sansen, "A high-frequency saturated CMOS floating resistor for fully differential analog signal processors," *Electron. Lett.*, pp. 1609–1610, August 29, 1991.

[12] M. Banu and Y. Tsividis, "Fully integrated active *RC* filters," *Proc. IEEE ISCAS'83*, pp. 602–605, 1983.

[13] W. R. Patterson and F. S. Shoucair, "Harmonic suppression in unbalanced analogue MOSFET circuit topologies using body signals," *Electron. Lett.*, vol. 25, pp. 1737–1739, December 7, 1989.

[14] C. Toumazou and D. G. Haigh, "Linear tunable resistance circuit using Gallium Arsenide MESFETs," *Electron. Lett.*, vol. 27, no. 8, pp. 655–657, April 11, 1991.

[15] S. I. Liu, H. W. Tsao, J. Wu, M. O. Yang, and J. H. Tsay, "New CMOS NIC-based MOSFET-C filters," *Electron. Lett.*, vol. 27, pp. 772–774, April 25, 1991.

Continuous-Time MOSFET-C Filters in VLSI

YANNIS TSIVIDIS, FELLOW, IEEE, MIHAI BANU, AND JOHN KHOURY

Abstract—The desirable features of fully integrated, VLSI-compatible continuous-time filters are discussed. A recently proposed integrated continuous-time filtering technique is reviewed, in which MOS transistors are used in place of resistors along with nonlinearity cancellation and on-chip automatic tuning. The filters obtained using this technique are compared to switched-capacitor (SC) filters, digital filters, and continuous-time filters using different techniques. Representative experimental results are given, demonstrating the high performance that can be achieved.

I. INTRODUCTION

THE ARRIVAL of VLSI (Very Large Scale Integration) is causing a drastic change in the field of continuous-time active filters. Traditional active filter implementations (using discrete components or hybrid techniques) are coming to an end in many applications, due to increased competition from fully integrated switched-capacitor or digital filters. On the other hand it has been recently demonstrated [1] that, using new techniques, it is possible to make fully integrated high-performance continuous-time active filters which may offer advantages over SC and digital filters in certain applications. These continuous-time filters are derived from classical *RC* active filters, and use MOS field-effect transistors (MOSFET's), capacitors, and active elements. They are thus referred to as MOSFET-C active filters. This paper reviews these new techniques, and combines the main points of related discussions which have been scattered over several publications and oral presentations. Several new points are also made. Although the only circuits discussed in this paper are filters, it will be apparent that the techniques presented can be applied to other types of circuits such as oscillators, voltage-controlled amplifiers, automatic gain control circuits, modulators, etc.

In Section II we discuss several features that are desirable in integrated filtering techniques. In Sections III–X we review techniques that make possible integrated MOSFET-C filters, and in Section XI we compare these filters to switched-capacitor and digital filters, and continuous-time filters using different techniques. Section XII presents experimental results, and Section XIII contains the main conclusions.

II. DESIRABLE FEATURES FOR FULLY INTEGRATED CONTINUOUS-TIME FILTERS

In attempting to implement working active filters in integrated form, it is quickly realized that some of the constraints and objectives involved are different from those in discrete-component or hybrid implementations. For an integrated filtering technique to have a chance for wide application, it is desirable that it possess several features, which are outlined below.

Compatibility with VLSI

Extensive work is under way in industry and universities to improve fabrication techniques for VLSI chips, constantly decreasing cost and improving performance. In the middle of such intense activity, it is desirable that a filtering technique be VLSI-compatible. Special technologies should be avoided if possible, since it is often advantageous to have continuous-time filters share the same chip with digital logic, and, therefore, they should be implemented in the same way as the latter. The implementation of continuous-time filters in MOS technology is especially attractive, since this technology is presently dominant in the implementation of digital logic in VLSI. In addition to the choice of technology, attention should be paid to design philosophy if possible. A large effort is currently under way to simplify the design of VLSI systems. Thus a continuous-time filtering technique is more likely to be accepted if it is compatible with this trend. Just as is the case with digital circuits, the "standard cell" approach is attractive. In this approach, the filter designer uses predesigned circuits like op amps as building blocks, without getting involved in the design of the blocks themselves. Here there is a similarity to discrete-component design. In the latter, op amp chips were connected with resistors and capacitors to make a filter. In the "standard cell" approach the op amp is not a separate chip, but rather a circuit cell stored in the memory of a CAD system. The designer "calls" this cell and "connects" it to other elements on the computer terminal screen. The complete filter design is then fabricated as one chip, or as part of a larger chip containing other systems as well. If a filtering technique is such that active elements can be viewed as "black boxes", it is suitable for "standard-cell" design, and makes possible a

Manuscript received June 5, 1985; revised September 30, 1985. This work was supported in part by the National Science Foundation under Grant ECS-83-10227. Part of this material was presented at ISCAS 1984 and 1985.

Y. Tsividis is with the Department of Electrical Engineering and the Center for Telecommunications Research, Columbia University, New York, NY 10027.

M. Banu and J. Khoury are with AT&T Bell Laboratories, Murray Hill, NJ 07974.

IEEE Log Number 8406494.

Reprinted from *IEEE J. Solid-State Circuits*, vol. SC-21, no. 1, pp. 15–30, Feb. 1986.

51

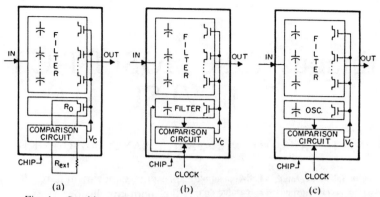

Fig. 1. On-chip automatic indirect tuning schemes. (a) With an external resistor as reference. (b) With a clock signal as reference and a voltage-controlled filter in the tuning loop. (c) With a clock signal as reference and a voltage-controlled oscillator in the tuning loop.

large degree of decoupling between filter synthesis and device-level circuit design.

Immunity to Parasitic Effects, Fabrication Tolerances, and Environmental Variations

There are many parasitic elements on integrated circuits. A viable filtering technique should be largely immune to such elements. In addition, accurate element values are not possible; e.g., RC products can vary by 50 percent or more due to fabrication tolerances, temperature variations, and aging. One thus needs a means to keep the filter's frequency response precise. Since doing so manually is clearly impractical, one must use some means for automatic tuning, accomplished by an on-chip system.

Large Signal Handling Capability

While it is desirable to keep the random noise internally generated by resistors and active elements at a low level, low random noise is not sufficient for large dynamic range. Since the filter is envisioned as part of a VLSI chip, a multitude of parasitic signals are likely to be present in its immediate environment, generated by other circuits on the same chip. These parasitic signals can contaminate the desired signal even more seriously than internally generated random noise can. Thus, in order to maintain a large dynamic range it is very important that the filtering technique inherently possess large signal handling capability. Since the filter will normally be used with automatic tuning which will vary certain voltage and/or current levels in the circuit, it is important to ensure that adjacent adequate signal handling capability is maintained *over all fabrication tolerances and temperature variations.*

Good Power Supply Rejection

The dynamic range can, of course, be helped if the above extraneous signals can be rejected to a significant extent. Since many of these signals are coupled to the filter through the power supply lines (for example, spikes due to switching of digital circuits on the same chip), it is important that the filter exhibit good power supply rejection. To this end, differential topologies are known to be helpful.

Low Power and Small Chip Area

These are well-known desirable features for any integrated circuit; integrated filters are no exception.

The objective of the work reviewed in this paper was to develop integrated filters exhibiting the above features.

III. On-Chip Automatic Tuning

To make possible the automatic tuning of integrated filters, RC products (or equivalent quantities) must be adjustable. In our technique, this is accomplished by using MOS transistors as voltage-controlled resistors. The effect of transistor nonlinearities can be accurately and reliably cancelled by suitable means, discussed in Section V. A review of automatic tuning schemes is now presented.

Indirect Tuning Schemes

Indirect automatic tuning schemes rely on the tight matching achievable for elements in close proximity on a chip. To our knowledge, the first such scheme was described by Canning and Wilson in a 1976 patent [2]. In our technique, automatic tuning schemes can take the forms shown in Fig. 1 [3]. These schemes are derived from similar techniques using other technologies [2], [4]–[11].

In Fig. 1(a), an on-chip resistor (R_o), realized by a MOS transistor, is compared to an external high-quality resistor (R_{ext}) by an on-chip circuit [8]. The value of R_o is automatically adjusted through a control voltage (V_C) until it becomes equal to R_{ext} (or until R_o/R_{ext} attains a fixed, predetermined value). The same control voltage V_C is applied to all other MOS resistors on the chip. Since the geometrical dimensions of the filter resistors are ratio-matched to those of R_o, their resistances attain desired, predetermined values, properly ratioed to R_o. Since the capacitor values are not accurately controlled during fabrication (although their ratios are), the scheme must be tuned externally once, by adjusting R_{ext}, until the frequency response is as desired. Following this, frequency response variations will be due to variations of R_{ext} (which, for a high-quality resistor will be small), and variations of the on-chip capacitances; for the latter, temperature coefficient as low as 15 ppm/°C have been reported [12].

If the use and initial adjustment of R_{ext}, or the subsequent small variations of the response are not acceptable, one can automatically tune RC products rather than just resistance values, by comparison to an external, highly accurate clock signal. If the filter is on the same chip with digital logic, the digital clock can be used. Tuning can be accomplished in two ways. In the scheme of Fig. 1(b), a "reference" filter is made out of the same types of basic structures as the main filter, and is fed by the clock signal. A phase comparator continuously compares the phase of the reference filter's output to that of the clock signal, and adjusts V_C until the two differ by a predetermined value. At this point, the RC products within the reference filter attain fixed, predetermined values. Since the main filter's resistances and capacitances are ratio-matched to those of the reference filter, the RC *products* in the main filter are stabilized, and so is the main filter's response. Note that this scheme automatically corrects for the variations of both resistances and capacitances, and requires no initial adjustment. The reference filter can be a replica of the main filter or, for economy, a replica of one basic cell of the latter. For example, if the main filter consists of coupled biquads, the reference filter can consist of one biquad. Note that the clock frequency should be *outside* the filter passband [1], since it is possible for the clock signal to appear at the output due to parasitic coupling.

A technique related to the above is shown in Fig. 1(c). Here the reference circuit is an oscillator made out of the same basic structures as the filter, and the phase comparator's output V_C attains such a value that the oscillator tracks the clock. The RC products in the oscillator thus become stabilized, and so are the RC products in the main filter due to matching. Again, the clock frequency should be outside the filter's passband.

All of the above techniques rely on tight element matching in order to provide satisfactory results. It is well known that two identical capacitors next to each other on a chip can be matched to about 0.1–0.5 percent. It is less well known that MOSFET "resistors" can attain a similar degree of matching [1], [13]. This is confirmed by direct matching measurements, as well as by the achievable accuracy of filter chips [1] and A/D converter chips using such "resistors" [13].

Direct Tuning Schemes

If very precise frequency response is desired, the degree of matching quoted above may be inadequate. A means to circumvent this problem may be to automatically tune the main filter itself [14], rather than a reference circuit next to it. This is shown in Fig. 2(a). The filter is periodically taken out of the signal path by on-chip switches, and placed in an automatic tuning loop, similar to the one used to tune the lower filter in Fig. 1(b). Such operation will be possible if the nature of the application is such that the filtering of the input signal is only needed part of the time. If uninterrupted filtering is necessary, one can use the system of Fig. 2(b). With the switch positions as shown, filter B is being tuned while filter A processes the input signal. Next, the

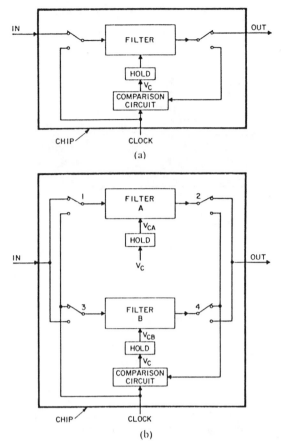

Fig. 2. On-chip automatic direct tuning schemes. (a) Interrupted filtering. (b) Uninterrupted filtering.

roles of filters A and B are to be interchanged; however, one cannot move all four switches downwards simultaneously, as then the build-up transients of filter B would appear at the output. Accordingly, switch 3 is first moved to the input. After the transient in filter B diminish, switches 1,2, and 4 are moved down. Filter A is now tuned while filter B processes the input signal, with the proper control voltage V_{CB} being held by the bottom "hold" circuit at the value established during the previous tuning half cycle. Following the tuning of filter A, switch 1 is moved to the input; after the transients in filter A die out, switches 2,3, and 4 are moved up, with the proper value of the control voltage V_{CA} held by the top "hold" circuit. The process is then repeated periodically. The output switching must be done carefully to ensure a smooth transition. What constitutes a "smooth transition" depends on the application; for example, in the case of an AM receiver IF stage followed by an envelope demodulator, nonperfect transitions are not likely to be of serious consequence. The "hold" circuits can consist of capacitors, with the V_C values to be held carefully deposited on them to avoid "switch feedthrough" errors [15]. Instead of tuning a whole filter at a time, one can also consider tuning its basic cells (e.g., biquads) one at a time. It is noted that direct tuning, to the best of our knowledge, has not yet been tried on an actual chip.

More information on the various automatic tuning techniques can be found in [3]–[11], [14], [16]. However, a

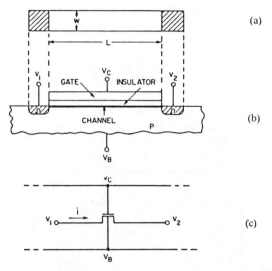

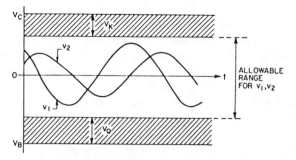

Fig. 4. Terminal voltages for the transistor of Fig. 3.

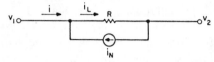

Fig. 3. A n-channel MOSFET. (a) Top view. (b) Side view. (c) Symbol.

Fig. 5. Low-frequency large-signal model for the MOS transistor.

detailed study of such techniques, and a detailed comparison of them is currently lacking.

IV. THE MOSFET AS A VOLTAGE-CONTROLLED RESISTOR

A n-channel MOSFET is shown in Fig. 3. The device has its gate connected to a dc control voltage V_C (e.g., 3–5 V) which is assumed to be produced by an automatic tuning scheme, as in Figs. 1 or 2. The substrate is connected to a fixed dc bias V_B (e.g., -5 V). The terminal voltages v_1 and v_2 are assumed to remain below V_C by at least an amount V_K as shown in Fig. 4, to allow operation in the "nonsaturation" region (Appendix). Also, v_1 and v_2 are assumed to remain above V_B by a noncritical quanity V_Q; the value of V_Q is 1–2 V and is discussed below. The transistor current i can be written in the form ([17] and Appendix)

$$i = i_L - i_N \qquad (1)$$

where i_N is a nonlinear term in v_1 and v_2 discussed in detail later, and i_L is a linear term given by

$$i_L = G(v_1 - v_2). \qquad (2)$$

The conductance G is given by

$$G = \left(\frac{W}{L}\right)\mu C'_{ox}(V_C - V_{TB}) \qquad (3)$$

with W and L the channel width and length, respectively (Fig. 3), μ the effective mobility (which will be assumed independent of terminal voltages until further notice), C'_{ox} the oxide capacitance per unit area, e.g., 0.5 fF/μm^2 and V_{TB} the threshold voltage of the transistor, corresponding to a substrate bias V_B (e.g., $V_{TB} = 1.9$ V at room temperature for the typical parameters given in the Appendix). A typical value for $\mu C'_{ox}$ at room temperature is 30 μA/V^2. Both V_{TB} and μ decrease with temperature.

Clearly, if one cancels the effect of i_N, the transistor behaves like a linear resistor with a conductance given by (3); the resistance $R = 1/G$ can be written in the form

$$R = \left(\frac{L}{W}\right)R_s \qquad (4)$$

where L/W is the "aspect ratio" of the transistor which is a design parameter, and R_s is a "sheet resistance" which, from (3), is given by

$$R_s = \frac{1}{\mu C'_{ox}(V_C - V_{TB})}. \qquad (5)$$

A model for the MOS transistor at low frequencies is, according to (1), as shown in Fig. 5. The above material holds also for p-channel devices, with appropriate changes in the signs of voltages and currents.

V. TRANSISTOR NONLINEARITIES AND THEIR CANCELLATION

The nonlinear term in (1) can be written in the following form (Appendix):

$$i_N = g(v_1) - g(v_2) \qquad (6)$$

where the function $g(v)$ is independent of V_C, and can be written as:

$$g(v) = g_e(v) + g_o(v) \qquad (7)$$

where $g_e(V)$ and $g_o(V)$ are even and odd functions, respectively, so that;

$$g_e(v) = g_e(-v) \qquad (8)$$

$$g_o(v) = -g_o(-v). \qquad (9)$$

Expressions for $g_e(v)$ and $g_o(v)$ are given in the Appendix. From the above we have

$$i_N = [g_e(v_1) - g_e(v_2)] + [g_o(v_1) - g_o(v_2)]. \qquad (10)$$

The term $[g_o(v_1) - g_o(v_2)]$ is very small compared to the linear term i_L in (1) (e.g., 0.1 percent of it or less). The term $[g_e(v_1) - g_e(v_2)]$, depending on v_1 and v_2, can be large and its effect must be eliminated.

Many different techniques have been proposed for eliminating the effect of nonlinearities. Some cancel the nonlinearities in the current of one device; others cancel the nonlinearities in the sum or difference of the currents in two or more devices. The various techniques are summarized in Fig. 6. The substrates are not shown for simplic-

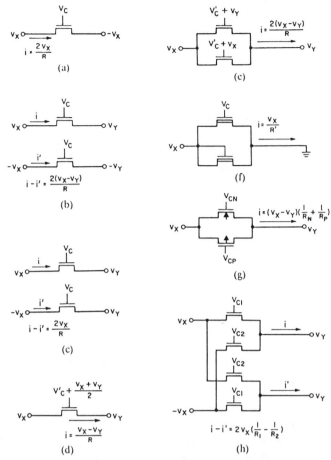

Fig. 6. Principles for eight ways to achieve nonlinearity cancellation in MOSFET-C filters. In all cases except (g), the substrate is assumed connected to V_B. In (g), the p-channel device's substrate is connected to the opposite of V_B. (a)–(c) achieve in principle complete cancellation of even nonlinearities; (d)–(g) achieve partial cancellation of even nonlinearities; (h) achieves in principle complete cancellation of both even and odd nonlinearities (see discussion on this scheme from a practical point of view in Section X).

This problem can be eliminated if a signal-dependent substrate voltage is supplied [18], using voltage level shifters.

It is easy to verify that the scheme in Fig. 6(e) will work even if the control voltage components on each gate are different. In particular, if the control component of the bottom transistor's gate is set to zero, and if $v_Y = 0$, one obtains the circuit of Fig. 6(f) [21]–[23]. To keep the bottom transistor on, this circuit requires the use of "depletion-mode" devices ($V_{TB} < 0$). This scheme does not eliminate even nonlinearities completely. The tranistors can purposely be mismatched to improve linearity [23], by an amount dependent on fabrication process parameters. The scheme has limited resistance variability compared to the other schemes, since one of the transistors is not controlled by V_C and represents a practically fixed resistance in parallel with the other transistor. In practical situations with a limited range for V_C, this may make it difficult to compensate for all fabrication tolerances and environmental changes. The expression for the resistance R' for this circuit is different from before, in that V_{TB} should be replaced by $2V_{TB}$. In CMOS technology, where usually depletion-mode tranistors are not available, for nondemanding applications it may be adequate to use the crude linearization scheme shown in Fig. 6(g). This circuit has been used as a crude linear resistor for several years in CMOS op amps and other analog circuits. If the n- and p-channel devices are purposely mismatched (based on a knowledge of fabrication process parameters), their nonlinearities can be shown to approximately cancel out. Since n- and p-channel devices are made differently, one cannot expect this scheme to provide high linearity.

The circuit in Fig. 6(h) [24] accomplishes in principle complete cancellation of both even and odd nonlinearities. In this figure R_1, R_2 are resistance values obtained from (4) and (5) with V_C equal to V_{C1} and V_{C2}, respectively. The performance of this circuit and of those in Fig. 6(a), (b), and (c) is so good that a meaningful evaluation and comparison of them must take into account high-order effects due to various nonidealities, which are discussed in Section X. Using these circuits, it is found that a 0.1-percent nonlinearity occurs with signal amplitudes of 1–2 V. The signal handling capability can be increased further using a simple technique discussed in Section X.

The above ideas can be used to produce linear integrated MOSFET-C filters in various ways, some of which are better than others. A review of possible techniques follows:

(a) Each transistor can be linearized separately [20]–[23], using, for example, the principles in Fig. 6(d)–(g). The transistors then become linear voltage-controlled resistors and can be used as resistors in an active "RC" filter, along with automatic tuning, as shown in Figs. 1 and 2.

(b) The transistors can be used with balanced signals, as in Fig. 6(a). However, it is not clear how one can generate useful filter topologies which achieve this.

(c) A rather *poor* way, in most cases, to accomplish some nonlinearity cancellation is the following. If, for a given RC filter topology, direct replacement of the resistors by unlinearized MOS transistors does not cause excessive odd-harmonic distortion at the filter output, one can build

ity; they are assumed connected to V_B except for the substrate of the p-channel device in Fig. 6(g), which is assumed connected to the opposite of V_B. All transistors within each scheme are assumed matched except for Fig. 6(f) and (g). For each scheme, the quantity being linearized is shown along with the resulting value. The residual nonlinear terms (if any) are not shown, but can be evaluated from the relations given. It is easily verified from the relations given above that in Fig. 6(a), (b), (c), [3], [18] the even nonlinearities are eliminated. The remaining odd nonlinearities are minute for most practical purposes, and can be reduced by increasing V_Q in Fig. 4 (Appendix). As an example, for a typical fabrication process, $V_B = -5$ V, and signal amplitudes of 1 V, the residual odd nonlinearities in the quantities indicated can be 0.1 percent of the linear term.

The scheme in Fig. 6(d) [3], [18] is a generalization of the early idea in [19]. In this scheme, and in the one in Fig. 6(e) [3], [20] the gates are not tied to a control voltage directly as before, but instead to voltages containing a control component (V_C') and a signal-dependent component. These schemes do not eliminate even nonlinearities completely as can be easily verified using relation (A.1) in the Appendix.

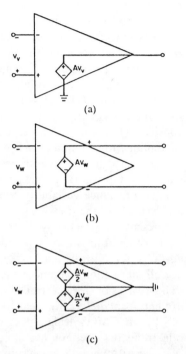

Fig. 7. Three kinds of op amps. (a) Single-ended output. (b) Differential output. (c) Balanced output.

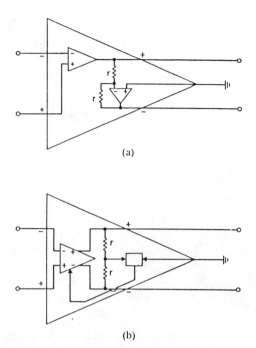

Fig. 8. Possible implementations of balanced-output on amp. (a) With two single-ended output op amps. (b) With a differential op amp and common-mode feedback.

two identical filters, drive them with opposite inputs, and take the output differentially (from the output of one filter to the output of the other). It is emphasized that the odd harmonics will not be cancelled in such a scheme. Odd harmonics can be large in such topologies since, despite the fact that individual transistors have mostly even-order nonlinearities, even harmonics can "mix" with the fundamental to produce large odd-order harmonics within the filter.

(d) To avoid the problem just mentioned, one can use the following technique: The filter is built out of building blocks *each* of which is individually linearized as far as its input-output characteristics are concerned. Such building blocks can easily be produced using balanced input/balanced output structures, in conjunction with the idea in Fig. 6(c). In the rest of this paper this approach is emphasized, but much of the material is relevant to other approaches as well.

More information on nonlinearity cancellation can be found elsewhere [18]. A phenomenon whereby both even and odd order nonlinearities cancel out in the filter structure as a whole, is discussed in [25].

VI. "Balanced" versus "Differential"

In our discussion we will need to make clear distinction between three kinds of op amps, as shown in Fig. 7. In Fig. 7(a), a conventional *single-ended-* output op amp is shown. In Fig. 7(b) a *differential* output op amp is shown. The output of this op amp is defined as the voltage difference between the two output terminals as indicated; the voltages at each of these terminals with respect to ground, however, are not individually defined. This type of op amp is in general useless for our purposes, and is included only to make clear its distinction from the *balanced-output* op amp, shown in Fig. 7(c). Here, the two outputs with respect to

ground are assumed to be accurately balanced as indicated. For the op amp to accomplish this, it needs a fifth terminal to which the ground is connected, so that it can serve as a reference for balancing the output. It is this type of op amp that will be used in this paper. Two possible implementations of such an op amp are shown in Fig. 8. The circuit in Fig. 8(a) has the advantage that it can be implemented from two single-ended op amps, which are available as "standard cells' in many design libraries. It has the disadvantage that, at high frequencies, the extra phase of the inverter can destroy the balance of the two outputs. For voiceband applications, however, this approach has given excellent results [1]. The approach shown schematically in Fig. 8(b) involves a differential-output op amp, the common-mode (average) output of which is sensed and compared to ground potential; corrective feedback is internally applied to make the common-mode output value equal to zero, thus maintaining the two outputs properly balanced. This scheme has the advantage that it is perfectly symmetric in principle; at high frequencies, additional phase shift is present in equal amounts at both outputs, and proper balancing is maintained. It has the disadvantage that it is not widely available yet as a standard cell, since it is newer and trickier to design. In addition, certain op amps using the general principle of Fig. 8(b), when in a loop can be subjective to "latch-up" if the overall common-mode loop gain becomes positive due to signal overload. The two resistors in Fig. 8(b) are only meant as a schematic representation of common-mode sensing; other sensing techniques can be used. Note, however, that crude common-mode sensing schemes, which may be accurate enough for differential switched-capacitor filters, may not provide output balancing accurate enough for continuous-time MOSFET-C filters.

VII. A BASIC LINEAR CELL

Fig. 9(a) shows the basic cell used in one MOSFET-C approach. The op amp gain is assumed infinite. We can write, for the upper output:

$$v_O(t) = v_Y(t) - \frac{1}{C_F} \int_{-\infty}^{t} i_F(\tau) d\tau. \qquad (11)$$

Similarly, for the lower output we can write

$$-v_O(t) = v_Y(t) - \frac{1}{C_F} \int_{-\infty}^{t} i'_F(\tau) d\tau. \qquad (12)$$

Subtracting (12) from (11) we obtain

$$V_O(t) = -\frac{1}{2C_F} \int_{-\infty}^{t} [i_F(\tau) - i'_F(\tau)] d\tau. \qquad (13)$$

From the circuit we see that

$$i_F - i'_F = (i_1 - i'_1) + (i_2 - i'_2) \qquad (14)$$

which, using the result in Fig. 6(c), and writing the current for each capacitor in terms of $\pm v_Z$ and v_Y, becomes

$$i_F - i'_F = \frac{2v_X}{R} + 2C_A \frac{dv_Z}{dt}. \qquad (15)$$

Using this in (13) we obtain

$$v_O(t) = \frac{1}{RC_F} \int_{-\infty}^{t} v_X(\tau) d\tau - \frac{C_A}{C_F} v_Z(t). \qquad (16)$$

This equation is identical to the input–output equation of the circuit in Fig. 9(b), which is composed wholly of linear elements and is the balanced version of the well-known single-ended cell in Fig. 9(c). If the op amp gain is assumed to be finite, it is easy to see that to maintain full correspondence between the circuits in Fig. 9(c) and (b), the op amp gains must be related, as shown in Fig. 7(a) and 7(c).

The circuit in Fig. 9(a) can be generalized to include more than one transistor and capacitor pairs connected the op amp inputs. (In fact one of the transistor pairs can be connected from the op amp outputs to the op amp inputs, with the analysis remaining valid). Again, it is easy to show that the outputs will be linear functions of the inputs, and equal to those of a corresponding circuit using linear resistors.

Note that above it is *not* claimed that voltages other than the output, and currents, are linear functions of the input. In fact, a calculation of such quantities or a computer simulation reveals clearly nonlinear *internal* behavior, as illustrated in Fig. 10. Note that, despite the fact that a balanced structure is used, the nonlinearities of the transistors result in currents which are *not* balanced, and each of these is a nonlinear function of the input. Also, the two op amp inputs v_Y (which are the same, under our assumption of infinite op amp gain) are *not* at "virtual ground". They instead contain a common-mode component (this can have an amplitude of, say 20 percent of the input amplitude; hence the op amp input common-mode requirements are modest). The voltages v_Y are also nonlinear functions of the input signal; in fact, they are practically second

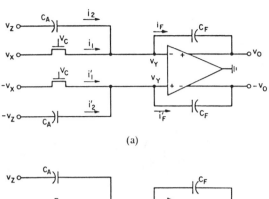

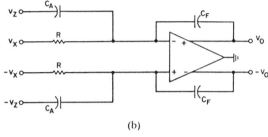

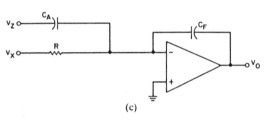

Fig. 9. (a) Basic MOSFET-C cell with linear input-output behavior. (b) Corresponding circuit using linear resistors. (c) Single-ended version of (b).

harmonics of it along with a dc component. These internal nonlinearities are such that the input–output characteristic is highly linear as shown above. An analysis including practical nonidealities such as finite gain, offsets, and mismatches, predicts that very satisfactory linearity is maintained [27]. This is verified by measurements on real chips (see below).

It has recently been shown [28] that MOSFET-C techniques can be used in the so-called balanced time-constant integrator. This is an interesting example of a circuit in which nonlinearity cancellation can be achieved without using a balanced structure. However, one must exercise care when using the balanced time-constant integrator, as it suffers from certain practical problems. Mismatches can cause significant phase errors at the unity-gain frequency [29], in contrast to the circuit of the Fig. 9(a); also, compared to the latter, the balanced time-constant integrator needs an op amp with larger common-mode input range and a capacitance twice as large, and can have lower power supply rejection due to the lack of balanced structure.

VIII. FILTER SYNTHESIS

Any active *RC* filter structure using the basic cell of Fig. 9(c) can be converted to one suitable for integration, using MOS transistors. A possible conversion procedure follows from Fig. 9, and is outlined below.

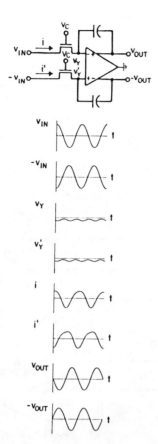

Fig. 10 An input–output balanced MOSFET-C integrator and associated voltage and current waveforms. The internal nonlinearities are such that the input–output behavior is highly linear.

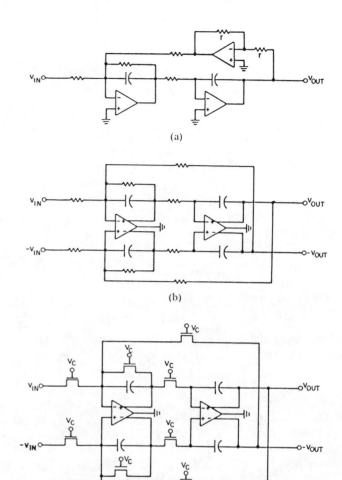

Fig. 11. Steps in designing a MOSFET-C filter. (a) Active RC prototype. (b) The fully-balanced version of (a). (c) The circuit in (b) with resistors replaced by MOSFET's. All substrates are connected to V_B.

(a) An active RC prototype is drawn [30]–[32], with a topology such that all resistor terminals are connected to op amp outputs, virtual grounds, or input voltage sources (for example, the Tow–Thomas biquad, shown in Fig. 11(a), falls in this category).

(b) The fully balanced version of the circuit in (a) is developed, using balanced-output op amps. Since such op amps inherently provide inversion at one of their outputs, all unity-gain inverters that may exist in step (a) can be eliminated (Fig. 11(b)) unless they happen to be part of an "active frequency compensation" scheme [30]–[32]. If full correspondence of op amp finite gain–bandwidth effects is to be maintained between the circuits of Fig. 11(a) and (b), the op amp gains should be related as those in Fig. 7(a) and (c).

(c) All resistors in the circuit of step (b) are replaced by MOS transistors (Fig. 11(c)), with their gates connected to the same control voltage V_C, and their substrates connected to the same bias V_B. As follows from (4), for any two transistors corresponding to two resistors, say R_1 and R_2 in Fig. 11(b), one must choose the L/W ratios in such a way that $(L/W)_1/(L/W)_2 = R_1/R_2$. The actual values of L/W must be such that the value of V_C required to provide the correct RC products does not exceed a given convenient maximum limit (e.g., the positive power supply voltage), over all temperature variations and fabrication tolerances. Once this is ensured, the on-chip automatic tuning scheme can be relied upon to provide the appropriate V_C value. A worst-case design procedure for

choosing L/W ratios is possible if the worst-case fabrication process parameters are known [33], [34].

To complete the design procedure, one must correct for the effects of transistor distributed capacitance and op amp finite gain–bandwidth product. This is discussed in the following section.

IX. Effect of Parasitic Capacitances, Op Amp Finite Gain–Bandwidth Product, and Op Amp Output Resistance

The MOS transistor in Fig. 3 exhibits a significant parasitic distributed capacitance between its channel and the gate, which is at small-signal ground. The total value of this capacitance is given by

$$C_g = C'_{ox}(WL) \qquad (17)$$

with C'_{ox} as defined in Section IV. Another distributed capacitance corresponds to the depletion region between the channel and the substrate. The total value of this capacitance is of the form [35], [36]

$$C_b = C'_b(WL) \qquad (18)$$

where the depletion region capacitance per unit area, C'_b,

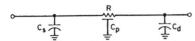

Fig. 12. Small-signal equivalent circuit for a MOSFET "resistor".

decreases with increasing $|V_B|$. It is normally small (e.g., one tenth of C'_{ox}).

Finally, there are two lumped parasitic capacitances from each "resistor" terminal to small-signal ground; these are due to the pn junctions in Fig. 3(a), and to the overlap of the gate and the n regions. These capacitances can typically be about 20 fF, and will be denoted by C_s and C_d.

The small-signal equivalent for a MOS "resistor" is shown in Fig. 12, where

$$C_p = C_g + C_b. \qquad (19)$$

For the topologies we are considering, the effect of capacitances C_s and C_d will not be significant if the op amp approximates ideal behavior. These capacitances are either voltage driven, or are connected to one of the op amp input terminals in Fig. 9(a). Due to the fact that matched transistors are used, the total capacitance between either op amp input terminal and ground is the same. As long as the op amp gain is very high, both capacitors see practically the same voltage v_Y across them. As v_Y varies with time, these capacitances add equal currents to i_F and i'_F, which cancel out in the difference in (13) even if these capacitances are nonlinear.[1] The effect of C_p however can be very important and can distort the frequency response if not taken into account at the design stage, even if the op amps are ideal. Several techniques have been proposed to deal with this effect, as outlined below.

The earliest technique is empirical [1], [17]. The filter is first designed assuming ideal resistors with no distributed capacitance, as in the previous section (Fig. 11(a) or (b)). Next, distributed capacitances are added and the filter is computer-simulated to determine whether such effects have significantly affected the frequency response. For the circuit of Fig. 11(b) this can be done conveniently if a simulator is available that can handle distributed RC elements. Otherwise, one can use a lumped RC approximation. Suitable such circuits are discussed elsewhere [37], [38]. Alternatively, one can perform the simulation directly at the transistor level (Fig. 11(c)), using some "tricks" and extra care [1], [34]. Computer simulation usually predicts a certain effect on the frequency response (e.g., peaking at the band edge). Provided this effect is small, it can be eliminated by empirically modifying slightly the value of one or two capacitor pairs in the filter, using computer simulation as a guide (a similar empirical technique is sometimes used to correct for "imperfect terminations" in switched-capacitor LDI ladder filters). This method is fast, and has resulted in successful chips from the first run [1], [17]. Note that the capacitor value adjustment described above can be used to simultaneously correct for the effects

of both the distributed capacitances and the op amp finite gain–bandwidth product, and even for op amp nonzero output resistance, as long as these are high-order effects.

An alternate technique is to develop analytical results for the distributed capacitance and finite gain–bandwidth effects (such as the center frequency shift and the change in Q for a biquad), and use frequency response predistortion techniques. The only such results presently available are for the Tow–Thomas biquad and for a modified version of the Vogel (Akerberg–Mossberg) biquad [37], [38].

Yet a third technique is to compensate each filter cell (such as the one in Fig. 9(a)) using passive or active compensation [30]–[32]. It is to be noted here that, whereas passive compensation may not be very popular in discrete-component filters due to lack of component value tracking, in integrated filters the results are more positive since all elements are made on the same chip and can be made to track adequately. For a discussion of passive compensation for both distributed capacitance effects and finite gain–bandwidth effects in the Tow–Thomas biquad the reader is referred to [38]. Regarding active compensation, we should warn the reader that schemes which work "in principle" assuming single-pole op amps and ideal resistors may not work due to excess phase in the op amps and in the MOSFET resistors (caused by the distributed capacitance). Phase margins in active compensation loops must be carefully considered.

All of the above techniques result in satisfactory corrections only if the distributed effects are rather small to begin with. If this is not the case, the filter can be modified by increasing all capacitor sizes and decreasing all resistor sizes proportionately, thus making the effect of distributed capacitances less pronounced. Corrections can then be applied using any of the above techniques. For a detailed design example, the reader is referred to [1]. Before finalizing the design one must of course be convinced that whatever compensation is used works well over fabrication tolerances and temperature variations, assuming the automatic tuning system has been activated.

Now let $\omega_0 = 1/RC$, where R and C are an integrator's resistance and capacitance, respectively. Let $\omega_p = 1/RC_P$, where C_p is the parasitic distributed capacitance associated with the transistor implementing R. For the distributed effects to be small, one needs a large ratio ω_p/ω_0. Note from (4) that $R \sim L/W$ (where $\sim$ denotes proportionality), and thus $\omega_0 \sim W/L$. From (17) to (19), $C_p \sim LW$ and, therefore, $\omega_p \sim 1/L^2$. Thus $\omega_p/\omega_0 \sim 1/(LW)$. To help make ω_p/ω_0 large, W can be set at the minimum value which, for a given fabrication process, will allow satisfactory resistor matching (e.g., a few micrometers). To further maximize ω_p/ω_0 a small L should be use (i.e., small R), which will mean a large C for a given ω_0. However this cannot be taken to extremes for two reasons. First, if the channel is made too short (e.g., several micrometers) "short-channel effects" will set in, and matching will deteriorate. Second, C cannot be made arbitrarily large because then the area of the chip will be excessive. Unlike discrete-component active filters, where the number of capacitors may be of concern, in integrated implementations it is the total chip

[1]Similar comments hold for the parasitic capacitances from either terminal of a filter capacitor to the substrate. Note that in MOS technology one of these parasitics (the so-called "bottom plate parasitic" is dominant (e.g., one-tenth the value of the corresponding filter capacitor). In critical cases, one should take this into account in deciding how to connect a capacitor in the circuit).

capacitance that must be kept within reasonable limits (e.g., a few hundred picofarads for a fifth-order filter). Assume then that, due to such considerations, C is fixed. Then to frequency-scale the design to a new critical frequency $\omega_0' = \beta\omega_0$ (with the scaling factor less than unity), one must scale L to $L' = L/\beta$. This will scale ω_p to $\omega_p' = \beta^2\omega_p$, giving $\omega_p'/\omega_0' = \beta(\omega_p/\omega_0)$. Thus the parasitic distributed capacitance effects become more serious at *low* frequencies. The design of, say, a 60-Hz or 50-Hz notch filter is challenging.

Rather than having to contend with the distributed capacitance as a parasitic element, an interesting idea would be to actually use this capacitance as a filter element [39]. From (4), (5), (19), and (17), assuming $\dot{C}_b$ is very small we obtain

$$RC_P \simeq \frac{L^2}{\mu(V_C - V_{TB})}. \tag{20}$$

Thus the inherent RC product of a MOSFET is approximately independent of C_{ox}', and is also independent of W, which may result in improved matching for RC products. Note that the above product is voltage controllable through V_C, and may be used to produce automatically tuned distributed filters. Also, such an implementation is economical in terms of chip area since it is in a sense "three-dimensional", with the resistance physically located under the capacitance on the chip (Fig. 3(a)). However, it is not clear how or if nonlinearity cancellation can be achieved in such filters; the analysis of Section V is certainly not valid when distributed effects dominate.

Op amps available as standard cells are often operational transconductance amplifiers (with a large output resistance). The effective output impedance will of course be lowered in the feedback configuration in which the op amps are employed. If this effective impedance is sufficiently lower than the impedances being driven, such op amps will be adequate. For voiceband filters the filter resistances are very high (several megaohms [1]), so they do not present a problem. One must, however, also make sure that the op amp can drive the resistors used in the various inverters or common-mode sensors (Fig. 8(a) and (b)).

For sufficiently high frequencies of operation one has to consider several effects. First, the filter impedance levels can be sufficiently low to require low-output impedance op amps. Second, when using balanced integrators it should be made sure that the op amp gain at these frequencies is not so low as to prevent nonlinearity cancellation (recall that both of these cancellations rely on the op amp's input voltages being nearly identical). Finally, the well-known op amp finite gain–bandwidth product effects on the filter's frequency response must be taken into account. At very high frequencies one may have to make the op amp biasing dependent on the control voltage, so that a certain degree of tracking can be achieved between the op amp's unity-gain frequency and the filter's critical frequencies.

It should be noted that a commercial chip using continuous-time MOSFET-C filters operating in the megahertz range has already been announced [40], [41].

X. Mismatches, Nonconstant Mobility, Effects, Distortion, Noise, and Dynamic Range

For exact cancellation of even-order distortion in the schemes presented, one would need exact transistor matching. In practice, mismatches will cause some residual even-order distortion. The dominant source for such mismatches appears to be threshold voltage mismatch. However, in the filters we are reviewing $V_C - V_{TB}$ in (5) can be large, thus reducing this effect and allowing matching as good as 0.1 to 0.5 percent for adjacent MOSFET resistors. Another nonideality is that the mobility μ is not really constant, but varies somewhat with the terminal voltages [35], [36]. Although even-order distortion is not really affected by this, odd-order distortion can be somewhat different than expected by assuming μ is constant. Another reason for this distortion to be different is that transistor channels are actually implanted, a fact not taken into account in the models used (Appendix). These practical effects make the comparison of the various techniques in Fig. 6 less than clear-cut. In fact, the behavior of the circuits in Fig. 6(a), (b), (c), and (h) may be rather similar, especially if their distortion is dominated by even-order terms due to mismatches. The reader is warned here that the value of computer simulation in predicting distortion, especially when the distortion is very low, is doubtful. This is because device models commonly used in CAD, with accuracies no better than, say, 5 percent, do not in general retain the fine details needed to correctly predict distortions of, say 0.1 percent. Other pitfalls to avoid when using computer simulation for the circuits presented, are discussed elsewhere [34]. Actual measurements show that, in the presence of all nonidealities, very low distortion levels are still obtained. Complete fifth-order filter chips can handle signals of several volts with total harmonic distortion of 0.1 percent.

The MOS "resistors" are found to produce thermal noise corresponding to actual resistors of the same resistance. In our implementations, this noise dominated the noise produced by the op amps, but was nevertheless low enough to give a dynamic range of about 100 dB for complete filters [1].

If it is desired to handle very large external signals, one can use the approach shown in Fig. 13. In this scheme the external signals are attenuated, processed by the filter, and amplified. If α is modest (e.g., 3) the resulting loss of dynamic range is not severe [1]. The V value of α can be chosen once the worst-case signal-handling capability of the filter by itself, over all fabrication tolerances, and temperature variations, has been determined.

As already mentioned, the dynamic range can be restricted due to extraneous signals generated by other circuits on a chip of which the filter is part (e.g., by digital circuits). The effect of extraneous signals on op amp power supply lines is largely eliminated due to the balanced topology. However, it is important to ensure that such signals are not present on the V_C and V_B lines. Otherwise, they can modulate the resistance values as seen from (5) (V_B can affect R through V_{TB}, if the automatic tuning loop

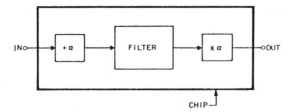

Fig. 13. Method to increase the external signal-handling capability of a filter.

cannot respond fast enough to eliminate its effect). One can ensure that V_C and V_B are clean DC voltages in several ways [34]. Note that this problem is in principle not present in the scheme of Fig. 6(h). This scheme has the advantage that $1/R_1 - 1/R_2$ depends only on $V_{C1} - V_{C2}$, rather than on quantities of the form $V_C - V_{TB}$. Thus extraneous signals on the V_B line do not affect the circuit. Also, extraneous signals on V_{C1} and V_{C2}, as long as they are common, cancel out in the difference. In practice this will not be exactly so due to the nonidealities discussed above. It should also be noted that this circuit has higher thermal noise and is more susceptible to mismatches than the one in Fig. 6(c). Depending on practical constraints in a given application, one or the other circuit may be preferable. At the time of this writing, the scheme of Fig. 6(h) has not yet been tried on an actual chip.

XI. COMPARISON TO OTHER INTEGRATED FILTERING TECHNIQUES

The fully integrated MOSFET-C active filters described above will now be compared to switched-capacitor filters, digital filters, and filters using other continuous-time techniques. Since in the preceeding sections we have discussed in detail the problems encountered in the design of MOSFET-C filters, the emphasis in the comparison to follow will be the corresponding problems of the other types of integrated filters [34].

Comparison to Switched-Capacitor Filters

Switched-capacitor techniques were the first to make possible the efficient implementation of monolithic signal processors. The frequency response of switched-capacitor filters can be scaled by varying their clock frequency, a feature desirable for some applications. These circuits suffer however from some drawbacks, not all of which are apparent from theoretical treatments, and which complicate chip-level design. A list of such drawbacks follows.

(1) Switched-capacitor filters are sampled-data systems, and as such they usually need input anti-aliasing and/or output smoothing filters. Of course continuous-time filters need an automatic tuning circuit instead, which occupies a similar amount of chip area. Note however that for a bank of such filters on the same chip one is likely to need only one automatic tuning circuit (assuming indirect tuning—Fig. 1), whereas for a bank of switched-capacitor filters one would need a bank of anti-aliasing and/or smoothing filters.

(2) In SC filters, internally generated op amp noise at high frequencies is aliased into the baseband due to sampling by each switch. One should make sure that this aliased noise is not excessive.

(3) Power supply noise at out-of-band high frequencies (at which the power supply rejection of the op amps is poor) is aliased into the baseband due to switching, and contaminates the signal. Differential techniques have been devised to alleviate this problem, resulting in switched-capacitor filter structures similar to the balanced continuous-time filter structures reviewed in this paper. In such continuous-time structures an inbalance of very small parasitic capacitances can cause power supply noise coupling at high frequencies, outside the baseband and may be ignored. In a switched-capacitor filter though, the coupled noise caused by a corresponding inbalance can be aliased into the baseband. Thus, in differential switched-capacitor filter structures even small parasitic capacitances should be balanced. This does not represent an easy design problem.

(4) In switched-capacitor filters, switching causes "clock feedthrough" which is difficult to predict and eliminate. Switch "charge injection" can depend on the signal level and if not properly taken into account can cause distortion. Clock feedthrough effects worsen at high switching rates. In continuous-time filters, if a clock is used as a reference (Figs. 1(b) or (c)) there will be some feedthrough to the output (e.g., 110 μV in [1]). By choosing the clock frequency outside the baseband, though, such feedthrough can be made inconsequential in many cases. In switched-capacitor filters, instead, clock feedthrough can create problems in the baseband due to sampling.

(5) In switched-capacitor filters, mixing products are created between the input signal frequencies and the switching frequency with its harmonics. This can be especially troublesome in some large systems, with many switched-capacitor filters coexisting on the same chip with other switching circuits and employing asynchronous clock rates. Modems are a typical example of a system where mixing products can be a problem [42].

(6) For a given technology, as the baseband frequency is raised an abrupt deterioration of performance is observed [43]. This is due to the effect of switch resistance and op amp slewing and settling behavior (which can be especially complicated where continuous-path loops are present, such as in some leap frog topologies). The prediction of such effects is difficult and requires extensive computer simulation of transient responses. The abruptness of the appearance of these effects as one attempts to use higher baseband frequencies makes "frequency predistortion" techniques difficult. Also, as the ratio of band-edge frequency to clock frequency is raised, the implementation of anti-aliasing and/or smoothing filters becomes critical. In continuous-time filters, high-frequency effects start becoming significant at lower frequencies than in switched-capacitor filters (assuming the same op amp performance) but, as baseband frequency is raised, worsen only gradually. At very high frequencies, such effects in switched-capacitor filters become worse than in continuous-time

61

filters [43]. Due to only gradual deterioration in continuous-time filters, high-frequency effects can be compensated using techniques analogous to those for classical active filters. The prediction and computer simulation of high-frequency effects in continuous-time filters is rather easy, requiring only ac analysis.

In view of the problems of switched capacitor circuits at high frequencies, some professional designers have opted for continuous-time MOSFET-C solutions instead [40], [41].

Comparison to Digital Filters

Digital filters are finally being implemented in single-chip form today. Design and testing automation is easier for them than for analog filters. Integrated digital filters are likely to be used extensively in situations where the signal is already in digital form, where long chains of filtering must be used, and where programmability is desired. A meaningful comparison to analog filters can, of course, only be done for the cases in which *analog* signals must be processed (e.g., in telephony, radio, and TV systems, which require a total number of filters numbering in the billions). Then, digital filters can be seen to suffer from the following drawbacks:

(1) An A/D and/or a D/A converter is needed. This complicates the system design. Also, since the A/D and D/A converters contain analog parts, the drawbacks sometimes claimed for analog circuitry (e.g., noise, accuracy etc.) are really there, in the A/D-digital filter–D/A combination [44]. Conversely, if techniques are devised to eliminate such problems from the analog parts of the A/D and D/A converters such techniques can probably also be used to eliminate the corresponding problems in analog filters (for example, the development of switched-capacitor techniques for precision A/D and D/A converters lead, within a couple of years, to the development of precision switched-capacitor filters). We note here that the "quantization noise" produced by the sampling and A/D conversion processes is actually a form of distortion at frequencies dependent on both the signal and the sampling rate. This distortion is in general nonharmonically related to the signal itself [45] and has been claimed to be more objectionable to humans than noise or harmonic distortion of comparable power. In some applications, the undesired signals are orders of magnitude larger than the desired ones (e.g., in receiver IF filtering). Then one must use a sufficient number of bits to process and reject the undesired signal, plus an extra number of bits to handle the desired signal adequately with low quantization noise. This can mean a large total number of bits making the design of the A/D and D/A coverters difficult and expensive. Note that to make possible a dynamic range of 100 dB (which has been attained with MOSFET-C filters [1]) one needs 17 bits. At the time of this writing, no fully integrated A/D converter has been reported with such resolution. Oversampling techniques are attractive for some applications but they trade bandwidth for resolution and can present certain complications [44].

(2) Anti-aliasing and/or output smoothing filters are needed. Comments here are the same as in point (1) of the preceeding subsection on switched-capacitor filters.

(3) Power dissipation is often larger in digital filters.

In concluding this part, it should be noted that, in cases where an A/D-digital filter–D/A combination is found attractive the continuous-time techniques proposed in this paper represent a good solution to the problem of implementing the input anti-aliasing and output smoothing filters (with or without automatic tuning, depending on requirements).

Comparison to Other Continuous-Time Filters

Other continuous-time filters, using a variety of technologies, and including on-chip automatic tuning systems, have been described [2], [6]–[8], [10], [11], [46]–[49]. The filter designer using these techniques will at present have to deal with the detailed device-level design of the active elements (gyrators, transconductance elements, etc.) since these are not standard building blocks and must be developed for the specific filter application. On the other hand, in this way one can optimize the active elements and, especially if their circuitry is sufficiently simple, attain good high-frequency performance. Several attempts have been made towards linearization of the active elements charaterics in these filters; by the time such linearization is reliably achieved, though, the extra circuitry needed deteriorates the high-frequency performance, at least in the attempts known to these authors. Thus the problems of linearity and high frequency operation are coupled. In addition, to realistically access the linearity of these schemes one should consider them with today's low-power supply voltages, and determine the worst-case signal-handling capability as the tuning voltage/current is varied to compensate for fabrication tolerances and temperature variations. It is then usually found that this worst-case capability is still limited.[1] We also note that of the techniques referred to above, most [2], [6]–[8], [47] do not use MOS technology and thus cannot be part of a MOS VLSI chip. This is a disadvantage in many applications, although we are not overlooking the importance of other technologies.

In the MOSFET-C filters reviewd in this paper, op amps are used instead as active elements. One can design a MOSFET-C filter treating the op amps basically as black boxes with known characteristics (e.g., bandwidth, dc gain, output impedance), just like in the design of discrete-component active *RC* filters. In a typical design environment, a chip designer can choose from a variety of ready and proven op amp cells, which have been developed from a multitude of other applications (again, just like in the case of discrete-component design). Linearization does not rely much on the internal circuitry of the active elements, which helps decouple the problems of linearity and high-frequency operation. For large signal handling capability, one uses a balanced topology (which is desirable anyway for good

---

[1]As the proofs for this paper are being corrected, it appears that a very recently developed transconductance cell may offer linearity as good as that of MOSFET-C techniques described here [50].

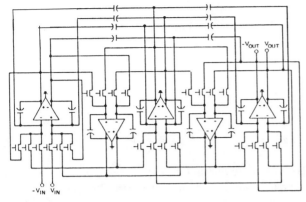

Fig. 14. Schematic of a fifth-order elliptic low-pass integrated filter [1].

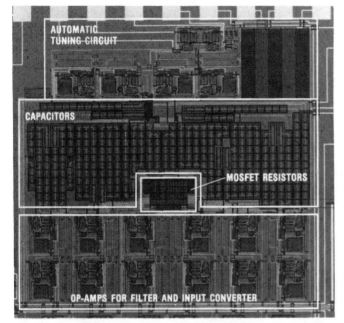

Fig. 15. Microphotograph of chip including the filter of Fig. 14, an input unbalanced-to-balanced converter, and the automatic tuning system.

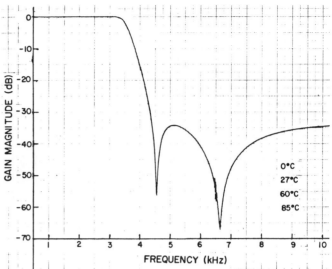

Fig. 16. Measured frequency response for the chip of Fig. 15.

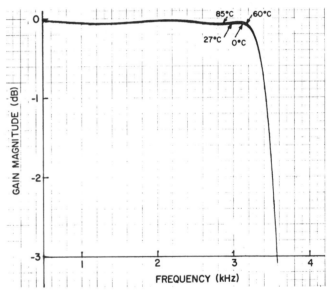

Fig. 17. Expanded version of the frequency response in Fig. 16.

power supply rejection) or individually linearized MOSFET's; for high-frequency operation, one uses high-frequency operational amplifiers and possibly passive or active compensation.

A fair comparison of the high-frequency performance of MOSFET-C techniques to that of the other continuous-time techniques referred to above, can be done after the latter have been adequately modified to provide the degree of linearity possible with MOSFET-C techniques. Also, in such a comparison one should allow for custom-designing the op amps in the MOSFET-C filters, as in done with the active elements in the other techniques. Under such assumptions, the outcome of the comparison is not clear at this point.

XII. EXPERIMENTAL RESULTS

Using the techniques described, an experimental monolithic MOSFET-C active filter with on-chip automatic tuning has recently been developed [1]. The filter topology is as in Fig. 14; an input unbalanced-to-balanced converter

has been included (not shown). The automatic tuning system is that of Fig. 1(c). The chip has been implemented in CMOS technology, and its microphotograph is shown in Fig. 15. With the tuning circuitry deactivated, the 3-dB frequency was found to vary by more than 40 percent over the commercial temperature range. Connecting the on-chip tuning system, the frequency response becomes as shown in Fig. 16 and is stable to better than 0.1 percent over the same temperature range. An expanded part of this response is shown in Fig. 17. With ± 5-V power supplies, the complete integrated system of Fig. 13 can handle differential signals of over 5-V peak-to-peak before its distortion rises to 0.1 percent and over 15 V peak-to-peak before it rises to 1 percent. The chip demonstrates that frequency response precision on par to that of today's switched-capacitor circuits is possible, without the complications arising from sampled-data operation.

XIII. Conclusions

We have reviewed techniques for implementing monolithic, VLSI-compatible active MOSFET-C filters with on-chip automatic tuning. Attractive features of these filters are precise frequency-response, low-noise operation, and large signal handling capability. The feasibility of the techniques has been demonstrated with a filter chip which exhibits high performance. We have found that significant assets in the design of these filters are the wealth of knowledge accumulated over three decades of intensive work on active filters by many researchers, as well as the relative ease of computer simulation. It is hoped that this will help make possible further improvements, notably techniques for high-frequency design. The recent development of a commercial chip with MOSFET-C filters operating in the megahertz range is only the beginning in this direction, but is certainly very encouraging. In certain cases, MOSFET-C filters can offer advantages over switched-capacitor filters, digital filters, and continuous-time filters using different techniques. Thus they can find their own range of applications and, along with other filtering techniques, they can play a complementary role in future mixed analog/digital VLSI systems. The techniques presented can be applied to circuits other than filters such as oscillators, voltage-controlled amplifiers, automatic gain control circuits, modulators, etc.

Appendix

The accurate analysis of MOS transistor nonlinearities requires the use of models more sophisticated than the quadratic equations common in circuit design. Thus in our work we have used the accurate strong inversion model instead [35], [36]. For this model, the current i in the device of Fig. 3 is, in the nonsaturation region, given by

$$i = \left(\frac{W}{L}\right)\mu C'_{ox}\left\{(V_C - V_B - V_{FB} - \phi_B)(v_1 - v_2)\right.$$
$$-\frac{1}{2}\left[(v_1 - V_B)^2 - (v_2 - V_B)^2\right]$$
$$\left.-\frac{2}{3}\gamma\left[(v_1 - V_B + \phi_B)^{3/2} - (v_2 - V_B + \phi_B)^{3/2}\right]\right\} \quad (A.1)$$

where V_{FB} is the transistor's "flatband voltage" (e.g., 0 V), ϕ_B is typically 0.7 V at room temperature, γ is the "body effect coefficient" (e.g., 0.5 $V^{1/2}$) and the rest of the quantities have the meaning discussed in Section IV. If, in this model, the linear components are extracted from the 3/2-power terms, and lumped with the main linear term, one easily obtains (1)–(3), (6), and (7), with

$$V_{TB} = V_{FB} + \phi_B + \gamma\sqrt{V_R} \quad (A.2)$$

$$g_c(v) = \left(\frac{W}{L}\right)\mu C'_{ox}\left\{\frac{1}{2}v^2 + \frac{1}{3}\gamma\left[(V_R + v)^{3/2} + (V_R - v)^{3/2}\right]\right\} \quad (A.3)$$

$$g_o(v) = \left(\frac{W}{L}\right)\mu C'_{ox}\left\{\gamma\left[\frac{1}{3}(V_R + v)^{3/2}\right.\right.$$
$$\left.\left.-\frac{1}{3}(V_R - v)^{3/2} - V_R^{1/2}v\right]\right\} \quad (A.4)$$

with

$$V_R = \phi_B - V_B. \quad (A.5)$$

To guarantee operation in the nonsaturation region, the voltage V_K in Fig. 3 should have the following value, as can be easily derived from basic device considerations [35], [36]:

$$V_K = V_{FB} + \phi_B - \frac{\gamma^2}{2} + \gamma\sqrt{V_C - V_B - V_{FB} + \frac{\gamma^2}{4}}. \quad (A.6)$$

It can be verified from (A.4) to (A.5) that in order to keep the odd nonlinearities negligible, γ should not be too large and v should not get too close to the value of V_B; hence the "safety margin" V_Q in Fig. 4.

If the gate potential contains a signal-dependent component, as in Fig. 6(d), (e), and (f), it is probably more convenient to use (A.1) and (A.6) directly, with V_C replaced with the actual gate potential.

References

[1] M. Banu and Y. Tsividis, "An elliptic continuous-time CMOS filter with on-chip automatic tuning," *IEEE J. Solid-State Circuits*, vol. SC-20, pp. 1114–1121, Dec. 1985.

[2] J. R. Canning and G. A. Wilson, "Frequency discriminator circuit arrangement," UK Patent 1 421 093, Jan. 1976.

[3] Y. Tsividis and M. Banu, "Integrated nonswitched active *RC* filters with wide dynamic range," in *Proc. 1983 European Conf. Circ. Theory and Design*, Stuttgart, pp. 111–113.

[4] K. Radhakrishna Rao, V. Sethuraman, and P. K. Neelakantan, "A novel 'Follow the master' filter," *Proc. IEEE*, vol. 65, pp. 1725–1726, 1977.

[5] J. R. Brand, R. Schaumann, and E. M. Skei, "Temperature stabilized active *R* filters," in *Proc. 20th Midwest Symp. on Circuits and Systems*, pp. 295–300, 1977.

[6] K. S. Tan and P. R. Gray, "Fully integrated analog filters using bipolar-JFET technology," *IEEE J. Solid-State Circuits*, vol. SC-13, pp. 814–821, Dec. 1978.

[7] K. W. Moulding, J. R. Quartly, P. J. Rankin, R. S. Thompson, and G. A. Wilson, "Gyrator video filter IC with automatic tuning," *IEEE J. Solid-State Circuits*, vol. SC-15, pp. 963–968, Dec. 1980.

[8] J. O. Voorman, W. H. A. Bruls, and P. J. Barth, "Integration of analog filters in a bipolar process," *IEEE J. Solid-State Circuits*, vol. SC-17, pp. 713–722, Aug. 1982.

[9] T. R. Viswanathan, S. Murtuza, V. H. Syed, J. Berry, and M. Staszel, "Switched-capacitor frequency-controlled loop," *IEEE J. Solid-State Circuits*, vol. SC-17, pp. 775–778, Aug. 1982.

[10] D. Senderowicz, D. A. Hodges, and P. R. Gray, "An NMOS vector-locked loop," in *Proc. 1982 IEEE Int. Symp. Circuits and Systems*, pp. 1164–1167.

[11] H. Khorramabadi and P. R. Gray, "High frequency CMOS continuous-time filters," *IEEE J. Solid-State Circuits*, vol. SC-19, pp. 939–948, Dec. 1984.

[12] J. L. McCreary, "Matching properties and voltage and temperature dependence of MOS capacitors," *IEEE J. Solid-State Circuits*, vol. SC-16, pp. 608–616, Dec. 1981.

[13] R. J. Apfel, Advanced Micro Devices Corporation, private communication.

[14] Y. Tsividis, "Self-tuned filters," *Electron. Lett.*, vol. 17, no. 12, pp. 406–407, June 1981.

[15] E. J. Swanson, "Echo cancellers: their role and construction, Chapter

16 in *Design of MOS VLSI Circuits for Telecommunications*, (Eds. Y. Tsividis and P. Antognetti), Englewood Cliffs, NJ: Prentice-Hall, 1985, p. 557.

[16] R. Schaumann and C. F. Chiou, "Design of integrated analog filter," in *Proc. 1981 European Conf. on Circuit Theory and Design*, The Hague, The Netherlands, pp. 407–411.

[17] M. Banu and Y. Tsividis, "Fully integrated active *RC* filters in MOS technology," *IEEE J. Solid-State Circuits*, vol. SC-18, pp. 644–651, Dec. 1983.

[18] M. Banu and Y. Tsividis, "Fully integrated active *RC* filters," in *Proc. 1983 Int. Symp. Circuits Systems*, pp. 602–605.

[19] A. Bilotti, "Operation of a MOS transistor as a variable resistor," *Proc. IEEE*, vol. 54, pp. 1093–1094, Aug. 1966.

[20] M. Banu and Y. Tsividis, "Floating voltage-controlled resistors in CMOS technology," *Electron. Lett.*, vol. 18, no. 15, pp. 678–679, July 1982.

[21] L. N. M. Edward, U.K. Patent 1251671, 27 Oct. 1971.

[22] I. S. Han and S. B. Park, "Voltage-controlled linear resistor by two MOS transistors and its application in active MOS integration," *Proc. IEEE*, vol. 72, pp. 1655–1657, Nov. 1984.

[23] J. N. Babanezhad and G. C. Temes, "A linear NMOS depletion resistor and its application in an integrated amplifier," *IEEE J. Solid-State Circuits*, vol. SC-19, pp. 932–938, Dec. 1984.

[24] Z. Czarnul, "Modification of the Banu–Tsividis continuous-time integrator structure," to be published.

[25] Y. Tsividis and B. X. Shi, "Cancellation of distortion of any order in integrated active *RC* filters," *Electron. Lett.*, vol. 21, no. 4, pp. 132–134, Feb. 1985.

[26] T. C. Choi, R. W. Brodersen, P. R. Gray, W. B. Jett, and M. Wilcox, "High-frequency CMOS switched-capacitor filters for communications application," *IEEE J. Solid-State Circuits*, vol. SC-18, pp. 652–664, Dec. 1983.

[27] M. Banu and Y. Tsividis, "Detailed analysis of nonidealities in MOS fully integrated active RC filters based on balanced networks," *IEEE Proc. Part G (Electronic Circuits and Systems)*, vol. 131, no. 5, pp. 190–196, Oct. 1984.

[28] M. Ismail, "A new MOSFET-capacitor integrator," *IEEE Circuits Syst.*, vol. CAS-32, pp. 1194–1196, Nov. 1985.

[29] L. C. Thomas, "The biquad: Part I—Some practical design considerations," *IEEE Circuits Theory*, vol. CT-18, pp. 350–357, May 1971.

[30] A. S. Sedra and P. O. Brackett, *Filter Theory and Design: Active and Passive*, Portland, OR: Matrix, 1978.

[31] L. T. Bruton, *RC Active Circuits*, Englewood Cliff, NJ: Prentice-Hall, 1980.

[32] M. S. Ghausi and K. R. Laker, *Modern Filter Design*, Englewood Cliffs, NJ: Prentice-Hall, 1981.

[33] M. Banu, Y. Tsividis and I. Papananos, "Adequacy of voltage control for compensating process and temperature variations in MOS active RC filters," in *Proc. 1984 Int. Symp. Circuits and Systems*, Montreal, Canada, pp. 936–939.

[34] Y. Tsividis, "Fully integrated filters," in *Design of MOS VLSI Circuits for Telecommunications*, (Eds. Y. Tsividis and P. Antognetti) Englewood Cliffs, NJ: Prentice-Hall, 1985, ch. 11.

[35] R. S. C. Cobbold, *Theory and Applications of Field-Effect Transistors.* New York: Wiley-Interscience, 1970.

[36] Y. Tsividis, *Operation and Modeling of The MOS Transistor.* New York: McGraw-Hill, 1986.

[37] J. M. Khoury, B. X. Shi, and Y. Tsividis, "Considerations in the design of high frequency fully integrated continuous time filters," in *Proc. 1985 Int. Symp. Circuits and Systems*, Kyoto, Japan, pp. 1439–1442.

[38] B. X. Shi, J. Khoury, and Y. Tsividis, "High frequency effects in a fully integrated Tow–Thomas biquad," to be published.

[39] J. Khoury, Y. Tsividis, and M. Banu, "Use of MOS transistor as a tunble distributed RC filter element," *Electron. Lett.*, vol. 20, no. 4, pp. 187–188, Feb. 1984.

[40] 82502 Ethernet transceiver chip, preliminary specification sheet, Intel Corporation, Aug. 1985.

[41] R. Van Brunt, Intel Corporation, private communication.

[42] K. Hanson, "Switched capacitor modems," in *Design of VLSI Circuits for Telecommunications*, (Eds. Y. Tsividis and P. Antognetti), Englewood Cliffs, NJ: Prentice-Hall, 1985, ch. 15.

[43] P. R. Gray and R. Castello, "Performance limitations in switched-capacitor filters," in *Design of VLSI Circuits for Telecommunications*, (Eds. Y. Tsividis and P. Antognetti), Englewood Cliffs, NJ: Prentice-Hall, 1985, ch. 10.

[44] P. R. Gray and D. A. Hodges, "Analog-digital conversion techniques for telecommunications applications," in *Design of VLSI Circuits for Telecommunications*, (Eds. Y. Tsividis and P. Antognetti), Englewood Cliffs, NJ: Prentice-Hall, 1985, ch. 7.

[45] P. B. Fellgett, "Some comparisons of digital and analogue audio recording," *Radio and Electronic Eng.*, vol. 53, no. 2, pp. 55–62, Feb. 1983.

[46] W. Kellner, "A continuous-time analog filter using MOS technology," *Frequenz*, vol. 35, pp. 340–343, 1981.

[47] K. Fukahori, "A bipolar voltage-controlled tunable filter," *IEEE J. Solid-State Circuits*, vol. SC-16, pp. 729–737, Dec. 1981.

[48] R. L. Geiger, P. E. Allen, and D. T. Ngo, "Switched resistor filters —a continuous time approach to monolithic MOS filter design," *IEEE Trans. Circuits Syst.*, vol. CAS-29, pp. 306–315, May 1982.

[49] G. Tröster and W. Langheinrich, "Monolithic continuous-time analogue filters in NMOS technology," in *Proc. 1984 Int. Symp. Circuits and Systems*, pp. 924–927.

[50] Y. Tsividis, Z. Czarnul, and S. C. Fang, "MOS transaconductors and integrators with high linearity," to be published.

On Balanced Integrator Filters

J. O. VOORMAN, A. VAN BEZOOIJEN AND N. RAMALHO

PHILIPS RESEARCH LABORATORIES

P.O. BOX 80.000

5600 JA EINDHOVEN

THE NETHERLANDS

Abstract—Principles and design theory of balanced-integrator filters (with balanced amplifiers) are surveyed. In addition to CMOS circuits, examples are given of bipolar and biCMOS implementations. Experiments on silicon with resonance circuits and examples of integrated filters, delay equalizers, and oscillators are described.

1. INTRODUCTION

IN 1983 Banu and Tsividis proposed a new method for the design of filters for continuous-time signals [1] (see also [2]). They use pairs of MOS transistors in the triode region as variable resistive elements controlled by the gate voltage in combination with fixed capacitors and fully balanced amplifiers. A fifth-order elliptic lowpass filter was worked out using a signal-flow-graph design method and it has been integrated as an example.

The MOS-transistor resistors are nonlinear. The idea of Banu and Tsividis was to fully symmetrize the circuits (integrators) to improve the linearity. By antimetric excitation of the fully symmetric circuits, all even-order harmonics are canceled. Even when employing simple transistor equations [3], the circuit with nonlinear resistors yields a perfectly linear integrator (see Fig. 1).

Studying the method in greater detail, we observe that

(1) the method permits the use of relatively large signal voltages, with the advantages of high signal-to-noise ratio, low bias currents, and small capacitors (small chip area)

(2) the balanced amplifiers can be relatively simple, in particular when bipolar transistors can be used (in biMOS or biCMOS processes)

(3) even-order cancellation of harmonics works well for the combination of fixed capacitors with variable MOS-transistor resistors but practical circuits can also be made with combinations of

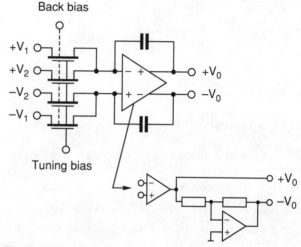

Fig. 1. Balanced integrator with MOS transistors as resistive elements, a pair of capacitors, and a balanced amplifier. The function of the balanced amplifier (in terms of a common operational amplifier and a pair of equal resistors) has been indicated in the lower right-hand part of the figure. In the case of antimetric excitation of the symmetric arrangement all even order harmonics are canceled. Using the simple equation below to describe the MOS transistors

$$I_d = b\left(V_g - V_{th} - \frac{V_d + V_s}{2}\right)(V_d - V_s)$$

with $b = \mu\epsilon_{ox}/t_{ox}W/L$, we arrive at

$$b(V_g - V_{th})(V_1 + V_2) + C\frac{dV_o}{dt} = 0.$$

One can see that we have a summing integrator and that to this degree of approximation it is perfectly linear, although nonlinear resistive elements are used. The effective conductance:

$$b(V_g - V_{th})$$

is a linear function of the gate voltage.

—fixed resistors with variable junction capacitors [4] (Fig. 2),
and
—fixed capacitors with variable transconductors [5] (Fig. 3)

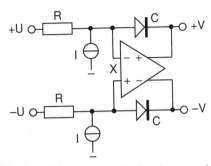

Fig. 2. Balanced integrator with junction capacitors. The currents of the bias current sources cause a DC voltage drop $I.R$ across the integrator resistors. Usually, in a filter, all amplifier outputs are at the same DC level (fixed by the common-mode control of the balanced amplifier). The DC level of the left-hand and the right-hand nodes in the figure is the same. The DC voltage drop also occurs across the junction capacitors, and varies the capacitor values and tunes the integrators.

(4) the method yields circuits with a high supply-power efficiency (i.e., ratio of signal handling to supply power) in theory as well as in practice

(5) the circuits are integration-friendly:
  —owing to the balancing, the circuits are insensitive to common-mode effects such as leakage and crosstalk, and signal currents in the supply lines are canceled out automatically, and
  —because the filter nodes are either virtual earth or low-ohmic (i.e., amplifier input and output, respectively), strays hardly affect the filter performance.

Resonance circuits form the basis of electronic filters. Common continuous-time resonance circuits are of second order. In the case of balanced integra-

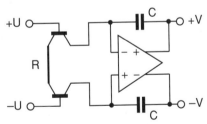

Fig. 3. Transconductor integrator principle using a balanced amplifier. The transconductor (*left part of the figure*) has been indicated by a simple symbol. The time constant of the integrator is $R.C/2$. Generally, the variability of the transconductor as a resistive element is used for tuning the integrator(s). All kinds of balanced transconductors can be employed (provided that the resulting integrators have a low common-mode gain).

tors, a resonance circuit is made from two balanced integrators and a cross-coupling. The circuit requires four capacitors (and, hence, is of fourth order). It is incorrect to state that the need for twice the number of capacitors is a waste. For a given noise level, the total capacitance is what counts. Equivalently, one can say that the resistive noise is not higher, because the common-mode part of the noise has no influence.

Below we shall consider these and further principles regarding balanced-integrator resonance circuits. We shall compare them with common (transconductor-C) second-order circuits. Stability items such as latch-up, overflow limit-cycle oscillations, and stability at high frequencies will be considered. Distortion and noise will be analyzed. The part on principles is followed by the design of (transistor) circuits. Subsequently, the circuits are employed in electronic resonators, oscillators, and in filters. Filter design methods as well as practical results on silicon will be given.

2. PRINCIPLES

2.1. Eigen Frequencies and Common-Mode Gain

Transconductor-C (gyrator-type) resonance circuits and integrator-type resonance circuits consist of two integrators and an inverter in a feedback loop. The equation for the eigen frequencies is

$$(-1/pRC)(-1)(-1/pRC) = 1, \qquad (1)$$

with imaginary solutions: $p = \pm j/RC$. We have a true lossless resonance circuit. In balanced filters, the inversion is commonly implemented as a cross-coupling (see fig. 4). The cross-coupling is an inversion only for differential-mode signals, not for common-mode signals. For common-mode signals, the eigen frequencies are determined (assuming that there is no common-mode rejection) by

$$(-1/pRC)(+1)(-1/pRC) = 1, \qquad (2)$$

with the solutions $p = \pm 1/RC$. The fourth-order resonance circuit has four eigen frequencies—the imaginary solutions correspond with antimetric signals on the circuit and the real solutions correspond with symmetric (common-mode) signals. Differential-mode stability and common-mode stability are different items. We have common-mode stability only if the common-mode gain of the integrators is sufficiently low. Preferably, for all frequencies, the magnitude of the common-mode loop gain of the resonance circuit in Fig. 4 should be lower than 1; that is, the magnitude of the common-mode gain of each of the integrators should be lower than 1.

2.2. Balanced Amplifiers

In Fig. 1 the asymmetric operational-amplifier/ inverter combination (to implement the balanced amplifier) has been introduced, only to simplify the understanding of the operation of the balanced amplifier. In practice, balanced amplifiers can be relatively simple symmetric circuits. Ideally, the balanced amplifier in Fig. 1 is defined by the equations:

$$i_1 = 0, \qquad v_1 = 0, \qquad v_2 + v_3 = 0, \qquad (3)$$

where 1 denotes the input port and 2 and 3 the output terminals of the amplifier (see also Fig. 5). Resonance circuits can be made equally well with amplifiers with balanced current outputs. The corresponding equations are

$$i_1 = 0, \qquad v_1 = 0, \qquad i_2 + i_3 = 0. \qquad (4)$$

These are the equations of an ideal operational amplifier or nullor (see [6], the first two equations describe the nullator part and the third is the definition of a port). In the latter case the balancing of the signal voltages is provided by the symmetry of the embedding, that is, the symmetry of the filter elements around the amplifier.

The principle of an electronic implementation of a balanced amplifier with bipolar transistors is shown in Fig. 6. The circuit has balanced voltage outputs. It may be seen as an operational amplifier without a

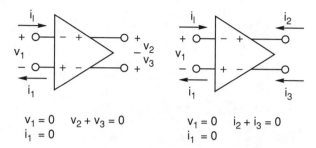

$$v_1 = 0 \qquad v_2 + v_3 = 0 \qquad\qquad v_1 = 0 \qquad i_2 + i_3 = 0$$
$$i_1 = 0 \qquad\qquad\qquad\qquad i_1 = 0$$

Fig. 5. Ideal balanced amplifiers. The inputs are described by nullator equations $v_1 = 0$, $i_1 = 0$. The left-hand amplifier has balanced voltage outputs. The right-hand amplifier has balanced current outputs (and balanced output voltages, provided that the embedding is symmetric). The right-hand amplifier is described by the equations of a nullor.

differential to single-ended converting output stage. The electronic implementation of an amplifier with balanced current outputs can be even simpler (see Fig. 7). This amplifier has been worked out to greater detail in one of the sections below. Simplicity of the amplifier circuit is important because a complex filter needs many amplifiers. A CMOS amplifier, in general, needs more stages than a bipolar one (for an example, see [7]). A simpler version has been depicted in Fig. 8. Another circuit, which shows the simplicity of balanced amplifier circuits, has been depicted in Fig. 9. It is a transconductor-integrator

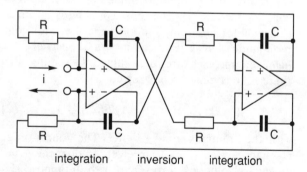

integration   inversion   integration

Fig. 4. Balanced-integrator resonance circuit (with input current i). For antimetric signals the circuit is a feedback loop of two (inverting) integrators and an inverter (cross-coupling). The eigen frequencies are $p = \pm j/(R.C)$. We have a second-order resonance circuit. For common-mode signals the cross-coupling does not work as an inversion. The circuit is absolutely common-mode–stable if the magnitude of the common-mode gain of the integrators is lower than 1 for all frequencies ω ($p = j.\omega$).

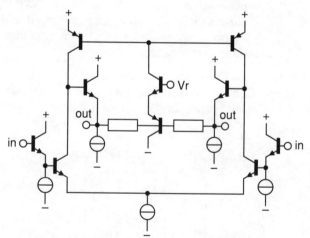

Fig. 6. Circuit example of a symmetric amplifier of bipolar transistors with balanced voltage outputs. It consists of a buffered long-tailed pair input stage and a load circuit. The Darlington buffer transistors at the inputs increase the input impedance and are against latch-up (incorrect biasing states). In the center is the common-mode feedback path (V_r is a reference voltage, which fixes the DC level of the filter). The circuit can be seen as an operational amplifier without a differential to single-ended converting output stage.

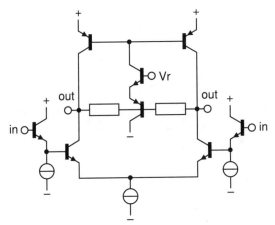

Fig. 7. Symmetric amplifier with balanced current outputs. Starting from the version with balanced voltage outputs, the output stages are left out. We thus arrive at an even simpler amplifier with balanced current outputs. The high transconductance of the bipolar transistors, relative to common filter impedance levels, can yield voltage gains of the order of magnitude of 40 dB. The amplifier can be used up to high frequencies.

arrangement of the type shown in Fig. 3 for filters in a bipolar IC process. The left-hand part is a transconductor with current multiplier and a load circuit. The right-hand part is the balanced amplifier with balanced voltage outputs.

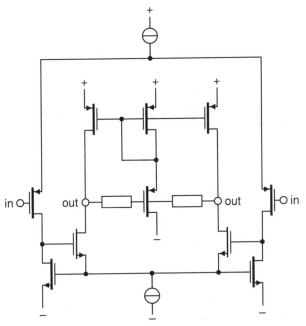

Fig. 8. Two-stage CMOS balanced amplifier. A PMOS input stage is followed by an NMOS gain stage (with PMOS load circuit). Both stages have a low common-mode gain. The output signal voltages are balanced, provided that the embedding is symmetric. The resistors in the common-mode control part of the load circuit should be equal (and as linear as possible) to provide accurate balancing.

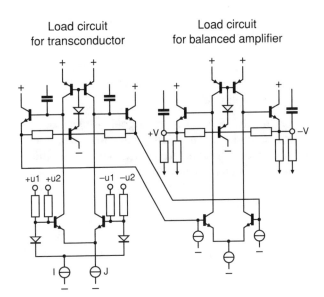

Load circuit for transconductor   Load circuit for balanced amplifier

Transconductor with current multiplier for frequency control

Balanced amplfier

Fig. 9. Balanced integrator using transconductors and a balanced amplifier. The upper terminals ($+u_1$, $-u_1$, $+u_2$, $-u_2$) of the resistors in the lower left part of the figure are voltage inputs to the integrator. In filter applications they are fed by outputs of balanced amplifiers. The voltages are converted to currents. The currents are added (or subtracted) and multiplied by the ratio J/I of two bias currents (*lower left part of the figure*). The output currents of the multiplier are fed to filter capacitors (see *top left part of the figure*) at the input of the balanced amplifier (*right-hand part of the figure*).

The NPN buffer transistors of the left-hand load circuit are at the same time Darlington transistors for the input stage of the amplifier (*bottom right*). The balanced amplifier has a similar load circuit. Resistors of the next transconductors are connected to the balanced amplifier outputs ($+v$, $-v$) of the integrator. To save supply-current consumption, the output stage of the balanced amplifier and the diodes of the multiplier share the same bias current.

2.3. Efficiency

For a low supply power consumption of integrated filters, it is important that the circuits, in particular resonance circuits, can handle a high signal power at the lowest possible supply power consumption. This applies to gyrator-type as well as to integrator-type resonance circuits.

The efficiency (η) of a gyrator is the ratio of the maximum *gyrated* signal power (p) to the supply-power consumption (P) for a resonance circuit with equal capacitors and in resonance. Theoretical values are of the order of magnitude of few percent, practical values are even lower [8, 9]. The concept of efficiency can be applied equally well to different types of electronic resonance circuit.

For a balanced-integrator type of resonance circuit of two equal integrators the amplifier output voltages near resonance are quadrature sine waves of equal amplitude.

Let the RMS value of the signal voltages be v (single-ended). The signal currents i in the integrator resistors are v/R. We define the gyrated signal power p as $p = v.i$. Signal voltages (peak-to-peak value) are lower than the supply voltage E. Hence, $2.v.\sqrt{2} < E$. In resonance an amplifier has to handle the signal current $i = v/R$ of next integrator resistors and equally large, but 90 degrees phase-shifted, currents of the integrator capacitors, together having a peak value of $2.i$. To avoid cross-talk along supply lines, signal dependent excess phase-shifts and to keep nonlinear distortion low, generally class-A type amplifier output stages are used. To handle peak currents of $2.i$, the output stage of the balanced amplifier needs this value as an absolute minimum bias current: $I_{amp} > 2.i$. Hence,

$$P = E \, 2.I_{amp} > (2.v)\sqrt{2} \; 2 \, 2.i \quad = p \, 8.\sqrt{2} \quad (5)$$

The efficiency

$$\eta = p/P < 9\%. \quad (6)$$

The balanced-integrator type of resonance circuit can have an unusually high efficiency (or, equivalently, a relatively low supply-power consumption).

2.4. Noise

In integrated filters, capacitors cost chip area and are taken as small as possible. The resistance level of integrated filters is high (but not so high that the signal-to-noise ratio requirements are not met). Signal voltages are relatively high. The main part of the noise is noise of the filter resistors. The common-mode part of the resistor noise can have negligible influence (see Fig. 10).

For a well-designed amplifier, noise can almost always be ignored in filter applications. The equivalent noise voltages at the input of the amplifier (related to the transconductance of the input stage and of base-series resistances in the case of a bipolar-transistor input stage) are generally significantly lower than the noise voltages of the large filter resistors. Base-current–related noise currents generally are low because otherwise the base currents

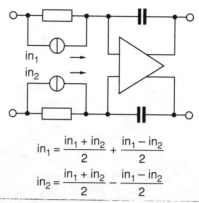

$$in_1 = \frac{in_1 + in_2}{2} + \frac{in_1 - in_2}{2}$$

$$in_2 = \frac{in_1 + in_2}{2} - \frac{in_1 - in_2}{2}$$

Fig. 10. Noise. The noise of the resistors (i_{n_1}, i_{n_2}) has a common-mode part: ($i_{n_1} + i_{n_2}$)/2 and a differential-mode part: ($i_{n_1} - i_{n_2}$)/2. If the common-mode gain of the integrator is low and there is an accurate balancing, the contribution of the common-mode part of the noise currents can be neglected. The amplifier noise can be low (relative to the noise of the large filter resistors).

would cause unwanted high DC offsets across the integrator resistors. In fact, because the amplifiers are applied in a noisy environment, their noise can often be ignored in filter applications.

2.5. Symmetry and Quadratic Losslessness

Next we consider the question, is symmetry critical? For example, is symmetry critical for obtaining high Q-factors?

LC filters are designed as lossless ladders between resistive terminations. For accurate filters, it is important that the inductors and capacitors have low dissipation factors.

In the case of electronic filters, we know that a gyrator is a nonenergic (or instantaneously lossless) element. A gyrator can be implemented using two transconductors. A resonance circuit of this gyrator and two capacitors is lossless—even when the two transconductances are not equal in value! We say that the circuit is structurally lossless (i.e., lossless independent of element values, not lossless by compensation). Structural losslessness of the building blocks is a precondition for the design of accurate filters.

Balanced-integrator circuits are not lossless by their structure. In Fig. 11 we consider an integrator. Minor asymmetries have been added to signals and element values. In the resulting descriptive equation, all errors are second-order small. Hence, symmetry is not too critical for obtaining low losses (see also [10]). We can say that balanced integrators are "quadratically lossless."

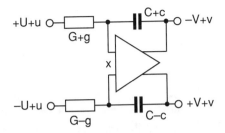

Fig. 11. Integrator symmetry is not critical. Small deviations u, g, c, v have been added to ideal values U, G, C, V, respectively. This also results in a small common-mode signal voltage x. Hence,

$$(+U + u - x)(G + g) = (x + V - v)p(C + c),$$
$$(-U + u - x)(G - g) = (x - V - v)p(C - c).$$

Subtraction yields

$$U.G + u.g - x.g = p(x.c + V.C - v.c).$$

All error terms ($u.g$, $x.g$, $x.c$, $v.c$) are second-order small. Omitting error terms: $U.G = p.C.V$.

3. STABILITY

Let us consider the stability of the resonance circuits (for detailed principles, see [11]). We start with the case of a resonance circuit with two balanced amplifiers with balanced voltage outputs.

3.1. Latch-Up and Overflow Limit-Cycle Oscillations for a Resonance Circuit with Amplifiers with Balanced Voltage Outputs

Electronic circuits behave as they are expected to do only if their biasing is correct. Unintentionally, a circuit can be designed to have more than one solution for the biasing (a well-known design error). After switching on the supply, it can adopt any of the biasing states—the correct one but also the wrong one(s). The circuit may "latch" in a wrong DC state. For a theory on the uniqueness of the DC solution, see [12, 13].

Let us consider the uniqueness of the DC solution for a balanced integrator resonance circuit. We see the resonance circuit as a resistive four-port with capacitors connected across all ports (see Fig. 12). We assume that overflow is limited by nonlinear resistors across the capacitors. The power P delivered via the ports to the four-port

$$P = 2(X^2 + Y^2)/R \qquad (7)$$

is non-negative and has to be supplied by the capacitors. The common-mode voltages X and Y will go to

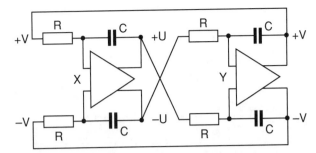

Fig. 12. DC stability (amplifiers with balanced output voltages). We see the resonator as a resistive four-port with capacitors connected across all ports. Overflow is limited by putting nonlinear resistors (not indicated) across the capacitors. We assume that the amplifiers behave correctly. For the upper left port the port voltage is $X - U$ and the port current is $(X - V)/R$ (the current in the capacitor). The power fed via this port to the four port network is $(X - U)(X - V)/R$. The total power transferred via the four ports to the resistive network is:

$$P = (X - U)(X - V)/R + (X + U)(X + V)/R$$
$$+ (Y - V)(Y + U)/R + (Y + V)(Y - U)/R,$$
$$= 2(X^2 + Y^2)/R.$$

Because the power that the capacitors with nonlinear resistors (diodes) can deliver is finite (finite initial charge), the common-mode voltages X and Y will go to the correct (zero) values. Neither the capacitors nor the amplifier inputs carry bias currents. Hence, the resistors do not. On average $U \to 0$ and $V \to 0$. The circuit goes to the correct DC-state.

the correct (zero) values and the circuit will assume the correct DC state.

Hence, in the case that overflow is limited by nonlinear capacitor losses, the circuit is DC-stable. Moreover, overflow limit-cycle oscillations (nonlinear oscillations) are damped. Capacitor losses may be introduced intentionally or they may occur because of the (deliberately designed) overflow behavior of the amplifiers.

3.2. High-Frequency Stability for a Resonance Circuit with Amplifiers with Balanced-Voltage Outputs

Next we consider the stability at high frequencies. We assume a finite voltage gain (A) for the amplifiers (the gain-bandwidth product is GB) (see Fig. 13),

$$1/A = 1/A_o + p/GB. \qquad (8)$$

There result four eigen frequencies: two with a large negative real part (high-frequency-stable) and two near $p = \pm j.\omega_o$, with $\omega_o = 1/RC$, which represent the resonance. The corresponding quality factor (Q_o)

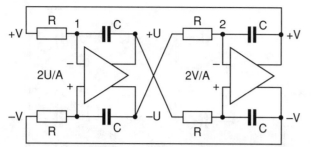

Fig. 13. High-frequency stability and accuracy (amplifiers with balanced voltage outputs). Let the gain of the amplifiers be A. The gain-bandwidth product is GB. Then $1/A = 1/A_o + p/GB$.

$$(+V + U/A)/R + (U + U/A)pC = 0 \text{ node (1)},$$
$$(-U + V/A)/R + (V + V/A)pC = 0 \text{ node (2)}.$$

The eigen frequencies follow from a zero determinant.

$$(pRC + pRC/A + 1/A)^2 + 1 = 0,$$
$$p + p/A + \omega_o/A = \pm j.\omega_o,$$

with $\omega_o = 1/RC$. With the expression for the amplifier gain we obtain

$$p^2 + \underbrace{p(GB + GB/A_o + \omega_o)}_{2.B} + GB.\omega_o/A_o = \pm j.GB.\omega_o,$$

$$p = -B \pm \sqrt{B^2 - GB.\omega_o/A_o \pm j.GB.\omega_o}\,.$$

There are four solutions. Those where $\pm\sqrt{....}$ has a negative real part: $p = -GB \mp j.\omega_o$ (approximately) do not lead to continuing oscillations (high-frequency stable). The other two solutions are near $p = \pm j.\omega_o$. They represent the resonance. We have, approximately,

$$p/\omega_o = -1/A_o + \omega_o/GB \pm j(1 - 1/A_o - \omega_o/GB).$$

The quality factor (Q_o) of the resonance circuit and the deviation ($d\omega$) of the resonance frequency from its design value $\omega_o = 1/RC$ are

$$Q_o = \frac{1}{2(1/A_o - \omega_o/GB)}, \quad \frac{d\omega}{\omega_o} = -\frac{1}{A_o} - \frac{\omega_o}{GB}.$$

of the resonance circuit and the deviation ($d\omega$) of the resonance frequency from its design value (ω_o) are

$$Q_o = \frac{1}{2(1/A_o - \omega_o/GB)},$$

$$\frac{d\omega}{\omega_o} = -\frac{1}{A_o} - \frac{\omega_o}{GB}. \tag{9}$$

For higher resonance frequencies, the circuit has a negative (unloaded) Q_o. The formulas give an impression of the requirements for the amplifiers.

3.3. Latch-Up and Overflow Limit-Cycle Oscillations for a Resonance Circuit with Amplifiers with Balanced-Current Outputs

Similar arguments apply in the case that we have a resonance circuit with balanced transconductance amplifiers. The DC convergence (latch-up) is considered first (see Fig. 14). In this case the power delivered to the 4 ports of the resistive network is given by

$$P.R = (X - U)(X - V) + (X - U')(X - V')$$
$$+ (Y - V)(Y - U') + (Y - V')(Y - U) \tag{10}$$

or

$$P.R = (X + Y)^2 + (U + U')^2 R/(2.r)$$
$$\cdot \{2 + R/(2.r)\} \geq 0, \tag{11}$$

by which we conclude unconditional DC stability. Overflow limit-cycle oscillations are damped.

3.4. High-Frequency Stability for a Resonance Circuit with Amplifiers with Balanced-Current Outputs

For stability at high frequencies, we model the balanced transconductance amplifier as $S = S_o/(1 + p/B)$, where B is the 3-dB bandwidth of the amplifier. We again find four eigen frequencies, two with large negative real parts predicting stability at high frequencies and two at resonance, with

$$Q_o = \frac{S_o.r}{2},$$
$$\frac{d\omega}{\omega_o} = -\frac{2}{S_o.R} - \frac{1}{S_o.r} \tag{12}$$

(see Fig. 15). One can remark that in this case (and to this degree of approximation) the amplifier bandwidth has no influence yet.

We have two resonator types with all the good properties one could wish to have: DC stability, free of overflow limit-cycle oscillations, and with high-frequency stability. It should be observed that there are not many circuits that have the combination of the above properties unconditionally.

In the above, the amplifier was assumed to be ideal. We can prove for resonators with prototype transistor amplifiers (Fig. 16) that we need not add diodes for overflow limitation (the proof is lengthy and has been omitted). The circuits are latch-up free by themselves.

The former circuits use bipolar transistors. In the case of MOS transistors, a difference is observed:

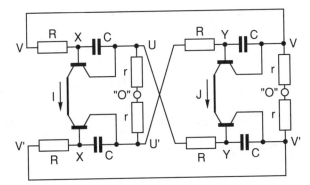

Fig. 14. DC stability (amplifiers with balanced output currents). Extra resistors r refer the circuit to ground. The total current to the ground node $U/r + U'/r + V/r + V'/r = 0$. Hence, $U + U' + V + V' = 0$. Further

$$I = (V - X)/R - U/r + (Y - U)/R,$$
$$I = (X - V')/R + U'/r + (U' - Y)/R.$$

Subtraction yields

$$X - Y = -\{1 + R/(2.r)\}(U + U').$$

The power delivered to the ports of the capacitively terminated 4-port network is given by

$$P.R = (X - U)(X - V) + (X - U')(X - V')$$
$$+ (Y - V)(Y - U') + (Y - V')(Y - U),$$
$$= (X + Y)^2 + (X - Y)^2 - (U + U' - V - V')^2/4,$$
$$= (X + Y)^2 + (U + U')^2 R/(2.r)\{2 + R/(2.r)\}.$$

We see that $U + U' \to 0$, $V + V' \to 0$, $X + Y \to 0$, $X - Y \to 0$, $X \to 0$ and $Y \to 0$. We have unconditional DC stability.

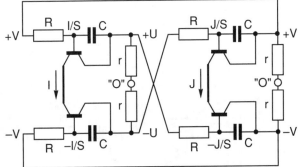

Fig. 15. High-frequency stability and accuracy (amplifiers with balanced output currents). The transconductance of the balanced amplifier is $S/2$. The descriptive equations are:

$$I = +(V - I/S)/R - U/r - (U + J/S)/R,$$
$$J = -(U + J/S)/R - V/r - (V - I/S)/R,$$
$$O = +(V - I/S)/R + (U - I/S)pC,$$
$$O = -(U + J/S)/R + (V - J/S)pC.$$

The equation for the eigen frequencies is

$$\left\{p\left(1 + \frac{2}{S.R} + \frac{1}{S.r}\right) + \frac{\omega_o}{S.r}\right\}^2 + \omega_o^2 = 0,$$

where $\omega_o = 1/RC$. We insert $S = S_o/(1 + p/B)$, where B is the 3-dB amplifier bandwidth. The four eigen frequencies are (approximately), $p = -(S_o/2)R.B \pm j.\omega_o$ (with large negative real parts: stable at high frequencies) and two poles which represent the resonance, with (approximately)

$$Q_o = \frac{S_o.r}{2}, \frac{d\omega}{\omega_o} = -\frac{2}{S_o.R} - \frac{1}{S_o.r}$$

when transistors are "bottoming," the gate currents remain zero. Although in some cases this leads to a completely different latch-up behavior, we arrive at the same conclusion regarding latch-up freedom.

More complex amplifier circuits will be equally latch-up free when the overflow behavior of the amplifier is similar to the overflow behavior of the single-transistor-pair prototype amplifiers.

4. Linearity

Linearity is almost entirely determined by the variable elements. We consider nonlinear effects for the simplest circuits: integrators with MOS-transistor resistors and with junction capacitors.

4.1. MOS Transistor Resistors

According to the simple quadratic description for the MOS transistor, we make a perfectly linear integrator. For a more detailed analysis one is obliged to go to a more accurate modelling for the MOS transistor. We shall use a general description, for which we refer to [1]:

$$I_d = K_1(V_d - V_s) + K_2(V_d^2 - V_s^2)$$
$$+ K_3(V_d^3 - V_s^3) + \cdots \quad (13)$$

With input voltages U, $-U$, output voltages V, $-V$, and X being the common-mode voltage at the amplifier input we arrive at the following equations for a balanced integrator (see Fig. 1 and [14])

$$K_1(+U - X) + K_2(U^2 - X^2) + K_3(+U^3 - X^3)$$
$$+ \cdots = C\frac{d(X - V)}{dt}, \quad (14)$$

$$K_1(-U - X) + K_2(U^2 - X^2) + K_3(-U^3 - X^3)$$
$$+ \cdots = C\frac{d(X + V)}{dt}. \quad (15)$$

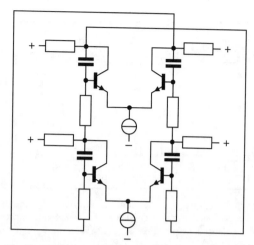

Fig. 16. Prototype resonance circuit. Any transistor can assume different states: inversely working, bottoming, not conducting, or working. The bias-current sources are assumed to be transistors, too. We can prove (under certain conditions regarding supply voltage and supply current) that none of the transistors can be inversely working, bottoming, or not conducting. Apparently, all transistors cannot but be working properly. The transistor circuit is latch-up-free (even without limiting diodes across the capacitors). More complex amplifiers with an overflow behavior similar to the overflow behavior of the prototype amplifier also lead to latch-up–free and overflow-limit-cycle–free filter circuits.

Subtraction yields,

$$K_1.U + K_3.U^3 + \cdots = -C\frac{dV}{dt}. \quad (16)$$

We introduce $U = a.\sin(\omega.t)$. Hence,

$$(K_1.a + \cdots)\sin(\omega.t) - \left(\frac{1}{4}K_3.a^3 + \cdots\right)$$

$$\cdot \sin(3.\omega.t) + \cdots = -C\frac{dV}{dt}. \quad (17)$$

$$V = \frac{K_1}{\omega.C}a.\cos(\omega.t)$$

$$- \frac{K_3}{12.\omega.C}a^3\cos(3.\omega.t) + \cdots. \quad (18)$$

We arrive at the third-order intercept point, the extrapolated signal amplitude a for which the third-order harmonic in the output voltage V would be equally strong as the signal itself:

$$a\{IP_3\} = \sqrt{12\frac{K_1}{K_3}}. \quad (19)$$

In the case that we use the MOS-transistor equation

$$I_d = b\Bigg\{\left(V_g - V_{th} - \frac{V_d + V_s}{2}\right)$$

$$\cdot(V_d - V_s) - \frac{2}{3}K\big((V_d + 2.\varphi)^{3/2}$$

$$- (V_s + 2.\varphi)^{3/2}\big)\Bigg\} \quad (20)$$

we have (approximately):

$$a\{IP_3\} = \sqrt{\frac{288}{K}(V_g - V_{th})(2.\varphi)^{3/2}}. \quad (21)$$

This leads to values of the order of magnitude of 20 V. For clarity, $a\{IP_3\} = 20$ V means that the signal-to-(third-order) distortion ratio will be 40 dB for a signal of 2 V (peak value, single-ended), 60 dB for a signal of 0.67 V, 80 dB for a signal of 0.2 V, and so on.

In general, the circuits have still more problems with intermodulation. Assuming two sine waves: $U = a.\sin(p.t) + a.\sin(q.t)$ at frequencies near to each other, distortion terms with frequencies $2.p - q$ and $2.q - p$ are found near the original signals (particularly important in the case of bandpass filters). For the intercept point, where the intermodulation ($2.p - q$ and/or $2.q - p$, extrapolated) would be equal to the signal (p and/or q), we find

$$a\{IP_{\text{intermod}}\} = a\{IP_3\}/3. \quad (22)$$

Hence, in the case of equal signal amplitudes, intermodulation is some 19 dB higher than third-order distortion!

The above modeling is not exact. Mobility saturation makes the situation worse. Also, temperature feedback on the chip is a nonlinear effect that should not be forgotten. On the other hand, back-gate effects may give surprising improvements; see, for example, [15].

The above concerns third-order distortion. In cases where a very low distortion is required, second-order distortion can be the limiting factor (see also [14]). The cause is unbalance. For the analysis, we return to the quadratic equation for the MOS transistor

$$I_d = K\left(V_g - V_{th} - \frac{V_d + V_s}{2}\right)(V_d - V_s). \quad (23)$$

In the case of unbalance, see Fig. 17,

$$M(V_g - V_{th})U - M.U.u + m.U^2/2$$

$$+ M.dV_{th}.X + \frac{dV}{dt} = 0. \quad (24)$$

The second, third, and fourth terms in the equation are nonlinear terms (mainly second-order distortion) caused by an unbalance in the excitation, the time constants, and the threshold voltages, respectively. In practice, u/U, m/M, dV_{th}/V_{th} all are of the order of magnitude of 1%, resulting in signal-to-distortion levels of the order of magnitude of 60 dB and not much higher (this is a serious limitation, in particular for low-pass filters).

It should be observed that in filters distortion is enhanced by resonance effects, it can be attenuated by filtering and, in some cases, distortion can be canceled (for example, an inverter with two identical nonlinear resistors can be distortion-free)—see also [16]. Nonlinear effects of an integrator only give an indication of the distortion in filters.

4.2. Junction Capacitors

We continue with integrators with linear resistors and junction capacitors. To a first approximation, an

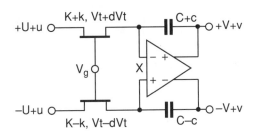

$$M+m = \frac{K+k}{C+c} \qquad M-m = \frac{K-k}{C-c}$$

Fig. 17. Nonlinearity by unbalance. All values are given some asymmetry (positive or negative values). The descriptive equations are:

$$(M + m)\{V_g - V_t - dV_t - (+U + u + X)/2\}$$
$$\cdot(+U + u - X) + d(+V + v - X)/dt = 0,$$

$$(M - m)\{V_g - V_t + dV_t - (-U + u + X)/2\}$$
$$\cdot(-U + u - X) + d(-V + v - X)/dt = 0,$$

where $M + m = (K + k)/(C + c)$ and $M - m = (K - k)/(C - c)$. Addition yields (as the main terms):

$$-V_g.X + V_t.X + X^2/2 = U^2/2.$$

Subtraction (omitting second-order and higher-order small terms and application of the above approximation in the smaller terms) yields:

$$M(V_g - V_t)U - M.U.u + m.U^2/2$$
$$+ M.dV_t.X + dV/dt = 0.$$

The second, third, and fourth terms are nonlinear. They can be the largest contributions to the distortion, in particular in applications with lowpass filters.

input signal voltage is applied to the linear resistors, converting the voltage linearly to a current. The current is fed to the nonlinear capacitors, giving distorted output voltages. The descriptive equations (see Fig. 2) are

$$(+U - X)/R + dQ\{+V - X\}/dt = I \quad (25)$$
$$(-U - X)/R + dQ\{-V - X\}/dt = I \quad (26)$$

where Q is charge on the nonlinear capacitors. Subtraction yields

$$2.U/R + (Q'\{+V - X\} + Q'\{-V - X\})\frac{dV}{dt} = 0 \quad (27)$$

where $Q' = dQ/dV$. Commonly, a junction capacitor is modeled as

$$dQ/dV = C_o/(1 + V/V_d)^p \quad (28)$$

where C_o is the capacitance at zero bias, V_d the diffusion voltage, and p the grading exponent ($1/3 < p < 1/2$).

$$2\frac{U}{R} + C_X\left[\left(1 + \frac{V}{V_d - X}\right)^{-p}\right.$$
$$\left. + \left(1 - \frac{V}{V_d - X}\right)^{-p}\right]\frac{dV}{dt} = 0 \quad (29)$$

where

$$C_X = C_o/(1 - X/V_d)^p. \quad (30)$$

Hence,

$$\frac{U}{R} + C_X\left[1 + \frac{p(p + 1)}{2}\left(\frac{V}{V_d - X}\right)^2 + \cdots\right]\frac{dV}{dt} = 0. \quad (31)$$

For a first approximation we insert $X = -V_b$, where $V_b = I.R$ is the invariant bias voltage. $C_X = C_b$. We arrive at

$$\frac{dV}{dt} = -\frac{U}{R.C_b}\left[1 - \frac{p(p + 1)}{2}\left(\frac{V}{V_d + V_b}\right)^2 + \cdots\right]. \quad (32)$$

We apply the signal $U = a.\sin(\omega.t)$. Using the linear part of the equation $V = b.\cos(\omega.t)$ with $b = a/(\omega.R.C_b)$. This result is inserted in the small nonlinear terms. After some calculations we arrive at an approximation for the third-order intercept point

$$b\{IP_3\} = \frac{V_d + V_b}{\sqrt{p(p+1)/24}}. \qquad (33)$$

In this case

$$b\{IP_{\text{intermod}}\} = b\{IP_3\}/\sqrt{3}. \qquad (34)$$

For example, with $p = 0.4$, $V_d = V_b = 0.6$ V we arrive at $b\{IP_3\} = 7.8$ V and $b\{IP_{\text{intermod}}\} = 4.5$ V. These are useful values for filters in bipolar IC processes in particular. Although reliable junction capacitors with capacitances of 2 to 4 nF/mm^2 ($V_b = 0$ V) can easily be made, they are not always available for designers.

It can be proved that the distortion of an integrator with an amplifier with balanced current outputs and one with balanced voltage outputs is not significantly different.

5. AN ACCURATE BIPOLAR BALANCED AMPLIFIER

We have already mentioned the simplicity of balanced amplifiers, in particular, of amplifiers with bipolar transistors. Below we consider the design of a high-performance balanced amplifier for high-frequency applications. The circuit consists of two parts: the amplifier stage and the load circuit.

5.1. Amplifier Stage

For the amplifier stage we start from a long-tailed pair with bipolar transistors. In Fig. 18 the transconductance has been enhanced by the inclusion of "negative" diode resistances. The output currents are taken from a separate long-tailed pair so as to ensure that the input transistors cannot bottom: against latch-up.

With this amplifier, we obtain, in practice, an order of magnitude higher transconductance than with a long-tailed pair without cross-coupled transistors (at the same total bias current). For example, for video frequencies, using a supply current of 500 μA/amplifier, a transconductance of $1/(20$ Ohm$)$ can be obtained, a value three orders of magnitude higher than common filter admittances. The ratio of the filter admittances to the transconductance of the amplifier determines the effective voltage gain of the amplifier (typically 50 to 70 dB).

In Fig. 19, more circuit details have been included: base-current compensation to increase the

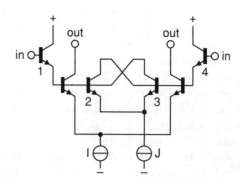

Fig. 18. Transconductance enhancement (using cross-coupled transistors). Transistors 1 and 3 carry the same current ($V_{be1} = V_{be3}$). Transistors 2 and 4 carry the same current ($V_{be2} = V_{be4}$). The voltage between the inputs is

$$V_{be1} + V_{be2} - V_{be3} - V_{be4} = 0, \text{ (approximately)}.$$

(almost) independent of the value of the output current. The emitter diode resistances of transistors 1 and 4 have been nearly compensated by the "negative" emitter diode resistances of transistors 2 and 3. A minor change in input voltage has large consequences for the output current—the transconductance of the amplifier is high. We need a separate long-tailed pair as the output stage (the collectors of the input transistors are connected to the positive supply voltage: against latch-up).

For greater detail, the transconductance of the amplifier is

$$\frac{1}{4\frac{k.T}{q}\left(\frac{1}{I} + \frac{1}{J}\right)\left(\frac{1}{h_{FE_o}} + \frac{1}{h_{FE}}\right)},$$

where h_{FE} is the current gain of the bipolar transistors. $1/h_{FE} = 1/h_{FE_o} + j.\omega/\omega_T$, where $\omega_T = 2.\pi.f_T$ is the cut-off frequency of the bipolar transistors. The formula shows the transconductance enhancement and the fact that the transconductance becomes inductive at higher frequencies.

current gain (transistors in dashed lines), large resistors R_p against slewing, neutrodyne capacitors C_n to compensate for feedback from the output terminals (via collector-base capacitances), and a series RC circuit (in dashed lines) to improve stability at high frequencies. Which of the additions are needed depends on the application and on the IC process.

5.2. Load Circuits

The output signal currents (differential mode currents) of the amplifier should be drawn from the filter. The load circuit should provide a high impedance for differential mode signals. The bias currents (common mode currents) should be drawn from the load circuit. The common-mode impedance of the load circuit should be low.

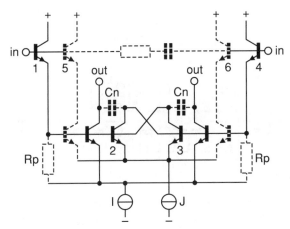

Fig. 19. Practical amplifier circuit. Not all parts are needed in all applications and in all IC processes. The base signal currents of transistors 1 and 5 (and also of 4 and 6) compensate, resulting in low input base signal currents (high amplifier current gain). Large resistors R_p can solve slew-rate problems in the case of applications at high frequencies. Small capacitances C_n may provide neutrodynization of the collector-base capacitances of the output transistors. For applications at high frequencies, in particular when the base-current compensation has been omitted, a series RC circuit (in dashes) between the amplifier inputs can be a remedy against instability at high frequencies (and against peaking of the filter gain).

Circuit examples for load circuits are depicted in Fig. 20. The left-hand circuit is a solution with bipolar transistors (for a bipolar IC process). The right-hand circuit uses PNP transistors, one PMOS transistor, and a pair of large NMOS filter resistor-type resistors—a true biCMOS circuit. For applications at higher frequencies (with larger bias currents), vertical PNP transistors are preferred to lateral ones.

5.3. Gain-Bandwidth Product

The equivalent gain-bandwidth product of the amplifier (with load circuit) in filter applications can be higher than the f_T of the NPN transistors. The high-frequency roll-off of the amplifier can be more than 20 dB/decade provided that a sufficient phase margin is achieved. We have obtained effective gain-bandwidth products of 2 to 4 GHz in different IC processes. The amplifier is useful for the design of accurate filters, in particular for video frequencies and higher.

5.4. Peaking at High Frequencies

A balanced high-transconductance-amplifier (with low input signal current) to a first approximation can

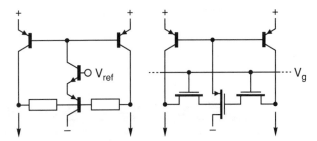

Fig. 20. Load circuits (examples). The left-hand circuit uses bipolar transistors. When the two resistors are larger than the filter resistors, they hardly influence the voltage gain of the amplifier. V_{ref} is a reference voltage, which fixes the DC-voltage level of the filter. In the right-hand part of the figure we have a true biCMOS circuit. The resistors in the load circuit have been implemented in the same way as filter resistors (at the cost of extra distortion).

be modeled as

$$S = \frac{S_o}{1 + p/B}, \qquad (35)$$

where B is the 3-dB cut-off frequency. The amplifier assumes an inductive character at higher frequencies. In filter applications, the inductive amplifier together with the capacitive embedding shows resonance. The result can be a spurious peaking of the filter gain. This typically occurs somewhere between 100 and 500 MHz. An RC series circuit between the amplifier inputs (see Fig. 19) can damp the peaking.

5.5. Predistortion

The high-frequency roll-off of the transconductance amplifier can be predistorted by modifying the filter elements. To this end we start from a design with filter admittances G_k, $p.C_k$ and amplifier transconductances S_o. We divide all admittances by the factor $1 + p/B$ and we implement the new filter admittances (see Fig. 21). The voltage transfer function remains the same. One should be aware that the predistortion may lead to higher peaking or, possibly, instability.

6. DESIGN METHODS

We have considered the electronic design of balanced integrators. Below we discuss methods for using the integrators in filters.

6.1. Signal Flow-Graph Methods

Design methods using signal-flow graphs (SFGs) are well-known—see for example [2, 17] and Fig. 22.

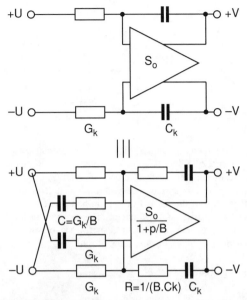

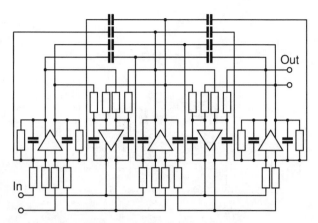

Fig. 22. SFG balanced-integrator filter. The figure shows a typical Cauer-elliptic filter derived from a signal-flow graph. Pairwise, the integrators constitute resonance circuits. The upper capacitive couplings provide transmission zeroes.

Fig. 21. Predistortion. We start from a design with filter admittances G_k, $p.C_k$ and amplifier transconductances S_o (see *top part of the figure*). We divide "all" admittances by the factor $1 + p/B$. The voltage transfer function remains the same. The new admittances are

$$\frac{S_o}{1 + p/B},$$

$$\frac{p.C_k}{1 + p/B} = \frac{1}{1/(B.C_k) + 1/(p.C_k)},$$

$$\frac{G_k}{1 + p/B} = G_k - \frac{1}{1/G_k + B/(p.G_k)}.$$

Now, the amplifier transconductance has its high-frequency roll-off. Any capacitor C_k has a series resistance $(1/B.C_k)$. The conductances have been shunted by a negative RC-series circuit (implemented using a cross-coupling)—see *bottom part of the figure*. Thus, the filter has been predistorted for first-order high-frequency roll-off of the amplifiers (the transfer function is as it had been without amplifier roll-off).

The network equations and element equations of a lossless LC ladder are drawn in a signal-flow graph with additions, subtractions, and integrations (in some cases also differentiations). The signal-flow graph is implemented with balanced integrators. The method can also be based upon a state variable formulation of the network equations; see for a survey [18].

6.2. Canonic Filter Sections

The SFG method has no solution to implement lossless allpass sections (which we have in the case of transconductor-C filters, see [19]). For allpass sections we have devised canonic filter sections, see

[20] and Fig. 23. An nth-order canonic filter section can implement any nth-order (stable) transfer function without subtractions in the coefficients (compare with [21]). The sections can also be used for the design method where the filter function is written as a product of low-order factors, which are implemented as a cascade of low-order filter sections.

6.3. Single-Amplifier Design

A third interesting design method (see [22]) is based on the circuit in Fig. 24. We divide numerator and denominator of the transfer function by a polynomial $R(p)$, with all zeroes distinct and on the

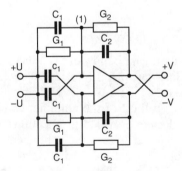

Fig. 23a. First-order canonic filter section. The transfer function is

$$\frac{V}{U} = \frac{G_1 + p(C_1 - c_1)}{G_2 + p.C_2}.$$

For a lowpass: $C_1 = c_1 = 0$. For a highpass: $G_1 = 0$, $c_1 = 0$. For an allpass: $G_1 = G_2$, $C_1 = 0$, $c_1 = C_2$. Any first-order (stable) filter function can be implemented.

78

negative real frequency axis:

$$H(p) = \frac{N(p)}{D(p)}$$

$$= \frac{N(p)/R(p)}{D(p)/R(p)}$$

$$= \frac{N_1/R - N_2/R}{D_1/R - D_2/R}$$

$$= \frac{Y_1 - Y_2}{Y_3 - Y_4}. \tag{36}$$

Denominator and numerator are expanded in partial fractions. All fractions with positive residues and all fractions with negative residues are taken together. We arrive at four admittance functions: $N_1/R = Y_1$, $N_2/R = Y_2$, $D_1/R = Y_3$, and $D_2/R = Y_4$. If the degree of polynomial R is high enough, all admittances can be implemented as passive RC admittances. For details on the decomposition, refer to [23]. With a single amplifier and 4 pairs of RC admittances, any transfer function can be implemented. The resulting circuits are sensitive to tolerances but they show no internal enhancement of the signals. In Fig. 25, an example of a resonance circuit (or selective amplifier) has been depicted.

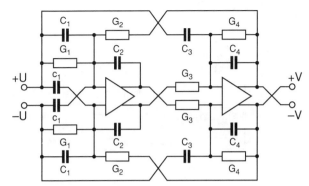

Fig. 23b. Second-order canonic filter section. The transfer function is

$$\frac{V}{U} = \frac{G_1.G_3 + p(C_1 - c_1)G_3 + p^2 C_2.C_3}{G_2.G_3 + p.C_2.G_4 + p^2 C_2.C_4}.$$

For a lowpass (all-pole): $C_1 = c_1 = C_3 = 0$. For a highpass: $G_1 = 0$, $C_1 = c_1 = 0$. In the case of a transmission zero $p = j.\omega$: $C_1 = c_1 = 0$. For an allpass: $G_1 = G_2$, $G_3 = G_4$, $C_1 = 0$, $c_1 = C_2$, $C_3 = C_4$. All equal resistors or all equal capacitors can be used.

7. EXPERIMENTS AND MEASURED RESULTS

Several circuits have been integrated in experiments and applications. We have designed in bipolar IC processes and in biCMOS processes. Often, bipolar or CMOS experiments have been carried out in the bipolar part or only the CMOS part of a biCMOS

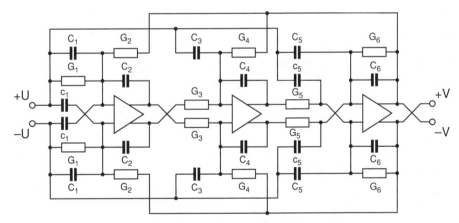

Fig. 23c. Third-order canonic filter section. The transfer function is

$$\frac{V}{U} = \frac{G_1.G_3.G_5 + p(C_1 - c_1)G_3.G_5 + p^2 C_2.C_3.G_5 + p^3 C_2.C_4(C_5 - c_5)}{G_2.G_3.G_5 + p.C_2.G_4.G_5 + p^2 C_2.C_4.G_6 + p^3 C_2.C_4.C_6}.$$

The section can implement any third-order filter transfer function. Fourth-order and higher-order sections (although less practical) can be made similarly.

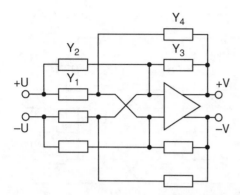

Fig. 24. Single-amplifier filter design. All admittances of the balanced arrangement are passive *RC* admittances. The transfer function is

$$\frac{V}{U} = \frac{Y_1 - Y_2}{Y_3 - Y_4} = H(p).$$

Any transfer function $H(p)$ can be written in this form by the division of denominator and numerator by an auxiliary polynomial (with all zeroes distinct and on the negative real axis), partial fraction expansion of denominator and numerator, and taking fractions with residues of the same sign together.

process. Some experiments have been carried out in IC processes that were still in a laboratory phase. But apart from the corresponding uncertainties, all measurements (except some cases of distortion measurements) were in agreement with the simulations. Filter gains agree with design targets within tenths of decibels, up to frequencies of almost 100 MHz. Noise is less than 2 dB higher than simulations indicate. Distortion and supply rejection ratio proved to be less predictable, for CMOS designs in particular. More than 10 dB higher distortion (compared with simulations) have been measured. In some cases with modified MOS-transistor models, the accuracy of the simulations has been improved.

7.1. Circuits in Standard-Digital-CMOS

For applications in standard digital CMOS processes, we have thus far preferred transconductor-*C* (gyrator) techniques. In the case of standard digital CMOS, the preferred gate tuning voltage of the MOS-transistor resistors of Banu-Tsividis-type balanced integrator filters are often outside (i.e., higher or lower than) the supply voltage. This is the case because we want to handle large signals with low distortion and we need a certain tuning range to cope with tolerances in the process. We have used biCMOS processes with a standard (5 V) CMOS combined with a bipolar part for higher supply volt-

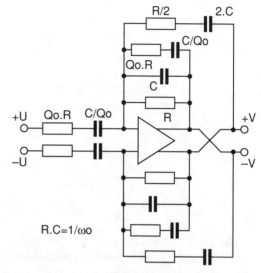

Fig. 25. Single-amplifier resonance circuit.

$$H(p) = \frac{\dfrac{p.\omega_o}{Q_o}}{p^2 + \dfrac{p.\omega_o}{Q_o} + \omega_o^2}$$

$$= \frac{\dfrac{p.\omega_o/Q_o}{p + \omega_o}}{\omega_o + p + \dfrac{p.\omega_o/Q_o}{p + \omega_o} - \dfrac{2.p.\omega_o}{p + \omega_o}},$$

where we have divided by the common factor $p + a$ (with $a = \omega_o$). Hence,

$$Y_1 = \frac{p.\omega_o/Q_o}{p + \omega_o}, Y_2 = 0,$$

$$Y_3 = \omega_o + p + \frac{p.\omega_o/Q_o}{p + \omega_o}, Y_4 = \frac{2.p.\omega_o}{p + \omega_o},$$

which leads to the circuit in the figure. If desired, the last term of Y_3 can be included in Y_4.

ages (e.g., 8 V or 12 V). In that case, the bipolar part takes care of the control of the gates of the MOS-transistor resistors.

7.2. Some Experiments in biCMOS

Figure 26 shows chip photographs of two experiments, each with a pair of resonance circuits for video frequencies. The resonance circuits consist of two balanced integrators and a cross-coupling. One resonance circuit of each of the pairs has been damped using small capacitors to arrive (as accurately as possible) at a Q_o of 16.

In Fig. 26a, the filter resistors are NMOS transistors, which can be varied in the range between 10

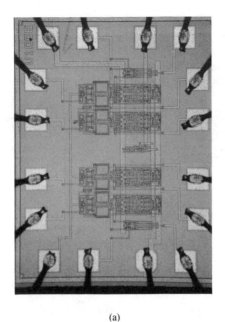
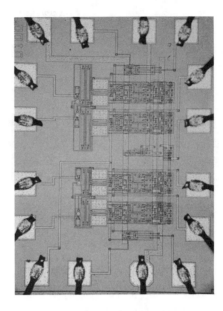

(a)   (b)

Fig. 26. Resonance circuits (chip photos). Shown are two pairs of balanced-integrator resonance circuits for video frequencies (approximately 4 MHz). One of each pair of resonance circuits has been accurately damped to a quality factor of 16 using small capacitors. The unloaded Q-factors are amply above 100 (designed and measured).

The circuits in photo (a) have been made with NMOS resistors (10 to 20 kOhm), (gate-)dielectric capacitors, and bipolar balanced amplifiers. The NMOS resistors have been frequency-corrected (corrected for their transmission line effect) by putting a series circuit of a capacitor $C/6$ (C = gate capacitance) and a resistor $0.7\,R$ (R = filter resistor) between drain and source.

In photo (b) we show a similar pair of video frequency resonance circuits but in a different circuit technique—with implanted resistors (10 kOhm) and variable junction capacitors. We have applied distributed bootstrapping to the filter resistors to correct for high-frequency phase shifts.

The process is a 2.5 μm biCMOS process. The area of the chips on the photos (including bond pads) is 1.5 mm^2.

and 20 kOhm by control of the gate voltage. Figure 26b shows the same pair of resonance circuits with fixed (implanted) resistors of 10 kOhm and variable junction capacitors. In the latter case, bias currents cause common-mode voltages across the junction capacitors for tuning. The measured tuning of the version with NMOS-transistor resistors is shown in Fig. 27.

An analog tapped delay line is shown in Fig. 28. It is a cascade connection of 4 Nyquist sections having a delay-bandwidth product of 0.5. Each section has a third-order transfer function. The sections have been designed for a nominal delay per section of 100 ns

(signal bandwidth: 5 MHz). Tuning varies the bandwidth and the delay (see Fig. 29). The tapped delay line can be used for adaptive filters and short (luminance) delay lines.

7.3. Compatibility with Multipliers

MOS-transistor filter resistors can be linearized by putting half the signal voltage on the gate (and, for greater accuracy, also on the backgate) in addition to the bias voltage (see [24]). A simple electronic solution for balanced integrator circuits has been depicted in the upper part of Fig. 30 (see also [25]).

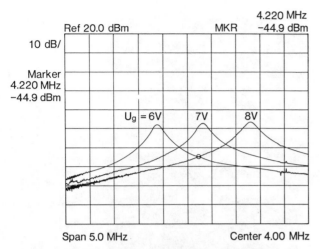

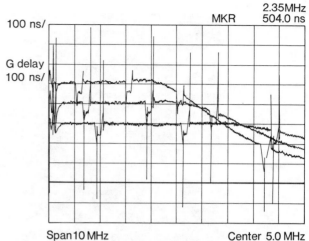

Fig. 27. Tuning the resonance circuit (version with NMOS filter resistors). The supply voltage for the CMOS is 5 V. The gate voltage is provided by the bipolar part of the biCMOS process. Three measured filter gain curves are shown as a function of frequency, each with a different tuning voltage. Equal maxima would mean equal Q-factors.

Fig. 29. Tuning the overall delay of the tapped delay line. The measured group delay of the delay line is shown as a function of frequency for three different gate control voltages. The bandwidth varies proportionally and the delay varies inversely proportionally with the control voltage.

Third-order distortion (including intermodulation $2p - q$) is reduced by 12 dB.

Multipliers can be made using double-balancing; see [26, 27]. Also, in that case, signal voltages have to be applied to the gates in addition to bias volt-

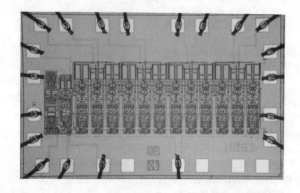

Fig. 28. Tapped delay line (chip photo). One delay section has a third-order equal-ripple approximation to a constant group delay d over a bandwidth $b = 1/(2.d)$ Hz: a Nyquist delay section. The roll-off at high frequencies is first-order (to limit noise and the effect of the spurious peaking at around 200 MHz). On the chip, 4 delay sections (for video frequencies) have been cascaded. The circuit technique is with NMOS-transistor resistors, dielectric gate-oxide capacitors and biCMOS balanced amplifiers. The process is a 2.5 μm biCMOS process. The chip area of the circuits on the photo is 1 mm^2. The tapped delay line can be used for short delay lines and in adaptive filters.

ages. For this purpose, the same technique can be applied as in the top part of Fig. 30. Multipliers are used in mixer circuits, correlators for adaptive filters, and in squarers—for example, for amplitude detection in sine-wave quadrature oscillators.

7.4. Sine-Wave Quadrature Oscillator

A sine-wave quadrature oscillator provides two signals: $a.\sin(\omega.t)$ and $a.\cos(\omega.t)$. The main part of the oscillator is a resonance circuit of two integrators and a cross-coupling (see Fig. 31). The integrators consist of a voltage-to-current conversion with transconductance G, followed by the integration of the current in a capacitor C. The descriptive equations for the oscillator are

$$C\frac{du_1}{dt} + g(a).u_1 + G.u_2 = i_{n_1}, \qquad (37)$$

$$C\frac{du_2}{dt} + g(a).u_2 - G.u_1 = i_{n_2}, \qquad (38)$$

where u_1 and u_2 are integrator input/output signals (single-ended), $g(a)$ is a variable positive or negative conductance: damping or undamping (for Q-control) across the capacitors C, and i_{n_1} and i_{n_2} are the differential-mode parts of the noise currents of the (trans)conductances. Approximately

$$\langle i_{n_1}^2 \rangle = \langle i_{n_2}^2 \rangle = 2.k.T.G.df. \qquad (39)$$

The resonance circuit is damped or undamped when the signal amplitude is too high or too low. The

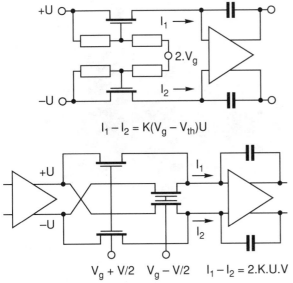

$$I_1 - I_2 = K(V_g - V_{th})U$$

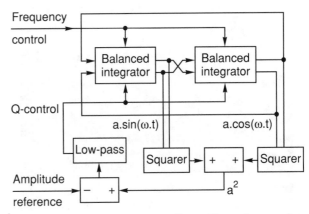

$$V_g + V/2 \quad V_g - V/2 \quad I_1 - I_2 = 2.K.U.V$$

Fig. 30. Application of a combination of tuning and signal voltages to the gates of the MOS-transistor resistors.
Linearization—in the upper part of the figure we show a circuit technique to apply half the signal voltage to the gate and, preferably, also to the back gate (not drawn) of the transistors in addition to the bias voltages. Thus, third-order distortion terms are reduced by a factor 4 (12 dB).
Multiplication (*lower part of the figure*)—if for a MOS transistor (in the triode region) we use the equation

$$I_d = K\left(V_g - V_{th} - \frac{V_d + V_s}{2}\right)(V_d - V_s),$$

we obtain

$$I_1 = K(U + V)U, \ I_2 = K(U - V)U, \ I_1 - I_2 = 2.K.U.V.$$

From the last equation we see that the left part of the lower circuit is a multiplier. Together with the right-hand integrator a correlator has been made. Also in this case we apply bias voltages and signal voltages to the gates. For the implementation, the same electronic circuit technique as in the upper circuit can be applied.

square of the amplitude is obtained using two squarers and an adder (see Fig. 31). The equations are the same as for a gyrator oscillator. Amplitude control and frequency control are independent (see also [28, 29]. A version for video frequencies, using the above circuit principles, has been integrated (for a chip photo, see Fig. 32).

7.5. Video Low-Pass Filter

The chip photo in Fig. 33 shows a fifth-order Cauer-elliptic video low-pass filter. On the same chip the group delay has been equalized using 3 second-order allpass sections (not shown on the photo). The fifth-order filter is a signal-flow-graph

Fig. 31. Sine-wave quadrature oscillator. The main part of the oscillator is a resonance circuit of two balanced integrators and a cross-coupling (inversion). There are two output signals: $a.\cos(\omega.t)$ and $a.\sin(\omega.t)$. The resonance circuit is damped or undamped when the signal amplitude is too high or too low. Insertion of $u_1 = a.\cos(\varphi)$ and $u_2 = a.\sin(\varphi)$ in the noise-free descriptive equations yields

$$d\varphi/dt = G(t)/C, \quad C.da/dt + a.g(a) = 0.$$

We see that frequency control is instantaneous. Amplitude control and frequency control are independent. Writing $u_1 = a.\cos(\varphi) + i_{n_1}$ and $u_2 = a.\sin(\varphi) + i_{n_2}$ and using $R = 1/G$, the noise spectrum of the oscillator can be calculated:

$$\langle u_{n_1}^2 \rangle = \langle u_{n_2}^2 \rangle = \frac{1 + (f/f_o)^2}{\left(1 - (f/f_o)^2\right)^2} \, 2.k.T.R.df.$$

design. The allpass sections are canonic filter sections. The balanced integrators use biCMOS balanced amplifiers (with high transconductance), NMOS resistors, and gate-dielectric capacitors. All NMOS transistor resistors have been frequency corrected ($C/6$ across the resistor, where C is the total gate capacitance of the resistor). No further corrections for strays have been made. The measured filter function proves to be remarkably accurate (see also [30]). The signal-to-noise ratio (1% distortion) is 70 dB. The active chip area is 0.05 mm² per filter order.

7.6. 216 MHz Matched Oscillator

In many applications where one or more filters have to be designed, there is already a clock oscillator for the system. When we design (or redesign) the clock oscillator in the same technique as the filter(s), there is a natural matching between them. In Fig. 34, a 216 MHz clock oscillator is shown, which after frequency-doubling provides us with a clock signal of 432 MHz. A part of its spectrum has been shown in Fig. 35 (measured). The clock oscillator matches a

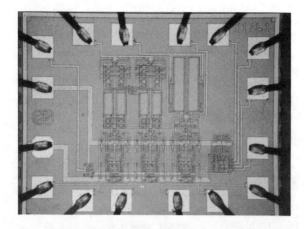

Fig. 32. Sine-wave quadrature oscillator (chip photo). From left to the right we see the two balanced integrators of the resonance circuit, a balanced amplifier with squarers for amplitude detection (with ripple filter), and the circuit that provides a reference for the amplitude. The nominal frequency of the oscillator is 5 MHz. The design has been made in a 2.5 μm biCMOS IC process. The area of the chip (including bond pads) is 1.5 mm^2. The area of the oscillator circuits is 0.4 mm^2.

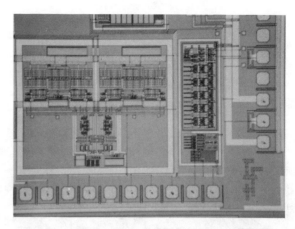

Fig. 34. 216 MHz matched oscillator. The oscillator is a quadrature sine-wave oscillator. It has been designed as a resonance circuit with a negative Q_o factor and hard amplitude limiting (which barely influences the oscillation frequency). With a frequency doubler using the sinewave and the cosine wave we arrive at a clock signal of 432 MHz. The oscillator matches within $\pm 4\%$ to a third-order lowpass loop filter for a sigma-delta modulator (with 5 MHz bandwidth, having an accurate transfer function up to 144 MHz). The main part of the layout consists of vertical PNP transistors in the load circuits. The oscillator and filters are designed in a still experimental 1.5 μm biCMOS process with NPN transistors with an f_T of 8 GHz.

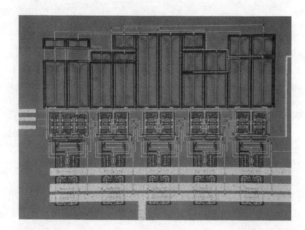

Fig. 33. Video lowpass filter (chip photo). A fifth-order Cauer-elliptic lowpass filter is shown. It has a nominal bandwidth of 3 MHz. The group delay of the filter has been equalized using three second-order allpass sections (on the same chip but not on the photograph). The implementation uses NMOS-transistor resistors (nominal value: 10 kOhm), biCMOS-balanced amplifiers, and gate-dielectric capacitors. The supply voltage is 5 V (the gate control voltage is higher). The supply current is 250 μA per amplifier. The signal-to-noise ratio (at 1% distortion) is 70 dB. The active chip area is 0.05 mm^2 per filter order. The design has been made in a 1.5 μm biCMOS process ($f_{T\max}$ of NPN 3 GHz).

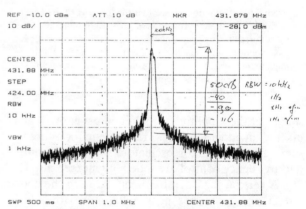

Fig. 35. Oscillator spectrum. The figure shows a part of the spectrum of the oscillator (around the carrier). In the design phase of the oscillator the requirement for the noise was derived from requirements on jitter and amounted to a design value for the carrier-to-noise ratio of 117 dB (noise at a distance of 2 MHz in a band of 1 Hz). The noise converted from the value, which is measured at a distance of 100 kHz and with a bandwidth of 10 kHz, is less than 2 dB higher than the predicted value.

third-order lowpass loop filter (with 5 MHz bandwidth) for a sigma-delta modulator (part of ESPRIT project 412: biCMOS).

7.7. Circuits in Bipolar Processes

We have also designed balanced-integrator filters with transconductors in bipolar IC processes, but they are still too preliminary to be reported.

8. CONCLUSION

In the literature, much information can be found on balanced-integrator filters. Nevertheless, we feel that we have treated several items in a different way and that we are contributing to new design methods and are presenting new circuit designs.

We have considered integrators and resonance circuits that form the basis for filter design, eigen frequencies, balanced-amplifier principles, circuit design, efficiency, noise, (quadratic) losslessness, three types of stability, and (non-)linearity of MOS-transistor resistor integrators and junction capacitor integrators. Three design methods have been reviewed: SFG, canonic filter sections, and single-amplifier filters.

A set of circuit examples completes the overview. The examples show, in particular, that balanced-integrator filters and biCMOS IC processes go well together.

ACKNOWLEDGMENTS

We would like to mention the enthusiastic discussions, in particular on stability items, that we had with Mr. K. W. Moulding of the Philips Research Laboratories in Redhill, U.K. We would like to thank Mr. P. van Veghel (a former colleague) for the design of the 5 MHz oscillator, Miss Gearty (at the time a student from Trinity College in Dublin, Ireland) for her assistance with the design of the video lowpass filter, and last but not least, all the people who cooperated on the ESPRIT-412 project —biCMOS, in technology, modeling, CAD, and circuit design—without whom several designs would not have been successful.

REFERENCES

[1] M. Banu and Y. Tsividis, "Fully integrated active *RC* filters in MOS technology," *IEEE J. Solid-State Circuits*, vol. SC-18, pp. 644–651, 1983.

[2] Y. Tsividis, M. Banu, and M. Khoury, "Continuous-time MOSFET-C filters in VLSI," *IEEE J. Solid-State Circuits*, vol. SC-21, pp. 15–30, 1986.

[3] R. H. Crawford, "MOSFET in circuit design," New York: McGraw-Hill, 1967.

[4] J. O. Voorman, "Filter arrangement," US Patent 4,786,880, 1988.

[5] J. O. Voorman, "Filter arrangement having a transconductance circuit," US Patent 4,780,690, 1988.

[6] H. J. Carlin, "Singular network elements," *IEEE Trans. on Circuit Theory*, vol. CT-11, pp. 67–72, 1964.

[7] M. Banu, J. M. Khoury and Y. Tsividis, "Fully differential operational amplifiers with accurate output balancing," *IEEE J. Solid-State Circuits*, vol. SC-23, pp. 1410–1414, 1988.

[8] D. Blom and J. O. Voorman, "Noise and dissipation of electronic gyrators," *Philips Research Reports*, vol. 26, pp. 103–113, 1971.

[9] J. O. Voorman and D. Blom, "Noise in gyrator-capacitor filters," *Philips Research Reports*, vol. 26, pp. 114–133, 1971.

[10] J. M. Khoury and Y. P. Tsividis, "Analysis and compensation of high-frequency effects in integrated MOSFET-C continuous-time filters," *IEEE Trans., Circuits Syst.*, vol. CAS-34, pp. 862–875, 1987.

[11] J. O. Voorman, "The gyrator as a monolithic circuit in electronic systems," Thesis, University of Nijmegen, 1977.

[12] R. O. Nielsen and A. N. Willson, "A fundamental result concerning the topology of transistor circuits with multiple equilibria," *Proc. IEEE*, vol. 68, pp. 196–208, 1980.

[13] T. Nishi and L. O. Chua, "Topological criteria for nonlinear resistive circuits containing controlled sources to have a unique solution," *IEEE Trans., Circuits Syst.*, vol. CAS-31, pp. 722–741, 1984.

[14] M. Banu and Y. Tsividis, "Detailed analysis of nonidealities in MOS fully integrated active RC filters based on balanced networks," *IEE Proceedings, Part G* (Electronic Circuits and Systems), vol. 131, pp. 190–196, 1984.

[15] W. R. Patterson and F. S. Shoucair, "Harmonic suppression in unbalanced analogue MOSFET circuit topologies using body signals," *Electron. Lett.*, vol. 25, pp. 1737–1739, 1989.

[16] Y. P. Tsividis and B. X. Shi, "Cancellation of any order in integrated active RC filters," *Electron. Lett.*, vol. 21, pp. 132–134, 1985.

[17] M. Banu and Y. Tsividis, "An elliptic continuous-time CMOS filter with on-chip automatic tuning," *IEEE J. Solid-State Circuits*, vol. SC-20, pp. 1114–1121, 1985.

[18] W. Heinlein and H. Holmes, "Active filters for integrated circuits," München Oldenbourg, Ch. 8, 1974.

[19] J. O. Voorman, W. H. A. Brüls and P. J. Barth, "Integration of analog filters in a bipolar process," *IEEE J. Solid-State Circuits*, vol. SC-17, pp. 713–722, 1982.

[20] J. O. Voorman, "Balanced integrator-filter arrangement," US Patent 4,926,135, 1990.

[21] P. V. Ananda Mohan, "New structures of MOSFET-C filters," *Proc. IEEE*, vol. 75, pp. 957–960, 1987.

[22] J. O. Voorman, "Gebalanceerde filterschakeling," Dutch Patent Application, PHN 13.097, 1989.

[23] H. Y-F. Lam "Analog and digital filters: design and realization," Englewood Cliffs, NJ: Prentice Hall, pp. 359–361, 1979.

[24] A. Bilotti, "Operation of the MOS transistor as a variable resistor," *Proc. IEEE*, vol. 54, pp. 1093–1094, 1966.

[25] J. O. Voorman, "Analog integrated filters or continuous-time filters for LSI and VLSI," *Revue de Physique Appliquée*, vol. 22, pp. 3–14, 1987.

[26] B. Song, "CMOS RF circuits for data communications applications," *IEEE J. Solid-State Circuits*, vol. SC-21, pp. 310–317, 1986.

[27] Z. Czarnul, "Modification of Banu-Tsividis continuous-time integrator structure," *IEEE Trans. Circuit Syst.*, vol. CAS-33, pp. 714–716, 1986.

[28] J. O. Voorman, "Ideal frequency modulator," *Electron. Lett.*, vol. 10, pp. 387–388, 1974.

[29] J. O. Voorman, "Continuous-time analog integrated filters," in *Integrated Continuous-Time Filters: Principles, Design, and Applications*, Y. P. Tsividis and J. O. Voorman, Eds., Piscataway, NJ: IEEE PRESS, 1993.

[30] A. van Bezooijen, N. Ramalho and J. O. Voorman, "Balanced integrator filters at video frequencies," *ESSCIRC*, pp. 1–4, 1991.

Section 2-B   Balanced Circuits

This section is devoted to fully balanced MOSFET-C filters. These filters are based on integrators consisting of capacitors, MOS transistors, and a balanced-output op amp, connected in such a way that the even-order nonlinearities cancel out. The remaining odd-order nonlinearities are negligible for many applications. The principle is explained and demonstrated in an all-pole, voltage-controlled filter in Paper 2-B.1. Further demonstration is given in Paper 2-B.2 in which, in addition to an elliptic filter, a MOSFET-C VCO is presented and is used as part of an on-chip automatic tuning system. The successful implementation of filters like these depends on careful consideration of the various nonidealities involved. Paper 2-B.3 discusses such nonidealities, mostly at low frequencies, and comes up with the fortunate conclusion that most of these can be kept at a safely low level by adhering to certain straightforward precautions. Paper 2-B.4 concentrates on high-frequency nonidealities and their compensation, proposes new biquad topologies, and demonstrates the latter in a bandpass high-Q filter implemented in CMOS technology, operating in the 0.5 MHz range. Better results can be obtained in BiCMOS technology, as illustrated with a video filter in paper 2-B.5. In addition to frequency response accuracy, noteworthy here are the small chip area and power dissipation, which are both vital to the competitiveness of an integrated continuous-time filter. It is also demonstrated in this paper that no output stage for driving the MOSFET resistors is necessary if a sufficiently large transconductance is used in a single-stage op amp; this greatly extends the frequency range of application for MOSFET-C filters.

Achieving a large dynamic range in integrated continuous-time filters is difficult because of the need to use modern fabrication processes with low supply voltages (which implies small signal swings) as well as small chip area and thus small capacitances (which implies large noise levels). These problems can be attacked in various ways. One is, of course, the optimization of dynamic range in the classical sense, assuming given maximum signal swings. This topic is discussed elsewhere [1]. Another is the minimization of noise in the active elements; an example is presented in paper 2-B.6 by V. D. Plas, in which a balanced op amp with resistive loads in the input stage is used. Yet another way is to increase the maximum signal swing. In this solution, reduction of the effect of odd-order nonlinearities (which are not cancelled in balanced operation) can be important. In certain cases, "structural" cancellation of such nonlinearities can occur in the filter structure as a whole [2]. This effect has been demonstrated only for part of a filter's passband, and has not yet been fully explored. However, an ingenious way to reduce odd-order nonlinearities in integrator building blocks is described by Czarnul in paper 2-B.7, and in a related patent [3], and consists of modifying the basic MOSFET-C integrator by adding two cross-coupled transistors.* It is worth noting that the technique was first disclosed by Czarnul to one of the editors (Y. T.) in a letter in April, 1985, and was mentioned in Paper 2-A.1 with Czarnul's permission and due reference to him; preprints of the paper were freely distributed. However, because that first publication mentioning Czarnul's technique was not written by Czarnul himself, the origin of the technique is sometimes not clearly pointed out in some of the literature. We should remark that the technique, while increasing the signal swing, also increases the noise level and the sensitivities to transistor mismatch in comparison to the two-transistor MOSFET-C integrator, so one must apply it carefully. An extensive comparison of the two approaches can be found in [5]. An interesting possibility results from exchanging the signal and control terminals in the circuit suggested by Czarnul, resulting in a circuit discussed elsewhere [6]. That circuit, as well as some others, are really a cross between MOSFET-C and transconductor-C–op amp circuits; the latter are covered in Part 4 of this volume.

All circuits in this section are based on integrators, thus requiring one op amp per pole of the transfer function. In general, replacement of resistors by MOSFETs in nonintegrator-based structures does not work, because nonlinearities are usually not cancelled. It has been demonstrated, however, that in some cases it does work [7] and can lead to MOSFET-C circuits with a low op amp count. This direction remains largely unexplored.

An application of MOSFET-C filters is illustrated in Paper 7-A.1.

---

* A similar circuit was proposed independently by B.-S. Song for use in multipliers [4].

A Note on the Design of Balanced-Output Op Amps

As explained in the above papers, proper balancing of op amp outputs is essential. The quick way of using a single-ended op amp followed by an op amp-based inverter is totally inadequate at high frequencies since the inverter causes extra phase lag that destroys balancing. Thus, for high frequency work the design of fully balanced output (not just differential output) op amps is a must. Design considerations for such op amps for medium frequencies are presented in detail elsewhere [8, 9], but could not be included in this volume because of the decision to exclude papers purely on active elements (i.e., op amps and transconductors). Discussions of such op amps appropriate for high frequency work can be found, though, in filter papers in this volume (Papers 2-A.2 and 2-B.5). An important conclusion in these papers is that, if properly designed, some fully balanced op amps can be simpler than single-ended designs since they do not require the use of a differential-to-single-ended converter; op amp gain-bandwidth products of several GHz become possible in BiCMOS technology.

REFERENCES

[1] G. Groenewold, "The design of high dynamic range continuous-time integratable filters," *IEEE Trans. Circuits Syst.*, vol. 38, pp. 838–852, August 1991.

[2] Y. P. Tsividis and B. X. Shi, "Cancellation of distortion of any order in integrated active RC filters," *Electron. Lett.*, vol. 21, pp. 132–134, February 14, 1985.

[3] Z. Czarnul, "Semiconductive MOS resistance network," U.S. patent 4710726, December 1, 1987.

[4] B.-S. Song, "CMOS RF circuits for data communications applications," *IEEE J. Solid-State Circuits*, vol. SC-21, pp. 310–317, April 1986.

[5] Z. Czarnul, S. C. Fang, and Y. Tsividis, "Improving linearity in MOS fully integrated continuous-time filters," *Proc. IEEE ISCAS'86*, pp. 1169–1172, San Jose, 1986.

[6] P. J. Ryan and D. G. Haigh, "Novel fully differential MOS transconductor for integrated continuous-time filters," *Electron. Lett.*, vol. 23, pp. 742–743, July 2, 1987.

[7] Z. Czarnul and Y. Tsividis, "Implementation of MOSFET-C filters based on active *RC* prototypes," *Electron. Lett.*, vol. 24, no. 3, pp. 184–185, February 4, 1988.

[8] M. Banu, J. M. Khoury and Y. Tsividis, "Fully differential operational amplifiers with accurate output balancing," *IEEE J. Solid-State Circuits*, vol. 23, pp. 1410–1414, December 1988; errata, ibid., vol. 24, p. 847, June 1989.

[9] J. N. Babanezhad, "A low-output-impedance fully differential op amp with large output swing and continuous-time common-mode feedback," *IEEE J. Solid-State Circuits*, vol. 26, pp. 1825–1833, December 1991.

Fully Integrated Active *RC* Filters in MOS Technology

MIHAI BANU, STUDENT MEMBER, IEEE, AND YANNIS TSIVIDIS, SENIOR MEMBER, IEEE

Abstract —A fully integrated continuous-time low-pass filter has been fabricated in CMOS technology. The device implements an active *RC* network using integrated capacitors and MOS transistors operated in the nonsaturation region as voltage-controlled resistors. The filter topology is fully balanced for good linearity and for good power supply rejection. The cutoff frequency is voltage adjustable around 3 kHz allowing compensation for process and temperature variations. With ± 5 V power supplies a dynamic range of over 94 dB has been achieved.

I. INTRODUCTION

THE basic problem that has hindered the straightforward monolithic realization of active *RC* filters has been the unpredictability of element values due to fabrication process and temperature variations. These variations can cause time constant errors of over 100 percent. Therefore, approaches based on fixed time constant implementation relying on absolute element values are naturally doomed to failure in the context of IC processes available today. However, these processes do allow for accurate realization of element value ratios and hence, of time constant ratios. If these time constants are voltage- or current-controlled, they can be automatically tuned to predetermined values by an on-chip control system; the latter uses an off-chip reference, such as a crystal clock [1], [2] or an external resistor [3]. Control circuits for achieving this automatic tuning have been discussed elsewhere [1], [2], [4], [5] and are not considered here; instead, we will focus on the implementation of the filters themselves.

Several filters have been proposed based on the above principle, and utilizing no switching. As adjustable elements they have used gyrators with variable junction capacitance [2], variable transconductance elements [1], [3], [6], and special operational amplifiers with a variable junction capacitor [7]. A common characteristic of all these approaches is that, like switched-capacitor filters, they are based on nonstandard techniques requiring specialized design. In contrast to this, the filters most extensively studied and best understood, namely those consisting of resistors, capacitors, and operational amplifiers (henceforth referred to as active *RC*), had not yielded to integration so far. In

this paper, a method will be presented to integrate such filters on a chip, attaining excellent performance [8].

In active *RC* networks, the time constants can be made adjustable by using voltage-controlled resistors. MOS technology is naturally suited for this approach. Indeed, in this technology high quality capacitors and operational amplifiers are routinely implemented and the MOS transistor, operated in the nonsaturation region, is basically a voltage-controlled resistor. However, there is a potential major drawback in the arbitrary replacement of resistors with transistors. The strong nonlinearity of the MOSFET prohibits the use of large signals, limiting drastically the dynamic range [9]. In the following sections it will be shown how, by proper use of fully balanced networks, the bothersome transistor nonlinearities can be cancelled out, allowing the implementation of filters with wide dynamic range. The resulting filters operate in continuous time utilizing no switching, and thus they have none of the disadvantages associated with analog sampled-data filters. Specifically, there is no need for input antialiasing and output smoothing filters, no Nyquist rate limitations, no potential for operational amplifier high-frequency noise being aliased into the baseband, and no extraneous components at the output due to clock feedthrough. Further, in cases where switched-capacitor or digital filters are desirable, the filters proposed here represent an attractive candidate for implementing input antialiasing and output smoothing filters.

II. TECHNIQUE FOR THE LINEARIZATION OF MOSFET CHARACTERISTICS

A. Transistor Nonlinearities

The drain current of an n-channel MOS transistor in nonsaturation is given by [10]

$$
\begin{aligned}
I_D = 2K\Big\{ & (V_C - V_B - V_{FB} - \phi_B)(V_1 - V_2) \\
& - \frac{1}{2}\big[(V_1 - V_B)^2 - (V_2 - V_B)^2\big] \\
& - \frac{2}{3}\gamma\big[(V_1 - V_B + \phi_B)^{3/2} - (V_2 - V_B + \phi_B)^{3/2}\big]\Big\}
\end{aligned}
$$

$$(1a)$$

Manuscript received April 5, 1983; revised July 14, 1983 and August 20, 1983.

The authors are with the Department of Electrical Engineering, Columbia University, New York, NY 10027 and Bell Laboratories, Murray Hill, NJ 07974.

Reprinted from *IEEE J. Solid-State Circuits*, vol. SC-18, no. 6, pp. 644–651, Dec. 1983.

with

$$\gamma = \frac{1}{C'_{\text{ox}}} (2qN_A\epsilon_s)^{1/2} \qquad (1b)$$

$$K = \frac{1}{2}\mu C'_{\text{ox}} \frac{W}{L} \qquad (1c)$$

where I_D is the drain current in the triode region, V_C, V_B, V_1, V_2 are the gate, substrate, drain, and source potentials with respect to ground, W and L are the channel width and length, μ is the carrier effective mobility in the channel, V_{FB} is the flat-band voltage, N_A is the substrate doping concentration, C'_{ox} is the gate oxide capacitance per unit area, ϵ_s is the silicon dielectric constant, q is the electron charge and ϕ_B is the approximate surface potential in strong inversion for zero backgate bias (classically, this potential has been taken to be $2\phi_F$ with ϕ_F the Fermi potential, but ϕ_B is actually higher by several kT/q [11]). It is assumed that the source and the drain voltages V_1 and V_2 never become too low to forward bias the drain and the source junctions and never become too high to drive the device into saturation. The ground potential is defined such that V_1 and V_2 vary around zero. In that case the substrate voltage should be negative in order to keep the drain and the source junctions reversed biased (such a definition for ground potential is convenient when two power supplies of opposite values are present).

The 3/2 power terms in (1a) can be expanded in Taylor series with respect to V_1 and V_2. Then I_D can be written in the general form

$$I_D = K\left[a_1(V_1 - V_2) + a_2(V_1^2 - V_2^2) + a_3(V_1^3 - V_2^3) + \cdots\right] \qquad (2)$$

where the coefficients a_1 are independent of V_1 and V_2 and are functions of the gate and substrate potentials (V_C and V_B) and all the process and physical parameters involved in the making of the device. The inverse of (Ka_1) is the small-signal resistance R of the transistor; it can be shown that

$$R = \frac{1}{Ka_1} = \left[\mu C'_{\text{ox}} \frac{W}{L}(V_C - V_T)\right]^{-1} \qquad (3)$$

where V_T is the threshold voltage corresponding to $-V_B$ backgate bias. The value of R may be varied with V_C (henceforth called the control voltage); therefore, for small signals, the MOSFET can be used as a voltage-controlled resistor.

An indication on how the nonlinear higher order terms in (2) affect the transistor characteristics is given by the relative magnitude of the coefficients a_i compared to a_1. Fig. 1 shows the ratios $a_2/a_1, a_3/a_1$, etc., for common process parameters, as computed from (1a). A typical practical situation is illustrated by taking $V_2 = 0$ V, $V_1 = 1$ V, $V_C - V_T = 2$ V, $\mu C'_{\text{ox}}(W/L) = 10\ \mu\text{A/V}^2$ and $V_B = -5$ V (for usual power supplies of ± 5 V the n-channel transistor substrate is considered connected to the minimum available potential). Then, the first term in the right-hand side of

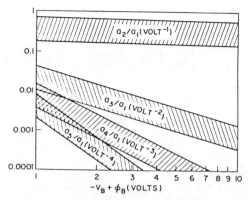

Fig. 1. Coefficients of the nonlinear components in the MOS transistor characteristics normalized to a_1 for different substrate biases and different control (gate) voltages. Each band corresponds to 4 V $< V_C - V_T < 1$ V (bottom of band for 4 V); $\phi_B = 0.7$ V, $\gamma = 1$ V$^{1/2}$.

(2) is 20 μA, the second term is $-6\ \mu$A, the third term is $3 \times 10^{-2}\ \mu$A, the forth one is $-2 \times 10^{-3}\ \mu$A, etc. It is seen that the dominant deviation from linearity comes from the second-order term. In the next subsection a simple circuit technique for the cancellation of this term will be presented.

B. Nonlinearity Cancellation

The proposed technique will be illustrated by developing an active *RC* integrator in which MOSFET's are used instead of resistors. The classical implementation is shown in Fig. 2(a). The gain factor of this integrator is given by $(1/RC)$. Consider replacing the resistor with a MOSFET whose small-signal channel resistance is R, as shown in Fig. 2(b). Using the relation (2) with $Ka_1 = 1/R$ we have

$$V_{\text{out}} = -\frac{1}{RC}\int_{-\infty}^{t} V_{\text{in}}\, dt'$$
$$- \frac{K}{C}\int_{-\infty}^{t}\left(a_2 V_{\text{in}}^2 + a_3 V_{\text{in}}^3 + \cdots\right) dt'. \qquad (4)$$

The first term in (4) represents the ideal response of the integrator [identical with the response of the circuit of Fig. 2(a)] and the second one represents the error due to transistor nonlinearities. For large signals, the error term in the output becomes significant and produces excessive second-order harmonic distortion which limits the dynamic range. Considering the same transistor as in the example of the previous paragraph ($V_C - V_T = 2$ V, $V_B = -5$ V, coefficients a_i given as in Fig. 1) the total harmonic distortion (THD) is approximately 7.5 percent for an input signal of 2 V$_{\text{p-p}}$. If THD of less than 1 percent is desired, it is easy to calculate that input signals no larger than 250 mV$_{\text{p-p}}$ should be applied. However, if the $a_2 V_{\text{in}}^2$ term in (4) were cancelled, the remaining integrator output error due to the higher order terms would be considerably less, resulting in only 0.03 percent THD for the same device and 2 V$_{\text{p-p}}$ signal level. A partial cancellation of this type was effectively accomplished in a circuit proposed quite early [12] which implemented a grounded linearized resistor with parasitic dc paths. A fully floating linearized resistor without dc

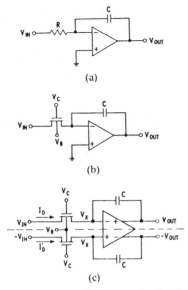

Fig. 2. (a) Classical active *RC* integrator. (b) Small-signal active *RC* integrator with variable gain factor. (c) Large-signal active *RC* integrator with variable gain factor realized as a fully balanced circuit.

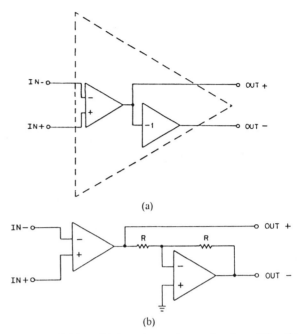

Fig. 3. (a) Definition of balanced output operational amplifier. (b) A possible implementation of the balanced output operational amplifier.

parasitic paths was proposed recently [13]. Both schemes in [12] and [13] use extra circuitry in addition to the MOS transistor to implement the device linearization. It will be shown below that overall linearity can be accomplished without necessarily having to linearize every transistor separately and without the need for any extra circuitry; linearization schemes are considered further elsewhere [14]–[16].

The cancellation of the second-order term in the output of the circuit of Fig. 2(b) can be accomplished simply by using the fully balanced version of the latter as shown in Fig. 2(c). It consists of two identical capacitors, two identical transistors with identical gate and substrate bias, and one operational amplifier whose output voltages are required to be always symmetric with respect to ground (V_{out} and $-V_{out}$). The two input voltages are also assumed balanced (V_{in} and $-V_{in}$). One can regard this scheme as the combination of the circuit in Fig. 2(b) with its own mirror image taken with respect to the symmetry axis shown in Fig. 2(c).

The fully balanced integrator will now be analyzed. Assuming infinite op amp gain and zero offset voltage, the two inputs of the operational amplifier are at the same potential V_x (not virtual ground in general). Writing the *KVL* equations for the two outputs we have

$$V_{out}(t) = -\frac{1}{C}\int_{-\infty}^{t} I_D \, dt' + V_x \tag{5a}$$

$$-V_{out}(t) = -\frac{1}{C}\int_{-\infty}^{t} I_D' \, dt' + V_x. \tag{5b}$$

The solution for V_{out} is obtained by subtracting (5b) from (5a):

$$V_{out}(t) = -\frac{1}{2C}\int_{-\infty}^{t} (I_D - I_D') \, dt'. \tag{6}$$

The values of the currents I_D and I_D' are given according to (2):

$$I_D = K\left\{ a_1\left[V_{in} - V_x\right] + a_2\left[V_{in}^2 - V_x^2\right] \right.$$
$$\left. + a_3\left[V_{in}^3 - V_x^3\right] + \cdots \right\} \tag{7a}$$

$$I_D' = K\left\{ a_1\left[(-V_{in}) - V_x\right] + a_2\left[(-V_{in})^2 - V_x^2\right] \right.$$
$$\left. + a_3\left[(-V_{in})^3 - V_x^3\right] + \cdots \right\}. \tag{7b}$$

When (7b) is subtracted from (7a), all the even order terms in V_{in} and all the terms in V_x cancel out:

$$I_D - I_D' = 2K\left[a_1 V_{in} + a_3 V_{in}^3 + a_5 V_{in}^5 + \cdots \right]. \tag{8}$$

Since the terms containing $a_3, a_5, \cdots$ are much smaller than the linear one (see previous subsection), the right-hand side of (8) is practically linear in V_{in}. Using (8) in (6), we obtain

$$V_{out}(t) \cong -\frac{1}{RC}\int_{-\infty}^{t} V_{in} \, dt'. \tag{9}$$

This result proves that the fully balanced integrator of Fig. 2(c) has practically the same transfer characteristic as the circuit of Fig. 2(a), even for large signals. It is emphasized that the circuit developed is not a differential scheme since it does not act on the difference of two arbitrary signals, say V_a and V_b; instead, $V_a = V_{in}$ and $V_b = -V_{in}$. The circuit thus accepts *one* balanced input (V_{in} and $-V_{in}$) and produces *one* balanced output (V_{out} and $-V_{out}$). The requirement of the operational amplifier to balance the output can be met as shown in Fig. 3(a). The circuit contains a high gain stage followed by an inverter. Clearly, no matter how it is connected in an external network, the two outputs will always be balanced. Fig. 3(b) shows a simple practical implementation.

In many filter applications multiple input integrators are

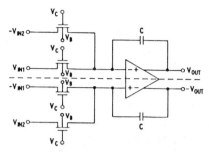

Fig. 4. Fully balanced differential integrator.

needed. Fig. 4 shows a fully balanced differential integrator. This time the circuit operates on two independent large signals: V_{in1} and V_{in2}, performing the integral of their difference. In a completely analogous fashion to our previous analysis, it can be shown that the transistors of each pair cancel their nonlinearities among themselves independently of the others, just as before. The same principle can be used to implement various other linearized filter building blocks of the active *RC* type, such as [16] summers (replacing the capacitors with MOS transistors), differentiators (interchanging the capacitors with the transistors), variable gain amplifiers (replacing the capacitors with resistors), etc. These filter building blocks are input–output compatible and can be connected to each other without any additional interfacing circuitry. Due to the automatic balancing at the output of the operational amplifiers, signal inversion is available at any node pair. The filters thus obtained are naturally balanced from input to output which is a desirable feature for good power supply rejection and increased signal level.

III. NONIDEALITIES

When the ideas introduced in the previous section are applied in practice, the actual circuits will exist in the presence of many nonideal conditions such as device mismatches, errors in the signal balancing, operational amplifier offsets, etc. Analyzing the effects of the latter, it can be shown that the proposed circuits still exhibit good performance [17]; a similar conclusion is suggested by the experimental results to be presented in this paper.

In the previous section only the resistive part of the channel was considered and therefore, strictly speaking, the results derived there are valid only at dc. In fact there are parasitic distributed capacitances from the channel to the gate and to the substrate. These capacitances together with the channel resistance form an intrinsic time constant of the device which will influence the frequency response of the filter in which the MOSFET is used. In order to minimize this effect, the filter should be designed such that the intrinsic transistor time constants are much smaller than the actual time constants needed to be implemented. This strategy usually requires the use of transistors with channel length not larger than several hundred μm [17], or the use of large capacitance values. That is why this filtering technique is more naturally suited for high frequencies where shorter transistors are required.

It was mentioned before that the signal at the balanced operational amplifier inputs [V_x in Fig. 2(c)] is not at virtual ground due to the nonlinearities of the MOS transistors. The question arises whether this introduces any complications in the design of the op amps with respect to the input common mode rejection. It can be calculated [16] that for usual cases, the signal at the amplifier summing nodes is no more than a fifth of the integrator input signal. This indicates that the op amp common mode input signal is relatively small and does not pose any special design problems.

IV. FILTER DESIGN AND CMOS IMPLEMENTATION

Based on the principles presented before, we have designed and fabricated a fifth-order low-pass filter in CMOS technology. The circuit, whose diagram is shown in Fig. 5, is the fully balanced version of a standard active *RC* ladder filter. It is synthesized from multiple-input balanced integrators identical with the one developed before (see Fig. 4). The gates of all transistors used as resistors are connected to the same potential V_C (control voltage). Varying V_C, one can change the frequency response in a manner equivalent to frequency axis scaling.

The process used is a Bell Laboratories standard twin-tub CMOS [18], having the capability to implement capacitors between the gate polysilicon and a second polysilicon layer. The design rules were based on 3.5 μm minimum linewidth.

Since MOSFET's and poly1-to-poly2 capacitors are readily available the only remaining circuit element needed is the balanced-output operational amplifier. The key specification in the design of this element is the proper matching of its outputs; they should be balanced within 1 percent [17] for low filter distortion. For speedy and reliable first-time design, the straightforward implementation shown in Fig. 3(b) was chosen. It uses two regular operational amplifiers and two p-tub resistors matched to each other. One problem with the use of p-tub resistors is their nonlinearity. to reduce this effect, they had to be designed with relatively large dimensions: 40×600 μm for approximately 35 kΩ; in this twin-tub CMOS technology the p-tub resistor nonlinearity comes from its width and length modulation with the signal (due to depletion regions in the junction between the p-tub and the n-tub). The operational amplifiers used are based on a previously designed circuit [19]. With respect to these op amps, two design factors had to be considered; capability to drive resistors and stability when connected as in Fig. 3(b) and in the actual filter. Since the filter MOST resistors are of the order of several MΩ (see below), the effective loads of the operational amplifiers are given by the p-tub resistors used in the inverters [see Fig. 3(b)]. Therefore, the output stage of the op amps was designed to drive low impedances which was reflected in a power dissipation of 2 mW per amplifier. Good output driving capability also increases the amplifier phase margin. This is desirable in order to avoid possible

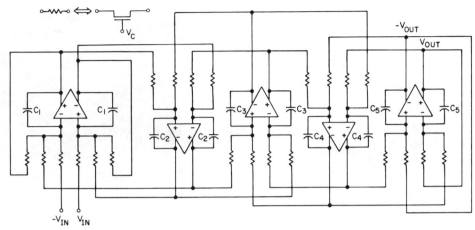

Fig. 5.   Fully balanced active *RC* ladder filter (fifth-order all-pole).

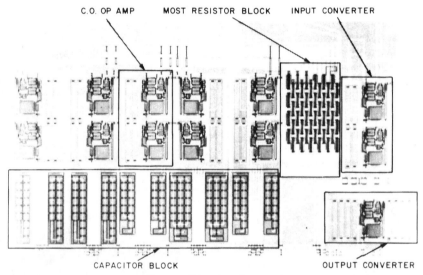

Fig. 6.   Chip microphotograph.

stability problems caused by cascading two operational amplifiers inside a feedback loop. For the same reason, each op amp had to be overcompensated.

The pole locations of the filter were chosen to implement a Chebyshev transfer function with 0.1 dB passband ripple and a cutoff frequency tunable around 3 kHz. These specification require the implementation of large time constants. For practical values of total integrated capacitance, large resistance values must be used (on the order of a couple of MΩ). They were implemented with p-channel MOSFET's having very small shape factors: $W/L = 0.01$ realized with $W = 4$ μm and $L = 400$ μm (p-channel devices were used because they have smaller mobility than the n-channel ones, and thus larger resistances). For such device sizes, the parasitic capacitances to the gate and to the substrate cannot be neglected despite the fact that the actual filter time constants were designed to have much larger values than the transistor intrinsic time constants [16]. This distributed capacitance effect can be simulated simply by modeling each transistor as a series combination of many shorter transistors. Using such simulation it was found that the previous effect produces a peaking of al-

most 1 dB near the band edge. An empirical optimization was performed by perturbing the value of each capacitor separately and observing the effect on the computer simulated frequency response. The peaking could be eliminated very easily by increasing C_2 and C_4 by the same properly chosen amount. However, by doing this, the passband ripple was increased to about 0.2 dB near the band edge. It should be mentioned that this simulation predicted very well the behavior of the actual device and the above compensation worked as expected (see Section V).

Fig. 6 shows a microphotograph of the experimental chip. For precise control over the shape of the frequency response, proper accuracy in the ratios between the filter time constants had to be insured (1 percent accuracy is usually enough to give passband deviations of less than 0.1 dB for filters of this type because they are naturally insensitive to parameter variations). This was accomplished by matching both the resistors and the capacitors. Because there is better control over the latter, the MOST resistors were designed to be identical and the time constant ratios were implemented as capacitor ratios. In order to improve the MOST resistor matching, a layout strategy was used

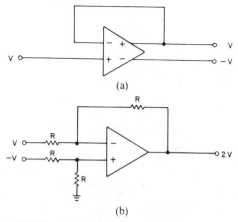

(a)

(b)

Fig. 7. (a) Unbalanced-to-balanced input converter. (b) Balanced-to-unbalanced output converter.

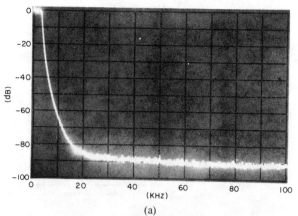

(a)

Fig. 8. Filter frequency response.

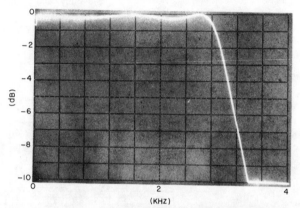

Fig. 9. Passband details of filter frequency response.

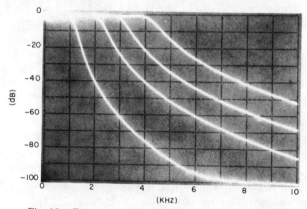

Fig. 10. Frequency response for various control voltages.

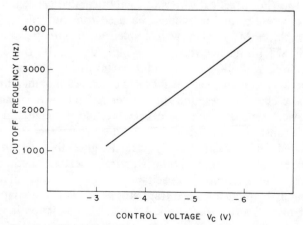

Fig. 11. Cutoff frequency (−3 dB point) versus control voltage.

where each resistor was used split into four identical parts and the parts were interleaved with all the others (see Fig. 6). In this way local process variations influence evenly all resistors. The capacitors were fabricated over a grounded p-tub to reduce the power supply coupling through the substrate.

Included in the chip was also a "single-ended to balanced" input converter and a "balanced to single-ended" output converter. These were implemented with p-tub resistors, according to the diagrams shown in Fig. 7. The active chip area including the converters is 4 mm².

V. EXPERIMENTAL RESULTS

All the data to be presented were measured for the complete system including the balanced filter and the input and output converters. The filter dc gain is 0 dB and the power supplies used were ±5 V.

Figs. 8 and 9 show the frequency response of the filter with stopband and passband details. Input signals of up to 10 MHz were also applied and the filter stopband rejection was found always better than 60 dB; this reflects the continuous time nature of the system. Varying the control voltage V_C, the frequency response could be changed as shown in Fig. 10. Clearly, this effect is similar to a frequency axis scaling. A more exact characterization of the frequency response dependence on V_C is contained in Fig. 11; the experimentally observed cutoff frequency (−3 dB point) is plotted versus the control voltage. It should not be surprising that the curve is a straight line because the dependence of $1/R$ in V_C in (3) is practically of the first degree (neglecting the small variation of mobility with the gate voltage).

The linearity performance of the filter is illustrated in Fig. 12. Here, the measured total harmonic distortion is shown as a function of the signal level for different values of $V_C - V_T$. In generating these plots, the input signal frequency was taken at one-third of the respective filter bandwidth such that the second and the third harmonic distortion components fall into the passband. The points

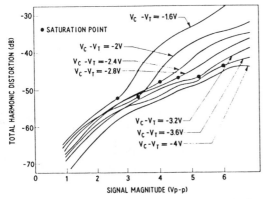

Fig. 12. Total harmonic distortion for various control voltages.

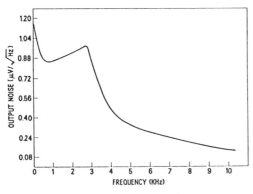

Fig. 13. Filter output noise.

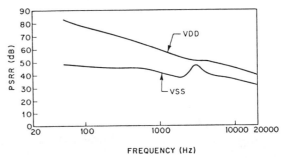

Fig. 14. Power supply rejection ratio (PSRR) versus frequency.

TABLE I
PERFORMANCE PARAMETERS OF THE FILTER INCLUDING
INPUT AND OUTPUT CONVERTERS

Power supply voltages	± 5 V
C-message weighted noise	34 μV rms
Wide band noise (2 Hz–12 MHz)	50 μV rms
Dynamic range[a] (based on -40 dB THD and C-message weighted noise)	94–96 dB
PSRR (1 kHz)	
$+V_{DD}$	-60 dB
$-V_{SS}$	-40 dB
Power dissipation	20 mW

[a] Depending on the value of control voltage.

where the transistors get into the saturation region of operation (shown on the distortion curves) mark a change in the shape of these curves. If a certain application requires the use of large signals with THD smaller than that indicated by Fig. 12 (e.g., -50 dB THD at signals of 6 V_{p-p}), the input signal could be first attenuated by an appropriate factor, then passed through the filter and finally amplified by the same factor. From the curves of Fig. 12 notice that a prefiltering attenuation and post-filtering amplification by only a factor of 2 would accomplish at least 10 dB improvement in THD. Such a strategy would inherently increase the output noise level and a penalty in overall dynamic range would be paid; however, this should not be critical for many applications because the starting dynamic range of the filter itself is very large (see below).

The output noise of the filter was measured to be 34 μV rms for C-message weighting, 42 μV rms for 3 kHz-flat weighting and 50 μV rms for 15 kHz-flat weighting. The wide band noise (2 Hz–12 MHz) remains at 50 μV rms which shows that practically all of it comes at low frequencies. This can be verified from the noise spectrum plotted in Fig. 13. Comparing these experimental results with simulations indicates that, in this implementation, the noise is mostly due to the resistor thermal noise at all but very low frequencies, where the $1/f$ noise of the operational amplifiers becomes predominant.

The power supply rejection performance is shown in Fig. 14 for both positive and negative supplies. It is emphasized that the PSRR is dominated by the performance of the

balanced operational amplifiers and not by the other components of the filter. This is indicated by the fact that the curves of Fig. 14 are similar to those of a single balanced output operational amplifier. In addition, the coupling from the negative supply (V_{SS}) can only come from the operational amplifiers because the MOST resistors are p-channel (substrate connected to V_{DD}) and all the capacitors were fabricated over a grounded p-tub.

The power dissipation was 20 mW. This reflects the fact that two regular operational amplifiers were used for each integrator.

A summary of the filter performance is shown in Table I.

VI. CONCLUSIONS

A method has been described for the integration of active RC filters with wide dynamic range in MOS technology. MOSFET's operated in nonsaturation are used as voltage-controlled resistors and are linearized with a simple circuit technique based on fully balanced operation. As an application, a CMOS fifth-order low-pass filter for voice-band was fabricated. The filter works in continuous-time (no switching) and therefore offers natural advantages over sampled-data systems, such as no need for antialiasing or smoothing filtering, no Nyquist rate limitations, no switching noise, and no operational amplifier noise aliasing into the baseband. In addition, the filter design is straightforward, based on well established active RC filter theory. The simplicity and predictability of the design were reflected in successful results from the first trial. The behavior of the actual implementation was in good agreement with computer simulations and analytical results. The filter exhibited low noise and good linearity, resulting in wide dynamic range.

REFERENCES

[1] K. S. Tan and P. R. Gray, "Fully integrated analog filters using bipolar JFET technology," *IEEE J. Solid-State Circuits*, vol. SC-13, pp. 814–821, Dec. 1978.

[2] K. W. Moulding, J. R. Quartly, P. J. Rankin, R. S. Thompson, and G. A. Wilson, "Gyrator video filter IC with automatic tuning," *IEEE J. Solid-State Circuits*, vol. SC-15, pp. 963–968, Dec. 1980.

[3] J. O. Voorman, W. H. A. Bruls, and P. J. Barth, "Integration of analog filters in a bipolar process," *IEEE J. Solid-State Circuits*, vol. SC-17, pp. 713–722, Aug. 1982.

[4] D. Senderowicz, D. A. Hodges, and P. R. Gray, "An NMOS integrated vector-locked loop," in *Proc. Int. Symp. Circuits Syst.*, May 1982, pp. 1164–1167.

[5] Y. Tsividis, "Self-tuned filters," *IEE Electron. Lett.*, vol. 17, no. 12, pp. 406–407, June 1981.

[6] K. Fukahori, "A bipolar voltage-controlled tunable filter," *IEEE J. Solid-State Circuits*, vol. SC-16, pp. 729–737, Dec. 1981.

[7] R. Schaumann and C. F. Chiou, "Design of integrated analog active filters," in *Proc. 1981 Europ. Conf. Circuit Theory Des.*, The Hague, The Netherlands, Aug. 1981, pp. 407–411.

[8] M. Banu and Y. Tsividis, "Fully integrated active *RC* filters in CMOS technology," in *Dig. Tech. Papers, IEEE Int. Solid-State Circuits Conf.*, New York, Feb. 1983, pp. 244–245.

[9] R. L. Geiger, P. E. Allen, and D. T. Ngo, "Switched-resistor filters —A continuous time approach to monolithic MOS filter design," *IEEE Trans. Circuits Syst.*, vol. CAS-29, pp. 306–315, May 1982.

[10] W. M. Penney and L. Lau, Eds., *MOS Integrated Circuits.* New York: Van Nostrand-Reinhold, 1972.

[11] Y. Tsividis, "Problems with precision modeling for analog MOS LSI," in *Proc. Int. Electron Devices Meeting*, San Francisco, CA, 1982.

[12] A. Bilotti, "Operation of a MOS transistor as a variable resistor," *Proc. IEEE*, vol. 54, pp. 1093–1094, Aug. 1966.

[13] M. Banu and Y. Tsividis, "Floating voltage-controlled resistors in CMOS technology," *IEE Electron. Lett.*, vol. 18, no. 15, pp. 678–679, July 1982.

[14] ——, "Fully integrated active *RC* filters," in *Proc. Symp. Circuits Syst.*, May 1983, pp. 602–605.

[15] Y. Tsividis and M. Banu, "Integrated nonswitched active *RC* filters with wide dynamic range," in *Proc. Europ. Conf. Circuit Theory and Design*, Stuttgard, Germany, Sept. 1983.

[16] M. Banu and Y. Tsividis, to be published.

[17] ——, "Detailed analysis of nonidealities in MOS fully integrated active *RC* filters based on balanced networks," to be published.

[18] L. C. Parillo, R. S. Payne, R. E. Davis, G. W. Reutlinger, and R. L Field, "Twin-tub CMOS—A technology for VLSI circuits," *IEEE Int. Electron Device Meeting, Tech. Dig.*, Dec. 1980, pp. 752–755.

[19] V. R. Saari, "Low power, high drive CMOS operational amplifiers," *IEEE J. Solid-State Circuits*, vol. SC-18, pp. 121–127, Feb. 1983.

An Elliptic Continuous-Time CMOS Filter with On-Chip Automatic Tuning

MIHAI BANU, MEMBER, IEEE, AND YANNIS TSIVIDIS, SENIOR MEMBER, IEEE

Abstract —A voice-band continuous-time filter is described which was designed based on the technique of fully balanced networks and was fabricated in a 3.5-μm CMOS technology. The filter implements a fifth-order elliptic low-pass transfer function with 0.05-dB passband ripple and 3.4-kHz cutoff frequency. A phase-locked loop (PLL) control system fabricated on the same chip automatically references the frequency response of the filter to an external fixed clock frequency. The cutoff frequency was measured to vary by less than 0.1 percent for an operating temperature range of 0–85° C. The absolute value accuracy of the cutoff frequency was 0.5 percent (standard deviation). With ±5-V power supplies the measured dynamic range of the filter was approximately 100 dB.

I. INTRODUCTION

PRECISION ACTIVE *RC* filters have traditionally been fabricated with discrete components and hybrid circuits. Recently it was shown that they can be integrated on a single MOS chip by the concurrent use of two circuit techniques. The first one, discussed in [1] and [2], gives a general method for designing integrated active *RC* networks with tunable characteristics. The second technique deals with the on-chip automatic tuning of these networks [3]. The resulting monolithic circuits have frequency responses which are insensitive to fabrication process tolerances, operating temperature variations, and aging. Thus, a solution is found to the problem of implementing precision active *RC* filters with inherently imprecise integrated components.

The tuning technique in [3] has been previously used in context with other types of continuous-time filters [4]–[9]. Its main idea is to reference the unpredictable but tunable frequency response of a network to an external fixed clock frequency. This is sufficient to make the frequency response well defined in spite of arbitrary variations of network internal parameters. The technique relies on the "master and slave" concept [4] taking advantage of the integrated circuits process capability for accurate component matching. Only a "master" subsystem has to be directly tuned, the rest of the network consisting of one or more "slave" circuits being indirectly referenced to the clock frequency. If the accuracy of component matching is

not adequate for certain applications fully integrated continuous-time networks are still feasible based on "self-tuning" as proposed in [10]. Also, it is possible to use an external temperature-insensitive resistor as the reference instead of the clock [11].

The only structural difference between the MOS active *RC* networks proposed in [1] or [2] and their classical counterparts is the use of MOS transistors operated in nonsaturation instead of fixed-value resistors. The transistors effectively act as voltage-controlled resistors creating the capability to voltage-tune the circuits through their gate potential. Fully balanced topologies and operation ensure that the dominant nonlinearities of the MOS transistors are canceled out and the filters obtained have a wide dynamic range [1]. The calculations in [18] have also shown that these circuits are insensitive to the dominant practical nonidealities.

This paper discusses in detail the design and performance of the CMOS active *RC* filter reported in [3]. It has a fifth-order elliptic low-pass transfer function with specifications similar to those of the PCM channel bank filters.

II. FILTER DESIGN

A. General Design Strategy

The method used to synthesize the filter was the classical simulation of signals in a double terminated reactance ladder. A general advantage of this approach is that the resulting circuit has a low passband sensitivity to element value variations just like the ladder. The design was carried out in three steps. First the classical ladder prototype was represented by an appropriate signal-flow graph. Then, a fully-balanced filter containing resistors, capacitors, and operational amplifiers was derived based on the graph. Finally, the resistors were replaced with MOS transistors and the effects related to the monolithic implementation were considered.

B. Classical Ladder Prototype and Corresponding Graph

The classical ladder prototype was simply selected from standard passive filter design tables [12]. A fifth-order elliptic low-pass response was chosen whose corresponding ladder is shown in Fig. 1. The structure implements five

Manuscript received April 22, 1985; revised August 2, 1985. This work was supported in part by National Science Foundation Grant ECS-83-10227.
M. Banu is with AT&T Bell Laboratories, Murray Hill, NJ 07974.
Y. Tsividis is with the Department of Electrical Engineering and the Center for Telecommunications Research, Columbia University, New York, NY 10027.

Reprinted from *IEEE J. Solid-State Circuits*, vol. SC-20, no. 6, pp. 1114–1121, Dec. 1985.

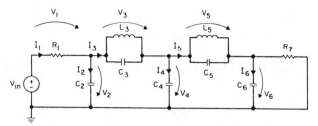

Fig. 1. RLC ladder prototype.

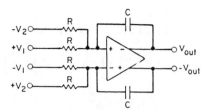

Fig. 3. Fully balanced differential integrator.

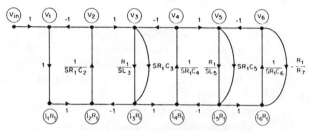

Fig. 2. Signal-flow graph for the ladder in Fig. 1.

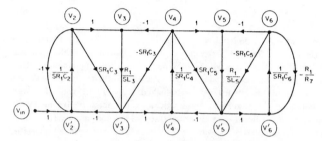

Fig. 4. Modified signal-flow graph for the ladder in Fig. 1.

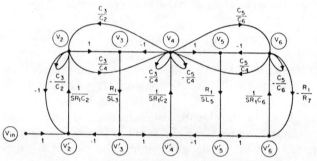

Fig. 5. Final version of signal-flow graph for the ladder in Fig. 1.

poles and two finite transmission zeros. The element values normalized to unity cutoff frequency and unity load resistors are given in [12] for the case: $n = 5$ (filter order), $\theta = 47°$ (modular angle), and $\rho = 10$ percent (reflection coefficient). The filter obtained has approximately 0.043-dB passband ripple and 34-dB minimum stopband rejection.

The circuit of Fig. 1 can be represented with a signal-flow graph as in Fig. 2 [13]. The vertices correspond to the ladder branch voltages and branch currents. The topolgy and the edge gains are such as to satisfy the KVL and KCL network equations. Notice that in this signal-flow graph all vertex variables have dimensions of a voltage, a fact accomplished by multiplying all current variables by R_1. This is a necessary condition since the active filter to be developed is intended to work with voltage signals.

In Fig. 2 the gain of any graph edge is either a constant, or it is proportional to $s^{\pm 1}$. By the proper combination of several signal-processing operations into single active RC building blocks, the filter will be implemented using only five operational amplifiers. This requires some modification of the signal-flow graph.

A useful signal-processing block which combines the functions of signal inversion, signal summation, and signal integration is the differential integrator. In practice it is realizable using resistors, capacitors, and a single operational amplifier; a fully balanced version is shown in Fig. 3. There are five subgraphs representing this block within the signal-flow graph of Fig. 2. They correspond to the five vertical edges whose gains are proportional to s^{-1}. These differential integrator blocks are connected into a "leapfrog" configuration just like in an all-pole filter.

The transmission zeros are generated by the two edges with gains proportional to s. Since these edges do not originate from differential integrator outputs they are not consistent with the "leapfrog" configuration and must be removed, for example, by splitting them, as shown in Fig. 4. In the new graph the vertices on the bottom have been renamed to reflect the fact that they represent voltage

variables. Also, a simplification was obtained by shifting the input edge to enter directly the vertex V_2'. The four new edges have gains representing the operation of differentiation; however, at the integrator outputs V_2, V_4, and V_6, their total effect is that of multiplication with constants. It can be verified by inspection that any differentiation is followed by an integration. Based on this observation, a final version of the graph is obtained (Fig. 5) that can be used to synthesize an active RC elliptic filter with five operational amplifiers. A corresponding graph has previously been developed by different means for switched-capacitor circuits [14].

C. Balanced Active RC Filter

The signal-flow graph of Fig. 5 is constructed from five subgraphs, two of which represent pure differential integrators, and the remaining three being combinations of multiple-input integrators with weighted summers. These latter subsystems can be readily implemented with classical active RC blocks whose fully balanced versions are shown in Fig. 6 (fully balanced circuits are needed for nonlinearity cancellation when the resistors are replaced by MOS transistors below [1], [2]). The function of integration is implemented with resistors and capacitors and that of "multiplication by a constant" is implemented only with capacitors.

Signals are added in the conventional manner at the input of the operational amplifiers. Since some of the input voltages in the circuits of Fig. 6 are available as output voltages of the same block, the corresponding inputs will be connected to the respective outputs and the resulting parallel capacitors will be lumped together.

The complete filter synthesized from the building blocks of Fig. 6 and two balanced differential integrators as in Fig. 3 is shown in Fig. 7. Because of the way the filter was derived, it has an identical transfer function with its ladder prototype. The element values for this circuit are shown in the second column of Table I after denormalizing [15] to a cutoff frequency of 3400 Hz and an impedance level of 4 MΩ. The impedance denormalization is seen to result in practical element values for monolithic implementation.

The last step in the design of the classical active RC filter is the optimization of its dynamic range, i.e., the relative adjustment of its element values such that all operational amplifier outputs attain the same maximum signal level (not necessarily at the same frequency) [15]. However, a design based on the largest dynamic range theoretically possible requires ratios of resistor values which are not fractions of small integers. Since the resistors will be implemented ultimately as series combinations of identically sized MOS transistors (in order to attain a high degree of matching), such a design is not practical. Thus, a close to optimum solution was used which resulted in resistor value ratios convenient to implement as explained below. For all practical purposes the loss of dynamic range due to this approximate optimization is insignificant, e.g., less than 1 dB.

A computer simulation of the filter response at all operational amplifier outputs shows that an acceptable equalization of levels is obtained if the signals at the first and third operational amplifiers outputs are decreased by a factor of 2 and if the signals at the second and fourth operational amplifiers outputs are decreased by a factor of 2.5. This is done by properly adjusting the elements in the feedback paths of the operational amplifiers as well as those driven by the respective outputs such that the filter time constants remain unchanged [15]. In addition, in order to have a dc gain of 0 dB, signals at all nodes internal to the filter must be increased by a factor of 2 with respect to the input signal. To accomplish this the two input resistors can be simply divided by two. The resulting active filter optimized for dynamic range is shown in Fig. 8. The ratios of the resistor values are seen to be easily realizable because all resistors can be considered to be composed of either four, five, or ten identical units. Each unit has the value $R_1/10$. The actual filter element values can be calculated using Fig. 8 and the last column of Table I.

It is not necessary to carry the design of the classical active RC circuit any further, for example, by compensating the nonidealities of the operational amplifiers. The fine tuning of the design will be done after the resistors are replaced with MOS transistors so that all practical nonidealities are treated at the same time.

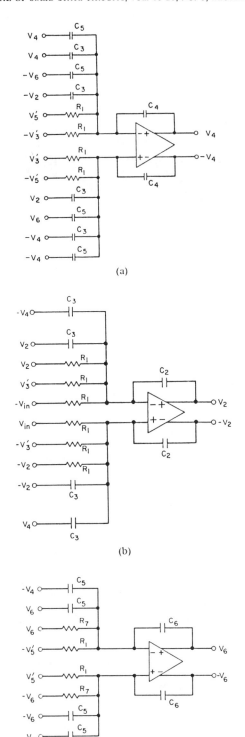

Fig. 6. (a) Fully balanced building block implementing a subgraph from Fig. 5. (b) Fully balanced building block implementing another subgraph from Fig. 5. (c) Fully balanced building block implementing a third subgraph from Fig. 5.

D. Resistor Replacement with MOS Transistors and Optimization

Each of the "unit resistors" mentioned above was next replaced by a corresponding "unit transistor." All unit transistor gates were connected to the same control voltage V_C. The channel-length-to-channel-width ratio (L/W) for

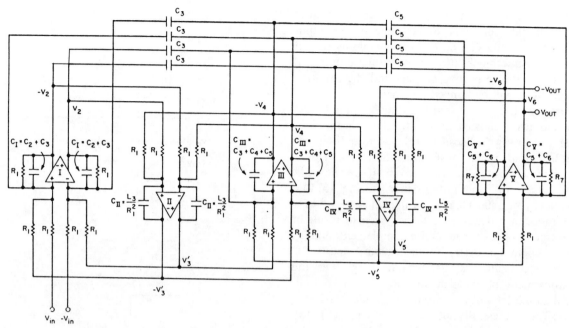

Fig. 7. Complete balanced active RC filter.

TABLE I
VALUES OF OPERATIONAL AMPLIFIER FEED-
BACK CAPACITORS IN FIGS. 7 AND 8

Element	Value for Fig. 7		Value for Fig. 8	
C_I	11.9697	pF	23.9394	pF
C_{II}	13.5949	pF	33.9873	pF
C_{III}	26.3272	pF	52.6544	pF
C_{IV}	9.1731	pF	22.9327	pF
C_V	13.8730	pF	13.8730	pF
C_3	2.34344	pF	2.34344	pF
C_6	7.45653	pF	7.45653	pF *
R_1	4	MΩ	4	MΩ
R_7	4	MΩ	4	MΩ

*The two capacitors marked by an asterisk in Fig. 8 were perturbed from the value shown above in order to optimize the design (see Section II-D).

each unit transistor was chosen such that all fabrication process and temperature variations can be eliminated by automatically adjusting V_C (Section III), with V_C attaining a given maximum value (in our case 5 V) under worst-case conditions. The proper L/W was found using ac computer simulations [16] and observing the −3-dB frequency of the filter. Using a gate width of 4 μm it was found that the proper unit transistor gate length L was 40 μm. (Actually, simulating a single integrator would suffice for determining L; also, an analytical procedure can be used in lieu of computer simulations if desired [17], [18]).

The next step in the design involved the simulation and compensation of the effects of op amp nonidealities and the distributed capacitance of the transistors. During simu-

lations the full circuit of the op amps was used [19]; each balanced op amp was implemented using two single output CMOS op amps [1], with somewhat reinforced output stages for driving the 35-kΩ p-tub resistors of the unity gain inverters within each balanced op amp. Since distributed channel capacitance effects are not normally accounted in CAD transistor models, we used a lumped approximation: Each 40-μm unit transistor was simulated as four 10-μm-long fictitious transistors with their channels in series, with a common gate connection and a common substrate connection. Of course, in this series combination the three internal nodes are artificial and thus in the model statements the corresponding junction and gate overlap capacitances were forced to zero. (Similarly, if the length of each fictitious device were short enough to cause "short-channel" effects in the simulations, one would have to eliminate such effects in the model statement.) A detailed simulation of the passband showed that the filter frequency response had a peaking of 0.4 dB near the cutoff point. This was partly because of the op amp's finite gain-bandwidth product (1 MHz), but mostly a result of the transistor channel distributed capacitance. Since this small peaking was a high-order effect, it was easy to eliminate it by a slight perturbation of the design. In order not to upset transistor matching, the perturbation was done on capacitor values (with both capacitors in a pair being perturbed identically, of course, in order to preserve symmetry and maintain the conditions for nonlinearity cancellation [1]). Simulations showed that the peaking could most effectively be eliminated by decreasing slightly the values of the capacitors between the outputs of the fifth amplifier and the inputs of the third amplifier, marked by an asterisk in Fig. 8. Similar design perturbations are commonly done in "LDI ladder" switched-capacitor filters and are very easy to perform. Finally, the filter was simulated under extreme

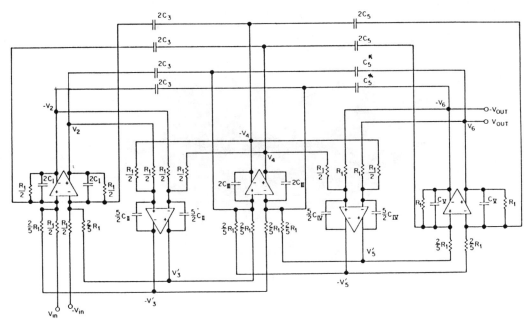

Fig. 8. Balanced filter scaled for optimum dynamic range. The capacitors marked with an asterisk have been slightly modified in order to optimize the design (see Section II-D).

process conditions and a temperature variation of 0–85°C to ensure that the above compensation was adequate in all cases. This was indeed found to be the case and the passband response was seen to vary by only 0.05 dB, so the design was ready for layout.[1]

III. PHASE-LOCKED LOOP CONTROL SYSTEM

A scheme for the automatic tuning of the filter developed in the previous section is illustrated in Fig. 9 [3]. The "master" voltage-controlled oscillator (VCO) is phase-locked to a reference clock and the "slave" filter uses the same control voltage that is applied to the oscillator. Therefore, the conventional phase-locked loop (PLL) shown in the figure tunes the VCO directly and the filter indirectly. Naturally, the operation of the scheme depends on the "master" capability to track the behavior of the "slave" for arbitrary fabrication process and temperature variations. This is guaranteed by implementing both circuits with the same technique, and placing their passive elements closely using well-known matching techniques.

The VCO is a second-order fully balanced active *RC* network. Ideally this state-variable topology realizes poles precisely on the *jω* axis. Since the predictable nonidealities of this circuit automatically ensure its instability, no special care has to be taken to produce oscillations. In order to limit the output signal level, thus preserving good spectral

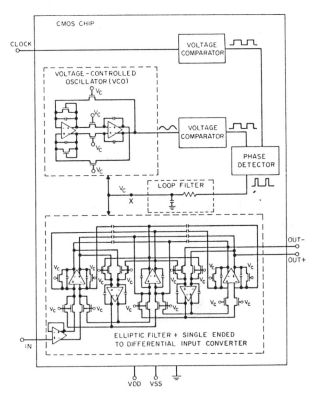

Fig. 9. Complete system containing a "master" VCO which is phase-locked to an external clock and the "slave" filter.

purity, two "diode-connected" transistors are added. If the oscillating frequency of the VCO were designed to be much larger than the filter cutoff point errors in the matching between the "master" and the "slave" would develop owing to unequal operational amplifier finite gain-bandwidth effects. On the other hand, the VCO nominal frequency cannot be set within the filter bandwidth because in practice the parasitic couplings between the "mas-

[1] Note that if one had chosen smaller capacitances and larger resistances in Table I, the capacitance effects would be excessive. Then, a perturbation as above would not be able to eliminate the peaking without significantly changing the frequency response at other points. In such a case one would simply have to increase the capacitances and decrease the resistances by the same factor, and try again. Choosing the gate width of the unit transistors as small as 4 μm helped keep the distributed capacitance effects small, and it did not affect matching as will be obvious from the measured chip performance below.

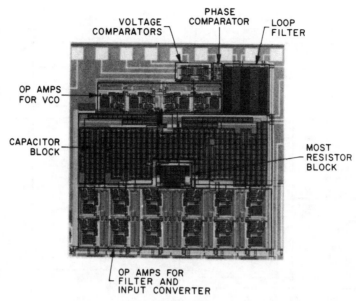

Fig. 10. Chip microphotograph.

ter" and the "slave" which are both on the same chip would result in clock feedthrough into the passband. A reasonable value for the VCO frequency is 6.5 kHz which is close enough to the filter cutoff point and still within its stopband. In fact, since this frequency is quite close to the second filter transmission zero it is reasonable to expect that any undesired clock feedthrough into the filter input will be attenuated.

In addition to the VCO the PLL contains a phase comparator, two voltage comparators, and a loop filter. The phase comparator is a simple EXCLUSIVE-OR gate whose output "digital" levels are adjusted such that the dc component of the resulting signal has the right values for the tuning of the elliptic filter. The purpose of the voltage-comparators is to guarantee that the inputs to the phase comparator are square waves of fixed amplitudes even when the signal level at the output of the VCO and/or the signal level of the clock change. This eliminates the PLL jitter due to such sporadic signal level changes. The loop filter is a single time-constant RC network. It must practically reject all ac components from the phase comparator output signal. An MOS transistor operated in nonsaturation followed by a grounded capacitor is the natural implementation in MOS technology. Notice that the inherent nonlinearities of this circuit are of no consequence since the operation of the PLL is not required to be linear. In an actual practical application the PLL would need additional capture circuitry to automatically guarantee an eventual lock state when the device is turned on. For the experimental purpose of this design, no such capture circuitry was used.

IV. CHIP IMPLEMENTATION

The above design was implemented in a standard 3.5-μm linear CMOS process [20] with capacitors fabricated between the gate polysilicon and a second polysilicon level. A photomicrograph of the chip is shown in Fig. 10. During the layout stage care was taken to place the various elements of the system in such a way as to accomplish proper matching between the filter components and also between the "master" and the "slave". Thus, all MOSFET resistors and all MOS capacitors of the chip were laid out in respective separate blocks to keep them bunched together as close as possible. However, contrary to the strategy in [1] where the resistors were interleaved, no such technique was applied in this case despite the channel length value of only 4 μm. The filter and the VCO resistors were simply placed parallel to each other simplifying the interconnections and generating a very tight layout. As it will be seen in the next section, this aggressive approach still guaranteed an excellent resistor matching resulting in an accurate filter response.

In all other respects the implementation of the filter followed standard practices for analog MOS circuits. For example, the capacitor block was laid out over a grounded p-tub to minimize the parasitic coupling to the substrate. Also, separate ground lines were used for the filter and the PLL to avoid potential injection of noise into the signal path. An additional balanced operational amplifier connected as a single-ended-to-differential converter [1] was also put on the chip whose active size was 4 mm².

V. EXPERIMENTAL RESULTS

All results to be presented were obtained with ± 5-V power supplies. Because of a mistake in handling a computer file the chip was fabricated using a process whose tolerances were much different from the ones assumed in the design of the filter (e.g., the minimum and maximum threshold voltages were approximately half a volt larger than assumed and the nominal channel width was only 2 μm instead of the assumed 4 μm ± 0.5 μm). These errors were easily compensated during testing by breaking the

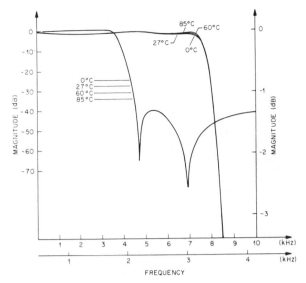

Fig. 11. Measured filter frequency response with PLL connected. Axis for passband detail curve shown on the right and on the bottom.

Fig. 12. Simple way to increase the filter signal handling capability by trading off some of its dynamic range.

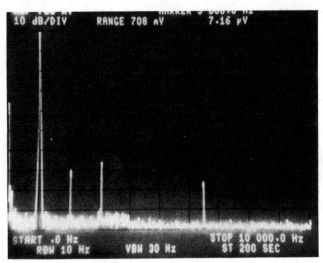

Fig. 13. Single-ended output spectrum for the system of Fig. 12 when the signal processed is 4 Vp-p differentially measured (horizontal 1 kHz/division; vertical 10 dB/division).

connection at point "X" in Fig. 9 and inserting a 1.1-V battery (see footnote at the end of this section). With this the circuit exhibited the performance expected from the intended process. Also, an external resistor and capacitor were substituted for the loop filter in Fig. 9 which was open-circuited because of a mask error. The filter frequency response for various operating temperatures is shown in Fig. 11. The measured cutoff point for each chip was controlled to better than 0.1 percent as the temperature was varied from 0° to 85°C (if the control system is disconnected and a fixed voltage is applied to the filter control terminal a variation of approximately 40 percent in the cutoff frequency is observed for this temperature range!). The absolute accuracy of the cutoff frequency was measured to vary from chip to chip according to a Gaussian distribution with a standard deviation of 0.5 percent. A part of this error is attributed to the device mismatches between the VCO and the filter and another part is attributed to the nonidealities in the PLL, e.g., nonlinearities in the VCO. It may be possible to make this error even smaller by using a voltage-controlled filter (VCF) in lieu of a VCO [4], [9].

The input of the filter was grounded and the differential output C-massage weighted noise was measured to be 42-μV rms. The differential output signal level at room temperature for 1-percent total harmonic distortion (THD) was 11.7 Vp-p thus accomplishing a dynamic range of approximately 100 dB. The THD for a 1-kHz input signal and a differential output of 4 Vp-p was −51 dB. This figure could be improved by trading off some of the dynamic range. To demonstrate this, the filter was tested in the setup of Fig. 12 which can be implemented on-chip

(e.g., by using poly resistors). For the purposes of the test, the 1/3 attenuator was a simple resistive voltage divider and the ×3 amplifier was an integrated fully-balanced CMOS circuit using p-tub resistors from a different test chip. The resulting distortion for the same 1-kHz input signal and 4 Vp-p differential output was better than −64 dB. The corresponding spectrum for the single-ended output is shown in Fig. 13. The differential output noise of the system in Fig. 12 was 140-μV rms. The clock feedthrough seen in Fig. 13 at 6.5 kHz is 110-μV rms.[2]

VI. Conclusions

This paper has described the design and the performance of a precision monolithic active RC filter based on the technique of fully balanced networks. The circuit presented implements a fifth-order low-pass elliptic transfer function with specifications similar to those of the PCM channel bank filters. The CMOS chip contains a PLL control system which tunes the filter continuously to a relative precision of better than 0.1 percent for temperature variations of 85°C and to an absolute precision of 0.5 percent (standard deviation). The measured dynamic range of the filter is approximatively 100 dB.

The design of the system was based on classical active RC networks. The additional considerations required by this monolithic implementation took into account the effects of the MOS transistor parasitic capacitances and the effects of process and temperature variation compensation. With the exception of transistor matching considerations the chip design followed standard MOS analog circuit practices.

---

[2]A new chip was fabricated without the error mentioned earlier, thus eliminating the need for the external battery. The main filter exhibited a THD of −40 dB at 8.4 Vp-p differential input. The complete integrated system of Fig. 12 exhibited a THD of −40 dB at 15.7 Vp-p differential input; a THD of −65 dB was measured at 5 Vp-p differential input.

REFERENCES

[1] M. Banu and Y. Tsividis, "Fully integrated active *RC* filters in MOS technology," *IEEE J. Solid-State Circuits*, vol. SC-18, pp. 664–651, Dec. 1983.

[2] Y. Tsividis, M. Banu, and J. Khoury, "Continuous-time MOSFET-C filters in VLSI," to be published in *IEEE J. Solid-State Circuits*, vol. SC-21, no. 1, Feb. 1986; also to be published in *IEEE Trans. Circuits Syst.*, vol. CAS-33, no. 2, Feb. 1986.

[3] M. Banu and Y. Tsividis, "On chip automatic tuning for a CMOS continuous-time filter," in *Dig. of Tech. Papers*, IEEE International solid-state circuits conference, New York, Feb. 1985.

[4] J. R. Canning and G. A. Wilson, "Frequency discriminator circuit arrangement," U.K. pat. 1 421 093, January 1976.

[5] J. R. Brand, R. Schaumann, and E. M. Skei, "Temperature-stabilized active *R* bandpass filters," in *Proc. 20th Midwest Symp. Circuits Syst.*, Aug. 1977, pp. 295–300.

[6] K. Radhakrishna Rao, V. Sethuraman, and P. K. Neelakantan, "A novel 'follow the master' filter," *Proc. IEEE*, vol. 65, no. 12, pp. 1725–1726, Dec. 1977.

[7] K. S. Tan and P. R. Gray, "Fully integrated analog filters using bipolar-JFET technology," *IEEE J. Solid-State Circuits*, vol. SC-13, pp. 814–821, Dec. 1978.

[8] K. W. Moulding, J. R. Quartly, P. J. Rankin, R. S. Thompson, and G. A. Wilson, "Gyrator video filter IC with automatic tuning," *IEEE J. Solid-State Circuits*, vol. SC-15, pp. 963–968, Dec. 1980.

[9] H. Khorramabadi and P. R. Gray, "High-frequency CMOS continuous-time filters," *IEEE J. Solid-State Circuits*, vol. SC-19, pp. 939–948, Dec. 1984.

[10] Y. Tsividis, "Self-tuned filters," *IEE Electron. Lett.*, vol. 17, no. 12, pp. 406–407, June 1981.

[11] J. O. Voorman, W. H. A. Bruls, and P. J. Barth, "Integration of analog filters in a bipolar process," *IEEE J. Solid-State Circuits*, vol. SC-17, pp. 713–722, Aug. 1982.

[12] A. I. Zverev, *Handbook of Filter Synthesis*. New York: Wiley, 1967, p. 214.

[13] O. Wing, "Ladder network analysis by signal-glow graph: application to analogue computer programming," *IRE Trans. Circuit Theory*, pp. 289–294, Dec. 1956.

[14] G. M. Jacobs, D. J. Allstot, R. W. Brodersen, and P. R. Gray, "Design techniques for MOS switched capacitor ladder filters," *IEEE Trans. Circuits Syst.*, vol. CAS-25, pp. 1014–1021, Dec. 1978.

[15] A. S. Sedra and P. O. Brackett, *Filter Theory and Design: Active and Passive*. Portland, OR: Matrix Publishers, 1978.

[16] L. W. Nagel, "ADVICE for circuit simulation," presented at 1980 ISCAS Conf. TX., Apr. 1980.

[17] M. Banu, Y. Tsividis, and I. Papananos, "Adequacy of voltage control for compensating process and temperature variations in MOS active *RC* filters," in *Proc. IEEE Int. Symp. Circuits Syst.*, May 1984, pp. 936–939.

[18] M. Banu and Y. Tsividis, "Detailed analysis of nonidealities in MOS fully integrated active *RC* filters based on balanced networks," in *IEE Proc.*, vol. 131, pt.G, no. 5, pp. 190–196, Oct. 1984.

[19] V. R. Saari, "Low power, high drive CMOS operational amplifiers," *IEEE J. Solid-State Circuits*, vol. SC-18, pp. 121–127, Feb. 1983.

[20] L. C. Parillo, R. S. Payne, R. E. Davis, G. W. Reutlinger, and R. L. Field, "Twin-tub CMOS–A technology for VLSI circuits," in *IEDM Tech. Dig*, Dec. 1980, pp. 752–755.

Detailed Analysis of Nonidealities in MOS Fully Integrated Active *RC* Filters Based on Balanced Networks

M. BANU AND Y. TSIVIDIS

Abstract—The paper gives a detailed account of the effects produced by practical nonidealities in fully integrated balanced *RC* filters, which are implemented using MOS transistors as replacements for resistors (MOSFET-capacitor continuous-time filters). It is found that the operation of such filters is insensitive to all typical nonidealities, with the exception of the intrinsic distributed parasitic capacitances of the transistors; there are cases when the latter have to be taken into account in the filter design.

1. INTRODUCTION

A new technique has recently been introduced for the implementation of fully integrated active *RC* filters in MOS technology [1–3]. The basic idea consists of replacing the resistors in a classical *RC* network with linearised MOS transistors, which effectively operate as voltage-controlled linear resistors. The resulting circuit contains only MOS transistors and capacitors as passive elements, and can therefore be fabricated in MOS technology, yielding an integrated tunable filter with a wide dynamic range. Such filters, hereafter referred to as MOSFET-capacitor continuous-time filters, can be stabilised against fabrication process tolerances and temperature variations, using the "master and slave" or the "self-tuning" techniques as described elsewhere [4–10]. References 2 and 3 introduce some general theoretical ideas on MOSFET-characteristic linearisation, which include the technique of balanced networks; experimental results regarding the latter are given in Reference 1.

In this paper we will show that typical practical

Paper 3365G (E10), first received 21st December 1983 and in revised form 5th June 1984.

The authors are with AT & T Bell Laboratories, Murray Hill, NJ 07974, USA: Prof. Tsividis is also with the Department of Electrical Engineering, Columbia University, New York, NY 10027, USA.

nonidealities do not seriously affect the performance of the proposed balanced filters. To this end, we will present a detailed analysis of these circuits, taking into account the practical errors due to device mismatches, nonideal operational amplifiers and parasitic capacitances. A balanced *RC* integrator will be used throughout as the prime example. Firstly, a Taylor expansion of the transistor characteristic is introduced, which indicates that the nonlinearity of the device is primarily given by the second-order term in the expansion. Then, the principle of balanced networks is reviewed, and the tolerance of the linearised effective resistor is calculated as a function of transistor matching. The linearity of a balanced integrator is estimated by calculating the harmonic distortion at the output of the circuit when a sinusoidal input signal is applied. Finally, the effects of parasitic capacitances and the noise performance are discussed.

2. MOSFET CHARACTERISTICS IN NONSATURATION REPRESENTED AS A TAYLOR SERIES

In the ensuing analysis, it will be useful to represent the MOSFET characteristics as a Taylor series in terms of the signals present on the source and drain of the device. Fig. 1 shows a MOS transistor with the source, drain, gate and substrate connected to the respective potentials V_S, V_D, V_G and V_B, all defined with respect to ground. If the drain and source voltages V_D and V_S consist of a DC value V_Q in addition to the actual signals V_1 and V_2, we have

$$V_D = V_Q + V_1 \qquad (1a)$$

$$V_S = V_Q + V_2 \qquad (1b)$$

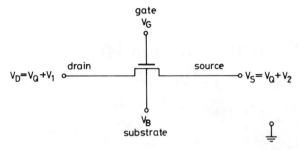

Fig. 1. Definition of terminal voltages applied to a MOS-FET.

For conventional long-channel transistors, the value of this current in nonsaturation (consider an n-channel device) is given [11] by

$$I_D = 2K(V_G - V_B - V_{FB} - \phi_B)(V_1 - V_2)$$
$$- 2K(\tfrac{1}{2})\big[(V_1 + V_Q - V_B)^2 - (V_2 + V_Q - V_B)^2\big]$$
$$- 2K(\tfrac{2}{3})\gamma\big[(V_1 + V_Q - V_B + \phi_B)^{3/2}$$
$$- (V_2 + V_Q - V_B + \phi_B)^{3/2}\big] \qquad (2a)$$

with

$$\gamma = \frac{1}{C'_{ox}}(2qN_A\varepsilon_S)^{1/2} \qquad (2b)$$

$$K = \frac{1}{2}\mu C'_{ox}\frac{W}{L} \qquad (2c)$$

where W and L are the channel width and length, μ is the carrier effective mobility in the channel, V_{FB} is the flatband voltage, N_A is the substrate doping concentration, C'_{ox} is the gate oxide capacitance per unit area, ε_S is the silicon dielectric constant, q is the electron charge and ϕ_B is the approximate surface potential in strong inversion for zero backgate bias; ϕ_B is commonly taken to be twice the Fermi potential, but is actually several (kT/q) higher than this value [12]. Expanding the last two terms in eqn. 2a in a Taylor series with respect to V_1 and V_2, and rearranging the other terms, one can obtain [13]

$$I_D = K\big[a_1(V_1 - V_2) + a_2(V_1^2 - V_2^2)$$
$$+ a_3(V_1^3 - V_2^3) + \cdots\big] \qquad (3)$$

with

$$a_1 = 2(V_G - V_Q - V_T) \qquad (4a)$$

$$a_2 = -\big[1 + \tfrac{1}{2}\gamma(V_Q - V_B + \phi_B)^{-(1/2)}\big] \qquad (4b)$$

$$a_n = \gamma A(n)(V_Q - V_B + \phi_B)^{-[(2n-3)/2]} \qquad \text{for } n \geq 3$$
$$(4c)$$

where $A(3) = -(1/12)$, $A(4) = +(1/32)$, $A(5) = -(1/64)$ etc., and V_T is the threshold voltage, corresponding to a "backgate" bias of $V_Q - V_B$ [11], as follows:

$$V_T = V_{FB} + \phi_B + \gamma(V_Q - V_B + \phi_B)^{1/2} \qquad (5)$$

The coefficient Ka_1 in eqn. 3 is the small-signal conductance of the transistor channel. As the latter can be varied with the quantity $(V_G - V_Q)$, a control voltage V_C will be defined as

$$V_C = V_G - V_Q \qquad (6)$$

With this notation, the channel small-signal resistance R (at $V_S = V_S = V_Q$) becomes

$$R = \frac{1}{2K(V_C - V_T)} \qquad (7)$$

Note that if the reference ground potential is chosen to be the same as V_Q, then V_C becomes the actual gate voltage of the transistor; such a convention was used in Reference 1.

Equation 3 can be written in a concise form if a function $f(V)$ is defined as follows:

$$f(V) = a_1 V + a_2 V^2 + a_3 V^3 + \cdots \qquad (8)$$

Using eqn. 8, eqn. 3 becomes

$$I_D = K[f(V_1) - f(V_2)] \qquad (9)$$

It must be pointed out that for long-channel transistors, eqns. 3 and 9, considered independently of the Taylor expansion of Equation 2a, are valid under more general conditions than those of eqn. 2a; for example, with the proper values for the coefficients a_i, eqn. 3 is valid even if the mobility μ depends on the gate and substrate voltages, and even if the substrate doping has a nonzero gradient transversal to the channel, situations not considered in eqns. 2a.

It was mentioned in Reference 1 that most of the contributions to the drain current I_D in eqn. 3 come from the first and second-order terms, higher-order ones being practically negligible (e.g., see Fig. 1 in Reference 1). All the MOSFET linearisation techniques introduced previously [1–3] are based on the cancellation of the even-order terms in eqn. 3, the remaining dependence of I_D on $(V_1 - V_2)$ being practically linear.

106

3. Fully Balanced MOS Circuits Implementing Equivalent Resistors

The principle of MOSFET-characteristic linearisation using fully balanced networks is now briefly reviewed. Fig. 2a shows an integrator using two identical transistors, two identical capacitors and one ideal operational amplifier (infinite gain and zero input offset) with balanced outputs. The output balancing voltage is V_{QO}. The inputs are assumed to be balanced with respect to a voltage V_Q; the relation of this notation to eqn. 1 will become clear shortly. Owing to the infinite gain of the operational amplifier, the potentials at its two inputs are identical. In general, the latter can be expressed as a time varying voltage V_x, in addition to the input balancing voltage V_Q. Note that V_x is different from zero, because the transistor characteristics are nonlinear. If I_1 and I_2 are the currents flowing through the two transistors, the circuit equations are

$$V_{QO} + V_{out} = -\frac{1}{C}\int_{-\infty}^{t} I_1 \, dt' + V_Q + V_x \quad (10a)$$

and

$$V_{QO} - V_{out} = -\frac{1}{C}\int_{-\infty}^{t} I_2 \, dt' + V_Q + V_x \quad (10b)$$

Subtracting eqn. 10b from 10a and dividing by two, we obtain

$$V_{out} = -\frac{1}{2C}\int_{-\infty}^{t} (I_1 - I_2) \, dt' \quad (11)$$

Note that the terminal potentials of each transistor in Fig. 2a are identical in form to the terminal potentials of the MOSFET in Fig. 1, with V_Q the integrator input balancing voltage; this justifies the notation V_Q. Therefore, the results from Section 2 (eqns. 3 and 9) can be applied to express the two currents in eqn. 11 in terms of the input voltage V_{in} and the voltage V_x. From eqns. 4a and 6–9, we have

$$I_1 - I_2 = K[f(V_{in}) - f(V_x)] - K[f(-V_{in}) - f(V_x)]$$
$$(12a)$$

$$= K[f(V_{in}) - f(-V_{in})] \quad (12b)$$

$$\cong 2Ka_1 V_{in} \quad (12c)$$

$$\cong \frac{2}{R} V_{in} \quad (12d)$$

where the odd-order nonlinearities have been neglected, due to their very small magnitude [1]. From

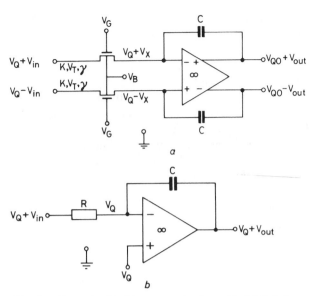

Fig. 2. Alternative ideal integrator circuits. a Ideal fully balanced integrator. b Ideal classical nonbalanced integrator.

eqns. 11 and 12d we obtain

$$V_{out} \cong -\frac{1}{RC}\int_{-\infty}^{t} V_{in} \, dt' \quad (13)$$

It is thus seen that the balanced integrator of Fig. 2a is functionally identical in practice with the classical linear RC implementation of Fig. 2b (except for the output DC offset $\Delta V_Q = V_{QO} - V_Q$); based on this equivalence, we define an effective resistance for the balanced integrator given by eqn. 7. Notice also that the technique works independently of the actual values taken by the voltage V_x. As mentioned previously, the latter is different from zero, in general, due to the nonlinear character of the individual transistor characteristics. It can be calculated that V_x is typically no larger than a fifth of the input voltage.

When several balanced integrators are used in a filter, the matching of equivalent resistances from stage to stage will not be perfect, owing to errors in the matching of V_T, K and V_Q (e.g., if the circuit of Fig. 2a drives another similar stage, the input balancing voltage of the latter will be V_{QO}). Using eqns. 6 and 7, and if all transistors in the filter are connected to the same gate voltage, it is easy to calculate the tolerance of the equivalent linearised resistors to be

$$\frac{\Delta R}{R} \cong \frac{|\Delta K|}{K} + \frac{|\Delta V_Q| + |\Delta V_T|}{V_C - V_T} \quad (14)$$

This equation determines the sensitivity requirements of the filters to be implemented given a particular fabrication process. For example, if ΔV_Q and ΔV_T are 3 mV, ΔK is 0.1% of K, and $V_C - V_T$ = 3 V, then the resistance tolerance is 0.3%. This number is consistent with the actual matching of the transistor pairs used in Reference 1 (each pair consists of two adjacent devices with $W = 4$ μm and $L = 400$ μm), which was measured to be typically 0.2% for $V_G - V_T = 3$ V.

The cancellation of device nonlinearities as described in this Section is valid in the ideal case, when aspects such as device mismatches, amplifier offset voltages etc., are disregarded. Next, an analysis of the effects introduced by practical error sources in the linearity of the fully balanced networks will be discussed.

4. LINEARITY OF THE FULLY BALANCED INTEGRATOR IN THE PRESENCE OF NONIDEALITIES

Fig. 3 shows a fully balanced integrator operating in the presence of the major nonideal conditions that are believed to be dominant in a practical circuit. The following error sources have been included:

(a) The two inputs and the two outputs are balanced with respect to different voltages V_Q and V_{QO}, and differ in magnitude by the factors α and β, respectively.

(b) The transistors are considered mismatched in the parameters K, V_T and γ.

(c) The capacitors have different values C_1 and C_2

(d) The operational amplifier has a nonzero input offset voltage V_{os} and a finite voltage gain A_v.

The ideal situation assumed previously corresponds to $K_1 = K_2$, $V_{T1} = V_{T2}$, $\gamma_1 = \gamma_2$, $C_1 = C_2$, $\alpha = 1$, $\beta = 1$, $V_{os} = 0$, and $A_v = \infty$. Because of the finite value of A_v, the inputs of the operational amplifier, after excluding the offset, are at different potentials V_x and V_y, just as before these potentials are considered in reference to V_Q. The purpose of the following considerations is to find the transfer characteristic of the circuit of Fig. 3.

If I_1 and I_2 are the currents flowing through the two parallel paths containing the transistors, the network equations can be written as

$$V_{QO} + V_{out} = -\frac{1}{C_1}\int_{-\infty}^{t} I_1\, dt' + V_Q + V_x + V_{os}$$

$$\tag{15a}$$

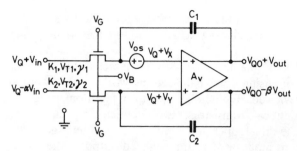

Fig. 3. Fully balanced integrator with major nonideal conditions.

$$V_{QO} - \beta V_{out} = -\frac{1}{C_2}\int_{-\infty}^{t} I_2\, dt' + V_Q + V_y \quad (15b)$$

$$V_{out} = (V_x - V_y)A_v \quad (15c)$$

Subtracting eqn. 15b from 15a, dividing by $(\beta + 1)$ and using eqn. 15c, we obtain

$$V_{out} = \frac{A_v}{(1 + \beta)A_v - 1}$$

$$\cdot \left[-\int_{-\infty}^{t} \left(\frac{I_1}{C_1} - \frac{I_2}{C_2} \right) dt' + V_{os} \right] \quad (16)$$

The currents I_1 and I_2 depend on V_{in}, according to eqn. 9, as follows:

$$I_1 = K_1 f_1(V_{in}) - K_1 f_1(V_x + V_{os}) \quad (17a)$$

$$I_2 = K_2 f_2(-\alpha V_{in}) - K_2 f_2(V_y) \quad (17b)$$

In these equations, the functions f_1 and f_2 describing the characteristics of the two transistors, will (see eqn. 8) be

$$f_1(V) = a_1 V + a_2 V^2 + a_3 V^3 + a_4 V^4 + \cdots \quad (18a)$$

$$f_2(V) = b_1 V + b_2 V^2 + b_3 V^3 + b_4 V^4 + \cdots \quad (18b)$$

where a_i and b_i are given in terms of the respective values of K, V_T and γ, and the biasing conditions are as shown in eqn. 4 (both transistors in Fig. 3 have the same V_G, V_Q and V_B). For perfect transistor matching, $a_i = b_i$ and $f_1 = f_2$. Defining a parameter η as

$$\eta = \left(\frac{K_2}{K_1} \right)\left(\frac{C_1}{C_2} \right) \quad (19)$$

and applying eqn. 17, one has

$$V_{out} = \frac{A_v}{(1 + \beta)A_v - 1}$$

$$\cdot \left\{ -\frac{K_1}{C_1} \int_{-\infty}^{t} [f_1(V_{in}) - \eta f_2(-\alpha V_{in})]\, dt' \right.$$

$$\left. + \frac{K_1}{C_1} \int_{-\infty}^{t} [f_1(V_x + V_{os}) - \eta f_2(V_y)]\, dt' + V_{os} \right\}$$

$$(20)$$

In the ideal case, eqn. 20 gives the output voltage in terms of the input voltage explicitly, because the second integral in the right-hand side is then null. This is not true when nonidealities are present, which makes the exact analysis of this case very complicated. However, for practical values of the nonidealities in Fig. 3, the second integrand in eqn. 20 can be neglected, except for a DC component (this can be seen if the two terms are expanded into series in terms of V_x and V_y [13]). The effect on the output of this DC term will be the addition of a ramp voltage, which would saturate a stand-alone integrator. In filters, however, there is negative feedback that cancels this undesired effect.

Introducing the notation

$$\tau = \frac{C_1}{K_1 a_1} \qquad (21)$$

where τ is the inverse of the integrator gain factor, neglecting the second integral in eqn. 20 and expanding the terms under the first integral according to eqn. 18, we obtain

$$V_{out} \simeq \frac{A_v}{(1 + \beta)A_v - 1} V_{os} - \frac{A_v}{(1 + \beta)A_v - 1} \frac{1}{\tau}$$

$$\cdot \left[\left(1 + \eta\alpha \frac{b_1}{a_1} \right) \int_{-\infty}^{t} V_{in}\, dt' + \frac{a_2}{a_1} \left(1 - \eta\alpha^2 \frac{b_2}{a_2} \right) \right.$$

$$\cdot \int_{-\infty}^{t} V_{in}^2\, dt' + \frac{a_3}{a_1} \left(1 + \eta\alpha^3 \frac{b_3}{a_3} \right) \int_{-\infty}^{t} V_{in}^3\, dt'$$

$$\left. + \frac{a_4}{a_1} \left(1 - \eta\alpha^4 \frac{b_4}{a_4} \right) \int_{-\infty}^{t} V_{in}^4\, dt' + \cdots \right] \quad (22)$$

This result gives an approximate solution for the output voltage of the nonideal integrator; note that all parameters describing the practical error sources appear explicitly in eqn. 22.

The following ratios of the coefficients a_i and b_i appearing in eqn. 22 can be calculated using the results of Section 2 (see eqn. 4):

$$a_1 = 2(V_C - V_{T1}) \qquad (23a)$$

$$b_1 = 2(V_C - V_{T2}) \qquad (23b)$$

$$\frac{b_1}{a_1} = 1 + \frac{\Delta V_T}{V_C - V_{T1}} \qquad (23c)$$

$$\frac{b_2}{a_2} = \frac{1 + \frac{1}{2}\gamma_2(V_Q - V_B + \Phi_{B2})^{-(1/2)}}{1 + \frac{1}{2}\gamma_1(V_Q - V_B + \Phi_{B1})^{-(1/2)}} \qquad (23d)$$

$$\frac{b_3}{a_3} = \frac{b_4}{a_4} = \cdots \simeq \frac{\gamma_2}{\gamma_1} = \left(\frac{N_{A2}}{N_{A1}} \right)^{1/2} \frac{d_{ox2}}{d_{ox1}} \qquad (23e)$$

$$\frac{a_2}{a_1} = -\frac{\frac{1}{2} + \frac{1}{4}\gamma_1(V_Q - V_B + \Phi_{B1})^{-(1/2)}}{V_C - V_{T1}} \qquad (23f)$$

$$\frac{a_3}{a_1} = \frac{1}{2}A(3)\gamma_1 \frac{(V_Q - V_B + \Phi_{B1})^{-(3/2)}}{V_C - V_{T1}} \qquad (23g)$$

$$\frac{a_4}{a_1} = -\frac{1}{2}A(4)\gamma_1 \frac{(V_Q - V_B + \Phi_{B1})^{-(5/2)}}{V_C - V_{T1}} \qquad (23h)$$

where ΔV_T is the difference between the threshold voltages of the two transistors, and d_{ox1} and d_{ox2} are the respective gate oxide thicknesses. In eqn. 23e we neglect the small variation between Φ_{B1} and Φ_{B2}. In all numerical calculations to be done in this Section, the following values will be used:

$$V_C - V_{T1} = 1.5\ \text{V} \qquad (24a)$$

$$\gamma = 1\ \text{V}^{1/2} \pm 0.2\% \qquad (24b)$$

$$V_Q - V_B + \Phi_B = 5.7\ \text{V} \pm 0.01\% \qquad (24c)$$

$$\Delta V_T = 5\ \text{mV} \qquad (24d)$$

The tolerance of γ above has been estimated as a worst case by assuming that this variation alone is responsible for the nonzero value of ΔV_T. Similarly, the tolerance in eqn. 24c (which is due to variations in Φ_B) was calculated by assuming that the variation in γ is due only to the parameter N_A, and that Φ_B is twice the Fermi potential. Using eqn. 24, one can estimate that

$$\frac{b_1}{a_1} = 1 \pm 0.34\% \qquad (25a)$$

$$\frac{b_2}{a_2} = 1 \pm 0.04\% \qquad (25b)$$

$$\frac{b_3}{a_3} = \frac{b_4}{a_4} = \cdots = 1 \pm 0.2\% \qquad (25c)$$

$$\frac{a_2}{a_1} = -0.4 \text{ V}^{-1} \qquad (25d)$$

$$\frac{a_3}{a_1} = 0.002 \text{ V}^{-2} \qquad (25e)$$

$$\frac{a_4}{a_1} = -0.00014 \text{ V}^{-3} \qquad (25f)$$

Note that in the ideal case ($\alpha = 1$, $\eta = 1$, $a_i = b_i$) the even-order terms in eqn. 22 vanish, as expected. In practice, however, the nonideal circuit of Fig. 3 will exhibit residual even-order nonlinearities, in addition to the odd-order ones shown by Eqn. 22, due to mismatches. Considering the actual values of (a_i/a_1) given by eqn. 25, it appears that practically all nonlinearities in the right-hand side of eqn. 22 are given by the second- and third-order terms. Next, the result of eqn. 22 will be used to analyse the manner in which the linearity of the fully balanced scheme is affected by practical nonidealities. In general, the circuit of Fig. 3, considered as part of a larger system, drives other similar circuits; these will be referred to as the "driven" stages.

Inspecting eqn. 22, one can see that the transfer characteristic is independent of V_{QO}. Therefore, the behavior of the circuit remains essentially unchanged for various values of the output balancing voltage. However, it is reminded that a V_{QO} not equal to V_Q creates errors in the equivalent integrating resistance matching between this stage and the driven stages (see Section 3).

As seen in eqn. 22, the amplifier input offset voltage V_{os} produces a DC component in the output signal, but the linearity of the current and following stages is not affected by this nonideality.

The accuracy of output balancing (as described by β) does not influence at all the linearity of the fully balanced circuit, because the only place where β enters in eqn. 22 is as a scaling factor. It should be clear, though, that a nonideal β value affects the driven stages, in the same way as a nonideal α value affects the driving circuit.

The amplifier gain A_v and the circuit gain factor τ^{-1} also do not influence the linearity of the circuit. This fact is seen from eqn. 22, where the only contributions of A_v and τ are in the scaling factor, assuming that the value of A_v is not too small to compromise the approximation made to derive eqn. 22.

Taking into account the previous observations, it results that the nonlinearity in eqn. 22 is determined solely by the values of the parameters η, α, and by ratios of the parameters a_1 and b_i. One way to

characterise this nonlinearity is to calculate the total harmonic distortion (THD) at the output if a signal $V_{in} = V_{in0} \sin(\omega t)$ is applied at the input. Neglecting the small terms that are generated when the function $\sin(\omega t)$ is raised to different powers and integrated, it is easy to estimate the second- and third-harmonic distortion, D_2 and D_3, as follows:

$$D_2 \simeq \frac{1}{4} \frac{a_2}{a_1} \frac{\left(1 - \eta \alpha^2 \frac{b_2}{a_2}\right)}{1 + \eta \alpha \frac{b_1}{a_1}} V_{in0} \qquad (26a)$$

$$\simeq \frac{1}{8} \frac{a_2}{a_1} \left(1 - \eta \alpha^2 \frac{b_2}{a_2}\right) V_{in0} \qquad (26b)$$

$$D_3 \simeq \frac{1}{12} \frac{a_3}{a_1} \frac{1 + \eta \alpha^3 \frac{b_3}{a_3}}{1 + \eta \alpha \frac{b_1}{a_1}} V_{in0}^2 \qquad (26c)$$

$$\simeq \frac{1}{12} \frac{a_3}{a_1} V_{in0}^2 \qquad (26d)$$

Note that D_3 is practically constant even for relatively large variations of η and α, and always has a nonzero value (only even-order harmonics are cancelled). Therefore, the presence of the third-order harmonic distortion gives a fundamental limitation of the technique, representing the minimum theoretically possible harmonic distortion for a given fabrication process and biasing conditions (see eqn. 25e). Using eqn. 25e and $V_{in0} = 1.25$ V (the value of 1.25 V is the maximum signal allowed to keep transistors in nonsaturation for the numerical example given above), the value of D_3 is -72 dB.

The second-harmonic distortion is much more sensitive to the matching of the transistors and to the accuracy of input signal balancing. In the ideal case ($\eta = 1$, $\alpha = 1$), D_2 is zero, as expected. The following practical values will be used in the calculation of worst-case D_2:

(a) $\alpha = 1 \pm 1\%$ ($\pm 1\%$ accuracy in input signal balancing)

(b) $\eta = 1 \pm 2\%$ ($\pm 2\%$ matching of η consisting of approximately $\pm 1\%$ matching of transistor K parameter and $\pm 1\%$ capacitor matching: see definition of η in eqn. 19). Considering the worst-case combination of the previous parameters and the values given by eqn. 25, the second-order harmonic distortion calculated using eqn. 26b and $V_{in0} = 1.25$ V is -52 dB. Clearly, then, the main sources of nonlinearities in the proposed circuits come from the practical device and balancing mismatches, rather than from the fundamental limitation of the principle (see discussion in connection with eqn. 26*b*). Therefore, the more accurately the MOS transistors are matched, and the more accurately the signals are balanced, the better the performance of the circuits. For example, if $\alpha = 1 \pm 0.5\%$ and $\eta = 1 \pm 0.5\%$, the worst case THD is less than -60 dB for the same input level. Even better performance seems to be achievable in view of our measured resistor matching of 0.2%.

5. PARASITICS

Equations 3 and 4 were derived from MOSFET static characteristics, and therefore they describe only the DC behavior of the device. In this Section, the effects of transistor parasitic capacitances on the performance of the fully balanced integrator will be discussed.

The capacitances associated with the MOSFET are divided into extrinsic and intrinsic ones. The former are due to the drain and source depletion regions and to the gate-diffusion overlap. In the second category enter the distributed capacitances from the inverted channel to the substrate and the gate.

Fig. 4 illustrates a fully balanced integrator where the extrinsic parasitic capacitances of the transistors are explicitly shown. They are lumped into four elements, connected between the sources or the drains of the transistors and ground. The two parasitic capacitors at the input of the integrator have a negligible influence on the operation of the stage, because they are connected to low-impedance nodes; in practice, the input nodes are driven by good voltage sources (operational amplifiers designed to drive resistors). Furthermore, the other two extrinsic parasitic capacitors practically do not interfere with the operation of the scheme. As they are identical (identical transistors have identical parasitics) and they are connected to identical potentials (ground on one terminal and operational amplifier common-mode input voltage on the other terminal), their currents are equal, even if the capacitors are nonlinear. The combined error in the output of the integrator produced by these equal parasitic currents is zero. This is easy to see because the fully balanced circuits inherently reject common-mode input signals. Strictly speaking, any mismatches between the previous capacitors would introduce an error in the output of the circuit. However, this error is usually completely negligible, because the integrating capac-

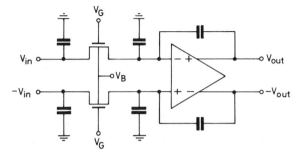

Fig. 4. Fully balanced integrator with transistor extrinsic parasitic capacitances.

itors are much larger than the parasitics, and the value of the common-mode voltage at the input of the operational amplifier is smaller than the integrator input voltage. Therefore, it is seen that the fully balanced circuits are inherently insensitive to the extrinsic parasitic capacitances of the transistors.

From the AC point of view, all intrinsic capacitances are connected to ground. In order to model the effects of the latter properly, the MOS transistors have to be represented as distributed RC lines rather than simple resistors. Thus, an actual integrator using MOST resistors is in fact as shown in Fig. 5A (the following considerations are valid for balanced as well as unbalanced circuits, but only the latter case is illustrated, for simplicity). Owing to its distributed nature, the circuit has an extra set of poles, infinite in number [14], in addition to the pole close to zero frequency, and the high frequency ones generated by the finite bandwidth of the operational amplifier. It will be seen below that in the worst case, as far as effects of the parasitics are concerned, the frequency corresponding to the lowest pole due to distributed capacitances can be much smaller than the frequencies corresponding to the poles due to amplifier finite gain-bandwidth effects. Thus, for the purpose of this Section, the nonideal operation of the integrator at low frequencies will be considered dominated by the parasitics, and the operational amplifier will be assumed ideal.

An approximate but simple way to evaluate the operation of the circuit in Fig. 5A at not too high values of frequency is to replace the distributed RC line with a lumped T-network, as shown in Fig. 5B. It can easily be verified that the transadmittances of the T-network and of the transmission line in Figs. 5A and B match to a first order. As far as the matching of the transadmittances is concerned, using a capacitance value of $(2/3)C_i$ in the T-network gives a better result than using simply C_i. The circuit

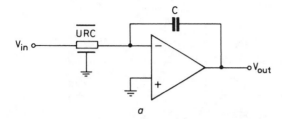

Fig. 5A. Integrator with distributed RC line used instead of a resistor.

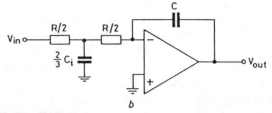

Fig. 5B. First-order approximation with lumped elements for the circuit in Fig. 5A.

in Fig. 5B is characterised by two RC products; τ given by the channel resistance in conjunction with the integrating capacitor, and τ_i, determined by the channel resistance in conjunction with the intrinsic parasitic capacitance. If the total channel resistance is R as in eqn. 7, the integrating capacitor is C, and the intrinsic parasitic capacitance per unit area is C_i', we have, using eqn. 2c, that

$$\tau = RC = \frac{C'Lab}{2K'W(V_C - V_T)} \qquad (27a)$$

$$\tau_i = \frac{RC_i}{6} = \frac{C_i'L^2}{12K'(V_C - V_T)} \qquad (27b)$$

where C' is the integrating capacitance per unit area, a and b are the integrating capacitor plate dimensions and K' is a constant. The values of C' and K' are

$$C' = \frac{\varepsilon_{ox}}{d_{oxC}} \qquad (28a)$$

$$K' = \frac{1}{2}\mu \frac{\varepsilon_{ox}}{d_{oxG}} \qquad (28b)$$

with d_{oxC} and d_{oxG} the capacitor and gate oxide thicknesses, respectively.

The transfer function of the nonideal integrator of Fig. 5B is

$$H(j\omega) = \frac{V_{out}(j\omega)}{V_{in}(j\omega)} = -\frac{1}{j\omega\tau}\frac{1}{1 + j\omega\tau_i} \qquad (29a)$$

$$= -\frac{1}{j\omega\tau - \omega^2\tau\tau_j} \qquad (29b)$$

A measure of the deviation from ideality in the integrator transfer function is given by the ratio between the imaginary and real parts of the denominator in eqn. 29b [15]. This ratio, the integrator Q-factor, is

$$Q = -\frac{1}{\omega\tau_i} \qquad (30a)$$

At the unity gain frequency of the ideal integrator $\omega_0(= \tau^{-1})$, the value of Q is

$$Q_0 = -\frac{\tau}{\tau_i} \qquad (30b)$$

From eqn. 27 one has that

$$|Q_0| = 6\frac{C}{C_i} = 6\frac{C'}{C_i'}\frac{ab}{WL} \qquad (31)$$

To minimise the effect of the intrinsic parasitic capacitances, the value of $|Q_0|$ should be designed to be very large. Practically, however, it is not always possible to maximise $|Q_0|$ to the point where the influence of τ_i becomes completely negligible. As shown by eqn. 31, the only way to increase $|Q_0|$ is by enlarging the integrating capacitance area and/or by decreasing the transistor sizes, a strategy that is obviously bound by limitations. For example, consider a typical situation where the integrating capacitance is implemented with twenty 40 μm $\times$ 40 μm plates in parallel (for an oxide thickness of 600 Å, a 40 μm $\times$ 40 μm square has a capacitance of about 1 pF; therefore, in this example, the total integrating capacitance is approximately 20 pF), and the transistor has the dimensions $W = 4$ μm and $L = 500$ μm (long transistors are needed to implement large values of time constants). If $C' = C_i'$, then, using eqn. 31, we obtain $|Q_0| = 96$. In precision filters it is not usually possible to neglect such low values of $|Q_0|$. Assuming the following typical value

$$\frac{C_i'}{K'} = 10^{-10} \text{ V s}/\mu\text{m}^{-2} \qquad (32)$$

one can estimate from eqn. 27b, for $V_C - V_T = 1$ V, that

$$\tau_i \simeq 8.3 \times 10^{-12} \text{ (s}/\mu\text{m}^{-2})L^2 \qquad (33)$$

For a transistor with a channel length of 500 μm, τ_i is calculated to be 2.08 μs. The integrating time constant τ in the previous example is 200 μs. Thus, the unity gain frequency of the integrator τ^{-1} is approximately 0.8 kHz, and the natural frequency corresponding to the main pole introduced by parasitics τ_i^{-1} is approximately 76 kHz. Comparing this with the natural frequencies of the poles due to operational amplifier finite bandwidth (OA unity gain at a few MHz), it is clear that for this example, the deviation from ideality at low frequencies is dominated by the effect of the parasitics. This justifies our treatment of the operational amplifier as an ideal element.

The previous example shows that, in general, when designing precision filters with the proposed technique, the intrinsic parasitic capacitances of the transistors should be taken into account. This can be done in the final stage of the design by performing an optimisation of the fully balanced circuits. Our experience so far has shown that this is easy to do, by empirically adjusting the value of one or two capacitors in the filter circuit. The distributed nature of the gate-to-channel and substrate-to-channel capacitances can be simulated on the computer simply by splitting each transistor into many shorter ones connected in series. This is equivalent to approximating the distributed RC line with a lumped ladder network. Naturally, when doing this, the values of the extrinsic capacitances of the unit transistors should be reduced to zero, except for the two extremes. An alternative approach for compensating the effects of the intrinsic parasitic capacitances is by connecting feed-through capacitors in parallel with the MOSFETs.

Even if the above compensation methods are used in the design of the MOSFET-capacitor continuous-time filters, and even assuming ideal operational amplifiers, an exact realisation of a given frequency response is not possible, because the effects of the transistor intrinsic parasitics are not totally predictable. The major cause for this is the fact that the capacitors C and C_i are usually fabricated in different processing steps, and their capacitances therefore cannot be matched accurately, i.e. C_i is mostly due to the gate oxide capacitance, while C may be fabricated between the gate polysilicon and a second polysilicon layer. As indicated by eqn. 31, Q_0 depends on the ratio between C and C_i and, typically, it can vary as much as $\pm 20\%$ from its nominal value. Such unpredictable variations will generate errors in the filter frequency response. However, by choosing large enough values for the nominal Q_0, these errors become practically insignificant [16]. For example, in the fifth-order filter chip described in Reference 1, we found that a nominal value of $Q_0 = 100$ was adequate.

6. NOISE

The noise performance of the balanced MOS filters discussed is identical with the noise performance of their classical prototypes, i.e. those with the same topology but containing only linear resistors. As each transistor is operated only in nonsaturation, its individual noise is the same as the noise of a linear resistor, whose value equals the transistor small-signal channel resistance [12]. It is emphasised that, in the absence of signal at the filter input, the transistors have no $(1/f)$ noise, because their drain-to-source voltages are zero.

7. CONCLUSIONS

The transistor linearisation technique proposed in References 1–3 is shown in this paper to be insensitive to practical deviations from ideal conditions. If the operational amplifiers are properly balanced (typically about 1%) and the devices are matched, good overall linearity is guaranteed. Therefore, in the design stage, one can practically disregard the nonlinear character of the individual transistors, treating the filter just as its classical active RC prototype. The equivalent resistors obtained have tolerances that depend directly on the matching of MOS transistor characteristics in nonsaturation and on the matching of the operational amplifier balancing voltage. Care should therefore be taken in the layout of the balanced filters discussed for best performance. The fully balanced circuits are inherently insensitive to the extrinsic parasitic capacitances of the transistors. The intrinsic parasitics cannot be neglected in certain cases, and must be considered when designing precision filters. This is especially important when implementing filters using transistors with very long channel lengths.

8. ACKNOWLEDGMENT

This work was supported in part by National Science Foundation grant ECS-83-10227.

REFERENCES

[1] Banu, M., and Tsividis, Y.: "Fully integrated active RC filters in MOS technology", *IEEE J. Solid-State Circuits*, 1983, **SC-18**, pp. 644–651.

[2] Banu, M., and Tsividis, Y.: "Fully integrated active *RC* filters". Proceedings of international symposium on circuits and systems, May 1983.

[3] Tsividis, Y., and Banu, M.: "Integrated nonswitched active *RC* filters with wide dynamic range". Proceedings of the European conference on circuit theory and design, Stuttgart, Sept. 1983.

[4] Tan, K. S., and Gray, P. R.: "Fully integrated analog filters using bipolar-JFET technology", *IEEE J. Solid-State Circuits*, 1978, **SC-13**, pp. 814–821.

[5] Brand, J. R., Schaumann, R., and Skei, E. M.: "Temperature-stabilized active *R* bandpass filters". Proceedings of 20th midwest symposium on circuits and systems, August 1977, pp. 295–300.

[6] Moulding, K. W., Quartly, J. R., Rankin, P. J., Thompson, R. S., and Wilson, G. A.: "Gyrator video filter IC with automatic timing", *IEEE J. Solid-State Circuits*, 1980, **SC-15**, pp. 963-968.

[7] Voorman, J. O., Bruls, W. H. A., and Barth, P. J.: "Integration of analog filters in a bipolar process", *ibid*, 1982, **SC-17**, pp. 713–722.

[8] Tsividis, Y.: "Self-tuned filters", *Electron. Lett.*, 1981, **17**, pp. 406–407.

[9] Radhakrishna Rao, K., Sethuraman, V., and Neelakan-Tan, P. K.: "A novel 'follow the master' filter", *Proc. IEEE*, 1977, **65**, pp. 1725–1726.

[10] Senderowicz, D., Hodges, D. A., and Gray, P. R.: "An NMOS integrated vector-locked loop". Proceedings of international symposium on circuits and systems, May 1982, pp. 1164–1167.

[11] Penney, W. M., and Lau, L.: "MOS integrated circuits" (Van Nostrand Reinhold Co., New York, 1972).

[12] Tsividis, Y., and Masetti, G.: "Problems in precision modelling of the MOS transistor for analog applications", *IEEE Trans.*, 1984, **CAD-3**, pp. 72–79.

[13] Banu, M.: "Theory and design of linear integrated MOS-FET-capacitor continuous-time filters". Ph.D. thesis, Department of Electrical Engineering, Columbia University, New York, 1983.

[14] Ghausi, M. S., and Kelly, J. J.: "Introduction to distributed-parameter networks with applications to integrated circuits" (Holt, Rinehart and Winston, 1968).

[15] Sedra, A. S., and Brackett, P. O.: "Filter theory and design: active and passive" (Matrix Publishers, Portland, Oregon, USA, 1978).

[16] Bruton, L. T.: "*RC*-active circuits theory and design" (Prentice Hall, New Jersey, USA, 1980).

Analysis and Compensation of High-Frequency Effects in Integrated MOSFET-C Continuous-Time Filters

JOHN M. KHOURY, MEMBER, IEEE, AND YANNIS P. TSIVIDIS, FELLOW, IEEE

Abstract —The high-frequency operation of MOSFET-C continuous-time filters is investigated. The degradation of performance of integrators due to the effects of op-amp finite gain–bandwidth product and the distributed capacitance of the MOS transistor is characterized. A solution to minimize these effects is presented and evaluated for practical designs. Op-amp requirements for good linearity performance at high frequencies are derived. The analyses and techniques shown are verified with computer simulation and demonstrated with an experimental chip.

I. INTRODUCTION

CONTINUOUS-TIME filters have recently received attention in the context of MOS VLSI technology. A main reason for this is that a number of drawbacks associated with switched-capacitor techniques are absent in continuous-time operation. Since continuous-time filters do not employ sampling, as do switched-capacitor filters, high-frequency noise is not aliased into the baseband. The sampling process in switched-capacitor circuits also has the practical problems of clock feedthrough and switch charge injection, which are difficult to predict and eliminate, especially at high frequencies; such problems are nonexistent in continuous-time filtering. At high frequencies, a switched-capacitor filter requires antialiasing and smoothing filters with sharp cutoff characteristics, due to low clock-frequency-to-baseband-frequency ratios, which makes necessary sophisticated continuous-time filtering methods, such as those being considered in this paper. Since such methods must be developed anyway, it is then natural to consider implementing the whole filtering function with continuous-time techniques. One continuous-time technique that has provided high linearity and high precision at voice-band frequencies is the MOSFET-C technique [1], [2]. A detailed comparison of MOSFET-C filters to switched-capacitor and digital filters, as well as to filters using different continuous-time techniques, is given

elsewhere [1]. To take advantage of the potential of MOSFET-C techniques at high frequencies, a number of high-frequency effects must be taken into account. This paper considers such effects in detail, develops design techniques, and evaluates an experimental integrated high-frequency bandpass filter. It is hoped that the results presented will help further the state of the art in high-frequency continuous-time integrated filters, which are already finding commercial application [3]–[5].

Low-frequency MOSFET-C filters have been implemented with the basic integrator building block shown with solid lines [1], [2] in Fig. 1(a). For the moment, the reader is asked to disregard the transistors shown with dotted lines. Transistors M_A and M_B operate in the nonsaturation region and act as voltage-controlled resistors. By matching M_A to M_B and C_A to C_B and using a balanced output op-amp, all even terms of the transistor nonlinearity cancel, provided that the inputs are also balanced. The odd terms of the transistor nonlinearity are not rejected, but they are much smaller in magnitude than the remaining linear term and can be neglected for most filter applications. For elimination of both even and odd nonlinearities (assuming a bias-independent mobility), the transistors shown with dotted lines can be added [6]; this connection will be considered further in Section IV. The cancellation of the transistor nonlinearity permits large-signal operation, in contrast to other continuous-time filtering techniques. The gate voltage V_{C1} (or both V_{C1} and V_{C2} in the four-transistor integrator) is used to automatically tune the integrator, as discussed in the following paragraphs.

Two nonidealities of the integrator in Fig. 1(a) must be taken into account for high-frequency applications. First, as is well known, the finite gain–bandwidth product of the op-amp results in a phase lag causing the integrator to deviate from the ideal response of 90°. Secondly, the MOS transistor is not a simple resistor as assumed, but rather can be modeled as a uniform RC transmission line for small-signal inputs, as shown in the circuit of Fig. 1(b) and the corresponding single-ended circuit of Fig. 1(c). The distributed capacitance of the MOS transistor, due to the gate oxide and depletion layer capacitances, produces a

Manuscript received April 23, 1986; revised December 2, 1986 and February 14, 1987. This work was supported in part by the National Science Foundation under Grant ECS-83-10027. Part was presented at the 1985 IEEE International Symposium on Circuits and Systems in Kyoto, Japan.
J. M. Khoury is with AT&T Bell Laboratories, Murray Hill, NJ 07974.
Y. P. Tsividis is with the Department of Electrical Engineering and the Center for Telecommunications Research, Columbia University, New York, NY 10027.
IEEE Log Number 8714909.

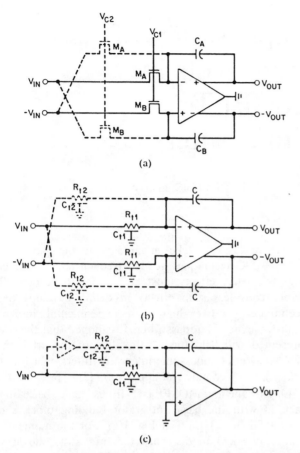

Fig. 1. (a) Balanced MOSFET-C integrator. (b) Equivalent small-signal circuit of (a). (c) Single-ended version of (b).

phase lag at the output of the two-transistor integrator in a similar way as the finite gain of the op-amp does. Even small phase errors at the integrator output can cause serious degradation in precision and high-Q filters. Therefore, a technique is needed which cancels the op-amp finite gain–bandwidth product effect and the distributed capacitance effect in the two-transistor integrator.

The equations formulated in this paper are primarily concerned with obtaining the proper Q in filter sections, and in the filter as a whole by use of passive compensation. Depending on filter specifications, enhancements to simple passive compensation may be required. Sensitivity equations derived in the paper will enable the designer to quantify expected performance of passive compensation and compare various alternatives.

MOSFET-C continuous-time filters require some kind of on-chip automatic tuning circuit for precise frequency response, since the RC products implemented with MOS transistors and capacitors can vary greatly due to fabrication processing tolerances, temperature, and aging. Without automatic tuning, the cutoff frequency can vary by as much as 50 percent, but with such tuning the precision is comparable to that obtainable with switched capacitor circuits [2]. Various automatic tuning schemes have been reviewed elsewhere [1].

Tuning of RC products will be performed with indirect or direct tuning depending on the filter requirements.

Indirect tuning, also referred to as "master–slave" tuning, consists of a master circuit whose MOS "resistors" and capacitors are ratio matched to the main filter, the slave. Once the RC products of the master cell are tuned, the main filter is also tuned because it uses the same control voltage as the master. In contrast, direct tuning (or "self-tuning") requires that the filter be periodically removed from the signal path by on-chip automatic means and has its RC products adjusted. Clearly, these tuning examples provide just one degree of freedom and cannot be used to compensate for errors such as Q enhancement. Depending on filter requirements, independent control of center frequency and Q in the master–slave scheme [7]–[9] may be necessary.

II. THE MOS TRANSISTOR AS A DISTRIBUTED RC ELEMENT

Understanding the origin of the RC transmission line characteristics of the MOS transistor is essential before attempting to analyze their effect in MOSFET-C filters. The following analysis considers small-signal operation of the MOSFET for simplicity. In the frequency range of interest, the harmonic distortion caused by large-signal operation of the MOSFET is well modeled by the low-frequency analysis in [10], and has been shown to be small even when the distributed capacitance of the MOSFET is nearly 7 percent of the value of the integrating capacitor (such distortion is, for example, less than 0.1 percent for signals of several volts peak-to-peak [1], [2]). Although a nonlinear analysis of the MOSFET including distributed capacitance is not presented here, such an analysis would have usefulness in the context of MOSFET-C filters.

The MOSFET-C continuous-time filters considered in this paper operate the MOS transistors in the strong inversion nonsaturation region around zero drain-to-source bias voltage. For this operating point, in contrast to the general case [11], the transistor can be modeled as a uniform RC transmission line for small signals. The total resistance of this RC transmission line, R_t, is simply the small-signal drain-to-source channel resistance; the total capacitance C_t is the parallel combination of the channel-to-gate oxide capacitance and the channel-to-substrate depletion capacitance. The two distributed capacitances appear in parallel because both the gate and substrate are at small-signal ground. In addition to the intrinsic distributed capacitances of the MOSFET, there are lumped extrinsic parasitic capacitors at the source and drain terminals due to the junctions and oxide overlap capacitances. Since the filters considered will always have the source and drain of the transistors connected to voltage sources, op-amp outputs, or virtual grounds, these extrinsic capacitances can be neglected [1]. Strictly speaking, at high frequencies the op-amp input terminals do not provide an ideal virtual short and the output is not an ideal voltage source. However, if both the drain and source lumped capacitors are much smaller than C_t, then they can be neglected with minimal error. Consequently, the MOS transistor is treated as a uniform RC transmission line in this paper.

The two-port admittance parameters for a uniform RC transmission line are given by [12]:

$$Y = \frac{\sqrt{s\tau}}{R_t \sinh \sqrt{s\tau}} \begin{bmatrix} \cosh \sqrt{s\tau} & -1 \\ -1 & \cosh \sqrt{s\tau} \end{bmatrix} \quad (1)$$

where

$$\tau = R_t C_t. \quad (2)$$

The filters considered in this paper operate at "low" frequencies relative to the $\omega_\tau = 1/\tau$ of the MOSFET's (e.g. $\omega \leqslant 0.2\omega_\tau$), so that the transmission line nature of the MOS transistor can be modeled with approximate admittance parameters. Expanding each of the hyperbolic functions in (1) in a series and retaining only the first two terms result in the following:

$$y_{11} = y_{22} = \frac{\dfrac{s\tau}{2} + 1}{R_t \left(\dfrac{s\tau}{6} + 1 \right)} \quad (3)$$

$$y_{12} = y_{21} = \frac{-1}{R_t \left(\dfrac{s\tau}{6} + 1 \right)}. \quad (4)$$

Such a formulation for the approximate y parameters was used in [13], and [14] so that the expansion corresponded to an equivalent "T-network" circuit consisting of two resistors and a capacitor when optimal modeling of only y_{21} and y_{22} was necessary.

III. THE UNCOMPENSATED TWO-TRANSISTOR MOSFET-C INTEGRATOR AT HIGH FREQUENCIES

As previously stated, the distributed capacitance of the MOS transistor and the finite gain–bandwidth product of the op-amp can cause the phase at the output of the two-transistor integrator to differ from 90°. Even a small phase error can be disastrous for a high-Q biquad. In this section, the nonideal behavior of the two-transistor MOSFET-C integrator shown with solid lines in Fig. 1 is characterized. The characterization will be in terms of phase errors at the integrator output, which are known to cause Q deviations in filters. The gain error at the integrator output is not characterized, since it will cause a shifting of the frequency axis, which can be easily corrected by the automatic tuning system.

A generally accepted figure of merit for an integrator is the quality factor Q_I, which is analogous to the quality factor of an inductor or capacitor [15]. If the transfer function of the integrator in Fig. 1 is placed in the following form:

$$\frac{V_{out}}{V_{in}}(j\omega) = \frac{1}{R(\omega) + jX(\omega)} \quad (5)$$

then the integrator quality factor is given by

$$Q_I(\omega) = \frac{X(\omega)}{R(\omega)}. \quad (6)$$

The transfer function of the two-transistor integrator in Fig. 1 is given by

$$\frac{V_{out}}{V_{in}} = \frac{y_{21}}{\left(1 + \dfrac{1}{A}\right) sC + \dfrac{y_{22}}{A}} \quad (7)$$

where A is the open-loop gain of the op-amp and y_{ij} is the (i, j) y parameter of the transistor. The first-order approximations for the y parameters in (3) and (4) are used throughout the derivations. We will substitute $s = j\omega$, and we write the op-amp gain as follows:

$$A(j\omega_0) = a + jb = |A|e^{j\psi} \quad (8)$$

where ω_0 is the nominal 0-dB frequency of the integrator, given by

$$\omega_0 = \frac{1}{R_{t1}C}. \quad (9)$$

R_{t1} is equal to the total drain-to-source resistance of the MOS transistors in the two-transistor integrator shown in Fig. 1. The following expression for the integrator Q_I is then obtained:

$$Q_I(\omega_0) = \left(\left[\frac{\cos \psi + \sin \psi}{|A|} \right] - \frac{\omega_0}{6\omega_{\tau 1}} \right)^{-1} \quad (10)$$

where

$$\omega_{\tau 1} = \frac{1}{\tau_1} = \frac{1}{R_{t1}C_{t1}}. \quad (11)$$

C_{t1} is the total distributed capacitance of the transistors with solid lines in Fig. 1(a). The above formula was derived assuming that $\omega_0 \leqslant 0.2\omega_{\tau 1}$ and has been verified with computer simulation. $Q_I(\omega_0)$ can in theory be made infinite by appropriately choosing the op-amp gain and phase in proper relation to the integrator unity-gain frequency and the distributed effects of the MOS transistor. Such a technique is likely to be unreliable since many differing parameters are required to match and, hence, will not be considered here. Note also that the integrator quality at ω_0 is independent of the op-amp gain if the op-amp phase at that frequency is $-45°$. This result indicates that the op-amp dominant pole should be made to coincide with ω_0. Although it is possible in MOS technology to have the op-amp pole and ω_0 coincide and track, such a technique would either limit the amount of dc gain in the op-amp or unnecessarily restrict ω_0 to too low a frequency.

The result in (10) can be simplified by assuming the op-amp has single-pole rolloff, with a transfer function of the form

$$A(s) = \frac{\omega_T}{s} \quad (12)$$

where ω_T is the unity-gain frequency of the op-amp. Assuming such an op-amp model, one obtains the follow-

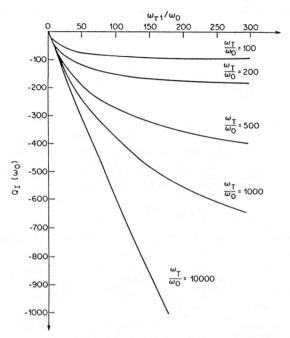

Fig. 2. Plot of the uncompensated two-transistor integrator quality factor at ω_0 for various ω_T/ω_0 and $\omega_{\tau 1}/\omega_0$ ratios.

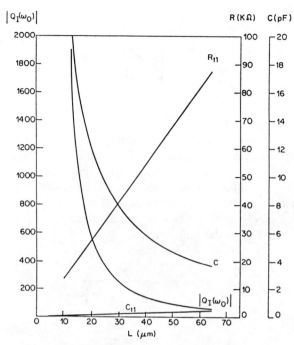

Fig. 3. Plot of $|Q_I(\omega_0)|$, C, C_{t1}, R_{T1} as a function of transistor length assuming the op-amp is ideal, ω_0 is held constant at $(2\pi)500$ krad/s, the per-unit-area transistor distributed capacitance is $1\mathrm{fF}/\mu\mathrm{m}^2$, the resistance per square of the transistor is 8.33 kΩ, and the transistor width is kept fixed at 6 μm.

ing two-transistor integrator quality factor:

$$Q_I(\omega_0) = \frac{-1}{\left(\dfrac{\omega_0}{\omega_T}\right) + \dfrac{1}{6}\dfrac{\omega_0}{\omega_{\tau 1}}}. \tag{13}$$

The resulting integrator quality factor at ω_0 is plotted versus $\omega_{\tau 1}/\omega_0$ for various ω_T/ω_0 ratios, as shown in Fig. 2. The graph shows how dramatically the quality is degraded as distributed effects become important in the uncompensated two-transistor integrator.

In order to determine how the integrator quality is affected by the various design parameters, (13) is evaluated and plotted in Fig. 3 along with the design parameters. The following assumptions have been made: the op-amp is ideal; ω_0 is held constant at $(2\pi)500$ krad/s; the per-unit-area transistor distributed capacitance is $1\mathrm{fF}/\mu\mathrm{m}^2$; the resistance per square of the transistor is 8.33 kΩ; and the transistor width is kept fixed at 6 μm for the plot. The integrator quality factor is seen to degrade rapidly as the transistor length L is increased and, in fact, is inversely proportional to L^2. The conclusion drawn from this graph is that for a given ω_0, the largest possible integrating capacitor and the smallest transistor length should be used to maximize the integrator quality factor. On the other hand, the transistor length should not be made too small (e.g., only a few μm), since then "short-channel effects" would be introduced.

Precision and high-Q filters require integrators with quality factors of several thousand. A loose upper bound on $|Q_I(\omega_0)|$ for an uncompensated two-transistor integrator in a particular technology can be obtained by assuming

ideal op-amps. If this is done, the following equation is derived from (13):

$$|Q_I(\omega_0)| = \frac{6C}{C_t'WL}. \tag{14}$$

C_t' is the per-unit-area distributed capacitance of the MOS transistor and W is the transistor width. As follows from this formula, one should choose C as large as possible, and W and L as small as possible, in a manner consistent, of course, with the desired $\omega_0 = 1/R_{t1}C$. The maximum integrating capacitor size is based on practical chip area constraints. Assuming $C_{\max} = 20\mathrm{pF}$, $C_t' = 1\mathrm{fF}/\mu\mathrm{m}^2$, $W_{\min} = 6\mu\mathrm{m}$, and $L_{\min} = 10\mu\mathrm{m}$, a loose upper bound on integrator quality is found to be 2000. If op-amp effects are included, assuming $\omega_T/\omega_0 = 1000$, the resulting upper bound on integrator quality is less than 700. For some practical combinations of op-amp gain and MOS distributed effects, the resulting Q_I of the integrator can be less than 100.

If the filter designer maximizes the magnitude of the integrator Q_I by using the largest practical integrating capacitor and minimum transistor widths, then the integrator quality factor and the unity-gain frequency are inversely proportional to the transistor length, provided that the op-amp is ideal. Under these assumptions, a low-frequency integrator requires an MOS transistor of great length and necessarily has an inherently lower quality factor than a high-frequency integrator based on the same assumptions.

IV. Inherent Cancellation of Distributed Capacitance Effects in the Four-Transistor MOSFET-C Integrator

As shown in the previous section, the two-transistor integrator suffers from phase errors due to the distributed capacitance of the MOS transistors operated as voltage-controlled resistors as well as the op-amp finite gain-bandwidth product. This section shows that the addition of the two transistors shown with dotted lines in Fig. 1, originally proposed for improved linearity [6], inherently cancels the phase errors due to the MOS transistors.

The small-signal transfer function of the four-transistor integrator, using the approximate y parameters in (3) and (4) and assuming a single-pole rolloff op-amp, as in (12), is given by

$$\frac{V_{\text{out}}}{V_{\text{in}}} = \frac{\left(1 - \frac{R_{t2}}{R_{t1}}\right) + \frac{s}{6} R_{t2}(C_{t1} - C_{t2})}{sR_{t2}C\left(\frac{s}{\omega_T} + 1\right)}. \tag{15}$$

R_{t1} and C_{t1} are the total distributed resistance and capacitance of the MOS transistors connected to V_{C1} in Fig. 1(a). Similarly, R_{t2} and C_{t2} are the total distributed resistance and capacitance of the MOS transistors connected to V_{C2}. All transistors in Fig. 1(a) have the same dimensions and substrate bias, so their distributed capacitance is identical. (However, their resistances differ because one pair of devices is connected to V_{C1} and the other to V_{C2}.) Consequently, C_{t1} equals C_{t2}. Equation (15) then becomes

$$\frac{V_{\text{out}}}{V_{\text{in}}} = \frac{1 - \frac{R_{t2}}{R_{t1}}}{sR_{t2}C\left(\frac{s}{\omega_T} + 1\right)}. \tag{16}$$

Notice that the transfer function is independent of transistor distributed capacitance. This indicates that the phase error at the integrator output must be solely attributable to the op-amp finite gain effects. The quality factor for the integrator is simply

$$Q_I(\omega) = \frac{-\omega_T}{\omega}. \tag{17}$$

The quality of the four-transistor integrator is identical to that of a simple RC integrator with no distributed effects [15]; hence, it is always superior to that of the uncompensated two-transistor MOSFET-C integrator. The inherent cancellation of distributed capacitance effects is robust since it depends only on the matching of devices of the same type. The reader is reminded that the proof of the cancellation of distributed capacitance effects is restricted to frequencies such that the approximations used for the y parameters of the transistors remain valid. The inherent insensitivity of the four-transistor integrator to parasitic capacitances was observed in [22].

Although the four-transistor integrator is superior to the two-transistor integrator in terms of quality factor, the four-transistor design has two disadvantages which must be considered. First, the thermal noise at the integrator output is higher in the four-transistor case, assuming identical integrating capacitances, identical ω_0, and negligible op-amp noise. Second, the sensitivity of ω_0 to transistor mismatches is worse in the four-transistor design. Both effects become more severe as the difference between V_{C1} and V_{C2} decreases. All these issues need attention prior to selecting either approach for a filter implementation.

V. Passive Compensation of the Integrator with a Lumped Capacitor

The integrator (two-transistor or four-transistor) of Fig. 1 can be compensated with the two identical capacitors C_C, as shown in Fig. 4(a), to produce a high-quality integrator. The corresponding small-signal single-ended circuit is shown in Fig. 4(b). The two C_C each introduce phase lead which exactly cancels the phase lag due to the finite op-amp gain (and the distributed capacitance of the MOS transistor, for the two-transistor integrator design) at one frequency. The transfer function for the two-transistor integrator is easily found to be

$$\frac{V_{\text{out}}}{V_{\text{in}}} = \frac{y_{21} - sC_C}{\left(1 + \frac{1}{A}\right)sC + \frac{y_{22} + sC_C}{A}}. \tag{18}$$

Assuming arbitrary open-loop gain and phase characteristics of the op-amp as in (8), the following formula can be derived for the required value of compensation capacitor to yield an integrator of infinite Q_I at ω_0:

$$C_C = \frac{|A|C}{2\cos\psi}$$
$$\times \left[-1 + \sqrt{1 - \frac{4\cos\psi(\cos\psi + \sin\psi)}{|A|^2} + \frac{2\omega_0\cos\psi}{3\omega_{\tau1}|A|}} \right]. \tag{19}$$

If the op-amp is assumed to have a single-pole rolloff and a unity-gain frequency of ω_T, the value of C_C can be rederived, resulting in the following:

$$C_C = \frac{\left[\left(\frac{\omega_T}{\omega_0}\right) + 3\right]\frac{C_{t1}}{4} + \frac{3}{2}C}{\frac{3}{2}\left(\frac{\omega_T}{\omega_0}\right) + \frac{\omega_0}{8\omega_{\tau1}}\left[\frac{\omega_T}{3\omega_{\tau1}} + \frac{\omega_0}{\omega_{\tau1}}\right]}. \tag{20}$$

The value of C_C in (19) and (20) is directly applicable to the two-transistor integrator design. If the four-transistor design is used, the equations should be evaluated with ω_{t1} set to infinity and C_{t1} set to zero. Passive compensation forces the phase to 90° at ω_0; however, it will not guarantee 90° at all frequencies; nor will it guarantee zero gain error at ω_0. The basic reason is that C_C introduces a single zero which cannot cancel the infinite number of poles of the RC transmission line and the pole resulting from the finite gain-bandwidth product of the op-amp. However, the cancellation is quite good in the region around ω_0,

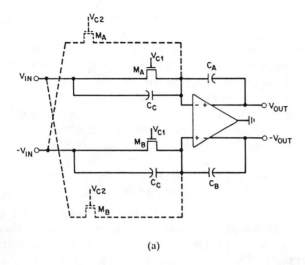

(a)

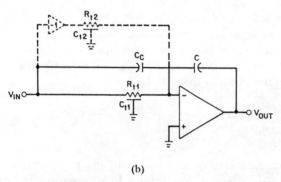

(b)

Fig. 4. Passive compensation of the integrator. (a) Balanced integrator with passive compensation. (b) Equivalent small-signal half circuit.

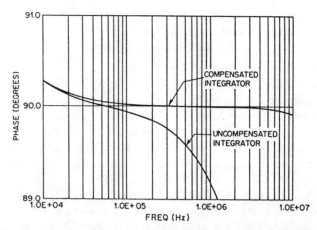

Fig. 5. Phase response of the uncompensated and compensated two-transistor integrator with a nominal unity-gain frequency of 500 kHz.

where the MOSFET can be modeled with the approximate y parameters of (3) and (4). As an example, consider a two-transistor integrator with a nominal unity-gain frequency of 500 kHz. If a 15.28-pF integrating capacitor is chosen, the small-signal resistance of the MOS transistor is 20.83 kΩ. The transistor is chosen to be 6 μm wide and 15 μm long, resulting in a distributed capacitance of 0.09 pF. Although smaller transistor dimensions are possible, such dimensions (and thus the corresponding distributed capacitance) have purposely been chosen large in order to show the effectiveness of passive compensation. The op-amp is assumed to be nonideal with a dc gain of 80 dB, a unity-gain frequency of 80 MHz, and a phase margin of 60°. Approximating the op-amp response using a single-pole transfer function, the required compensation capacitor is found by (20) to be 0.111 pF. The phase of the compensated and uncompensated integrator is shown in Fig. 5. Clearly, compensation has greatly reduced the phase error and does indeed provide a high-quality integrator over a range of frequencies around the nominal unity-gain frequency.

Assuming that $\omega_T \gg \omega_0$ and $\omega_0 \leqslant 0.2\omega_{t1}$, (20) can be simplified to

$$C_C = \frac{C_{t1}}{6} + \frac{\omega_0}{\omega_T} C. \tag{21}$$

Finally, if the distributed capacitance goes to zero, the expression for C_C in (21) reduces to the familiar form for the two-transistor integrator [15]:

$$C_C = \frac{C}{\left(\dfrac{\omega_T}{\omega_0}\right)} = \frac{1}{\omega_T R_{t1}}. \tag{22}$$

The compensation capacitor for the case of no distributed capacitance will, in theory, compensate for the finite gain of the op-amp and produce no phase errors for all frequencies. Therefore, using filter structures with MOS transistors having small distributed capacitance will make the technique presented more effective.

The equations derived show that infinite-Q integrators can be obtained if parameters are exact. Below, the integrator Q_I's that can be achieved with passive compensation in a practical circuit with nonzero tolerances are determined. The analysis will assume single-pole op-amps for simplicity.

The phase at the output of the integrator shown in Fig. 4 can be written in the following form:

$$\phi(\omega_0) = \frac{\pi}{2} + \phi_E(\lambda_C, \xi, \eta). \tag{23}$$

Here, ϕ_E is the error in the integrator phase and is nominally zero if C_C is chosen as prescribed in (20). The other variables represent the following ratios:

$$\lambda_C = \frac{C_C}{C} \tag{24}$$

$$\xi = \frac{\omega_T}{\omega_0} \tag{25}$$

$$\eta = \frac{C_{t1}}{C}. \tag{26}$$

The sensitivities of the integrator phase to λ_C, ξ, and η have been derived and verified with computer simulation;

120

they are

$$S_{\lambda_C}^{\phi} = \frac{2\lambda_C}{\pi(1+\lambda_C^2)} \qquad (27)$$

$$S_{\xi}^{\phi} = \frac{2(\lambda_C+1)}{\pi\xi} \qquad (28)$$

$$S_{\eta}^{\phi} = \frac{-\eta}{3\pi}. \qquad (29)$$

The viability of passive compensation will be shown by performing a sensitivity analysis on the 500-kHz integrator example given above. The sensitivities are $S_{\lambda_C}^{\phi} = 4.62 \times 10^{-3}$, $S_{\xi}^{\phi} = 4.01 \times 10^{-3}$, and $S_{\eta}^{\phi} = -6.25 \times 10^{-4}$. The "worst case" phase error will be calculated by assuming that all variations in λ_C, ξ, and η are in the appropriate direction to maximize the error. The error in λ_C is assumed to be 0.5 percent since λ_C represents the ratio of two capacitors of the same type, known for their excellent matching properties. The tolerance of ξ is assumed to be 50 percent since the unity-gain frequency of an op-amp is not well controlled (which can be remedied—see next paragraph). Note that ω_0 will be correctly maintained by the tuning system. Finally, η represents the ratio of the distributed capacitance to that of the integrating capacitance. Since the oxide of these two different "devices" is often grown during the same process step, loose tracking of 10 percent can be expected. Using the above assumed tolerances, the compensated integrator can have a phase error of up to 0.188° at the nominal ω_0, corresponding to $|Q_I(\omega_0)| > 304$. Such a lower bound may be high enough depending on the application.

Note that in the above example ξ was assumed to have a tolerance of 50 percent. It was implicitly assumed that the value of ω_0 was fixed and all variation was due to op-amp effects. If one desires to have a filter where the desired ω_0 may be programmed (e.g., a bandpass filter with programmable center frequency), the tolerance in ξ will be larger than that assumed here. Also, if the minimum value of $|Q_I(\omega_0)|$ must be maximized for acceptable filter performance, the tolerance of ξ can be minimized by forcing the op-amp open-loop frequency response to track the frequency response of the basic filter [1]. This can be achieved by appropriately biasing the op-amps from the filter tuning voltage taking advantage of the fact that ω_T for single-pole op-amps is of the form g_m/C, where g_m is a device transconductance, and g_m is dependent on the bias current. The transconductance of the op-amp will track the filter conductances, and the op-amp compensation capacitor will closely match the filter capacitors since they are fabricated in the same processing steps. If op-amp tracking is performed and the tolerance in ξ is reduced to 2 percent for the above example, the resulting quality of the integrator will be at least 3839. The increase in performance of the integrator is achieved with only a modest increase in circuit complexity.

VI. PRACTICAL FILTERS REALIZABLE WITH PASSIVE COMPENSATION

Characterizing and improving integrator performance is fundamental to the design of precision filters, since the integrator is the basic building block for the active filters addressed by this paper. The next higher order building block, the biquad, is analyzed here. The balanced biquad shown in Fig. 6(a) was proposed earlier [13], and its small-signal half circuit is shown in Fig. 6(b). The two-transistor integrator is assumed, without loss of generality. The circuit uses capacitive damping, provided by C_Q, and ac coupling of the input through C_K, which is possible for bandpass and high-pass responses. The main advantage of using C_Q and C_K, as opposed to resistive damping and dc coupling, is that for high-Q biquads the large distributed capacitance of the MOS transistor that would be needed to provide damping is avoided. Assuming that all transistors in a resistively damped biquad, such as the Tow–Thomas biquad, are of the same width, the distributed RC product of the damping "resistor" is Q^2 times larger than that of the transistor in each integrator [14]. Such a large RC product means that for high-Q biquads, the frequency of operation may be well beyond the first pole of the RC transmission line providing damping. In this case, the transfer function is no longer that of a biquad with minor degradation. Similar statements apply to the case of input dc coupling.

The balanced op-amp used in the biquad of Fig. 6(a) must be properly designed to guarantee dc stability of the two-integrator loop. Specifically, the common-mode output of each balanced op-amp must not deviate appreciably from its nominal value (e.g., 0 volts) even if the common-mode input range of that op-amp is exceeded. Some balanced op-amp designs are such that both outputs will simultaneously swing in the same direction when the input common-mode range is exceeded. Use of these latter types of balanced op-amps can cause positive feedback of the common-mode signal in the main loop of the biquad, resulting in possible latchup.

The biquad in Fig. 6 has both bandpass and high-pass outputs; analysis will be performed for the bandpass output only. The idealized transfer function for the bandpass output is

$$\frac{V_{out}}{V_{in}} = \frac{s\omega_0(\lambda_K)}{s^2 + \frac{\omega_0}{Q}s + \omega_0^2} \qquad (30)$$

where

$$\lambda_K = \frac{C_K}{C_1} \qquad (31)$$

$$Q = \frac{C_1}{C_Q} \qquad (32)$$

$$\frac{1}{\omega_0} = R_{t1}C_1 = R_{t2}C_2. \qquad (33)$$

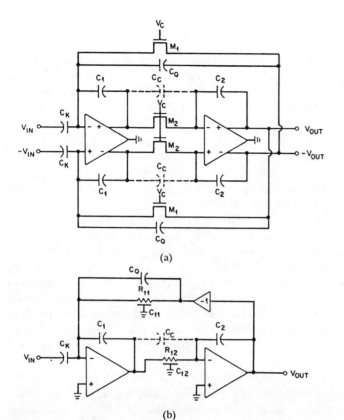

(a)

(b)

Fig. 6. Proposed biquad. (a) Balanced version of the proposed biquad. (b) Equivalent small-signal half circuit.

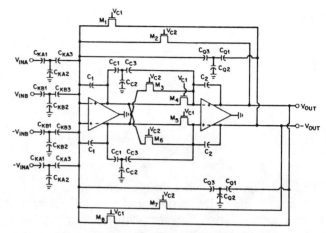

Fig. 7. High-Q MOSFET-C bandpass biquad.

If the idealized equations are used in the design of the biquad, Q enhancement will occur due to the phase lag of the two integrators. However, if C_Q is increased to provide passive compensation for one integrator, as well as biquad damping, and C_C is added to compensate the other integrator, the result is a near-ideal transfer characteristic. C_C can be eliminated and C_Q used to provide biquad damping and compensation for both integrators; however, better matching to the ideal biquad characteristic is obtained with the additional zero introduced by C_C. Assuming that both op-amps are identical and single pole, and that M_1 and M_2 are identical, the following value of C_Q is derived:

$$ C_Q = C_1 \left[\frac{\frac{\xi}{Q} + \frac{\eta\xi}{6} + (\xi+1)\left(\frac{2+\lambda_K}{\xi} + \frac{\eta}{6} - \lambda_C\right)}{\xi - 1} \right]. \quad (34) $$

C_C, ξ, and η are as defined in (20), (25), and (26), respectively. The resulting biquad Q is of the form

$$ Q = Q(\lambda_Q, \lambda_K, \lambda_C, \eta, \xi) \quad (35) $$

where

$$ \lambda_Q = \frac{C_Q}{C_1}. \quad (36) $$

The sensitivities of the biquad Q to the parameters shown above are useful in determining the limits of perfor-

mance. The sensitivities are derived assuming that $\xi \gg 1$ and that $\eta \ll 2$, and are as follows:

$$ S_{\lambda_C}^Q = \frac{-\lambda_C\xi}{(\lambda_C + \lambda_Q)\xi - \eta\xi/3 - 2 - \lambda_K} \quad (37) $$

$$ S_{\lambda_Q}^Q = \frac{-\lambda_Q\xi}{(\lambda_C + \lambda_Q)\xi - \eta\xi/3 - 2 - \lambda_K} \quad (38) $$

$$ S_{\lambda_K}^Q = \frac{\lambda_K}{(\lambda_C + \lambda_Q)\xi - \eta\xi/3 - 2 - \lambda_K} \quad (39) $$

$$ S_{\eta}^Q = \frac{\frac{\eta\xi}{3}}{(\lambda_C + \lambda_Q)\xi - \eta\xi/3 - 2 - \lambda_K} \quad (40) $$

$$ S_{\xi}^Q = \frac{-(2+\lambda_K)}{(\lambda_C + \lambda_Q)\xi - \eta\xi/3 - 2 - \lambda_K}. \quad (41) $$

VII. IMPLEMENTATION OF HIGH-Q BANDPASS BIQUADS

The bandpass biquad presented in the previous section and shown in Fig. 6 requires large capacitor ratios for high-Q biquads. Specifically, C_K and C_Q will be roughly equal to $1/Q$ the value of C_1. The bandpass biquad shown in Fig. 7 uses capacitive T-networks to alleviate the problem of large capacitor ratios.

The four-transistor integrator is assumed as opposed to the two-transistor integrator to eliminate biquad Q errors which could result from nonideal tracking of the lumped compensation capacitors and the distributed capacitance of the MOS transistors (see (26)). Equations (20) and (34) are modified below. The new formulations account for T-network implementations, assume a dominant op-amp pole at frequency ω_p, ignore distributed capacitance effects since the four-transistor integrator is assumed (see Section IV), and for generality include an extra input signal path. The additional balanced input facilitates summation of two signals, as is required in leapfrog active filter implementations [15]. (See Section XII below.)

The op-amp frequency response is assumed to be single pole, of the form

$$A(j\omega) = \frac{\dfrac{\omega_T}{\omega_P}}{1 + j\dfrac{\omega}{\omega_P}} \qquad (42)$$

where ω_P is the dominant pole frequency of the op-amp.

The T-network design approach fixes the "1" and "3" capacitors (e.g., C_{C1} and C_{C3}) at the unit capacitance size, and the "2" capacitor (e.g., C_{C2}) is adjusted to give the proper equivalent capacitance size for the T-network. Referring to Fig. 7, capacitor C_{C2} is given by

$$C_{C2} = \frac{C_{C1}\left(\dfrac{\omega_T}{\omega_0}\right) - \left(\dfrac{\omega_0 - \omega_p}{\omega_0}\right)\left(\dfrac{C_2}{C_{C3}}\right)(C_{C1} + C_{C3})}{1 + \left(\dfrac{\omega_0 - \omega_p}{\omega_0}\right)\left(\dfrac{C_2}{C_{C3}}\right)}. \qquad (43)$$

Similarly, capacitance values for implementation of λ_{KA} and λ_{KB} or, generically, λ_K are related by

$$C_{K2} = \frac{C_{K1}C_{K3}}{\lambda_K C_1} - C_{K1} - C_{K3}. \qquad (44)$$

Finally, capacitance values of the T-network controlling the biquad Q are related by

$$C_{Q2} = \frac{1}{\dfrac{C_1}{QC_{Q1}C_{Q3}} + \dfrac{1}{C_{Q1} + C_{Q3} + C_Y}} - C_{Q1} - C_{Q3} \qquad (45)$$

where C_Y is given by

$$C_Y = \frac{\left(\dfrac{\omega_T}{\omega_0 - \omega_p}\right)C_{Q1}C_{Q3} - C_1(C_{Q1} + C_{Q3}) - \left(\dfrac{\omega_0}{\omega_0 - \omega_p}\right)C_X(C_{Q1} + C_{Q3})}{C_1 + \left(\dfrac{\omega_0}{\omega_0 - \omega_p}\right)(C_X + C_{Q3})}. \qquad (46)$$

C_X represents capacitive loading on the input terminals of the first op-amp and is due to the loading of the K capacitor T-networks. C_X is given by

$$C_X = (C_{KA1} + C_{KA2})\frac{C_{KA3}}{C_{KA1} + C_{KA2} + C_{KA3}} + (C_{KB1} + C_{KB2})\frac{C_{KB3}}{C_{KB1} + C_{KB2} + C_{KB3}}. \qquad (47)$$

VIII. SELECTING THE PROPER TUNING SCHEME FOR A FILTER DESIGN

The previous sections have provided design equations for maximizing the Q_I of integrators as well as accurate implementation of biquad Q's. In addition, sensitivity formulas indicated the range of expected variations in integrator Q_I and biquad Q. These results are used in this section to estimate overall filter performance due to expected integrator phase errors.

In order to estimate deviations in the magnitude response of a filter prior to design, one may use the following equation [15]:

$$\Delta A_{\max} < 13.65 N \left(\frac{Q}{Q_I}\right) \text{ dB}. \qquad (48)$$

$\Delta A_{\max}$ is the maximum attenuation deviation in the passband, expressed in decibels, N is the filter order, Q is the filter quality, and Q_I is the "average" quality factor of all the integrators. The designer must first choose the acceptable frequency response deviation in decibels. Since the filter order and nominal Q are known, a lower bound is placed on the integrator Q_I. Use of (27)–(29) permits the designer to determine if simple passive compensation with the expected device mismatches can achieve a large enough minimum Q_I. If passive compensation cannot work by itself, the next degree of complexity is to make the op-amp gain–bandwidth product track with filter RC product tuning by appropriately biasing the op-amp from the tuning voltage. Such a method may reduce variations in ξ from 50 percent to 2 percent. Finally, if op-amp tracking cannot guarantee an acceptable minimum Q_I, then a Q-control scheme [7]–[9] employing indirect or direct tuning may be necessary. Use of passive compensation in conjunction with the Q control loop will reduce the required tuning range. An important reason to use a closed-loop Q control circuit in very high Q filters is that the nondominant pole of the op-amp (not modeled in this paper) can cause second-order phase errors. The nondominant pole is a function of the transistor drain small-signal conductance in the saturation region, often poorly modeled. Accurate prediction and cancellation of the nondominant pole effect cannot be easily achieved with methods depending on matching of devices or tracking with filter tuning.

In this section, emphasis on filter performance has been in terms of integrator and biquad quality factors. Other effects can also degrade filter performance. For example, the filter magnitude response is roughly $2Q$ times more sensitive to biquad center frequency mismatches than to errors in biquad Q. Therefore, for high-Q filter applications, one must be able to ratio-match biquad center frequencies well in the case of master–slave tuning. If the achievable matching is not sufficient, then direct tuning may be necessary [1].

IX. ACTIVE COMPENSATION

Although passive compensation is quite adequate for many applications, active compensation may at first seem to provide superior results since the method depends on matching the same types of devices rather than tracking different devices. The basic idea, as proposed by Vogel [16] and Akerberg–Mossberg [17], is to place an op-amp in the inverting unity-gain configuration in the feedback loop of another op-amp which implements a Miller integrator. This configuration depends on the op-amps matching and will provide an integrator with phase lead. Such a phase lead integrator can be used in conjunction with a phase lag integrator, as in Fig. 1, to produce a high-quality biquad. The authors of this paper have shown that the same configuration can be used to cancel not only finite gain–bandwidth effects, but also the distributed capacitance of the MOS transistor [13]. As pointed out in [18], however, the phase lead integrator can become unstable due to the reduced phase margin of the two op-amp loop. Although it is possible to increase the phase margin with appropriate techniques [18], the increase is typically not large and is often not adequate due to the effect of the distributed capacitance. Due to the drawbacks of active compensation, it appears better to use passive compensation when possible.

X. BALANCING REQUIREMENTS ON THE TWO-TRANSISTOR MOS INTEGRATOR

Up to this point, all the derivations have assumed that the balanced integrator is completely symmetric and that the inputs are perfectly balanced. If there are mismatches or imbalanced inputs, the Q_I of the integrator will be degraded and even-order harmonic distortion will result. Below, the effect of mismatches on the quality of the two-transistor integrator is addressed. Consider the balanced two-transistor integrator in Fig. 1(a). In the analysis which follows, the op-amp is assumed ideal, the input signals are perfectly balanced, and the distributed capacitance of the MOSFET is neglected. Transistors M_A and M_B are assumed mismatched, as are capacitors C_A and C_B, resulting in the following RC products:

$$\tau_A = R_{t1A}C_A = \tau_0 - \Delta\tau_0 \qquad (49)$$

$$\tau_B = R_{t1B}C_B = \tau_0 + \Delta\tau_0 \qquad (50)$$

where R_{t1A} and R_{t1B} are the small-signal resistances of transistors M_A and M_B and

$$\tau_0 = \frac{1}{2}(\tau_A + \tau_B). \qquad (51)$$

The resulting integrator quality can be derived and is found to be

$$Q_I(\omega)\big|_{\omega = \frac{1}{\tau_0}} = \frac{2}{\left(\dfrac{\Delta\tau_0}{\tau_0}\right)^2}. \qquad (52)$$

If the time constants are mismatched such that $(\Delta\tau_0/\tau_0) = 0.01$, the integrator Q_I is found to be 20000. Clearly, this Q_I corresponds to a very small phase error, 0.0029°, which will be masked by phase errors resulting from tolerances in λ_C, ξ, and η of the passive compensation technique already presented. Therefore, the previous derivations which were based on the half-circuit modeling of the balanced integrator and the balanced biquad are justified since the mismatches are seen to be a second-order effect.

The two-transistor integrator in Fig. 1(a) can be modified as suggested in [19] when only a single-ended output

is required. Specifically, the bottom plate of capacitor C_B is connected to ground and the balanced op-amp is replaced with a single-ended one. This alternative integrator design is now seen to be far more sensitive to mismatches in RC products than the fully balanced integrator, as evidenced by the following formula, which can easily be derived:

$$Q_I(\omega)\big|_{\omega = \frac{1}{\tau_0}} = \frac{-2}{\left(\dfrac{\Delta\tau_0}{\tau_0}\right)}. \qquad (53)$$

If again $(\Delta\tau_0/\tau_0) = 0.01$, the integrator quality is seen to be only -200. Such a result may be acceptable for low-Q applications, but not for high-quality filters.

When comparing the two integrator designs, assuming an ideal op-amp, one notices that for the implementation recommended in [19], the voltage at the op-amp input terminals is determined solely by R_{t1B}, C_B, and $-V_{IN}$, whereas in the fully balanced integrator design in Fig. 1(a) the voltage is determined by R_{t1A}, R_{t1B}, C_A, C_B, V_{IN}, and $-V_{IN}$. The integrator of Fig. 1(a) couples the two signal paths to yield the high performance.

The degree to which transistor nonlinearities can be canceled is crucially dependent on the matching of "identical" devices and the design of the balanced op-amp. The effect of mismatches and the imbalance of signals in magnitude has been extensively analyzed in [10] and will not be repeated here. Instead, the effect of phase errors between the nominally balanced signals on distortion in high-frequency filters is explored in this section. The following derivation assumes that all operation is ideal, except that the phase error between the input signals, θ_I, is nonzero.

The drain current of an MOS transistor in the nonsaturation region can be expressed with a Taylor series [10]:

$$I_D = K\left[a_1(V_1 - V_2) + a_2(V_1^2 - V_2^2) + a_3(V_1^3 - V_2^3) + \cdots\right] \qquad (54)$$

where V_1 and V_2 are the voltages on the drain and source. The coefficients a_i are functions of the transistor parameters, gate bias, and substrate bias. Typically, the second-order term is much larger than any of the other nonlinear terms. If the integrator is perfectly balanced and all devices are perfectly matched, the effect of all even terms in the above equation will be eliminated assuming infinite op-amp gain. The remaining terms will be much less than the first-order term. However, nonideal effects often cause a_2 to be the limiting factor in performance. Assuming only a phase imbalance θ_I is present, the integrator input signals are given by

$$V_{INP} = V_p\cos(\omega t) \qquad (55)$$

$$V_{INN} = V_p\cos(\omega t + \pi + \theta_I). \qquad (56)$$

The resulting output signal is

$$
\begin{aligned}
V_{\text{out}}(t) =\ & \frac{K}{2C}\left[\left(2a_1 V_p + \frac{3a_3 V_p^3}{2} + \cdots\right)\sin\left(\frac{\theta}{2}\right)\right] \\
& \times \left(\frac{1}{\omega}\right)\cos\left(\omega t + \frac{\theta}{2}\right) \\
& + \frac{K}{2C}\left[\left(a_2 V_p^2 + a_4 V_p^4 + \cdots\right)\sin(\theta)\right] \\
& \times \left(\frac{1}{2\omega}\right)\cos(2\omega t + \theta) \\
& + \frac{K}{2C}\left[\left(\frac{a_3 V_p^3}{2} + \cdots\right)\sin\left(\frac{3\theta}{2}\right)\right]\left(\frac{1}{3\omega}\right) \\
& \times \cos\left(3\omega t + \frac{3\theta}{2}\right) \\
& + \frac{K}{2C}\left[\left(\frac{a_4 V_p^4}{4} + \cdots\right)\sin(2\theta)\right]\left(\frac{1}{4\omega}\right) \\
& \times \cos(4\omega t + 2\theta) \\
& + \cdots \\
& + V_{\text{dc}}
\end{aligned}
\tag{57}
$$

where V_{dc} is a dc component, and

$$
\theta = \pi + \theta_I. \tag{58}
$$

The distortion due to the second and third harmonics is given approximately by

$$
D_2 = \frac{a_2 V_p \sin(\theta)}{4a_1 \sin\left(\frac{\theta}{2}\right)} \tag{59}
$$

and

$$
D_3 = \frac{a_3 \sin\left(\frac{3\theta}{2}\right) V_p^2}{12 a_1 \sin\left(\frac{\theta}{2}\right)}. \tag{60}
$$

The coefficients a_i are given by [10]:

$$
a_1 = 2(V_C - V_T) \tag{61}
$$

$$
a_2 = -\left(1 + \frac{\gamma}{2\sqrt{V_B + \phi_B}}\right) \tag{62}
$$

$$
a_3 = \frac{\gamma}{12}(V_B + \phi_B)^{-3/2}. \tag{63}
$$

V_T is the transistor threshold voltage, V_B is the substrate bias, and γ and ϕ_B are bias independent transistor constants. Consider an example with $V_C = 2.5$ V, $V_T = 1.1$ V, $V_B = -2.5$ V, $\gamma = 0.4\sqrt{V}$, and $\phi_B = 0.7$ V. If $V_p = 0.5$ V and $\theta = 179°$, $D_2 = -61.2$ dB and $D_3 = -87.3$ dB. If we keep $V_p = 0.5$ V but change $\theta = 178°$, $D_2 = -55.2$ dB and D_3 remains practically unchanged. Finally, if an input is applied with $V_p = 1.0$ V and $\theta = 178°$, the result is that $D_2 = -49.2$ dB and $D_3 = -75.2$ dB. It is thus seen that for the second harmonic distortion to be adequately reduced, θ_I should be less than 1°.

Since the input balancing must be better than 1°, certain balanced op-amp configurations cannot be used. (Note that the inputs to the integrator described are assumed to be driven from the output of a similar stage, hence the requirement on op-amp output balancing.) For example, [2] constructs the balanced op-amp from two single-ended op-amps, one of which is used as an inverter. Although this method performs very well for low-frequency applications, it is not adequate for very high frequencies (i.e., low ω_T/ω_0). If the single-ended op-amps have single-pole rolloff and an ω_T/ω_0 of 100, the inverting amplifier will introduce a phase error of 1.15°. Optimum balancing of the op-amp outputs indicates that the op-amp design must be completely symmetrical and must employ some form of common-mode feedback [1]. Some common-mode feedback techniques used in the design of differential op-amps for switched-capacitor filters do not provide adequate balancing for the MOSFET-C continuous-time filters considered here.

In summary, for adequate cancellation of transistor nonlinearities, the most crucial design requirements are precise balancing of the op-amp outputs (in both phase and magnitude) and precise matching of the MOS transistors and the integrating capacitors.

The reader should note that [20] indicates that the use of balanced op-amps constructed with two single-ended op-amps is superior for high-frequency operation, in an apparent contradiction to what is presented here. The discrepancy arises because [20] is considering frequency response precision whereas the focus of this section is distortion.

XI. OP-AMP OFFSET REQUIREMENTS

Special attention must be paid to keep op-amp offset as low as possible, especially in high-Q applications. Op-amp differential output offset causes mismatches in the operating points of the transistors it drives and can result in degraded power supply rejection of the filter and integrator Q_I errors (see (52)). Similarly, op-amp output common-mode offset changes the resistance of the transistors it drives and thus the integrator unity-gain frequency.

XII. DESIGN AND EVALUATION OF AN EXPERIMENTAL MOSFET-C BANDPASS FILTER

An experimental bandpass filter has been designed using the results of the analyses developed in previous sections and implemented in a 5-V, 1.5-μm CMOS technology. A challenging example is the implementation of the frequency response required for a typical intermediate frequency (IF) filter found in AM receivers. Frequency response characteristics of the IF filter vary from one design to another; however, we assumed as typical specifications a center frequency of 455 kHz, passband ripple of 3 dB, a bandwidth of 7 kHz, and -50-dB attenuation at 455 ± 10 kHz. Anticipating some deviation from ideality in the implemented chip, a passband ripple of 2 dB was assumed. Such specifications are achievable with an eighth-order Chebychev bandpass filter. The normalized low-pass LC

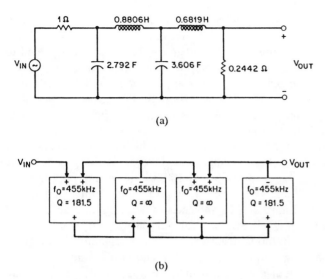

(a)

(b)

Fig. 8. (a) Normalized low-pass LC prototype. (b) Leapfrog bandpass filter.

prototype is shown in Fig. 8(a). Notice that the termination resistors are not equal as this is impossible for an even-order Chebychev design. For low passband sensitivity, the leapfrog active filter structure was chosen. Following well-known design techniques [15], the LC prototype can be converted to the leapfrog filter in Fig. 8(b) by use of the low-pass-to-bandpass transformation. All signals shown in the leapfrog structure, although indicated with a single line, are balanced.

Since the Q of this filter is high, 65, the type of tuning required must be studied. Does the filter Q need to be tuned and does each biquad need to have its center frequency tuned independently? For the passband ripple not to deviate more than 1 dB from the nominal 2 dB design, (48) indicates that each individual integrator must have a Q_I greater than approximately 7100. Use of the integrator phase sensitivity formulas (27) and (28) will indicate whether or not such a quality factor can be guaranteed without a Q control loop. For this calculation, distributed capacitance is ignored, the compensation capacitor and the 7.5-pF integrating capacitor are assumed to match within 0.5 percent, and the ξ of 119 is kept to within 2 percent by making the op-amp gain track filter tuning. The resulting sensitivity calculation indicates that the phase error is large enough to result in a Q_I less than 4800. Clearly, the filter must possess a Q control circuit for this application. The integrator Q_I was maximized by using the four-transistor approach, by providing nominal passive compensation to account for op-amp dominant pole effects, and by using a Q control circuit to correct slight variations around the nominal compensation caused by mismatches and higher order op-amp poles.

Since the filter Q is so high (the passband is only 1.5 percent of the center frequency), each biquad must resonate at very nearly the same frequency. Even a 1-percent error in a single biquad center frequency is unacceptable. Master–slave center frequency tuning cannot be used because it would require that RC time constants across the

chip match within about 0.1 percent. Direct tuning is therefore required to adjust the center frequency of each biquad in the filter.

The op-amp used in the filter design has a dominant pole nominally at 68 kHz and an extrapolated unity-gain frequency of 54 MHz. All integrating capacitor sizes were chosen to be 7.5 pF, with the unit capacitor set at 0.5 pF. All transistors used as voltage-controlled resistors were chosen to be P channel devices 9.25 μm wide and 12 μm long. The chip photograph is shown in Fig. 9. Filter tuning was performed manually, through the control voltages (on-chip automatic tuning is now being considered). All biquad ω_0's were tuned separately; however, a single Q control signal was applied to all biquads simultaneously. The frequency response of the filter is shown in Fig. 10(a). It has a passband ripple of 3 dB as shown in Fig. 10(b) and predicted by simulation.

Although the frequency response shown in Fig. 10 is suitable for an AM receiver IF stage, other specifications for such usage would not be met by the experimental chip (nor was it attempted to meet them). One notable such specification is dynamic range, as will now be explained. For compatibility with VLSI trends, a single 5-V power supply was used (as opposed to ±5 V). This limits the achievable signal swings (due to both op-amp output stages and a low value of control voltage) to about 1 V_{p-p}, differentially measured. The in-band noise power in active RC leapfrog structures can be calculated to be proportional to Q/C_{INT}, where C_{INT}, the total capacitance used in each balanced integrator, must be limited in order to avoid an excessive chip area (we used two 7.5-pF capacitors). The noise can be expected to be high for integrated high-Q filters [21]. The output noise of the experimental chip was measured to be 2.5 mV$_{rms}$, which is close to the simulated value and what one would expect for a discrete-component active RC filter with the same structure, total capacitance, and Q. Simulation indicated that the op-amp noise contribution was negligible. The dynamic range using a two-tone third-order intermodulation distortion of 1 percent (a relevant test for IF work) is 40 dB. Here we emphasize that one should exercise caution when comparing dynamic range for different filters. A bandpass filter with high Q, small total capacitance, and low power supply voltage will tend to have lower dynamic range than a low-Q filter with large total capacitance and high power supply voltage. The discussion of limited dynamic range for high-Q integrated filters applies to continuous-time as well as switched-capacitor filters [21].

In the active filter literature, the subject of noise has received little attention because relatively large capacitances can be used in discrete-component implementations to achieve low noise. Since integrated filters must use small capacitances, their noise can be high and should be an important factor when comparing alternative filter structures. Such comparisons and the development of low-noise filter structures (in the context of small total capacitance constraints imposed by VLSI) constitute an important research topic. Since the future of active filters is tied to

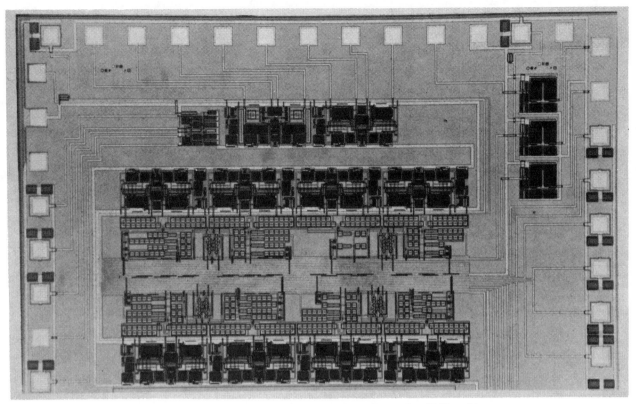

Fig. 9. Microphotograph of MOSFET-C continuous-time IF filter chip.

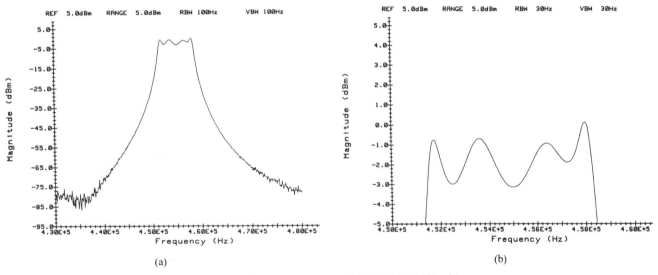

(a)

(b)

Fig. 10. (a) Frequency response of MOSFET-C IF filter chip.
(b) Passband frequency response.

VLSI, the importance of work on low-noise structures cannot be overemphasized.

XIII. Conclusions

We have investigated several high-frequency effects in integrated MOSFET-C active filters, including the op-amp finite gain–bandwidth product, the distributed channel capacitance of MOS "resistors," and the effect of imbalance on integrator quality and nonlinearity. It has been shown that passive compensation techniques can be reliably used to correct for such effects, and quantitative results have been devised for use in such correction. An experimental chip has been designed and fabricated in order to verify the theory. The chip is a voltage tunable MOSFET-C leapfrog bandpass filter which achieves a center frequency of 455 kHz and a Q of 65 when manually tuned. Further success in high-frequency, high-Q integrated filters will require work on automatic tuning and noise performance in active filter structures.

REFERENCES

[1] Y. Tsividis, M. Banu, and J. Khoury, "Continuous-time MOSFET-C filters in VLSI," *IEEE J. Solid-State Circuits*, vol. SC-21, no. 1, pp. 15–30, Feb. 1986; also *IEEE Trans. Circuits Syst.*, vol. CAS-33, pp. 125–140, Feb. 1986.

[2] M. Banu and Y. Tsividis, "An elliptic continuous-time CMOS filter with on-chip automatic tuning," *IEEE J. Solid-State Circuits*, vol. SC-20, no. 6, pp. 1114–1121, Dec. 1985.

[3] 82502 Ethernet Transceiver Chip Preliminary Specifications Sheet, Intel Corp., Aug. 1985.

[4] R. Van Brunt, Intel Corp., private communication.

[5] J. Hein, "LSI architectures for data/clock recovery," in *Proc. IEEE Int. Symp. Circuits Syst.*, 1986, pp. 1298–1301.

[6] Z. Czarnul, "Modification of the Banu–Tsividis continuous-time integrator structure," *IEEE Trans. Circuits Syst.*, vol. CAS-33, pp. 714–716, July 1986.

[7] P. Neelakantan and V. Sethuraman, "Realization of stable electronic systems using nonlinear feedback," Bachelor of Technology thesis, Dept. Elect. Eng., Indian Institute of Technology, May 1977.

[8] D. Senderowicz, D. Hodges, and P. Gray, "An NMOS integrated vector-locked loop," in *Proc. IEEE Int. Symp. Circuits Syst.*, May 1982, pp. 1164–1167.

[9] C. Chiou and R. Schaumann, "Design and performance of a fully integrated bipolar 10.7-MHz analog bandpass filter," *IEEE Trans. Circuits Syst.*, vol. CAS-33, pp. 116–124, Feb. 1986.

[10] M. Banu and Y. Tsividis, "Detailed analysis of nonidealities in MOS fully integrated active *RC* filters based on balanced networks," *Proc. Inst. Elect. Eng.*, vol. 131, pt. G, no. 5, pp. 190–196, Oct. 1984.

[11] M. Bagheri and Y. Tsividis, "A small-signal dc-to-high-frequency nonquasistatic model for the four-terminal MOSFET valid in all regions of operation," *IEEE Trans. Electron Devices*, vol. ED-32, pp. 2383–2391, Nov. 1985.

[12] M. Ghausi and J. Kelly, *Introduction to Distributed-Parameter Networks; With Applications to Integrated Circuits*, New York: Holt, Rinehardt and Winston, 1968.

[13] J. Khoury, B-X Shi, and Y. Tsividis, "Considerations in the design of high frequency continuous time filters," in *Proc. IEEE Int. Symp. Circuits Syst.* (Kyoto) 1985, pp. 1439–1442.

[14] B-X Shi, J. Khoury, and Y. Tsividis, "High frequency effects in MOSFET-C Tow–Thomas biquads," *IEEE Trans. Circuits Syst.*, vol. CAS-33, pp. 648–651, June 1986.

[15] A. Sedra and P. Brackett, *Filter Theory and Design: Active and Passive*. Beaverton, OR. Matrix, 1978.

[16] P. W. Vogel, "Method for phase correction in active *RC* circuits using two integrators," *Electron. Lett.*, vol. 7, no. 10, pp. 273–275, May 20, 1971.

[17] D. Akerberg and K. Mossberg, "A versatile active *RC* building block with inherent compensation for the finite bandwidth of the amplifier," *IEEE Trans. Circuits Syst.*, vol. CAS-21, pp. 75–78, Jan. 1974.

[18] K. Martin and A. Sedra, "On the stability of the phase-lead integrator," *IEEE Trans. Circuits Syst.*, vol. CAS-24, pp. 321–324, June 1977.

[19] M. Ismail, "A new MOSFET capacitor integrator," *IEEE Trans. Circuits Syst.*, vol. CAS-32, pp. 1194–1196, Nov. 1985.

[20] M. Ismail and D. Rubin, "Effect of the finite amplifier gain–bandwidth on the performance of fully-balanced MOSFET-capacitor filters," in *Proc. 28th Midwest Symp. Circuits Syst.*, Aug. 1985.

[21] B-S Song and P. R. Gray, "Switched-capacitor high-*Q* bandpass filters for IF applications," *IEEE J. Solid-State Circuits*, vol. SC-21, no. 6, pp. 924–933, Dec. 1986.

[22] M. Ismail and D. Rubin, "Improved circuits for the realization of MOSFET-capacitor filters," in *Proc. IEEE Symp. Circuits Syst.* (San Jose, CA), 1986, pp. 1186–1189.

Balanced Integrator Filters at Video Frequencies

A. VAN BEZOOIJEN, N. RAMALHO AND J. O. VOORMAN

PHILIPS RESEARCH LABORATORIES, P.O. BOX 80.000, 5600 JA EINDHOVEN, THE NETHERLANDS

Abstract—Two balanced integrator video filters are presented. They are a choice from a series of experiments on silicon including filters, delay equalizers and oscillators. A 4MHz resonance circuit has been realized as an example of a purely bipolar implementation. It makes use of variable junction capacitors, fixed diffusion resistors and balanced transconductance amplifiers. A 5th-order elliptic low-pass filter has been realized in a BICMOS technology. The amplifiers are mainly bipolar while the NMOS resistors and gate-oxide capacitors make use of the CMOS part. These two examples show that high-performance, low-cost, integrated video filters can be realized with balanced integrators.

1. INTRODUCTION

THE trend towards even larger scale integration of analog and mixed analog/digital systems is still going on. While the functions of these systems become more and more complex, the aim (and challenge) of integration is to improve the performance and reliability and to reduce cost price and power consumption. In these (partly) analog systems continuous-time analog filters are often required for analog signal processing [1].

In the last decade many new circuits and filter techniques have been published for the implementation of integrated filters. A major objective of these new approaches is to arrive at a more linear tunable filter element. This is because of two contradictory requirements. On one hand, in continuous-time analog filters, time constants must be variable in order to be able to tune out process spreads and temperature variations. Thus, either the resistors or capacitors must be made bias-current- or bias-voltage-dependent, but, on the other hand, the value of the resistors and capacitors must be independent of signal current and signal voltage.

In this respect the balanced integrator technique as proposed in [2] is very attractive because it combines a sufficiently large tuning range (factor 2) of an NMOS resistor with the large signal handling capability of this resistor (theoretically more than 1

V for 1% third-order distortion). A balanced amplifier provides for the rejection of common-mode signals (second-order distortion of the NMOS resistors).

A resonance circuit is described as an example of a purely bipolar implementation. Sufficient gain is obtained from an amplifier with enhanced transconductance. The resonance frequency can be tuned with junction capacitors. A 5th-order elliptic low-pass filter is presented as an example for a BICMOS technology. The transconductance amplifier is bipolar while the NMOS-resistors and gate-oxide capacitors make use of the CMOS part. This filter can be tuned by the gate voltage of the NMOS filter resistors. Instability of the amplifier was a major problem encountered during the design of the filter circuitry. However, some effective countermeasures can be taken.

2. RESONANCE CIRCUIT

Relatively simple second-order resonance circuits have been designed in order to show the feasibility of balanced integrator filters at video frequencies. Fig. 1 shows, as an example, an implementation for a purely bipolar technology. The transfer function of this filter equals:

$$\frac{Y}{V} = \frac{pRgCi}{(pRgCg)^2 + pRgCq + 1}$$

The resonance frequency $fo = 1/(2\pi RgCg)$ can be tuned with current sources that provide a DC voltage drop, $Icon \cdot Rg$, across the junction capacitors Cg and Cq. The quality factor of the resonator, $Qo = Cg/Cq$, is independent of the resonance frequency.

A bipolar balanced amplifier (Fig. 2) with an unusually high transconductance is used. The cross-coupled (negative) diodes partly cancel the (positive) emitter impedance of the input transistors. The rela-

Reprinted from *Digest ESSCIRC'91*, pp. 1–4, 1991.

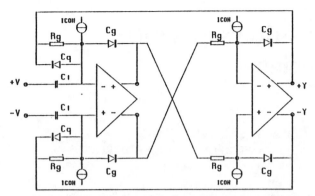

Fig. 1. Resonance circuit. The current sources cause a bias voltage drop Icon · Rg across the junction capacitors. fo = 4MHz. Qo = 16.

tively large signal current through the cross-coupled diodes is mirrored to the output pair with a multiplication factor m. If the influence of Rp is neglected, then the transconductance equals:

$$gm = \frac{m(\beta + m + 1)}{2(m + 1)(m + 1)} \cdot \frac{q}{kT} \cdot \frac{\beta}{\beta + 1} \cdot \frac{Ibias}{2}$$

For $\beta = 150$ and m = 4 the transconductance is enhanced by a factor 12.4 compared to the transconductance of a long-tailed pair at the same bias current. The bias current of the amplifier is $500\,\mu A$ which results in a gm of 0.1A/V. However, the resistors Rp are necessary to prevent slew-rate oscillations and they approximately halve the transconductance. At high frequencies gm reduces further because of the first-order roll-off of β. The emitter

size of all npn transistors is $7\mu m * 9\mu m$ and the ft is 2.5GHz.

The active load circuit delivers the bias current of the amplifier and attenuates common-mode signals at the output of the amplifier because its common-mode impedance is small (1kΩ approx.) compared to the filter impedance (10kΩ). Rg is a p-type diffusion resistor. The capacitors Cg and Cq are implemented as unit capcitors. The ratio Cg/Cq is 15 in order to obtain (according to simulations) a desired Q of 16.

A bootstrapping technique (Fig. 5a) is used to keep excess phase shift in the filter resistors Rg small. Therefore, Rg is embedded in the load resistor Rl (40kΩ n-well resistor) and because the signal voltage across Rg and across Rl are equal, no signal current will flow through the parasitic junction capacitor of Rg.

At higher frequencies the transconductance amplifier becomes inductive because of the roll-off of β. The capacitive loading of the amplifier together with other second-order effects cause instability of the amplifier around 200MHz. The oscillation can be damped with Rs (1kΩ) and Cs (1pF) in series across the amplifier input.

Fig. 3 shows a chip photograph with two resonators. The active chip area is 0.15mm^2 per resonator. Measured resonance curves are shown in Fig. 4. The measured quality factor Qm is 16.2, which means that the total excess phase shift in the circuit is $1/Qo - 1/Qm = -0.005$rad or -0.3 degree. The noise voltage integrated over the pass-band is 0.15mVeff and 1% distortion (1% detuning of fo) is measured for a signal amplitude of 0.2Veff, which

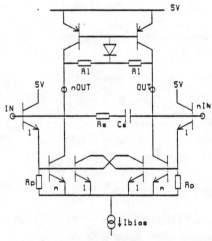

Fig. 2. Bipolar amplifier with enhanced transconductance. gm = 0.05V/A. The active load circuit provides common-mode rejection.

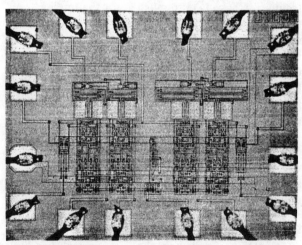

Fig. 3. Chip photograph of a pair of resonance circuits. The active chip area is 0.15mm^2 per resonator.

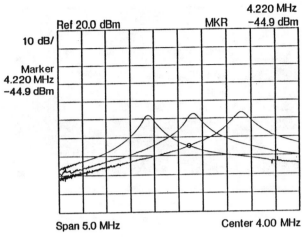

Fig. 4. Amplitude characteristics of the resonator A small Q-enhancement is noticeable.

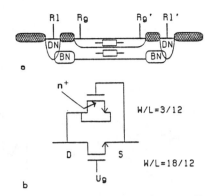

Fig. 5. Two phase compensation techniques. a. Bootstrapping of a diffusion resistor. b. A matched NMOS capacitor in parallel with a NMOS filter resistor.

results in 62dB signal-to-noise ratio. A 5V power supply is used and the circuit takes 1.4mA.

3. 5TH-ORDER ELLIPTIC LOW-PASS FILTER

In [3] Tsividis presented a 5th-order elliptic low-pass filter at audio frequencies. Starting from an LC prototype, he arrives, via a signal-flow graph technique, at a balanced integrator implementation. The filter is tuned by controlling the gate voltage of NMOS resistors. We took this filter structure (Fig. 6), as an example, to implement a video filter in a 1.5μm BICMOS technology with a ft of 3GHz. In this technology the balanced amplifier with enhanced transconductance (Fig. 2) turned out to be stable even without the use of Rp, Rs and Cs. The transconductance is approximately 0.05A/V for a reduced bias current of 250μA and the voltage gain is about 50dB at 5MHz for a filter impedance of $10k\Omega$.

The size of the NMOS resistors (W/L = 18/12) is a compromise between matching and excess phase shift (after compensation) of the resistors. This phase shift between the drain input voltage and the output current of the virtually grounded source is caused by the distributed gate capacitance (and backgate capacitance) of the NMOS. From transmission line theory [4] it is known that this phase shift equals approximately: $\delta = -1/6\omega RgCgate$. It can be compensated with a capacitance of Cgate/6 in parallel with Rg. The compensation of the distributed gate capacitance (Fig. 5b) is fairly accurate (process independent) because it is implemented as a gate capacitance (W/L = 3/12) also.

Fig. 7 shows measured amplitude characteristics for three different gate voltages. The almost frequency independent, deep transmission zeroes are an indication of the high intrinsic Q of the circuitry. The measured noise voltage integrated over the 3MHz pass-band is 36μVeff and 1% third-order distortion is measured for a signal amplitude of 0.12Veff, which results in 70dB signal-to-noise ratio. The power supply is 5V and the total power dissipation is 12.5mW. Fig. 8 shows a photograph of the filter that occupies 0.3mm^2.

4. CONCLUSIONS

In a bipolar technology a 4MHz resonance circuit has been realized with balanced integrators. The measured -0.3 degree excess phase shift of this resonator is very small. The S/N is 62dB and the

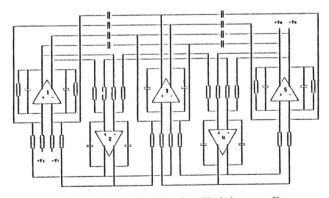

Fig. 6. Circuit diagram of a 5th-order elliptic low-pass filter. All resistors ($10k\Omega$) are made of NMOS.

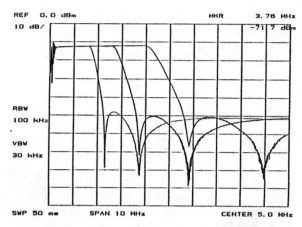

Fig. 7. Amplitude characteristics of the low-pass filter. The filter is tuned by the gate voltage of the NMOS-resistors.

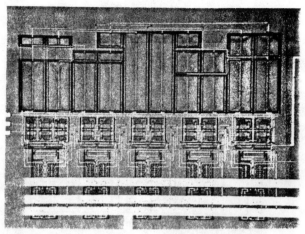

Fig. 8. Chip photograph of the low-pass filter. The active chip area is $0.3mm^2$. S/N = 70dB. Power dissipation is 12.5mW.

power dissipation is 7mW. The active chip area is $0.15mm^2$.

A 5th-order elliptic low-pass filter has been realized in a BICMOS technology. The measured signal-to-noise ratio is 70dB (1% third-order distortion), the power dissipation is 12.5mW and the active chip area is $0.3mm^2$.

These two examples, from a series of experiments on silicon, show that high performance, low-cost, integrated video filters can be realized with balanced integrators.

REFERENCES

[1] J. O. Voorman, "Analog integrated filters or continuous-time filters for LSI and VLSI," Revue de Physique Appliquee 22 (1987) 3–14.

[2] M. Banu and Y. Tsividis, "Fully integrated active RC filters in MOS technology," IEEE Journal of Solid-State Circuits SC-18 (1983) 644–651.

[3] M. Banu and Y. Tsividis, "An elliptic continuous-time CMOS filter with on-chip automatic tuning," IEEE Journal of Solid-State Circuits SC-20 (1985) 1114–1121.

[4] Chirlian, "Integrated and active network analysis and synthesis," Prentice-Hall (1967).

MOSFET-C Filter with Low Excess Noise and Accurate Automatic Tuning

Jaap van der Plas

Abstract —Continuous-time integrated filters having a maximum dynamic range at the audio-frequency range are obtained using MOSFET-C filters. In combination with a careful design of the applied symmetrical amplifiers in a BiCMOS technology, the detrimental influence of $1/f$ noise can be minimized. A 98-dB dynamic range (THD < 0.3%) is obtained in a realized fifth-order Butterworth low-pass filter, while the overall $1/f$ noise corner frequency is limited to 250 Hz. Automatic adjustment of the filter cutoff frequency is performed using a novel all-silicon automatic tuning system that, compared with traditional automatic tuning systems, demands reduced overhead circuitry.

I. Introduction

THE achievement of a sufficiently high dynamic range in combination with a high linearity, a minimum chip area, and minimum power consumption is generally the main objective for continuous-time integrated filters. An important figure of merit that combines noise performance with linearity is the intermodulation-free dynamic range (IMFDR). The IMFDR is defined as the ratio between that level of two sine waves with equal amplitude for which the level of the intermodulation products is equal to the noise floor and the noise floor itself.

A major limitation of integrated technology is the absence of usable inductors, while only small capacitors are available as reactive elements. Consequently, the requirement of a filter transfer with complex poles can only be met using active filters. A basic building block of continuous-time active filters is an active integrator. Maximization of the (intermodulation-free) dynamic range of the entire filter implies both optimization of a single integrator and optimization of the filter structure [1]. The implementation of active integrators having a maximum (intermodulation-free) dynamic range for audio frequencies for a given chip area and power consumption is dealt with in Section II. Subsequently, Section III describes the design of a symmetrical amplifier applied in MOSFET-C filters.

The transfer of a filter in the frequency domain can be normalized with respect to a certain cutoff frequency (or central frequency). In integrated active filters, the (dimensionless) coefficients of the normalized filter transfer can

Manuscript received November 26, 1990; revised March 11, 1991. This work was supported by the Dutch Technology Foundation (STW).

The author is with the Department of Electrical Engineering, Delft University of Technology, 2628 CD Delft, The Netherlands.

IEEE Log Number 9100045.

be established as ratios of on-chip component values, which are generally well matched. The cutoff frequency, however, is determined by absolute component values. The large absolute tolerance generally makes tuning of this cutoff frequency necessary. Section IV presents a novel automatic tuning system that, compared with traditional tuning systems, requires a reduced amount of overhead circuitry.

As an application example, Section V presents a prototype continuous-time filter, implemented in a BiCMOS technology. The application of this filter as an output filter of a synchronous detector for an AM shortwave upconversion receiver [2], [3] requires a fifth-order Butterworth low-pass filter with a 3.3-kHz cutoff frequency, having a dynamic range of at least 90 dB (THD < 0.3%) and a second- and third-order IMFDR of at least 70 and 77 dB, respectively. The applied calculation model for MOS transistors is outlined in the Appendix.

II. Integrator Implementations

An active integrator is realized around a resistive voltage-to-current transfer and a capacitor as a current-to-voltage integrator. In order to facilitate automatic tuning, the integration time constant has to be electrically adjustable. Since (fixed) oxide capacitors are largely preferred because of the excellent linearity and matching, this facility requires electrically adjustable resistive voltage-to-current transfers.

Electrically adjustable resistive transfers are commonly realized using MOS transistors as transconductance elements or as gate-controlled resistors. Balanced integrator structures are applied in order to cancel even-order nonlinearity emerging from the quadratic behavior of MOS transistors. For low-frequency applications (< 100 kHz), special attention must be paid to the detrimental influence of $1/f$ noise (also called excess noise or flicker noise) upon the dynamic range.

Fig. 1 shows an elementary integrator architecture, built up around a source-coupled pair as a transconductance element. Using the square-law drain-current model in the saturation region, given in the Appendix, the small-signal integrator transfer is calculated as

$$\frac{V_o(s)}{V_i(s)} = \frac{1}{s\tau} = \frac{\sqrt{\beta I_T}}{2sC} = \frac{g_m}{2sC}. \tag{1}$$

Reprinted from *IEEE J. Solid-State Circuits,* vol. SC-26, no. 7, pp. 922–929, July 1991.

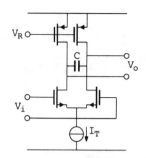

Fig. 1.   Elementary integrator architecture.

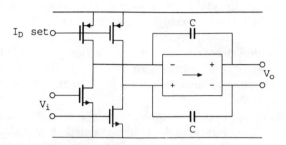

Fig. 2.   Alternative transconductance integrator.

The small-signal transconductance g_m and hence the integration time constant τ are adjusted by the tail current I_T.

From the Appendix (equation (A6)), it follows that the equivalent input noise voltage in a frequency range Δf can be calculated as

$$V_{ni}^2 = \frac{8kT\tau}{3C} \int_{\Delta f} \left[1 + \frac{f_{ln}}{f} + \frac{g_{mp}}{g_{mn}}\left(1 + \frac{f_{lp}}{f}\right) \right] df \quad (2)$$

where the indexes n and p indicate the NMOS and PMOS transistor, respectively. The frequency f_l expresses the noise corner frequency for which the $1/f$ noise level equals the thermal noise level. For drain currents of about 10 μA, f_{ln} is in the order of magnitude of 300 kHz and f_{lp} is in the order of magnitude of 10 kHz in the applied process. Comparable results are obtained for a PMOS source-coupled pair using NMOS current sources.

An alternative transconductance integrator, depicted in Fig. 2, uses NMOST's biased in the triode region. According to the Appendix, a constant drain–source voltage results in a linear transfer from the gate–source voltage to the drain current. With V_{DS} the drain–source bias voltage, the integrator transfer is equal to

$$\frac{V_o(s)}{V_i(s)} = \frac{1}{s\tau} = \frac{\beta V_{DS}}{sC} = \frac{g_m}{sC}. \quad (3)$$

This drain–source bias voltage and hence the integration time constant is adjusted by the PMOS current sources.

In analogy with the saturated transconductance integrator, the equivalent input noise voltage in a frequency

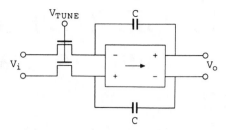

Fig. 3.   Principle of MOSFET-C integrator using gate-controlled MOS resistors.

range Δf is calculated as

$$V_{ni}^2 = \frac{8kT\tau}{C} \int_{\Delta f} \left[\frac{V_G}{V_{DS}}\left(1 + \frac{f_{l'n}}{f}\right) + \frac{2g_{mp}}{3g_{mn}}\left(1 + \frac{f_{lp}}{f}\right) \right] df. \quad (4)$$

The $1/f$ noise corner frequency $f_{l'}$ in the triode region is much smaller than the corner frequency in the saturation region. In the applied process, this corner frequency is in the order of magnitude of 50 kHz for NMOST's using $I_D \approx 10$ μA. If the amplifier is optimally designed, its noise contribution can be kept lower than that of the triode transconductance transistors.

Fig. 3 shows the principle of a MOSFET-C integrator that uses gate-controlled MOS resistors. According to the Appendix, the equivalent resistance of a gate-controlled MOS resistor with zero bias current is calculated as

$$R_m = \left.\frac{dV_{DS}}{dI_D}\right|_{V_{DS}=0} = \frac{1}{\beta V_G} \quad (5)$$

which results in the integrator transfer

$$\frac{V_o(s)}{V_i(s)} = \frac{1}{s\tau} = \frac{1}{sR_mC}. \quad (6)$$

The thermal noise of a MOS resistor with zero bias current corresponds to that of its ohmic equivalent, while the $1/f$ noise is totally absent. Provided that the symmetrical amplifier is well designed, the equivalent input noise voltage of this integrator is completely determined by the thermal noise of the MOS resistors:

$$V_{ni}^2 = 8kTR_m\Delta f = \frac{8kT\tau\Delta f}{C}. \quad (7)$$

If we compare the equivalent input noise voltages of the given integrator implementations for equal values of the time constant τ and the capacitance C, the MOSFET-C integrator has the lowest noise level, especially for low frequencies. The signal handling capability of these integrators does not significantly differ, since they are bounded by the available supply voltage. Consequently, MOSFET-C filters provide the highest dynamic range for audio-frequency applications.

Calculation of the distortion of MOSFET-C filters is based upon the drain current model given in the Appendix. From (A4), the differential-mode input current as a function of the differential-mode input voltage of the

MOSFET-C integrator is derived as

$$i_{d1} - i_{d2} = \beta \left\{ V_G v_i - \frac{\epsilon}{2} v_i^2 + \frac{\gamma}{96} V_B^{-3/2} v_i^3 \right\}. \quad (8)$$

In this equation, ϵ denotes a small imbalance in transistor parameters. Measurements of the applied MOS resistors show that the effect of mobility degradation can practically be ignored in this specific case. As a result, the second- and third-order IMFDR's are calculated as

$$\text{IMFDR}_2 = \sqrt[4]{\frac{V_G^2 C}{4 \epsilon^2 kT \tau \Delta f}} \quad (9)$$

$$\text{IMFDR}_3 = \sqrt[3]{\frac{8 V_B^{3/2} V_G C}{\gamma kT \tau \Delta f}}. \quad (10)$$

The maximum input voltage for which the MOS transistors remain in the triode region is almost equal to $2V_G$, which results in a dynamic range:

$$\text{DR} = \sqrt{\frac{V_G^2 C}{4 kT \tau \Delta f}}. \quad (11)$$

Additional odd-order nonlinearity cancellation by the double-MOSFET method is not applied, since this method increases the thermal noise level and does not compensate for the residual even-order nonlinearity due to component mismatches [5].

III. DESIGN OF A SYMMETRICAL AMPLIFIER

A MOSFET-C integrator requires a fully balanced amplifier with a sufficiently high differential-mode voltage gain and an accurate output common-mode voltage. The limited value of on-chip capacitances combined with a low cutoff frequency requires large MOS resistors R_m in the order of magnitude of 100 kΩ to 1 MΩ. The equivalent input noise voltage of the amplifier must not exceed the noise voltage of these resistors.

Optimum noise matching with the MOS resistors in combination with a maximum gain and a high common-mode rejection is obtained using a PMOS source-coupled pair as input stage. The transfer and noise behavior of a similar source-coupled pair was already dealt with in Section II. As mentioned before, the $1/f$ noise corner frequency of PMOS transistors is much lower than that of NMOS transistors. The common-mode rejection is important in order to prevent common-mode instability by parasitic common-mode loops within the filter.

The current sinks of the input stage are commonly implemented using NMOS transistors. At low frequencies, the $1/f$ noise of these NMOS transistors dominates over the noise of the PMOS input stage and even over the thermal noise of the MOS resistors. If these current sinks are replaced by ordinary resistors, the resulting loss of amplifier gain is generally unacceptable, unless a bipolar second stage is applied. Current sinks using bipolar transistors are not considered as a useful alternative because of the high level of the collector-current shot noise.

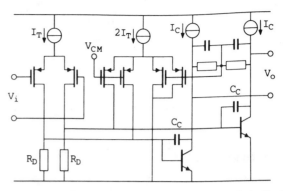

Fig. 4. Two-stage BiCMOS amplifier with common-mode feedback.

A two-stage BiCMOS amplifier, using a bipolar common-emitter stage as second stage, is depicted in Fig. 4. The output voltage swing of this bipolar output stage is nearly rail to rail. Accurate common-mode sensing is performed using two diffused resistors and the double source-coupled pair provides for a maximum common-mode accuracy [3], [4]. The capacitors C_C are added for phase compensation.

The small-signal low-frequency differential-mode voltage gain of the amplifier according to Fig. 4 is calculated as

$$G_{dm} = g_{mp} \frac{R_D}{R_D + r_\pi} \beta_f R_L \quad (12)$$

where $g_{mp} = \sqrt{\beta_p I_T}$ is the transconductance of the PMOS input transistor and β_f is the current gain of the n-p-n transistors. The common-mode sense resistors are part of the effective load resistance R_L, calculated from each output to ground. The input impedance r_π of the bipolar output stage is equal to

$$r_\pi = \frac{\beta_f V_T}{I_C} \quad (13)$$

in which V_T is the thermal voltage. With $R_D = V_{BE}/I_T$, (12) can be written as

$$G_{dm} = \sqrt{\beta_p I_T} \frac{V_{BE}}{V_{BE} + \beta_f V_T I_T / I_C} \beta_f R_L. \quad (14)$$

If the base current is ignored, a maximum voltage gain for a given collector current I_C is found if

$$I_T = \frac{V_{BE} I_C}{\beta_f V_T} \quad (15)$$

and consequently, $R_D = r_\pi$. This maximum voltage gain is equal to

$$G_{dm} = \frac{1}{2} g_{mp} \beta_f R_L. \quad (16)$$

The equivalent input noise voltage of the amplifier for $R_D \approx r_\pi$ is completely determined by that of the input

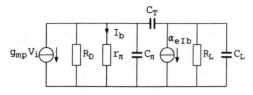

Fig. 5. Single-ended amplifier model for calculation of high-frequency behavior.

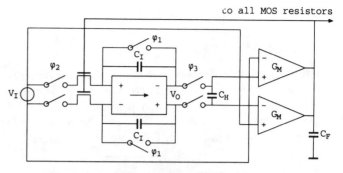

Fig. 6. Novel elegant tuning technique.

source-coupled pair:

$$S(v_{ni}) = \frac{16kT}{3g_{mp}}\left(1 + \frac{f_{lp}}{f}\right). \tag{17}$$

With a low bias current I_T of some tens of microamperes, the $1/f$ noise corner frequency f_{lp} of the PMOS transistors is limited to 10 kHz or even lower. The $1/f$ noise can be neglected in the weighed audio spectrum if the overall corner frequency of the integrator does not exceed 500 Hz, which results in the condition

$$g_{mp} > \frac{40}{3R_m}. \tag{18}$$

In this case, the filter noise is determined by the noise of the integration resistors only.

For high frequencies ($f \gg 1/\tau$), the integration capacitors can be regarded as a unity feedback. A single-ended amplifier model for the calculation of the high-frequency behavior is depicted in Fig. 5. In this figure, C_π is the bipolar transistor base–emitter capacitance, while the collector–base capacitance is incorporated in the compensation capacitance C_T. The input capacitance of the PMOS input stage and the parasitic substrate capacitance of the filter capacitors are part of the total load capacitance C_L. The drain resistor R_D is assumed to be equal to r_π.

If we assume $\beta_f \gg 1$ and $\beta_f R_L \gg r_\pi$, the poles in the amplifier transfer can be calculated as

$$p_1 \approx -\frac{1}{R_L(C_L + \beta_f C_T/2)} \tag{19}$$

$$p_2 \approx -\frac{2 + \beta_f C_T/C_L}{r_\pi(C_T + C_\pi)} \tag{20}$$

in which p_1 is the most dominant one ($p_1 \ll p_2$). The resulting unity-gain angular frequency ω_t is equal to

$$\omega_t = -G_{dm}p_1 = \frac{g_{mp}}{C_T + 2C_L/\beta_f}. \tag{21}$$

Since the most dominant pole p_1 gives a phase lag of 90° at ω_t, the phase margin ϕ_m is calculated as

$$\phi_m = 90° - \arctan\left(\frac{G_{dm}p_1}{p_2}\right) \tag{22}$$

in which

$$\frac{G_{dm}p_1}{p_2} = \frac{g_{mp}}{g_{mn}}\frac{(C_T + C_\pi)C_L}{(C_T + 2C_L/\beta_f)^2}. \tag{23}$$

In this equation, $g_{mn} = I_C/V_T$ is the transconductance of the bipolar output transistors. A minimum required phase margin of 45° results in the relation

$$\frac{g_{mn}}{g_{mp}} \geqslant \frac{(C_T + C_\pi)C_L}{(C_T + 2C_L/\beta_f)^2}. \tag{24}$$

The small-signal behavior of the common-mode feedback loop is similar to the unity-feedback differential-mode behavior. The common-mode loop gain, however, is approximately half the differential-mode gain G_{dm}. Since the phase lag of the common-mode sense resistors is compensated by two bypass capacitors (see Fig. 4), differential-mode stability also implies common-mode stability.

In an implementation of a fifth-order MOSFET-C filter, described in Section V, the symmetrical amplifier is dimensioned using a 0.1-mA collector current for the bipolar output transistors. With $V_{BE} = 0.7$ V, $\beta_f \approx 190$ μA/V^2, and $\beta_p = 250$ μA/V^2, a maximum voltage gain is obtained if $R_D = r_\pi = 48$ kΩ and $I_T = 15$ μA. The transconductance of the input transistor $g_{mp} = 61$ μA/V. The maximum voltage gain is 49 dB for an effective load resistance $R_L = 50$ kΩ. Using a 1-pF compensation capacitance, the calculated unity-gain bandwidth is 6.4 MHz with a 57° phase margin. The output capacitance in this case is 50 pF for each output to ground. The measured transfer does not significantly differ from the calculated one ($G_{dm} = 52$ dB, GBW = 6 MHz, and $\phi_m = 55°$).

IV. AUTOMATIC TUNING

In continuous-time integrated filters, tuning of the cutoff frequency is usually performed automatically by means of indirect tuning techniques. The integration time constants of one or more additional integrators, implemented on the same chip as the filter itself, are related to a reference frequency. If *all* integrators are simultaneously tuned, the value of the cutoff frequency is related to the reference frequency as well. The accuracy of such tuning techniques is determined by the matching of on-chip component values.

Traditional indirect automatic tuning concepts use two active integrators configured as a two-integrator oscillator in a PLL or as a frequency discriminator in a frequency control loop [5]. Fig. 6 shows a novel elegant tuning technique, in which the integration time constant of only

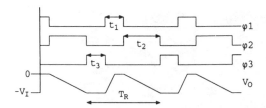

Fig. 7. Timing diagram.

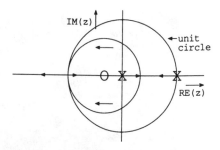

Fig. 8. Root locus of sampled feedback system as a function of k.

one additional integrator is compared with a time reference. The timing and control is performed directly with switches, which are driven by the reference timing signals φ_1, φ_2, and φ_3. This technique is called the direct sample tuning technique.

The timing diagram is shown in Fig. 7. During the time φ_1 is active, the integration capacitors are short circuited, forcing the output differential-mode voltage to zero. During the time interval t_2, in which φ_2 is active, a fixed differential input voltage is connected to the integrator input, which results in a ramp voltage at the integrator output. Finally, when φ_3 gets active, the integrated voltage is sampled into the capacitor C_H. This sampled voltage passes through the low-pass filter, consisting of two transconductances G_M and a capacitor C_F, to the gates of all MOS resistors.

In the stationary state, the final sampled voltage V_O is equal to the reference voltage V_I, which is also the integrator input voltage. Consequently, the integration time constant τ_I is tuned to the time interval t_2, which is derived from a reference frequency. The sampled and filtered tuning voltage, applied to all MOS resistors, remains constant with no ripple. Now all absolute values of all time constants, and hence the cutoff frequency, are related to the reference time t_2.

The stability of the sample control loop would pose no problems if the time constant C_F/G_M is made much larger than the autotuning cycle time T_R. However, if all capacitors including C_F have to be implemented on chip, only a limited time constant C_F/G_M can be realized. Because the autotuning circuitry inherently produces no ripple on the resistor tuning voltage in the stationary state, the minimum C_F/G_M mainly depends on the loop stability. Using the z transform [3], the poles of the sample control loop are found with the root-locus equation:

$$\frac{-1}{k} = \frac{3z+1}{8z^2-8z}. \tag{25}$$

The time interval t_2 is assumed to be half the tuning cycle time T_R, while the root-locus factor k is equal to

$$k = \frac{2\beta V_I G_M T_R^2}{C_I C_F}. \tag{26}$$

In this equation β is the proportionality factor of the MOS resistors. The root locus of this sampled feedback system as a function of k is drawn in Fig. 8.

The breakaway point in the root locus at the real axis occurs for $k = 8/9$ at $z = 1/3$ and for $k = 8$ at $z = -1$.

For a stable autotuning system without complex poles, we have to choose $k \leqslant 8/9$. However, a smaller value of k is preferred for minimum noise and interference on the tuning voltage. In a prototype integrated filter, described in Section V, $\beta = 1$ μA/V^2, $V_I = 1$ V, $T_R = 32$ μs, and $C_I = 33$ pF. A value of $k = 0.4$ is obtained taking $G_M = 1.25$ μA/V and $C_F = 200$ pF. Both C_I and C_F are implemented on-chip.

V. APPLICATION EXAMPLE

This section presents a prototype fifth-order Butterworth filter, designed as an output filter of a synchronous detector for an AM shortwave upconversion receiver. For HF interference suppression purposes, this filter has to be implemented as a fourth-order active filter preceded by a first-order passive RC filter [2], [3]. Fig. 9 shows a photomicrograph of the evaluation chip, on which the fourth-order MOSFET-C filter part (Fig. 11) including a first-order MOSFET-C test section (Fig. 10) and the automatic tuning circuitry (see Section IV) have been integrated.

A maximum signal-handling capability for signals within the filter passband requires a unity transfer from the filter input to the output of the integrators for frequencies below the cutoff frequency. For this reason, all integration resistors of one integrator section have the same value.

In order to obtain a Butterworth transfer:

$$|H(s)|^2 = \frac{|V_o|^2}{|V_i|^2} = \frac{1}{1+(\omega/\omega_c)^{10}} \tag{27}$$

the integration time constants have to fulfill the relations:

$$a_1 = \omega_c \tau_1 = 1 \tag{28}$$

$$a_2 = \omega_c \tau_2 = 0.5\sqrt{5} \tag{29}$$

$$a_3 = \omega_c \tau_3 = 0.8\sqrt{5} \tag{30}$$

$$a_4 = \omega_c \tau_4 = 0.5\sqrt{5} \tag{31}$$

$$a_5 = \omega_c \tau_5 = 0.2\sqrt{5}. \tag{32}$$

The angular cutoff frequency is equal to

$$\omega_c = \frac{1}{\sqrt[5]{\tau_1 \tau_2 \tau_3 \tau_4 \tau_5}}. \tag{33}$$

The dimensionless normalized filter coefficients a_i are in

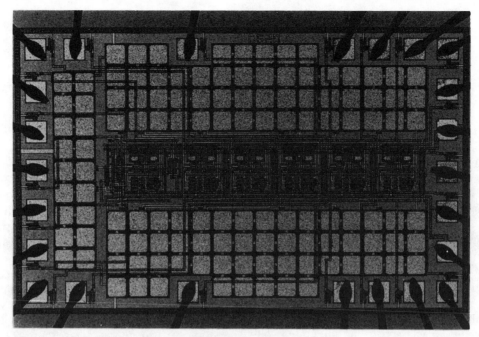

Fig. 9. Photomicrograph of evaluation chip.

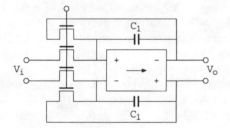

Fig. 10. First-order MOSFET-C test section.

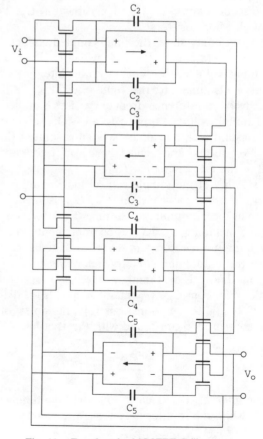

Fig. 11. Fourth-order MOSFET-C filter part.

fact ratios of component values. If all time constants are tuned with the same scale factor, the cutoff frequency can be adjusted without affecting the normalized coefficients and hence shape of the filter transfer. For MOSFET-C filters, this factor depends on the gate control voltage of the MOS resistors (see Section II), which is generated by the automatic tuning system.

The equivalent output noise voltage of the first-order section is calculated as

$$V_{no1}^2 = \frac{16kTR_{m1}}{2\pi} \int_0^\infty \frac{d\omega}{1 + \omega^2 \tau_1^2} = \frac{4kT}{C_1} \qquad (34)$$

which is, independent of the integration resistance, inversely proportional with the available capacitance. In analogy with this first-order section, the equivalent output noise of the fourth-order section is calculated as

$$V_{no4}^2 = 4kT \sum_{i=2}^{5} \frac{1}{C_i} \qquad (35)$$

and the equivalent output noise voltage of the complete filter is equal to

$$V_{no}^2 = 4kT \sum_{i=1}^{5} \frac{1}{C_i}. \qquad (36)$$

138

If all MOS resistors are equal and the ratios of the time constants are established as ratios of the capacitor values, the output noise as a function of the total capacitance C_T is expressed by

$$V_{no}^2 = \frac{8kT}{C_T} \sum_{i=1}^{5} \frac{1}{a_i} \sum_{j=1}^{5} a_j \approx \frac{244kT}{C_T}. \qquad (37)$$

However, if all capacitor values are equal and the ratios of the time constants are established as ratios of the MOS resistor values of each integrator section, the output noise as a function of the total capacitance C_T is expressed by

$$V_{no}^2 = \frac{200kT}{C_T} \qquad (38)$$

which is only 1 dB lower. For a maximum tracking accuracy of the MOS resistors, all MOS resistors are taken as equal and a 1-dB higher noise floor is accepted.

In a silicon prototype, all MOS resistors R_m have the nominal value of 500 kΩ, which results in the capacitor values:

$$C_1 = 99 \text{ pF}$$
$$C_2 = 110 \text{ pF}$$
$$C_3 = 176 \text{ pF}$$
$$C_4 = 110 \text{ pF}$$
$$D_5 = 44 \text{ pF}.$$

With a total capacitance $C_T = 1.078$ nF, the calculated equivalent output noise voltage is 31 μV. Within the filter passband, the calculated noise density of the output voltage corresponds to that of a 10-MΩ resistor ($S(V_{no}^2) = 80$ kTR_m).

Fig. 12 shows the measured filter transfers from the filter input to the integrator outputs. Within the passband of the filter, all integrators have to handle the same signal level. With a maximum 2-dB overshoot around the cutoff frequency, the signal-handling capability of the complete filter is almost equal to that of a single integrator. The measured filter output noise corresponds to the calculated output noise within 1 dB, while the measured overall $1/f$ noise corner frequency does not exceed 250 Hz.

Using a nominal gate voltage $V_G = 2.2$ V, the measured maximum input signal level for which the total harmonic distortion of one sine wave does not exceed 0.3% is 3.5 V$_p$ (2.5 V rms). In combination with an output noise voltage $V_{no} = 31$ μV, the dynamic range is 98 dB. If we consider two interfering signals in the stopband, the intermodulation distortion is determined by the first MOS resistor pair. In this case, the IMFDR is calculated as

$$\text{IMFDR}_2 = \sqrt[4]{\frac{2V_G^2}{\epsilon^2 V_{no}^2}} \qquad (39)$$

$$\text{IMFDR}_3 = \sqrt[3]{\frac{64V_B^{3/2}V_G}{\gamma V_{no}^2}}. \qquad (40)$$

With $\epsilon = 1\%$, $V_B = 3.5$ V, and $\gamma = 0.28$, the calculated

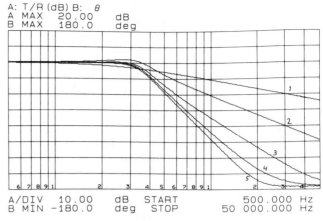

A: T/R (dB) B: θ
A MAX 20.00 dB
B MAX 180.0 deg

A/DIV 10.00 dB START 500.000 Hz
B MIN -180.0 deg STOP 50 000.000 Hz

Fig. 12. Measured filter transfers from filter input to integrator outputs.

second- and third-order IMFDR's are 70 and 83 dB, respectively. The measured second- and third-order IMFDR's are 73 and 82 dB, respectively, which is very close to the calculated ones.

VI. Conclusions

In conclusion, we can state that for continuous-time integrated filters in the audio-frequency range, MOSFET-C filters are preferred over transconductance implementations. Using MOSFET-C filters in combination with a well-designed BiCMOS amplifier, the detrimental influence of $1/f$ noise can practically be eliminated and the filter noise is completely determined by the unavoidable thermal noise of the filter resistors.

The novel direct sample tuning system proposed in Section IV provides for an all-silicon tuning system with minimum overhead circuitry.

Appendix
Applied MOS Model

The applied MOS drain current formula in the triode region is derived from the Ihantola and Moll model, which can be found in [6, p. 120]:

$$I_D = \beta \left((V_{GS} - V_{FB} - \phi_B)V_{DS} - \frac{1}{2}V_{DS}^2 \right.$$
$$\left. + \frac{2}{3}\gamma(V_{SB} + \phi_B)^{3/2} - \frac{2}{3}\gamma(V_{SB} + V_{DS} + \phi_B)^{3/2} \right). \qquad (A1)$$

In this equation, V_{SB} denotes the source–bulk voltage, V_{FB} denotes the flat-band voltage, ϕ_B denotes the surface Fermi potential, and γ denotes the body coefficient.

A simplified expression with a minimum loss of accuracy can be obtained using a Taylor-series expansion up to the third order:

$$I_D = \beta \left((V_{GS} - V_{TH})V_{DS} - \left(\frac{1}{2} + \frac{\gamma}{4}V_B^{-1/2} \right)V_{DS}^2 \right.$$
$$\left. + \frac{\gamma}{24}V_B^{-3/2}V_{DS}^3 \right). \qquad (A2)$$

In this equation, $V_{SB} + \phi_B$ is written as V_B for short, while the threshold voltage V_{TH} is equal to

$$V_{TH} = V_{FB} + \phi_B + \gamma\sqrt{V_B}. \qquad (A3)$$

For (Bi)CMOS processes with lightly doped substrates, the body factor γ is small $(0.3 \sqrt{V})$ and the drain current formula can be further simplified to

$$I_D = \beta\left(V_G V_{DS} - \frac{1}{2}V_{DS}^2 + \frac{\gamma}{24}V_B^{-3/2}V_{DS}^3\right). \qquad (A4)$$

The term $V_{GS} - V_{TH}$ is written as V_G for short. This equation is valid for $V_G > V_{DS}$. In the saturation region, for which $V_G < V_{DS}$, the drain current is modeled according to the square law:

$$I_D = \frac{\beta}{2}V_G^2. \qquad (A5)$$

The drain-current spectral noise density of a MOS transistor is given by

$$S(I_{dn}) = 4kT\beta V_G \frac{2}{3}\frac{1+\alpha+\alpha^2}{1+\alpha} + \frac{K_F I_D^{A_F}}{WLC_{ox}}\frac{1}{f}. \qquad (A6)$$

The left-hand term expresses the thermal noise according to [6], where k is the Boltzman constant and T is the absolute temperature. In the triode region, the factor α is equal to:

$$\alpha = 1 - \frac{V_{DS}}{V_G} \qquad (A7)$$

while in the saturation region, $\alpha = 0$. The right-hand part of (A6) expresses the $1/f$ noise according to [7], where K_F and A_F are technology-dependent constants, W is the transistor length, L is the transistor width, and C_{ox} is the oxide capacitance per unit area.

ACKNOWLEDGMENT

Silicon prototypes of the filters were processed by Philips Nijmegen, The Netherlands.

REFERENCES

[1] G. Groenewold, "Design of high dynamic range continuous-time integrable bandpass filters," to be published in *IEEE Trans. Circuits Syst.*, vol. 38, 1991.

[2] J. van der Plas and E. H. Nordholt, "A novel extended dynamic range synchronous detector for AM shortwave upconversion receiver," *IEEE Trans. Consumer Electron.*, vol. 35, no. 3, pp. 390–396, Aug. 1989.

[3] J. van der Plas, "Synchronous detection in monolithically integrated AM upconversion receivers," Ph.D. dissertation, Delft Univ. of Technology, Delft, The Netherlands, Nov. 1990.

[4] M. Banu, J. M. Khoury, and Y. Tsividis, "Fully differential operational amplifiers with accurate output balancing," *IEEE J. Solid-State Circuits*, vol. 23, no. 6, pp. 1410–1417, Dec. 1988.

[5] Y. Tsividis, B. Banu, and J. Khoury, "Continuous-time MOSFET-C filters in VLSI," *IEEE Trans. Circuits Syst.*, vol. CAS-33, no. 2, pp. 125–139, Feb. 1986.

[6] Y. P. Tsividis, *Operation and Modeling of the MOS Transistor*. New York: McGraw-Hill, 1987.

[7] A. Vladimirescu and S. Liu, "The simulation of MOS integrated circuits using Spice2," College of Engineering, Univ. of Calif., Berkeley, Memo. UCB/ERL M80/7, Feb. 1980.

Paper 2-B.7

Modification of Banu-Tsividis Continuous-Time Integrator Structure

ZDZISLAW CZARNUL

Abstract —Addition of a matched pair of MOS transistors is proposed as a modification to the Banu–Tsividis fully balanced integrator structure [1]. Its application allows a high linearity of the balanced integrator to be obtained. Additionally, its transfer function does not depend on the threshold voltage V_T, and it minimizes temperature and body effects.

INTRODUCTION

Extensive research has been conducted on the fully balanced integrator with MOS resistors by Banu and Tsividis. The structure of this integrator is shown in Fig. 1. Recently, some interesting results were obtained [1]–[3] by means of an analysis based on a Taylor series expansion of the MOSFET characteristic in terms of the signal present on the source and drain of the device. In this paper the analysis is repeated using the exact formulas [4] (without expanding the drain current dependence in a Taylor series), in order to show some disadvantages of this circuit and to show some advantages of the modified integrator.

ANALYSIS

For a long channel MOSFET transistor the drain current in the nonsaturation region can be written [4] as (1) and (2)

$$I_D = F(V_D, V_G) - F(V_S, V_G) \tag{1}$$

where

$$F(V_x, V_y) = 2K(V_y - V_B - V_{FB} - \phi_B)V_x$$
$$- K(V_x - V_B)^2 - \tfrac{4}{3}K\gamma(V_x - V_B + \phi_B)^{3/2} \tag{2a}$$

with

$$K = \frac{1}{2}\mu C'_{ox} \cdot \frac{W}{L}; \qquad \gamma = \frac{1}{C'_{ox}} \cdot (2qN_A\epsilon_s)^{1/2}. \tag{2b}$$

The symbols have the following meaning:

V_D, V_S, V_G, V_B drain, source, gate and substrate potentials with respect to the ground,

L, W length and width of the channel,

V_{FB} flat-band voltage,

ϕ_B approximate surface potential in strong inversion for zero backgate bias,

μ carrier effective mobility in the channel,

N_A substrate doping concentration,

C'_{ox} gate oxide capacitance per unit area,

ϵ_s silicon dielectric constant,

q electron charge.

Manuscript received April 3, 1985; revised October 10, 1985. This work was performed while the author was on leave at the Institute of Circuit Theory and Telecommunication of the Technical University of Denmark.

The author is with the Center for Telecommunication Research, Columbia University, New York, NY 10027, on leave from the Institute of Electronic Technology, Technical University of Gdansk, Poland.

IEEE Log Number 8608533.

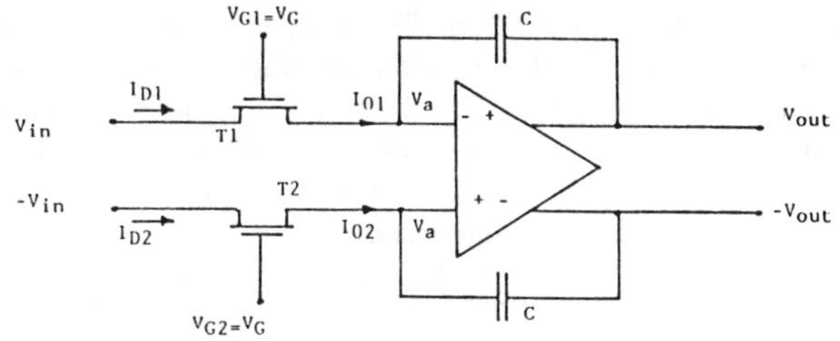

Fig. 1. Banu–Tsividis continuous-time integrator structure [1].

As is well known from the ideal fully balanced integrator, the output voltage V_{out} with respect to the ground is given by

$$V_{out} = -\frac{1}{2C}\int_{-\infty}^{t} (I_{01} - I_{02})\, dt. \tag{3}$$

For the circuit shown in Fig. 1 the differential input current is given by

$$I_{01} - I_{02} = I_{D1} - I_{D2}. \tag{4}$$

Assuming that the two inputs of the operational amplifier are at the same potential V_a and inserting (1) and (2) into (4) with $V_{G1} = V_{G2} = V_G$ we obtain

$$I_{01} - I_{02} = F(V_{in}, V_G) - F(V_a, V_G)$$
$$- F(-V_{in}, V_G) + F(V_a, V_G)$$
$$= F(V_{in}, V_G) - F(-V_{in}, V_G)$$
$$= 4K(V_G - V_{FB} - \phi_B)V_{in}$$
$$+ \tfrac{4}{3}K\gamma\big[(\phi_B - V_B - V_{in})^{3/2} - (\phi_B - V_B + V_{in})^{3/2}\big]. \tag{5}$$

Equation (5) can be rewritten as follows:

$$I_{01} - I_{02} = 4K(V_G - V_T)V_{in} + \tfrac{4}{3}K\gamma\big[(\phi_B - V_B - V_{in})^{3/2}$$
$$- (\phi_B - V_B + V_{in})^{3/2} + 3V_{in}\sqrt{\phi_B - V_B}\,\big] \tag{6}$$

where $V_T = V_{FB} + \phi_B + \gamma\sqrt{\phi_B - V_B}$.

In (6) the second term on the right-hand side does not include a linear component with respect to V_{in} (after expanding in a Taylor series).

The first component in (6) represents the input current of the ideal integrator and the second one represents the total current error due to nonlinearities of the MOS transistors. The current value of the first component is tuned by the voltage difference $V_G - V_T$ with V_G assumed to be provided by a p-n-chip automatic tuning circuit [5].

The dynamic range of the Banu–Tsividis integrator is limited by the current error (second component in (6)), which becomes significant for large signals. The total harmonic distortion (THD) can be calculated from (6) [6]. At this point it should be stated,

Reprinted from *IEEE Trans. Circuits Syst.*, vol. CAS-33, no. 7, pp. 714–716, July 1986.

141

that the dynamic range is limited a priori by the nonsaturation region of MOS transistors, i.e.,

$$|V_{in}| < |V_G - V_T|, \qquad \text{for } V_a \to 0. \tag{7}$$

MODIFIED INTEGRATOR STRUCTURE

We suggest a modification of the Banu–Tsividis integrator as shown in Fig. 2. It needs four matched transistors (only two more than in the original circuit), which are designated $T1$, $T2$, $T3$, and $T4$. Note that the drains of $T1$ and $T3$ are connected to the same node, whereas their sources are separated. A similar connection scheme applies for $T2$ and $T4$. In the proposed integrator the noninverting input terminal of the integrator is the common node of $T1$ and $T3$ drains, whereas the inverting input terminal of the integrator is the common node of $T2$ and $T4$ drains. The common node of $T1$ and $T2$ sources is connected to the inverting input of the operational amplifier and the common node of $T3$ and $T4$ sources is connected to the noninverting input of the op amp. The common node of $T1$ and $T4$ gates is used as the first control voltage terminal (V_A) and the common node of $T2$ and $T3$ gates is used as the second control voltage terminal (V_C). The differential input current $I_{01} - I_{02}$ is calculated in the same way as above. If we put

$$V_{G1} = V_{G4} = V_A \quad \text{and} \quad V_{G2} = V_{G4} = V_C \tag{8}$$

as shown in Fig. 2, we obtain

$$
\begin{aligned}
I_{01} - I_{02} &= (I_{D1} + I_{D2}) - (I_{D3} + I_{D4}) \\
&= F(V_{in}, V_A) - F(V_a, V_A) + F(-V_{in}, V_C) \\
&\quad - F(V_a, V_B) - F(V_{in}, V_C) + F(V_a, V_C) \\
&\quad - F(-V_{in}, V_A) + F(V_a, V_A) \\
&= F(V_{in}, V_A) - F(V_{in}, V_C) \\
&\quad - [F(-V_{in}, V_A) - F(-V_{in}, V_C)].
\end{aligned} \tag{9}
$$

Inserting (1) and (2) into (9), the differential input current is given by

$$I_{01} - I_{02} = 4K(V_A - V_C)V_{in}. \tag{10}$$

For the modified integrator using matched four transistors as outlined in Fig. 2, the output voltage V_{out} with respect to the ground is exactly the same as for the ideal active integrator, if the mobility μ, and, therefore K, is assumed independent of terminal voltages. Inserting (10) into (3), we obtain

$$V_{out} = -\frac{2K(V_A - V_C)}{C} \int_{-\infty}^{t} V_{in}(t)\, dt. \tag{11}$$

From this relation the value of "resistance" (in the sense of active integrator resistance) is given by

$$"R" = \frac{1}{2K(V_A - V_C)} \tag{12}$$

where differential tuned voltage of "resistance" is equal to $V_A - V_C$. Of course, the MOS transistors operate in nonsaturation region, which requires

$$|V_{in}| < \min\{|V_A - V_T|, |V_C - V_T|\} \qquad \text{for } V_a \to 0. \tag{13}$$

Thus the proposed configuration of integrator with MOS transistor ideally performs as a perfect active integrator, provided the mobility μ is assumed constant. In practice, this assumption does not hold precisely, since the mobility is somewhat dependent on the terminal voltages. In addition, mismatches between the transistor sizes will cause some distortion. Finally, because the circuit operation contains signal subtractions, the noise and sensitivity to mismatches may be somewhat increased. A detailed compari-

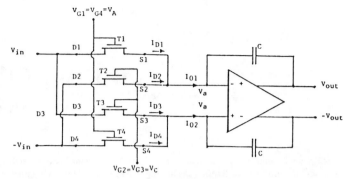

Fig. 2. Modification of Banu–Tsividis continuous-time integrator structure.

son in the presence of nonidealities of the proposed circuit to that in [1] will be performed in the near future. Although the temperature dependent threshold voltage does not appear in (12), automatic tuning may be needed because K depends on temperature through the mobility μ.

CONCLUSION

The properties of the modified integrator proposed here improve those of Banu–Tsividis integrator. In particular, its transfer function:

1) is ideally the same as an ideal active integrator because linearity perturbation is cancelled, when using identical transistors, provided the mobility μ is assumed constant;

2) does not depend on the threshold voltage V_T and the body effect term $\sqrt{\phi_B - V_B}$. This is of special importance when realizing very high values of the equivalent integrator time constant which requires a small value of $V_A - V_C$. However, the noise in such cases may increase;

3) is tuned only by differential voltage $V_A - V_C$ and the dynamic range can be increased simply by simultaneously increasing V_A and V_C, which does not affect the transfer function;

4) A major advantage is that the resistance value does not depend on the substrate voltage V_B, and thus substrate parasitic signals cannot modulate the resistance value. In [1], instead, one must provide a clear substrate bias to avoid such problems. Also, parasitic signals common to the tuning voltages V_A and V_B cancel out, whereas in [1] one must ensure that V_G is well filtered.

ACKNOWLEDGMENT

The author wishes to thank Prof. E. Lindberg and Jan Erik Karlskov Jensen from the Technical University of Denmark for their fruitful discussions. Particularly, the author is grateful to Prof. R. W. Newcomb from the University of Maryland, College Park, for his encouragement to undertake the research in this area and Prof. Y. Tsividis from the Columbia University, New York, for his detailed comments and discussions.

REFERENCES

[1] M. Banu and Y. Tsividis, "Fully integrated active *RC* filters in MOS technology," *IEEE J. Solid-State Circuits*, vol. SC-18, pp. 644–651, Dec. 1983.
[2] ——, "Detailed analysis of nonidealities in MOS fully integrated active *RC* filters based on balanced networks," *Proc. Inst. Elect. Eng.*, vol. 131, pt. G. no. 5, pp. 190–196, Oct. 1984.
[3] Y. Tsividis, M. Banu, and J. Khoury, "Suitability of MOS circuits for integrated high performance active filters," in *Proc. 1984 IEEE Int. Symp. on Circuits and Systems*, (Montreal, Canada), pp. 928–931.
[4] N. M. Penney and L. Lau, *MOS Integrated Circuits*. New York: Van Nostrand Reinhold 1972, pp. 60–92.
[5] Y. Tsividis and M. Banu, "Integrated nonswitched active *RC* filters with wide dynamic range," in Proc. European *Conf. on Circuit Theory and Design*, (Stuttgart, Germany Sept. 1983, pp. 111–113.
[6] Z. Czarnul and E. Lindberg, "A new IC-MOS continuous-time integrator structure," to be published.

Section 2-C   Single-Ended Circuits

Although MOSFET-C filters are best integrated in fully balanced form, in principle they can also be used in special nonbalanced forms. A method to do this involves Czarnul's four-transistor circuit, which was proposed in Paper 2-B.7. This method is discussed by Czarnul in Paper 2-C.1. The method is also discussed by Ismail et al. in Paper 2-C.2, and is demonstrated in an integrated biquad filter. Other approaches are presented elsewhere [1, 2]. A different technique, in which individual MOSFETS are driven in a balanced fashion but the overall topology is not balanced, is presented in [3]; the approach in that paper, though, may suffer from practical problems because of the use of differentiators and the lack of DC paths to some nodes. A different approach to this principle, which is not subject to such limitations, is presented in [4]; also, in this paper resistors are used in such a way that the signal swing across the MOSFETs is limited, thus lowering distortion.

It should be noted that circuits using single-ended op amps (and thus not fully balanced) are likely to produce more distortion than fully balanced circuits, even if simple device equations do not reveal this. This is considered in [5]. In addition, nonbalanced circuits can suffer from interference from the power supply and via the substrate. Thus, nonbalanced circuits may be adequate for stand-alone filters in certain cases but may be inadequate when the filter must be part of a large, mixed analog to digital chip since, in the latter case, the interference from digital circuits can be large.

REFERENCES

[1] S. Takagi, N. Fujii, and T. Yaganisawa, "Highly linear canonical MOSFET-capacitor filters," *Trans. IEICE*, Japan, vol. E-71, pp. 562–566, June 1988.

[2] S. I. Liu, H. W. Tsao, J. Wu, M. O. Yang, and J. H. Tsay, "New CMOS NIC-based MOSFET-C filters," *Electron. Lett.*, vol. 27, pp. 772–774, April 25, 1991.

[3] C. Acar and M. S. Ghausi, "Fully integrated active-RC filters using MOS and nonbalanced structure," *Int. J. Circuit Theory Appl.*, vol. 15, no. 2, pp. 105–121, April 1987.

[4] T. Inoue, F. Ueno, S. Sonobe, and M. Kawasaki, "A design of automatically tunable active MOSFET-RC filters using a single-ended structure," *Electronics and Communications in Japan, Part 3*, vol. 73, no. 10, pp. 1–12, 1990.

[5] Z. Czarnul, S. C. Fang and Y. Tsividis, "Conversion of certain *RC*-active networks to MOSFET-C integrated structures," *Proc. 29th Midwest Symposium on Circuits and Systems*, pp. 196–199, 1987.

Novel MOS Resistive Circuit for Synthesis of Fully Integrated Continuous-Time Filters

ZDZISLAW CZARNUL

Abstract —This paper describes a new MOS resistive circuit containing four matched MOS transistors. It allows to fully integrate known active *RC* filter structures on a single chip without externals components. Integrator, summer and lossy integrator circuits with a single operational amplifier are shown. The new circuits improve on previously suggested MOS active filters.

INTRODUCTION

Fully integrated continuous-time linear circuits can be realized in MOS technology by using MOS transistors (or MOS elaborate circuitry) in lieu of conventional resistors [1]-[5]. Many attempts have been made to utilize such circuits as nonlinearity cancellation can be achieved in them. The MOS balanced linear circuit structures minimize or cancel the nonlinearity, but they require an operational amplifier with differential output [1], [6], which increases power consumption. The novel MOS resistive circuit proposed in this paper avoids this disadvantage and the input–output behavior of the filter based on this device is the same (without nonlinearities), as the prototype active *RC* filter.

DC MODEL OF MOS TRANSISTOR IN NONSATURATION REGION

To introduce the proposed MOS resistive circuit (MRC), we assume that the MOS transistors used have a long n-channel and operate in the nonsaturation region. Complete expressions describing the MOS transistor channel current I_D in nonsaturation region are given by (1) and (2) [7]

$$I_D = F(V_D, V_G) - F(V_S, V_G) \qquad (1)$$

where

$$F(V_X, V_G) = 2K(V_G - V_B - V_{FB} - \phi_B)V_X$$
$$- K(V_X - V_B)^2 - \tfrac{4}{3}K\gamma(V_X - V_B + \phi_B)^{3/2} \qquad (2)$$

with

$$K = \frac{1}{2}\mu C_{ox}\frac{W}{L}, \quad \gamma = \frac{1}{C_{ox}}(2qN_A\epsilon_s)^{1/2}. \qquad (3)$$

The symbols have the following meaning.

V_D, V_S, V_G, V_B	drain, source, gate and substrate potentials with respect to the ground,
L, W	length and width of the channel,
V_{FB}	flat-band voltage,

Manuscript received May 14, 1985; revised November 19, 1985. This work was performed while the author was on leave from the Institute of Circuit Theory and Telecommunication of the Technical University of Denmark.

The author is with the Center for Telecommunication Research, Columbia University, New York, NY 10027, on leave from the Institute of Electronic Technology, Technical University of Gdansk, Poland.

IEEE Log Number 8608536.

ϕ_B	approximate surface potentials in strong inversion for zero backgate bias,
μ	carrier effective mobility in the channel, assumed independent of the terminal voltages,
N_A	substrate doping concentration,
C_{ox}	gate oxide capacitance per unit area,
ϵ_s	silicon dielectric constant,
q	electron charge.

From (1) and (2) the following relation is obtained:

$$F(V_X, V_{G1}) - F(V_X, V_{G2}) = 2KV_X(V_{G1} - V_{G2}). \qquad (4)$$

NOVEL MOS RESISTIVE CIRCUIT (MRC)

We assume that the output nodes of the proposed circuit have exactly the same potential V as depicted in Fig. 1, and it is described by

$$I_1 - I_2 = G(V_1 - V_2) \qquad \text{for any voltage } V. \qquad (5)$$

The MOS transistor realization of the above circuit is shown in Fig. 2, where all transistors are matched and operate in the nonsaturation region. We note that if the proposed MRC consists precisely of matched transistors then in and out are interchangeable. Assuming that the potentials of the nodes 1,2,3,4 are the same as in Fig. 1, the current difference $I_1 - I_2$ according to (1) is given by

$$\begin{aligned}
I_1 - I_2 &= (I_{D1} + I_{D3}) - (I_{D2} + I_{D4}) \\
&= F(V_1, V_{G1}) - F(V, V_{G1}) + F(V_2, V_{G2}) - F(V, V_{G2}) \\
&\quad - F(V_1, V_{G2}) + F(V, V_{G2}) - F(V_2, V_{G1}) + F(V_1, V_{G1}) \\
&= F(V_1, V_{G1}) - F(V_1, V_{G2}) - [F(V_2, V_{G1}) - F(V_2, V_{G2})].
\end{aligned} \qquad (6)$$

Inserting (4) to (6) we obtain

$$I_1 - I_2 = 2K(V_{G1} - V_{G2})\cdot(V_1 - V_2). \qquad (7)$$

The relation (7) is fundamental for the analysis to follow. Comparing the relation (7) and (5) the value of the conductance G is given by

$$G = 2K(V_{G1} - V_{G2}) \qquad (8)$$

where the differential control voltage of the conductance G is equal to $V_{G1} - V_{G2}$.

Assuming that the input voltages V_1 and V_2 can be positive or negative and the transistors operate in nonsaturation region, the relation (9) have to satisfied:

$$\max\{V_1, V_2, V\} < V_M \qquad (9a)$$

$$\min\{V_1, V_2, V\} > V_B \qquad (9b)$$

Reprinted from *IEEE Trans. Circuits Syst.*, vol. CAS-33, no. 7, pp. 718–721, July 1986.

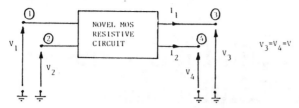

Fig. 1. Definition of a novel MRC.

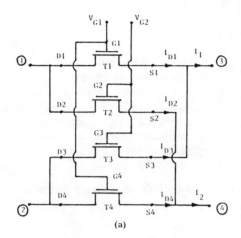

(a)

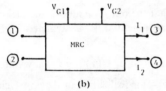

(b)

Fig. 2. (a) MOS transistors realization of MRC. (b) Symbol of MRC.

where

$$V_M = \min\{V_{G1} - V_{K1}, V_{G2} - V_{K2}\} \quad (10a)$$

and the voltage V_{Kn} have the following value [11]:

$$V_{Kn} = V_{FB} + \phi_B - \frac{\gamma^2}{2} + \gamma\sqrt{V_{Gn} - V_B - V_{FB} + \frac{\gamma^2}{4}} \quad (10b)$$

with $n = 1, 2$.

The proposed MRC is supposed to respond to the differential signals only, but according to (9) the differential and common mode input voltage ranges have to be limited as follows:

$$V_B < V_{ic} = \frac{1}{2}(V_1 + V_2) < V_M \quad (11a)$$

$$-\frac{1}{2}(V_M - V_B) < V_{id} = \frac{1}{2}(V_1 - V_2) < \frac{1}{2}(V_M - V_B) \quad (11b)$$

where $V_M > 0$ and $V_B < 0$ for assumed n-channel MOS transistors. According to (11) the op amp common mode input voltage V satisfies the following relation:

$$V_B < V < V_M. \quad (12)$$

INTEGRATOR CIRCUIT WITH MRC

The structure of an integrator using above circuit is shown in Fig. 3, where MRC realization was shown in Fig. 2(a). From the circuit in Fig. 3 the differential current $I_1 - I_2$ is given by

$$I_1 - I_2 = -C\frac{dV_0}{dt}. \quad (13)$$

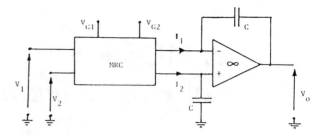

Fig. 3. Circuit diagram of an integrator with MRC.

The two expressions in (7) and (13) can be combined to give

$$V_0 = -\frac{2K(V_{G1} - V_{G2})}{C}\int_{-\infty}^{t}(V_1 - V_2)\,dt. \quad (14)$$

This result proves that the integrator of Fig. 3 has the same transfer characteristic as the classical active RC integrator as long as the mobility is assumed constant [13]. The integrator's "RC product" is given by

$$\tau = \frac{C}{2K(V_{G1} - V_{G2})}. \quad (15)$$

It is interesting that it is possible in the same circuit to obtain an noninverting or inverting transfer function, if we put $V_1 = 0$, $V_{G1} > V_{G2}$ or $V_2 = 0$, $V_{G1} < V_{G2}$ and $V_1 = 0$, $V_{G1} < V_{G2}$ or $V_2 = 0$, $V_{G1} > V_{G2}$, respectively. Additionally, its transfer function does not depend on the threshold voltage V_T and the extraneous signals in the substrate do not modulate the time constant value. Similarly, the extraneous signals common to the control voltages cancel out. The time constant of the proposed integrator (equation (15)) is voltage-controlled and can be automatically tuned to predetermined value by an on-chip automatic control system, e.g., as described in [8].

SUMMER CIRCUIT WITH MRC

A summer circuit with MRC is shown in Fig. 4, where the suitable difference currents according to (7) are given as follows:

$$I_1 - I_2 = -2K(V_{G1} - V_{G2})V_0 \quad (16a)$$

$$I_1' - I_2' = 2K'(V_{G1}' - V_{G2}')(V_1 - V_2) \quad (16b)$$

$$I_1'' - I_2'' = 2K''(V_{G1}'' - V_{G2}'')(V_3 - V_4). \quad (16c)$$

Subtracting the KCL equations for the nodes A and B we have

$$I_1 - I_2 = (I_1' - I_2') + (I_1'' - I_2''). \quad (17)$$

The expressions (16) and (17) can be combined to give

$$V_0 = -\frac{K'}{K}\frac{V_{G1}' - V_{G2}'}{V_{G1} - V_{G2}}(V_1 - V_2)$$
$$-\frac{K''}{K}\frac{V_{G1}'' - V_{G2}''}{V_{G1} - V_{G2}}(V_3 - V_4). \quad (18)$$

The proposed summer is linear again, assuming mobility independent of terminal voltages and each component can be tuned independently by single external voltages V_{G1}' and V_{G1}'', if the voltage V_{G2}' and V_{G2}'' terminals are connected to a common potential V_{G2}. To secure negative feedback of op-amp in Fig. 4, it requires $V_{G1} > V_{G2}$, but the relation between $V_{G1}', V_{G2}', V_{G1}'', V_{G2}''$ can be chosen arbitrary.

If we decide to use only one control voltage $V_{G1} = V_{G1}' = V_{G1}''$ or $V_{G2} = V_{G2}' = V_{G2}''$ (one of them is constant) we can achieve a factor sign reversal by interchanging V_{G1} and V_{G2} in the corresponding MRC. In this case, the value of factor can be set by the

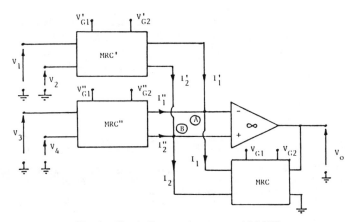

Fig. 4. Circuit diagram of a summer with MRC.

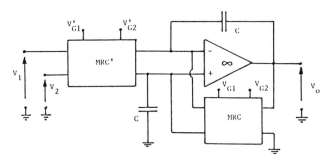

Fig. 5. Circuit diagram of a lossy integrator with MRC.

transistor geometry ratios (W/L) as follows:

$$\frac{K'}{K} = \left(\frac{W}{L}\right)' \cdot \frac{L}{W} \tag{19a}$$

$$\frac{K''}{K} = \left(\frac{W}{L}\right)'' \cdot \frac{L}{W}. \tag{19b}$$

LOSSY INTEGRATOR CIRCUIT WITH MRC

The structure of a lossy integrator with MRC is realized by combining the above described circuits, i.e., as shown in Fig. 5. If we put the analysis in the same way as above we obtain

$$-2K'(V'_{G1} - V'_{G2})(V_1 - V_2) = C\frac{dV_0}{dt} + 2K(V_{G1} - V_{G2})V_0. \tag{20}$$

Thus the Laplace transfer function of the circuit in Fig. 5 is given by

$$\frac{V_0}{V_1 - V_2} = -\frac{K'}{K}\frac{V'_{G1} - V'_{G2}}{V_{G1} - V_{G2}}\frac{1}{1 + s\dfrac{C}{2K(V_{G1} - V_{G2})}}. \tag{21}$$

The comments above for the integrator and summer circuits are valid for the lossy integrator circuit.

EXAMPLE OF FILTER REALIZATION

An example of a filter design using the integrator and lossy integrator structures with identical MOS transistors is shown in Fig. 6(b). The filter is derived from the well-known Tow–Thomas structure as in Fig. 6(a) [9]. The transfer functions for the original T-T filter and its realization in MOS technology proposed here,

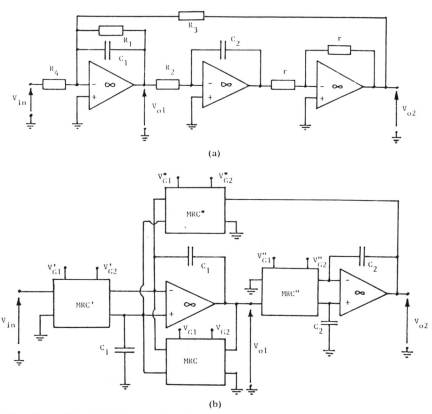

(a)

(b)

Fig. 6. (a) The Tow–Thomas biquad. (b) Continous-time MOS Filter using single op amps, capacitors and MRC's, resulting from the Tow–Thomas biquad.

are given by (22a), (22b), and (22c), respectively.

$$\frac{V_{01}}{V_{in}} = -\frac{1}{R_4 C_1} \frac{s}{s^2 + \frac{1}{R_1 C_1} s + \frac{2}{R_2 C_2 R_3 C_1}} \qquad (22a)$$

$$\frac{V_{01}}{V_{in}} = -\frac{2K(V_{G1}' - V_{G2}')}{C_1} \frac{s}{s^2 + as + b} \qquad (22b)$$

where

$$a = \frac{2K(V_{G1} - V_{G2})}{C_1}$$

$$b = \frac{4K^2(V_{G1}'' - V_{G2}'')(V_{G1}''' - V_{G2}''')}{C_1 C_2}. \qquad (22c)$$

It is interesting to note that the structure of Fig. 6(b) assures fully cancelation of nonlinearities and needs sixteen matched MOS transistors, four capacitors and two single op amps. In contrast, the Tsividis and Shi concept requires two amps with differential output, four capacitors and eight MOS transistors. It allows to cancel distortion only in a limited frequency range [10].

CONCLUSION

If an active *RC* filter structure is realized in MOS technology by the method proposed here, full cancelation of nonlinearities is achieved. The properties and restrictions of the resulting circuit will be the same as described by author in [6]. We note that the above development is based on a simplified analytical model of MOS transistor [7]. The practical problems (nonconstant mobility, mismatches, noise) will be discussed elsewhere [12].

ACKNOWLEDGMENT

The author wishes to thank Prof. E. Lindberg and Mr. Jan Erik Karlskov Jensen from the Technical University of Denmark for their fruitful discussions. The author is grateful particularly to Prof. R. W. Newcomb from the University of Maryland for his encouragement to undertake the research in this area and Prof. Y. Tsividis from Columbia University for his detailed comments and discussions.

REFERENCES

[1] M. Banu and Y. Tsividis, "Fully integrated active *RC* filters in MOS technology," *IEEE J. Solid-State Circuits*, vol. SC-18, pp. 664–651, Dec. 1983.

[2] K. Nay and A. Budak, "A voltage-controlled resistance with wide dynamic range and low distortion," *IEEE Trans. Circuits Syst.* vol. CAS-30, pp. 770–772, Oct. 1983.

[3] I. S. Han and S. B. Park, "Voltage-controlled linear resistor by two MOS transistors and its application to active *RC* filter MOS integration," *Proc. IEEE*, vol. 72, pp. 1655–1657, Nov. 1984.

[4] J. N. Babanezhad and G. C. Temes, "A linear NMOS depletion resistor and its application in an integrated amplifier," *IEEE J. Solid-State Circuits*, vol. SC-19, pp. 932–938, Dec. 1984.

[5] Z. Czarnul, "Design of voltage-controlled linear transconductance elements with matched pair of FET transistors," to be published.

[6] ——, "Modification of Banu–Tsividis continuous-time integrator structure," pp. 714–716, this issue.

[7] N. M. Penny and L. Lau, *MOS Integrated Circuits.* New York: Van Nostrand Reinhold, 1972, pp. 60–92.

[8] H. Khorramabadi and P. R. Gray, "High-frequency CMOS continuous-time filter," *IEEE J. Solid-State Circuits*, vol. SC-19, pp. 939–948, Dec. 1984.

[9] L. C. Thomas, "The biquad," *IEEE Trans. Circuit Theory*, vol. CT-18, pp. 350–361, 1971.

[10] Y. Tsividis and B. Shi, "Cancelation of distortion of any order in integrated active *RC* filters," *Electron. Lett.*, vol. 21, no. 4, pp. 132–134, Feb. 1985.

[11] Y. Tsividis, M. Banu, and J. Khoury "Continuous-time MOSFET-C filters in VLSI," *IEEE Trans. Circuits Syst.*, vol. CAS-32, pp. 125–140, Feb. 1986.

[12] Z. Czarnul, S. C. Fang, and Y. Tsividis "Improving linearity in MOS fully-integrated continous-time filters," to be published.

[13] For similar work independently proposed elsewhere see M. Ismail, "New fully integrated MOSFET capacitor active filters," in *Proc. ISCAS '85* (Kyoto, Japan), pp. 1435–1438.

A New MOSFET-C Universal Filter Structure for VLSI

MOHAMMED ISMAIL, SENIOR MEMBER, IEEE, SHIRLEY V. SMITH, AND
RICHARD G. BEALE

Abstract —A new continuous-time all-MOS universal filter structure is proposed. The new structure is based on the MOSFET-C design approach. It achieves complete MOS nonlinearity cancellation and does not require the use of fully balanced op amps. General topological requirements that are necessary for the conversion of active-*RC* prototypes to MOSFET-C counterparts, such that MOS nonlinearity cancellation is achieved, are established. Accordingly, a new universal active-*RC* prototype filter structure, which meets the necessary requirements, is presented and its MOSFET-C version is developed. Nonideal effects that may degrade the performance at high frequency are discussed and ways for improvement are proposed. Results obtained from a test chip have verified the viability of the proposed structure. The chip is an implementation of a MOSFET-C universal filter in a 3.5-μm CMOS process. The filter is successfully tuned over a wide range of pole frequencies ($0 \rightarrow 100$ kHz) using op amps with a measured gain bandwidth (GB) of only 1.2 MHz.

I. INTRODUCTION

CONTINUOUS-TIME integrated filters, implemented in MOS VLSI technology, have recently been receiving considerable attention. They have important applications in mixed analog/digital MOS VLSI systems such as high-speed computer communication transceiver chips, retrieval and storage systems, radio and TV receivers, and analog interface systems in general. In addition, continuous-time MOS circuits may have a significant impact on the field of neurocomputing where massive application of scaled analog MOS VLSI is expected.

MOSFET-C filters [1]–[9] represent a new class of continuous-time MOS integrated filters. The elements of such filters are MOS op amps, MOS transistors, and capacitors. MOSFET-C filters are different from other existing types of continuous-time MOS filters in that they avoid the usually complicated transistor-level design [10]. Instead, they use predesigned MOS op amps which are usually available in any standard cell computer library. The result is MOS integrated filters that require less design time and make effective use of available VLSI CAD tools.

The starting point in the MOSFET-C filter design is an active-*RC* prototype network whose resistors are replaced by MOS transistors operating in the triode region in such a way that the input–output operation of the resulting MOS filter is linear over an extended voltage range. The gate voltage of the MOS transistors is used to automatically tune the filter and compensate for time-constant unpredictabilities due to process or temperature variations.

The development of new MOSFET-C filter structures is desirable and highly motivated by the fact that there are a host of good active-*RC* filters available for the designer to choose from. However, conversion of popular active-*RC* networks to MOSFET-C implementation does not always result in MOS nonlinearity cancellation [4]. Generally, some topological requirements must be satisfied [5], [8], [9] in the prototype active-*RC* network. Therefore, one should be aware of the fact that what used to be classified as a popular or good active-*RC* filter for discrete implementation may not be suitable to the new fully integrated MOSFET-C approach. Hence, reassessment of popular active-*RC* filters is necessary [3], [4]. As a result, new prototype structures may emerge as good candidates for MOS implementation [4], [9].

The universal filter, usually referred to in the classical literature as the Kerwin–Huelsman–Newcomb (KHN) [11] biquad, or the state-variable filter, is a fundamental second-order building block in many analog signal processing applications. It provides the three basic filtering functions of low pass (LP), high pass (HP), and bandpass (BP). Recently [6], a MOSFET-C version of the universal filter using fully balanced op amps has been developed. The circuit [6] achieves cancellation of the even-ordered MOS nonlinearities.

In this paper, we propose a novel universal MOS filter that uses regular single-ended output op amps and achieves complete cancellation of MOS nonlinearities both even and odd. First, a fundamental MOS nonlinearity cancellation is described in Section II. Basic building blocks are then introduced in Section III and used in the development of the new filter. Section IV discusses nonideal effects and practical considerations, and proposes ways for performance improvement. Design and evaluation of an experimental test chip is included in Section V followed by some concluding remarks.

Manuscript received July 6, 1987; revised October 9, 1987. This work was supported by the National Science Foundation under Grant MIP.8451103, the Semiconductor Research Corporation under Contract 85-11-066, and by a grant from AT&T Technology Systems.
M. Ismail and S. V. Smith are with the Department of Electrical Engineering, University of Nebraska-Lincoln, Lincoln, NE 68588-0511.
R. G. Beale is with AT&T Bell Laboratories, Reading, PA 19612-3566.
IEEE Log Number 8718434.

Reprinted from *IEEE J. Solid-State Circuits,* vol. SC-23, no. 1, pp. 183–194, Feb. 1988.

II.   MOS Nonlinearity Cancellation

The analysis of MOS transistor nonlinearities requires the use of models more sophisticated than the common square-law model. Therefore, we use the accurate strong inversion model [12]–[14]. For this model, the triode region current I_D in the MOS device of Fig. 1(a) is given by

$$I_D = \frac{W}{L}\mu c_{ox}\Big\{ (V_C - V_B - V_{FB} - \phi_B)(V_1 - V_2)$$
$$- \frac{1}{2}\big[(V_1 - V_B)^2 - (V_2 - V_B)^2\big]$$
$$- \frac{2}{3}\gamma\big[(V_1 - V_B + \phi_B)^{3/2} - (V_2 - V_B + \phi_B)^{3/2}\big]\Big\} \quad (1)$$

where W and L are the channel width and length, respectively, μ is the carrier effective mobility, V_{FB} is the flat-band voltage, c_{ox} is the gate oxide capacitance per unit area, γ is the body effect, and ϕ_B is the approximate surface potential in strong inversion for zero backgate bias. The voltages V_1, V_2, V_C, and V_B are defined with respect to ground.

The 3/2 power terms in (1) can be expanded in Taylor series with respect to V_1 and V_2. Then I_D can be written in the general form [14]

$$I_D = K\big[a_1(V_1 - V_2) + a_2(V_1^2 - V_2^2) + a_3(V_1^3 - V_2^3) + \cdots \big] \quad (2)$$

where

$$K = \frac{1}{2}\mu c_{ox}\frac{W}{L} \quad (3)$$

$$a_1 = 2(V_C - V_{TB}) \quad (4)$$

and

$$V_{TB} = V_{FB} + \phi_B + \gamma[\phi_B - V_B]^{1/2}. \quad (5)$$

The second- and higher-order coefficients a_i ($i \geq 2$) are independent of V_1 and V_2 and are functions of all the process and physical parameters involved in the making of the device.

The inverse of Ka_1 of (2) is the small signal resistance R of the transistor and is given by

$$R = \frac{1}{Ka_1} = \frac{1}{\mu c_{ox}\dfrac{W}{L}(V_C - V_{TB})} \quad (6)$$

where the aspect ratio L/W is used as a design parameter for R. R can also be tuned automatically or manually by changing V_C (henceforth called the control voltage).

The second- and higher-order terms in (2) are nonlinear. Note that these terms are independent of V_C. If these terms are cancelled, the MOS transistor behaves like a linear resistor as long as the device is operating in the triode region, i.e.

$$V_1 \leqslant V_C - V_{TB}. \quad (7)$$

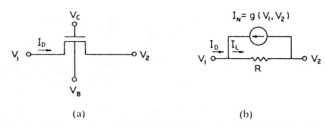

Fig. 1.   (a) An n-channel MOSFET. (b) Large-signal model of the MOS transistor.

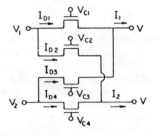

Fig. 2.   The general four-transistor transconductor.

Referring to Fig. 1(b), and in order to simplify the analysis, the current equation (2) is written as follows:

$$I_D = I_L - I_N \quad (8)$$

where I_N is a nonlinear term in V_1 and V_2 and I_L is a linear term given by

$$I_L = \frac{1}{R}(V_1 - V_2). \quad (9)$$

I_N can be expressed as follows:

$$I_N = g(V_1) - g(V_2) \quad (10)$$

where $g(V_1)$ and $g(V_2)$ are nonlinear functions in V_1 and V_2, respectively, and are *independent* of the gate voltages.

Now consider the four identical MOS devices shown in Fig. 2, driven by the voltages V_1 and V_2 and a common-mode (virtual short) voltage V, all referred to ground. Using (8)–(10), one can express I_1 and I_2, respectively, as follows:

$$I_1 = I_{D1} + I_{D3}$$
$$= \frac{V_1 - V}{R_1} + \frac{V_2 - V}{R_3} - \big[g(V_1) - g(V)\big]$$
$$- \big[(g(V_2) - g(V)\big] \quad (11)$$

$$I_2 = I_{D2} + I_{D4}$$
$$= \frac{V_1 - V}{R_2} + \frac{V_2 - V}{R_4} - \big[g(V_1) - g(V)\big]$$
$$- \big[g(V_2) - g(V)\big] \quad (12)$$

where R_i ($i = 1$–4) is given by (6) with $V_C = V_{Ci}$. Inspection of (11) and (12) results in the interesting fact that the nonlinear components of I_1 and I_2 are equal. Now con-

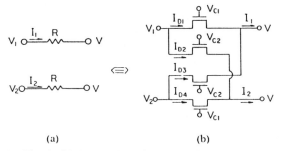

(a)   (b)

Fig. 3. The double-MOSFET method for nonlinearity cancellation. (a) Resistor pair R. (b) Equivalent MOS structure.

sider the difference between the two currents, i.e.

$$I_1 - I_2 = \left(\frac{1}{R_1} - \frac{1}{R_2}\right)V_1 + \left(\frac{1}{R_3} - \frac{1}{R_4}\right)V_2$$
$$+ \left(\frac{1}{R_2} + \frac{1}{R_4} - \frac{1}{R_1} - \frac{1}{R_3}\right)V \quad (13)$$

which has no nonlinear terms. The voltage V, however, is a nonlinear function of the signals V_1 and V_2. Therefore, for a truly linear current difference $I_1 - I_2$, the V term in (13) must be forced to zero. This results in the following general nonlinearity cancellation condition that [2]

$$\frac{1}{R_2} + \frac{1}{R_4} = \frac{1}{R_1} + \frac{1}{R_3} \quad (14a)$$

or

$$V_{C2} + V_{C4} = V_{C1} + V_{C3}. \quad (14b)$$

A possible choice of the control voltages to satisfy (14) is to let $V_{C1} = V_{C4}$ and $V_{C2} = V_{C3}$. The resulting MOS structure is shown in Fig. 3(b). Note that the four-MOS structure of Fig. 3(b) has recently been proposed in [15] and has also been used in the development of fully balanced biquads in [7]. However, the condition for nonlinearity cancellation given by (14) is an interesting generalization and provides insight as to how the cancellation is achieved. With $V_{C1} = V_{C4}$ and $V_{C2} = V_{C3}$, (13) reduces to

$$I_1 - I_2 = \frac{1}{R}(V_1 - V_2) \quad (15a)$$

where

$$\frac{1}{R} = \frac{1}{R_1} - \frac{1}{R_2} = \mu c_{ox}\frac{W}{L}(V_{C1} - V_{C2}). \quad (15b)$$

To ensure triode region operation, one must have

$$V_1, V_2 \leq \min[V_{C1} - V_{TB}, V_{C2} - V_{TB}]. \quad (15c)$$

Equation (15a) suggests that the four identical MOS devices simulate a pair of identical resistors R, as shown in Fig. 3. In other words and as far as the difference $I_1 - I_2$ is concerned, the four-MOSFET structure is equivalent to the resistor pair R. This is an important observation that helps in the design of MOSFET-C filters from active-RC

prototypes. It leads to the fact that the active-RC prototype circuit must meet the following necessary requirements for MOSFET-C conversion:

1) the resistances must occur in matched pairs;
2) the voltage at one end of the pair must be the same, generally the differential inputs of an ideal op amp; and
3) the voltages at the other end must be different, i.e., $V_1 \neq V_2$. This includes the special case of V_1 (or V_2) = 0, but not both, and the fully balanced case [7] in which $V_1 = -V_2$.

We will call the above nonlinearity cancellation scheme "the double-MOSFET" method [7], [8]. This indicates the need of two MOS devices per resistor for the conversion of active-RC circuits to MOSFET-C counterparts. It is also important to point out the fact that the MOS devices used could be enhancement or depletion, n or p type. Depletion devices can accept positive as well as negative gate voltages, e.g., one can use $V_{C1} = -V_{C2}$ with V_{C1} positive [27]. For p-channel devices, V_C and V_{TB} are interchanged in (6) and (15c). Also, V_{C1} and V_{C2} are interchanged in (15b).

III. THE NEW MOSFET-C UNIVERSAL FILTER STRUCTURE

The block diagram representation of the universal filter is shown in Fig. 4(a). The classical filter structure is shown in Fig. 4(b). The filter provides the three basic filtering functions at the three op-amps outputs. It is well known [16] that the classical structure of Fig. 4(b) is not capable of independently realizing the three design parameters of interest, namely, the pole Q, Q, pole frequency ω_0, and the multiplicative constant H_0. Typically one designs the circuit to meet specified ω_0 and Q while H_0 is not free to be chosen. However, this problem can be solved by adding a grounded resistor connected to the positive input terminal of op-amp A_1. The circuit is also known to have low sensitivities to circuit element variations.

Obviously the structure of Fig. 4(b) does not meet the necessary topological requirements stated in the previous section for MOSFET-C conversion. To satisfy these requirements, a new active-RC universal filter is developed as shown in Fig. 5. The new filter implements the functions indicated in the block diagram representation of Fig. 4(a) by means of the integrator and weighted-summer building blocks shown in Figs. 6(a) and (b), respectively. Let us now verify that nonlinearity cancellation does indeed take place. First consider the integrator of Fig. 6(a). Its output is given by

$$V_0 = -\frac{1}{C}\int_{-\infty}^{t} I_1 \cdot d\tau + V_x$$
$$= \frac{1}{C}\int_{-\infty}^{t}(I_2 - I_1)\,d\tau. \quad (16)$$

Using the results of Section II, particularly (15), one can

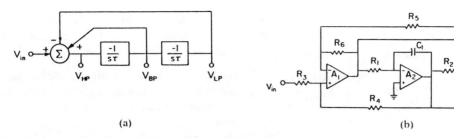

(a)   (b)

Fig. 4.   (a) Block diagram representation of a state-variable universal filter. (b) Classical active-RC universal filter.

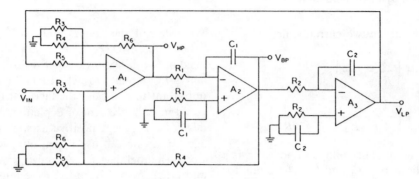

Fig. 5.   New active-RC universal filter for MOSFET-C implementation.

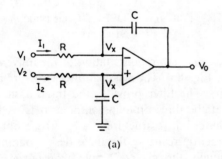

(a)

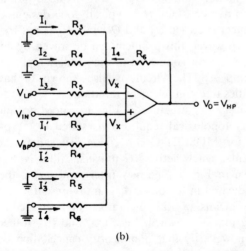

(b)

Fig. 6.   Basic building blocks. (a) Integrator. (b) Weighted summer.

express V_0 as

$$V_0 = \frac{1}{RC} \int_{-\infty}^{t} (V_2 - V_1) \, d\tau. \qquad (17)$$

This means that the R pair of the integrator can be replaced by MOS transistors according to the double-

MOSFET method (Fig. 3) such that the input–output relationship is a linear one. As a result, R in (17) is given by (15b). Next, consider the weighted summer of Fig. 6(b). If one writes the node equations at V_X, he gets

$$I_1' + I_2' + I_3' = -I_4' \qquad (18)$$

and

$$I_1 + I_2 + I_3 = -I_4 \qquad (19)$$

subtracting (19) from (18)

$$(I_1' - I_1) + (I_2' - I_2) + (I_3' - I_3) = (I_4 - I_4') \qquad (20a)$$

using (15a) in (20a)

$$\frac{V_{in} - 0}{R_3} + \frac{V_{BP} - 0}{R_4} + \frac{0 - V_{LP}}{R_5} = \frac{V_0 - 0}{R_6} \qquad (20b)$$

where

$$R_i = \frac{1}{\mu c_{ox} \left(\dfrac{W}{L} \right)_i (V_{C1} - V_{C2})}, \qquad i = 3,4,5,6. \qquad (20c)$$

Again here, if we replace the four resistor pairs in Fig. 6(b) with MOSFET's, according to the double-MOSFET method, one obtains (20b) which is expressed as the following weighted sum:

$$V_0 = \frac{R_6}{R_3} V_{in} + \frac{R_6}{R_4} V_{BP} + \frac{R_6}{R_5} V_{LP}. \qquad (21)$$

The MOSFET-C version of the new filter is developed as shown in Fig. 7. Using (17) and (21), one can arrive at

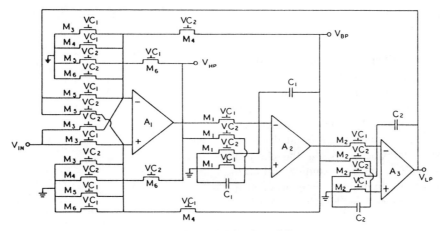

Fig. 7.   The new MOSFET-C universal filter structure.

the following filter transfer function:

$$\frac{V_0}{V_{in}} = \frac{N(s)}{s^2 + \dfrac{R_6}{R_1 R_4 C_1} s + \dfrac{R_6}{R_1 R_2 R_5 C_1 C_2}} \qquad (22)$$

where $N(s)$ is given by

$$\text{for } V_0 = V_{HP}, \qquad N(s) = \frac{R_6}{R_3} s^2$$

$$V_0 = V_{BP}, \qquad N(s) = -\frac{R_6}{R_3} \cdot \frac{1}{R_1 C_1} \cdot s \qquad (23)$$

and

$$V_0 = V_{LP}, \qquad N(s) = \frac{R_6}{R_3} \cdot \frac{1}{R_1 R_2 C_1 C_2}.$$

If one assumes $R_6 = R_5$ and equal time constants for the two integrators, to maximize the filter dynamic range [17], i.e., $R_1 = R_2 = R$ and $C_1 = C_2 = C$, the filter pole Q and pole frequency are given, respectively, by

$$Q = \frac{R_4}{R_6} = \frac{(W/L)_6}{(W/L)_4} \qquad (24a)$$

$$\omega_0 = \frac{1}{RC} = \mu \frac{c_{ox}}{C} \frac{W}{L} (V_{C1} - V_{C2}). \qquad (24b)$$

Also, the high-pass gain at infinity equals the low-pass gain at dc:

$$= \frac{R_6}{R_3} = \frac{R_5}{R_3} = \frac{(W/L)_3}{(W/L)_6} \qquad (24c)$$

and the bandpass gain at resonance is

$$\frac{R_4}{R_3} = \frac{(W/L)_3}{(W/L)_4}. \qquad (24d)$$

Hence, the filter is capable of independently realizing the three parameters of interest, namely, ω_0, Q, and gain H_0. It also possesses the low-sensitivity properties of a

two-integrator loop structure [17]. Furthermore, it is interesting to note that the design equations of the new filter are much more simpler than those of the classical structure. To see this consider the weighted-summer subcircuit of the classical structure. Its output is given by

$$V_{0HP} = K_1(1 + K_3)V_{in} + K_2(1 + K_3)V_{0BP} - K_3 V_{0LP} \qquad (25)$$

where

$$K_1 = \frac{1}{1 + R_3/R_4}$$

$$K_2 = \frac{1}{1 + R_4/R_3}$$

and

$$K_3 = \frac{R_6}{R_5}. \qquad (26)$$

Comparing (25) to (21) one can clearly see the simplicity of (21) in which the weights are simple resistor (W/L) ratios. This ultimately results in simpler filter design equations. However, if one is to implement the filter using discrete active-RC components the classical structure uses fewer circuit elements in comparison to the new structure of Fig. 5.

IV. NONIDEAL EFFECTS

The main goal of this paper is to introduce the new universal filter structure and show how to "capitalize" on the wealth of knowledge gained in the field of active RC and put it to use in the context of MOS VLSI technology. However, there are several practical considerations that may affect the performance of MOSFET-C filters particularly at higher frequencies where it is desirable to take advantage of the continuous-time technique. This section briefly discusses some of the nonideal effects and provides ways to mitigate or eliminate such effects in the proposed filter structure.

153

A. Op-Amp Dynamics

One of the limiting factors in realizing high-frequency high-precision MOSFET-C filters is the finite gain-bandwidth (GB) of the op amps [7], [8]. The new filter structure belongs to the two-integrator loop class of filters. Such filters suffer from a rather drastic pole-Q enhancement effect due to finite GB [19]–[21]. The Q-enhancement phenomenon is due to excess phase lag, around the loop, contributed by op-amp parasitic poles. In the classical universal filter case this effect has been studied and compensation methods that result in dramatic improvement in the filter useful frequency range have been proposed [20], [21].

Obviously, one has to study the effect of limited GB on the performance of the new prototype topology of Fig. 5. It is desirable to analytically study these effects at this early stage to avoid complicated analysis of the MOSFET-C version of Fig. 7. The analysis can be verified by computer simulation using a program such as SPICE. In some cases breadboarding the prototype active-RC circuits in the laboratory [18] may prove necessary to take a closer look at the circuit useful frequency range, dynamic range, stability, etc.

Now consider the prototype circuit of Fig. 5. Assume a first-pole model for the op-amp open-loop gain given by $A(s) = GB/s$ and assume identical op amps. Using well-known analysis methods [16], [17], one can show that the excess phase lag around the loop, ϕ, is given by

$$\phi \simeq \left(4 + \frac{R_6}{R_3} + \frac{1}{Q}\right) \frac{\omega}{GB}, \qquad \omega \ll GB \qquad (27)$$

with each integrator providing a phase lag of ω/GB, and assuming $R_5 = R_6$, the weighted summer provides a phase lag of $\phi - 2\omega/GB$.

Fortunately, compensation methods, both passive [19] and active [20], [21], are available in the active-RC literature and can effectively be used to mitigate excess phase lag effects. Fig. 8(a) and (b) shows two variable phase lead integrator blocks using passive and active compensation, respectively. The compensating capacitors C_c in Fig. 8(a) is used to provide the necessary amount of phase lead. If one of the two integrators, say A_3, in the new filter structure is modified according to Fig. 8(a), one can easily show that the design equation for C_c is

$$C_c R = \left(4 + \frac{R_6}{R_3} + \frac{1}{Q}\right) \cdot \frac{1}{GB} \qquad (28)$$

where R is given by (15b). Passive compensation, which has not been recognized as an effective compensation technique for discrete active-RC filters, seems attractive for MOSFET-C integrated filters [5]. This is because of the fact that the op-amp compensation capacitor will closely track the filter capacitors since they are fabricated in the same processing steps. The concern here is due to the fact that the time constant $C_c R$ is voltage controlled, i.e., it can be tuned, around a nominal design value to compensate

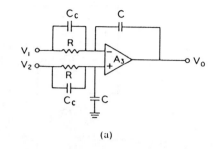

(a)

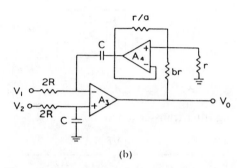

(b)

Fig. 8. Phase lead integrators employing (a) passive compensation, and (b) active compensation.

for process or temperature variations, whereas the op-amp GB which is of the form g_m/C is not well controlled. However, since g_m is dependent on the bias current, one can appropriately bias the op amp from the filter tuning voltage [23] such that (28) is always valid. This might be acceptable for fixed frequency response applications. In variable frequency filter applications, where it is desirable to design filters with constant pole Q over a wide range of pole frequencies, passive compensation might be difficult to implement on chip. This is because changing ω_0 is achieved by changing the nominal value of $V_{C1} - V_{C2}$ to a new value that might be three or four times less or more. This in turn changes R by the same factor. So, in order to always keep (28) valid, one has to either use variable GB op amps or variable compensating capacitors C_c, or both.

On the other hand, active compensation depends on matching the same type of devices (op amps) rather than the tracking of different devices. The actively compensated phase lead integrator of Fig. 8(b) uses op-amp A_4 and the associated resistive circuit to provide the necessary amount of phase lead. If $b = 1$, this ensures integrator stability with respect to the op-amp second pole [21]. The phase lead provided by the integrator is given by $(a/2)\omega/GB$. For instance, if $Q = 10$ and $R_6/R_3 = 1$ then the required value of $a = 10.2$. The resistors r and r/a can be fabricated in MOS technology using tub, poly, or diffusion resistances. Unlike passive compensation, active compensation is independent of the filter time constant and therefore is more suitable for variable frequency range applications. This has been verified using intensive computer simulation [24], [25].

B. Parasitic Capacitances

Another important limiting factor that must be taken into account is the effect of MOS parasitic capacitances.

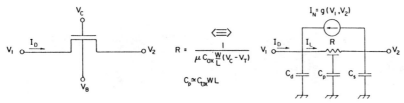

Fig. 9.   MOS model with high-frequency parasitics.

Fig. 9 shows an n-channel MOS model with the high-frequency parasitic capacitances. The capacitances C_d and C_s are either voltage driven or connected to one of the op-amp inputs. Therefore their effect is not significant if the op amp approximates ideal behavior [5]. The effect of the distributed capacitance C_p, however, can be more significant and can result in frequency response degradation in a manner similar to the effect of finite op-amp GB. Fortunately, it has been shown in [7], [22], and [24] that the four-MOS structure, originally developed for nonlinearity cancellation, inherently cancels the effect of C_p over an extended frequency range. Specifically, it has been shown [24] that when the pair of resistors in the integrator of Fig. 6(a) is replaced by MOSFET's according to Fig. 3, the resulting integrator transfer function is free from phase errors due to C_p for frequencies such that $\omega^2 R_1 R_2 C_p^2/36 \ll 1$, where R_1 and R_2 are given by (6) for $V_C = V_{C1}$ and $V_C = V_{C2}$, respectively, and with the assumption that the distributed effects are modeled as a uniform RC transmission line.

C. Mismatches and Mobility Degradation

The analysis adopted earlier in the paper assumed matched MOS devices with constant mobility. This is, of course, not the case in practice. Mismatch in MOS aspect ratios and threshold voltage cause residual even-order harmonic distortion. Further, the mobility is dependent on the gate voltage V_C through a process known as "mobility degradation" [26]. This causes residual odd-order harmonic distortion [5]. At higher frequencies the op-amp gain decreases and the assumption of virtual short at the op-amp inputs is no longer valid. These nonideal effects combined with noise due to thermal effects and extraneous signals can restrict the dynamic range. Fortunately, since R is dependent on $(V_{C1} - V_{TB}) - (V_{C2} - V_{TB})$, noise signals generated on the V_C as well as the V_B lines does not affect the performance. Also, one has to exercise extreme care in the layout of the MOS transistors to improve matching. Finally, higher values for V_{C1} and V_{C2} (to realize the same $V_{C1} - V_{C2}$) would reduce harmonic distortion.

V.   DESIGN EXAMPLE

Based on the principles presented earlier, we designed a MOSFET-C universal filter to meet the following specifications:

$Q = 5$,
$f_0 = 30$ kHz,
BP gain at resonance $= 1$, and
LP gain at dc $= 0.2 =$ HP gain at ∞.

TABLE I
OP-AMP SPECIFICATIONS

A_0	80 dB
f_T	1.2 MHz
PSRR+, 1KHz	-45dB
PSRR-, 1KHZ	-55dB
Equivalent input Thermal noise	$12nV/\sqrt{Hz}$
Slew rate, 50pF	+5, -4 V/µ sec.
CMVR	± 3.5 V
Power Consumption ± 5V	7mw
Area	0.15 mm

The filter is fabricated using a Bell Laboratories standard twin-tub CMOS process, having the capability to implement capacitors between the gate polysilicon and a second polysilicon layer. The design rules are based on 3.5-µm minimum line width. The gate oxide thickness is 500 Å and the capacitor oxide thickness is 800 Å. P-channel MOS devices are used as voltage-controlled resistors. PMOS devices are used because they have smaller mobility than NMOS devices, and thus smaller channel length for the same resistance value R. Op amps with high driving capability are used. The op-amp specifications are listed in Table I. The values for the control voltages are chosen to be $V_{C1} = -5$ V and $V_{C2} = -4$ V. In order to achieve a high degree of matching between the MOS transistors a "unit transistor" layout strategy is adopted such that identically sized MOS transistors are used. We used parallel combination (all sources (drains) are tied together) of identical MOS devices; e.g., if the unit transistor has an aspect ratio of 1/5 then a transistor with a 1/1 aspect ratio would be implemented using a parallel combination of five unit transistors. The five unit transistors share the same gate–source voltage and provide equivalence to the transistor with 1/1 aspect ratio. Our unit device is 30 µm long and 6 µm wide. All MOS devices were laid out as close to each other as possible. Four 9.55-pF capacitors are used. A photomicrograph of the filter is shown in Fig. 10. An extracted version of the layout was simulated using the program ADVICE, a simulation tool used at Bell Laboratories. The simulation results are shown in Fig. 11 which indicates a slight Q-enhancement effect (about 2 dB). The experimental results of the LP and HP frequency responses are shown in Fig. 12(a) whereas the BP response is shown in Fig. 12(b). Due to absence of an automatic

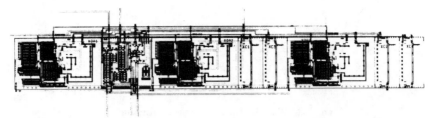

Fig. 10.   Photomicrograph of the filter.

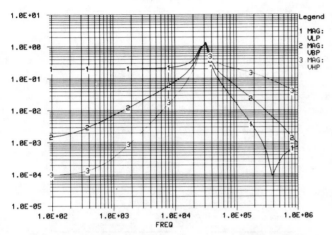

Fig. 11.   Frequency response simulation results using ADVICE.

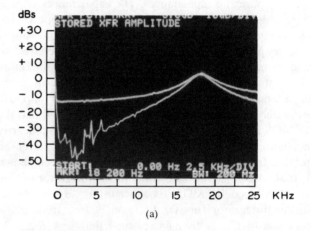

(a)

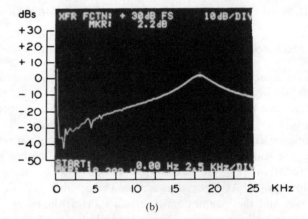

(b)

tuning, the pole frequency f_0 is shifted to 18.2 kHz. The filter was tuned manually and a 30-kHz pole frequency was obtained by changing V_{C2} from -4 to -3.5 V. Here, we should point out that if an automatic tuning system is used (currently under consideration), the system should not necessarily change both V_{C1} and V_{C2} automatically, e.g., V_{C1} can be held constant while V_{C2} is controlled by the tuning system. In order to see the filter capability of realizing transmission zeros, the LP and HP outputs were summed using an off-chip summer. The result is the symmetrical notch response of Fig. 12(c). The filter was then tuned over a wide frequency range (0–63 kHz) by keeping V_{C1} constant (-5 V) and changing V_{C2} (-5 to -1.6 V). Fig. 13(a) shows a plot of the pole frequency f_0 versus $\Delta V_C = V_{C2} - V_{C1}$. The filter was also tuned at higher frequencies (up to 100 kHz) using lower values of V_{C1} and V_{C2} without affecting signal handling capability. The pole Q was measured at different values of f_0 and Q was plotted versus f_0 as shown in Fig. 13(b) to investigate the filter Q-enhancement effect. The input terminals of op-amp A_3 were connected to bonding pads in the chip layout. The op-amp GB was measured using an op amp that was available on chip. Compensating capacitors were then calculated using (28) (R in (28) is determined as $1/\omega_0 C$ with $C = 9.55$ pF) and were connected according to Fig. 8(a): one capacitor between the op-amp negative input and the BP output, the other between the op-amp positive input and ground. Different pairs of compensating capacitors C_c were tried at different f_0's and successfully restored the pole Q to the desired $Q = 5$, as shown in Fig. 13(b).

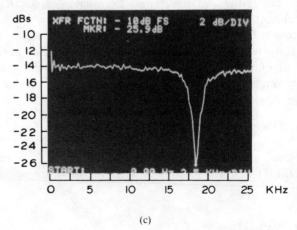

(c)

Fig. 12.   (a) LP and HP frequency responses. (b) BP frequency response. (c) Symmetrical notch frequency response.

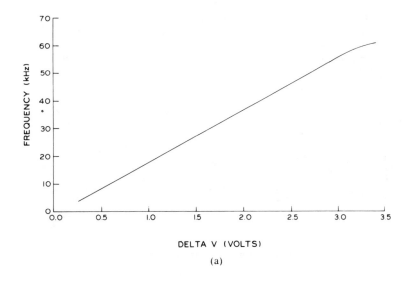

(a)

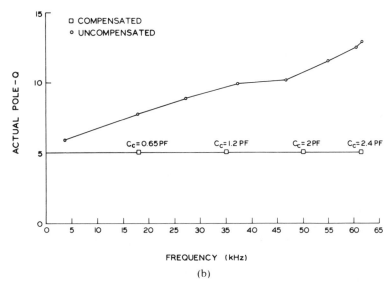

(b)

Fig. 13. (a) f_0 versus ΔV_C. $\Delta V = |V_{C1} - V_{C2}|$, $V_{C1} = -5$ V. (b) Q versus f_0.

The linearity performance of the filter is illustrated in Fig. 14. The measured total harmonic distortion (THD) using a constant $\Delta V_C = V_{C2} - V_{C1}$ but different values of V_{C1} and V_{C2} is shown in Fig. 14(a). The THD is also measured at different values of ΔV_C as shown in Fig. 14(b). In generating these plots, the input signal frequency was taken at one-third f_0 which gives maximum third harmonic distortion and the LP output was measured. The results are very reasonable for a single-ended (unbalanced) topology. Fig. 14(a) and (b) shows that improvement in THD is achieved with larger control voltages (magnitudes) and smaller ΔV_C. It is also evident from Fig. 14(a) and (b) that a significant improvement in THD can be achieved by attenuating the input signal, say by a factor of 2 or 3, and amplifying the output signal by the same factor. The dominant even and odd harmonic components relative to the fundamental are plotted versus input voltage in Fig. 14(c). This shows that at lower signal levels distortion is dominated by device mismatches whereas at relatively higher signal levels the mobility degradation effect becomes stronger.

The total in-band output noise was measured to be 300-, 270-, and 320-μV rms for the LP, BP, and HP outputs, respectively. The noise spectrum of the BP output is shown in Fig. 15. The LP and HP outputs exhibited very similar spectra [24]. This, combined with 1-percent THD for 4.5-$V_{p\text{-}p}$ input at 1 kHz (with 0.2 dc gain, the LP output signal is 900 m$V_{p\text{-}p}$), results in 61-dB dynamic range. This figure could be improved by trading off THD. The BP and HP power supply rejection performances are shown in Figs. 16 and 17, respectively. The PSRR peaks at f_0 with a higher peak in the case of V_{DD}. This is due to the fact that PMOS devices are used (substrate connected to V_{DD}). The LP PSRR performance is very similar to that of the BP [24]. Table II summarizes the measured filter performance.

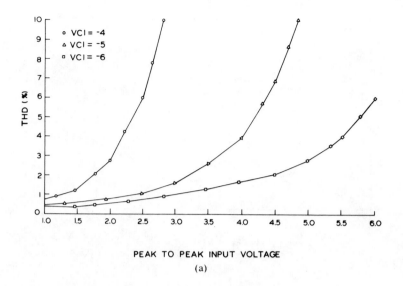

PEAK TO PEAK INPUT VOLTAGE

(a)

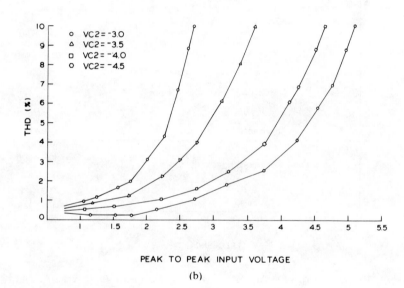

PEAK TO PEAK INPUT VOLTAGE

(b)

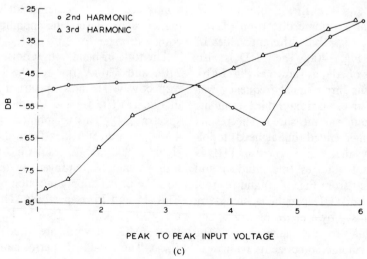

PEAK TO PEAK INPUT VOLTAGE

(c)

Fig. 14. (a) THD versus input voltage (p-p). Different V_{C1} and V_{C2}, constant ΔV_C. $\Delta V = |V_{C1} - V_{C2}| = 1$. (b) THD versus input voltage (p-p). Different ΔV_C. $V_{C1} = -5$ V. (c) Second and third harmonic distortion versus input voltage. $V_{C1} = -5$ V; $V_{C2} = -4$ V. $f = 1$ kHz.

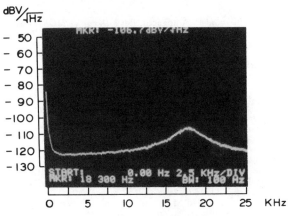

Fig. 15. Bandpass noise spectrum.

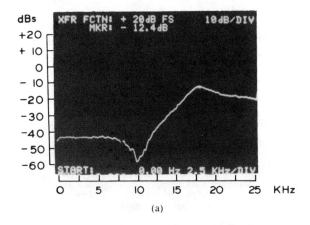

(a)

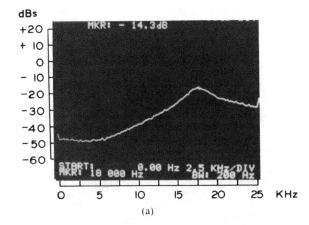

(a)

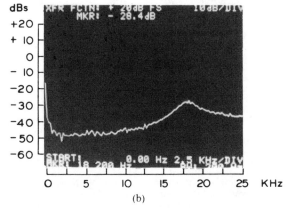

(b)

Fig. 17. (a) HP PSRR—V_{DD}. (b) HP PSRR—V_{SS}.

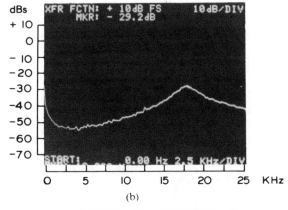

(b)

Fig. 16. (a) BP PSRR—V_{DD}. (b) BP PSRR—V_{SS}.

TABLE II
MEASURED FILTER PERFORMANCE ($V_{C1} = -5$ V, $V_{C2} = -4$ V)

Power Supply		± 5V
In-band noise		
	LP	300 μV rms
	BP	270 μV rms
	HP	320 μV rms
Dynamic range (1KHz - 1% THD - 0.2 dc gain)		61dB
PSRR (1KHz)		
	LP	-45dB
V_{DD}	BP	-47dB
	HP	-44dB
	LP	-52dB
V_{SS}	BP	-50dB
	HP	-49dB
Area		0.7 mm^2

VI. CONCLUSIONS

A new continuous-time MOSFET-C universal filter structure is presented. The structure is simple and the design process is easy as it uses regular single-ended op amps. Nonideal effects and practical limitations due to op-amp dynamics, MOS parasitic capacitances, device mismatches, and mobility degradation are investigated and simple compensation techniques and design methods to mitigate or eliminate such effects are described. An experimental test chip has been designed and fabricated in order to verify theoretical expectations. Needless to say, circuit techniques that are insensitive to device mismatches and mobility degradation with low noise performance as well as sophisticated high-precision automatic tuning schemes constitute important areas for future research. Furthermore, the availability of high-speed op amps with good driving capability is an important factor in the implementation of high-frequency MOSFET-C filters.

In conclusion, the paper provides a good example of how to bridge the gap between classical analog circuits and VLSI.

IEEE JOURNAL OF SOLID-STATE CIRCUITS, VOL. 23, NO. 1, FEBRUARY 1988

ACKNOWLEDGMENT

The authors are grateful to J. Steininger for his help and cooperation, to L. Mantz for chip layout, and to N. Khachab for his assistance in testing the chip.

REFERENCES

[1] M. Banu and Y. Tsividis, "Fully-integrated active-RC filters in MOS technology," *IEEE J. Solid-State Circuits*, SC-18, pp. 644–651, Dec. 1983.

[2] M. Ismail, "Four-transistor continuous-time MOS transconductor," *Electron. Lett.*, vol. 23, no. 20, pp. 1099–1100, Sept. 1987.

[3] M. Ismail, "A new MOSFET-capacitor integrator," *IEEE Trans. Circuits Syst.*, vol. CAS-32, pp. 1194–1196, Nov. 1985.

[4] M. Ismail, "New fully-integrated MOSFET-capacitor active filters," in *Proc. IEEE Int. Symp. Circuits Syst.* (Kyoto, Japan), pp. 1435–1438, June 1985.

[5] Y. Tsividis, M. Banu, and J. Khoury, "Continuous-time MOSFET-C filters in VLSI," *IEEE Trans. Circuits Syst.*, vol. CAS-33, pp. 125–139, Feb. 1986.

[6] M. Ismail and D. Ganow, "MOSFET-capacitor continuous-time filter structures for VLSI," in *Proc. IEEE Int. Symp. Circuits Syst.* (San Jose, CA), May 1986, pp. 1196–1200.

[7] M. Ismail and D. Rubin, "Improved circuits for the realization of MOSFET-C filters," in *Proc. IEEE Int. Symp. Circuits Syst.* (San Jose, CA), May 1986, pp. 1186–1189.

[8] S. Smith, F. Liu, and M. Ismail, "Active-RC building blocks for MOSFET-C integrated filters," in *Proc. 1987 IEEE Int. Symp. Circuits Syst.* (Philadelphia, PA), May 1987, pp. 342–346.

[9] M. Ismail and S. Smith, "A new MOSFET-C universal filter structure for VLSI," in *Proc. 1987 VLSI Circuits Symp.* (Karuizawa, Japan), May 1987, pp. 71–72.

[10] A. P. Nedungadi and P. E. Allen, "A MOS integrator for continuous-time monolithic filters," in *Proc. IEEE Int. Symp. Circuits Syst.* (Montreal, Canada), May 1984, pp. 932–935.

[11] W. J. Kerwin, L. P. Huelsman, and R. W. Newcomb, "State-variable synthesis for insensitive integrated circuit transfer functions," *IEEE J. Solid-State Circuits*, vol. SC-2, pp. 87–92, Sept. 1967.

[12] W. M. Penny and L. Lau, Eds., *MOS Integrated Circuits.* New York: Van Nostrand-Reinhold, 1972.

[13] Y. Tsividis, *Operation and Modeling of the MOS Transistor.* New York: McGraw-Hill, 1986.

[14] Y. Tsividis and P. Antognetti, Eds., *Design of MOS VLSI Circuits for Telecommunications.* Englewood Cliffs, NJ: Prentice-Hall, 1985.

[15] Z. Czarnul, "Modification of the Banu–Tsividis continuous-time integrator structure," *IEEE Trans. Circuits Syst.*, vol. CAS-33, pp. 714–716, July 1986.

[16] L. P. Huelsman and P. E. Allen, *Introduction to the Theory and Design of Active Filters.* New York: McGraw-Hill, 1980.

[17] A. S. Sedra and P. O. Brackett, *Filter Theory and Design: Active and Passive.* Champaign, IL: Matrix, 1977.

[18] M. Ismail and D. Rubin, "Effect of the finite amplifier gain-bandwith on the performance of fully-balanced MOSFET-capacitor filters," in *Proc. 28th Midwest Symp. Circuits Syst.* (Louisville, KY), Aug. 1985, pp. 592–595.

[19] A. M. Soliman and M. Ismail, "Phase correction in two-integrator loop filters using a single compensating resistor," *Electron. Lett.*, vol. 14, pp. 375–376, 1978.

[20] A. M. Soliman and M. Ismail, "A universal variable phase 3-port VCVS and its application in two-integrator loop filters," in *Proc IEEE Int. Symp. Circuits Syst.* (Houston, TX), May 1980, pp. 83–86.

[21] A. M. Soliman, "Novel phase lead inverting integrator and its application in two-integrator loop filters," *Electron Lett.*, vol. 16, pp. 475–476, June 1980.

[22] D. Rubin, "Analysis and compensation of nonidealities in continuous-time fully-balanced MOSFET-capacitor active filters," M.S. thesis, Dept. Elec. Eng., Univ. of Nebraska-Lincoln, Dec. 1985.

[23] J. M. Khoury and Y. P. Tsividis, "Analysis and compensation of high-frequency effects in integrated MOSFET-C continuous-time filters," *IEEE Trans. Circuits Syst.*, vol. CAS-34, pp. 862–875, Aug. 1987.

[24] S. V. Smith, "Design, analysis and compensation of single-ended MOSFET-C integrated filters," M.S. thesis, Elec. Eng. Dept., Univ. of Nebraska, Lincoln, 1987.

[25] M. Ismail and S. Smith, "MOSFET-C filter structures homologous to the conventional KHN structure," in *Proc. 30th Midwest Symp. Circuits Syst.* (Syracuse, NY), Aug. 1987.

[26] J. L. Pennock, "CMOS triode transconductor for continuous-time active integrated filters," *Electron. Lett.*, vol. 21, pp. 817–818, Aug. 1985.

[27] N. I. Khachab and M. Ismail, "Novel continuous-time all-MOS four-quadrant multipliers," in *Proc. IEEE Int. Symp. Circuits Syst.* (Philadelphia, PA), May 1987, pp. 762–765.

Part 3
Filters Using Capacitors and Transconductors

SECTIONS 3-A and 3-B are devoted to filters using only transconductors (voltage-controlled current sources) and capacitors. An advantage of these filters is that parasitic poles of transconductors often can be accounted for by correction of the filter time constants. For example, in many cases all or many signal voltage-carrying nodes are intended filter nodes (the transconductors have none or only a few internal signal–voltage–carrying nodes). Stray capacitances on signal–voltage–carrying nodes shunt filter capacitances and can be included in them. Moreover, the capacitive embedding of the transconductors decreases the loop gain at high frequencies and helps to keep the circuits stable. In CMOS technology, the resulting filters are capable of higher frequencies of operation than MOSFET-C filters (in BiCMOS, extremely wideband op amps are possible and MOSFET-C filters become competitive; see Papers 2-A.2 and 2-B.5). The disadvantage of transconductance-C filters is that they are sensitive to parasitic capacitances (which can be nonlinear) and, thus, they usually require device-level design based on the knowledge of such parasitics.

The name *operational transconductance amplifier* (OTA) is sometimes used in lieu of the name *transconductor*. Filter configurations using transconductors and capacitors are introduced in Papers 1-1 and 1-2 in this volume and are considered in a number of publications [1–18] as well as in the papers in this and the following section. Of the large number of topologies that have been proposed, the ones most amenable to reliable filter integration contain a capacitor connected to every node; otherwise, parasitic capacitances can introduce new parasitic poles. Note that the well-known classic gyrator-C filters can be implemented as transconductor-capacitor filters since each gyrator can be implemented as two transconductors connected back to back.

The first reported integrated transconductor-capacitor filters were single-ended and based on gyrators. They are described in Paper 3-A.1 by Moulding and Wilson and Paper 3-A.2 by Moulding et al. These filters operate in the video range and are made using bipolar technology. Junction capacitors with variable bias voltage are used for the tuning of the time constants of the filters.

Paper 3-A.3 by Voorman, Brüls, and Barth shows accurate filter circuits for audio frequencies using dielectric capacitors (a process option) and transconductor–multiplier combinations. Next we return to the simplest bipolar transconductor that one can imagine: a differential pair of transistors. The transconductor and the multiplier (multiplication being achieved by the bias current) have been merged. Linearization is obtained by placing stages in parallel (Paper 3-A.4 by Voorman, Brüls, and Barth and Paper 3-A.5 by Tanimoto, Koyama, and Yoshida). These circuits operate with supply voltages as low as 1 V.

For bipolar NPN transistors, the exponential relationship between collector current and base–emitter voltage holds true for many decades of collector current and the circuits can be tuned over this range. The tuning range of MOSFET transconductors is much smaller, of the order of magnitude of one-half to one decade. MOSFET transconductors are, however, more linear and can handle higher signal voltages. Some single-ended circuit approaches can be found in Paper 3-A.6 by Nedungadi and Geiger, Paper 3-A.7 by Park and Schaumann, and Paper 3-A.8 by Bult and Wallinga. The first paper uses extended long-tailed pair transconductors, the second uses extended CMOS inverter transconductors, and the third is based on the use of a simple two-transistor linear resistive element.

The optimization of transconductance-C and other filters with respect to dynamic range is discussed in [19]. Frequency response deviations caused by transconductor nonlinearities are discussed in [20, 21]. We note that transconductance-C techniques (just like any other filter implementation technique) can be extended for use in oscillator circuits; see, for example, [22–24]. Several other discussions on oscillators can be found in papers included in this volume as part of descriptions of automatic tuning based on VCOs.

A Note on the Design of Transconductors

The design of transconductors for transconductor-capacitor continuous-time filters differs significantly from that of op amps in that (1) the input stage must be able to handle large signals, (2) the input and output must be of very high impedance, (3) the 3-dB bandwidth must be wide, and (4) the transconductance must be well-defined and usually must be tunable. Several examples of transconductors can be found in the papers of this and the following section. Although we could not include papers purely on the electronics of transconductors in the volume, many such papers can be found in the literature. Most transconductor designs reported employ MOS transistors based in either the saturation region ([10, 25–43], and Papers 3-A.6, 3-A.7, 3-A.8, 3-B.1 and 3-B.10) or in the nonsaturation (triode) region ([44–49] and Papers 3-B.2 to 3-B.9, 7-D.1, and 7-D.3). In nearly all of these, the input is symmetrical and the output currents can be either single-ended or differential. Differential outputs can be converted to single-ended outputs using current mirror circuits (or NIC circuits). Alternatively, differential outputs can be used in a balanced way when the common-mode gain is low (for example, reduced by common-mode feedback) as required for the balanced filters of the next section. In either case, linearization techniques are a must, since lack of linearity will not only produce distortion but also signal-level dependent frequency response deviations in filters, and even jump phenomena may occur [20, 21].

References

[1] M. Białko and R. W. Newcomb, "Generation of all finite linear circuits using the integrated DVCCS," IEEE Trans. Circuit Theory, pp. 733–736, November 1971.

[2] D. W. H. Calder, "Audio frequency gyrator filters for an integrated radio paging receiver," *Proc. Int. Conf. on Mobile Radio Techniques*, IEE, York, pp. 21–26, September 1984.

[3] R. L. Geiger and E. Sánchez-Sinencio, "Active filter design using operational transconductance amplifiers: a tutorial," *IEEE Circuits and Devices Mag.*, vol. 1, pp. 20–32, March 1985.

[4] P. Kwa, "Homogeneous gyrator-chain networks," *Electron. Lett.*, vol. 21, pp. 1080–1081, November 7, 1985.

[5] N. Jöhl and F. Krummenacher, "Filtres continus MOS intégrés à large échelle," *Mitteilungen AGEN*, no. 43, pp. 49–55, May 1986.

[6] C.-S. Park and R. Schaumann, "Fully integrated analog filters in CMOS technology," *Proc. ISCAS*, pp. 1161–1164, May 1986.

[7] M. A. Tan and R. Schaumann, "Generation of transconductance-grounded-capacitor filters by signal-flow-graph methods for VLSI implementation," *Electron. Lett.* vol. 23, pp. 1093–1094, September 1987.

[8] M. A. Tan and R. Schaumann, "Design of a general biquadratic filter section with only transconductors and grounded capacitors," *IEEE Trans. Circuits Syst.*, vol. 35, pp. 478–480, April 1988.

[9] R. Nawrocki, "Building set for tunable component simulation filters with operational transconductance amplifiers," *Proc. 30th Midwest Symposium on Circuits and Systems*, pp. 227–230, 1988.

[10] T. G. Kim and R. L. Geiger, "Monolithic programmable RF filter," *Electron. Lett.*, vol. 24, no. 25, pp. 1569–1571, December 8, 1988.

[11] E. Sánchez-Sinencio, R. L. Geiger and H. Nevarez-Lozano, "Generation of continuous-time two integrator loop OTA filter structures," *IEEE Trans. Circuits Syst.*, vol. 35, pp. 936–945, August 1988.

[12] A. C. M. de Queiroz, L. P. Calôba and E. Sánchez-Sinencio, "Signal-flow-graph OTA-C integrated filters," *Proc. IEEE ISCAS '88*, pp. 2165–2168, 1988.

[13] L. P. Calôba, A. C. M. de Queiroz, and E. Sánchez-Sinencio, "Signal-flow graph OTA-C band-pass and band-reject integrated filters," *Proc. IEEE ISCAS '89*, pp. 1624–1627, 1989.

[14] L. P. Calôba, A. C. M. de Queiroz, "OTA-C simulation of passive filters via embedding," *Proc. IEEE ISCAS 89*, pp. 1083–1086, 1989.

[15] M. A. Tan and R. Schaumann, "Simulating general-purpose LC-ladder filters for monolithic realizations with only transconductance elements and grounded capacitors," *IEEE Trans. Circuits Syst.*, vol. 36, pp. 299–307, February 1989.

[16] P. V. Ananda Mohan, "Generation of OTA-C filter structures from active RC filter structures," *IEEE Trans. Circuits Syst.*, vol. 37, pp. 656–660, 1990.

[17] B. M. Al-Hashimi and J. K. Fidler, "Novel high-frequency continuous-time low-pass OTA-based filters," *Proc. IEEE ISCAS '90*, pp. 1171–1172, 1990.

[18] A. L. M. de Queiroz and L. P. Calôba, "Some practical problems in OTA-C filters related with parasitic capacitances," *Proc. IEEE ISCAS*, pp. 2279–2282, 1990.

[19] G. Groenewold, "The design of high dynamic range continuous-time integratable filters," *IEEE Trans. Circuits Syst.*, vol. 38, pp. 838–852, August 1991.

[20] S. Szczepanski and R. Schaumann, "Effects of weak nonlinearities in transconductance-capacitance filters," *Proc. IEEE ISCAS*, pp. 1055–1058, 1989.

[21] D. L. Hiser and R. L. Geiger, "Impact of OTA nonlinearities on the performance of continuous-time OTA-C filters," *Proc. IEEE ISCAS*, pp. 1167–1170, 1990.

[22] A. Rodríguez-Vázquez, B. Linares-Barranco, J. L. Huertas and E. Sánchez-Sinencio, "On the design of voltage-controlled sinusoidal oscillators using OTA's," *IEEE Trans. Circuits Syst.*, vol. 37, pp. 198–211, February 1990.

[23] B. Linares-Barranco, E. Sánchez-Sinencio, A. Rodríguez-Vázquez, and J. L. Huertas, "Very high frequency CMOS OTA-C quadrature oscillators," *Proc. IEEE ISCAS*, pp. 3189–3192, 1990.

[24] B. Linares-Barranco, A. Rodríguez-Vázquez, E. Sánchez-Sinencio and J. L. Huertas, "CMOS OTA-C high-frequency sinusoidal oscillators," *IEEE J. Solid-State Circuits*, vol. 26, pp. 160–165, February 1991.

[25] A. Nedungadi and T. R. Viswanathan, "Design of linear CMOS transconductance elements," *IEEE Trans. Circuits Syst.*, vol. CAS-31, pp. 891–894, October 1984.

[26] R. R. Torrance, T. R. Viswanathan and J. V. Hanson, "CMOS voltage to current transducers," *IEEE Trans. Circuits Syst.*, vol. CAS-32, pp. 1097–1104, 1985.

[27] T. L. Viswanathan, "CMOS transconductance element," *Proc. IEEE*, vol. 74, pp. 222–224, January 1986.

[28] C.-S. Park and R. Schaumann, "A high-frequency CMOS linear transconductance element," *IEEE Trans. Circuits Syst.*, vol. CAS-33, pp. 1132–1138, November 1986.

[29] K. Bult and H. Wallinga, "A class of analog CMOS circuits based on the square-law characteristic of an MOS transistor in saturation", *IEEE J. Solid-State Circuits*, vol. SC-22, pp. 357–365, June 1987.

[30] E. Seevinck and R. F. Wassenaar, "A versatile CMOS linear transconductor/square-law function circuit," *IEEE J. Solid-State Circuits*, vol. SC-22, pp. 366–377, June 1987.

[31] A. Guzinski, M. Bialko, and J. C. Matheau, "Body-driven

differential amplifier for application in continuous-time active-C filter," *Proc. ECCTD '87*, pp. 315–320, Paris, September 1987.

[32] S. W. Kim and R. L. Geiger, "Design of a CMOS differential amplifier using a source-coupled back-gate pair," *Proc. 30th Midwest Symposium on Circuits and Systems,* pp. 929–932, 1988.

[33] B. Nauta and E. Seevinck, "Linear CMOS transconductance element for VHF filters," *Electron. Lett.*, vol. 25, pp. 448–450, March 30, 1989.

[34] E. Klumperinck, E. v. d. Zwan, and E. Seevinck, "CMOS variable transconductance circuit with constant bandwidth," *Electron. Lett.,* vol. 25, no. 10, pp. 675–676, May 11, 1989.

[35] S. Noceti Filho, M. C. Schneider, and R. N. G. Robert, "New CMOS OTA for fully-integrated continuous-time circuit applications," *Electron. Lett.*, vol. 25, no. 24, pp. 1674–1675, November 23, 1989.

[36] Z. Wang, "Novel linearisation technique for implementing large-signal MOS tunable transconductor," *Electron. Lett.*, vol. 26, pp. 138–139, January 1990.

[37] Z. Wang and W. Guggenbühl, "A voltage-controllable linear MOS transconductor using bias offset technique," *IEEE J. Solid-State Circuits*, vol. 25, pp. 315–317, 1990.

[38] P. M. VanPeteghem, H. M. Fossati, Glenn L. Rice and Y.-Y. Lee, "Design of a very linear MOS transconductance input stage for continuous-time filters," *IEEE J. Solid-State Circuits*, vol. 25, pp. 497–501, April 1990.

[39] P. Wu, R. Schaumann and S. Szczepanski, "A CMOS OTA with improved linearity based on current addition," *Proc. IEEE ISCAS*, pp. 2296–2299, 1990.

[40] G. Wilson and P. K. Chan, "Low-distortion CMOS transconductor," *Electron. Lett.*, vol. 26, no. 11, pp. 720–722, May 24, 1990.

[41] Z. Czarnul and N. Fujii, "Highly linear transconductor cell realized by double MOS transistor differential pair," *Electron. Lett.*, vol. 26, pp. 1819–1821, 1990.

[42] Z. Czarnul and S. Tagaki, "Design of linear tunable CMOS differential transconductor cells," *Electron. Lett.*, vol. 26, pp. 1809–1811, 11 October 1990.

[43] P. Wu and R. Schaumann, "Tunable operational transconductance amplifier with extremely high linearity over very large input range," *Electron. Lett.*, vol. 27, pp. 1254–1255, July 1991.

[44] J. L. Pennock, "CMOS triode transconductor for continuous-time active integrated filters," *Electron. Lett.*, vol. 21, pp. 817–818, August 29, 1985.

[45] Y. Tsividis, Z. Czarnul and S. C. Fang, "MOS transconductors and integrators with high linearity," *Electron. Lett.*, vol. 22, pp. 245–246, February 27, 1986; errata: *ibid.*, p. 619, May 22, 1986.

[46] Z. Czarnul and Y. Tsividis, "MOS tunable transconductor," *Electron. Lett.*, vol. 22, pp. 721–722, June 19, 1986.

[47] B. Stefanelli and A. Kaiser, "CMOS triode transconductor with high dynamic range," *Electron. Lett.*, vol. 26, pp. 880–881, June 21, 1990.

[48] U. Gatti, F. Maloberti, and G. Torelli, "A novel CMOS linear transconductance cell for continuous-time filters," *Proc. IEEE ISCAS '90*, pp. 1173–1176, 1990.

[49] I. Silva-Martinez, M. J. Steyaert and W. M. C. Sansen, "A large-signal very low-distortion transconductor for high-frequency continuous-time filters," *IEEE J. Solid-State Circuits*, vol. 26, pp. 946–955, July 1991.

Paper 3-A.1

A Fully Integrated Five-Gyrator Filter at Video Frequencies

KENNETH W. MOULDING AND GORDON A. WILSON

Abstract—An experimental single-chip silicon integrated-circuit filter is described for use in color television receivers. It comprises five gyrator resonators operating in the range 4–6 MHz. This chip provides all the selectivity required to separate the sound, luminance, and chrominance components from the composite video signal, and is tuned by a single bias potential applied to the p-n junction capacitors on the chip. The chip replaces an equivalent *LC* filter of about 20 discrete components (coils, capacitors, and resistors) which are bulky, are relatively expensive, and suffer from the need for individual screening and alignment.

The theory of gyrators related to providing fully integrated selectivity at high frequency is outlined. Performance boundaries in terms of *Q*-factor, frequency setting accuracy, noise, distortion, and temperature are considered. Design aspects are discussed, first for a gyrator and then for the complete experimental filter chip.

Introduction

NOW THAT MOST of the signal-processing functions in a color television receiver have been integrated there is a strong incentive to integrate the few remaining components, particularly the tuned circuits in the video frequency stages.

In a typical receiver there are a number of tuned circuits which can be brought together to form a video selectivity block (Fig. 1). In it the composite signal is separated into the luminance, chrominance, and sound components so that the information can be processed by the PAL color decoder and the sound detector. The filter conventionally consists of discrete coils and capacitors which are relatively bulky and expensive and also suffer from the need for individual screening and alignment. This is a particularly suitable application for integrated gyrators, and the present paper describes a single-chip filter, employing five gyrator resonators, designed to replace the conventional filter.

The Gyrator

The ideal gyrator, Fig. 2, is a passive lossless nonreciprocal two-port whose admittance matrix is

$$\begin{vmatrix} 0 & g_0 \\ -g_0 & 0 \end{vmatrix}.$$

If we apply a load $Y_{L2} = j\omega C_2$, we obtain

$$Y_{\text{in}} = g_0^2/j\omega C_2$$

Manuscript received November 4, 1977; revised January 20, 1978.
The authors are with the Philips Research Laboratories, Redhill, Surrey, England.

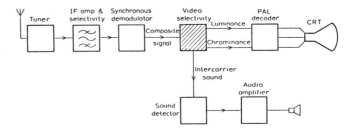

Fig. 1. Typical television receiver.

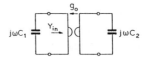

Fig. 2. Gyrator resonator.

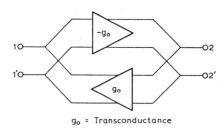

g_0 = Transconductance

Fig. 3. Gyrator realization using two transconductance amplifiers.

which is the admittance of an equivalent inductor of value C_2/g_0^2. Now by tuning the input with a load $Y_{L1} = j\omega C_1$, we form a tuned circuit of resonant frequency

$$\omega_c = g_0/\sqrt{C_1 C_2}.$$

A gyrator can be produced by the closed-loop connection of two transconductance amplifiers (Fig. 3), one with transconductance g_0 and the other $-g_0$. However, at high frequencies the admittance matrix contains finite port conductances (g_s) and significant phase shift ($-\phi/2$) in each transadmittance

Reprinted from *IEEE J. Solid-State Circuits*, vol. SC-13, no. 3, pp. 303–307, June 1978.

167

$$\begin{vmatrix} g_s & g_0 e^{-j(\phi/2)} \\ -g_0 e^{-j(\phi/2)} & g_s \end{vmatrix}.$$

Now assuming $\phi \ll 1$ and $g_s \ll g_0$, $Y_{L1} = Y_{L2} = j\omega C$ gives

$$y_{in} \simeq 2g_s - \phi g_0^2/\omega C + j\omega C - jg_0^2/\omega C$$

which contains a negative real term proportional to ϕ and yields the results

$$\omega = g_0/C$$

and

$$1/Q = 2g_s/g_0 - \phi.$$

Furthermore, the sensitivity of Q to ϕ can be obtained by differentiating the last expression to give [1]

$$S_\phi^Q = \partial Q/Q \div \partial\phi/\phi = \phi Q$$

which demonstrates that the resonator becomes more critical as ϕ or Q increase.

GYRATOR INTEGRATION

The gyrator conductance (g_0) is normally defined by resistors within the transconductance amplifiers. With integrated amplifiers and high-stability close-tolerance discrete resistors, it is possible at low frequencies to obtain near-ideal gyrators, and these can be combined with close-tolerance capacitors to obtain very high-quality tuned circuits [2], [3]. At higher frequencies, say above 1 MHz, S_ϕ^Q will deteriorate due to the increasing phase shift in the amplifiers, and this discrete component approach becomes unattractive.

However, the capacitors required at high frequency are small enough to integrate as junctions. If we integrate the capacitors and resistors, then the inherent matching of the components on an IC chip allows us to produce economically a number of tuned circuits whose resonant frequencies match to within about 1 percent. Furthermore, by varying the bias voltage on the junction capacitors, all the resonators can be tuned with a single adjustment. It should therefore be possible to make a viable IC to replace a group of high-frequency tuned circuits provided the Q-factors and other specifications are not too exacting.

PERFORMANCE BOUNDARIES FOR FULLY INTEGRATED GYRATOR RESONATORS

A. Q-Factor

Amplifier phase shift, and therefore its spread, is normally proportional to frequency. For a typical integrated gyrator using a 400-MHz f_T process, the spread in total amplifier phase shift is in the region of $\pm 0.1°$/MHz. For a permitted spread in Q (say ± 20 percent), we can calculate the maximum allowable Q as a function of frequency using the sensitivity equation previously given. The result (Fig. 4) shows a Q limit of 20 at 6 MHz and indicates that gyrators made in this IC process would be of little use above the HF range.

B. Frequency-Setting Accuracy

Typical spreads in resistors and junction capacitors between IC batches give rise to a variation in resonant frequency of

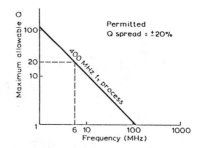

Fig. 4. Gyrator Q limitations.

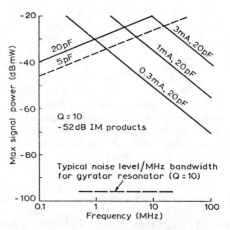

Fig. 5. Gyrator signal-handling limitations.

about ± 20 percent, and this must be corrected by adjusting the capacitor bias voltage. However, the mismatch between the frequencies of resonators on the same chip is very much less and depends upon the geometry and spacing of these critical components. Matching can be improved by designing the degeneration resistors with generous dimensions and grouping them in close proximity. This minimizes the variations due to mask alignment, etching tolerances, and doping gradient. Similar considerations apply to junction capacitors, although in this case there has to be a compromise between narrow fingers that suffer from dimensional tolerance and wide fingers that yield low Q-factor. It has been found that with careful design, matching of better than 0.5 percent is possible.

C. Noise and Distortion

An extension to the noise analysis of Blom and Voorman [4] shows that the optimum noise factor of a gyrator resonator at center frequency is given by $F_{opt} = 1 + 2Q(F_0 - 1)$, where F_0 is the noise factor of each amplifier. Similarly, intermodulation is increased by a factor of $2Q$ at fixed signal voltage or by $2Q^2$ at fixed power (allowing for the change of circuit impedance). Hence the dynamic range reduces by a power ratio of nearly $4Q^3$. Intermodulation in integrated gyrators arises from two sources: the emitter junction characteristics of transistors and the nonlinearity of junction capacitance, which forms the resonating capacitors and is also present as transistor-collector capacitance, etc. Fig. 5 shows the theoretical signal-handling performance for bipolar IC components. The lines of positive slope show the limit imposed by capacitor

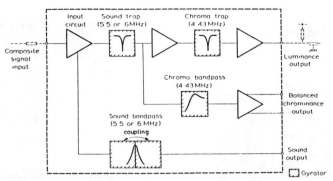

Fig. 6. Video-selectivity system using gyrators.

nonlinearity ($P \propto \omega_0 C/Q$), while those of negative slope show the limit due to emitter distortion ($P \propto I_e^3/\omega_0^2 C^2 Q^2$). At lower frequencies the capacitor size is the limitation while at higher frequencies it is the emitter current. Once the Q-factor and dynamic range are known, optimum values for C and I_e can be determined. However, the value of C should not be chosen too low in relation to the stray circuit capacitance, and also it is preferable to have a single design which is adequate for all the stages of a filter.

D. Temperature

The temperature coefficient for integrated resistors is approximately 0.002 K, although for capacitors it is an order of magnitude less than this. Consequently, temperature compensation is necessary for many applications.

THE INTEGRATED VIDEO FILTER

A block diagram of a suitable video-selectivity system is shown in Fig. 6. This includes bandpass and trap filters to separate the components of the composite signal, namely luminance information (0–5 MHz), a 4.43-MHz chrominance subcarrier, and a 5.5- or 6-MHz sound subcarrier. An experimental single-chip realization of this selectivity block, using gyrators, has been designed and made in a standard bipolar process.

A. The Gyrator

The gyrator design for this filter is based on degenerated long-tailed pair amplifiers, Fig. 7. These have the advantage that the V_{be} of the transistors are balanced and both phases of output are available. The degeneration resistors R determine the transconductance g_0 of the amplifiers. The emitter-follower transistors (T_1, T_4, T_5, and T_8) provide level shifting for dc coupling and also reduce the effect of β spread on the overall Q of the resonator. The use of dc current sources allows high-Q circuits to be achieved with a low supply rail. The current sources in the collectors (Ip) employ lateral p-n-p transistors, while the emitter sources (In) are vertical n-p-n devices. The resistor Rd, in series with the capacitor C_2, compensates for the frequency-dependent phase shift in the amplifiers [5], [6].

Gyrator resonators involving floating-load capacitors are avoided wherever possible because of the difficulty in providing bias. To obtain a floating-junction capacitor one uses two

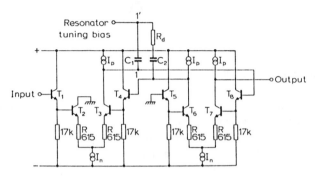

Fig. 7. Gyrator resonator.

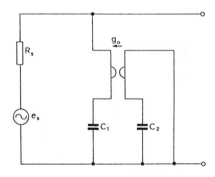

Fig. 8. Gyrator trap circuit with grounded capacitors.

capacitors in series, with a variable bias applied at the center tap. The chip area used is increased four times and the bias has to be applied through a high-value resistor in order not to disturb the Q of the circuit. This is avoided in the trap circuits by using a semifloating gyrator, Fig. 8. The circuit of Fig. 7 can be adapted to provide this configuration by joining the base of T_1 and the collector of T_7 to form the floating-trap terminal.

In the grounded gyrator configuration for a bandpass resonator (Fig. 7), the input signal is not applied directly to the gyrator port 1–1'. Instead, it is convenient to use the base of T_1 and the collector of T_7 as input and output points. (These points would otherwise have been earthed.) This arrangement provides buffering which makes the gyrator resonance independent of the source and load circuits. A series or parallel

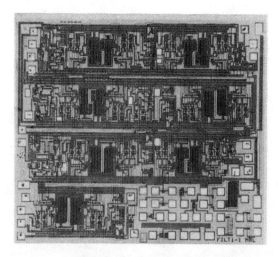

Fig. 9. Video filter chip.

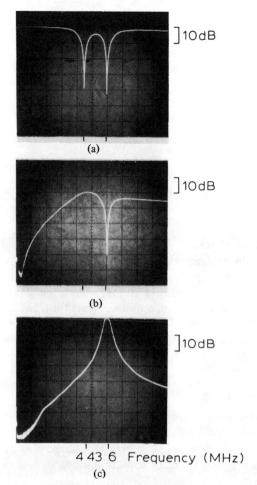

Fig. 10. Measured responses of filter chip. (a) Luminance. (b) Chrominance. (c) Sound.

damping resistor at the port 1–1′ is used to define the working Q of the resonator.

To minimize chip area the capacitors C_1 and C_2 are formed from the parallel connection of emitter-base and collector-base junctions of a transistor structure. The capacitors for the 6-MHz gyrator resonator are each 19 pF. Resonators at 4.43 and 5.5 MHz use values of 26 and 21 pF, respectively. The following table shows the performance of the 6-MHz gyrator:

6-MHz Gyrator Performance	
Gyrator transconductance	0.7 mS
Load capacitors	19 pF
Useful Quality Factor	
As a bandpass	up to 20
As a trap	∞
Amplifier phase shift	2°
Emitter current	
(long-tailed pair transistors)	0.35 mA
Input level for −52-dB IM Products	20-mV rms (Q = 20)
Chip area	0.8 mm²

B. The Filter Chip

Fig. 9 is a photograph of the complete experimental filter, using the arrangement shown in Fig. 6. Of this 14-mm² chip, 9 mm² is occupied by the filter and the rest by test circuits. The filter contains five gyrator-C resonators together with a buffer amplifier, input and output interfacing circuits, and a voltage reference circuit; a total of 350 components. The input circuit attenuates the video signal from the synchronous detector IC to prevent distortion in the gyrators. The video level from the synchronous detector is fixed at 1.7-V black to white by the automatic gain control loop of the receiver and allows the filter always to operate with its optimum signal-to-noise ratio. The luminance output circuit drives signal current into an external shunt resistor, selected to match the characteristic impedance of the luminance delay line. The resonant circuits are completely buffered from the circuits external to the IC. A single preset control is used to supply the tuning bias to the junctions of the gyrator resonator capacitors. A variation in junction voltage from 0.5 to 6 V gives a frequency tuning range of ±27 percent, which is suffi-

cient to cover the full range of component variations. The filter dissipation is about 300 mW. Peak-to-peak signal to weighted rms noise ratios measured for the luminance and chrominance channels (with filters complying to the CCIR Standard Rec. 451-1) are better than 64 dB for IM products less than −52 dB. The rms signal-to-noise ratio for the FM sound channel is about 48 dB, giving in excess of 60 dB after demodulation. Because breadboard measurements give only a very rough prediction of IC behavior at high frequencies, and integration strays are important in the performance of such a circuit, most of the design work was carried out using an IC modeling program, MANIC. This also performed a dc analysis and gave the ac expansion for the circuit-analysis programs.

Fig. 10 shows the measured response curves of a typical integrated filter sample: Fig. 10(a), the luminance response, with two traps each with a 3 dB bandwidth of 1 MHz; Fig. 10(b), the chrominance response consisting of a low-Q (2.5) bandpass filter and a 40-dB-deep 6-MHz trap; and Fig. 10(c), sound bandpass response using a coupled second-order Butterworth filter. Samples have been very successfully tested in a color receiver where the results were indistinguishable from the LC equivalent. However, the temperature dependance of resonant frequency f_0 without any temperature compensation circuits is too high ($\delta f_0/f_0 \simeq 0.2$ percent/°C) while the temperature dependence of Q is just acceptable ($\delta Q/Q \simeq 0.4$ percent/°C for $Q = 36$). With current advances in MSI technology, such a filter should be cost effective in the very near future.

CONCLUSIONS

This work has demonstrated that a multigyrator filter can be made on a single chip of silicon with the desired frequency-response characteristics and adequate distortion and noise performance for the television video frequency application. The next step must be to include stabilization of resonant frequency against the effects of temperature variation. This is included in our current work, in which we will also optimize the layout design to meet a requirement for frequency matching of better than 0.5 percent. A further objective is to provide for compensation of batch-to-batch variations in Q-factor to satisfy a tighter specification for the sound trap (Q always better than 200). The latter involves an extensive analysis of IC component spreads and correlations.

ACKNOWLEDGMENT

The team responsible for this work has included P. S. Kasbia, J. R. Quartly, P. J. Rankin, A. S. Taylor, R. S. Thompson, the authors, and the late J. R. Canning.

REFERENCES

[1] K. W. Moulding, "Fully integrated selectivity at high frequency using gyrators," *IEEE Trans. Broadcast Telev. Receivers*, vol. BTR-19, pp. 176-179, Aug. 1973.
[2] J. O. Voorman and A. Biesheuvel, "An electric gyrator," *IEEE J. Solid-State Circuits*, vol. SC-7, pp. 469-474, Dec. 1972.
[3] J. O. Voorman, "The gyrator as a monolithic circuit in electronic systems," Ph.D. dissertation, Nijmegen, The Netherlands, 1977.
[4] D. Blom and J. O. Voorman, "Noise and dissipation of electronic gyrators," *Philips Res. Rep.*, vol. 26, pp. 103-113, 1971.
[5] H. T. Van Looij and K. M. Adams, "Phase compensation in electronic gyrator circuits," *Electron. Lett.*, vol. 4, pp. 430-431, Oct. 1968.
[6] J. G. Wade and D. W. Parker, "Stability of a wideband gyrator circuit," *Electron Lett.*, vol. 7, pp. 224-225, May 1971.

Gyrator Video Filter IC with Automatic Tuning

KENNETH W. MOULDING, JONATHAN R. QUARTLY, PAUL J. RANKIN, ROGER S. THOMPSON,
AND GORDON A. WILSON

Abstract—A single-chip gyrator filter for separating the components of the video signal in a TV receiver is described which is suitable for mass production in a standard bipolar process ($f_T \approx 400$ MHz). The 11 mm^2 filter chip operates at frequencies up to 10 MHz, requires no tuning or alignment and has Q-factors which are stable with temperature.

The IC contains an automatic tuning system which tunes the five resonators of the filter by aligning an auxiliary gyrator resonator with the crystal oscillator present in the color decoder of a TV receiver. Problems of matching the frequencies of the individual gyrator resonators are discussed, showing how alignment accuracy of 0.5 percent can be obtained when resistivities and specific capacitances have production spreads of at least 10 percent. Various gyrator circuit configurations are given which minimize the circuit complexity and, hence, the chip area. Computer aided design techniques for the filter using geometrically scaled models and macromodeling are presented and it is shown how a complete simulation of the chip led to a significant improvement in bandstop performance. Finally, the measured responses are presented and the filter performance is discussed in the light of present day requirements. Ideas for larger scale integration of the TV system are prompted by the advent of this IC.

INTRODUCTION

ALTHOUGH large sections of the signal path of the color television receiver (Fig. 1) have been integrated, further progress is restricted by the number of components which defy integration, in particular, the filter coils and trimmers. Integration to avoid these components is, therefore, very desirable, especially if it can be achieved using a process which is compatible with the other IC's in the receiver. The integrated filter described in this paper replaces the *LC* video filter required to separate the components of the video signal and is manufactured in a standard bipolar process. Fewer external connections and the freedom from adjustments and alignment provided by this IC should give greater reliability than its *LC* counterpart. At the same time, designed-in flexibility allows the IC to interface with many current video demodulator and color decoder arrangements.

Two versions of the filter have been designed, one for use with PAL television system *I* (sound carrier at 6 MHz) and the other with PAL television system *B* or *G* (sound carrier at 5.5 MHz), and the design can easily be adapted for NTSC or SECAM. The description of the filter in this paper relates to the European system *G*.

Manuscript received May 20, 1980; revised July 24, 1980.

K. W. Moulding, P. J. Rankin, R. S. Thompson, and G. A. Wilson are with Philips Research Laboratories, Redhill, Surrey, England.

J. R. Quartly was with Philips Research Laboratories, Redhill, Surrey, England. He is now with the Welding Institute, Abington, Cambridge, England.

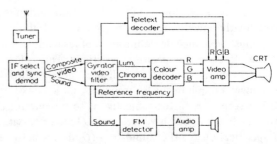

Fig. 1. Television receiver using a gyrator video filter IC.

In the television receiver, the video filter is placed after the synchronous demodulation of the composite signal (Fig. 1) which consists of an 0–5 MHz luminance signal, a 4.43 MHz color subcarrier and a 5.5 MHz FM sound carrier. *LC* resonators in the filter are simulated with gyrators terminated by junction capacitors, the voltage dependence of the latter being exploited for tuning the filter. Each gyrator employs two voltage controlled current sources, and uses a total of 14 transistors. Using these techniques, resonant frequencies in the range of at least 1–10 MHz can be achieved. One of the main problems encountered in designing such a filter is to achieve accurate resonant frequencies and Q factors which are tolerant of process spreads.

An earlier paper [1] described a basic video filter chip which demonstrated the feasibility of fully integrated selectivity, and also discussed some of the features of the gyrator and its performance limitations with regard to signal handling and Q-factor. The use of gyrator-simulated inductances provides active filters which are least sensitive to component variations and have the widest dynamic range [2], [3]. This paper describes the gyrator filters and new innovations which make the IC very tolerant of process spreads and suitable for mass production, focussing particularly on the automatic tuning circuit, dc biasing and layout design. Computer aided design methods are also discussed as these have featured strongly in the development.

GENERAL DESCRIPTION

The separation of the composite signal is performed by five gyrator resonators. First, the input signal is stripped of the intercarrier sound in a two-stage sound trap (Fig. 2) and a low impedance takeoff for a teletext decoder or VCR is provided. The signal is then applied to a single gyrator resonator, with two outputs, to separate luminance and chrominance signals. In the sound channel, a coupled bandpass pair of gyrator resonators provide the necessary selectivity. Further, the chip

Reprinted from *IEEE J. Solid-State Circuits*, vol. SC-15, no. 6, pp. 963–968, Dec. 1980.

172

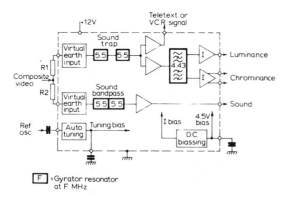

Fig. 2. Schematic of gyrator video filter IC.

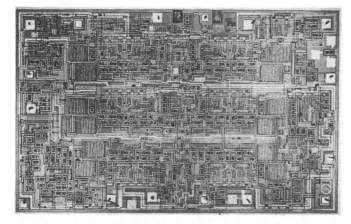

Fig. 3. Gyrator video filter (chip photograph).

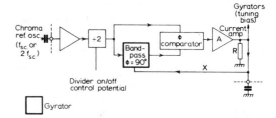

Fig. 4. Automatic tuning circuit.

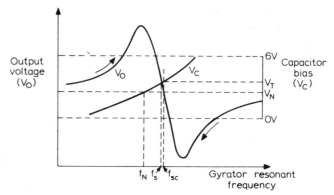

Fig. 5. Open loop characteristics of the tuning circuit (loop broken at X).

contains an automatic tuning system which tunes the five resonators of the filter by aligning a sixth auxiliary gyrator resonator with the crystal oscillator present in the color decoder of the TV receiver. A bandgap voltage reference circuit is used to set voltage and current levels throughout the filter giving immunity to supply voltage variations.

The present filter has in-built flexibility to interface with most color television receiver circuit designs. Interfacing circuits are included to match to the signal levels of adjacent IC's and to isolate the resonators from the effects of external loading. By changing the values of the series resistors R_1 and R_2 at the virtual earth inputs, the filter can accommodate a wide range of video amplitudes from a standard 1 V p-p video, to the 3 V video from a synchronous demodulator IC (e.g., TDA2541). Also, the provision of two inputs allows for separate IF demodulation of video and sound subcarrier signals and permits the individual adjustment of the signal levels applied to the IC. To give optimum signal-to-noise ratio without distortion, the video signal level (black to white) across the port of the first sound trap gyrator internal to the IC is arranged to be ≈ 120 mV p-p.

The 11 mm² chip (Fig. 3), dissipates 650 mW and uses resonating capacitors of about 20 pF. Each gyrator resonator occupies an area of ≈ 0.7 mm², of which ≈ 0.12 mm² are the capacitors. The complete filter IC has 567 components comprising 216 transistors, 339 resistors, and 12 capacitors.

AUTOMATIC TUNING

Thanks to the good matching of components on a single chip, all resonators can be tuned with a common capacitor bias voltage. This bias must be adjusted to allow for ambient temperature variations and the relatively large batch-to-batch spreads. Adequate compensation circuits for use with preset adjustment are problematical. An automatic tuning arrangement was therefore chosen [4] in which the filter is kept tuned by locking a reference gyrator to the crystal oscillator in the color decoder (Fig. 4). This oscillator may be either at subcarrier frequency, f_{sc} (4.43 MHz) or at $2f_{sc}$ (8.87 MHz). The reference signal is fed into a limiter amplifier followed by a divider which can be switched on or off as required by the receiver design. The resultant signal is passed through a single 4.43 MHz gyrator bandpass resonator where it suffers a nominal 90° phase shift. This is then compared in phase with a sample of the incoming reference. If the resonant frequency of the gyrator is $<f_{sc}$, the phase shift across the bandpass is $<90°$. This gives a positive-going output voltage at the phase comparator which is amplified and smoothed (Fig. 5). Applying the dc output to the resonating capacitors closes the control loop and tunes the gyrator up towards f_{sc}. When the gyrator resonant frequency is $>f_{sc}$, a negative-going output voltage tunes the gyrator down to f_{sc}.

The residual tuning error δf depends on how far the gyrator is initially off-tune, and on the slope K of the open loop characteristic near f_{sc} in Fig. 5. This figure also shows the typical characteristic of resonant frequency versus capacitor bias. The output voltage swing available to the control loop is restricted to protect the capacitors from forward bias or breakdown. An approximate tuning voltage V_N is first derived by a simple network. With no reference signal present, this voltage, applied to the capacitors, tunes the gyrator to frequency f_N. (V_N also corresponds to the zero-error voltage from the phase comparator when $\phi = 90°$.) When the reference signal f_{sc} is applied, a voltage is generated which is applied to the capacitors and tunes the gyrator to f_s. The tuning frequency error can be shown to be given approximately by $\delta f = (V_N - V_T)/K$ for large loop gains.

The slope of the open loop characteristic K is dependent on a number of factors:

$$K = \frac{d\phi}{df} \cdot \frac{dI}{d\phi} \cdot A \cdot R \quad \text{V/Hz}$$

where $d\phi/df$ is the rate of change of phase with frequency of the gyrator bandpass and is proportional to Q; $dI/d\phi$ is the rate of change of output current with phase for the phase comparator; A is the amplifier current gain and R is the load resistor. The present circuit gives a worst-case tuning error of 10 kHz ($\frac{1}{4}$ percent) using a gyrator bandpass with $Q = 25$, and a loop gain of 100.

It is vital that the phase of the two signals arriving at the comparator should differ by exactly 90° when the gyrator is correctly tuned as any deviation from this would cause an additional tuning error. Account is therefore taken during the design of any parasitic phase lags in the two paths.

The useful capacitor bias range is 0.5–6 V, limited at one end by increasing distortion, and at the other by junction breakdown. This can control the capacitance over a range of ±28 percent which is sufficient to accommodate the spread in $R \cdot C$ due to variations in the process and an ambient operating temperature range of 0–60°C.

The temperature coefficient of the filter frequencies with automatic tuning has been measured to be 60 ppm/°C, which is satisfactory.

FILTER DESIGNS

The gyrators, with ports 1–1' and 2–2', are formed from degenerated long-tailed pair amplifiers (voltage controlled current sources) as shown in Fig. 6. These amplifiers have the advantage that the V_{be}'s of the transistors are balanced and both phases of output are available to form the forward and reverse transconductances, $-g_o$ and g_o. Also, the gyrators so formed are floating. When the gyrator is grounded (that is ac grounded) at terminals 1' and 2' and the ports loaded with grounded p-n junction capacitors, tuning bias voltages can be easily applied. Grounded ports also allow indirect input and output points to be used which buffer the resonator from the effects of loading without affecting the operation of the gyrator. A buffered output signal proportional to the port voltage across 1–1' is provided by a series load resistor R_L connected between the earthed terminal and the corresponding transistor collector. Buffered input is obtained by connecting the source in series with the earthed terminal 2' and transistor base B1, which then injects signal current into the resonator across the gyrator port 1–1'.

The circuit shown in Fig. 7 is a practical gyrator resonator with load capacitors C_1 and C_2. It employs indirect input and output points, and gives a simple bandpass response. The

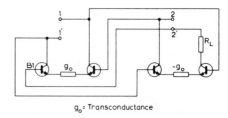

Fig. 6. Gyrator realization using two transconductance amplifiers.

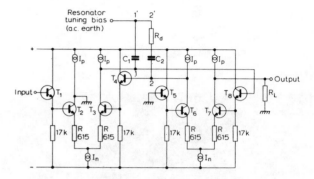

Fig. 7. Gyrator resonator giving a bandpass response.

degeneration resistors R determine the transconductance g_o of the amplifiers. Emitter-follower transistors (T_1, T_4, T_5, and T_8) provide level shifting for dc coupling and, together with the use of dc current sources as collector loads, give a low gyrator port conductance. The current sources in the collectors (I_p) employ lateral p-n-p transistors, while the emitter sources (I_n) are vertical n-p-n devices. A resistor R_d is included in series with one of the terminating capacitors to give the desired Q factor for each resonator. In calculating the value of R_d, the nonideal nature of the gyrator and its terminating capacitors must be modeled. Both gyrator port conductance and capacitor Q are finite and these lower the resonator Q, while phase shift in the amplifiers (due mainly to finite transistor f_T) has the effect of enhancing Q. Port conductance is kept low as indicated above and has only a small effect on Q, but parasitic damping associated with the internal resistance of the terminating capacitors is more significant, especially for the emitter-base capacitance which is used. Nevertheless, the damping arising from these two sources is outweighed by the Q enhancement due to amplifier phase shifts [1] and the resonator Q would be negative. The value chosen for R_d is therefore made up of two contributions: first, the resistance needed to compensate for the amplifier phase shift and give a resonator Q of infinity, and, second, the resistance needed to damp this infinite Q resonator to the Q required for the particular circuit application.

A simplified representation of the symmetric bandpass resonator is shown in Fig. 8(a). Fig. 8(b) shows a single gyrator used to give both trap and asymmetric bandpass functions. For a trap connection, one floating gyrator port is needed to allow the series capacitor to be grounded. The buffered bandpass output shows a positive tilt which arises from the intrinsic high-pass character of this connection. This configuration is used for the chroma filtering at 4.43 MHz (Fig. 2), where it is

174

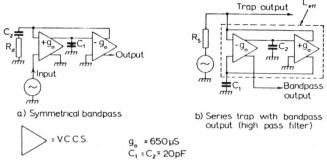

a) Symmetrical bandpass

b) Series trap with bandpass output (high pass filter)

$g_o = 650\,\mu S$
$C_1 = C_2 = 20\,pF$

Fig. 8. Gyrator filter arrangements.

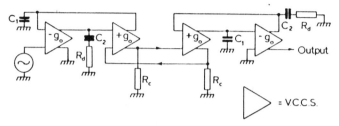

Fig. 9. Actively coupled second-order bandpass.

acceptable to have the same bandwidth of 1.5 MHz for both trap and bandpass responses.

The sound bandpass is a second-order Butterworth filter. Active coupling [6] has been used rather than the more common top-C coupling, since the latter would require a floating capacitor. Fig. 9 shows the separate forward and reverse coupling paths, where the coupling coefficient is given by the product $R_c \cdot g_o$. The −3 dB bandwidth of the response is 280 kHz at 5.5 MHz and requires gyrator resonators with Q factors of 27. For the sound trap, the severe specification in the chroma channel demands two stages of trapping in order to guarantee the necessary rejection of >40 dB over the sound bandwidth.

PROCESS TOLERANCE

Batch-to-batch spreads in the parameters of a standard bipolar process can be up to ±20 percent while across one chip, ±2 percent variation might be found. However, this application demands very close control of frequency characteristics, and, therefore, particular attention has been paid to the effects of processing variations when choosing circuits and their layout.

The resonance of a gyrator resonator is given by $\omega = 1/\sqrt{R_1 R_2 C_1 C_2}$ where R_1 and R_2 are the resistances defining the transconductances and C_1 and C_2 are the load capacitances. In the filter, the sound trap must track the reference gyrator to ±0.5 percent implying component matching of a similar accuracy.

Resistor matching is a function of resistivity, etching, and contact resistance variations. These can be minimized by placing the resistors in close proximity with the same orientation and by using generous dimensions with large contacts.

The capacitors are formed by the parallel connection of the emitter-base and collector-base junctions of a transistor. For best matching of the emitter-base contribution, a single large emitter would be preferred. Unfortunately, the series resistance of such a structure is too high and a striped geometry must be used. As with resistors, close proximity and common orientation are beneficial. The capacitor areas are scaled to obtain the two resonant frequencies required in the filter. This scaling must be applied equally to the two junctions to maintain a constant ratio as the specific capacitances of each vary independently. In the present design, using 60 μm wide resistors and 25 μm wide emitter junction stripes for the capacitors, a 90 percent yield in respect of frequency matching is anticipated.

The chip uses the 12 V ± 10 percent supply normally available in a television receiver. An internally generated 4.5 V supply provides a suitable bias potential for the gyrator amplifiers. This circuit uses a bandgap reference [7] to generate 1.5 V which is then amplified to 4.5 V with low output impedance so that signal currents flowing into it do not give rise to excessive crosstalk between the gyrators. The choice of 4.5 V optimizes the available capacitor bias range while giving sufficient headroom to the n-p-n current sinks in the gyrators.

Extensive use is made of n-p-n and p-n-p current sources and sinks to give immunity to supply rail variations. Special current setting circuits ensure that the absolute values of the operating currents are the same from one gyrator to the next and do not vary too widely with temperature and process spreads. It is impractical to distribute bias *voltages* over the chip to set the gyrator current sources and sinks because of the potential drops down the supply rails. Therefore, to overcome this problem, a "master" current setting circuit is used to produce three equal reference currents from the 4.5 V supply. These *currents* are fed to "slave" circuits close to the gyrators where local bias voltages are generated. Within one gyrator, it is also most important that the p-n-p current sources accurately match the n-p-n current sinks. Offset currents at the ports are then kept low, thus avoiding problems of dc shifts between stages.

CAD TECHNIQUES

The design of the filter has relied on extensive computer modeling and simulation. Breadboarding methods for high frequency applications are unsuitable because of their poor representation of the parasitic electrical effects associated with IC components. CAD methods provide for the component tracking and allow experimentation with changes in component dimensions, etc. In designing the filter, only the frequency divider and phase comparator circuits were breadboarded because of their grossly nonlinear mode of operation.

The CAD programs take two files of input data (Fig. 10). The circuit designer manipulates one file by giving the circuit topology and his choices for component dimensions such as resistor widths, length of emitters, number of base contacts, etc. The other file is a process description common to a number of designers; it contains about 110 values of mask clearances, nominal sheet resistances, specific junction capacitance laws, temperature coefficients, etc. The effects of process changes can then be readily tested by altering these values.

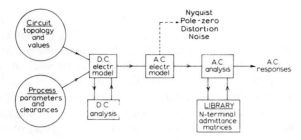

Fig. 10. CAD for modeling and analysis of IC's.

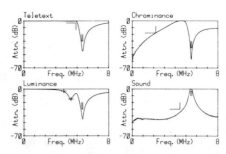

Fig. 11. Measured responses of video filter (with HP 3042A Automatic Network Analyzer).

The two files are combined using geometrically scaled component models, to give a complete circuit representation. These models have evolved in the course of a continuing activity of on-slice dc and HF measurements for the necessary process characterization. Particular attention is paid to accuracy at high frequencies, for example, interconnections are modeled with resistance and stray capacitance.

The filter is first partitioned into circuit blocks which are analyzed, individually. The programs find the dc operating points of the components, then expand the models into a linearized equivalent circuit for interactive ac analysis. Other programs are available for investigating stability via Nyquist plots or pole-zero computation, noise, or nonlinear distortion performances. When a satisfactory design has been reached, the small-signal performance of each circuit block is stored in an admittance matrix library. For instance, a gyrator circuit is stored as a 12-terminal matrix with the gyrator ports, supply and bias rails, and buffered inputs and outputs as terminals of the macromodel.

Although most of the design can be done by considering the circuit blocks separately, it is essential that the complete filter of about 600 components is simulated to study crosstalk effects and to verify the overall responses. This is done efficiently by recalling the macromodels from the admittance matrix library and adding any further components, interconnections, and encapsulation strays. ac analysis on the full circuit, which is equivalent to about 3000 linearized elements can then be rapidly performed.

Crosstalk between the sound channel or tuning circuit and the luminance or chrominance output must be very low for adequate filter rejection performance. This means that any common paths must be carefully considered. Complete simulation of the filter by the methods described above revealed that the common impedances due to bias and supply rails and bonding wire inductances could be a problem. A significant improvement in the bandstop performance was obtained by a rerouting of power rails and an isolation of the resonant currents of individual gyrators.

PERFORMANCE

Fig. 11 shows the measured responses of a filter for the European TV system *G* with the specification points marked.

Samples show very consistent performance and agree closely with design predictions of amplitude and phase response. The tightest specification to be met is the sound trap in the chrominance channel where a minimum attenuation of 40 dB is required over the sound bandwidth of 100 kHz. The trap has been designed to give a tuning tolerance of ±0.5 percent which allows for automatic tuning errors and component mismatch on the chip. The crosstalk performance is very good, thus maintaining deep traps. The signal-to-noise performance is fully adequate, with values better than 80 dB, 70 dB, and 60 dB[1] in the teletext, luminance, and chrominance channels, respectively. This is confirmed by good performance in a television receiver.

CONCLUSIONS

This video filter IC is fully compatible with most other television IC's produced in a standard bipolar process and is suitable for mass production. It requires no adjustment and is free of alignment drift. This filter represents an important step towards larger scale integration in television signal processing, as the filtering function could now be combined on one IC with the synchronous demodulator, color decoder, or sound detector.

REFERENCES

[1] K. W. Moulding, G. A. Wilson, "A fully integrated five-gyrator filter at video frequencies," *IEEE J. Solid-State Circuits*, vol. SC-13, pp. 303–307, June 1978.
[2] A. Fettweis, "Noise performance of capacitor-gyrator filters," *Int. J. Circuit Theory Appl.*, vol. 2, pp. 181–186, June 1974.
[3] J. O. Voorman, "The gyrator as a monolithic circuit in electronic systems," Ph.D. dissertation, Nijmegen, The Netherlands, 1977.
[4] British Patent 1 421 093.
[5] H. T. Van Looij and K. M. Adams, "Phase compensation in electronic gyrator circuits," *Electron. Lett.*, vol. 4, pp. 430–431, Oct. 1968.
[6] British Patent Application 7916112.
[7] R. J. Widlar, "New developments in IC voltage regulators," *IEEE J. Solid-State Circuits*, vol. SC-6, pp. 2–7, Feb. 1971.

[1] Peak-to-peak signal to weighted rms noise ratios measured with filters complying to the CCIR Standard Rec. 451-1.

Paper 3-A.3

Integration of Analog Filters in a Bipolar Process

J. O. VOORMAN, W. H. A. BRÜLS, AND P. J. BARTH

Abstract—Monolithic analog filters are described which are based on the integration of electronic transconductors and capacitors. The method used allows simulation of inductor capacitor filters.

The transconductors are voltage-controlled current sources provided with a scaling multiplier. The value of one external resistor and matching of integrated elements determine the transconductances. Capacitors are made with an oxide/nitride dielectric on the low-ohmic emitter diffusion and with an aluminum top electrode.

Applications include PCM low-pass filters, Viewdata modem filters, etc. The method is extendable from the audio band up to video frequencies. Simple breadboarding, no need for special CAD, and an extremely low supply power consumption are features of the filter type.

The filters are on-chip compatible with analog and digital system parts.

I. INTRODUCTION

INITIALLY, electric filters were built from coils, transformers, and capacitors. In the 1960's and 1970's attempts were made to eliminate the (expensive and bulky) coils and transformers by the introduction of active parts. *RC*-active filters came up. In 1966 Orchard drew attention to the fact that the "classical" ladder filters from inductors, transformers, and capacitors exhibit a natural insensitivity to element value variations (Fig. 1; see also [19]). This insensitivity permits the design of extremely accurate filters considering the tolerances on the inductor and capacitor values.

A search began for active filters with similar properties. Two ways were followed.

On the one hand, attempts were made to replace the coils by electronic inductors. Tellegen's gyrator [18] terminated by a capacitor yields an inductor. A difficulty encountered was that it is impossible to make a proper gyrator with a floating port using resistors, capacitors, and common operational amplifiers (with earthed output port [24]). Special-purpose integrated circuits were designed to simulate floating coils [20], [22].

On the other hand, efforts were directed at transforming the filters and at simulating the filter equations so as to have all electronic parts earthed:

1) reactive-active filters were proposed [13] using the elements R, C and earthed L and $-C$,

2) the Bruton transformation [4] led to generalized immittance converter filters [5], [15] with R, C and earthed L, superinductor (*FDNR*), and supercapacitor (*FDNC*),

Manuscript received July 9, 1981; revised October 5, 1981.
The authors are with Philips Research Laboratories, Eindhoven, The Netherlands.

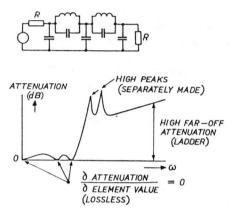

Fig. 1. The three properties which are so much appreciated with the classical filters: zero first-order sensitivity of the gain with respect to element value variations at points of zero insertion loss; individually tunable high attenuation peaks in the stopband(s); and large far-off attenuation (addition of the attenuations of all ladder sections).

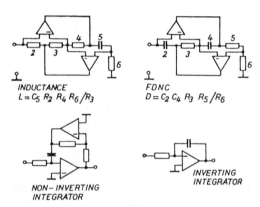

Fig. 2. Some electronic components for hybrid integrated filters (filters constructed from resistors, capacitors, and common operational amplifiers on thin or thick film).

3) direct implementation of the filter equations yielded signal-flowgraph and leapfrog filters [1] with positive and negative integrators (with earthed output ports).

All earthed components, which have been mentioned above, can be constructed from resistors, capacitors, and common operational amplifiers (see Fig. 2).

The resistor-capacitor-operational amplifier filters have become the most popular because of the low price of mass-produced operational amplifiers (compared with the more expensive special-purpose gyrator IC's).

Even the above hybrid integrated filters do not fit in with thinking in LSI and VLSI. Filters need to be integrated on the same chip together with analog and digital system parts. Digital

Reprinted from *IEEE J. Solid-State Circuits,* vol. SC-17, no. 4, pp. 713–722, Aug. 1982.

filters, of course, meet the above requirement. Moreover, they feature excellent stability and reliability. However, in those cases where chip area or power consumption are (too) large, switched capacitor filters can offer an interesting alternative [3], [6], [8], [14]. They are integrated on MOS processes (extended with integrated capacitors).

We present an alternative for integration in bipolar processes with capacitors. The filters are gyrator type analog filters. They are based on the integration of capacitors and electronic transconductors.

II. THE FILTER ELEMENTS: CAPACITOR AND TRANSCONDUCTOR

Linear capacitors can be integrated either between two interconnection layers or between an interconnection layer and a low-ohmic diffusion. In our case the capacitors are made on the emitter diffusion with a silicon oxide/nitride sandwich as a dielectric and covered with an aluminum top electrode (Figs. 3 and 4). Second-layer interconnection lines may run freely across the capacitors. The capacitor value is of the order of magnitude of 1 nF/mm². Leakage, losses, temperature dependence and voltage dependence compare favorably with the properties of capacitors in common use for filter applications. Usually, integrated capacitors deviate less than 10 percent from the design value and matching is well within 1 percent.

Integrated resistors (base diffusion) have a large temperature coefficient and their value can deviate by up to 10 percent from the design value. By scaling their value to the value of an external resistor we obtain the following:

1) the effective value of the conductor is made to depend on ratios of values of integrated elements (instead of absolute values) and on the value of an external conductor, and

2) an adjustment of the value of the external conductor can correct for the initial deviation of the "capacitor" values from their design value.

The use of "trans" conductors (with a voltage input and a current output) instead of conductors permits them to be combined into gyrators and gyrator type circuits.

The principle of the transconductor is shown in Fig. 5. The input voltage v yields a signal current $i = G_k v$ in the integrated conductor G_k. This current is scaled. The collector currents of the input transistors $I_1 - i$ and $I_1 + i$ (I_1 is a supply current) are fed to a current multiplier. The multiplication is based on addition and subtraction of base–emitter voltages, which corresponds to multiplication and division of collector currents, respectively, because of the logarithmic characteristic of bipolar transistors. Let the collector currents of the output transistors be $I_2 - j$ and $I_2 + j$, where I_2 is another supply current. Then $(I_1 - i)/(I_2 - j) * (I_2 + j)/(I_1 + i) = 1$, provided that the multiplier transistors are pairwise identical and they are at the same temperature. The output signal current $j = (I_2/I_1)i$. The effective value of the transconductance is

$$G_{k\text{ eff}} = j/v = (I_2/I_1) G_k. \qquad (2.1)$$

The supply current ratio is controlled according to the rule

$$I_2/I_1 = G_2/G_1 \qquad (2.2)$$

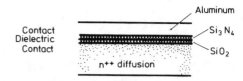

Fig. 3. Cross section of an integrated dielectric capacitor.

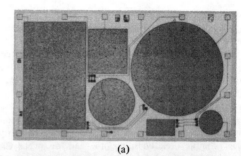

(a)

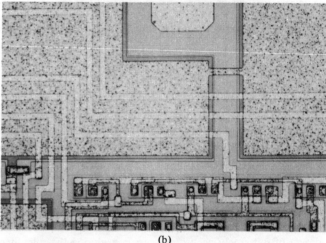

(b)

Fig. 4. (a) Photograph of a test chip with integrated capacitors. (b) Electronic circuitry combined with integrated dielectric capacitors.

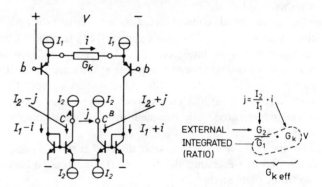

Fig. 5. Transconductor principle. A transconductor consists of a voltage-controlled current source and a current multiplier.

(Fig. 6) from which it follows that

$$G_{k\text{ eff}} = (G_2/G_1) G_k. \qquad (2.3)$$

One control circuit controls several or all transconductors. All conductors G_k and the reference conductor G_1 are integrated. G_2 is kept outside the chip. The transconductances are fixed by ratios of values of integrated elements (for instance, G_k/G_1, and not by their absolute values) and the value of an external conductor G_2.

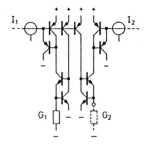

Fig. 6. Control circuit principle. The ratio of the values of the two sets of supply currents for the transconductors becomes equal to the ratio of the values of an integrated and an external reference conductor.

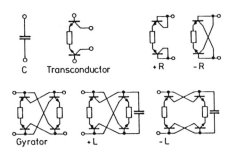

Fig. 7. Some components for filter design from capacitors and transconductors (resistor, negative resistor, gyrator, inductor, negative inductor).

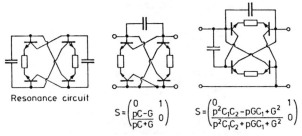

$$S = \begin{pmatrix} 0 & 1 \\ \dfrac{pC-G}{pC+G} & 0 \end{pmatrix} \qquad S = \begin{pmatrix} 0 & 1 \\ \dfrac{p^2C_1C_2 - pGC_1 + G^2}{p^2C_1C_2 + pGC_1 + G^2} & 0 \end{pmatrix}$$

Fig. 8. A resonance circuit and some constant resistance phase-shifters. The phase-shifters give a frequency-dependent delay from the left to the right and zero delay from the right to the left (S = scattering matrix).

Matching of transconductances relies upon the matching of integrated transistors and resistors. The external conductor fixes the absolute value. Variation of the conductance G_2 scales the filter characteristic along the frequency axis.

The effective transresistance yields a multiplication factor. For instance, with $R_1 = R_k = 40$ kΩ and $R_2 = 400$ kΩ ($R_1 = 1/G_1$, etc.), the effective transresistance (400 kΩ) is ten times larger than the values of the integrated resistors. This permits them to be used in filters for relatively low frequencies without the need of large chip areas.

III. COMPONENTS FROM CAPACITORS AND TRANSCONDUCTORS

As a first element for filter design we have the capacitor. A transconductor with paralleled input and output ports yields a resistor (Fig. 7), the value of which is controlled by the external conductor. A negative resistor is made introducing a cross-coupling. Two transconductors can be combined to form a gyrator (positive immittance inverter). Addition of a capacitor yields an electronic inductor. A negative inductor can be made.

A resonance circuit and some nonreciprocal constant resistance phase-shifters are shown in Fig. 8.

IV. FILTER DESIGN

The most direct method of filter design with transconductors and capacitors is to start from an inductor-capacitor filter configuration and to implement all inductors as electronic inductors consisting of a gyrator and a capacitor each (Fig. 9). The terminating resistors are in the form of transconductors with paralleled input and output ports.

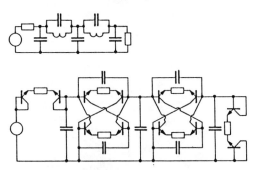

Fig. 9. A fifth-order inductor-capacitor low-pass filter (for example, for a PCM codec) and its transconductor-capacitor counterpart. Every inductor is replaced by a gyrator (from transconductors) and a capacitor. Every resistor is implemented as a transconductor with paralleled input and output ports.

The filter can be breadboarded by interconnecting transconductor boards and capacitors (Fig. 10). The resistance level of the filters (100–500 kΩ for filters in the audio band) still permits direct (unscaled) breadboarding. The filters can even be more accurate than the corresponding inductor-capacitor filters because of lower losses, for example. Any inductor-capacitor-resistor network can thus be implemented, provided that the inductors and resistors have a dc path to earth in order to fix the dc levels of the electronic transconductors.

The advantages of small size (low price) and ease of breadboarding (as compared with inductor-capacitor filters) are accompanied by the disadvantages of a (low) supply power consumption, a higher noise level (due to the noise of the electronic parts), and a possibility of instability. The following three types of instability can be distinguished (corresponding to the values of the time constants in the circuitry):

1) at dc (latch-up);

2) at filter frequencies (overflow limit cycle oscillations); and

4) at high frequencies.

If the transconductors are properly designed it is unlikely that any of the three instabilities will occur [24]. However, a general proof of stability in a network of capacitors and a given type of transconductor has not yet been given. Stability should still be considered from case to case.

Stability analysis is relatively simple in cases where all transconductors are earthed (with one side of the input port). A monotonous dependence of the output current on the input

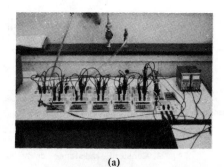

(a)

(b)

Fig. 10. Transconductor boards (breadboard transistor circuits) are interconnected with capacitors for the breadboarding of a receive filter for a Viewdata modem. Integrated transconductors can be employed for a higher order breadboarding.

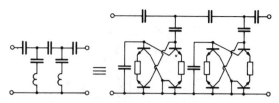

Fig. 11. A high-pass filter (with earthed inductors) can be made with capacitors and earthed transconductors. Stability analysis is relatively simple.

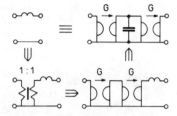

Fig. 12. A floating inductor can be made with a gyrator with a floating port and a capacitor, but also with two earthed gyrators and a capacitor. In the latter case a 1:1 transformer (two identical cascaded gyrators) is introduced and the inductor becomes a capacitor in the center.

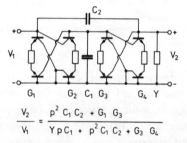

$$\frac{V_2}{V_1} = \frac{p^2 C_1 C_2 + G_1 G_3}{Y p C_1 + p^2 C_1 C_2 + G_3 G_4}$$

Fig. 13. A low-pass filter section with four earthed transconductors and two capacitors. The voltage transfer function shows a true transmission zero, regardless of proper matching of the transconductor values.

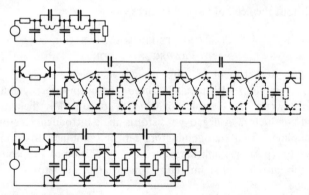

Fig. 14. An inductor-capacitor low-pass filter and an equivalent circuit with earthed transconductors and capacitors. Pairs of transconductors can be combined to obtain the lower implementation with six earthed transconductors (the same number that we need in a direct inductor simulation).

voltage and damping of the filter at overflow (these are requirements for a properly designed transconductor) can assure stability.

It is useful, therefore, to study filter design with capacitors and "earthed" transconductors. We shall show that for common filters this does not lead to a larger number of components.

In a high-pass filter all transconductors can be earthed (Fig. 11). A floating inductor can be implemented using two gyrators with earthed ports and a capacitor [9] (see Fig. 12). The above, however, is not a direct inductor simulation which automatically preserves the insensitivity properties of the inductor capacitor filters. Referring to Fig. 1 we may ask: do the attenuation peaks remain very high, regardless of the degree of matching of the transconductor values? That there is no problem can be shown by a calculation of the voltage transfer function of a low-pass filter section equipped with two earthed gyrators (four transconductors) and loaded by an admittance Y (see Fig. 13). The transmission zero is deep, independent of the values of the transconductors.

In Fig. 13 we use four earthed transconductors for something that can be done with one floating gyrator. However, the two inner transconductors are connected to the same voltage and each has a spare output (to earth). The two transconductors can be combined into one. Similarly, pairs of earthed transconductors can be combined in a low-pass ladder

filter (Fig. 14). Also the load resistor of the filter is involved in the contraction. The first- and second-order delay sections in Fig. 8 can be dealt with in the same way (Fig. 15). In conclusion, Figs. 11, 14, and 15 show a way to implement inductor-capacitor filters and delay sections with a minimum

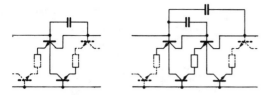

Fig. 15. First- and second-order delay sections (see Fig. 8) constructed from capacitors and "earthed" transconductors.

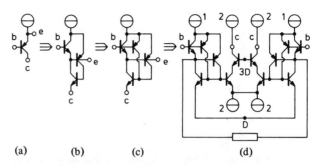

Fig. 16. The accuracy of the (a) input transistors of the transconductors has been improved by the introduction of (b) supertransistors. (c) An extra transistor has been added to protect against latch-up. In (d) the supertransistors have been fitted in the transconductor.

number of capacitors and transconductors, the latter of which are all earthed.

V. The Design of Transconductors and Control Circuit

Various types of transconductors can be designed for general purposes, simple special-purpose circuits, low frequencies, high frequencies, and for a low supply voltage, etc. First, we shall describe general-purpose circuits for filters in the audio band and later—in view of the application in a receive filter for a Viewdata modem—simplified special-purpose designs.

Let us start with the general-purpose transconductor. The input transistors should have a high current gain and transductance so that the transistor parameters need not explicitly be taken into account in the transconductor value. The input p-n-p transistor [Fig. 16(a)] has been made, therefore, as a supertransistor from two n-p-n transistors and a p-n-p transistor [Fig. 16(b)]. Another p-n-p is added to prevent latch-up [Fig. 16(c)]. In Fig. 16(d) the transconductor has been equipped with the improved input transistors. The latter circuit needs certain voltage levels (D and $3D$, D = diode voltage) which have been provided in the complete circuit in Fig. 17 (the part in dotted lines). "0" is the filter earth level. Its value can be chosen from a wide range. The output transistors have been drawn in a dashed circle, which indicates a provision to kill their parasitic p-n-p transistors (for instance, a collector wall diffusion all around the transistor) in order to avoid latch-up. The circuitry in dashed lines represents the lower supply current sources fed from above via a current mirror. The circuitry has been designed with base current compensation and early effect compensation (for the method, see [24]). Therefore, the supply currents 1 and 2 deliberately deviate a little from the currents in the conductors G_1 and G_2 (see Fig. 18).

Fig. 18 shows the control circuit for the transconductor in Fig. 17. The circuitry in continuous lines corresponds to the diagram in Fig. 6. Two p-n-p transistors have been replaced by more accurate supertransistors with base current compensation. The circuitry in dashed lines adds some base currents. The dotted lines indicate a "start" provision and some overvoltage protection diodes.

Fig. 19 shows various types of supply current sources. For low losses in the filters, very high collector resistances are required (the resistors may directly shunt reactive filter elements).

Filter circuits can be designed for a supply voltage as low as 3 V. A transconductor for filters in the audio band will have $R_k = 1/G = 20$–50 kΩ. Typical values for the supply currents are $I_1 = 10$–25 μA and $I_2 = 1$–3 μA. The result is a

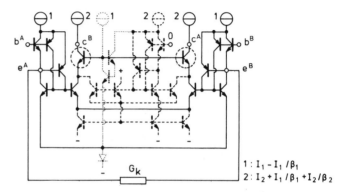

Fig. 17. The complete diagram of the general-purpose transconductor. Compared with Fig. 16(d), the voltage levels D and $3D$ have now been provided (in dotted lines) and the lower supply currents are fed via a current mirror (in dashed lines).

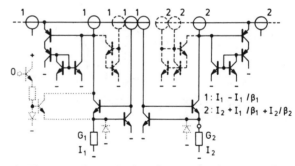

Fig. 18. The control circuit for the transconductor in Fig. 17 (the principle has been given in Fig. 6).

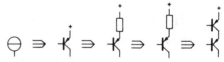

Fig. 19. Some supply current source implementations. From left to right: a lateral p-n-p transistor, the same, but with emitter feedback to increase the collector impedance and to reduce the noise, the same, but the Early effect of the lateral p-n-p is reduced by increasing the basewidth, and a cascode circuit with a still higher collector impedance.

minimum supply power of the order of magnitude of 0.1 mW/ transconductor with a maximum signal-to-noise ratio of, typically, 60–80 dB.

Similar circuits can be developed for higher frequencies, for instance, for the video band (0–5 MHz).

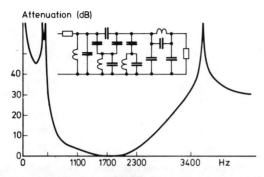

Fig. 20. Inductor-capacitor receive filter for a Viewdata modem and its attenuation as a function of frequency. It has a passband (around 1700 Hz) for the incoming FSK signal and it rejects the return channel (around 420 Hz).

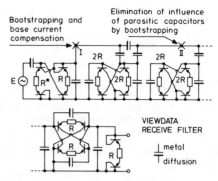

Fig. 23. The transconductor-capacitor Viewdata receive filter. Parasitic capacitances of the floating filter capacitors are eliminated by bootstrapping (see also Fig. 24).

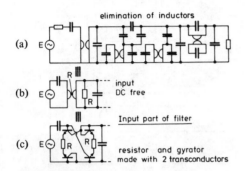

Fig. 21. (a) All inductors of the Viewdata receive filter in Fig. 20 have been eliminated. The input is made dc free. (b) The input resistor is placed behind the gyrator. (c) The gyrator and the resistor together are made from two transconductors.

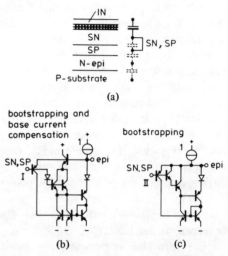

Fig. 24. (a) Cross section of a capacitor on the emitter diffusion (*SN*), the base diffusion (*SP*), the epitaxial layer (*N*-epi), and the substrate. Voltage followers (b) and (c) let the epitaxial layer signal voltage follow the *SN*, *SP* capacitor terminal voltage, thus eliminating the influence of parasitic capacitors on the filter characteristic.

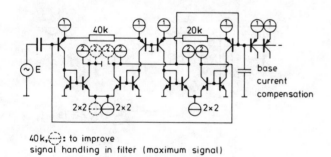

40k, ⊖: to improve signal handling in filter (maximum signal)
Input part of filter

Fig. 22. Increasing the signal handling capacity of one transconductor substantially improves the signal handling capacity of the filter.

VI. RECEIVE FILTER FOR A VIEWDATA MODEM

We have breadboarded several filter types. In order to show the feasibility of the method a first example had to be worked out completely and was to be integrated. We chose the receive filter for a Viewdata modem.

The purpose of the receive filter is to transfer the incoming FSK signal (frequencies: 1300, 2100 Hz, speed: 1200 bits/s) and to reject the return channel (frequencies: 390, 450 Hz, speed: 75 bits/s); see Fig. 20. It was supplied to us as a ninth-order inductor-capacitor filter.

We directly eliminated all inductors [Fig. 21(a)]. We obtained a dc free input [Fig. 21(b)]. The gyrator and the filter input resistor are made using two transconductors [Fig. 21(c)].

The filter was breadboarded (Fig. 10). The signal margins in

the transconductors were checked by computer simulation. It was observed that the maximum (undistorted) signal in the filter can be roughly a factor of two higher if we increase the signal handling capacity of one transconductor (Fig. 22). We now arrive at the filter configuration in Fig. 23. Two gyrators in resonance circuits for the rejection of the return channel have been made with twice the nominal gyrator resistance in order to have lower capacitor values (saving of chip area).

The parasitic capacitor at the bottom side of (floating) integrated capacitors cannot be ignored. Bootstrapping eliminates them. To achieve this the epitaxial layer was separated from the lower terminal of the capacitor by application of a base diffusion [*SP*, Fig. 24(a)]. Two voltage follower circuits [Fig. 24(b) and (c)] are needed to eliminate the influence of five parasitic capacitors.

A special-purpose simple transconductor (or voltage-controlled current source V_{CCS}) was designed to further reduce chip area and power consumption. We chose the transconductor in Fig. 25 with cascoded supply current sources, simplified supertransistors, and centralized provisions for the levels D and $3D$ and for the control of the lower supply current source. Fig. 26 shows the control circuit for the Viewdata modem

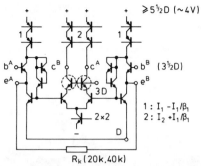

Fig. 25. Simplified transconductor. It is equipped with resistors of 20 or 40 kΩ.

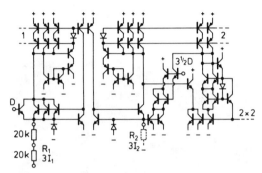

Fig. 26. Control circuit for the Viewdata filter. It controls the p-n-p type supply current sources 1 and 2 and the n-p-n type 2 × 2. In order to have more tractable (lower) values for the reference resistors they carry three times the supply currents of the current sources.

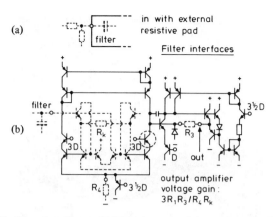

Fig. 27. Filter interfaces. (a) There is no need for an integrated interface at the input of the filter. (b) An output amplifier has been coupled to the transconductor of the load resistor.

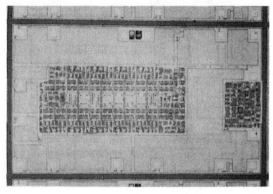

Fig. 28. Photo of the Viewdata filter chip. The nine transconductors, control circuitry, and output amplifier (with resistors in the center) are surrounded by capacitors. The smaller separate circuit is the slicer/two-phase rectifier.

receive filter. It is provided with the appropriate base current compensations. Typical resistor values are $R_1 = 40$ kΩ ($I_1 = 5$ μA) or 20 kΩ ($I_1 = 11$ μA) and $R_2 = 10 R_1$ ($I_2 = 0.1 I_1$). This leads to total supply current consumptions of 160 and 320 μA. With a supply voltage of 4 V the power consumption of the filter is 0.6 and 1.2 mW, respectively.

VII. INTERFACES

In order to simplify the use of the filter it was decided to design some interfaces.

Maximum input signal voltages of the order of magnitude of 100 mV can be made with a relatively low-ohmic resistor pad (low-ohmic relative to the resistance level of the filter: 200 kΩ). At the input of the filter there is no need for an integrated interface circuit [Fig. 27(a)].

At the filter output a voltage amplifier has been coupled to the transconductor of the load resistor [Fig. 27(b)].

In a Viewdata modem the output signal of the filter is sliced (hard limited) and it should be detectable whether the signal amplitude is higher or lower than some specified values. To this end a slicer and a two-phase rectifier have been developed with a large dynamic range considering the low supply voltage.

VIII. LAYOUT, INTEGRATION, AND PERFORMANCE

The filter, the control circuitry, the output amplifier, and the slicer/two-phase rectifier have been put on one chip of 2.9 × 5 mm² (inclusive 16 bonding pads).

The layout can be seen from the photo in Fig. 28.

The performance of the filter can be assessed against various criteria. Fig. 29 shows the transmission of the filter. The characteristic at low frequencies and the behavior at high frequencies have been photographed separately.

Variation of the external reference resistor R_2 scales the characteristic along the frequency axis. This is shown in Fig. 30. The total range for linear scaling is of the order of magnitude of three decades.

An increase in the supply voltage of the filter from 4 to 12 V does not result in a visible modification of the filter characteristic. The supply current increases slightly. A signal sine wave voltage on the supply is found at the filter output attenuated by 40–50 dB.

The temperature coefficient of characteristic frequencies of the filter curve is approximately 120 ppm/°C (inclusive the influence of the external metal film resistor).

Although the supply power consumption of the filter is of the order of magnitude of 1 mW the maximum-undistorted-signal-to-noise distance is satisfactory. It can be estimated roughly from Fig. 31, where the filter characteristic has been given at maximum signal together with the characteristic in the case of a 40 dB lower input signal level. Fig. 32 gives the spot noise power (with 10 Hz resolution). We have integrated the

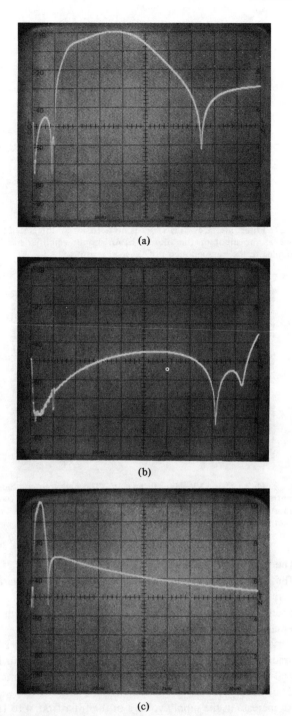

(a)

(b)

(c)

Fig. 29. Transmission of the integrated receive filter. The vertical scale is 10 dB/div. Horizontally we have different scales: (a) 500 Hz/div, (b) 50 Hz/div, (c) 5 kHz/div.

noise power in the frequency band 500–2900 Hz. A maximum-signal-to-noise distance was found of almost 70 dB (even in the case of 0.6 mW supply power consumption).

IX. Former, Alternative, and Further Results

The principle of our filter method was already described in [23] and employed in a tone encoder/decoder for paging applications [25], however, still with external capacitors. The integration of the capacitors became feasible after the technology of high quality integrated capacitors had been developed.

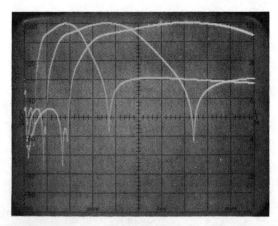

Fig. 30. Scaling of the external reference resistor by factors of 0.5 and 2 scales the frequency characteristic by factors of 2 and 0.5, respectively. The corresponding three characteristics have been photographed (successively) in one picture.

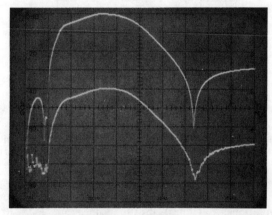

Fig. 31. The filter characteristic at maximum (undistorted) signal and in the case of a 40 dB lower input signal (the curve tracer bandwidth is 10 Hz) to roughly estimate the noise of the filter.

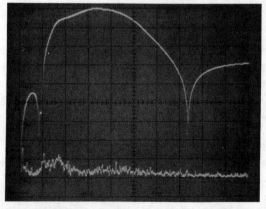

Fig. 32. The spot noise as measured (with 10 Hz bandwidth) of the integrated Viewdata filter. Over a frequency band from 500 to 2900 Hz we have a maximum-undistorted-signal-to-noise distance of almost 70 dB.

In the literature the following several alternatives for the integration of analog filters in bipolar processes have been reported (for a survey of principles, see Fig. 33).

1) Active-R filters [Fig. 33(a)]: the 6 dB/octave frequency roll-off of the gain of operational amplifiers is used to make

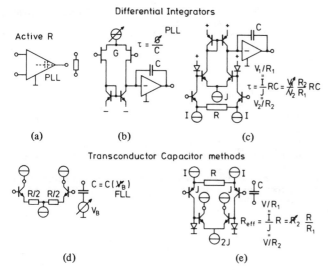

Fig. 33. Principles for the integration of analog filters in bipolar processes. (a) Active *R* methods. (b) Integrator with variable JFET input stage. (c) Integrator with variable multiplier input stage. Transconductor-capacitor methods: (d) with fixed transconductors and variable depletion layer capacitors; (e) with variable transconductors and fixed capacitors.

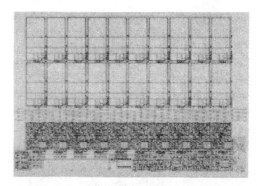

Fig. 34. Mask programmable filter principle. The pattern shows a row of 10 transconductors and two rows of capacitor banks. In between is an interconnection field of first-layer aluminum. Components are connected to the interconnection lines (nodes) by mask programmable second-layer interconnections. Control circuitry, level provisions, and bootstrap circuits complete the pattern.

earthed integrators as components for filter design [2], [16]. The fixing of time constants relies upon matching of gain-bandwidth products and their control by an additional phase-locked loop (on an external reference frequency).

2) Two more specific designs of amplifier integrators have been presented by Tan and Gray [17], who use a variable input stage with junction field effect transistors [Fig. 33(b)] and by Fukahori [7], who uses a variable input stage with a bipolar multiplier [Fig. 33(c)]. In the latter case the control of the time constants is by way of a voltage ratio. The temperature coefficient of the integrated resistors is in the time constants.

3) Another method with transconductors (Fig. 33(d); [10], [11]) employs variable depletion layer capacitors. The time constants are tuned by variation of the capacitor values with a bias voltage. The method is employed for video filtering. A frequency-locked loop on the color subcarrier controls the time constants.

Fig. 33(e) reviews the elements for our transconductor-capacitor filter method.

Apart from our first example, the Viewdata modem filter with its extremely low supply power consumption, we have integrated the filter elements (capacitors, transconductors, and control circuit) in various ways and in different integration processes. The area has been reduced significantly.

Several filters have been breadboarded and a layout design has been made for a mask programmable filter (Fig. 34). It consists of a row of transconductors, two rows of capacitor banks $(1 + 2 + 4 + 8 + 16 + 32 + 64 + 128$ pF each), control circuitry, and some bootstrap circuits. The user can design filters by completing one mask: the mask of the second-layer interconnection pattern.

NB the same bipolar integration process type (extended with integrated dielectric capacitors) has been used for the integration of an adaptive filter for automatic echo reduction in Teletext data (7 Mbits/s) (see [26]).

X. CONCLUSION

A method has been given for the integration of analog filters in a bipolar integration process. It is based on the integration of capacitors and electronic transconductors. The capacitors are of a high quality and stability and they exhibit proper matching. The transconductors consist of accurate voltage-controlled current sources with integrated resistors, the values of which are scaled to an external resistor by means of current multiplication.

The above two types of elements permit a direct simulation of inductor-capacitor filters (including their natural insensitivity to element value deviations). Gyrators are used for inductor simulation. On the other hand, transformations have been given to achieve filter configurations with (the same number of) all transconductors earthed.

The feasibility of the method has been demonstrated by the integration of a ninth-order receive filter for a Viewdata modem. This has illustrated the simple breadboarding, shown that there is no need for special CAD, and that the supply power consumption is extremely low (1 mW). The supply power consumption is an order of magnitude lower than values reported for switched capacitor filters.

After the integration of this first filter we further optimized the filter parts. A mask programmable filter has been designed. It contains transconductors and capacitor banks, which can be interconnected by completing the pattern of the second-layer interconnection mask.

The filter method can be used for all types of filters for signal handling at baseband (low-pass, high-pass, and phase (delay) filters). In narrow-band filters for signals at intermediate frequencies one should be aware of noise and signal enhancement effects which may lead to a higher supply power consumption (as for all nonpassive filters [21]).

The method is extendable from the audio band up to video frequencies (0–5 MHz). It is well suited for application in oscillators and in variable and programmable filters.

ACKNOWLEDGMENT

The authors are pleased to thank J. G. de Groot and L. A. Daverveld who carried out extensive and decisive technological

IEEE JOURNAL OF SOLID-STATE CIRCUITS, VOL. SC-17, NO. 4, AUGUST 1982

work on the integration of the capacitors and the Viewdata filter. They also wish to thank Dr. B. Huber for his enthusiasm and the design of the inductor-capacitor version of the Viewdata filter, which has served as a basis for the transconductor-capacitor implementation.

Furthermore, they would like to express their gratitude to all who have contributed in any way whatsoever, among whom they are particularly indebted to L. J. W. van Loon for his coordinating activities.

REFERENCES

[1] P. O. Brackett and A. S. Sedra, "Direct *SFG* simulation of *LC* ladder networks with applications to active filter design," *IEEE Trans. Circuits Syst.*, vol. CAS-23, pp. 61-67, 1976.

[2] J. R. Brand and R. Schaumann, "Active *R* filters: Review of theory and practice," *IEE J. Electron. Circuits Syst.*, vol. 2, pp. 89-101, 1978.

[3] R. W. Brodersen, P. R. Gray, and D. A. Hodges, "MOS switched-capacitor filters," *Proc. IEEE*, vol. 67, pp. 61-75, 1979.

[4] L. T. Bruton, "Network transfer functions using the concept of frequency-dependent negative resistance," *IEEE Trans. Circuit Theory*, vol. CT-16, pp. 406-408, 1969.

[5] L. T. Bruton, "Multiple-amplifier *RC*-active filter design with emphasis on GIC realizations," *IEEE Trans. Circuits Syst.*, vol. CAS-25, pp. 830-845, 1978.

[6] A. Fettweis, "Basic principles of switched-capacitor filters using voltage inverter switches," *Archiv für Elektronik und Übertragungstechnik*, vol. 33, pp. 13-19, 1979; and "Switched-capacitor filters using voltage inverter switches: Further design principles," *Archiv der Elektrischen Übertragung*, vol. 33, pp. 107-114, 1979.

[7] K. Fukahori, "Monolithic tunable notch filter," in *Dig. Tech. Papers, IEEE Int. Solid-State Circuits Conf.*, Philadelphia, PA, vol. 266, pp. 130-131.

[8] D. A. Hodges, P. R. Gray, and R. W. Brodersen, "Potential of MOS technologies for analog integrated circuits," *IEEE J. Solid-State Circuits*, vol. SC-13, pp. 285-294, 1978.

[9] A. G. J. Holt and J. Taylor, "Method of replacing ungrounded inductors by grounded gyrators," *Electron. Lett.*, vol. 1, p. 105, 1965.

[10] K. W. Moulding and G. A. Wilson, "A fully integrated five-gyrator filter at video frequencies," *IEEE J. Solid-State Circuits*, vol. SC-13, pp. 303-307, 1978.

[11] K. W. Moulding, J. R. Quartly, P. J. Rankin, R. S. Thompson, and and G. A. Wilson, "Gyrator video filter IC with automatic tuning," *IEEE J. Solid-State Circuits*, vol. SC-15, pp. 963-968, 1980.

[12] H. J. Orchard, "Inductorless filters," *Electron. Lett.*, vol. 2, pp. 224-225, 1966.

[13] H. J. Orchard and D. F. Sheahan, "Inductorless bandpass filters," *IEEE J. Solid-State Circuits*, vol. SC-5, pp. 108-118, 1970.

[14] J. Pandel, "Switched-capacitor elements for VIS-SC-filters with reduced influences of parasitic capacitances," *Archiv für Elektronik und Übertragungstechnik*, vol. 35, heft 3, pp. 121-130, 1981.

[15] W. Saraga, D. Haigh, and R. G. Barker, "A design philosophy for microelectronic active-*RC* filters," *Proc. IEEE*, vol. 67, pp. 24-33, 1979.

[16] M. A. Soderstrand, "Active *R* ladders: High-frequency high-order low-sensitivity active *R* filters without external capacitors," *IEEE Trans. Circuits Syst.*, vol. CAS-25, pp. 1032-1038, 1978.

[17] K. Tan and P. R. Gray, "Fully integrated analog filters using bipolar-JFET technology," *IEEE J. Solid-State Circuits*, vol. SC-13, pp. 814-821, 1978.

[18] B. D. H. Tellegen, "The gyrator, a new electric network element," *Philips Res. Rep.*, vol. 3, pp. 81-101, 1948.

[19] G. C. Temes and H. J. Orchard, "First-order sensitivity and worst case analysis of doubly terminated reactance two-ports," *IEEE Trans. Circuit Theory*, vol. CT-20, pp. 567-571, 1973.

[20] H. R. Trimmel and W. E. Heinlein, "Fully floating chain-type gyrator circuit using operational transconductance amplifiers," in *Dig. Tech. Papers, IEEE Int. Symp. Electr. Network Theory*, 1971, pp. 61-62.

[21] J. O. Voorman and D. Blom, "Noise in gyrator-capacitor filters," *Philips Res. Rep.*, vol. 26, pp. 114-133, 1971.

[22] J. O. Voorman and A. Biesheuvel, "An electronic gyrator," *IEEE J. Solid-State Circuits*, vol. SC-7, pp. 469-474, 1972.

[23] J. O. Voorman, "The adaptive gyrator," in *Proc. IEEE Int. Symp. Circuits Syst.*, Munich, Germany, 1976, pp. 34-37.

[24] J. O. Voorman, "The gyrator as a monolithic circuit in electronic systems," thesis, University of Nijmegen, The Netherlands, 1977.

[25] J. O. Voorman and A. Wijker, "Pagyr: A new component for selective calling," *Philips Telecommun. Rev.*, vol. 36, pp. 31-40, 1978.

[26] J. O. Voorman, P. J. Snijder, P. J. Barth, and J. S. Vromans, "A one-chip automatic equalizer for echo reduction in Teletext," *IEEE Trans. Consumer Electron.*, vol. CE-27, pp. 512-529, 1981.

Bipolar Integration of Analog Gyrator and Laguerre Type Filters (Transconductor-Capacitor Filters)

J.O. Voorman, W.H.A. Brüls and P.J. Barth
Philips Research Laboratories, P.O.Box 80.000, 5600 JA Eindhoven
The Netherlands

New electronic circuit principles are given for the integration of analog filters in bipolar processes with dielectric capacitors. They extend the application to lower supply voltages(> 1.2 V) and to higher frequencies (< 10 MHz) and they give a reduction of chip area.

Introduction

In the past few years we have developed several bipolar integrated circuits with integrated analog filters (gyrator type fixed filters [1,3] and Laguerre type adaptive filters [2,4]).

Below we give a short survey of results earlier obtained and we report on new developments towards lower supply voltages, higher frequencies and reduction of chip area.

Transconductor-capacitor filters

The integration of analog filters proved possible after a major technological breakthrough: the development of high-quality integrated dielectric capacitors, as an option to standard bipolar processes [1,2,3].

In addition to capacitors, electronic transconductors (as resistive elements) were used for filter design (fig. 1). The inherent advantages of lossless ladder filters are preserved (see e.g. [1]). Resistors, capacitors, gyrators, inductors, transformers, etc. are available (fig. 2).

The values of the transconductors are determined by electronic scaling of the value of one external reference resistor (fig. 3). Values of integrated resistors and emitter areas are used as ratios.

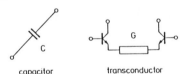

capacitor   transconductor

Fig. 1. The capacitor and transconductor (or voltage-controlled current source (VCCS)) are a basis for analog filter design.

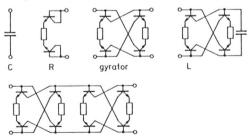

C   R   gyrator   L

transformer

Fig. 2. All components for classical filters can be made from transconductors and capacitors.

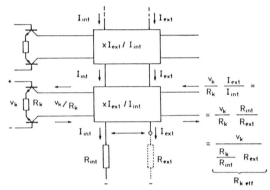

Fig. 3. Control of transconductor values. Integrated resistors R_k convert the input signal voltages v_k to signal currents v_k/R_k, which are all multiplied by the ratio of two control currents. The latter are derived from an external and an integrated reference resistor. The effective transconductance is $(R_{int}/R_k)/R_{ext}$.

When the external reference resistor is varied, all transconductances vary and the filter characteristic scales along the frequency axis.

The above has been worked out in a first example: a receive filter for a viewdata modem [3]. The chip area is $12\,mm^2$, the lowest supply voltage 4 V and the supply power 1 mW (important in view of powering via the telephone line).

A second example is a filter master chip of $9\,mm^2$ with capacitor banks, ten transconductors and control circuitry. Completion of one mask (second interconnection layer) defines the filter [3].

More recent developments

We start from the capacitor and transconductor (fig. 1).

As far as the transconductor is concerned, we have so far reduced the influence of the transistor parameters by feedback and compensation. Highly linear and accurate transconductors have been made.

When we omit the resistor (in fig. 1) we are left with a non-linear differential stage. For one transistor (fig. 4a):

$$V_{be} = \frac{kT}{q} \ln(I_c/X), \qquad (1)$$

where X is the saturation current. For the differential stage with transistors 1 and 2 (fig. 4b):

Reprinted from *Proc. ECCTD'83*, Stuttgart, pp. 108–110, Sept. 1983.

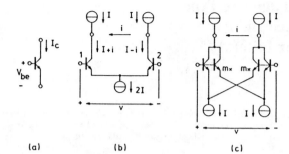

(a)   (b)   (c)

Fig. 4. Linearization of a transistor
differential stage. (a) transistor, (b)
differential stage and (c) two differential stages in parallel for linearization.

$$v = \frac{kT}{q}\left\{\ln\frac{I+i}{I-i} - \ln(X_1/X_2)\right\}. \quad (2)$$

The ratio of saturation currents is a
ratio of emitter areas. Conversely,

$$i = I\tanh\{y + \ln(X_1/X_2)/2\}. \quad (3)$$

where $y = v/(2kT/q)$.

The above non-linear relation can be
linearized by putting two stages in
parallel with emitter area ratios of 1:r
and r:1, respectively (fig. 4c). We
obtain:

$$\frac{j}{I} = \frac{1}{2}\left\{\tanh(y + a) + \tanh(y - a)\right\}, (4)$$
$$= (1-d)\left\{y + (d-1/3)y^3 + ...\right\}, \quad (5)$$

where $a=\ln(r)/2$ and $d=\{(r-1)/(r+1)\}^2$. For
$d=1/3$ or $r=2+\text{sqrt}(3)=3.732...$ the relation is maximally linear. Some over-
compensation is obtained in the more
practical case of r=4.

Fig. 5 gives the distortion as a
function of the input signal voltage. For
input peak voltages below 27 mV (peak cur-

rents below I/3) the harmonic distortion
of the linearized stage is below -68 dB.
With r=4 the transconductance is:

$$\frac{i}{v} = \frac{8}{25}\frac{qI}{kT}. \quad (6)$$

The linearized differential stage is
used for the design of several transconductor types: one for low supply voltages,
a very accurate transconductor, and a version for low frequencies (fig. 6).

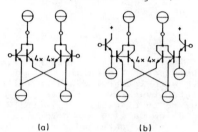

(a)   (b)

Fig. 6. At the left: a transconductor for
low supply voltages (>1.2 V), at the
right: a very accurate transconductor,
and below: a transconductor with a (2n+1)x
lower transconductance (for low-frequency
filters).

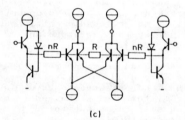

(c)

The transconductance is temperature-
stabilized when the supply currents are
derived from a current stabilizer with a
current of the type:

$$I = (kT/qR_{ext})\ln(m), \quad (7)$$

where R_{ext} is an external reference resistor and m is a geometric ratio of
emitter areas (for a circuit example;
see fig. 7).
The transconductance is ((6),(7)):

$$G_{k\ eff} = (8/25)\ln(m)/R_{ext}. \quad (8)$$

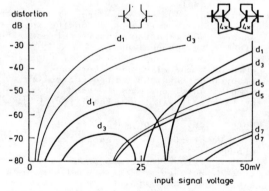

distortion
dB

Fig. 5. Distortion:
-in thin lines of a common differential
 stage,
-in thick lines of the linearized differential stage (r=4).
We have a sinewave input voltage (peak
value in mV). In the output signal current: d_1 is the deviation from linearity,
$d_3, d_5, ...$ are (odd) harmonics (all in dB
relative to the main signal current).

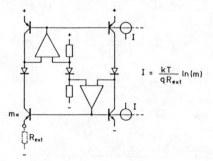

$$I = \frac{kT}{qR_{ext}}\ln(m)$$

Fig. 7. Current stabilizer circuit principle. The currents are $(kT/qR_{ext})\ln(m)$.

A further reduction in chip area is obtained when we apply electronic multiplication methods for the capacitances (see e.g. fig. 8).
Capacitance multiplication reduces the impedance level of the filter.

When we apply the above principles to the 9th order receive filter for a viewdata modem, the chip area can be reduced to 3 mm^2 and the supply voltage to 2 V. Less stringent requirements can be met even at lower supply voltages (>1.2V). Filters for frequencies between 10 Hz and 10 MHz can be made.

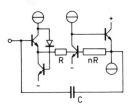

Fig. 8. Electronic magnification of capacitances. Seen at the input terminal the capacitance is : (n+1)C.

Laguerre type video filters

Adaptive filters generally consist of a cascade of tapped delay sections. The (variable) tapweights are adjusted automatically. A well known method for automatic adjustment is correlation of the tap signal with some error signal (fig. 9).

We have made an adaptive equalizer for reduction of echoes in Teletext data signals (7 Mb/s) [2,4]. All analog circuit implementation has given a cheap one-chip solution. The transversal filter is a cascade of seven first-order allpass sections (Laguerre filter). The correlator integrators and the allpass sections have been made with integrated dielectric capacitors.

With the transconductors in fig. 6 new allpass sections (of first and second order) have been made (fig. 10).
The first-order allpass sections have been applied in an adaptive delay-line of ten sections (chip area : 8 mm^2) for ghost cancelling for the TV picture (fig. 11).

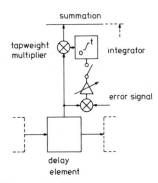

Fig. 9. Adaptive delay section. The tapweights are automatically adjusted by correlation of the tapsignal with an error signal. The delay can be made with an allpass section.

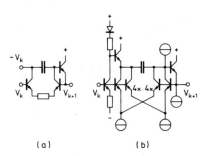

Fig. 10. First-order transconductor-capacitor allpass section; at the left : principle, at the right : circuit diagram (the delay can be varied over a wide range by adjustment of the supply currents of the transconductor). Below : principle of a second-order delay section.

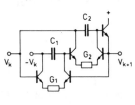

(c)

Conclusion

New principles have been given for the integration of analog filters in bipolar processes. A lowest supply voltage of 1.2 V and a highest frequency of 10 MHz can be obtained at a small chip area.

The examples show the power of bipolar electronics for the integration of fixed and adaptive filters.

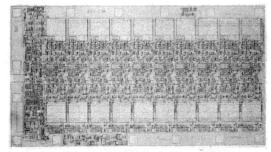

Fig. 11. Photograph of a chip with ten analog adaptive delay sections (for automatic ghost cancelling in the TV picture).

References

1 J.O. Voorman (1980),Eurocon '80, Stuttgart, 246-250.
2 J.O. Voorman, P.J. Snijder, P.J. Barth and J.S. Vromans (1981) IEEE Transactions on Consumer Electronics CE-27, 512-529.
3 J.O. Voorman, W.H.A. Brüls and P.J. Barth (1982) IEEE Journal of Solid-State Circuits SC-17, 713-722.
4 J.O. Voorman, P.J. Snijder, J.S. Vromans and P.J. Barth (1982) Philips Technical Review 40, 11/12.

Realization of a 1-V Active Filter Using a Linearization Technique Employing Plurality of Emitter-Coupled Pairs

Hiroshi Tanimoto, Mikio Koyama, and Yoshihiro Yoshida

Abstract —A low-voltage (1 V), low-power (100 μW), and low-frequency (9 kHz) fifth-order fully integrated active low-pass filter (LPF) using a bipolar technology is described. Novel highly linear transconductors consisting of N emitter-coupled pairs were designed for low-voltage operation. The linear input range is expanded to about 100 mV$_{p-p}$ at 1% error with $N = 4$, which is about twice that of the conventional linearization technique.

The filter is basically a gyrator–capacitor type, in which gyrators are implemented by using the linearized transconductors. Large time constants were realized with very low current (540 nA/transconductor) owing to the high transconductance-to-operating-current ratio of the linearized transconductors. Measured results show a passband ripple of 1.5 dB, a minimum stopband rejection of 70 dB, and a dynamic range of 56 dB, despite a very high nominal impedance (400 kΩ). Practical limitations of this approach are also discussed, such as the sensitivity of the linearized transconductors against process variations, noise, and frequency limitations.

I. Introduction

RECENT advances in hand-carried electronic equipment demand smaller and smaller components. Typical examples are hand-carried radiotelephones and radio pagers. Filters are very important components in these telecommunication equipments. Reducing the equipment size and power dissipation are very important in realizing such equipment, which is small and easy to maintain.

As the size of batteries is now becoming the limiting factor for such equipment, it is not sufficient to reduce the size of bulky components such as filters by integrating them; the reduction of their power dissipation is also very important. A key point is to develop, simultaneously, both low-power and low-voltage operating LSI's in order to reduce the battery size. Here, low voltage means a single battery operation, i.e., about 1 V.

This paper describes a low-voltage (1 V) and low-power (100 μW) fifth-order fully integrated active low-pass filter using a bipolar technology.

Manuscript received November 30, 1990; revised March 14, 1991.

H. Tanimoto and M. Koyama are with Toshiba Research and Development Center, 1, Komukai Toshiba-cho, Saiwai-ku, Kawasaki 210, Japan.

Y. Yoshida is with the Semiconductor Division, Toshiba Corporation, 1, Komukai Toshiba-cho, Saiwai-ku, Kawasaki 210, Japan.

IEEE Log Number 9100257.

There are several types of active filters that can be integrated; however, the transconductor–capacitor type of filter is one of the few choices considering a 1-V operation [1]. The well-known gain-cell type variable transconductors are not applicable because they require an extra V_{BE} for logarithmic compression, and thus need at least about 2 V to operate. Another possibility is to utilize a class-AB variable transconductor [4]; however, this transconductor requires buffers at the input or output in order to absorb its relatively low input resistance. This will lead to a larger power consumption or will require a similar power supply voltage to the gain-cell type transconductor.

In contrast, the ordinary bipolar emitter-coupled pair with current source loads can operate from a 1-V power supply as a variable transconductor. Also, this circuit has a high transconductance-to-quiescent-current ratio, which is essential for a low-power operation.

Examining the above emitter-coupled pair, the output voltage can swing only about 0.3 V peak to peak in this situation. Unfortunately, a conventional emitter-coupled pair has only a 10-mV linear input range and cannot fully exploit the limited dynamic range. Although a conventional linearized differential pair using two emitter-coupled pairs with 1:4 ratioed emitter sizes [2] has about a 40-mV linear input range, it is not sufficient when used in practical circuits, which often produce tens of millivolt offsets. Thus, further linearization of the differential pair as a transconductor is of foremost concern.

This paper introduces highly linear transconductors consisting of N bipolar transistor differential pairs and gives the conditions to implement such transconductors in Section II. For the $N = 4$ case, a linear input range of 100 mV$_{p-p}$ at 1% error can be realized theoretically. Sensitivity analysis results on the proposed circuit structure indicated that the circuit is very robust against changes in processing parameters (Section III). Section IV describes the practical implementation of a 1-V filter IC and related design considerations such as low-voltage operation, noise, and frequency limitations. The measured results of the experimental active-low-pass filter IC using the linearized transconductors are described in Section V. The test chips have demonstrated the usefulness of the approach for low-voltage and low-power realization of filter IC's.

Reprinted from *IEEE J. Solid-State Circuits*, vol. SC-26, no. 7, pp. 937–945, July 1991.

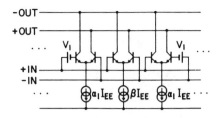

Fig. 1. General circuit topology of linearization technique.

II. Linearized Variable Transconductors

A. Basic Idea for Linearization

The basic idea for linearization is to give each differential pair operating in parallel ($N \geqslant 2$) an appropriate input offset voltage and a tail current in such a way that the combined input–output characteristic of those N pairs in parallel has a flatter slope. Fig. 1 shows the general transconductor circuit using this technique. This is an extension of an idea mentioned in [2], which corresponds to the $N = 2$ case.

Neglecting the emitter resistance and the output resistance of the core differential pair and considering the symmetry of the circuit, we have the resulting transconductance $G(\cdot)$:

$$G(V_{\text{in}}) = \sum_{k=1}^{[N/2]} \alpha_k \{ g_m(V_{\text{in}} - V_k) + g_m(V_{\text{in}} + V_k) \}$$
$$+ \beta g_m(V_{\text{in}}) \quad (1)$$

where $g_m(V_{\text{in}}) = dI_{\text{diff}}/dV_{\text{in}}$, $I_{\text{diff}} = \alpha_F I_{EE} \tanh(V_{\text{in}}/2V_T)$; V_{in} is differential input voltage; V_k is the kth offset voltage; N is the number of differential pairs operating in parallel; $[N/2]$ is the integer part of $N/2$; α_k is the kth tail current multiplier; I_{diff} is the differential output current of a differential pair; α_F is the common-base forward current gain; I_{EE} is the tail current value; V_T is the thermal voltage ($= kT/q$); and β is the tail-current multiplier for an odd N ($\beta = 0$ for an even N).

The offset V_k's are assumed to be ordered in ascending magnitude. Note that α_k's and β are normalized by the largest one without loss of generality.

B. Maximally Flat Approximation and Equiripple Approximation

We first use a "maximally" flat approximation to approximate the flat characteristics. The condition for (1) to have a maximally flat transconductance can be obtained by setting the parameters α_k, β, and V_k in such a way that the derivatives of G at $V_{\text{in}} = 0$ are zero to as high an order as possible. For the sake of simplicity, we make the following normalizations and definitions:

$$x = V_{\text{in}}/2V_T$$
$$y = I_{\text{diff}}/\alpha_F I_{EE} (= \tanh x)$$
$$G_m(x) = dy/dx = 1 - y^2 (= 1 - \tanh^2 x)$$
$$v_k = V_k/2V_T. \quad (2)$$

This leads to a simpler version of (1):

$$G(x) = \sum_{k=1}^{[N/2]} \alpha_k \{ G_m(x - v_k) + G_m(x + v_k) \} + \beta G_m(x).$$
$$(1')$$

As the function $G(x)$ is an even function of the argument x, the nth derivative $G^{(n)}(x)$ is an odd function of x for odd n's, and is an even function for even n's. Thus, the odd-order derivatives of $G(x)$ are always zero at $x = 0$, and we only have to check the even-order derivatives. The number of parameters that can be set independently is $N - 1$, because only the ratios among α_k's and β have a meaning (we will set $\alpha_{[N/2]} = 1$ arbitrarily without loss of generality). Thus, we can set the parameters to satisfy the following set of simultaneous $N - 1$ nonlinear equations:

$$G^{(2)}(0) = G^{(4)}(0) = G^{(6)}(0) = \cdots = G^{(2(N-1))}(0) = 0.$$
$$(3)$$

As the odd-order derivatives are zero at $x = 0$, we can expect to have a $(2N-1)$th-order maximally flat characteristic at best. The authors have solved the $N = 1, 2, 3$ cases analytically and the $N = 4$ case numerically. The resulting parameter sets are shown in Table I.

For the maximally flat cases, N equaling one and two corresponds to conventional circuits. For N equaling three and four, we can obtain the fifth- and seventh-order maximally flat characteristics, respectively.

Similarly, $G(x)$ can be approximated to have an equiripple characteristic. The conditions for $G(x)$ to have equiripple characteristics are equivalent to having all the minima and maxima of $G(x)$ with the same values. It is rather easy and straightforward to apply any numerical optimization technique, for example, the least mean-square error optimization technique, directly to the original problem, because this condition leads to a set of nonlinear equations. Such an example of a parameter set obtained by using the LMS optimization technique for a 0.8% equiripple is shown in Table I.

Table I also summarizes the transconductance value per total quiescent current for the $N = 1$ to 4 maximally flat cases. The values are normalized such that the value for the ordinary emitter-coupled pair is unity. From this table, the transconductance value per total quiescent current for the $N = 4$ case is about half that of an emitter-coupled pair, and 72% of a conventional linearized transconductor ($N = 2$).

C. Results of the Linearization Technique

Fig. 2(a) shows the theoretical transconductance plots of the proposed linearization. The horizontal axes are the differential input voltage, and the vertical axes are the normalized transconductance. The inner four curves are maximally flat designs, and the outermost curve is an equiripple design example.

TABLE I
OBTAINED PARAMETER SETS FOR $N = 1-4$

N	$V_1/2V_T$	$V_2/2V_T$	α_1	α_2	β	$G(0)/(I_{\text{total}}/2V_T)$	Comment
1	—	—	—	—	1.0	1.000	Common diff. pair
2	0.65848	—	1.0	—	—	0.667	Conventional [2]
3	1.03172	—	1.0	—	0.64	0.545	5th-order max. flat
4	0.35407	1.29773	0.54785	1.0	—	0.480	7th-order max. flat
4	0.550	1.794	0.720	1.0	—	0.357	0.8% equiripple

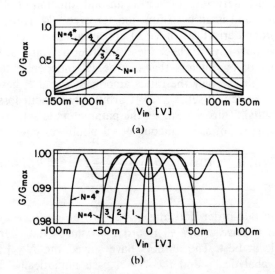

(a)

(b)

Fig. 2. Theoretical results of linearization technique: (a) transconductance versus input voltage level plots, and (b) its detail. * 0.8% equiripple design. The other curves are all maximally flat designs.

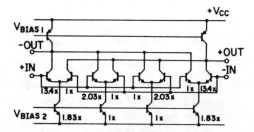

Fig. 3. Circuit realization of maximally flat transconductor ($N = 4$).

Fig. 2(b) shows a detail of the flat portion of Fig. 2(a). This clearly demonstrates the usefulness of the linearization technique. For the $N = 4$ maximally flat case, the linear range at 1% transconductance falloff is about 100 mV$_{\text{p-p}}$. As the $N = 1$ case is a standard differential pair, the improvement is about a factor of 10. Compared with the conventional linearized transconductor [2], that is the $N = 2$ case, the improvement is about double. A linear range of about 160 mV$_{\text{p-p}}$ can be achieved for the $N = 4$ equiripple design.

D. Practical Circuit Realization of the Linearization Technique

In order to realize the offset voltage V_k, an asymmetric emitter-coupled pair with $m:1$ ratioed emitter areas was used, where $m = e^{V_k/V_T}$ [2].

The largest emitter area ratio was 13.4 in the $N = 4$ maximally flat case. A linear input range of about 160 mV$_{\text{p-p}}$ can be achieved for a 0.8% equiripple design ($N = 4$). The largest emitter area ratio was 36.2 in this case. As the emitter area ratio increases exponentially with N, this ratio exceeds 30 in an $N = 5$ maximally flat case, as an example. These values may be too large for most applications; however, a wider linear input could be obtained at the cost of an increased transistor area.

Fig. 3 shows an $N = 4$ circuit realization, which was used to implement the experimental low-pass filter IC described in Sections IV and V.

III. SENSITIVITY TO PARAMETER VARIATIONS

A. Sources of Transconductance Variation

Transistor mismatches affect the transconductor characteristics in two aspects. First, they result in a transconductance value deviation. Second, they cause a linearity degradation.

Parameters subject to change in the authors' linearization technique are α_k's, β, and V_k's. The α_k's and β are determined by the ratioed tail-current sources, and the V_k's are determined by the emitter area ratio of each asymmetric differential pair. It is sufficient to consider only the saturation current "I_s" mismatch among the transistor parameter mismatches, because mismatches in V_{BE} and the emitter area can be treated equivalently as mismatches in the saturation currents. Or more practically, the emitter-area-ratio variations are rather indistinguishable from the variations in the saturation currents by electrical measurements.

The transconductance value deviation is mainly caused by mismatches among the ratioed tail-current source values. This is related to variations in α_k's and β. It is a common practice to utilize emitter-degeneration resistors against the variations in V_{BE}. Unfortunately, the authors' experimental low-pass filter (LPF) operated at a very low current level, making the use of the emitter-degeneration technique impractical.

Linearity degradation is attributed to mismatches in the asymmetric differential pairs and the tail-current sources. That is, mismatches in the tail-current sources cause the parameters α_k to change, and ratio mismatches in the asymmetric differential pairs cause the parameters V_k to change. For ratio mismatches in the differential pairs, a pair-wise mismatch does not affect total linearity because V_k's are solely determined by the emitter area ratios; however, a mismatch within a pair can cause V_k to deviate from its nominal value.

We next calculate the effect caused by saturation current variation.

B. Transconductance Sensitivities to Saturation Current Variation

As the total transconductance is given by the summation of $\alpha_k G_m(x \pm v_k)$ type terms, we can obtain the total sensitivity formula by first calculating its sensitivity and then summing them up for all k's. Considering that the variations in "I_s" occur to individual transistors independently, we define the following "partial" transconductance:

$$G_k(x) = \alpha_k G_m(x - v_k) + \tilde{\alpha}_k G_m(x + \tilde{v}_k)$$
$$G_0(x) = \beta G_m(x).$$

There are parameters with and without "~", because these parameters have the same nominal value but change independently and need to be distinguished. Therefore, we have the total differential:

$$dG_k = \frac{\partial G_k}{\partial \alpha_k} d\alpha_k + \frac{\partial G_k}{\partial v_k} dv_k + \frac{\partial G_k}{\partial \tilde{\alpha}_k} d\tilde{\alpha}_k + \frac{\partial G_k}{\partial \tilde{v}_k} d\tilde{v}_k. \quad (4)$$

In (4), we assumed that the emitter area ratio "m" does not change. Using the following relations:

$$\frac{\partial G_k}{\partial \alpha_k} = \frac{G_k}{\alpha_k}$$

$$\frac{\partial G_k}{\partial \tilde{\alpha}_k} = \frac{G_k}{\tilde{\alpha}_k}$$

$$\frac{\partial G_k}{\partial v_k} = -2\alpha_k \tanh(x - v_k)\left[\tanh^2(x - v_k) + 1\right]$$

$$\frac{\partial G_k}{\partial \tilde{v}_k} = 2\tilde{\alpha}_k \tanh(x + \tilde{v}_k)\left[\tanh^2(x + \tilde{v}_k) + 1\right]$$

and relations between I_s and α_k, v_k:

$$\frac{d\alpha_k}{\alpha_k} = \frac{dI_s}{I_s}, \quad \frac{dv_k}{v_k} = \frac{V_T}{v_k}\left(\frac{dI_{s1}}{I_{s1}} - \frac{dI_{s2}}{I_{s2}}\right) \quad (5)$$

we obtain

$$dG_k = G_k\left(\frac{dI_s}{I_s} + \frac{d\tilde{I}_s}{\tilde{I}_s}\right) - 2\alpha_k V_T \tanh(x - v_k)$$

$$\cdot \left\{\tanh^2(x - v_k) + 1\right\}\left(\frac{dI_{s1}}{I_{s1}} - \frac{dI_{s2}}{I_{s2}}\right)$$

$$+ 2\tilde{\alpha}_k V_T \tanh(x - \tilde{v}_k)\left\{\tanh^2(x - \tilde{v}_k) + 1\right\}$$

$$\cdot \left(\frac{d\tilde{I}_{s1}}{\tilde{I}_{s1}} - \frac{d\tilde{I}_{s2}}{\tilde{I}_{s2}}\right). \quad (6)$$

Likewise, we get

$$\frac{dG_0}{G_0} = \frac{d\beta}{\beta} = \frac{dI_s}{I_s}.$$

In (5) and (6), I_{s1} and I_{s2} are the saturation currents for the individual transistors of a differential pair. Again, "~" is used to distinguish statistically independent variables.

If the I_s's are uncorrelated and their variations are small, the following equation holds approximately:

$$\sigma_G^2\Big|_{V_{in}=0} \approx \left\{\sum_{k=1}^{[N/2]}\left(2 + \left[\frac{8\alpha_k V_T}{G_k(0)}\tanh v_k\left[\tanh^2 v_k + 1\right]\right]^2\right)\right.$$
$$\left. + \frac{1 - (-1)^N}{2}\right\}\sigma_{I_s}^2 \quad (7)$$

where $\sigma_G^2 = (\Delta G/G)^2$ and $\sigma_{I_s}^2 = (\Delta I_s/I_s)^2$. The last term is introduced for mathematical adjustments for odd n's, and is zero for even n's. As the second term in the brackets of (7) is usually small, say a few tenths, the term "2" dominates over the variation in $G(0)$. This means that the variation in the offset voltage v_k has a small effect on the transconductance value variation in the proposed linearization technique. Therefore,

$$\sigma_G^2\Big|_{V_{in}=0} \approx N\sigma_{I_s}^2. \quad (8)$$

Because the term "2" comes from mismatches in α_k's and β, the variation in the total transconductance G can be very small if the emitter-degeneration technique is employed for suppressing the tail-current mismatches. In such cases, the mismatches in α_k's and β can be made negligible, and the variation will become

$$\sigma_G^2\Big|_{V_{in}=0} \approx \left\{\sum_{k=1}^{[N/2]}\left(\frac{8\alpha_k V_T}{G_k(0)}\tanh v_k\left[\tanh^2 v_k + 1\right]\right)^2\right\}\sigma_{I_s}^2.$$

C. Numerical Example for the N = 4 Transconductor

Using the parameter values for the $N = 4$ case from Table I and (7), we can obtain an estimate of the variation in $G(0)$. This resulted in $\sigma_G^2 \approx 4.37 \cdot \sigma_{I_s}^2$. The result predicts about 2.1% $G(0)$ variation caused by 1% random I_s variation. Note that this value is very close to the value predicted by (8). If we utilized the emitter-degeneration technique, the variance could be reduced to only 0.37.

In order to estimate a practical transconductance variation, the authors carried out a Monte-Carlo simulation on the circuit of Fig. 3 ($N = 4$ case). In this simulation, only the SPICE BJT model parameter "I_s" was taken as a Gaussian random variable with $\pm 1\%$ standard deviation, while the other parameters were kept constant. This is equivalent to ± 1.3-mV standard deviation in V_{BE}, and is a modest estimate in a typical bipolar process. A result of 49 SPICE runs indicated that the resulting standard deviation in the flat portion of the transconductance curve was less than $\pm 1.6\%$ of the nominal transconductance value $G(0)$. This supports the above sensitivity analysis result and the reproducibility of the very flat measured transconductance curve of Fig. 9 over processing variations.

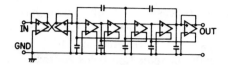

Fig. 4.   Schematic circuit diagram of fifth-order active ladder LPF [3].

$$V_{CC} > V_{BE} + 2V_{CE\,min.}$$

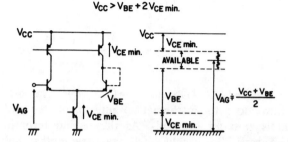

Fig. 5.   Limitation and conditions for maximum output swing in low-voltage operation.

IV. A 1-V ACTIVE FILTER IC

A. Filter Design

An experimental 1-V active LPF was designed with $N = 4$ transconductors. The filter was an active ladder type derived from a doubly terminated fifth-order elliptic LC ladder filter prototype with 9-kHz cutoff, 1-dB passband ripple, and 75-dB stopband rejection. Each floating inductor was realized by one capacitor and two gyrators which consisted of two transconductors connected back to back. Considering the total capacitor area and the noise level, the nominal impedance was chosen to be 400 kΩ, and this resulted in a total required capacitance of 400 pF. Seven transconductors were used in total. Redundant transconductors were eliminated following the techniques in [3]. The total quiescent current per transconductors was about 540 nA, in which the minimum quiescent collector current was about 12 nA. Fig. 4 shows a schematic circuit diagram of the filter. The triangles were replaced by the proposed transconductors of Fig. 3.

B. Low-Voltage Operation Considerations

Next, let us consider the operating voltage. Fig. 5 serves as a model for the linearized transconductor used in the filter, which is basically a parallel connection of emitter-coupled pairs. Because the transconductors are used as gyrators, the output node and the input node must be at the same potential as in Fig. 5. Assume that the power supply voltage is V_{CC}, and the minimum allowable emitter-to-collector voltage is $V_{CE\,min}$ for both n-p-n and p-n-p current sources.

Then, V_{CC} must satisfy the following relation for proper operation:

$$V_{CC} > V_{BE} + 2V_{CE\,min}.$$

So, only the voltage exceeding this value is available for signal swing. For a typical bipolar process, this minimum V_{CC} may be around 0.9 V at room temperature, assuming that V_{BE} is 0.6 V and $V_{CE\,min}$ is between 0.1 and 0.2 V.

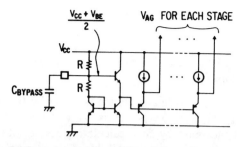

Fig. 6.   Analog ground voltage generator for maximum output swing.

The analog ground voltage V_{AG} must satisfy the next equation to exploit the entire dynamic range:

$$V_{AG} \approx \frac{V_{CC} + V_{BE}}{2}.$$

Fig. 6 is a circuit diagram of an analog ground voltage generator that satisfies the above condition. Using this circuit, the filter IC operated at its optimal operating point. A bypass capacitor was connected externally to improve the power supply rejection ratio.

C. Noise Considerations

The noise performance of the linearized transconductors is essentially the same as a conventional emitter-coupled pair, as the proposed linearized transconductors consist of N ordinary emitter-coupled pairs with offsets at their input connected in parallel.

The effect of the base resistance r_b basically remains unchanged when compared with an ordinary emitter-coupled pair; however, the input-referred collector shot noise increases somewhat because the linearized transconductors have a lower transconductance value per total quiescent current. This is one of the penalties paid for linearization.

The seventh column of Table I ($G(0)/(I_{\text{total}}/2V_T)$) summarizes the transconductance value per total quiescent current for the $N = 1$ to 4 maximally flat cases. A net enhancement in the dynamic range is possible because of drastic improvements in the linear input ranges. For the $N = 4$ case, we can expect a 14-dB improvement in the dynamic range over the conventional emitter-coupled pair, because the improvement in the linear input range is about a factor of 10 and the transconductance-to-total-operating-current ratio is about one half.

D. Frequency Limitation Considerations

The lowest realizable cutoff frequency of the gyrator–capacitor filters is determined by the upper limit of capacitor value C and the lower limit of realizable transconductance value $G_{\min}$, because the cutoff frequency is proportional to $G_{\min}/C$. The maximum capacitor value available on a chip is typically limited on the order of 100 pF. The minimum attainable transconductance value is limited by the h_{FE} falloff in the small current region because the transconductance is proportional to the quiescent current. In this type of filter, the dc gain of each transconductor stage is nearly equal to its h_{FE} value by the authors' analysis, and a lower dc gain degrades the filter pole Q values [5].

Another limiting factor is the leakage current when the quiescent current becomes comparable to it. In fact, the minimum collector current for the transistors within the linearized transconductor is only 2.2% of the total quiescent current, for the $N = 4$ case. If there were a fabrication process which guaranteed h_{FE} down to 10 pA, which is typical leakage current level, it would be possible to realize a $G_{min} = 1/(228\ M\Omega)$. Then, a monolithic filter with cutoff frequency as low as several hertz may be theoretically possible; however, it is not practical to deal with such a high impedance.

The highest realizable frequency of this type of gyrator–capacitor filter is determined by the excess phase shift mainly due to the second poles of the capacitively loaded transconductors, i.e., integrators [5], [6].

A conventional simple emitter-coupled pair is assumed for a transconductor for simplicity. Then the second pole p_2 is determined by the input device's time constant, i.e., $p_2 \approx 1/r_b \cdot C_{BE}$. As an example, consider a simple second-order filter with a center frequency ω_0 and a quality factor $Q = 20$. Simulation results indicated that the p_2 must 200 times larger than ω_0 in order to keep $\Delta Q/Q < 30\%$. If the dc gain is adjusted to compensate the excess phase shift at ω_0 [6], this condition can be alleviated to $p_2 > 50 \cdot \omega_0$. With parameters for the fabrication process used, $r_b \approx 300\ \Omega$ and $C_{BE} \approx 0.5$ pF, we get $p_2 \approx 1$ GHz; that is, this filter can be expected to operate up to 20 MHz.

The emitter-coupled pair has been assumed above; however, the result is true for the linearized transconductors, because the time constant $r_b \cdot C_{BE}$ remains almost the same. This is because the use of transistor with N times larger emitter area results in $N \cdot C_{BE}$ and r_b/N. Usually r_b tends not to scale very well, however, the magnitude of p_2 remains on the same order despite a larger emitter area. Thus the low-Q filters can be expected to operate beyond 100 MHz easily with a modern fine-line process. In fact, simulation results on the LPF described in the subsection A confirmed that it works up to 50 MHz for a quiescent current 500 times larger, and capacitors one-tenth the designed size. Therefore, this type of monolithic realization is potentially well suited for high-frequency filters [7].

E. Test Chip

A block diagram of the filter test chip is shown in Fig. 7. Besides the filter block there are two simple emitter-follower buffers at both ends of the filter to internally preserve the high filter impedance.

A simple bias current reference circuit using a V_T generator was included for temperature compensation, because the transconductance value of the transconductor is inherently inversely proportional to the absolute temperature. Unfortunately, there was a pattern error and

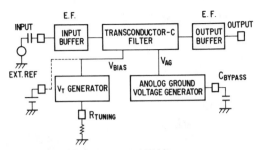

Fig. 7. Block diagram of experimental 1-V LPF IC.

Fig. 8. Microphotograph of test chip.

the measurements were carried out by using an external reference. An analog ground voltage reference circuit, mentioned above, was included.

As the minimum current level was extremely low (12 nA), an h_{FE} falloff in the low I_C region would normally be a significant problem. Fortunately, it was possible to utilize a suitable bipolar production line process shown to have practically no h_{FE} falloff down to the nanoampere region.

Also, care was taken to buffer and separate the bias line for each transconductor's current source loads. This greatly improves the stopband response degradation due to coupling through the bias line. Systematic offsets were carefully avoided by balancing the base currents, since the dynamic range of the transconductor was limited.

A filter test chip was fabricated by a bipolar process with a minimum emitter size of $4.8 \times 4.8\ \mu$m and $f_T = 1.5$ GHz.

A microphotograph of the filter IC is shown in Fig. 8. The active die area was $1.33 \times 1.33\ mm^2$ including the V_T generator circuit and all the capacitors totalling 400 pF. The capacitors occupied the upper half of the chip, and seven transconductors were located below the capacitors. The remaining were buffers and bias circuitry.

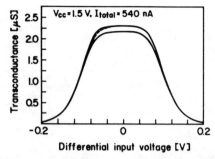

Fig. 9. Measured results of proposed linearized transconductor (*N* = 4).

A linearized transconductor of *N* = 4, separate from the filter, was also fabricated on the same wafer for testing purposes.

V. MEASURED RESULTS

A. Linearized Transconductor of N = 4

Fig. 9 shows the measured transconductance curve for the circuit shown in Fig 3. The power supply voltage was 1.5 V, and the total operating current was 540 nA. Note the flatness at the top of the curves. The linear input range was about 82 mV_{p-p} at 1% transconductance error and 100 mV_{p-p} at 2% error, which was slightly worse than predicted by theoretical calculations. The maximum transconductance for this case was calculated to be 2.5 μS, which closely matched the measured result. The three curves indicate deviations among separate chips from the same wafer.

The differences among $G(0)$ are attributed to bias current variations due to the base current error in the current mirror circuits used. This can be explained by the fact that the total collector current values deviated from their reference currents.

The measured result confirms the robustness of the circuit structure to process variations and supports the result of the sensitivity analysis.

B. 1-V Active Low-Pass Filter IC

Fig. 10(a) shows the measured frequency responses of the test chip for various power supply voltages from 0.9 to 1.5 V. Fig. 10(b) is the passband detail. Both were measured with a 100-mV_{p-p} input signal.

The measured passband response closely matched its simulated result except for a constant loss. This is attributed to a lower than expected h_{FE} value. The stopband rejection obtained was 69 to 74 dB, which was 6 to 1 dB worse than the design objective. This could be attributed to internal coupling due to the effect of a near-saturation operation, layout, etc., facilitated by the very high internal impedance level. The lower cutoff frequency was introduced by an external coupling capacitor needed for measurements. As seen from these results, the filter successfully operated down to 1 V at room temperature.

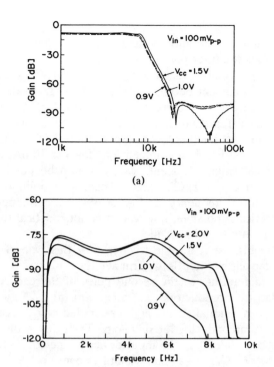

(a)

(b)

Fig. 10. (a) Measured frequency responses, and (b) passband detail for 0.9–2.0 V.

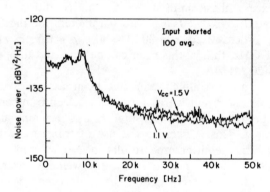

Fig. 11. Measured output noise spectra.

Varying V_{CC} while keeping the bias current constant caused slight shifts in the cutoff frequency. This was due to near saturation of the tail-current source transistor, which caused its bias currents to vary with V_{CC}. This shift can be easily corrected by adjusting the operating current appropriately.

The passband edge Q was degraded for the V_{CC} = 0.9-V case. This was due to the active load transistors fully entering the saturation region. Thus, the output impedance of the loads decreased and the Q factor of the simulated inductors was lowered. Devices with a lower saturation voltage are essential for further low-voltage operation.

Fig. 11 shows the measured output noise spectra with the input shorted. The total output noise was independent of V_{CC}, and was about 40 μV_{rms} in the passband (100 Hz to 10 kHz). The output noise was dominated by shot

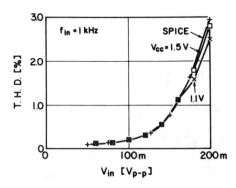

Fig. 12. Measured and simulated THD characteristics.

TABLE II
SUMMARY OF MEASURED CHIP CHARACTERISTICS

Power supply voltage	> 1.0 V
Power supply current	0.1 mA
Passband edge frequency	9 kHz
Passband ripple	1.5 dB
Stopband attenuation	> 70 dB
Passband noise	$40 \ \mu V_{rms}$ at V_{out}
THD	< 1% at $V_{in} = 150 \ mV_{p-p}$
Dynamic range	56 dB at 1% THD
Active die area	$1.3 \times 1.3 \ mm^2$

Minimum emitter size = $4.8 \times 4.8 \ \mu m$, $f_t = 1.5$ GHz

noise and thus very closely matched the simulation results. This output noise power is inversely proportional to the capacitor values, so that the noise in this type of circuit configuration may be improved only at the cost of increased chip area.

The linear input range for 1% total harmonic distortion was measured to be 150 mV$_{p-p}$, as shown in Fig. 12. This confirms the effectiveness of the linearization technique. This also closely matched the predicted value by SPICE simulation. Thus, the dynamic range of this filter was calculated to be about 56 dB.

The cutoff frequency of the filter IC was variable from 100 Hz to 50 kHz without significant degradation by simply varying V_{BIAS}, although the filter IC was not intentionally designed to vary its cutoff frequency such a wide range. The variable cutoff frequency range was not determined by the structure of the filter IC but simply by its bias circuitry design. This may support the frequency limitation considerations described in Section IV-D.

A summary of the measured filter IC characteristics is shown in Table II.

VI. CONCLUSION

A 1-V fully integrated active filter IC using the novel highly linear transconductor was fabricated using a bipolar technology. The filter IC is a gyrator–capacitor type, in which a gyrator is realized by two linearized transconductors. The 9-kHz fifth-order elliptic LPF test chip demonstrated operation down to 1 V with 100-μW power consumption, 56 dB of SNR, and over 3 decades of frequency tuning range. These result confirm that this is a viable approach to low-voltage and low-power filter realizations.

Low-voltage design considerations, noise, and frequency limitations were discussed on the filter IC. In particular, the analysis indicated that the approach is potentially well suited for high-frequency operation.

The technique for linearizing a variable transconductor using two emitter-coupled pairs has been extended to using three pairs or more in order to realize a low-voltage and low-power filter IC. The conditions for obtaining a maximally flat or equiripple transconductance characteristic were derived.

A sensitivity analysis showed the robustness of the linearization technique to parameter variations, which was confirmed by measurements on a test chip. In fact, a transconductor consisting of four emitter-coupled pairs was fabricated and tested to have about a 100-mV$_{p-p}$ linear input range, as predicted. This is an improvement of about a factor of 10 over a conventional emitter-coupled pair.

The linearized transconductors do not use the emitter-degeneration technique, so their transconductance values are high and proportional to the emitter currents. Thus, the transconductors are particularly well suited for low-power and/or low-voltage applications like active filters, analog multipliers, AGC amplifiers, and so on.

REFERENCES

[1] J. O. Voorman, "Analog integrated filters or continuous time filters for LSI and VLSI," in Proc. ESSCIRC '85, no. 292.
[2] J. C. Schmoock, "An input stage transconductance reduction technique for high-slew rate operational amplifiers," IEEE J. Solid-State Circuits, vol. SC-10, no. 6, pp. 407–411, Dec. 1975.
[3] D. W. H. Calder, "Audio frequency gyrator filters for an integrated radio paging receiver," in Proc. 1984 IEE Conf. Mobile Radio Syst. Tech., pp. 21–24.
[4] J. O. Voorman, "Transconductance amplifier," U.S. Patent 4 723 110.
[5] K. W. Moulding and G. A. Wilson, "A fully integrated five-gyrator filter at video frequencies," IEEE J. Solid-State Circuits, vol. SC-13, no. 3, pp. 303–307, June 1978.
[6] H. Khorramabadi and P. R. Gray, "High-frequency CMOS continuous-time filters," IEEE J. Solid-State Circuits, vol. SC-19, no. 6, pp. 939–948, Dec. 1984.
[7] M. Koyama, H. Tanimoto, and S. Mizoguchi, "A 10.7 MHz continuous-time bandpass filter bipolar IC," in Proc. CICC, May 1989, pp. 25.2.1–25.2.4.

High-Frequency Voltage-Controlled Continuous-Time Lowpass Filter Using Linearised CMOS Integrators

A. P. NEDUNGADI AND R. L. GEIGER

DEPARTMENT OF ELECTRICAL ENGINEERING, TEXAS A&M UNIVERSITY, COLLEGE STATION, TX
77843, USA

Abstract—The design and implementation of a continuous-time lowpass filter with voltage-controlled cutoff frequency and pass-band ripple is presented. The circuit uses a linearised CMOS transconductor as a basic integrating building block. A voltage-controlled phase-adjusting scheme is employed in the integrator to compensate for excess phase in the transconductance at high frequencies. The fabricated filter is capable of realising cutoff frequencies as high as 2 MHz and handles single-ended input signals up to 4 V p-p with less than 1% distortion.

INTRODUCTION

RECENTLY, several techniques for realising continuous-time filters in MOS technology have been proposed. Most of these techniques realise filters in the audio frequency range,[1] where switched-capacitor (SC) circuits have already been established as a viable approach. However, as operating frequencies are raised by an order of magnitude or more, the advantages of continuous-time processing become increasingly apparent.[2] To date, only a few fully MOS realisations of high-frequency continuous-time filters have been reported. The technique proposed in Reference 2 realises a 500 kHz bandpass filter but has limited signal swing capability due to nonlinearities in the MOSFETs used. Recently, a low-frequency linearising scheme has been extended to high frequencies,[3] but only simulated results using operational amplifiers with 200 MHz gain-bandwidth products are available. This letter discusses the implementation of a 1 MHz lowpass filter using linearised CMOS transconductance integrators with improved signal-handling capability. Experimental results obtained from a fabricated test chip are reported.

FILTER REALISATION

Fig. 1 shows the basic transconductance circuit used in the proposed filter. It employs a linearised input stage consisting of a simple source-coupled pair M_1, M_2 biased dynamically by a current component proportional to the square of the input voltage $V = V_1 - V_2$. This square-law current is generated by the crosscoupled configuration M_3–M_6 and coupled through a level-shifting device M_7. By properly scaling the W/L ratios of the source-coupled pair and the crosscoupled devices, the nonlinearities of the input stage can be largely cancelled out over a wide input voltage range.[4] The remaining devices M_8–M_{31} are used to bias the input stage and to sum device currents to obtain the final output current I_o. Assuming unity-gain current mirrors and a square-law model[5] for the input devices gives the following linear i/v characteristic for the complete transcon-

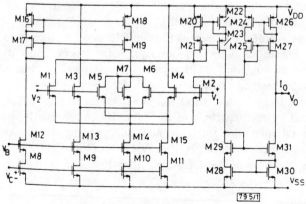

Fig. 1.   Linearised CMOS transconductance circuit.

Reprinted with permission from *El. Letters,* vol. 22, no. 14, pp. 729–731, July 3, 1986.

ductor:

$$I_o = g_m V = K(V_C - V_{Tn})V \qquad (1)$$

where K is a constant dependent on process parameters and the geometries of M_1–M_6 and M_8–M_{11}, and V_{Tn} is the n-channel threshold voltage. Note that the transconductance $g_m = K(V_C - V_{Tn})$ is adjustable by control voltage V_C. The range of V over which eqn. 1 is valid and further design details for the basic input stage are discussed elsewhere[4] and are not repeated here.

The complete transconductance circuit of Fig. 1 was fabricated using a standard 3 μm double-poly p-well CMOS process.[6] M_1, M_2 and M_5–M_7 had $W/L = 10$ μm/5 μm while M_3, M_4 had $W/L = 20$ μm/5 μm. The substrates of these devices were connected to their respective sources. The remaining n-channel devices were in a common p-well connected to V_{SS}. All p-channel devices shared a common substrate connected to V_{DD}. The circuit occupies a total area of 220×700 μm^2. Fig. 2 depicts the nonlinearity in the measured i/v characteristics of the fabricated circuit as a percentage of a 2 V (peak) full-scale value, using the nominal supply and bias voltage values indicated. The results are comparable to those for recently reported transconductor schemes.[7,8] However, the present circuit has the advantage of not requiring an accurately balanced input drive or a complicated output common-mode biasing circuit.[2] The circuit consumes 10 mW with the nominal bias values, and exhibits a short-circuit 3 dB bandwidth of 15 MHz.

Fig. 3 shows a 3rd-order Chebyshev lowpass ladder filter realised using the transconductor of Fig. 1 as a basic integrating building block. MOS Capacitors C_1–C_3 perform the required integration. The

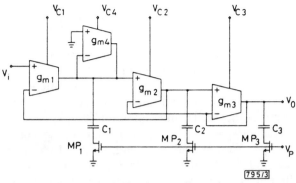

Fig. 3.   3rd-order Chebyshev lowpass filter using phase-compensated transconductance integrators.

$g_{m1} = g_{m2} = g_{m3} = g_{m4} = g_m, C_1 = C_3 \simeq 9.2$ pF, $C_2 \simeq 4.5$ pF

drain resistances of devices MP_1–MP_3 in series with the capacitors introduce a high-frequency zero in the transfer function of each integrator. This zero is used to compensate for excess phase shift within the transconductor at high frequencies. The location of this zero is controllable using V_P, resulting in a voltage-variable phase-compensation scheme. If the initial phase errors are not large, the zero frequency is much higher than the unity-gain bandwidth of the integrator. Therefore, at frequencies within the passband of the filter, the signal voltages across the compensating MOSFETs are very small, resulting in negligible distortion due to nonlinearities of these devices. It can be shown that, for a single integrator with input $V = V_A \sin \omega t$, the distortion caused by the nonlinear phase-compensating device is mainly due to the second-harmonic component and is approximately given by

$$HD \simeq \frac{(g_m r_d)^2 V_A}{(V_P - V_{Tn})\sqrt{4(g_m r_d)^2 + (g_m/\omega C)^2}} \qquad (2)$$

where g_m is the integrator transconductance, C the integrating capacitance and r_d the small-signal resistance of the compensating transistor. Equation 2 has been derived assuming a first-order model of the compensating MOSFET operating in the ohmic region of its i/v characteristic.[5] For typical values $g_m r_d = 0.02$, $V_A = V_P - V_{Tn} = 2$ V and $\omega = g_m/C$, eqn. 2 gives $HD < 0.05\%$.

The complete filter of Fig. 3 was designed to have a nominal cutoff frequency $f_c = 1$ MHz with a passband ripple of 1 dB and was fabricated using the process already mentioned.[6] MP_1–MP_3 had $W/L = 25$ and their substrates were short-circuited to their sources. The entire filter, including the capacitances,

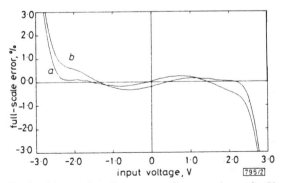

Fig. 2.   Measured nonlinear error of transconductor for V_{DD} = $-V_{SS} = 5$ V, $V_B = -2.5$ V, $V_C = 1.75$ V, $V_0 = 0$
   a   Input V_1, $V_2 = 0$
   b   Input V_2, $V_1 = 0$

phase-compensating devices and on-chip output buffers, occupies an area of $1500 \times 700\ \mu m^2$. A photomicrograph of an experimental chip including the proposed filter as well as single transconductor and buffer test cells is shown in Fig. 4. All measurements were made using ± 5 V supplies with $V_B = -2.5$ V. Fig. 5a shows the measured frequency response of the 1 MHz filter after adjusting $V_{C1} = V_{C2} = V_{C3} = V_{C4} = V_C$ and V_P to obtain the specified cutoff frequency and passband ripple. Expanded passband characteristics are given in Fig. 4b for four different values of (V_C, V_P) corresponding to f_c ranging from 250 kHz to 2 MHz. In each case the control voltages were adjusted to make the measured passband response within 0.1 dB of the ideal Chebyshev response. For f_c as high as 1.5 MHz, the variation in cutoff frequency is essentially linear with respect to V_C, as expected from the linear dependence of g_m in eqn. 1. Above this frequency, the increased value of V_C required drives M_8–M_{11} into their ohmic regions of operation, resulting in a nonlinear dependence of f_c on V_C. This also limits the maximum obtainable value of f_c to approximately 2.2 MHz. To test the effectiveness of the phase control scheme, the drain resistances of MP_1–MP_3 were made very small by applying a large V_P (+10 V). This effectively disabled the phase compensation and resulted in a 2 dB peaking at the edge of the passband due to excess phase shifts in the integrators. The distortion characteristics of the filter were investigated. Fig. 6 shows the output

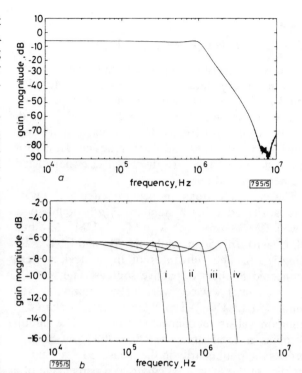

Fig. 5. Measured frequency response of filter.
a   Cutoff frequency $f_c = 1$ MHz, $V_C = 1.554$ V, $V_P = 1.845$ V
b   Expanded passband characteristics:
  (i) $f_c = 250$ kHz, $V_C = 1.155$ V, $V_P = 1.065$ V
  (ii) $f_c = 500$ kHz, $V_C = 1.288$ V, $V_P = 1.270$ V
  (iii) $f_c = 1$ MHz, $V_C = 1.554$ V, $V_P = 1.845$ V
  (iv) $f_c = 2$ MHz, $V_C 2.562$ V, $V_P = 4.320$ V

spectrum obtained for the 1 MHz filter with a 4 V p-p input signal at 250 kHz. The total harmonic distortion in this case is within 1%. This distortion is reduced to 0.2% for a 2 V p-p input. The measured output noise spectral density above 10 kHz in the passband of the 1 MHz filter is fairly constant at 0.1

Fig. 4. Photomicrograph of experimental chip.

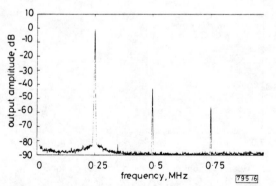

Fig. 6. 1 MHz filter output distortion spectrum for $V_i = 4$ V p-p at 250 kHz.

$\mu V / \sqrt{(Hz)}$. This value increases slightly at lower frequencies due to $1/f$ noise, rising to 1 $\mu V / \sqrt{(Hz)}$ at 100 Hz.

CONCLUSION

The design and implementation of a novel continuous-time filter technique using linearised high-frequency CMOS transconductors has been presented. A fabricated Chebȳshev lowpass prototype exhibits a 1 MHz nominal cutoff frequency and is capable of handling input signals as high as 4 V p-p with less than 1% distortion using ± 5 V supplies. Using a voltage-controlled phase-compensation scheme, accurate response can be obtained for cutoff frequencies as high as 2 MHz. The voltage-control feature allows the filter to be tuned on-chip against process and temperature variations using known tuning schemes. Extension of this technique to higher frequencies is currently being investigated.

REFERENCES

[1] Tsividis, Y., Banu, M., and Khoury, J.: 'Continuous-time MOSFET-C filters in VLSI', *IEEE Trans.*, 1986, **CAS-33**, pp. 125–140.

[2] Khorramabadi, H., and Gray, P. R.: 'High-frequency CMOS continuous-time filters', *IEEE J. Solid-State Circuits*, 1984, **SC-19**, pp. 939–948.

[3] Khoury, J., Shi, B-X, and Tsividis, Y.: 'Considerations in the design of high frequency fully integrated continuous time filters,' IEEE international symposium on circuits and systems, 1985.

[4] Nedungadi, A., and Viswanathan, T. R.: 'Design of linear CMOS transconductance elements', *IEEE Trans.*, 1984, **CAS-31**, pp. 891–894.

[5] Penney, W. M., and Lau, L.: 'MOS integrated circuits' (Van Nostrand Reinhold, New York, 1972), pp. 60–70.

[6] 'MOSIS User's Manual'. USC Information Sciences Inst., Marina Del Rey, CA, 1985.

[7] Fernandez, F. J., and Schaumann, R.: 'Techniques for the design of linear CMOS transconductance elements for video-frequency applications'. Midwest symposium on circuits and systems, 1985.

[8] Tsividis, Y., Czarnul, Z., and Fang, S. C.: 'MOS transconductors and integrators with high linearity', *Electron. Lett.*, 1986, **22**, pp. 245–246.

Design of a 4-MHz Analog Integrated CMOS Transconductance-*C* Bandpass Filter

CHIN S. PARK, MEMBER, IEEE, AND ROLF SCHAUMANN, FELLOW, IEEE

Abstract —Design and evaluation of a continuous-time eighth-order fully integrated CMOS transconductance-*C* bandpass filter for operation at 4 MHz is presented. A phase-locked loop (PLL) for frequency tuning and a four-point amplitude-locking loop for *Q*-factor tuning at the reflection zeros of the filter are implemented. The transfer characteristics were found to be essentially within specifications: less than 1-dB passband attenuation, 75-dB stopband attenuation and S/N ratio, and 0.5-percent harmonic distortion for 0.5-V_{p-p} signal were observed. Offset of the transconductances was internally controlled by an offset-control loop to less than 4 mV. Also a temperature-insensitive transconductance design and the noise characteristics of the filter building blocks are discussed.

I. INTRODUCTION

A NUMBER of approaches have been discussed in the recent literature [1]–[6] for the design of continuous-time ("analog") fully integrated filters. Their advantages have been pointed out [2] and it has been shown that continuous-time filtering is competitive with switched-capacitor (SC) methods even at low frequencies [2], the natural SC domain. For applications at higher frequencies, SC filters pose a number of challenging design problems caused by their sampled-data nature: decreasing amplifier gain results in SC filters no longer being insensitive to parasitics and the necessary high sampling frequencies increase the performance requirements, such as settling time, placed on the amplifiers. On the other hand, if the sampling frequency is reduced as far as possible, the design of anti-aliasing filters becomes increasingly difficult, requiring greater stability and higher tolerances. Because it is the performance of the *total filter system* and not just the intrinsic filter that is of relevance in practice, it can be reasoned that staying in the continuous-time domain, i.e., using *all-analog* filtering, may be preferable. In this way all "peripheral" problems caused by switching, sample-and-hold circuitry, and anti-aliasing and reconstruction circuits can be avoided. Of course, in the analog domain, the designer is confronted with the serious and challenging problem of having to *tune* his filter by some

automatic on-chip method [2]–[5], [7], [8] against fabrication tolerances, parasitic effects, and component drifts during operation.

With these trade-offs in mind, we discuss in this paper the design of an analog integrated eighth-order bandpass filter for nominal operation at a band-center frequency of 4 MHz, with 800-kHz bandwidth and 0.5-dB passband ripple. The circuit is built as a cascade of four second-order sections, each using only capacitors and transconductances. DC offset of the transconductance blocks is reduced to a few millivolts throughout the chip by a recently proposed [9] offset zeroing scheme. The circuit uses fully automatic tuning against deviations in frequency and bandwidth (*Q*) based on the "master–slave" concept (see, e.g., [4]); it employs a frequency-locking loop to stabilize the center frequency and a four-point magnitude locking scheme to control *Q*. Experimental evaluation of the final CMOS chip demonstrates that, except for a few minor problems caused by unexpectedly large processing tolerances, the filter and the tuning methods function correctly.

II. FILTER CIRCUIT AND STRUCTURE

The design is developed around the recently introduced simple linear tunable CMOS transconductance element [9] shown in Fig. 1. The device realizes

$$g_m = 2k_{\text{eff}}(V_{G1} + |V_{G4}| - \Sigma V_T) \tag{1a}$$

where

$$\Sigma V_T = V_{Tn1} + V_{Tn3} + |V_{Tp2}| + |V_{Tp4}| \tag{1b}$$

and $V_{Tn,pi}$, $i = 1, \cdots, 4$, are the threshold voltages of the corresponding devices. Note that g_m is tunable by adjusting the gate voltages V_{G1} and V_{G4}; usually, $V_{G1} = -V_{G4} = V_G$. The transconductance parameter for these composite devices is

$$k_{\text{eff}} = \frac{k_n k_p}{\left(\sqrt{k_n} + \sqrt{k_p}\right)^2}$$

with

$$k_{n,p} = 0.5 \left[\mu_{\text{eff}} C_{ox} \frac{W}{L} \right]\Big|_{n;p}. \tag{2}$$

Manuscript received November 9, 1987; revised February 19, 1988. This work was supported in part by the National Science Foundation under Grant 82-150001.

C. S. Park was with the Department of Electrical Engineering, University of Minnesota, Minneapolis, MN 55455. He is now with Intel Corporation, Santa Clara, CA 95052.

R. Schaumann is with the Department of Electrical Engineering, University of Minnesota, Minneapolis, MN 55455.

IEEE Log Number 8821663.

Reprinted from *IEEE J. Solid-State Circuits*, vol. SC-23, no. 4, pp. 987–996, Aug. 1988.

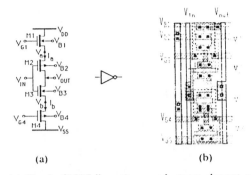

Fig. 1. (a) Simple CMOS linear transconductance element and circuit symbol. (b) Transconductance layout (size: $71 \times 154 \ \mu m^2$).

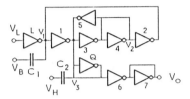

Fig. 2. g_m-C biquad building block.

The device parameters in (2) have their usual meaning and the equations are valid provided that all four CMOS devices are in saturation. It is shown in [9] that linearity and frequency response can be optimized by choosing proper aspect ratios for the devices; for the parameters of the MOSIS 3-μm bulk CMOS process [10] that was used for the implementation of the filter chip, the optimal gate sizes can be calculated to be $W/L = 25 \ \mu m/5 \ \mu m$ for the p-channel and $W/L = 20 \ \mu m/5 \ \mu m$ for the n-channel MOSFET's. With the transconductances introduced in Fig. 1, a CMOS biquad [11] (Fig. 2) is designed that can realize, depending on which terminals are chosen as input, highpass (HP), low-pass (LP), bandpass (BP) or bandreject (BR) functions.[1] For the intended application, four second-order BP sections are needed.

At high frequencies, it is unreasonable to expect that the biquads will be of second order; rather, parasitic elements will give rise to nondominant parasitic poles and zeros that may cause unacceptable performance at megahertz frequencies. To understand the behavior, a realistic transconductance model, as shown in Fig. 3, must be used in the analysis. In Fig. 3, the elements originate from the gate–drain capacitance (C_p), the gate–source capacitance (C_i), and the drain–substrate capacitance (C_o) of the MOSFET's. In addition, various coupling and loading capacitances between connection lines should be included, but to keep the model simple and the analysis tractable, these and other parasitic components are neglected because their effects become important only at frequencies much higher than the range of interest. Substituting the model in the circuit of Fig. 2, labeling the identical ele-

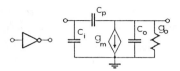

Fig. 3. Inverting transconductance element and small-signal model.

ments 1–5 as g_m, and assuming $C_i \gg (C_p, C_o)$, the following matrix description can be derived from the circuit, excluding the output buffer consisting of g_{m6} and g_{m7}:

$$AV = I \qquad (3)$$

where

$$A = \begin{pmatrix} 2g_0 + sc_1 & g_m - sC_p & -sC_p \\ -sC_p & g_m + 2g_0 + 3sC_i & g_m - 2sC_p \\ g_m - sC_p & g_m - 2sC_p & g_{mQ} + 2g_0 + g_{0Q} + sc_2 \end{pmatrix}$$
$$(4a)$$

$$I = \begin{pmatrix} -g_{mL}V_L + sC_1V_B \\ 0 \\ sC_2V_H \end{pmatrix} \qquad (4b)$$

$$V = \begin{pmatrix} V_1 & V_2 & V_3 \end{pmatrix}^t \qquad (4c)$$

and where we have defined

$$c_1 = C_1 + C_i + 2C_p + C_0 + C_{pL} + C_{0L} \approx C_1 + C_i \qquad (5a)$$

and

$$c_2 = C_2 + C_{\text{buffer}} + 2C_i + 3C_0 + 4C_p. \qquad (5b)$$

Superscript t means transpose. Evaluating these equations and neglecting insignificant terms results in

$$H_n(s) = \frac{V_0}{V_n}\bigg|_{V_i = 0;\, i \neq n} = \frac{N_n(s)}{D(s)} \qquad (6)$$

where n stands for BP, LP, HP, or BR and $V_{BR} = V_L = V_H$, i.e., V_L and V_H are tied together to obtain a bandrejection function. The various polynomials in (6) are

$$D(s) = 3c_1c_2C_is^3$$
$$+ \left[c_1c_2g_m + 3c_1C_ig_{mQ} + c_2C_pg_m + 4c_1C_pg_m \right]s^2$$
$$+ \left[c_1g_m(g_{mQ} - g_m) + 2c_1g_{mQ}g_0 + c_2g_mg_0 \right.$$
$$+ 2c_1g_mg_0 + c_1g_mg_{0Q}$$
$$+ \left. C_pg_mg_{mQ} - 3C_pg_m^2 \right]s + g_m^3 + g_mg_0(g_{mQ} - g_m)$$
$$(7a)$$

$$N_{BP}(s) = C_1\left(3C_iC_ps^3 - 3C_ig_ms^2 - g_m^2s\right) \qquad (7b)$$

$$N_{LP}(s) = g_{mL}\left(-3C_iC_ps^2 + 3C_ig_ms + g_m^2\right) \qquad (7c)$$

$$N_{HP}(s) = C_2\left(3c_1C_is^3 + c_1g_ms^2 + g_mg_0s\right) \qquad (7d)$$

$$N_{BR}(s) = 3c_1C_2C_is^3 + c_1C_2g_ms^2$$
$$+ g_m\left(C_2g_0 + 3C_ig_{mL}\right)s + g_{mL}g_m^2. \qquad (7e)$$

For clarity, the dominant ideal terms are highlighted by **bold** print. From (7a) and (7b), including the inverting output buffer g_{m6}, g_{m7}, the nominal bandpass function—the case of most interest in this paper—is given by

$$H_{BP}(s) = -\frac{g_{m6}}{g_{m7}} \frac{C_1 g_m s}{C_1 C_2 s^2 + C_1 (g_{mQ} - g_m) s + g_m^2}. \quad (8)$$

Note from (7) that in $N_{BP}(s)$ the second-order term $3C_1 C_i g_m s^2$ can be significant at high frequencies; thus, roll-off on the high-frequency side of the passband will not be as steep as on the low-frequency side. Similarly, in $N_{BR}(s)$, the Q factor of the transmission zero, given by the nonzero term $g_m(C_2 g_0 + 3C_i g_{mL})$, is severely affected by parasitics in high-frequency applications. Both these phenomena were actually observed on the experimental chips [6] and during simulation. Also observe that the s^3 terms indicate that high-frequency signal feedthrough must be expected, as is indeed verified by experiment (see Fig. 12).

From (6) or (8), the biquads' nominal pole frequency is given by

$$\omega_0 = \frac{g_m}{\sqrt{C_1 C_2}} \quad (9)$$

which shows that ω_0 tuning is necessary in principle, even if parasitic effects could be neglected, because g_m depends on the operating conditions and because the absolute values of both g_m and C_i are subjected to large process tolerances.

The pole-quality factor Q is ideally determined by element ratios

$$Q = \frac{g_m}{g_{mQ} - g_m} \sqrt{\frac{C_2}{C_1}} \quad (10)$$

but evidently, from (7a), parasitics—in particular g_0—will have a strong effect on the actual value of Q; this is the case especially for large Q, i.e., small values of $g_{mQ} - g_m$, and at high frequencies where the size of parasitic capacitances is of the same order as the circuit capacitors.[2] If the realized passband shape and bandwidth are to be correct in high-frequency applications, it should be apparent, therefore, that Q *tuning will be unavoidable*, even if some of the effects may be eliminated through predistortion after careful modeling.

A final factor to be observed is the finite range of linear operation of the active transconductances. Thus, for optimum dynamic range, the signal level of the biquads has to be scaled appropriately [12], [13] which is accomplished by the buffer amplifiers consisting of g_{m6} and g_{m7}.

With these guidelines in mind, the eighth-order Chebyshev bandpass filter is constructed by cascading four BP sections with nominal pole frequencies and Q factors (f_{pi}/MHz, Q_i; $i = 1, \cdots, 4$) of values 3.5807/23.9, 3.8090/9.83, 4.1586/9.83, and 4.4237/23.9, respectively.

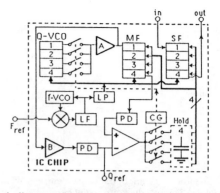

Fig. 4. Block diagram of fully tuned filter. SF: slave filter; MF: master filter; PD: peak detector; CG: clock generator; LF: loop filter; LP: low-pass filter. A and B are buffer amplifiers/attenuators. Note that the output of the hold circuitry contains four wires.

As shown below, to reduce internal device noise contributions, biquads with lower values of ω_0 and Q should precede those with higher values in the cascade connection.

III. CONTROL CIRCUITRY

As discussed in Section II, the filter IC must include means that permit the filter to tune itself against errors caused by fabrication tolerances and varying operating conditions, such as temperature. The approach adopted for this design is a "master–slave" system with a conventional phase-locked loop (PLL) for frequency tuning and a four-point amplitude-locking scheme for Q tuning. The method will be explained with the help of the block diagram in Fig. 4.

A. VCO Design

All VCO's in the control loops are biquads, identical in layout and design to the one shown in Fig. 2, except that signal input, $V_B = V_L = V_H$, is ground (no g_{mL}) and the Q factor is set to infinity. For a well-defined process, the Q-control voltage can be generated internally (≈ -3.5 V at 5-V power supply). For a wide-tolerance process, however, this control voltage should be accessible to avoid the possibility of shifting the VCO frequency when poles are too far in the right half plane.[3]

B. The Frequency-Control Loop

The frequency-control loop implemented on the chip is a conventional PLL with an infinite Q-factor biquad as f-VCO, an RC filter as loop filter (LF), and an EXCLUSIVE-OR (XOR) gate as phase detector. The f-VCO biquad oscillates at a frequency given by (9) which differs from the filter pole frequencies by at most a designable constant (a capacitor ratio). The VCO frequency error,

---

[2]Also the source impedance can have an effect on Q! (see (16)).

[3]Note from (7a) that for infinite Q the pole frequency is slightly reduced ($g_m = g_{mQ}$!). To compensate for this effect, by (9) the capacitances of VCO's should be designed slightly smaller than the nominal values of the biquads.

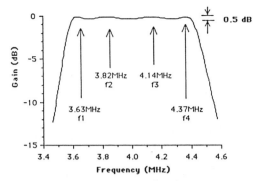

Fig. 5. Filter passband and Q-control frequencies.

when compared to f_{ref}, results at the LF output in a dc error signal that is applied in an appropriate manner to the g_m gates ($V_{G1,4}$ of g_{m1-5} in Fig. 1(a)) to change g_m and thereby tune the f-VCO oscillation frequency until the error is zero. The required loop gain is attained from the XOR gate. The time constant of the RC loop filter affects the tuning range of the PLL and was designed to be 0.5 μs. Additional RC filtering (LP) with much larger time constant is used for cleaning the bias signal from the remaining high-frequency noise and other interference before entering the filter blocks, including the master/slave filters and the Q-VCO's for the Q-control loop. Attention must be paid to designing the transition voltage of the XOR gate to match the center of the analog VCO output signal.[4] Sections 1–4 of the Q-VCO's and of the master and slave filters are matched to the f-VCO; therefore, the error correction signal generated by the f-VCO, when applied to the remaining 12 biquads, will correctly tune all frequency parameters throughout the chip. Experience has shown and it can be verified from (7) that pole frequencies, in contrast to pole-Q factors, are not very sensitive to parasitics; matching does not, therefore, appear to be a problem.

C. The Q-Control Loop

The Q-control loop consists of Q-VCO's, master filter, peak detector, comparator, holding circuitry, and time-sharing clock generators [6]. The master and slave filters are identical. The four Q-VCO's generate frequencies at the reflection zeros of the filter, i.e., points of perfect transmission, as illustrated in Figs. 5 and 12. The peak detector consists of a diode (a low-β n-p-n transistor with collector connected to V_{DD}; in low-frequency applications, the diode can be replaced by precision diode), a 10-pF hold capacitor, and a discharging resistor. The Q-control signals are stored on the hold capacitors in Fig. 4 which should sustain the voltages until the next update period. Note, though, that leakage through the reverse-biased di-

ode at the MOSFET of the multiplexing switch can be significant when the junction temperature is high. In that case, external hold capacitors may be necessary.[5] The clock circuitry generates four-phase nonoverlapping clock signals. As discussed in [6], the Q-VCO output signals (Fig. 5) are fed into the master filter one at a time under clock control and the amplitude response of the filter at the Q-VCO frequencies, which are nominally the reflection zeros, is compared to a reference voltage that is generated from the Q-VCO's.

Because by (8) the midband gain of the biquads is proportional to a designable g_m ratio and to Q, one may conclude that any measured gain error at the Q-VCO frequencies can be attributed to a Q error and can be corrected by tuning Q. Further, the heights of the passband ripple peaks of the cascade circuit (see Fig. 5) can be shown to be dominantly determined by the section Q values which in turn are affected by parasitics, in addition to source and load conditions as pointed out earlier. The adopted procedure is, therefore, a complete *functional tuning* scheme that corrects the Q errors *regardless* of their origin, because the biquad sections work in their natural environment, the full eighth-order filter, and master and slave are identical in all details. The errors are processed and fed back to the gate control terminals, $V_{G1,4}$, of the transconductances g_{mQ} in the corresponding master and slave biquads to set their Q factors [6]. The Q-VCO's can consist of either one biquad and a capacitor array with switches, or of separate biquads matched to the corresponding filter sections. The former scheme is found not practical for high-frequency applications because of parasitic switch capacitances [6]. In this paper, the second method was used. The amplitudes of the VCO outputs depend on frequency and cannot be adjusted exactly because only one Q-control voltage is applied to all VCO's of different oscillation frequencies. For applications at lower frequencies, the VCO output can be easily amplified to the maximum swing (square wave) that the transconductance can handle (2.5 V at 5-V power supply) and attenuated by either a resistive voltage divider or simply by resistive loading; therefore, the spectrum of VCO output signals can be set to be uniform in magnitude and thus one reference voltage for the peak detector is sufficient. Of course, higher harmonics are thereby added to the signal, but here the discussion is confined to the case of filters with reasonably narrow passband where these harmonics can be filtered out in the master filter. For high-frequency applications, the reference signal should be generated by

---

[4]If the transition voltage is larger than the magnitude of the VCO output, the XOR gate will never switch and the phase comparison breaks down. In situations where unmatched VLSI library components are to be used for convenience (as done in the present design), the problem can be avoided by amplifying the VCO output to assure sufficient signal swing to drive the XOR logic gate.

[5]In any junction-isolated process the leakage currents will be at least of the order of 1 pA and possibly much higher for high junction temperatures. Thus, with on-chip hold capacitors limited to a few picofarad, storage times, before drooping occurs, will be measured only in seconds or even fractions of seconds. External hold capacitors will, therefore, be difficult to avoid unless very frequent charge updating can be employed. As described in Section VI, external hold capacitors were used for our circuit; with these, the Q-control loop functioned correctly for clock frequencies (externally controllable for testing purposes) in the range 1 Hz $\leqslant f_c \leqslant 100$ kHz. Any clock feedthrough is thereby well outside the passband.

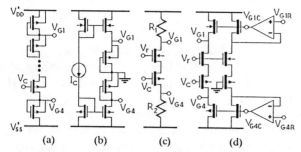

Fig. 6. (a)–(d) Different bias generation circuits.

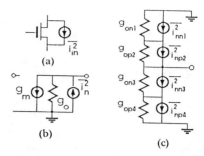

Fig. 7. (a)–(c) Noise circuit models.

an additional matched peak detector from the VCO outputs directly as shown in Fig. 4. The transfer functions of both paths (see Fig. 4), VCO–attenuator A–master filter–peak detector and VCO–A–peak detector–B, should, of course, be matched. A digital circuit version of this Q-control scheme can be found in [15].

D. Bias Generator Design

As pointed out before, the control loops generate bias signals which must be applied to the gates of the appropriate transconductances. Consequently, design of the bias generator (BG) is very important for the overall performance of the filter, including the tuning loops. BG generates two bias voltages, V_{G1} and V_{G4} in Fig. 1, which for most cases [9] satisfy

$$V_{G1} = -V_{G4} = V_G = V_{G0} - f(V_c). \quad (11)$$

In (11), V_c is the bias control voltage generated by the frequency- and Q-control loops, and $f(V_c)$ is not necessarily a linear function (apart from some special applications, such as analog multipliers). For the MOSIS bulk CMOS case with ± 5-V power supply, feasible ranges are $3.5\ \text{V} < V_G < 5\ \text{V}$ and $-1.5\ \text{V} < V_c < 1.5\ \text{V}$. Fig. 6 shows various bias generation circuits [15]. Each of the circuits in Fig. 6(a)–(d) has its advantages and disadvantages: for example, in circuit (a), V_G is process independent and a linear function of V_c; circuit (b) has high PSR; circuit (c) lends itself to designing a temperature-independent biasing scheme; and circuit (d) permits wide device tolerances. On the other hand, circuits (a), (c), and (d) have poor PSR and circuits (a) and (b) need one V_T between power supply and the maximum value of V_G.

For the complete tuning operation of the eighth-order filter, 13 biquads are needed: four each for master and slave filters, and for the Q-control VCO's, and one for the f-VCO. The biquads for the master and slave filters are identical; those for the VCO's differ slightly from those of the filters to account for the frequency shift caused by Q-factor differences (infinite Q for the VCO's).[3]

As shown in Fig. 2, eight inverting transconductance elements are required to build a completely tunable bandpass biquad. Reasonable tuning ranges, without affecting linearity and dynamic range severely, are, of course, determined by the type of transconductance circuit chosen; for the devices in this paper, Fig. 1, the ranges are around

a factor 2 of the nominal center frequency for frequency control and unlimited for Q control (unless parasitic output conductances g_o become comparable to the transconductances g_m as may be the case for short-channel MOSFET's).

E. Offset-Zeroing Loop

Although not part of the intrinsic tuning loops, offset zeroing is nevertheless an important aspect of the overall control scheme: if dc offset voltages become too large, not only will the filters suffer from reduced dynamic range and increased distortion, but more importantly, the tuning loops will not function correctly because the generated bias voltages will lose their required symmetry to ground. To assure negligible dc offset, the design includes an automatic offset-zeroing loop, consisting of reference transconductances that are matched to the filter transconductances. The dc offset of the reference devices is "compared to ground" and the appropriately amplified dc error signal is applied to the backgates (V_{B1}) of the devices $M1$ in Fig. 1 of all circuit transconductances to reduce dc offset to zero. Implementation details can be found in [9] and [15]; it can be shown that V_{B1} is always in the range $V_b < V_{B1} < V_a$ (see Fig. 1(a)). In the experimental circuit in this paper, dc offset was kept at less than 4 mV for all transconductances throughout the chip.

IV. NOISE AND ORDERING OF BIQUADS

Low-frequency noise sources of MOSFET's and also high-frequency gate-induced noise are not significant at the operating frequency of the filter. Therefore, thermal noise from the devices themselves is the major noise source. A noise equivalent circuit for a transconductance element and noise characteristics of the biquad from its transconductance elements can be easily derived as follows.

A. Noise Equivalent Circuit of the Transconductance Element [14], [17]

A noise-source representation of an individual transistor is shown in Fig. 7(a), with

$$\overline{i_{in}^2} = K4kTg_{mi}\Delta f \quad (12)$$

where $K \approx 2/3$, assuming hot-electron noise and induced gate noise are a small fraction of thermal noise. Also low-frequency noise is not included because it is insignificant at frequencies above 100 kHz. With (12), the MOSFET noise circuit shown in Fig. 7(b) and the simplified noise equivalent circuit of the transconductance including noise sources in Fig. 7(c) can be derived; it is assumed that the noise characteristics of all p-channel MOSFET's and of all n-channel devices, respectively, are identical. With

$$g_o = 2 \frac{g_{on} g_{op}}{g_{on} + g_{op}} \tag{13}$$

and

$$\bar{i}_n^2 = 2 \frac{g_{op}^2 \bar{i}_{nn}^2 + g_{on}^2 \bar{i}_{np}^2}{g_{on}^2 + g_{op}^2} \tag{14}$$

Fig. 7(b) is also an approximate equivalent noise model of the complete transconductance. Noise from the bias sources, V_{G1} and V_{G4}, can be considered by adding $g_{mn1}^2 \bar{v}_{nG1}^2$ to $\bar{i}_{nn1}^2$ and $g_{mp4}^2 \bar{v}_{nG4}^2$ to $\bar{i}_{np2}^2$, where $\bar{v}_{nG1}^2$ and $\bar{v}_{nG4}^2$ are noise voltages for the bias generators V_{G1} and V_{G4}, respectively. Noise coupling through power supply lines is not discussed here, because noise coupling through parasitic capacitors depends on unknown factors of layout and processing and the transconductances themselves have high power supply rejection (> 90 dB up to $f = 1$ MHz) [9].

B. Inherent Noise of the Biquad Building Block

Applying the equivalent circuit shown Fig. 7(b) to the bandpass biquad shown in Fig. 2, but without $g_{mL,6,7}$, nodal analysis results in $AV = I$ with

$$A = \begin{pmatrix} g_s + sC_1 & -sC_1 & 0 & 0 \\ -sC_1 & g_0 + sC_1 & g_m & 0 \\ 0 & 0 & g_m + 2g_0 & g_m \\ 0 & g_m & g_m & sC_2 + g_{mQ} + 3g_0 \end{pmatrix} \tag{15a}$$

$$V = (V_B \quad V_1 \quad V_2 \quad V_3)^t \tag{15b}$$

$$I = \begin{pmatrix} \sqrt{\bar{i}_{ns}^2} + g_s v_s \\ \sqrt{\bar{i}_{n2}^2} \\ \sqrt{\bar{i}_{n3}^2 + \bar{i}_{n4}^2} \\ \sqrt{\bar{i}_{n1}^2 + \bar{i}_{n5}^2 + \bar{i}_{nQ}^2} \end{pmatrix} \tag{15c}$$

where v_s is the input voltage source, connected to the bandpass input V_B in Fig. 2, and g_s its output conductance; $\bar{i}_{ns}^2$ is thermal noise current of g_s. An approximate solution, neglecting nondominant terms with $g_0 \ll g_m \ll g_s$, is

$$V_3 = \frac{g_m N(s)}{g_s \left\{ s^2 C_1 C_2 + sC_1 \left[g_{mQ} - g_m \left(1 - \frac{g_m}{g_s} \right) \right] + g_m^2 \right\}} \tag{16}$$

with

$$N(s) = -sC_1 \left(g_s v_s + \sqrt{\bar{i}_{ns}^2} \right) + (sC_1 + g_s) \sqrt{\bar{i}_{n2}^2}$$
$$+ \left[sC_1 \left(1 - \frac{g_s}{g_m} \right) + g_s \right] \sqrt{\bar{i}_{n3}^2 + \bar{i}_{n4}^2}$$
$$+ sC_1 \frac{g_s}{g_m} \sqrt{\bar{i}_{n1}^2 + \bar{i}_{n5}^2 + \bar{i}_{nQ}^2}$$
$$= -sC_1 g_2 \left(v_2 + \sqrt{\bar{v}_{sn}^2} \right)$$

where

$$\sqrt{\bar{v}_{sn}^2} = \frac{\sqrt{\bar{i}_{ns}^2}}{g_s} + \left(\frac{1}{sC_1} + \frac{1}{g_s} \right) \sqrt{\bar{i}_{n2}^2}$$
$$+ \left(\frac{1}{sC_1} + \frac{1}{g_s} - \frac{1}{g_m} \right) \sqrt{\bar{i}_{n3}^2 + \bar{i}_{n4}^2} + \frac{1}{g_m} \sqrt{\bar{i}_{n1}^2 + \bar{i}_{n5}^2 + \bar{i}_{nQ}^2}$$

is the equivalent input noise obtained by reflecting all noise sources to the biquad input. Note that the transfer function for the noise contributions to the output has a low-pass rather than a bandpass characteristic. For the devices used in the experimental circuit, the noise sources can be calculated to be $\bar{i}_{nn1}^2 = \bar{i}_{nn3}^2 = 3.47 \cdot 10^{-25}$ A^2/Hz, and $\bar{i}_{np2}^2 = \bar{i}_{np4}^2 = 2.86 \cdot 10^{-25}$ A^2/Hz; with these numbers and the same assumptions as above and $C_1 \approx C_2$, the equivalent input noise in midband, $\omega_p \approx g_m / \sqrt{C_1 C_2}$, of the biquad is 26.5 nV/$\sqrt{\text{Hz}}$. For a signal amplitude of 0.5 V and 800-kHz bandwidth, the intrinsic signal-to-thermal noise ratio is, therefore, approximately 80 dB.

As shown by (16), at the output, the internal device noise for a bandpass biquad has a low-pass characteristic proportional to Q, i.e., the lower stopband is more noisy than the upper stopband and the high-Q biquad has higher noise. Therefore, to reduce passband noise, lower center frequency and lower Q biquads should precede those with higher center frequency and higher Q factor to minimize internal device noise contributions. Note, however, that for a filter with fully operational automatic tuning, signal feedthrough from VCO's, digital parts, master filter, and control loops will generally be a more serious problem than inherent device noise.

V. TEMPERATURE DRIFT

From (7)–(10) it is apparent that temperature-induced changes of frequency and Q factor depend directly on the term $\partial g_m / \partial T$ and, by (7a), also on $\partial (g_m / g_o) / \partial T$. The change of transconductance with temperature T can be calculated from (1) as

$$\frac{\partial g_m}{\partial T} = \frac{g_m}{k_{eff}} \frac{\partial k_{eff}}{\partial T} + 4 k_{eff} \frac{\partial V_G}{\partial T} - 2 k_{eff} \frac{\partial \Sigma V_T}{\partial T} \tag{17}$$

where $\partial (\Sigma V_T) / \partial T \approx -8$ to -10 mV/°C and $\partial k_{eff} / \partial T \approx -0.005 \, k_{eff(300 \text{ K})}$/°C around room temperature. For the

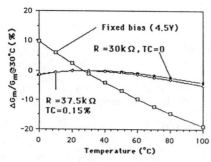

Fig. 8. Simulated transconductance change with temperature for temperature-tolerant biasing scheme.

transconductance element, the temperature coefficient equals $\partial g_m/\partial T \approx -0.4 \ \mu\text{S}/°\text{C}$ and that of the internal voltage gain, g_m/g_o, is $\partial(g_m/g_o)/\partial T \approx -0.06/°\text{C}$, assuming $\partial V_G/\partial T \approx 0$ [16].

As discussed in Section II, component drifts caused by temperature variations during operation are eliminated or reduced by the control loops. Nevertheless, the operating and tuning range of the filter can be increased if device parameter changes are intrinsically compensated. Although not included in the experimental chip, an appropriate scheme for accomplishing such compensation is presented in the following.

Most dc device parameters of MOSFET's change linearly or nearly linearly with temperature. Threshold voltage changes as -2 to -2.5 mV/°C according to the changes of bandgap, intrinsic carrier density, and junction potential. The transconductance element, $k = 0.5 \ \mu C_{ox}W/L$, varies as $T^{-1.5}$ because of mobility changes. Around room temperature, k changes by 0.5 percent/°C [16].

A. Temperature-Insensitive Transconductance Bias Design

From (17), g_m will be independent of temperature $(\partial g_m/\partial T = 0)$ if the temperature derivative of the bias voltage V_G satisfies

$$\frac{\partial V_G}{\partial T} = 0.5 \ \frac{\partial \Sigma V_T}{\partial T} - 0.25 \ \frac{g_m}{k_{\text{eff}}^2} \ \frac{\partial k_{\text{eff}}}{\partial T}. \quad (18)$$

One example of a suitable bias circuit is shown in Fig. 6(c), with $V_{G1} = -V_{G4}$. From Fig. 6(c), assuming $R_1 = R_2 = R_b$ and that all n-channel and p-channel FET's, respectively, are identical, it follows that

$$\frac{\partial V_G}{\partial T} = -R_b \frac{\partial I_b}{\partial T} - I_b \frac{\partial R_b}{\partial T} = -\hat{R}_b \frac{\partial I_b}{\partial T} \quad (19)$$

where

$$I_b = k_{\text{eff}}(V_{rc} - |V_{Tp}| - V_{Tn})^2 = k_{\text{eff}}(V_{rc} - 0.5\Sigma V_T)^2 \quad (20a)$$

$$\hat{R}_b = R_b + \frac{(\partial R_b/\partial T)}{(\partial I_b/\partial T)} I_b \quad (20b)$$

and

$$V_{rc} = V_r - V_c.$$

The temperature coefficient for diffused Si resistors is a few hundred to a few thousand ppm and that for metal-film resistors can be as low as a few tens ppm. Substituting (20a) into (19) yields

$$\frac{\partial V_G}{\partial T} = \hat{R}_b \left[k_{\text{eff}}(V_{rc} - 0.5\Sigma V_T) \frac{\partial \Sigma V_T}{\partial T} - \frac{I_b}{k_{\text{eff}}} \frac{\partial k_{\text{eff}}}{\partial T} \right] \quad (21)$$

which by comparison with (18) results in

$$k_{\text{eff}}(V_{rc} - 0.5\Sigma V_T)\hat{R}_b = 0.5$$

$$\hat{R}_b \frac{I_b}{k_{\text{eff}}} = 0.25 \frac{g_m}{k_{\text{eff}}^2}$$

and, with (1) and (20a)

$$V_G = I_b\hat{R}_b + 0.5\Sigma V_T$$

$$V_{rc} = 2I_b\hat{R}_b + 0.5\Sigma V_T = V_G + I_b\hat{R}_b$$

$$V_{DD'} = V_G + I_bR_b.$$

If the bias generator supply voltage V_{DD}' $(=V_{DD})$ and g_m are given, V_G and V_{rc} are determined in the above equations, assuming ΣV_T and $R_b' - R_b$ are constant. From (1a), V_G, ΣV_T, and β_c are calculated; also I_b is determined by (20a) so that R_b can be computed from the above equations. In practice, ΣV_T (including back-gate effects) depends on V_G and V_{DD}, and $R_b' - R_b$ depends on I_b, among other factors. Therefore, an approximate solution, R_b, can easily be found and can be further refined by a few simulations. Some SPICE results for the values and process parameters on the experimental chip are shown in Fig. 8. They indicate that the above relations can be satisfied with reasonable values of R_b and for different temperature coefficients. The predicted transconductance drift is less than 3 percent over the temperature range from 0 to 70°C (for a fixed bias, it is 22 percent).

VI. EXPERIMENTAL RESULTS AND DISCUSSION

Fig. 9 shows a photograph of the filter chip with all control circuitry and some additional test circuits not discussed in this paper. The filter system functioned correctly, but a few minor external components were necessary: in the frequency-control loop, a load resistor was connected to the f-VCO output to shift its dc level to the transition voltage of the following MOSIS-library XOR gate (see footnote 4 for methods to avoid this resistor). Once the f-VCO was locked to the external reference frequency, no frequency error between f-VCO, the filter, and the reference signal was noticeable on a spectrum analyzer. For the reference frequency (design value) of 2.9 MHz (away, but "not too far" [4], from the passband), the filter center frequency was 4 MHz as desired. No significant

Fig. 9. Photograph of the CMOS filter chip. Total area 6900×3400 μm; areas for the slave filter, master filter, and Q-control oscillators: 560×1100 μm each.

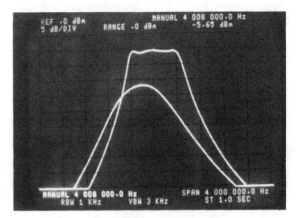

Fig. 11. Tuned and untuned filter performance.

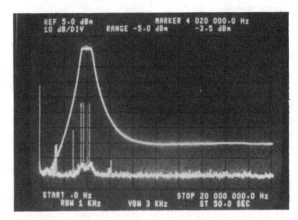

Fig. 12. Overall filter performance and, on lower trace, noise, Q-, and frequency-control signals.

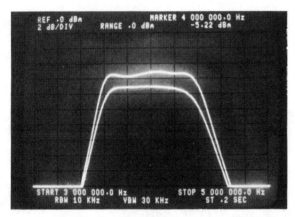

Fig. 10. Passband detail of the filter performance at 0°C (lower trace) and at 65°C.

frequency drift over the commercial temperature range could be observed (Fig. 10). In the experiment, the automatic frequency-tuning range was from 3.3 to 4.3 MHz and that for Q tuning was around 40 percent of its nominal value. (With manual control, by overriding the control loops, the corresponding ranges were 2.6 to 4.3 MHz for f tuning and unlimited for Q tuning, i.e., from very wide bandwidth (low Q) until oscillation.)

For the Q-control loop, charge leakage from the on-chip hold capacitors (40 pF each) of the Q-control voltages was observed to be too large so that external capacitors were connected to avoid drooping.[5] This leakage is caused by the reverse-biased diodes where the leakage current increases exponentially with temperature (a problem that gets more severe at high frequencies) and also depends on bias. One reverse-biased diode at the source or drain of a switch (Fig. 4) is unavoidable in the proposed scheme.

Furthermore, on the designed chip the capacitor nodes are connected to pads for testing purposes where reverse-biased junctions for input protection add additional parasitic diodes. On the chip, the Q-control comparator was designed with transconductances (Fig. 1) for a nominal gain of value three for stability of the loop. The actual gain was less than two because of a processing error in the bias circuitry which, together with a limited dc swing ($\leqslant \pm 2.5$ V), resulted in a narrower Q-tuning range than desired. Although the experimental performance was quite reasonable, evidently from Fig. 10, the Q-control range was insufficient to maintain the exact passband shape over the full design temperature range.[6]

Fig. 11 shows the filter characteristics in the vicinity of the passband at room temperature with both control loops closed and, for comparison, with both loops open (inactive). Note that the frequency parameters for the uncontrolled case are close to the design values, but that the quality factors, being very sensitive to parasitics, show large errors. Finally, Fig. 12 shows the overall filter performance between 0 and 20 MHz and, as reference, a second

---

[6] The main reason for this finding is the incorrect value of the p-well resistors R_1 and R_2 in the bias circuit of Fig. 6(c): the measured sheet resistance was found to be only one-third of the published nominal MOSIS specification which prevented the gate-tuning voltages from spanning the full design range.

TABLE I
EXPERIMENTAL FILTER DATA[7]

Control	Automatic	Manual
Passband ripple	1 dB	0.5 dB
Stopband attenuation	>60 dB	
Bandwidth	800 kHz	
S/N in passband	≈40 dB	75 dB
Distortion (for 0.5 V_{pp})	0.5%	
max. signal level	1.2 V_{pp}	
Frequency control range	1 MHz	1.5 MHz
Q-control range	40%	unlimited
Offset (reference inverter)	1 mV @ Gain≈50	

trace (obtained by grounding the filter input) with the system noise floor, the four multiplexed Q-control frequencies (compare with Fig. 5), and the 2.9-MHz frequency-control signal. Note that as predicted the high-frequency transition band is less steep than the low-frequency one and high-frequency attenuation is reduced due to parasitic feedthrough. Some additional measured performance characteristics of the filter are contained in Table I. Some dependence of center frequency on the Q factor was observed because the parasitic output conductance of the MOSFET's was larger than expected (see (7a)); therefore, the relative position of the center frequency of each biquad was not exact to filter specifications. This problem may be unavoidable at high frequencies due to the wide process tolerances necessitated by using different vendors.

Because of the several functional blocks on the test chip, unrelated to the filter system, accurate measured data of power consumption are not available; but approximately 900-mW power consumption can be estimated for the overall blocks (frequency-, Q-, offset-control loops, three eighth-order filters, and clock generation) of this filter (< 200 mW for one filter circuit itself).

VII. CONCLUSION

The paper shows that CMOS transconductance-C filters can be practically useful at video frequencies, with large S/N ratio and wide dynamic range. The proposed frequency-, Q-factor, and offset-control circuitry operated correctly. Some minor problems and possible solutions were pointed out in the text. Extreme attention must be paid to possible coupling of internal f- and Q-tuning signals as well as clock signals into the main filter; thus, very careful design and layout are necessary. In the experimental chip, signal interference among master/slave filters and VCO's through the frequency-control lines was ob-

served[7]; to reduce this problem, external grounded capacitors were used to reduce feedthrough. Signal or noise interference through power lines is negligible because of the high PSRR of the transconductances. In the layout shown in Fig. 1(b), a transconductance is designed like a polycell; therefore, chip layout design was more like that of a digital IC. Also in the layout, possible latch-up occurs only between M_2 and M_3; it can be easily suppressed by a vertical V_{DD} diffusion line as shown. Also this diffusion line works to isolate possible high-frequency interference.

Experimental results for an additional 10-MHz filter on the chip indicated that the methods adopted can work also at higher frequencies if appropriate care is taken. However, at even higher frequencies, signal interference between master and slave filters and the tuning blocks becomes a problem that requires careful attention to layout and design.

ACKNOWLEDGMENT

Processing of the final chips by the MOS Implementation Service (MOSIS), Marina Del Rey, CA, is gratefully acknowledged.

REFERENCES

[1] J. O. Voorman et al., "Integration of analog filters in a bipolar process," IEEE J. Solid-State Circuits, vol. SC-17, pp. 713–722, Aug. 1982.
[2] Y. Tsividis, M. Banu, and J. Khoury, "Continuous-time MOSFET-C filters in VLSI," IEEE J. Solid-State Circuits, vol. SC-18, pp. 15–30, Feb. 1986.
[3] H. Khorramabadi and P. R. Gray, "High-frequency CMOS continuous-time filters," IEEE J. Solid-State Circuits, vol. SC-21, pp. 939–948, Feb. 1984.
[4] C.-F. Chiou and R. Schaumann, "Design and performance of a fully integrated bipolar 10.7-MHz analog bandpass filter," IEEE J. Solid-State Circuits, vol. SC-21, pp. 6–14, Feb. 1986.
[5] K. Miura et al., "VCR signal processing LSIs with self-adjusted integrated filters," in Proc. Bipolar Circ. Tech. Meeting (BTCM), Sept. 1986, pp. 85–86.
[6] C. S. Park and R. Schaumann, "Design of an eighth-order fully integrated CMOS 4MHz continuous-time bandpass filter with digital/analog control of frequency and quality factor," in Proc. Int. Symp. CAS, May 1987, pp. 754–757.
[7] R. Schaumann and C.-F. Chiou, "Design of integrated analog filters," in Proc. 1981 European Conf. Circuit Theory and Design (ECCTD) (The Hague, The Netherlands), Aug. 1981, pp. 407–411.
[8] D. Senderowicz, D. A. Hodges, and P. R. Gray, "An NMOS integrated vector-locked loop," in Proc. IEEE Int. Symp. CAS, 1982, pp. 1164–1167.
[9] C. S. Park and R. Schaumann, "A high-frequency CMOS linear transconductance element," IEEE Trans. Circuits Syst., vol. CAS-33, pp. 1132–1138, Nov. 1986.
[10] MOSIS—Users' Manual, Inform. Sci. Inst., Univ. Southern Calif., Los Angeles.
[11] C. S. Park and R. Schaumann, "Fully integrated analog filters in CMOS technology," in Proc. Int. Symp. CAS, May 1986, pp. 1161–1164.
[12] K. R. Laker, R. Schaumann, and M. S. Ghausi, "Multiple loop feedback topologies for the design of low sensitivity active filters," IEEE Trans. Circuits Syst., vol. CAS-26, pp. 1–21, Jan. 1979.
[13] C.-F. Chiou and R. Schaumann, "A refined procedure for optimizing signal-to-noise ratio in cascaded active RC filters," Proc. Inst. Elec. Eng., vol. 128, part G, Electron. Circuits Syst., pp. 189–191, Aug. 1981.
[14] A. Van der Ziel and K. Amberiadis, "Noise in VLSI," in VLSI Electronics, vol. 7. New York: Academic, 1983.
[15] C. S. Park, "A CMOS linear transconductance element and its applications in integrated high-frequency filters," Ph.D. dissertation, Univ. of Minnesota, Minneapolis, Dec. 1987.

---

[7]For manual control, the Q-control oscillators are OFF so that the signal-to-thermal noise ratio is ≈ 75 dB (see Fig. 12). For automatic control, the Q-control loop is ON and the four multiplexed Q-control signals are found to couple into the slave filter, reducing the signal-to-"noise" ratio to ≈ 40 dB. Experimentally, the feedthrough paths were determined to be the gate-control bias lines. On the designed chip, the gate control lines are the same, i.e., direct connections for simplicity, for the Q-control oscillators, master and slave circuits without any HF isolation or additional low-pass filtering as adopted for the frequency control loop (see Fig. 4). It is not hard to show that a further simple low-pass filtering in the bias lines before they enter the slave filter or, better, using separate bias circuitry can reduce the four Q-control spectral lines in Fig. 12 by more than 30 dB so that an S/N ratio of the order of > 70 dB can be achieved.

A CMOS Analog Continuous-Time Delay Line with Adaptive Delay-Time Control

KLAAS BULT AND HANS WALLINGA, MEMBER, IEEE

Abstract — A CMOS analog continuous-time delay line has been developed composed of cascaded first-order current-domain all-pass sections. Each all-pass section consists of CMOS transistors and a single capacitor. The operation is based on the square-law characteristic of an MOS transistor in saturation. The delay time per section can either be controlled by an external voltage or locked to an external reference frequency by means of a control system which features a large capture range. Experimental verification has been performed on two setups: an integrated cascade of 26 identical all-pass sections and a frequency locking system breadboard built around two identical on-chip all-pass sections.

I. INTRODUCTION

ANALOG delay lines are useful elements in signal processing circuits such as adaptive filters. Charge-coupled device and switched-capacitor solutions are well known [1]–[3]. A drawback of these discrete-time circuits is the necessity of clocking and the occurrence of aliasing effects. A continuous-time approach may be attractive, particularly if the delay per section can be controlled electronically.

However, due to the dependence of time constants of continuous-time circuits on temperature- and process-dependent values of monolithic components such as capacitors and transistors, some extra circuitry is required to control the delay time. In [4]–[7] several techniques have been described which lock the performance of a filter to an external reference frequency. A similar approach is used here.

A delay-line section has to fulfill two important properties. First, the modulus of the transfer function has to equal unity over a broad frequency range, and second, the phase shift has to depend linearly on frequency in order to provide a frequency-independent group delay. A first-order

all-pass filter with a transfer function

$$H(j\omega) = \frac{1 - j\omega RC}{1 + j\omega RC} \quad (1)$$

satisfies the first condition, while the second condition is approximately true. The argument of $H(j\omega)$ is

$$\arg(H(j\omega)) = -2\arctan(\omega RC) \quad (2)$$

and the associated group delay is

$$D(\omega) = \frac{2RC}{1 + (\omega RC)^2}. \quad (3)$$

For

$$(\omega RC)^2 \ll 1 \quad (4)$$

the group delay is approximately constant. Hence, for band-limited signals a first-order all-pass filter may perform as a delay section. By cascading two or more first-order all-pass sections, with taps at the output of every stage, a tapped delay line is obtained.

The incorporation of frequency locking techniques requires that the RC products of the filter sections have to be adjustable. Recently a class of analog CMOS circuits has been presented based on the square-law characteristic of an MOS transistor in saturation [8]. This class comprises, among others, voltage-controlled linear $V–I$ and linear $I–V$ convertors, which lend themselves very well to realizing the desired time constants. In Section II it is shown how a voltage-controlled all-pass filter may be constructed using these circuits. Section III describes the delay line, and Section IV explains the time-delay control system. In Section V an analysis is given of errors that can occur in the performance of the all-pass filter and the control system. Section VI presents experimental results and Section VII finishes the paper with some conclusions.

II. A FIRST-ORDER ALL-PASS SECTION

Writing the all-pass transfer function (1) as

$$H(j\omega) = 2\frac{1}{1 + j\omega RC} - 1 \quad (5)$$

Manuscript received October 1, 1987; revised January 7, 1988. This work was supported by the Dutch Foundation for Fundamental Research (FOM).

K. Bult was with the IC Technology and Electronics Group, Department of Electrical Engineering, University of Twente, 7500AE Enschede, The Netherlands. He is now with Philips Research Laboratories, Eindhoven, The Netherlands.

H. Wallinga is with the IC Technology and Electronics Group, Department of Electrical Engineering, University of Twente, 7500AE Enschede, The Netherlands.

IEEE Log Number 8819979.

Reprinted from *IEEE J. Solid-State Circuits*, vol. SC-23, no. 3, pp. 759–766, June 1988.

211

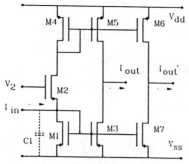

Fig. 1. The current invertor.

the all-pass function is split into two basic functions. The first term in (5) is a low-pass filter transfer function with a dc gain of two, and the second part represents a simple invertor. An analog CMOS current invertor circuit, which can provide both functions, has been described in [8] and is shown in Fig. 1. All transistors operate in the saturated region and the working of the circuit is based on the MOST square-law characteristic. The circuit features a linear input resistance

$$R = \frac{1}{2K(V_2 - 2V_t)} \qquad (6)$$

and furnishes an output current

$$I_{out} = I'_{out} = -I_{in}. \qquad (7)$$

Provided that

$$|I_{in}| = K(V_2 - 2V_t)^2 \qquad (8)$$

the circuit can handle positive as well as negative input currents.

With a capacitor connected between input and ground, as indicated by the dotted lines in Fig. 1, the current invertor is modified into a current domain low-pass filter with transfer function

$$H(j\omega) = \frac{-1}{1 + j\omega RC} \qquad (9)$$

where R is given by (6). Note that R, and also by means of R, the group delay $D(\omega)$ in (3) may be electronically controlled via V_2. A low-frequency gain of two may be obtained by adding the currents of the two output stages of Fig. 1. The all-pass filter function (5) can now be obtained by combination of a current invertor and a low-pass filter section in the way as shown in Fig. 2.

The first current invertor has three outputs. The first output ($M3$ and $M5$) provides an auxiliary output current I_{out1} (tap output). The second output ($M6$ and $M7$) contributes directly to the output current of the all-pass filter (I_{out3}) and realizes the second term in (5). The third output ($M8$ and $M9$) is connected to the input of the second current invertor. This second current invertor has a low-pass transfer function by action of the capacitor connected between input and ground. The double output branch of the second current invertor ($M15$–$M18$) is connected to

the output of the all-pass filter and provides the invertor with a gain of two. This realizes the first term in (5). Transistors $M12$ and $M14$ serve as an auxiliary output (I_{out2}). All MOS transistors have identical geometry.

III. THE DELAY LINE

By cascading several all-pass sections, as given in Fig. 2, a delay line is obtained. The auxiliary output of the first current invertor ($I_{out1,k}$) of each of the all-pass sections is used as a tap. The transfer function $H_k(j\omega)$ from the input current of the first stage to the output current $I_{out1,k}$ of stage k is given by

$$H_k(j\omega) = -\left(\frac{1 - j\omega RC}{1 + j\omega RC}\right)^{k-1}, \qquad k = 1, 2, \cdots, n. \quad (10)$$

For band-limited signals, satisfying condition (4), the delay time $t_{d,k}$ from input to the kth tap may be approximated by

$$t_{d,k} = 2(k-1)RC. \qquad (11)$$

The transfer function $H'_k(j\omega)$ from the input current to the auxiliary current output $I_{out2,k}$ is

$$H'_k(j\omega) = \frac{1}{1 + j\omega RC}\left(\frac{1 - j\omega RC}{1 + j\omega RC}\right)^{k-1},$$

$$k = 1, 2, \cdots, n. \quad (12)$$

The transfer functions described by (12) are Laplace transforms of Laguerre functions, which may be used advantageously in adaptive transversal filters [9]. As the relation between input current and input voltage of each stage is linear, both types of transfer functions are also available in the voltage domain at the gate of transistor $M1'$ and the gate of transistor $M11$ of the kth stage.

IV. THE DELAY-TIME CONTROL SYSTEM

Adaptive tuning of the delay time is possible by using the V_2 terminal. We will use an indirect tuning scheme [7] with one all-pass section as a reference filter as shown in Fig. 3. The functioning of this scheme is as follows. A reference signal with amplitude A and an accurately determined frequency ω_{ref} is fed into the input of the all-pass section and the input of a multiplier. The all-pass section will produce an output signal V_{out} of the same amplitude but with a phase shift given by (2):

$$V_{out} = A\sin(\omega_{ref}t + p) \qquad (13)$$

with

$$p = -2\arctan\left(\frac{\omega_{ref}C}{2K(V_2 - 2V_t)}\right). \qquad (14)$$

The output signal of the all-pass section is fed to the same multiplier as the input reference signal. The multiplier

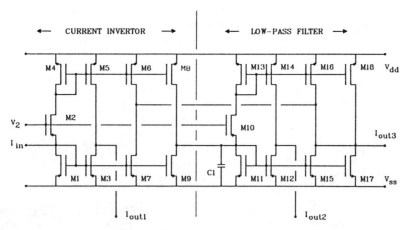

Fig. 2. The first-order all-pass circuit.

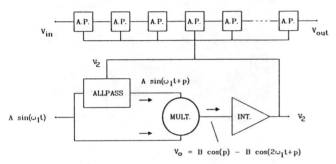

Fig. 3. Time-delay control system.

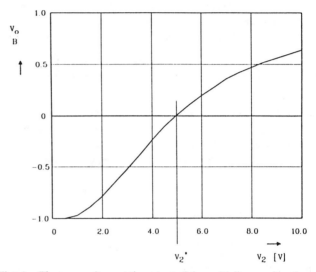

Fig. 4. The error voltage at the output of the multiplier as a function of V_2.

produces an output signal V_o containing two components:

$$V_o = B\cos(p) - B\cos(2\omega_{\text{ref}}t + p) \qquad (15)$$

in which B is determined by the amplitude of the input signal A and the multiplying constant of the multiplier. The multiplier is then followed by an integrator with a large time constant with respect to the reciprocal of the reference frequency. The second term in (15) is filtered out and will be neglected in this discussion. What remains is the first term in (15), a dc component. If the multiplier is connected correctly with respect to the sign of the inputs, the integrator will change its output signal V_2 in such a way that the dc component of (15) vanishes. In this situation the phase shift p of the all-pass filter is exactly 90° and the pole-zero frequency of the all-pass section is tuned to the reference input frequency.

The behavior of the system may be studied by finding an expression for the voltage V_o at the output of the multiplier as a function of the control voltage V_2. Substituting (14) into (15) and neglecting the second term in (15) we obtain

$$V_o = B\cos\left(2\arctan\left(\frac{V_2^* - 2V_t}{V_2 - 2V_t}\right)\right) \qquad (16)$$

with

$$V_2^* = 2V_t + \frac{\omega_{\text{ref}}C}{2K} \qquad (17)$$

the voltage V_2 for which the all-pass filter generates a phase shift of 90° for a given reference frequency. The voltage V_0 is plotted in Fig. 4 as a function of V_2 according to (16) for $V_2^* = 5.0$ V. This curve shows that in principle the system will always lock to the reference frequency irrespective of the initial value of V_2 and the value of the reference frequency. In practice, however, ω_{ref} has to be within a range, determined at the lower side by the deterioration of the circuit behavior due to weak inversion [8] and at the upper side by the supply voltage. Nevertheless the capture range of the system should be very large.

V. ERROR ANALYSIS

A. The All-Pass Section

The all-pass transfer function (1) is realized by adding the output signal of a low-pass filter with a low-frequency gain of two and the output signal of a current invertor, as described by (5). Transistor mismatch and channel-length shortening may lead to deviations of the low-frequency

213

TABLE I
MEASURED RESULTS FOR 26TH-ORDER ALL-PASS FILTER

Supply Voltage	V	8.0	8.0	8.0	8.0	8.0
Bias Current Ib	µA	80	40	20	10	5
Bias Voltage V2	V	7.18	5.31	4.08	3.26	2.69
Total Supply Current	mA	13.3	6.66	3.32	1.67	0.85
Group Delay	µS	8.1	10.6	14.3	19.6	27.9
DC-gain	dB	-2.9	-2.4	-3.0	-1.5	+0.8
Ripple	dB	3.7	4.7	5.0	4.5	3.0
RMS Noise volt. (100Hz...300KHz)	mV	0.115	0.099	0.082	0.079	–
RMS Max. inp. volt. (THD=1%)	mV	360	300	170	97	79

gains of these circuits and hence of the desired transfer function. We can analyze the effect of mismatch on the transfer function by assuming the low-frequency gain of the low-pass filter to be $2 + \Delta_{Ip}$ and the low-frequency gain of the current invertor $-(1 + \Delta_{ci})$, with Δ_{Ip} and Δ_{ci} being the deviations of the low-frequency gains. The transfer-function (1) is now written as

$$H(j\omega) = \frac{(1 + \Delta_{Ip} - \Delta_{ci}) - j\omega(1 + \Delta_{ci})RC}{(1 + j\omega RC)}. \quad (18)$$

As we can see, the pole frequency is not influenced. The zero frequency, however, is shifted, which means that the amplitude of the transfer function is not equal for all frequencies anymore. The low-frequency gain becomes

$$|H(0)| = (1 + \Delta_{Ip} - \Delta_{ci}) \quad (19)$$

whereas the high-frequency gain is

$$|H(\infty)| = (1 + \Delta_{ci}). \quad (20)$$

For use in a delay line we can tolerate only a small deviation from unity. If we allow the modulus of the transfer function of the delay line to be in the range

$$0.5 < |H_k(j\omega)| < 2.0, \quad (21)$$

and $k = 26$, we obtain the following restrictions for Δ_{Ip} and Δ_{ci}:

$$\max(|\Delta_{Ip} - \Delta_{ci}|, |\Delta_{ci}|) < 0.027. \quad (22)$$

This means that, in our situation, a deviation of the low-frequency gains of the current invertor and the low-pass filter of 2.7 percent may be tolerated.

B. The Delay-Time Control System

Mismatch, offsets, and other nonidealities in the subcircuits of the control system (Fig. 3) may lead to a deviation of the effective pole-zero frequency ω_{eff}, from the desired frequency set by the reference frequency ω_{ref}. It can be shown that

$$\left| \frac{\omega_{eff} - \omega_{ref}}{\omega_{ref}} \right| = \left| \frac{V_{zo} + CV_{xo}V_{yo} + V_{io} + V_2/A_0}{V_{in\,int}} \right| \quad (23)$$

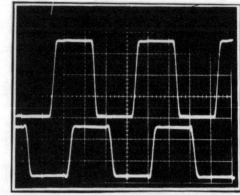

Fig. 5. Step response (lower trace) of the 26-stage delay line. The circuit is biased at $V_2 = 7.18$ V. The input signal (upper trace) has a magnitude of 0.4 V with a leading and a trailing edge time of 2.0 µs. The horizontal scale is 10 µs per division. The output load resistance was 360 Ω.

where

V_{zo} multiplier output offset voltage,
V_{xo} multiplier x-input offset voltage,
V_{yo} multiplier y-input offset voltage,
C multiplier constant,
V_{io} integrator input offset voltage,
A_0 integrator low-frequency gain, and
$V_{in\,int}$ signal amplitude at the input of the integrator.

As usually both input offset voltages are small, the product of both voltages is small with respect to the output offset voltage and may be neglected. Important is a low multiplier output offset voltage, a low integrator input offset voltage, a high integrator low-frequency gain, and a high signal level at the input of the integrator. For this reason an XOR circuit with two comparators is sometimes used instead of a multiplier (see also Fig. 12). In this situation (23) still holds with

$$V_{zo} = (V_{dd} - V_{ss})/2 - V_{GND} \quad (24)$$

and

$$V_{in\,int} = (V_{dd} - V_{ss}).$$

In this case special arrangements can be made to minimize V_{zo}, as will be explained in Section VI.

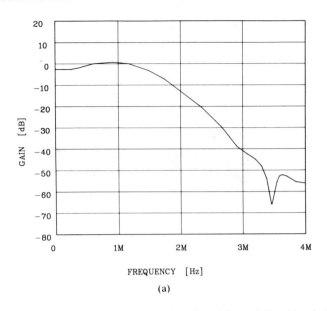

(a)

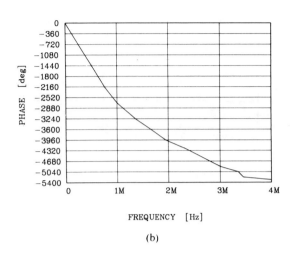

(b)

Fig. 6. (a), (b) Transfer function of the total filter biased with $V_2 = 7.18$ V; the dc current is 80 μA in each branch, 480 μA in each section, and 13.3 mA in the total filter.

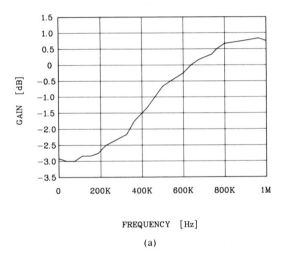

(a)

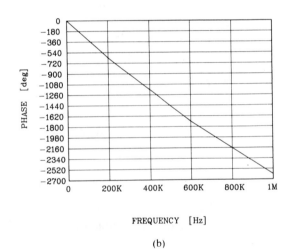

(b)

Fig. 7. (a), (b) Transfer function of the total filter biased at $V_2 = 7.18$ V.

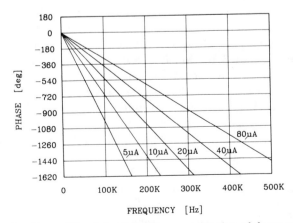

Fig. 8. Phase shift of the total filter as a function of frequency at several bias currents.

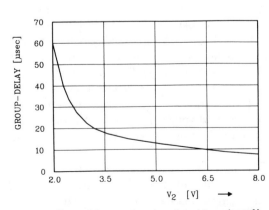

Fig. 9. Group delay as a function of the bias voltage V_2.

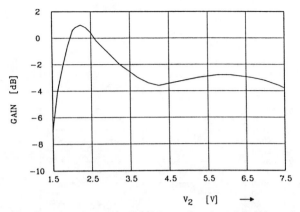

Fig. 10. Low-frequency gain (1 kHz) as a function of the bias voltage V_2.

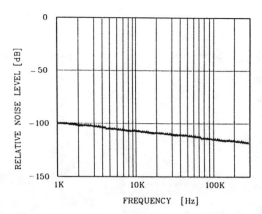

Fig. 11. The relative output noise level at $V_2 = 7.18$ V. The reference level in this measurement is the signal level at which a THD of 1 percent is measured.

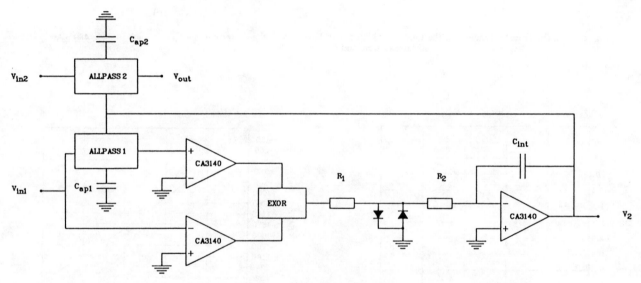

Fig. 12. Breadboard realization of the control system. Both all-pass sections are on the same chip.

VI. RESULTS OF MEASUREMENTS

Experimental verification has been performed on two setups: an integrated cascade of 26 identical all-pass sections, acting as a continuous-time delay line, and a frequency locking system breadboard built on breadboard around two identical on-chip all-pass sections. Both the delay-line and the two separate all-pass sections have been realized in the retrograde twin-well CMOS process of the University of Twente. Although all circuit schemes show NMOS transistors in the core of the circuits (transistors $M1-M3$ and $M7$ in Fig. 1), PMOS transistors were used to be able to reduce the body effect by connecting the source of each transistor to its own substrate well. The PMOST threshold voltage is -0.6 V. All transistors (in all circuits) have the same geometry: $W = 40$ μm and $L = 20$ μm.

Table I shows the measurement conditions for the 26th-order all-pass filter for five different bias currents. Fig. 5 shows the step response of the filter biased at $V_2 = 7.18$ V. At this bias voltage the bias current in each branch is

80 μA, in each section 480 μA, and in the complete filter 13.3 mA. The delay time is 8.1 μs.

For the same bias condition ($V_2 = 7.18$ V) the transfer function of the complete filter is measured. The results are shown in Fig. 6. Fig. 7 shows the same results for a smaller frequency span.

Fig. 8 shows the phase shift of the complete filter as a function of frequency at several bias currents, whereas Fig. 9 shows the group delay as a function of the bias voltage.

Fig. 10 shows the low-frequency gain at 1 kHz of the total filter as a function of the bias voltage V_2.

The noise spectrum has been measured between 1 and 300 kHz; Fig. 11 shows the results. The reference level (0 dB) in this measurement is defined as the input level at which the total harmonic distortion (THD) of the total circuit (26 stages) equals 1 percent.

The measurements on the delay-time control system have been performed on a breadboard setup with the electrical scheme of Fig. 12. This is basically the setup of Fig. 3. The multiplier has been realized with CA3140 op amps, used as comparators and an XOR circuit. The output

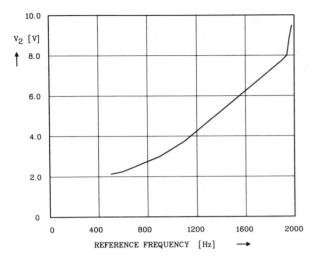

Fig. 13. Control voltage V_2 in the control loop as a function of the reference frequency with $C_{ap1} = 10$ nF.

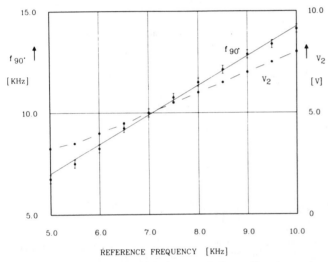

Fig. 14. The frequency at which the second all-pass filter has a phase shift of 90° as a function of the reference frequency. The control-loop voltage V_2 is also shown. In this measurement $C_{ap1} = 2.2$ nF and $C_{ap2} = 1.5$ nF.

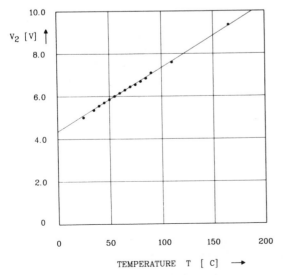

Fig. 15. The control-loop voltage V_2 as a function of temperature.

of the XOR circuit is connected via R_1 to two diodes to limit the voltage swing at the input of the integrator and to make the setup less susceptible to supply voltage variations. The integrator consists of R_2, C_{int}, and a CA3140 op amp. Both all-pass sections are on the same chip. ALLPASS1 is used in the loop as a reference filter whereas ALLPASS2 may be used for signal processing. The capacitors C_{ap1} and C_{ap2} are external capacitors. The supply voltage in this setup is 10 V whereas the ground level is 5.0 V. This setup functions very well. The system always locks to the reference frequency as long as V_2^* (see (17)) is within certain limits: 2.1 V < V_2^* < 8.0 V. The lower limit is in this case determined by the operation region of the integrator. The upper limit is set by the supply voltage.

The following measurements have been performed on the circuit of Fig. 12. The loop voltage V_2 has been measured as a function of the reference frequency. Fig. 13 shows the results measured with $C_{ap1} = 10$ nF. The scheme works properly for reference frequencies in the range 500–1950 Hz.

The performance of the ALLPASS2 filter (Fig. 12) has been determined in the following way. The frequency f_{90} at which the ALLPASS2 filter exhibits a phase shift of 90° has been measured as a function of the reference frequency f_{ref}. The result is shown in Fig. 14. This measurement has been performed with $C_{ap1} = 2.2$ nF and $C_{ap2} = 1.5$ nF. The theoretical results are plotted as a solid line. The figure shows a close agreement between theory and measurements. In this figure the loop voltage V_2 is also plotted.

Finally the loop voltage V_2 has been measured as a function of temperature; the result is shown in Fig. 15. During this measurement no change could be observed in the transfer function of the ALLPASS2 filter.

VII. DISCUSSION

Fig. 6(a) shows an approximately flat (3.8-dB ripple) amplitude response of the 26 sections for frequencies up to 1.5 MHz. This amounts to 0.14-dB ripple per section in this frequency range. With respect to the phase linearity, however, the input signal frequency has to be limited to a smaller range. Equation (3) predicts a nonlinearity of 2 percent for signals with $\omega < 0.2/RC$ which amounts to 176 kHz for $V_2 = 7.18$ V. Fig. 7(a) shows in this range a ripple in the amplitude response of about 0.2 dB for 26 sections, or about 0.077-dB per section.

The feasibility of the all-pass section of Fig. 1 is shown by Figs. 5–14. However, a first-order all-pass filter may not be the best solution. Higher order all-pass filters, as for instance, second-order filters with maximally flat phase response, have to be considered. This may lead to a larger usable bandwidth. Also, a larger delay time may be obtained with a smaller number of transistors.

It has yet to be investigated whether it is necessary to connect the source of each transistor to its own substrate. Connecting the substrate of each device to the power supply would largely reduce the parasitic capacitance on these nodes and the usable bandwidth would be much larger. Furthermore, NMOS transistors could be used in the core which also enhances the speed of the circuits.

The monotonously rising curve of the error voltage at the output of the multiplier as a function of V_2 (Fig. 4) gives the delay-time control system a very large capture range of about two octaves in frequency. This is due to the use of an all-pass filter as a reference filter. Other types of reference filters such as low pass, high pass, or bandpass will always show a decline of the error voltage as a result of the decreasing amplitude of the filter response towards the lower and/or higher frequencies. Consequently the application of such types of reference filters leads to capture ranges of 10–20 percent of the center frequency.

The deviation of V_2 from the straight line in Fig. 13, as predicted by the simple relation of (17), is probably due to carrier mobility reduction, which necessitates a higher gate voltage to obtain a certain value of the transconductance than the simple square-law would predict.

The temperature measurements shown in Fig. 15 have to be considered with ample wariness as the determination of the temperature could not be performed with great accuracy. However, it shows the range in which the system performs well and moreover, as no noticable difference could be observed in the behavior of the second all-pass filter (ALLPASS2), it shows the feasibility of the system.

VIII. CONCLUSION

A CMOS analog continuous-time delay line has been developed composed of cascaded current domain all-pass sections. The operation is based on the square-law behavior of an MOS transistor in the saturated region. An adaptive delay-time control system makes the delay time independent of processing and temperature variations. Measurements have been performed on an on-chip realization of the delay line of 26 stages and on a breadboard of the control system built around two all-pass sections on the same chip. The measurements show good results: a large capture range and good tracking of the reference frequency make the delay time very well controllable. We have demonstrated that it is possible to build an analog continuous-time delay line on the basis of analog CMOS circuits, using the square-law characteristic of an MOS transistor in saturation.

ACKNOWLEDGMENT

The authors are grateful to A. Kooy for processing the circuit at the IC-processing facility of the University of Twente. They also thank O. W. Memelink and W. J. A. de Heij for fruitful discussions.

REFERENCES

[1] M. H. White et al., "Charge-coupled devices (CCD) adaptive discrete analog signal processing," IEEE J. Solid-State Circuits, vol. SC-14, no. 1, pp. 132–146, Feb. 1979.

[2] C. F. N. Cowan, J. W. Arthur, J. Mavor, and P.B. Denyer, "CCD based adaptive filters: Realization and analysis," IEEE Trans. Acoustics, Speech Signal Processing, vol. ASSP-29, no. 2, pp. 220–229, Apr. 1981.

[3] K. Nagaraj, "Switched capacitor delay circuit that is insensitive to capacitor mismatch and stray capacitance," Electron. Lett., vol. 20, no. 16, pp. 663–664, Aug. 2, 1984.

[4] K. Tan and P. R. Gray, "Fully integrated analog filters using bipolar-JFET technology," IEEE J. Solid-State Circuits, vol. SC-13, no. 6, pp. 814–821, Dec. 1978.

[5] K. W. Moulding, J. R. Quartly, P. J. Rankin, R. S. Thompson, and G. A. Wilson, "Gyrator video filter IC with automatic tuning," IEEE J. Solid-State Circuits, vol. SC-15, no. 6, pp. 963–967, Dec. 1980.

[6] H. Khorramabadi and P. R. Gray, "High-frequency CMOS continuous-time filters," IEEE J. Solid-State Circuits, vol. SC-19, no. 6, pp. 939–948, Dec. 1984.

[7] Y. P. Tsividis, M. Banu, and J. Khoury, "Continuous-time MOSFET-C filters in VLSI," IEEE Trans. Circuits Syst., vol. CAS-33, no. 2, pp. 125–140, Feb. 1986.

[8] K. Bult and H. Wallinga, "A class of analog CMOS circuits based on the square-law characteristic of an MOS transistor in saturation," IEEE J. Solid-State Circuits, vol. 22, pp. 357–365, June 1987.

[9] J. O. Voorman et al., "An automatic equalizer for echo reduction in Teletext on a single chip," Philips Tech. Rev., vol. 40, no. 11/12, pp. 319–328, 1982.

Section 3-B   Balanced Circuits

Balanced transconductor-capacitor filters provide better linearity and better interference rejection than their single-ended counterparts. Most of the transconductor principles described in Sec. 3-A (including the references therein) can be used in balanced circuits by using differential output plus common-mode feedback. Paper 3-B.1 by Khorramabadi and Gray uses such an approach in a transconductor based on a simple differential pair operating in the saturation region; this principle is also adopted elsewhere [1]. Operation in the MHz range can easily be achieved in this way thanks to the simplicity of the circuitry. However, the lack of linearization circuitry limits signal swings. Thus, all other papers in this section use some form of linearization. Paper 3-B.2, by Pennock, Frith, and Barker, demonstrates a fifth-order elliptic CMOS filter operating in the audio and above-audio range, using a transconductor based on two balanced-driven, triode-operated grounded devices with constant drain-source voltage [2]. This principle, extended to differential pairs [3, 4], is also used by Alini, Baschirotto, and Castello in Paper 3-B.3; careful optimization of the transconductor, combined with the use of BiCMOS technology, makes possible operation at frequencies in the tens of MHz. As usual, significant power dissipation is needed at such frequencies. The next three papers use transconductors based on a single, balanced-driven, triode-operated transistor (see [5]) and demonstrate their use in filters at two opposite extremes: Kaiser, in Paper 3-B.4, presents a low-frequency micropower filter, whereas Gopinathan et al. present a video filter in Paper 3-B.5, and Wang and Abidi present a filter operating above the video range in Paper 3-B.6. The latter two papers also discuss general considerations for the implementation of high-frequency transconductance-C filters. Additional considerations of this nature are offered by Krummenacher and Joehl (Paper 3-B.7) and by Krummenacher (Paper 3-B.8). In these, a related transconductor is proposed, and a video filter using it is presented. Further modifications of the transconductor lead to the circuit used in Paper 3-B.9 by Steyaert, Silva-Martinez, and Sansen, who achieve low distortion in a 100 kHz filter. A feature of this filter is the use of tunable floating resistors for controlling the passband ripple. In Paper 3-B.10, Nauta uses a transconductor based on a very differ-

ent principle (the use of CMOS inverters plus positive feedback [6]) in a VHF filter (other VHF filters are presented in papers 5-B.3 and 5-B.4, and in [7]). In Paper 3-B.11, Koyama, Tanimoto, and Mizoguchi present a 10.7 MHz filter implemented in bipolar technology. It is our opinion that integrated continuous-time filters using present technologies are not competitive with passive filters for 10.7 MHz IF applications because of the combination of high Q and large dynamic range requirements; however, the paper contains useful general considerations related to filter implementation using bipolar transistors. Finally, another bipolar technology filter is presented in paper 3-B.12 by Takagi et al. The authors demonstrate the use of NIC (Negative Immitance Converter) circuits to avoid PNP active loads. In modern IC processes with high-speed NPN transistors and shallow epitaxial layers, it is becoming increasingly difficult to implement high-quality PNP transistors.

We should note that, although this section contains only balanced designs and the previous section only single-ended ones, many of the considerations presented for one of these types are transferable to the other type. This is particularly true of several synthesis techniques used, as well as of the input stages of the transconductors. We note that many of the transconductor principles presented in the literature (see, for example, refs. 25–49 of Sect. 3-A) apply to both single-ended and balanced designs.

The application of balanced transconductor-C filters is illustrated in Papers 7-B.1, 7-D.1, and 7-D.2.

References

[1] S. Masuda and Y. Kitamura, "Design considerations of monolithic continuous-time filters," *Proc. IEEE ISCAS*, pp.1165–1168, 1986.

[2] J. L. Pennock, "CMOS triode transconductor for continuous-time active integrated filters," *Electron. Lett.*, vol. 21, pp. 817–818, August 29, 1985.

[3] Z. Czarnul and Y. Tsividis, "MOS tunable transconductor," *Electron. Lett.*, vol. 22, pp. 721–722, June 19, 1986.

[4] B. Stefanelli and A. Kaiser, "CMOS triode transconductor with high dynamic range," vol. 26, pp. 880–881, June 21, 1990.

[5] Y. Tsividis, Z. Czarnul and S. C. Fang, "MOS transconductors and integrators with high linearity," *Electron. Lett.*, vol. 22, pp. 245–246, February 27, 1986; errata: *ibid.*, p. 619, May 22, 1986.

[6] B. Nauta and E. Seevinck, "Linear CMOS transconductance element for VHF filters," *Electron. Lett.*, vol. 25, pp. 448–450, March 30, 1989.

[7] W. M. Snelgrove and A. Shoval, "A balanced 0.9-μm CMOS transconductance-*C* filter tunable over the VHF range," *IEEE J. Solid-State Circuits*, vol. 27, pp. 314–333, March 1992.

Paper 3-B.1

High-Frequency CMOS Continuous-Time Filters

HAIDEH KHORRAMABADI, STUDENT MEMBER, IEEE, AND PAUL R. GRAY, FELLOW, IEEE

Abstract —Fully-integrated, high-frequency continuous-time filters can be realized in MOS technology using a frequency-locking approach to stabilize the time constants. A simple fully-differential integrator, optimized for phase-error cancellation, forms the basic element; a complete filter consists of intercoupled integrators. The center frequency of the filter is locked to an external reference frequency by a phase-locked loop. A prototype sixth-order bandpass filter with a center frequency of 500 kHz dissipates 55 mW and occupies 4 mm² in a 6 μm CMOS technology.

I. Introduction

HIGH-PRECISION, high-order monolithic filters in the frequency range of 100 kHz to 10 MHz have many applications in communication receivers such as AM and FM IF filtering and video processing in TV circuits. Additional applications include data communications and local area networks.

Monolithic filters have previously been successfully applied to voice band applications both by utilizing the switched-capacitor technique and the continuous-time filtering method [1], [2]. However, the extension of both techniques to higher frequencies has been delayed due to many problems.

One promising approach for the implementation of high-frequency filters is the switched-capacitor technique. Recently a switched-capacitor bandpass filter at the center frequency of 260 kHz has been designed which has shown excellent performance [3]. Another switched-capacitor filter with low-pass characteristics was reported at a roll-off frequency of 2.8 MHz [4]. One major drawback to this approach is the requirement of continuous-time prefilters to band limit the input spectrum to reduce the aliasing effects. Another problem peculiar to the implementation of high-frequency switched-capacitor filters is that due to settling time limitations in state-of-the-art operational amplifiers, the extension of this technique to higher frequencies requires the lowering of the ratio of clock rate to the center frequency of the filter which brings about the necessity of higher selectivity of the antialiasing prefilters.

Another alternative is to use continuous-time filtering techniques which do not have the aliasing problem of

sampled-data systems. However, due to the dependence of the center frequency of the filter on the absolute values of monolithic components such as capacitors and transistor transconductances, which are both process and temperature dependent, some extra circuitry is required to control the center frequency of this type of filters.

This paper describes a high-frequency CMOS continuous-time bandpass filtering technique which utilizes a modified version of the phase-locked loop scheme introduced by Tan [1] to precisely control the center frequency of the filter [5].

In Section II, Tan's approach is reviewed and the problems involved in the direct extension of this technique to higher frequencies are discussed. Solutions to the problems hindering the filter design are proposed in Section III, where a very simple fully differential integrator is described and a sixth-order bandpass filter is implemented. In Section IV, the center frequency control circuit is discussed. The experimental results are presented in Section V, and in the final section the capability of this technique in scaled technology is explored.

II. Extension of Low-Frequency Frequency-Locked Filtering Techniques to Higher Frequencies

The frequency-locked continuous-time filtering technique was first introduced in 1977 [1]. A low-pass voice-band filter was designed and a phase-locked loop scheme was utilized to control the roll-off frequency of the filter. Fig. 1 shows the block diagram of the system. The principle building block of the filter is an integrator. The time constant of the integrators are controlled through V_c. A voltage-controlled oscillator (VO), in conjunction with a phase-comparator, functions as a phase-locked loop. By choosing the same type of integrator for both the filter and the VCO, the bandwidth of the filter tracks the frequency of the oscillator. Thus, while the PLL is in lock, the roll-off frequency of the filter is exactly proportional to the external reference frequency.

The extension of this approach to higher frequencies involves several problems. The main problem is that the behavior of high-frequency filters is highly sensitive to analog integrator nonidealities, particularly the phase shift at the unity-gain frequency. The second problem is the

Manuscript received   ; revised   . This work was supported in part by the National Science Foundation under Grant ENG-442427 and also by the MOSTEK Corporation.

The authors are with the Department of Electrical Engineering and Computer Science, Electronics Research Laboratory, University of California, Berkeley, CA 94720.

Reprinted from *IEEE J. Solid-State Circuits,* vol. SC-19, no. 6, pp. 939–948, Dec. 1984.

221

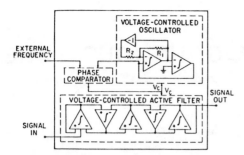

Fig. 1. Block diagram of Tan's approach to the design of low-frequency low-pass continuous time filter.

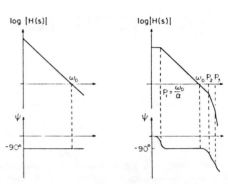

Fig. 2. Amplitude and phase response of an ideal integrator and a nonideal integrator.

realization of a CMOS VCO with stable and repeatable center frequency in the MHz range. Because the desired filters are often highly selective (high Q), the power supply rejection (PSRR) is a critical problem. Finally, the feed-through of the reference signal to the output of the filter can result in the degradation of the dynamic range.

The solution to the first problem will be discussed in detail in Section III. To overcome the second problem, an alternative scheme is discussed in Section IV which utilizes a voltage-controlled filter VCF instead of the conventional VCO. The last two problems are minimized by using fully differential architecture for the circuit design.

III. HIGH-FREQUENCY BANDPASS FILTER DESIGN

This section deals with the problems associated with the filter design. In Section III-A effect of the phase-shift error in analog integrators on the performance of high-frequency filters is analyzed. In Section III-B a simple integrator is designed and an optimum channel length is derived for which the phase error terms cancel. In Section III-C resonator design considerations are covered followed by the implementation of a sixth-order bandpass filter. In Sections III-E and F the filter dynamic range considerations are discussed.

A. Effect of Integrator Nonidealities on Filter Behavior

As mentioned earlier, the main building block for ladder type active filters is an integrator. In this section the frequency response of an integrator and its effect on the filter behavior is studied.

In Fig. 2 the amplitude and phase response of an ideal integrator is illustrated. It has a pole at the origin and exactly a 90° phase shift at the unity-gain frequency. Using the definition of quality factor, the Q of the ideal integrator is found to be

$$Q_{\text{intg}}^{\text{ideal}} = \infty. \tag{1}$$

For a real integrator with finite dc gain of a, the dominant pole is pushed from the origin to a frequency equal to ω_0/a, where ω_0 is the unity-gain frequency of the integrator. Also, it may have one or more high-frequency nondominant poles. The finite dc gain causes phase lead at the unity-gain frequency and the nondominant poles

result in excess phase shift. The quality factor of the real integrator Q_{intg}, assuming that all the nondominant poles p_i are at much higher frequency than the integrator unity-gain frequency, is found to be

$$\frac{1}{Q_{\text{intg}}} \approx \frac{1}{a} - \omega_0 \sum_{i=2}^{i=\infty} \frac{1}{p_i}. \tag{2}$$

The first term is equal to the phase lead at the unity-gain frequency in radian and the second-term corresponds to the excess phase. Note that as ω_0 is increased, the excess phase term becomes larger.

Fig. 3 demonstrates the effect of these two phase error components on the filter behavior. The bold curve in all three figures shows the frequency response of a sixth-order bandpass filter constructed with ideal integrators. The broken line in Fig. 3(a) shows the frequency response of the same filter made with integrators which have about 0.5° phase lead at their unity-gain frequency. This corresponds to a dc gain of 100 for the integrators. The Q is degraded in this case. In Fig. 3(b) the effect of 0.5° excess phase in integrators, which corresponds to a nondominant pole 100 times larger than the unity-gain frequency, is shown. In this case, the Q is enhanced and as mentioned earlier, as ω_0 is increased the excess phase becomes larger and may result in oscillation. Note that the error in the passband of the filter is directly proportional to $Q_{\text{filter}}/Q_{\text{intg}}$, where Q_{filter} is the quality factor of the filter. Fig. 3(c) shows the effect of exactly equal amounts of phase lead and excess phase at the unity gain frequency of the integrators, which results in phase error cancellation at this frequency. The frequency response of the filter in this case is very close to the ideal case.

These considerations suggest that it is very desirable to design the integrator in such a way that the two phase error components cancel each other right at the unity-gain frequency. However, the dependence of the two phase error components on temperature and process variations limits the accuracy of such phase error cancellation in high-frequency filtering applications and thus, in conjunction with the maximum allowable error in the passband, dic-

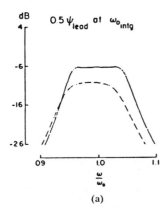

(a)

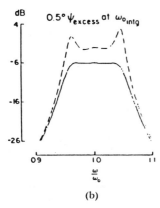

(b)

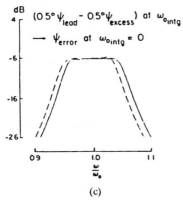

(c)

Fig. 3. Effect of integrator nonidealities on the filter behavior.

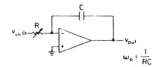

Fig. 4. Typical integrator configuration.

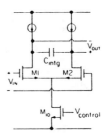

Fig. 5. Simple differential pair integrator.

tates an upper limit for the maximum Q of the filter. This will further be explored in Section VI.

B. Integrator Design

An *RC* integrator is typically constructed of a multistage operational amplifier connected in the feedback configuration, as shown in Fig. 4. In the previous section, it was shown that the frequency response of high-frequency filters is very sensitive to extra phase-shift in the integrator. The high-frequency poles of the multistage operational amplifier tend to contribute large amounts of excess phase causing large error in the filter response. An important objective, then, is to design an integrator with preferably no nondominant poles.

To achieve this goal, a one-stage source-coupled differential pair configuration was chosen to minimize Q enhancement effects, as shown in Fig. 5. The unity-gain frequency ω_0 of this integrator is given by

$$\omega_0 = \frac{g_{m(M1,2)}}{2C_{\text{intg}}} \tag{3}$$

where $g_{m(M1,2)}$ is the transconductance of the input transistors and C_{intg} corresponds to the integrating capacitor. It is evident that ω_0 is process dependent and can be controlled through $g_{m(M1,2)}$ by varying the drain current of the input transistors through V_{control}.

The quality factor of this integrator Q_{intg}, is found by using (2). The first term is derived by finding the dc gain of the integrator. The second term is estimated by finding an effective nondominant pole $p_{2_{\text{effective}}}$ for the integrator. The dc gain is found to be

$$a = \frac{g_{m(M1,2)}}{g_{0_{(M1,2)}} + g_{0_{\text{load}}}} \tag{4}$$

where $g_{0_{(M1,2)}}$ and $g_{0_{\text{load}}}$ are the small signal output conductance of the input transistors and the load transistors. Assuming that the output resistance of the load transistors is much larger than the output resistance of the input transistors, and by substituting for $g_{m(M1,2)}$ and $g_{0_{(M1,2)}}$, the gain is found to be

$$a = \frac{2}{\lambda(V_{GS} - V_{th})_{(M1,2)}} \tag{5}$$

where λ is the channel-length modulation coefficient. In practice λ is estimated from experimental data and is inversely proportional to the channel length. Here, for simplicity, a new parameter θ is introduced

$$\lambda = \frac{\theta}{L} \tag{6}$$

where θ is in the order of 0.1 $[\mu/V]$. Substituting for λ gives

$$a = \frac{2L}{\theta(V_{GS} - V_{th})_{(M1,2)}}. \tag{7}$$

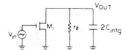

Fig. 6. Small-signal equivalent differential mode half-circuit of the integrator.

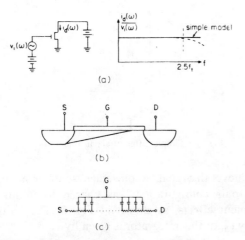

Fig. 7. The high-frequency behavior of an MOS transistor. (a) Drain current as a function of frequency. (b) Cross-sectional view of an MOS transistor in saturation. (c) The distributed channel resistance and gate capacitance.

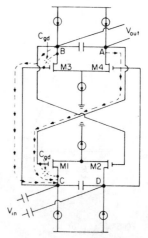

Fig. 8. Resonator implementation.

Fig. 6 shows the small-signal equivalent differential mode half-circuit of the integrator. The circuit has only two nodes, an input node and an output node. The simple IGFET model predicts no nondominant poles for this integrator, in other words, for a transistor biased in the saturation region, a constant drain current as a function of frequency is predicted when the gate is driven by a voltage source [Fig. 7(a)]. However, a more detailed consideration of the distributed nature of the channel resistance and gate capacitance, as illustrated in Fig. 7(b) and (c), shows that the frequency response of the transconductance falls off at high frequencies. It can be shown that this phenomenon gives rise to an infinite number of high-frequency poles and an effective nondominant pole can be approximated by [6]

$$p_{2_{\text{effective}}} \approx \frac{1}{\sum_{i=2}^{i=\infty} \frac{1}{p_i}} = 2.5\omega_{t_{(M1,2)}} \quad (8)$$

where

$$\omega_{t_{(M1,2)}} = \frac{3}{2}\frac{\mu(V_{GS}-V_{th})_{(M1,2)}}{L^2}. \quad (9)$$

Note that the integrator effective nondominant pole is at a much higher frequency than for a typical operational amplifier type integrator.

Substituting from (7), (8), and (9) in (2)

$$\frac{1}{Q_{\text{intg}}} \approx \frac{\theta(V_{GS}-V_{th})_{(M1,2)}}{2L} - \frac{4}{15}\frac{\omega_0 L^2}{\mu(V_{GS}-V_{th})_{(M1,2)}}. \quad (10)$$

Here it is assumed that the Q of the integrating capacitor is much larger than the other components quality factor and can be neglected, which is usually the case. The above equation shows that the excess phase shift due to this phenomena is proportional to $L^2_{(M1,2)}$, whereas the phase lead due to the finite dc gain is proportional to $1/L_{(M1,2)}$. From this, the conclusion can be drawn that, for a well-characterized well-controlled process, an optimum input transistor channel length can be chosen for first-order phase error cancellation at a given frequency, which makes the realization of high-Q filters possible. The optimum input channel length will be derived in the next section.

Inspecting the differential mode half circuit, it can be seen that there is a feed-forward path between the input and the output through the C_{gd} of the input transistors (a right-half plane zero). In the next section, it will be shown that connecting the integrators in a resonator configuration results in the disappearance of the right-half plane zero.

C. Resonator Design Considerations

In Fig. 8, a resonator is implemented by connecting two integrators back to back. Note that all parasitic capacitance at the output of each integrator, as well as the gate–source capacitance of the next integrator, adds up to the integrating capacitance of the previous stage. For the resonator quality factor Q_{res}, the effect of the gate–source capacitance quality factor $Q_{C_{gs}}$, which is connected in parallel with the integrating capacitor, must be taken into account. It can be shown that for an MOS transistor operating in the saturation region, due to the distributed channel resistance and gate capacitance, the input impedance behaves as a lossy capacitance with a quality factor of [7]

$$Q_{C_{gs}} \approx \frac{5\omega_t}{\omega}. \quad (11)$$

The resonator quality factor Q_{res} is given by

$$\frac{1}{Q_{\text{res}}} = \frac{2}{Q_{\text{intg}}} + \frac{2}{Q_{C_{gs}}} \quad (12)$$

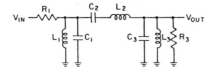

Fig. 9. Sixth-order LC ladder filter.

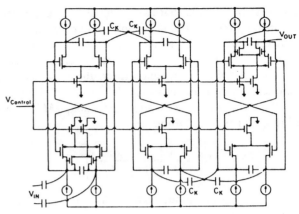

Fig. 10. Active implementation of the sixth-order ladder filter.

substituting from (10) and (11) in (12), the resonator quality factor is found to be

$$\frac{1}{Q_{res}} \approx \frac{\theta(V_{GS} - V_{th})_{(M1,2)}}{L} - \frac{4}{15} \frac{\omega_0 L^2}{\mu(V_{GS} - V_{th})_{(M1,2)}}.$$

(13)

It is interesting to note that the phase lag term is cut by exactly half due to the loss in the gate–source capacitances. From the equation above, by equating the two terms, an optimum channel length for the input transistor is found for which the phase error is cancelled

$$L_{opt} \approx \left[\frac{15}{4} \frac{\theta\mu(V_{GS} - V_{th})^2_{(M1,2)}}{\omega_0} \right]^{1/3}.$$

(14)

One interesting aspect of this resonator circuit configuration is that the right-half plane zero due to the gate–drain capacitances of the input transistors cancel out. This can be more clearly understood by inspecting Fig. 8. Lets consider node C, there are two signal feed-through paths to this node. One is from node A through the gate–drain capacitance of M_1; the other path runs from node B through the C_{gd} of M_3. As the circuit is fully balanced, the signals at nodes A and B are equal and of opposite signs, resulting in signal cancellation at node C.

D. Filter Design

The classical doubly-terminated LC ladder structure was used in the experimental chip described in Section V due to its low sensitivity to component variations (Fig. 9) [8]. The corresponding flowgraph is made of intercoupled resonators which in turn are constructed of integrators. All integrators are chosen to have the same time constant for optimum sensitivity [3].

Using the above integrator to implement the filter requires some extra buffers for both the Q-implementation and the unilateral coupling paths. To avoid the necessity of buffering and its inherent extra phase shift, the narrow-band approximation [9] is utilized to transform the unilateral coupling paths to bilateral ones. This scheme exhibits reasonable passband shape for Q greater than about 4. The realization of a sixth-order bandpass filter using the integrator described above is shown in Fig. 10. The coupling is implemented through C_k and the Q is set by adding termination devices, which will be discussed latter. The center frequency of the filter is controlled by $V_{control}$ through varying the transconductance of all input transistors which makes the matching of these transistors critical.

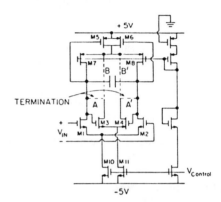

Fig. 11. Complete schematic of the integrator.

The complete schematic of the integrator is shown in Fig. 11. The common-mode output voltage is stabilized by M_5, M_6, which operate in the triode region. M_3, M_4 are the termination devices and are connected in the $(A–A')$ configuration for terminated integrators; $(B–B')$ connection is made for unterminated integrators. The quality factor of a terminated integrator Q_{intg}^{term} is given by

$$Q_{intg}^{term} = \frac{g_{m(M1,2)}}{g_{m(M3,4)}}.$$

(15)

By chosing equal channel lengths for $M_{1,2}$, $M_{3,4}$, and M_{10}, M_{11}, the Q can be implemented by scaling the channel widths of these transistors. To achieve high accuracy for the Q implementation, the termination transistor is chosen as a unit transistor and the input transistors are constructed of an array of Q unit transistors connected in parallel.

E. Maximum Voltage Swing Limitations

In this section the maximum voltage swing of the integrator with acceptable performance is discussed.

The source-coupled pair configuration used for the integrator design displays nonlinear behavior as the input voltage exceeds a certain value [11]. This nonlinearity, which is a function of the gate overdrive voltage ($V_{GS} - V_{th}$) of the input transistors, gives rise to two problems.

The first problem is that as the signal level is increased the transfer function becomes more nonlinear and in the presence of unwanted signals within the passband of the filter may result in spurious signals being generated within the filter itself. For a bandpass filter, the only distortion component which may fall within the passband of the filter is the third-order intermodulation distortion, $IM3$, and for the integrator is found to be

$$IM3 \approx \frac{3}{32}\left[\frac{\hat{v}_i}{(V_{GS} - V_{th})}\right]^2 \tag{16}$$

were $\hat{v}_i$ is the peak input voltage. As an example for a maximum allowable distortion $IM3 = 1$ percent and $(V_{GS} - V_{th})$ of 1.5 V the maximum peak input voltage is computed to be 490 mV.

The second problem is due to the fact that, as the equation below suggests, the input transistor transconductance G_m decreases as the input signal level is increased:

$$G_m \approx g_m\left[1 - \frac{3}{8}\left(\frac{\hat{v}_i}{(V_{GS} - V_{th})}\right)^2\right] \tag{17}$$

where g_m is the small signal transconductance. This in turn decreases the unity-gain frequency of the integrator and lowers the center frequency of the filter. The above consideration is of particular importance for the design of high-Q filters.

By simple circuit techniques, such as adding a cross-coupled pair to the input circuit, both problems can be improved. It can be shown that an increase of about 5 to 15 dB in the maximum input signal with acceptable performance can be achieved by properly scaling the W/L ratios of the source-coupled pair and the cross-coupled pair [7].

F. Filter Noise Performance

Assuming that for the frequency range of interest, the $1/f$ noise of the integrator transistors is negligible, and accounting for the thermal noise of both the input transistors and the load transistors, the input referred noise spectral density of the integrator is found to be

$$S_i(f)_{\text{intg}} = 8kT\frac{1}{g_{m_{(M1,2)}}} \tag{18}$$

for

$$\frac{g_{m_{(M1,2)}}}{g_{m_{(M7,8)}}} = 2.$$

The total output noise power of a typical doubly-terminated sixth-order ladder bandpass filter implemented with identical integrators is found to be [7]

$$\overline{v_{\text{out}}^2} = S_i(f)_{\text{intg}} \times \frac{3\pi}{2} \times Q \times f_0 \tag{19}$$

where $S_i(f)_{\text{intg}}$ is assumed to be frequency independent, f_0 corresponds to the center frequency of the filter, and Q is the quality factor of the terminated resonators which,

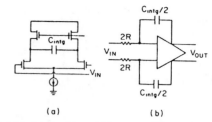

(a)   (b)

Fig. 12. (a) The simple differential pair integrator. (b) An operational amplifier type fully differential integrator.

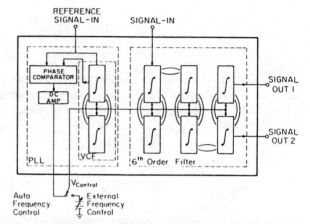

Fig. 13. Block diagram of the filter and the center frequency control circuit.

depending upon the desired shape of the filter frequency characteristics, ranges from one to two times the overall Q of the filter. Substituting for $S_i(f)$ and f_0, the total output noise power is found to be

$$\overline{v_{\text{out}}^2} = 3\frac{kT}{C_{\text{intg}}}Q. \tag{20}$$

It can be demonstrated that the same filter implemented with operational amplifier type fully differential integrators of Fig. 12(b) would exhibit four times more output noise power for equal total integration capacitance. This occurs because of the bridge connection of the integrating capacitance as illustrated in Fig. 12(a).

Since in recursive bandpass filters the output noise power is inversely proportional to the integrating capacitor value, for the above integrator the noise can be drastically reduced by choosing higher values for the integrating capacitors and paying a price in terms of higher power consumption and die area. Whereas in switched-capacitor technique the dependence of the operational amplifier settling time on the integrating capacitance limits the integrating capacitance to relatively small value for high-frequency filters. This in turn makes the achievement of low values of output noise easier in this techniques than in switched-capacitor filters.

IV. CENTER FREQUENCY CONTROL CIRCUITRY

The block diagram of the filter and the center frequency control circuitry is shown in Fig. 13. The center frequency of the filter can either be controlled externally, or an on-chip PLL locks the center frequency of the filter to an external reference frequency.

The PLL uses an exact replica of the main filter's second-order section instead of the conventional VCO. The phase detector compares the phase difference ϕ between the input and output of the filter and generates an error voltage ν_{error} proportional to this phase difference

$$\nu_{error} \approx K\nu_{in}\nu_{out}^{filt}\cos\phi \qquad (21)$$

where K is the phase detector conversion factor and ν_{in} and ν_{out}^{filt} are the rms values of the input voltage and the second-order filter output voltage. This voltage is then amplified and used to change the center frequency of the filter in a direction which reduces the difference between the two frequencies.

The second-order filter has two outputs. The bandpass output has a 180° phase shift at the center frequency with respect to the input signal. The other output has a high-pass characteristic with a peaking at the center frequency and 90° phase shift at this frequency. The fact that the output of the phase detector is proportional to $\cos\phi$, makes the high-pass output suitable to be used to generate the error voltage. Fig. 14(a) shows the amplitude and phase response of the second order filter output. In Fig. 14(b) the corresponding open loop error voltage is shown. The error voltage is zero for $f = f_0$ and is at its maximum for $f = f_0(1 \pm 1/2Q)$. Once the loop is closed, this voltage changes the center frequency of the filter and reduces the difference between the two frequencies.

The loop gain of the PLL is a function of the second-order filter Q, amplitude of the reference signal, phase detector conversion factor, and the dc amplifier gain. It can be shown that there exists an error between the locked center frequency f_0^{locked} and the reference frequency f_{ref} which tends to increase as the difference between the unlocked center frequency $f_0^{unlocked}$ and the reference signal is increased.

$$f_0^{locked} = f_{ref} + \frac{f_0^{unlocked} - f_{ref}}{A_{PLL}} \qquad (22)$$

where A_{PLL} corresponds to the phase-locked loop dc gain and is in the order of few hundreds. This error is usually negligible; as an example for a capture range of 30 percent and loop gain of 150 the maximum error is only 0.1 percent.

For the PLL circuit design a CMOS version of the Gilbert type phase-detector is used. The schematic of the dc amplifier and the voltage to current converter is shown in Fig. 15. C_{c1}, C_{c2}, and MA_8, MA_9 perform as a lag-lead type loop filter [10] which generate a pair of left-hand plane pole and zero. The compensation capacitor is Miller multiplied and the frequency response of the loop benefits from the pole-splitting effect of this configuration [11]. The pole location of the loop filter controls the bandwidth and thus, the capture range of the PLL. The zero location can be varied by changing the voltage on the gates of MA_8 and MA_9, and is utilized to increase the loop phase margin.

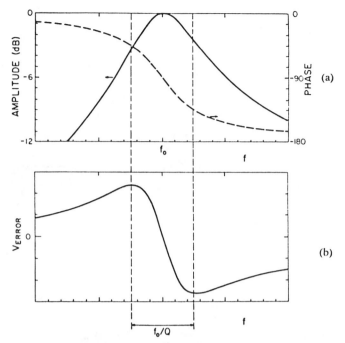

Fig. 14. (a) Amplitude and phase response of the filter output. (b) Open-loop error voltage.

Note that a significant source of extra phase shift, which can result in instability, is that $V_{control}$ has to drive a relatively high capacitance (in this case, eight current source transistor gates). To overcome this problem, $g_{m_{MI3}}$ must be chosen to be sufficiently high.

The fully differential architecture ensures low reference signal feed-through to the output of the filter.

V. EXPERIMENTAL RESULTS

An experimental prototype sixth-order bandpass filter with a center frequency of 500 kHz was designed and fabricated. Fig. 16 shows the microphotograph of the experimental chip. A 6 μm single-poly n-well CMOS technology was used and the die area is about 4 mm².

In Fig. 17(a) the overall frequency response of the filter is shown. The detailed passband of the two different outputs of the filter is seen in Fig. 17(b). The frequency response of the filter is very close to the designed shape and a ±10 percent variation in the power supply voltage produced no significant change in the filter frequency response.

The functionality of the PLL is shown in Fig. 18; note that the markers are added externally to indicate the reference frequency. First, a reference frequency at 450 kHz is applied, the filter frequency response locks to this frequency. Then the reference frequency is changed to 500 kHz, the filter follows this change. The last curve is for a reference frequency at 550 kHz. This corresponds to a 20 percent lock range for the phase-locked loop.

In Table I the results for the sixth-order bandpass filter for 10 V supply voltage is summarized. The total in-band noise is found from Fig. 19 to be about 30 μV rms for a

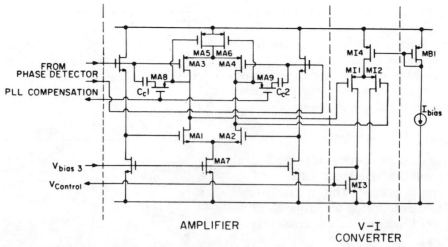

Fig. 15. Circuit schematic of the dc amplifier, voltage to current converter, and loop filter.

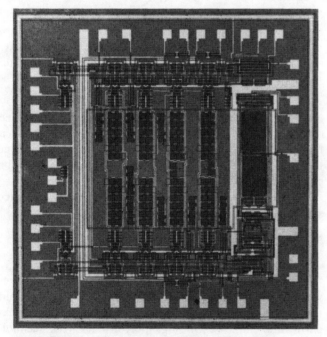

Fig. 16. Microphotograph of the experimental chip.

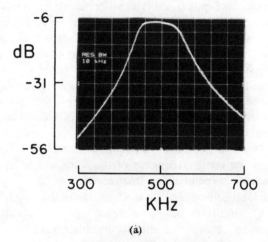

(a)

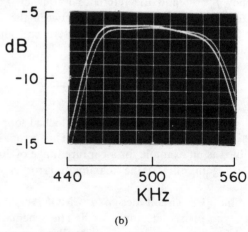

(b)

Fig. 17. (a) Overall frequency response of the prototype. (b) Detailed passband of two outputs of the filter.

bandwidth of 96 kHz. In order to compare the experimental noise to the theoretical noise, the prototype values of $C_{intg} = 38$ pF and $Q_{res} = 8$ is substituted in (20), which gives a total output noise of 50 μV rms. This is reasonably consistent with the experimental result as most of the noise power falls within the passband of the filter. The center frequency of the filter was controlled externally for the noise measurement. In Table I, the reference signal feedthrough at the output of the filter is given to be 100 μV rms which exceeds the output noise and degrades the dynamic range by 10 dB. The relatively high reference signal feedthrough is partly due to the fact that for debugging purposes some extra nodes were connected to bonding pads which increased the parasitic couplings. Another reason for this is due to some asymmetry in the filter layout. The

power supply rejection for both supplies is measured from Fig. 20(a) and Fig. 20(b) and is better than 35 dB. It is believed that a perfectly symmetrical layout and better component matching should improve both the power supply rejection and the reference signal feed-through.

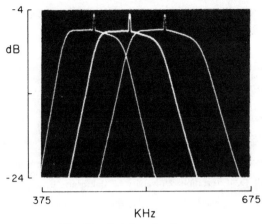

Fig. 18. PLL functionality test.

Center frequency	500KHz
-3dB bandwidth	96KHz
Total in-band noise	30μVrms
Reference signal feed-thru	100μVrms
Dynamic Range 1% intermodulation	60dB
Minimum PSRR (+V_{DD})	-35dB
Minimum PSRR (-V_{SS})	-38dB
Power dissipation	55mW

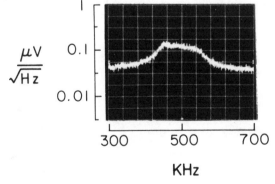

Fig. 19. Measured noise response of the filter.

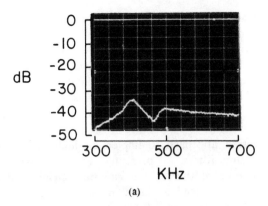

(a)

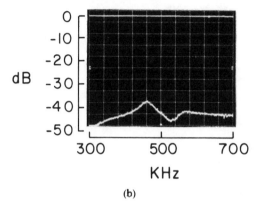

(b)

Fig. 20. (a) PSRR with respect to the positive supply. (b) PSRR for the negative supply.

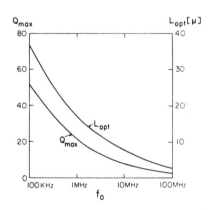

Fig. 21. The maximum achievable Q as a function of frequency. The optimum input transistor channel length for filters as a function of center frequency.

VI. CONCLUSION

To conclude, the capability of this technique in a scaled technology is projected. As was mentioned earlier, the Q of the integrator, due to phase error components, is process dependent and the error in the filter passband is propor-tional to $Q_{\text{filter}}/Q_{\text{intg}}$. A worst-case value for Q_{intg} for different center frequencies was found under the following conditions:

± 15 percent tolerance in process parameters (μ, λ)

1 μm uncertainty in polysilicon width.

Assuming 1 dB maximum error in filter passband and using the worst-case values of Q_{intg}, a maximum value for Q_{filter} as a function of center frequency is derived and sketched in Fig. 21. This figure shows a maximum Q of about 50 at the center frequency of 100 kHz and the maximum Q drops down to about 2.5 for 100 MHz. With the progress of processing technology (e.g., more accurate

IEEE JOURNAL OF SOLID-STATE CIRCUITS, VOL. SC-19, NO. 6, DECEMBER 1984

polysilicon etching), the maximum achievable Q can be improved.

The other curve shows the optimum input transistor channel length for different frequencies. From this curve it can be concluded that the implementation of filters with center frequencies up to 20 MHz can be realized in a 6 μm technology, and a 100 MHz filter requires a 3 μm technology.

A design approach to implement high-frequency continuous-time filters was presented. From the experimental performance of the filter it can be concluded that this technique is indeed a viable method for the implementation of high-frequency filters.

REFERENCES

[1] K. S. Tan and P. R. Gray, "Fully integrated analog filters using bipolar-JFET technology," *IEEE J. Solid-State Circuits*, vol. SC-13, pp. 814–821, Dec. 1978.

[2] M. Banu and Y. Tsividis, "Fully integrated active *RC* filters in MOS technology," *IEEE J. Solid-State Circuits*, vol. SC-18, pp. 644–651, Dec. 1983.

[3] T. C. Choi, R. T. Kaneshiro, R. W. Brodersen, P. R. Gray, W. B. Jett, and M. Wilcox, "High-frequency CMOS switched-capacitor filters for communication applications," *IEEE J. Solid-State Circuits*, vol. SC-18, pp. 652–664, Dec. 1983.

[4] S. Masuda, Y. Kitamura, S. Ohya, and M. Kikuchi, "CMOS sampled differential push–pull cascode operational amplifier," in *Proc. IEEE Int. Symp. Circuits Syst.*, May 1984, pp. 1211–1214.

[5] K. W. Moulding, J. R. Quartly, P. J. Rankin, R. S. Thompson, and G. A. Wilson, "Gyrator video filter IC with automatic tuning," *IEEE J. Solid-State Circuits*, vol. SC-15, pp. 963–968, Dec. 1980.

[6] J. R. Burns, "High frequency characteristics of the insulated gate field effect transistor," *RCA Rev.*, vol. 28, pp. 385, Sept. 1967.

[7] H. Khorramabadi, "High-frequency CMOS continuous time filters," Ph.D. dissertation, University of California, Berkeley, CA, to be published.

[8] H. J. Orchard, "Inductorless filters," *Electron. Lett.*, vol. 2, pp. 224–225, Sept. 1966.

[9] A. I. Zverev, *Handbook of Filter Synthesis.* New York: Wiley, 1967.

[10] F. M. Gardner, *Phaselock Techniques.* New York: Wiley, 1979.

[11] P. R. Gray and R. G. Meyer, *Analysis and Design of Analog Integrated Circuits.* New York: Wiley, 1984.

CMOS Triode Transconductor Continuous Time Filters

⋆JOHN PENNOCK, PETER FRITH, R. G. BARKER⋆⋆

WOLFSON MICROELECTRONICS LTD,
20 BERNARD TERRACE, EDINBURGH EH8 9NX

* now with Integrated Power Semiconductor Ltd, Livingston, Scotland.
** Admiralty Research Establishment, Portland, Dorset, U.K.

Abstract

A prototype 5th order Cauer CMOS continuous-time active integrated filter is described. It employs differential transconductance stages based on pairs of triode-mode MOSTs. The circuit occupies 2.2mm^2 and operates from a single 5V supply. Its cut-off frequency is programmable from 5 kHz to 90kHz by means of a single off-chip resistor. Such filters offer significant advantages over switched-capacitor filters, particularly in ease of design and systems compatibility.

Introduction

Silicon technology already delivers the cheapest and most compact active filters for large quantity requirements. The development of mask-programmable filters promises to extend this dominance to smaller volume markets, and future wafer commitment using electron beams could reduce production lead times to days. The active filter market is thus an important growth area for custom analog integrated circuits.

Almost all integrated filters to date have used switched-capacitor techniques [1]. These are by no means as ideal as sometimes claimed, largely because of the inherent sampled-data nature of such filters [2]. Considerable effort is now being expended world-wide to find better techniques for integrating filters in both MOS and bipolar technologies, principally various types of "continuous-time" filters [3-13]. Over the past two years we have developed what we consider to be a most promising approach in CMOS [14].

This approach uses voltage-controlled transconductance amplifiers ("transconductors") and on-chip capacitors. These emulate a doubly-terminated LC ladder with the required frequency response by defining time constants in a network of appropriate topology. Our transconductor design is based on a common-source pair of triode-mode MOSTs, operating with differential inputs and outputs. [15] In the remainder of this paper, we describe the detailed design of the transconductor, the filter network, the performance obtained and the advantages of this type of filter.

Basic Transconductor Principle

Fig 1 shows a pair of common-source n-channel MOS transistors. With a common drain-source bias Vds and input gate voltage Vgs0, the drain current through each transistor is given by the usual first-order equation:

$$Ids_{(Vgs0)} = k'(W/L)[(Vgs0-Vt)Vds-Vds^2/2] \quad (1)$$

Provided that Vgs0 is greater than Vds + Vt so that the transistor is in its linear or 'triode' region of operation,

If Vds remains constant while complementary signals +Vin/2 and -Vin/2 are superimposed on the quiescent gate biases Vgs0, as shown in Fig 1, a differential output current Iout is produced, where

$$Iout = Ids_{(Vgs0+Vin/2)} - Ids_{(Vgs0-Vin/2)} \quad (2)$$

$$= k'.(W/L).Vds.Vin \quad (3)$$

Thus a linear relationship is obtained between input gate voltage modulation Vin and resultant incremental drain current Iout.

The proportionality factor k'.(W/L).Vds includes the transistor gain factor k', the aspect ratio W/L of the transistor, and the bias voltage Vds. This bias voltage can be adjusted to obtain the desired transconductance despite thermal variation of k' and manufacturing tolerances of both k' and W/L. According to the simple equation (1), even a single triode mode transistor would give a linear transfer function. However, in practice a substantial second harmonic distortion is observed, caused by a variation of k' with Vgs (ascribed to mobility degradation by high transverse fields at the SiO2 interface). The symmetry of the differential circuit cancels the second and other even-order harmonic distortion output components, so the dominant distortion component is third harmonic.

Complete Transconductor

Fig 2 is a circuit diagram of the complete transconductor. This transconductor has two pairs of inputs, connected to transistors m1a, m2a and m1b, m2b. The buffer stages m3, m4, m5, m6 m7, and m8, fix the drain-source bias Vds of m1 and m2 and deliver the output currents at a high output impedance, so that the circuit operates as a good linear voltage-controlled current source. Cross-coupled feed-forward capacitors, CC1, CC2, CC3, CC4, compensate for the phase delay of the input and buffer devices.

The bias conditions are defined as follows: Devices m1x and m3x generate a reference current Iref, equal to that of one input device with its input at the desired mid-rail CM (common mode) output voltage. This is replicated by the current sources i1 to i8. Triode-mode devices m11 and m12 generate a total current dependent on the CM component of output voltage; this is reflected and amplified through current mirrors m15, m16, m17 and m20, m21, m22, to give equal currents through m23, m24 to the output nodes, and hence stabilise the CM output voltage.

Device mismatches may cause the CM output voltage to be offset from zero. This CM offset will be applied to the input terminals of following transconductors in the network. The triode transconductor has the advantage over MOS resistor schemes [3] in that the DM transconductance is only affected to second order by CM input voltage perturbations. The CM output current resulting from a DM (differential mode) input (i.e. DM-to-CM transconductance) is also only a second order effect. The low CM output impedance further reduces the DM-to-CM voltage conversion.

The simulated performance of this circuit is summarised in Table 1.

Reprinted from *IEEE CICC*, pp. 378–381, 1986.

Transconductance Stabilisation Loop

Transistor transconductance and filter cut-off frequency may be stabilised against temperature variations and process tolerances using a master-slave control loop, as mentioned earlier. For simplicity we chose to use a control circuit that references the transconductor transconductance (G) to an external resistor Rref. To compensate for small variations in the fabricated sheet capacitance and nominal transconductance, this single resistor is adjusted on test to set an accurate filter cut-off frequency; the low temperature coefficient of the integrated capacitors renders further adjustment with temperature unnecessary. An alternative control technique uses a phase locked loop (PLL) with a clock input replacing the reference voltage [13].

Fig 3 shows the circuit adopted. A voltage Vss/8 is applied across the inputs of master transconductor Gcell. (In this figure, ground is taken to be midrail between Vdd and Vss.) This transconductor is situated in close proximity to the filter slave transconductors comprising the filter network, and is identical to them except for a modified output stage incorporating differential to single-sided conversion. Its output current is thus 2.G.(Vss/8). The external resistor Rref is chosen such that this output current should develop a voltage equal to Vss across it, i.e., 2.G.(Vss/8). Rref = Vss. Any deviation in this voltage is detected by error amplifier A, whose output drives the bias line VB controlling the transconductance of transconductor GcellJcon to close the loop. The loop is stabilised by capacitor Ccon. The bias line VB is also distributed to the slave transconductors, to stabilise their transconductances to the same value.

Design of Integrated Filter

Fig 4 is a circuit diagram of a 5th order 0.18 dB Cauer low pass filter designed and fabricated using these transconductors. The network is derived from a doubly-terminated LC ladder prototype (CO520, Q = 30), in a similar way to the approximate method used in switched-capacitor ladder filters [1], but using transconductors driving load capacitors in place of switched-capacitor integrators. All transconductors have the same transconductance and are identical for good matching. Thus the shape of the frequency response is set by ratios of the capacitors, which can be set accurately and reproducibly by suitable layout techniques. Sensitivity to residual manufacturing variations is low, since the node capacitances correspond to L and C values of the prototype LC ladder.

Stray capacitance to ground from the top plates of the grounded capacitors arise from the input and output capacitances of the transconductors, from capacitance from the interconnect metallisation to substrate, and from capacitances from the top and bottom plates of floating capacitors to ground. These parasitics appear directly in parallel with the intended plate-to-plate capacitance, and have to be calculated and compensated for by adjustment of the capacitor values to obtain the desired frequency response. However, such strays are typically only a few per cent of the total effective capacitance on each node, so a small error in this correction will have minimal effect on filter response. This contrasts with the case of switched-capacitor filters, where the input switched capacitors are usually smaller than the switch and amplifier input capacitances, demanding the adoption of "parasitic-insensitive" techniques.

The load capacitance on each transconductor output is implemented by a combination of floating and grounded capacitance. The use of fully-floating capacitors can reduce the total capacitor area for a given circuit impedance by factor of four [4]. However, to ensure high-frequency common-mode stability, some grounded capacitance is necessary. In this first design, the total capacitor area was halved compared to a fully-grounded design.

Fig 5 is a microphotograph of the fabricated filter. The transconductors are distributed around a central routing channel. The input devices are placed as close as possible together next to the routing channel to optimise matching. The capacitors are placed outside the transconductors, in two banks. The capacitors of one bank correspond to the inductors of the prototype filter, those of the other bank to the capacitors, so that any consistent trend in sheet capacitance variation between the two blocks will result only in a slight shift in cut-off frequency rather than increased ripple.

Experimental Performance Characteristics

Figures 6 to 9 summarise results obtained from the first tested device. The response at the nominal 28kHz cut-off frequency shown in Figs 6 and 7 agrees closely with the theoretical 0.18dB passband ripple and 61.4dB stopband attenuation.

Simply by adjusting the control voltage VB (through changing Rref), the 3dB cut off-frequency can be varied from 5 to 90kHz before being limited by quiescent bias constraints. In the high frequency extreme there is about 0.2dB extra peaking at the passband edge, at the low-frequency extreme the first passband minimum is accentuated by 0.1dB. The small size of these deviations demonstrates the effectiveness of the phase neutralisation in reducing excess phase effects.

Fig 8 shows a plot of relative second and third harmonic distortion components against output signal amplitude at the worst-case frequency (10kHz) for a 28kHz filter. At low signal levels the distortion is dominated by the second harmonic, presently thought to be due to both device mismatches and test-board imperfections. The third harmonic increases at the expected 12dB/octave, being 64dB down at an output level of 2V peak-peak (-3dBV).

Fig 9 shows the spectral dependence of the output noise. This is dominated by the 1/f noise of the n-channel devices and peaks near the passband edge. The total noise integrated over the passband is 0.34mVrms, which gives a dynamic range of 69.4dB with respect to 1Vrms

Discussion

Compared to switched-capacitor filters, continuous-time filters have the following advantages:

(i) No aliasing of input or imaging of output signals: This simplifies the interface to unsampled systems, by removing the need for anti-aliasing prefilters and smoothing post-filters; sampled-data systems can include c-t filter blocks without clock-synchronisation problems.

(ii) No aliasing of high-frequency power supply or amplifier noise: In SC filters, the op amp PSRR reduces with frequency allowing high-frequency components of power supply ripple (e.g. from switching regulators) to be aliased down to baseband with little attenuation. Similarly the h.f. noise from wideband op amp output stages is aliased down to baseband. Such effects are particularly significant in the electrically noisy environment of combined analogue-digital chips.

(iii) Circuit simplicity: SC filters require the generation of multi-phase complementary clock wave-forms and their distribution to switches. This complicates the interconnect net, and constrains layout.

(iv) Simplicity of circuit synthesis: Conventional active filter methods can be used to obtain component values, rather than the complex sampled data algorithms required for accurate design of SC filters.

(v) Computer simulation: The complete circuit can be (and was!) simulated using SPICE down to the transistor level, to include the effects of all parasitics. Together with automated circuit extraction programmes, this allows a full CAD loop to be established between the circuit laid out and the desired performance specification. This is impossible with SC filters, even using special purpose simulators and with manual intervention to incorporate foreseen second order effects. This is perhaps the most significant advantage for custom integrated filters, where the risk of first-pass design malfunction and consequent re-design iterations must be minimised to provide an economic and credible customer interface.

The major disadvantages of c-t filters are the requirement for an on-chip control loop, and the residual distortion levels for large signals. The on-chip control loop is not a significant overhead for complex filters. Further advances can be expected in reducing the distortion levels as more experience is obtained with these circuits: certainly the performance obtained in this first-pass design could be improved by better common-mode control. Finally, the accuracy of the frequency response is affected by mismatching between transconductors in addition to errors in capacitor ratios: however the sensitivity of the response to such mismatches is low, and this problem is balanced by the absence of comparable SC filter problems such as finite SC integrator settling times.

In summary, we feel that the triode transconductor offers a most promising approach to integrated filter design. Synthesis, design and complete simulation of such filters is straightforward. The number of distortion sources is minimised, since Vbs (body effect voltage) and Vds are held constant. The common-mode output components are small, and sensitivity to common-mode inputs low. The circuit fits neatly into a single 5V supply rail. Its fully-differential architecture is an advantage rather than disadvantage in noisy environments such as combined A/D chips. The experimental results obtained, even from this first device, confirm our feelings. We confidently expect such filters to be included in the next generation of combined A/D integrated systems in 5V CMOS technology.

Acknowledgement

Much of our work in this field has been carried out with the support of the Procurement Executive, Ministry of Defence (UK).

Table 1. Transconductor performance

G_m/G_o	940
Output voltage swing	$\pm$ 0.9V
Input voltage swing	$\pm$ 1.05V
Nominal transconductance	8.5uA/V
Power dissipation	1mW

Fig1. Transconductor Principle

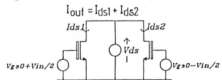

$$I_{out} = I_{ds1} + I_{ds2}$$

Fig 2. Transconductor Circuit Diagram

Fig3. Control Circuit

Fig 4. Circuit Diagram Of Fifth Order Filter

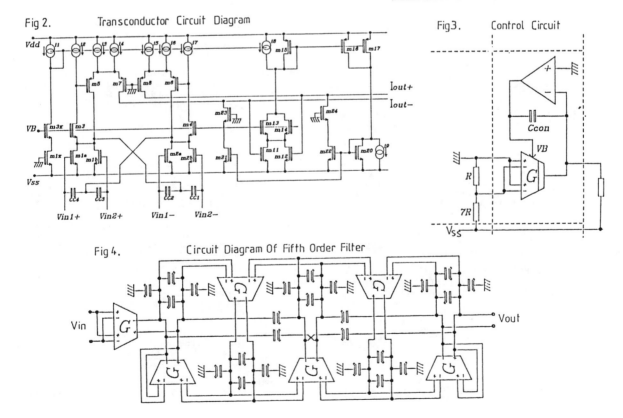

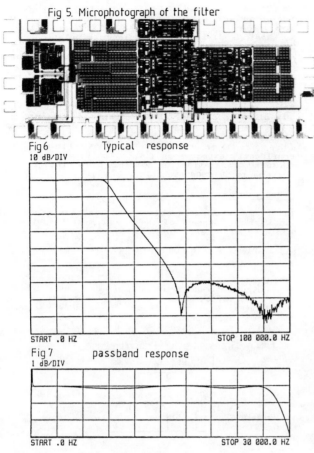

Fig 5. Microphotograph of the filter

Fig 6   Typical   response
10 dB/DIV

START .0 HZ   STOP 100 000.0 HZ

Fig 7   passband response
1 dB/DIV

START .0 HZ   STOP 30 000.0 HZ

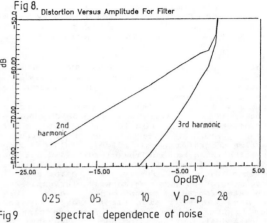

Fig 8. Distortion Versus Amplitude For Filter

2nd harmonic   3rd harmonic

OpdBV
−25.00   −15.00   −5.00   5.00

0·25   0·5   1·0   V p−p   2·8

Fig 9   spectral dependence of noise

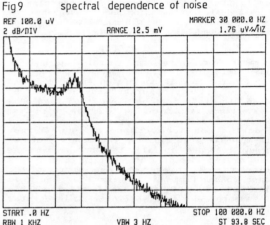

REF 100.0 uV   MARKER 30 000.0 HZ
2 dB/DIV   RANGE 12.5 mV   1.76 uV/√HZ

START .0 HZ   STOP 100 000.0 HZ
RBW 1 KHZ   VBW 3 HZ   ST 93.8 SEC

References

[1] Brodersen, R. W., P. R. Gray, and D. R. Hodges, "MOS switched capacitor filters," Proc. IEEE vol. 67, pp. 61-75, 1979.

[2] Tsividis, Y., and P. Antognetti (eds), "Continious-time filters," in Design of MOS VLSI circuits for telecommunications, p.p. 334-371, Prentice-Hall, N.J., 1985

[3] Banu, M. and Y. Tsividis, "Fully integrated active RC filters in MOS technology," IEEE J Solid State Circuits, vol. SC-18, pp. 644-651, Dec. 1983.

[4] Khorramabadi, H. and P.R. Gray, "High Frequency CMOS continuous-time filters," in Proc Int. Symp. Circuits Syst, vol. CAS- 31, pp. 891-894, 1984.

[5] Fukahori, K., "A bipolar voltage-controlled tunable filter," IEEE J. Solid State Circuits vol. SC-16, pp. 729-737, 1981.

[6] Voorman, J. O., W. H. A. Bruls, and P. J. Barth, "Integration of analog filters in a bipolar process," IEEE J. Solid State Circuits, vol. SC-17, pp. 713-722, Aug. 1982.

[7] Brinker, C.S. Den, W. Gosling, "The development of the voltage-to-current transactor (VCT)," Microelectron (GB), vol. 8, pp. 9-18, 1977.

[8] Nedungadi, A. and T. R. Viswantathan, "Design of linear transconductance elements," IEEE Trans. Circuits Syst, vol. CAS- 31, pp. 891-894, 1984.

[9] Troster,G. and W. Langheinrich, "Monolithic continuous-time analogue filters in MOS technology," in Proc Int Symp Circuits Symp, pp. 924-927, May 1984.

[10] Moulding, K.W. and G.A. Wilson, "A fully-integrated five gyrator filter at video frequencies, "IEEE J. Solid State Circuits, vol. SC-13, pp. 303-307, 1978

[11] Parpia, Z., C. A. T. Salama, G. C. Salter, and W. A. Cole, "Micropower monolithic filters using bipolar/JFET technology," in Proc. Int. Symp. Circuits Syst. (ISCAS), pp. 385-389, 1983.

[12] Moulding, K. W., J. R. Quartly, P. J. Rankin, R. S. Thompson, and G. A. Wilson, "Gyrator Video Filter IC with automatic tuning," IEEE J. Solid State Circuits, vol. SC-15, pp. 963-968, Dec 1980.

[13] Tan, K.S. and P.R. Gray, "Fully integrated analog filters using bipolar-JFET technology," IEE J. Solid State Circuits vol SC-13, pp 814-821, 1978.

[14] Pennock, J. L., "CMOS triode transconductor for continuous-time active integrated filters," Electron Lett., vol. 21, pp. 817-818, 29th August 1985.

[15] Pennock, J.L., "Transconductor circuit" UK provisional patent No. 8513329, May 28th 1985.

Paper 3-B.3

8-32MHz Tunable BiCMOS Continuous-Time Filter

R. ALINI, A. BASCHIROTTO, AND R. CASTELLO

UNIVERSITY OF PAVIA, DEPARTMENT OF ELECTRONICS

VIA ABBIATEGRASSO, 209-27100 PAVIA, ITALY

Abstract—A new transconductor stage in BiCMOS technology is presented. The main characteristics of the stage are: high linearity of operation, non-dominant poles in the range of gigahertzs, low noise and operation from a single 5V power supply. A 2nd-order lowpass filter cell based on this transconductor has been designed and realized in a 2μm BiCMOS technology. The cutoff frequency f_0 of the cell can be tuned in the range of 8-32MHz; the quality factor is 2. The filter THD stays lower than 40dB for an output signal up to 3.2Vpp at 5MHz frequency. The area of the cell is 500 mils^2 and the power consumption (with f_O = 25MHz) is 30mW.

I. INTRODUCTION

SEVERAL techniques have been proposed to realize Continuous-Time monolithic filters [1–7]. For high frequency the transconductance-C approach seems to be the most suitable. This is because, in a transconductance-C filter the key operation of voltage-to-current conversion is performed in an open-loop way. On the contrary in other approaches like the MOSFET-C a closed-loop operational amplifier that realizes a virtual ground is used. As a consequence the non-dominant pole of the voltage-to-current converter in a transconductance-C filter is not limited by the unity gain frequency of an operational amplifier while this is the case for a MOSFET-C filter. A higher frequency non-dominant pole for the transconductor is a key advantage since Continuous-Time filters are quite sensitive to excess phase errors especially if high selectivity is required. The main disadvantage of transconductance-C filters is their sensitivity to parasitic capacitances, which is a consequence of their open loop operation.

In this paper a BiCMOS transconductance-C filter for high frequency applications is reported. The filter is based on a new differential transconductor stage which uses MOS devices operating in the

triode region to give a linear voltage-to-current conversion. Very wide band operation is obtained by using only a signal high frequency n-p-n bipolar transistor (f_T = 7GHz) in the signal path between the input MOS transistor and the output node. Experimental data for a lowpass biquad cell with $Q = 2$ and cut-off frequency tunable in the range 8-32MHz is given.

II. THE BiCMOS TRANSCONDUCTOR STAGE

Key target specs for a transconductor with several MHz unity gain frequency are a moderate power consumption, good linearity for large voltage swings, small excess of noise compared with an equivalent passive realization, and small phase errors due to high frequency nonidealities.

A simplified schematic of the BiCMOS differential transconductor is shown in Fig. 1. The two input devices M1 and M2 are biased in the linear region of operation and determine the transconductance of the stage. The value of the battery E (typically from less than 100mV to several hundred millivolts) determines the drain-source voltage of M1 and M2 in quiescent conditions. Since M1 and M2 operate in the linear region, the following relationship holds:

$$g_m = \frac{\partial I_{out}}{\partial V_{in}} = \left(\frac{I_O}{(V_{GS} - V_T)_O}\right) = \mu C_{OX}\frac{W}{L}V_{DS} \tag{1}$$

where I_O is the current in each MOS device.

For a given g_m the $V_{GS} - V_T$ of the input pair (M1,M2) determines the value of the tail current source I_O and therefore the transconductor power dissipation. A small $V_{GS} - V_T$ is therefore desirable from this point of view. On the other hand, the input

Reprinted from *Digest ESSCIRC'91*, pp. 9–12, 1991.

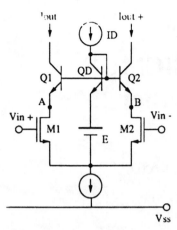

Fig. 1.   Basic BiCMOS transconductor.

voltage swing over which the circuit behaves linearly increases as the $V_{GS} - V_T$ of M1,M2 increases.

Taking into account all possible variations in the circuit operating conditions, the maximum value for the V_{DS} of M1,M2 can be obtained. From this the minimum $V_{GS} - V_T$ for the input transistors that gives the required linearity and swing is derived. The sum of the required $V_{GS} - V_T$ for M1 (M2), the maximum nMOS threshold and the required voltage for proper operation of the current source gives the minimum common mode input voltage.

III. STAGE NON-IDEALITIES

A complete scheme of the new $V - I$ converter is shown in Fig. 2. It includes the CMFB circuit (M3 and M4) and the loads realized with degenerated p-n-p current sources (Q3, Q4, R3, R4). Furthermore, the battery E is realized with the diode connected transistor QD and the resistance RD. Referring to eq. (1) if μ and V_{DS} are constant and bias-independent, there is a perfectly linear relation between I_{out} and V_{in}. Actually, as the current through bipolar device Q1 (Q2) changes, the voltage at node A (B) changes as well. This produces a change in the V_{DS} of the input devices which in turn causes a non-linear relation between I_{out} and V_{in}. To minimize the impedance at node A (B) while maintaining high speed of operation, bipolar transistors Q1 (Q2) are used as cascode devices.

A second cause of non-linearity in the $V - I$ characteristic is the dependency of the carrier mobility μ on the $(V_{GS} - V_T)$ of the input devices. On simulations, these two effects give a 0.3% THD for a 2.4V_{pp} input signal assuming 2% mismatch in the input transistors.

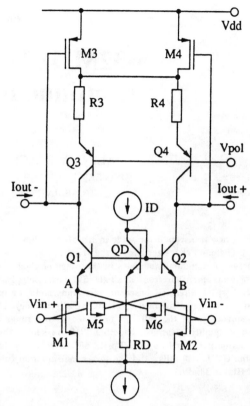

Fig. 2.   Complete transconductor scheme.

Another cause of non-ideal behaviour in a transconductor is its finite speed of response which causes excess phase error. The two main sources of phase error for the proposed transconductor are the transit-time in the input devices and the pole associated with common-base device Q1 (Q2). Both effects give rise to equivalent non-dominant poles above 1.5 GHz. One more cause of phase error is the feedforward path around M1 (M2) through the gate-to-drain parasitic capacitance. However, by connecting two dummy devices M5, M6 of area equal to 1/2 of that of M1 (M2) as shown in Fig. 2, a precise cancellation of the feedforward signal occurs.

The gain of the circuit for typical values of the transistor parameters and a voltage drop of 400mV across R3 (R4) is approximately 250 (about 48dB).

The dominant noise contribution is due to the input devices and to the load current sources. The total input referred noise can be written as follows:

$$V_n^2 = \left\{ 2\left[\frac{8}{3} \frac{kT}{g_m} \left(1 + \frac{1}{(g_m r_{ds})M1} \right) \right] \right\}_{input}$$
$$+ \left\{ 2\left[\frac{4kT}{g_m} \frac{V_{GS} - V_T}{\Delta V_R} \right] \right\}_{load} \qquad (2)$$

where ΔV_R is the dc voltage drop across R3, R4. From eq. (2) the load contribution can be reduced by increasing ΔV_R. A relatively small value of ΔV_R is, however, necessary to guarantee a sufficiently large output swing. Assuming a worst case supply voltage of 4.5V a typical ΔV_R of 400mV is chosen. In this case for $(V_{GS} - V_T) = 900$mV and V_{DS} that varies in the range 150mV $\div$ 450mV a total input noise in the range $13\frac{8kT}{3g_m} \div 21\frac{8kT}{3g_m}$ is obtained.

The offset of the stage is that of the input pair M1 and M2 plus that of Q1 and Q2 amplified by the ratio between the $(V_{GS} - V_T)$ and the V_{DS} of M1 (M2) plus that of Q3 and Q4 amplified by the ratio between the $(V_{GS} - V_T)$ of M1 (M2) and the voltage drop across R3 (R4). Since bipolar devices exhibit much less offset than MOS devices, the offset is dominated by M1 and M2.

The required area for a given g_m is small since the structure is very simple and M1 and M2 operate with large $V_{GS} - V_T$.

The main requirements of the Common Mode Feedback (CMFB) circuit are speed of operation and linearity. Linearity is achieved thanks to the large $(V_{GS} - V_T)$ of M3 and M4. The CMFB bandwidth is larger than the integrator unity gain bandwidth. This is due to the g_m of M3 and M4 that is only slightly smaller than that of the input devices and to the Common Mode capacitance.

IV. FILTER DESIGN

As an example of application of the proposed transconductor, a second-order (biquadratic cell) lowpass filter has been designed. The quality factor of this filter is 2 and the cut-off frequency f_0 can be tuned in the range 8-32MHz. The schematic of the filter is shown in Fig. 3.

The relative transconductance values are $g_{m1} = 2g_{m2}$. The total differential load capacitors have a nominal value of $C_T = 2.3$pF. The parasitic capaci-

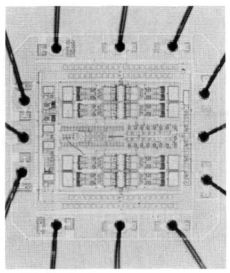

Fig. 4. Chip photograph.

tances C_P at the high-impedance output nodes of the transconductors have to be taken into account. These parasitic capacitances (about 1.1pF differential) are due to the junction capacitances of the bipolar transistor (C_{BC} and C_{CS}) and to the oxide capacitance of the MOS transistor in the CMFB stage and in the following input stage. These result in a reduced integrated capacitance $C_{1,2} = C_T - C_P$.

From eq. (1) it can be seen that the transconductance of the stage is a function of V_{DS}, i.e., of the current I_D across RD. For this reason a possible tuning strategy is to change I_D in order to obtained the desired value of $\omega_0 = g_m/C$ for all technological parameter variations. To maintain the linearity of the stage a constant value of $V_{GS} - V_T$ is required. This is obtained by changing also $I_{M1,M2}$ as I_D is changed.

V. EXPERIMENTAL RESULTS

The circuit has been integrated in a $2\mu m$ BiCMOS technology from SGS-Thomson Microelectronics

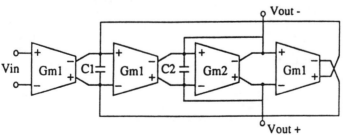

Fig. 3. Filter structure.

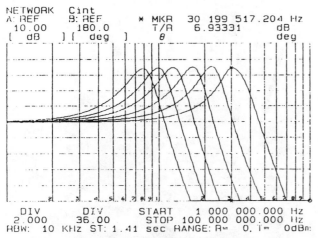

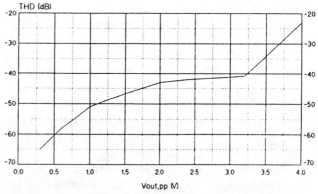

Fig. 6. Measured THD-vs-Vout @ 5MHz with $f_O = 25$MHz.

Fig. 5. Measured amplitude filter performance with tuning range.

(HF2CMOS). In the chip two identical biquad cells have been layed out to test the matching properties of the technology. The photograph of the chip is shown in Fig. 4. The area of one cell is 500 mils^2 and the power consumption (with $f_0 = 25$MHz) is 30mW with 5V power supply. The amplitude performance of the filter is shown in Fig. 5. The cut-off frequency is tuned (changing the bias current) in the range 8-32MHz with a slight (< 0.2dB) variation of the peak value. The Total Harmonic Distortion at the output as a function of differential signal amplitude at 5MHz is shown in Fig. 6 (with $f_0 = 25$MHz). The THD stays below -40dB up to 3.2 Vpp. The integrated output noise in the band $1 - 30$MHz is 200μV rms. It results in a dynamic range of 75dB (THD < -40dB).

VI. ACKNOWLEDGMENTS

This research has been developed in collaboration with SGS-Thomson Microelectronics. In particular the authors wish to acknowledge Dr. M. Zuffada and his group at SGS-Thomson Microelectronics for useful discussion and for supporting the lay-out. The authors wish to acknowledge also Prof. F. Montecchi (University of Pavia) for suggestions.

TABLE I-MEASURED PERFORMANCE CHARACTERISTICS
(5V POWER SUPPLY, 25° TEMPERATURE, 2 μm BICMOS TECHNOLOGY)

Power Consumption (@ fo=25MHz)	30mW
Active Area	500 mils^2
THD (3.2Vpp @5MHz)	-40dB
THD (1.2Vpp @5MHz)	-49dB
Integrated Output Noise (1-30MHz)	200μVrms
Dinamic range (THD<-40dB, @5MHz)	75dB
Tuning Range (peak variation<0.2dB)	8-32 MHz
Q Relative Maximum Deviation	5%

References

[1] Krummenacher and N. Joehl, "A 4-MHz CMOS Continuous-Time Filter With On-Chip Automatic Tuning," *IEEE J. Solid State Circuits*, 1988, SC-23, pp. 750–758.

[2] C. S. Park and R. Schaumann, "Design of a 4 MHz Analog Integrated CMOS Transconductance-C Bandpass Filter," *IEEE J. Solid State Circuits*, 1988, SC-23, pp. 987–996.

[3] Y. T. Wang, F. Lu, A. A. Abidi, "A 12.5 MHz CMOS Continuous-Time Bandpass Filter," Proc. of *Int. Solid State Circ. Conf.*, 1989, pp. 198–199.

[4] M. Banu and Y. Tsividis, "Fully Integrated Active RC Filters in MOS Technology," *IEEE J. Solid State Circuits*, 1983, SC-18, pp. 644–651.

[5] H. Khorramabadi and P. R. Gray, "High-Frequency CMOS Continuous-Time Filters," *IEEE J. of Solid-State Circuits*, 1984, SC-19, pp. 939–948.

[6] R. Castello, F. Montecchi, R. Alini, and A. Baschirotto, "A Very Linear BiCMOS Transconductor for High-Frequency Filtering Applications," IEEE ISCAS, New Orleans, 1990, pp. 1364–1367.

[7] J. L. Pennock, "CMOS Triode Transconductor for Continuous-Time Active Integrated Filters," *Electronics Letters*, 1985, Vol. 21, No. 18, pp. 817–818.

A Micropower CMOS Continuous-Time Low-Pass Filter

ANDREAS KAISER, MEMBER, IEEE

Abstract — A continuous-time third-order Butterworth low-pass filter with a nominal cutoff frequency of 945 Hz has been implemented in a standard 2.4-μm CMOS process. The filter is built from fully balanced linearized transconductors and capacitors. The power consumption of the filter, including bias and automatic-tuning circuits, is 12.6 μW from a single 3-V power supply. It achieves a dynamic range of 63 dB with a THD of less than 0.5 percent. The total chip area is 1 mm².

I. INTRODUCTION

IN THE PAST, micropower CMOS switched-capacitor filters in the audiofrequency range have been designed and employed successfully [1], [2]. However, for some applications SC filters are not well-suited, i.e., if strong high-frequency components are present at the input, as they would require costly analog pre- and post-filtering. Continuous-time filters, performing the required filter function directly without sampling of the input signal, could replace SC filters advantageously in those applications. This paper describes the design of such a micropower CMOS continuous-time filter, that realizes a third-order Butterworth low-pass transfer function with a nominal cutoff frequency of 945 Hz.

Low-power operation requires simple circuitry having only a small number of branches conducting current. A detailed discussion of specific design techniques can be found in [3]. Multistage amplifiers as required in active *RC* filters are not practical. The filter described here is built from transconductors and capacitors. The transconductors employ MOS transistors operated in the nonsaturation region as resistor equivalents. The fully balanced operation of the filter eliminates all even-order harmonic distortion components, and particularly the strong second-order harmonic distortion due to the nonlinearities of the MOS resistor equivalents [4]. For applications in battery-powered systems the circuit must also be able to operate from a single 3-V power supply while having large signal-handling capability. This requires careful optimization of the transistor sizes in order to reduce as much as possible the saturation voltages of the transistors, and special attention must be paid to the design of precise bias circuits.

Manuscript received September 20, 1988; revised January 16, 1989.
The author is with the Département Electronique, Institut Supérieur d'Electronique du Nord (ISEN), F-59046 Lille Cedex, France.
IEEE Log Number 8926937.

II. BASIC TRANSCONDUCTOR

A. Principle of Operation

The basic circuit diagram of the transconductor and its associated bias circuit is depicted in Fig. 1. It is composed of a voltage-to-current converter [5] (upper part) and a load circuit with a common-mode feedback loop [6]. Transistor $M2$ is operated in the nonsaturation region and works as a voltage-controlled resistor. The gate of $M2$ is the control terminal. The small-signal drain–source conductance of $M2$ is given by

$$g_{d_2} = K_2(V_c - V_{T2} - V_Q) \tag{1}$$

$$V_Q = V_{D2} = V_{S2} = V_{CM} - V_{GS1} \tag{2}$$

where K_2 is defined by

$$K_2 = \mu_p C_{ox}(W/L)_2. \tag{3}$$

V_{T2} is the effective threshold voltage of $M2$, V_C is the control voltage applied to the gate of $M2$, and V_Q is the quiescent potential at both the source and drain of $M2$. All other symbols have their usual meanings. In large-signal operation the drain–source conductance of $M2$ is strongly nonlinear due to the dependence of I_{D2} on the square of V_{DS2}. As shown in [5], fully balanced operation of the circuit cancels the second-order nonlinearities of $M2$ as long as $M2$ stays in the nonsaturation region. Fully balanced operation requires input and output voltages to be exactly symmetric with respect to the common-mode reference voltage $V_{CM\,REF}$. This is achieved by a common-mode feedback loop in the load circuit described below, that forces the common-mode voltage V_{CM} at the transconductor output to $V_{CM\,REF}$.

The transistors $M1A$ and $M1B$ form a differential pair, that is degenerated by transistor $M2$. Transistors $M3A$ and $M3B$ provide identical bias currents to $M1A$ and $M1B$. No bias current is flowing through $M2$, and thus no extra voltage drop due to the degeneration of the differential pair occurs. This is an important feature for low-voltage operation. Neglecting the drain conductance of $M3A$ and $M3B$, the small-signal transconductance for this circuit is

Reprinted from *IEEE J. Solid-State Circuits*, vol. SC-24, no. 3, pp. 736–743, June 1989.

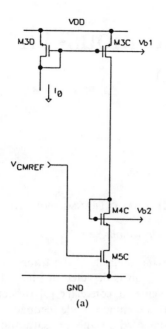

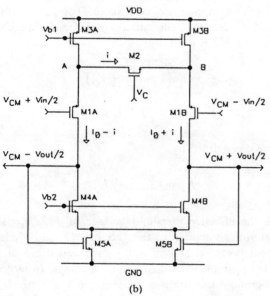

Fig. 1.   (a) Bias circuit. (b) Basic transconductor.

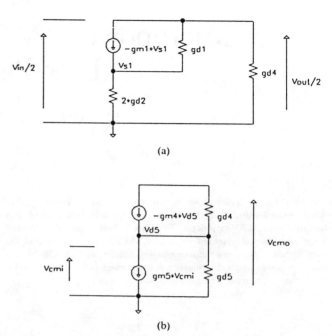

Fig. 2.   (a) Differential-mode half-circuit of the basic transconductor. (b) Common-mode half-circuit for calculation of CMFB-loop gain.

given by

$$G_m = i/V_{\text{in}} = \frac{1}{2/g_{m_1} + 1/g_{d_2}} \qquad (4)$$

where

$$g_{m_1} = \sqrt{2K_1 I_0} \qquad (5)$$

and

$$K_1 = \mu_p C_{ox} (W/L)_1. \qquad (6)$$

I_0 is the value of the drain currents of $M3A$ and $M3B$, and g_{d_2} has been defined in (1). Thus, the total transconductance is determined by the control voltage V_C, the bias current I_0, the geometries of $M1A$, $M1B$, and $M2$, and the input common-mode voltage V_{CM}. For audiofrequency

filters, the typical value of the transconductance will be on the order of 0.1 μA/V. This requires a very low W/L for transistor $M2$. For this reason the voltage-to-current converter was implemented with PMOS transistors, as they provide a lower transconductance than NMOS transistors for identical magnitude of the terminal voltages. All PMOS transistors of the voltage-to-current converter share the same n-well. The transconductance G_m may be tuned to a given value by applying the appropriate control voltage to the gate of $M2$. The minimum value of V_C is ground, and the maximum value of V_C is determined by the minimum allowable source-to-gate voltage of $M2$.

The load circuit is composed of transistors $M4A$, $M4B$, $M5A$, and $M5B$. Transistors $M4A$ and $M4B$ must be long-channel devices to provide high differential-mode output impedance. Transistors $M5A$ and $M5B$, operated in the nonsaturation region, sense the common-mode component of the output voltage. This common-mode component is then amplified through transistors $M4A$ and $M4B$. The bias circuit for the common-mode feedback (CMFB) loop is shown in Fig. 1(a). The CMFB loop fixes the common-mode output voltage of the transconductor at the common-mode reference voltage $V_{CM\,\text{REF}}$ applied to the gate of transistor $5C$ in the bias circuit. The differential output voltage of the transconductor is therefore exactly symmetric with respect to $V_{CM\,\text{REF}}$.

B. Small-Signal Analysis

Half-circuit concepts can be used to calculate the differential-mode dc gain of the transconductor and the open-loop dc gain of the CMFB loop. The small-signal differential- and common-mode half-circuits used for these calculations are depicted in Fig. 2(a) and (b), respectively. It can easily be shown that the differential-mode output conductance of the transconductor is

$$G_0 = g_{d_2} \cdot g_{d_1}/g_{m_1} + g_{d_4}/2. \tag{7}$$

The differential dc gain of the transconductor is

$$A_{DM} = G_m/G_0. \tag{8}$$

The finite dc gain of the transconductor causes phase lead in the integrators and modifies the expected filter transfer function. As the transconductance G_m is very low, and the low supply voltage does not allow the use of cascode transistors to boost the output impedance, the value of the dc gain will be typically on the order of 100. The pole frequency of the integrator is then located at a few hertz. Computer simulations did not indicate any serious degradation of the filter characteristics due to the low dc gain.

The common-mode output impedance of the voltage-to-current converter is very high and can be neglected. Therefore, the common-mode output impedance is simply

$$G_{0_{CM}} = g_{d_5} \cdot g_{d_4}/g_{m_4}. \tag{9}$$

The open-loop gain of the common-mode feedback amplifier is then given by

$$A_{CMFB} = g_{m_5} \cdot g_{m_4}/(g_{m_4} + g_{d_5}) \cdot g_{m_4}/(g_{d_4} \cdot g_{d_5}) \tag{10}$$

and the unity-gain bandwidth is given by

$$F_{u_{CMFB}} = \left(g_{m_5} \cdot g_{m_4}/(g_{m_4} + g_{d_5}) \right)/(2\pi \cdot C_p) \tag{11}$$

where C_p is the total capacitance to ground at the output of the transconductor. Offsets in the common-mode output voltage affect matching of the transconductors. The dc gain of the CMFB amplifier should be at least 20 dB to achieve reasonable accuracy, and the unity-gain bandwidth of the CMFB loop should be higher than the bandwidth of the filter.

C. Amplitude Limitations

The output of the transconductor is taken directly on the drains of $M1A$ and $M1B$. The input and output common-mode voltages of the transconductor must be identical to allow direct interconnection without any additional circuitry. As the input and output signal may be of opposite phase, the maximum allowable signal amplitude on any one of the input and output nodes is half the effective threshold voltage of $M1A$ and $M1B$, which results in a maximum allowable differential signal amplitude of $|V_{T1}|$. Higher signal amplitudes push $M1A$ and $M1B$ out of saturation and cause high distortion. A typical CMOS process will allow a differential signal amplitude of about 1 V under worst-case conditions.

D. Offset, Noise, and Distortion

Differential offset is of some concern due to the particular topology of the transconductor. The main offset sources are not the transistors of the input-differential pair, but the split current source $M3A/M3B$ and the transistors $M4A$ and $M4B$ of the load circuit. The differential drain-current offset δI_0 of $M3A/M3B$ can be as high as 10 percent of the nominal drain current, a typical value being $I_0/20$. This current offset creates an input-referred offset voltage of $\delta I_0/G_m$. To minimize this offset component, the nominal bias current I_0 should be as small as possible, and transistors $M3A$ and $M3B$ should have low transconductance. Typically I_0 will be two to four times the maximum signal current $G_m \cdot V_{in_{max}}$. $M4A$ and $M4B$ can be seen as a differential pair having its inputs grounded. The differential gain from the gates of $M4A$ and $M4B$ to the output is generally higher than the dc gain of the transconductor. Therefore, the input-referred offset due to $M4A$ and $M4B$ can be much greater than the threshold-voltage offset due to technological imperfections. Careful layout of transistors $M4A$ and $M4B$ will reduce the offset of the transconductor significantly.

Differential output noise is essentially due to transistors $M2$, $M3A$, $M3B$, $M4A$, and $M4B$. As no bias current flows through $M2$, this transistor contributes only white noise. Fortunately, transistors $M3A$, $M3B$, $M4A$, and $M4B$ can be implemented with relatively large gate areas without compromising overall circuit performance, and the $1/f$ noise can be reduced to a tolerable level.

As long as all transistors remain in their normal region of operation, distortion is due to two effects: the residual nonlinearity of the degenerated differential pair $M1A/M1B$ and the nonideal resistor equivalent $M2$. Both effects produce mainly third-order harmonic distortion. The distortion of the differential pair can be controlled by adjusting the bias current and the value of the degeneration resistor. The distortion of $M2$ can be influenced by a proper choice of the control-voltage range. Therefore, an acceptable compromise between power consumption, tuning range, and distortion has to be found. Actual circuits also produce second-order harmonic distortion, which is due to technological imperfections affecting the balance of the circuit.

III. Modified Transconductor

A. Input Common-Mode Voltage Limitations

In addition to the output nodes, the signal amplitude also appears across $M2$. Therefore, the quiescent potential of nodes A and B must be such that $M3A$ and $M3B$ will stay in saturation at the maximum signal amplitude. Taking into account the differential signal voltage drop due to $M1A$ and $M1B$, the signal amplitude across $M2$ may be approximated by

$$V_{DS2\,max} = V_{in_{max}} \cdot g_{m_1}/\left(g_{m_1} + 2 \cdot g_{d_2} \right). \tag{12}$$

$V_{in_{max}}$ is the maximum differential peak-to-peak input-signal amplitude. The quiescent potential of nodes A and B depends directly on the input common-mode voltage

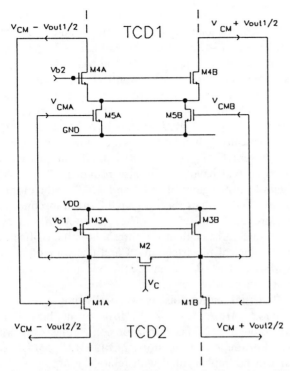

Fig. 3. Modified connection of the CMFB loop.

V_{CM}. The maximum value for V_{CM} is therefore

$$V_{CM\,max} = V_{DD} + V_{DS\,SAT3} - V_{DS2\,max}/2 + V_{GS1}. \quad (13)$$

Note that the body effect on V_{T1} and fabrication tolerances must be taken into account for correct evaluation of $V_{CM\,max}$.

A second constraint on the input common-mode voltage is imposed by the CMFB loop. The gate of transistors $M5A$ and $M5B$ must always remain at least 100 mV above V_{TN}. This guarantees that the transistors stay in strong inversion under all operating conditions. Therefore, the minimum common-mode output voltage is given by

$$V_{CM\,min} = V_{TN} + V_{in_{max}}/2 + 100 \text{ mV}. \quad (14)$$

Again, process tolerances on V_{TN} must be taken into account for the evaluation of $V_{CM\,min}$. Numerical evaluation of $V_{CM\,min}$ and $V_{CM\,max}$ for a standard 2.4-μm CMOS process, and assuming $V_{in_{max}} = 800$ mV, gives $V_{CM\,min} = 1.5$ V and $V_{CM\,max} = V_{DD} - 2$ V. Therefore the circuit in Fig. 1 will not allow operation from a 3-V power supply. The problem could be solved by adding a folded-cascode structure to the load circuit at the expense of extra power-supply current. A simpler solution consists in using the input-differential pair transistors of a succeeding transconductor as level shifters for the common-mode signal as shown in Fig. 3. The signal outputs of transconductor $TCD1$ are connected to the signal inputs of transconductor $TCD2$, whereas the nodes A and B of transconductor $TCD2$ are connected to the gates of $M5A$ and $M5B$ of $TCD1$. The gate voltages of $M5A$ and $M5B$ are now shifted by $|V_{GS1}|$. The complete circuit diagram of the modified transconductor is shown in Fig. 4. The transistor

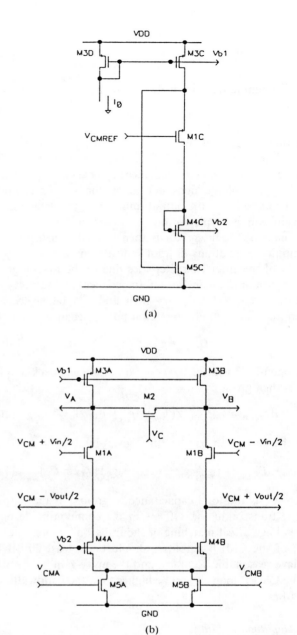

Fig. 4. (a) Modified bias circuit. (b) Modified transconductor.

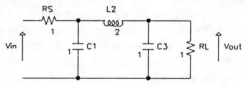

Fig. 5. Normalized prototype RLC ladder filter.

$M1C$ in the modified bias circuit shifts the common-mode reference voltage $V_{CM\,REF}$ by $|V_{GS1}|$, and the gate of $M5C$ is now connected to the source of $M1C$.

The minimum output common-mode voltage is now given by the following two expressions:

$$V_{CM\,min1} = V_{TN} + V_{in_{max}}/2 + 100 \text{ mV} - V_{TP} \quad (15)$$

$$V_{CM\,min\,2} = V_{DS5} + V_{DS\,SAT4} + V_{in_{max}}/2. \quad (16)$$

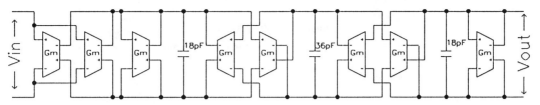

Fig. 6.   Fully differential transconductor–capacitor filter structure.

Expressions (13), (15), and (16) are easily satisfied by fixing the common-mode voltage V_{CM} to 1 V with $V_{DD} = 3$ V.

IV. Filter Structure

The filter-structure has been derived from a prototype third-order Butterworth *RLC* ladder filter (Fig. 5) by well-known signal-flow-graph techniques. The diagram of the fully differential transconductor–capacitor structure is shown in Fig. 6. All transconductors are identical. The filter has two internal gain peaks of about 1 and 3 dB close to the cutoff frequency. Adjustment of those gain peaks by scaling of the transconductors and capacitors was not practical. Noninteger ratios of the transconductance values would result in less accurate matching of the transconductors and degrade overall circuit performance. Therefore, only 6-dB steps are available for amplitude scaling, and no significant increase in dynamic range can be achieved. The 6-dB loss of the prototype filter has been compensated for by doubling the transconductance of the input transconductor. This is accomplished by connecting two transconductors in parallel.

The actual cutoff frequency of the filter may vary widely with process and environmental variations. Precision filtering functions make tuning necessary. Automatic tuning circuitry similar to [7] has been included on the chip to compensate for process and temperature variations and is shown in Fig. 7. The VCO is implemented as a two-integrator loop. The transconductors are identical to those in the filter. The differential oscillation amplitude is limited to V_{TN} by two shunt transistors connected across the outputs of one of the integrators. The oscillation frequency has been set to 2.52 kHz. The harmonic distortion due to the simple amplitude limitation circuit will cause a slight degradation of the tuning accuracy. An improved tuning scheme can be found in [8].

V. Filter Implementation

A. Filter Optimization

The filter has been implemented in an industry-standard 2.4-μm CMOS process. Process parameters are summarized in Table I. It was designed to operate from a single 3-V power supply. The common-mode reference voltage has been fixed to 1 V. The analytical expressions describing the characteristics of the transconductor have been implemented in a standard spreadsheet program. This en-

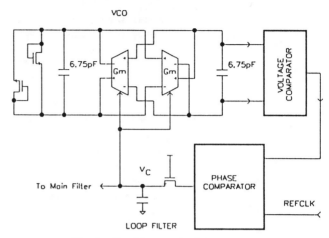

Fig. 7.   On-chip control voltage generator.

abled fast and effective optimization of the transistor sizes by taking into account worst-case process parameters and bias conditions. The predicted characteristics for a single transconductor are summarized in Table II. The CMFB-loop interconnections have been arranged in such a way that nodes *A* and *B* of every transconductor are connected to the CMFB inputs of one other transconductor. One exception had to be made, as the number of inputs and outputs does not match on the first internal node of the filter.

B. Layout

The layout of the transconductor is shown in Fig. 8. Transistor *M*2 has been implemented as a series connection of six shorter transistors in order to improve matching. The load circuit is separated from the voltage-to-current converter by a routing channel. Special care has been taken in the floorplan of the circuit to achieve good matching of the transconductors. All PMOS voltage-to-current converters have been grouped closely together. The placement of the load circuits minimizes the length of the CMFB-loop interconnection wires. The capacitors are implemented as a parallel connection of two poly I/poly II capacitors, one having the poly I terminal connected to the positive output of the integrator, the other one having the poly I terminal connected to the negative output of the integrator. This distributes the parasitic capacitance to the substrate equally between the two integrator outputs. The transconductors occupy 560×430 μm². Fig. 9 shows a photomicrograph of the filter. Total chip area is 1 mm².

TABLE I
CMOS PROCESS PARAMETERS

Minimum Gate Length	2.4 μm
V_{TN}	0.9 V
$\mu_N C_{OX}$	47 μA/V^2
V_{TP}	-0.9 V
$\mu_P C_{OX}$	17 μA/V^2
Metal Layers	2
POLY1/POLY2 Capacitance	0.4 fF/μ^2

TABLE II
CALCULATED TRANSCONDUCTOR CHARACTERISTICS

Power-Supply Voltage V_{DD}	3 V
Max. Differential Signal Amplitude	> 800 mV$_{PP}$
Nominal Bias-Current I_0	0.15 μA
Max. Power Consumption	< 1.2 μW
Transconductance Gm	0.107 μA/V
Control Voltage Range	100 - 500 mV
$(V_{GS2}-V_{T2})$ at V_C = 300mV	900 mV
gm_1	1.10 μA/V
gd_2	0.17 μA/V
Differential DC Gain	47 dB
Common Mode Reference Voltage V_{CMREF}	1 V
CMFB Loop Gain	40 dB
Input-Referred Noise (White Noise)	1 μV/$\sqrt{}$Hz

VI. EXPERIMENTAL RESULTS

During all measurements the chip operated from a single 3-V power supply. The reference current for the bias generator has been fixed externally as well as the 1-V common-mode reference voltage. Due to a layout error, the actual values of the capacitors in the VCO were far less than the intended 6.75 pF. The control loop did operate as expected with external capacitors connected to the VCO, but this does not allow appreciation of the accuracy of the tracking between the VCO and the filter cutoff frequency. Therefore most measurements had to be made with the filter tuned by an externally applied control voltage.

The measured amplitude response of the filter is shown in Fig. 10. Above 20-kHz the stopband attenuation stabilizes at about 80 dB. This is due to a small parasitic capacitance between the input and the output of the filter in the measurement setup. As shown in Fig. 11, the cutoff frequency can be varied by changing the value of the control voltage V_c. The dc gain error of the filter changes as well. This is due to the dependence of the dc gain of the integrators on the value of the transconductance. The differential output-noise spectrum is shown in Fig. 12. The white-noise spectral density in the passband is 2.4 μV$_{RMS}/\sqrt{Hz}$. $1/f$ noise is dominant below 500 Hz. The total noise voltage at the output, measured in the frequency band 10 Hz to 100 kHz, is less than 180 μV$_{RMS}$ under worst-case bias conditions. A typical value is 110 μV$_{RMS}$.

The total harmonic distortion at the filter output is below 1 percent for differential input-signal amplitudes of up to 900 mV$_{PP}$, and below 0.1 percent for signal amplitudes up to 200 mV$_{PP}$. The harmonic distortion is slightly frequency dependent with a maximum between 400 and 600 Hz. Fig. 13 shows the distortion at the filter output for a 400-Hz signal applied to the input. Second-order harmonic distortion is dominant at low signal levels, while third-order harmonic distortion is dominant at high signal levels. A sharp edge is apparent in the distortion figures located at a differential input level of 900 mV$_{PP}$. This results from the amplitude limitations in the filter discussed earlier. A summary of the measured filter performance is given in Table III.

VII. CONCLUSIONS

The feasability of micropower continuous-time filters has been demonstrated. The signal-handling capability of the continuous-time transconductor is excellent. The obtained performances in terms of power consumption and dynamic range is comparable to those of micropower

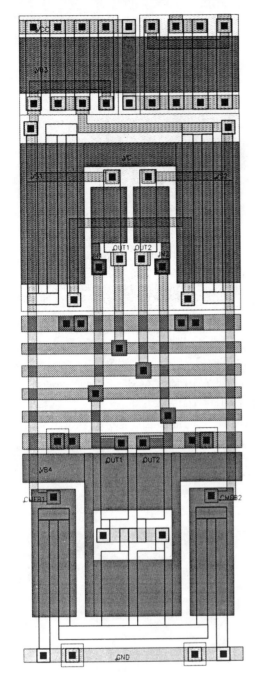

Fig. 8.   Layout of the transconductor.

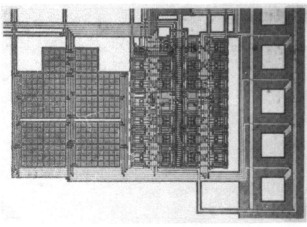

Fig. 9.   Photomicrograph of the filter.

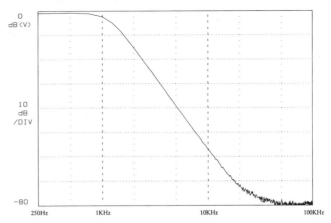

Fig. 10.   Measured filter transfer function.

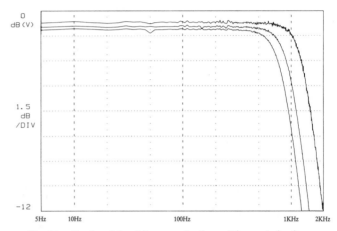

Fig. 11.   Passband detail for several values of the control voltage.

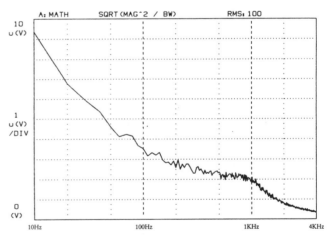

Fig. 12.   Differential output noise spectral density.

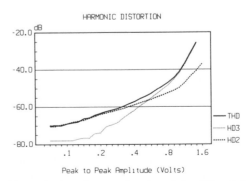

Fig. 13.   Harmonic distortion as a function of the differential peak-to-peak input voltage at $f = 400$ Hz.

245

TABLE III
MEASURED FILTER PERFORMANCE

Total Power Consumption at V_{DD} = 3V	12.6 μW
Nominal Cutoff Frequency	945 Hz
Total Differential Mode Output Noise Voltage (10Hz - 100KHz)	< 180 μV_{RMS}
THD at Vin = 500mV_{PP}	< 0.5 %
Dynamic Range	> 63 dB
PSRR	> 30 dB
CMRR	> 30 dB

switched-capacitor filters. The minimum power-supply voltage of 3 V compares favorably to SC filters. SC filters using the same fabrication process would require higher supply voltages or on-chip clock-voltage multipliers [9] due to high on-resistance of the analog CMOS switches. In many cases continuous-time filters may also simplify system design.

REFERENCES

[1] F. Krummenacher, "Micropower switched capacitor biquadratic cell," *IEEE J. Solid-State Circuits*, vol. SC-17, pp. 507–512, June 1982.
[2] M. Degrauwe and F. Salchli, "A multipurpose micropower SC filter," *IEEE J. Solid-State Circuits*, vol. SC-19, pp. 343–348, June 1984.
[3] E. A. Vittoz, "The design of high-performance analog circuits on digital CMOS chips," *IEEE J. Solid-State Circuits*, vol. SC-20, pp. 657–665, June 1985.
[4] M. Banu and Y. Tsividis, "Fully active *RC* filters in MOS technology," *IEEE J. Solid-State Circuits*, vol. SC-18, pp. 644–651, Dec. 1983.
[5] Y. Tsividis, Z. Czarnul, and S. C. Fang, "MOS transconductors and integrators with high linearity," *Electron. Lett.*, vol. 22, no. 5, pp. 245–246, Feb. 27, 1986.
[6] H. Khorramabadi and P. R. Gray, "High-frequency CMOS continuous-time filters," *IEEE J. Solid-State Circuits*, vol. SC-19, pp. 939–948, Dec. 1984.
[7] M. Banu and Y. Tsividis, "An elliptic continuous-time CMOS filter with on-chip automatic tuning," *IEEE J. Solid-State Circuits*, vol. SC-20, pp. 1114–1121, Dec. 1985.
[8] F. Krummenacher and N. Joehl, "A 4-MHz CMOS continuous-time filter with on-chip automatic tuning," *IEEE J. Solid-State Circuits*, vol. 23, pp. 750–758, June 1988.
[9] F. Krummenacher, H. Pinier, and A. Guillaume, "Higher sampling rates in SC circuits by on-chip clock-voltage multiplication," in *ESSCIRC'83 Dig. Tech. Papers* (Lausanne, Switzerland), Sept. 1983, pp. 123–126.

Design Considerations for High-Frequency Continuous-Time Filters and Implementation of an Antialiasing Filter for Digital Video

VENUGOPAL GOPINATHAN, YANNIS P. TSIVIDIS, FELLOW, IEEE, KHEN-SANG TAN, MEMBER, IEEE, AND RICHARD K. HESTER, SENIOR MEMBER, IEEE

Abstract —We report on an approach that has made possible the integration of video frequency continuous-time filters with wide dynamic range. Detailed design techniques specific to high-frequency operation are introduced to implement a 5-V, seventh-order elliptic analog magnitude filter for antialiasing in digital video applications. The filter, based on a G_m–C technique, exhibits a dynamic range of 61 dB and dissipates a power of 75 mW. Yield statistics are given.

I. Introduction

THE current trend in CMOS VLSI is to perform information processing more and more in the digital domain. However, the interface between the analog outside world and the digital processor will remain analog in nature. As the technology forges ahead, the performance/cost potential of the complete system cannot be fully realized until integrated circuits with analog input and output can be implemented. This paper deals with the design and implementation of one category of analog interface chips, viz., continuous-time filters, operating in the video frequency range. Many of the concepts described here could very well be extended to other filtering applications as well.

Several attempts at integrating continuous-time filters with on-chip tuning have been reported [1]–[12] in literature. High-precision continuous-time filters with large dynamic range have been demonstrated in the voice band [6]. However, extensions of these techniques to high frequencies have faced many problems. High levels of distortion, nonideal effects introduced by parasitic elements on the chip, and improper modeling of high-frequency operation of MOS transistors have been the chief impedi-

ments. Switched-capacitor (SC) techniques are relatively difficult to implement in these frequency ranges for the following reasons [13]: 1) sampling of signals occurs at many points inside the SC filter. Although the signal that is fed into the SC filter is band-limited, the noise that gets added to the signal internally often is not. These noise components get aliased into the baseband of the filter. 2) Switch feedthrough problems are severe at higher clock rates. 3) High-frequency effects caused by improper amplifier settling, switch resistance, etc. are difficult to model and simulate for an SC realization. In this paper, we introduce techniques that help surmount the problems in the design and implementation of continuous-time video filters and demonstrate their effectiveness with measured results from a video antialiasing filter fabricated in a 5-V, 1-μm CMOS technology.

In Section II, we describe briefly the tuning scheme necessary to maintain a stable and accurate frequency response in the presence of temperature variations, process tolerance, and aging. The design issues involved in the implementation of a video filter are described in Section III. Chip implementation and details of the circuitry used are elaborated in Section IV. Section V discusses the measured results from the chip and Section VI contains our conclusions.

II. Master–Slave Tuning (An Overview)

A continuous-time filter with a stable frequency response requires stable RC products (or C/G_m ratios) to be maintained within the chip. This is usually done using a master–slave tuning system [14] (refer to Fig. 1). Both the "slave" filter (which processes the signal) and the "master" filter are made of integrators with gain constant controlled by the voltage V_{freq}, and phase at unity-gain frequency controlled by another voltage V_{phase}. (The master can be a voltage-controlled oscillator, but in this

Manuscript received May 1, 1990; revised August 3, 1990.
V. Gopinathan and Y. P. Tsividis are with the Department of Electrical Engineering, Columbia University, New York, NY 10027.
K.-S. Tan and R. K. Hester are with the Semiconductor Process and Design Center, Texas Instruments Incorporated, Dallas, TX 75240.
IEEE Log Number 9039477.

Reprinted from *IEEE J. Solid-State Circuits*, vol. SC-25, no. 6, pp. 1368–1378, Dec. 1990.

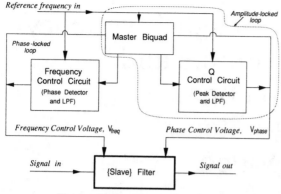

Fig. 1. Master–slave tuning scheme.

discussion we will restrict it to a voltage-controlled filter.) The master filter along with the feedback system, consisting of a phase detector and low-pass filter, forms a frequency-locked loop (FLL). When a stable reference frequency is fed into this loop, the negative feedback system locks the master filter to the incoming reference and thereby maintains a stable gain constant for the integrators in the master. The integrators in the slave also have a stable gain constant because they are also controlled by the same voltage and are well-matched to those in the master. Thus the slave filter maintains a stable frequency response.

The network within the dotted box in Fig. 1 constitutes an amplitude-locked loop. The topology of the master filter is such that any phase errors in its constituent integrators will manifest themselves as a change in its gain at the pole frequency. The amplitude-locked loop detects any changes in the gain at pole frequency from the ideal value and tunes them out using the control voltage V_{phase}. Since the same voltage controls the phase of the integrators in the slave, a stable and accurate frequency response is obtained from the slave filter.

III. DESIGN CONSIDERATIONS FOR VIDEO FREQUENCY OPERATION

In this section, we will describe the design issues involved using the example of a video antialiasing filter. The objective of the design discussed in this paper is to obtain high-frequency operation along with a wide dynamic range. The goal is to meet a set of video specifications with good yield, thus demonstrating the commercial viability of continuous-time filters in current VLSI.

A. Filter Order

Components cannot be matched to an arbitrary degree of precision within the chip. This inaccuracy leads to a mismatch in the gain constants of the various integrators in the slave filter, altering the shape of its frequency response. This problem is severe in video filters because the value of capacitors used in integrators are of the order of a few picofarads and matching them across the

chip to the required degree of precision is difficult. The first step in confronting this problem is to use filter topologies that are insensitive to component mismatches, viz., inductance simulation, leapfrog realization, etc. The second step is to overdesign the ripple amplitude and the roll-off rate so that there is more room within the specifications for response deviations due to component mismatches. This inevitably increases the order of the filter and leads to two different problems: 1) as the filter order increases, the physical size of the filter increases, thus deteriorating the matching between components now separated by larger distances; and 2) a more serious problem is the fact that the sensitivity of the passband edge to phase errors (at the unity-gain frequency of the integrators in the slave filter) increases with filter order [16]. Thus the order of the slave filter should be so chosen that the filter remains within specifications with finite tolerances of the components and worst-case phase error in the integrators of the slave. The extent to which the passband edge deviates from the nominal can be predicted early in the design process. Excess phase shift at unity-gain frequency is usually due to parasitic poles of the integrator. As an approximation, one can lump the effects of all the parasitic poles of the integrator into an effective pole corresponding to a frequency ω_p. Then the transfer function of integrator is given by

$$H_{\text{int}}(s) = \frac{1}{\left[1 + \left(\dfrac{s}{\omega_p}\right)\right]\left[\left(\dfrac{s}{\omega_u}\right)\right]} \tag{1}$$

where ω_u is the unity-gain frequency of the integrator. The magnitude transfer function $M_{\text{filt}_{NI}}(\omega)$, which includes the effect of integrator phase errors as a function of the ideal magnitude transfer function ($M_{\text{filt}_I}(\omega)$), and the group delay $\tau(\omega)$ of the ideal transfer function, can be predicted using the following relation (refer to the Appendix):

$$M_{\text{filt}_{NI}}(\omega) = M_{\text{filt}_I}(\omega)$$
$$\cdot \sqrt{\left(1 + \frac{\omega^2}{\omega_p}\tau(\omega)\right)^2 + \left(\frac{\partial M_I(\omega)}{\partial \omega}\frac{1}{M_I(\omega)}\frac{\omega^2}{\omega_p}\right)^2}. \tag{2}$$

This equation is plotted against an actually simulated transfer function for a 11th-order filter (seventh-order elliptic magnitude filter cascaded by a fourth-order delay equalizer) in Fig. 2. The integrators used in the filter had a phase error of 0.5° at their unity-gain frequencies.

B. Filter Topology

Transconductor-C topologies are usually preferred for high-frequency applications over MOSFET-C [6] topologies (made of op amps and MOSFET operating in the triode region) if device-level simulations can be carried out. This choice is preferred for two reasons: 1) transcon-

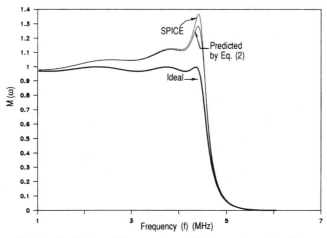

Fig. 2. Prediction of filter response with integrator nonidealities.

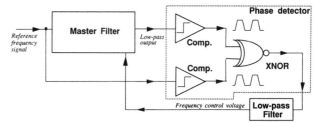

Fig. 3. Conceptual schematic of the frequency control loop.

able phase shift. Thus a small mismatch (say in aspect ratio or threshold voltage) from the desired value among these devices will introduce significant phase errors in the integrators, deteriorating the passband response of the filter.

ductance amplifiers are usually single-stage designs and hence they possess superior high-frequency performance; and 2) unlike op amps in MOSFET-C structures, transconductors do not need to drive resistors. So their design is simpler, leading to better high-frequency performance.[1]

Matching achievable between two transconductors with equal G_m's is better than that between two transconductors with noninteger G_m ratios. So the filter topology should not require noninteger G_m ratios for its implementation.

Node scaling, if needed for dynamic range optimization, can be performed with additional transconductors of the same G_m. This scales down the voltage gain at the nodes by integer multiples only.

C. Transconductance Amplifier

Low-distortion transconductance amplifiers are vital to a G_m–C filter with a wide dynamic range. In determining the distortion of the amplifier, nonquasi-static behavior of MOS transistors [18] needs to be taken into account. This problem is aggravated by the fact that devices which determine G_m need to be long to preserve good matching across the chip. Nonquasi-static effects are poorly modeled in most simulation programs or are not modeled at all. (One way to partially model these effects is to split the critical devices into a number of short but fictitious devices connected in series [18].)

In some applications, it is necessary to have an integrator whose phase at unity-gain frequency can be varied by a control voltage [14].[2] In such cases, the maximum variability of phase should not exceed approximately $\pm 1°$ over the complete range of control voltage. This is because a large tunability in phase also means large sensitivity of the phase to the device(s) that introduce this vari-

D. Tuning System

At video frequencies, the integrating capacitances in both the master and slave are of the order of a few picofarads. The parasitics then form a significant portion of the functional capacitance and their effect should also be considered when trying to match capacitors in different integrators. For a G_m–C topology, with identical transconductors, the parasitics are nearly the same from integrator to integrator. So to maintain a good matching between master and slave, the integrating capacitances in the master ($C_{\mathrm{integ}-M}$) should be nearly equal to those in the slave ($C_{\mathrm{integ}-S}$). Since the G_m's of all the transconductors in the master and slave are equal (as described in Section III-A, this "equal G_m" restriction helps in maintaining better matching of the G_m values), this means the unity-gain frequencies of the integrators in the master (given by $G_m / C_{\mathrm{integ}-M}$) should be approximately equal to those in the slave (given by $G_m / C_{\mathrm{integ}-S}$). The tuning process forces the pole frequency of the master filter ($= G_m / C_{\mathrm{integ}-M}$) to be equal to the frequency of the incoming reference signal. Thus for good master–slave matching, the reference frequency should be chosen to be as close to the unity-gain frequencies of the integrators in the slave as possible.

The frequency control part of a typical tuning circuit is redrawn with more details in Fig. 3. As an example, we chose a voltage-controlled filter as the master and a digital XNOR gate as the phase detector. The phase detector measures the phase difference between the low-pass output of the filter and the reference frequency signal. To convert the sinusoids that exist at two inputs of the phase detector to square waves, hard limiting comparators are used. At video frequencies, the square waves at the input and at the output of the XNOR gate have significant rise and fall times (which are not necessarily equal). The topology of the tuning system should be such that its performance is insensitive to these nonidealities. To minimize the error between the pole frequency of the master and the reference frequency (tuning error), the phase detector should also have low offsets.

---

[1] In BiCMOS, the good resistor-driving capability offered by bipolar transistors makes MOSFET-C filters [6] competitive at high frequencies [17].

[2] In most designs, this variation is obtained by changing the terminal voltages or bias current of some key MOS transistors in the cell.

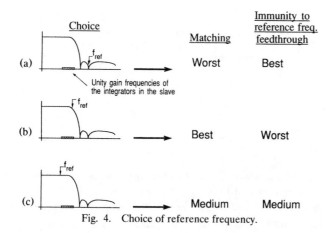

Fig. 4.   Choice of reference frequency.

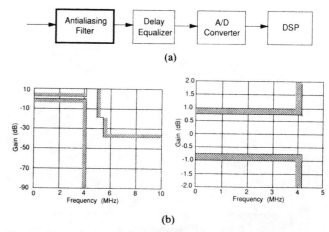

Fig. 5.   (a) Block diagram of the application for the antialiasing filter.
(b) Frequency response specifications for the filter.

One of the factors that limit the dynamic range of a continuous-time filter is the reference signal feedthrough, and the choice of reference frequency plays an important part in the amount of feedthrough. This feedthrough mostly arises from a small residual ripple that exists in the control voltage and various electrical couplings that exist within the chip.

Fig. 4 shows the relative merits and demerits of the various choices that can be made. The choices are grouped based on the location of reference frequency with respect to the frequency response of the slave. In Fig. 4(a), where the reference frequency is in the stopband, say at a transmission zero, the feedthrough will be minimum because the filter tends to filter out this frequency at least for the parasitic feedthrough paths to the input of the filter. However, this frequency can be quite far away from the unity-gain frequencies of the integrators in the slave (which are mostly near the passband edge, shown as a hatched area in the figure), and thus this choice suffers from poor master–slave matching. In Fig. 4(b), the reference frequency is located at the passband edge. Close proximity to the unity-gain frequencies of the slave give this choice very good master–slave matching characteristics. But it suffers from severe reference frequency feedthrough problems. This is because at the passband edge, high-gain paths exist from internal nodes of the filter to the output. So any coupling of the reference frequency signal to these internal nodes will lead to a large feedthrough. Fig. 4(c) has a medium level of master–slave matching and immunity to reference frequency feedthrough. The gains from various internal nodes of the filter are not as large as the same near the passband edge. This keeps the feedthrough to a medium level. Since the reference frequency is not very close to the unity-gain frequencies of the integrators in the slave, a medium level of master–slave matching will be seen.

A voltage-controlled filter is preferable to a voltage-controlled oscillator (VCO) as the master for the following reasons: 1) nonlinearities of a VCO tend to have significant influence on its oscillation frequency. So nonlinear limiting schemes need be used to restrict the oscillation amplitude [6], [8]. This is not necessary if the master is a voltage-controlled filter. 2) The design of a self-tuned filter with a wide capture and lock range is a lot easier than that for a PLL with similar characteristics. 3) Most circuit simulation programs have convergence problems and other difficulties in simulating circuits with positive feedback. A self-tuning filter has no positive feedback and hence its simulation is more accurate and easy. Although the tuning scheme with a VCO as the master is insensitive to phase detector offsets [8], in our case errors due to mismatches between VCO and slave filter are more severe than those due to phase detector errors in a self-tuned filter type tuning circuit.

IV. Chip Implementation

In this section, we use the design considerations introduced in the previous sections in designing a video antialiasing filter to a set of tight specifications.

A. Application and Specifications

Fig. 5(a) shows a block diagram of the kind of application for which this filter is designed. The antialiasing filter precedes a delay equalizer, a video A/D converter, and a digital signal processor. The specifications to be met by this filter are as shown in Fig. 5(b). These specs necessitate the use of an accurate slave filter with a precision on-chip automatic tuning circuit.

B. Filter Topology

To meet the specifications in spite of component tolerances, a seventh-order elliptic approximation was used. The ripple amplitude chosen was 0.25 dB and for design centering the cutoff frequency was set to be 4.4 MHz. For better high-frequency performance in standard CMOS (as opposed to BiCMOS), a $G_m - C$ topology was chosen; to maintain a low sensitivity to component mismatches, we used a leapfrog realization of a doubly terminated ladder. The active $G_m - C$ realization is as shown in Fig. 6. Using signal flow graph analysis, it can be shown that the

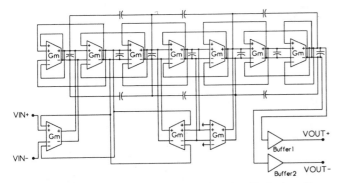

Fig. 6. Leapfrog realization of the seventh-order elliptic slave filter.

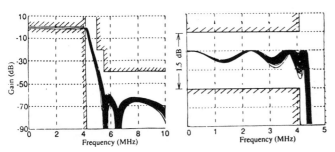

Fig. 7. Monte-Carlo analysis of the slave filter.

transmission zeros can be implemented by connecting capacitors between appropriate nodes as shown in the figure. Two-input-stage, single-output-stage transconductance amplifiers were used instead of conventional transconductors (the reasons for this choice will be clarified later). For dynamic range optimization, nodes were scaled with multiple equal valued transconductors.

In Fig. 7, we show the Monte-Carlo simulations superimposed on the magnitude specifications. The element mismatch standard deviation assumed in the simulation was 2% and 100 trials are plotted.

C. G_m–C Integrator

The frequency response of high-frequency, high-order filters is very sensitive to phase errors in the integrators. One source of phase error is the finite output impedance of the transconductance amplifier. So to improve the output impedance, a fully differential folded-cascode structure was chosen (refer to Fig. 8 and ignore, for now, the second input stage).

To obtain a high degree of output current linearity with input voltage, we use an input stage consisting of two source followers and a transistor MW, the latter operating in the triode region [19]. It can be shown that when the transconductor is driven by a pair of balanced input voltages, IN+ and IN−, the output current exhibits a sufficiently high degree of linearity to the input voltage. The G_m of the transconductor can be varied by changing the control voltage V_{FREQ}.

The folded-cascode amplifier was configured to have two identical input stages and a single output stage. This is useful in the following ways. a) It facilitates signal

addition required in the feedback paths of the leapfrog realization. b) The bias current required in the output stage of the ith integrator (say I_{bias}) is determined only by the maximum signal current flowing into the integrating capacitance (say $C_{int,i}$) (this prevents slewing of the output stage). This maximum signal current is a function of the integrating capacitance ($C_{int,i}$), maximum allowable peak-to-peak input swing ($V_{max,pp}$), and the frequency at which the integrator output has the maximum swing ($\omega_{c,i}$). To maintain identical designs for all the transconductors, a worst case can be chosen for all the output stages currents, with $\omega_{c,i} = \omega_c$ and $C_{int,i} = C_{int}$, where ω_c is the maximum of all $\omega_{c,i}$ and C_{int} is the maximum of all integrating capacitances. Thus

$$I_{bias} = \eta \omega_c C_{int} \frac{V_{max,pp}}{2} \qquad (3)$$

where η (>1) is a safety factor to prevent excessively high distortion (η, in our case was chosen as 1.5). Thus, the output stage bias current is independent of the number of input stages. The impedance at the output node of this two input transconductor is therefore about twice what it would be if the outputs of two separate transconductors were connected in parallel. c) Current sources in the output stage contribute significantly to the output noise current for the transconductor. Since two input stages drive a single output stage and the bias current in the output stage is not doubled, the total noise per input stage is reduced considerably. This reduction in noise translates directly to a lower total noise at the output of the filter. It is interesting to note here that if two separate transconductors (each with its own output stage) were connected in parallel, each of the output stages would have to be biased according to (3) to guarantee that neither of the output stages slews.

Fig. 9 shows the small-signal differential-mode half circuit of the tunable G_m–C integrator with some additions. The networks within the dotted lines have been added to introduce a variable phase lead or lag at the output for automatic tuning purposes. (As will be seen, the variable resistances in the figure are implemented with MOS transistors operating in the triode region.) If the input transistor is assumed to have a very large g_m, the complete transfer function of the integrator is

$$H_{int}(s) \approx \frac{1}{sR_\omega C_\omega}\left[\frac{1 + sC_{lead}(R_\omega + R_{lead})}{1 + sC_{lead}R_{lead}}\right]$$
$$\cdot \left[\frac{1 + sC_{lag}R_{lag}}{1 + sC_{lag}(R_{lag} + 1/g_{m1})}\right]. \qquad (4)$$

Thus R_{lead} and C_{lead} introduce a zero and a pole. By varying R_{lead}, a variable phase lead is introduced at the output. Along similar lines, R_{lag} and C_{lag} introduce a variable phase lag. The component values were chosen so that the maximum variability in phase is restricted to

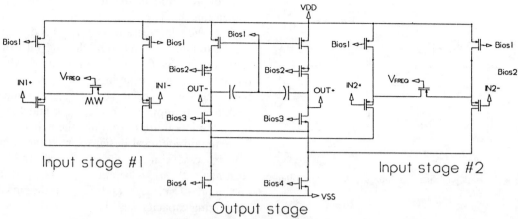

Fig. 8. Double-input folded-cascode transconductor.

$\pm 0.5°$. As explained in Section II, this keeps the sensitivity of phase to these component values quite small.

Fig. 10 shows the complete schematic of the transconductance amplifier with its biasing circuitry, phase-lead and phase-lag networks, and common-mode feedback. The output common-mode voltage is stabilized at 0 V using two separate feedback paths. The first one, consisting of transistors $MC1$ to $MC6$, is a modification of the common-mode feedback scheme used in [5]. Transistors $MC1$ to $MC4$ operate in the triode region. $MC1$, $MC2$, and $MC5$ are identical to $MC3$, $MC4$, and $MC6$, respectively. The current in $MC10$ is mirrored to $MC8$ (which sets the current in $MO1$ and $MO2$) by the combination of transistors $MC1$ to $MC6$. It can be seen that a small variation in the output common-mode voltage causes a large variation in the currents in $MO1$ and $MO2$. However, unlike in [5], the V_{DS}'s of the transistors operating in triode mode ($MC1$ to $MC4$) do not reduce the output voltage swing of the transconductor because they are not directly at the output stage. An examination of the closed-loop bandwidth of this common-mode feedback shows that the loop has insufficient loop gain for high-frequency operation. So an auxiliary feedback scheme is used that works better at high frequencies. This consists of capacitors $C1$ and $C2$ (of equal value) and the transistor $MC11$ operating in the triode region. The common-mode voltage is sensed at node CM. The voltage at node CM also controls the output stage current sources $MO3$ and $MO4$. This constitutes the second common-mode feedback loop. The open-loop frequency response of this common-mode feedback is high pass in nature. The pole location of this response is determined by the g_{DS} of the transistor $MC11$ and the capacitance of $C1$ and $C2$.

D. Tuning Circuit

The functional block diagram of the tuning circuit is as shown in Fig. 11. The master is a fully differential biquad with low-pass and bandpass outputs. A single-ended version of the biquad is as shown in Fig. 12. This is a well-known state-variable implementation where the inte-

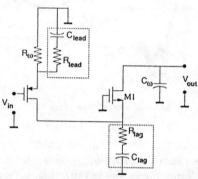

Fig. 9. Differential-mode small-signal half circuit of the tunable integrator.

grators are implemented using a $G_m – C$ topology [20], [21]. The bandpass and low-pass transfer functions are

$$H_{BP}(s) = \frac{V_{BP}(s)}{V_{in}(s)} = \frac{G_{m_{in}} s C_2}{s^2 C_1 C_2 + s C_2 G_{m_T} + G_{m_1} G_{m_1}}.$$

$$H_{LP}(s) = \frac{V_{LP}(s)}{V_{in}(s)} = \frac{G_{m_{in}} G_{m_2}}{s^2 C_1 C_2 + s C_2 G_{m_T} + G_{m_1} G_{m_2}} \quad (5)$$

respectively. The pole frequency ω_0, the filter quality factor Q, and the gain at the pole frequency $H_{BP}(\omega_0)$ of the biquad are given by

$$\omega_0 = \sqrt{\frac{G_{m_1} G_{m_2}}{C_1 C_2}}$$

$$Q = \frac{1}{G_{m_T}} \sqrt{G_{m_1} G_{m_2} \frac{C_1}{C_2}}$$

$$H_{BP}(\omega_0) = \frac{G_{m_{in}}}{G_{m_T}}. \quad (6)$$

In the actual implementation, $G_{m_1} = G_{m_2}$ and $G_{m_{in}} = G_{m_T}$. The transconductors $T1$ and $T4$ with G_m values $G_{m_{in}}$ and G_{m_T} are implemented using a double-input transconductor. Since the two input stages are physically close, they exhibit a high degree of matching. The quality factor

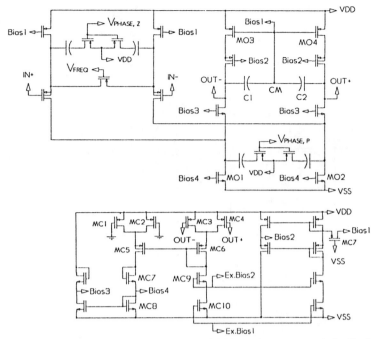

Fig. 10. Complete schematic of the transconductor with bias and common-mode feedback circuitry.

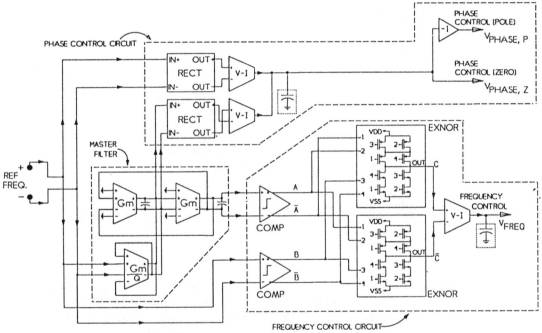

Fig. 11. Functional block diagram of the tuning circuit.

is set by scaling down the G_m of $T1$ and $T4$ by a factor Q. The proper functioning of the loop is independent of the exact value of Q as long as it is in the range of 8 to 10 to provide sufficient tuning sensitivity.

The bandpass output of the biquad is connected to the phase-control circuit and the frequency-control circuit is connected to the low-pass output of the biquad. The latter detects the phase difference between the input and the low-pass output of the filter and changes the pole frequency of the filter until the low-pass output is in quadrature with the input. Then the pole frequency of the

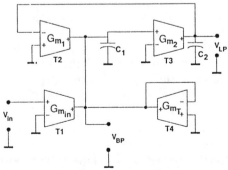

Fig. 12. Simplified single-ended version of the master filter.

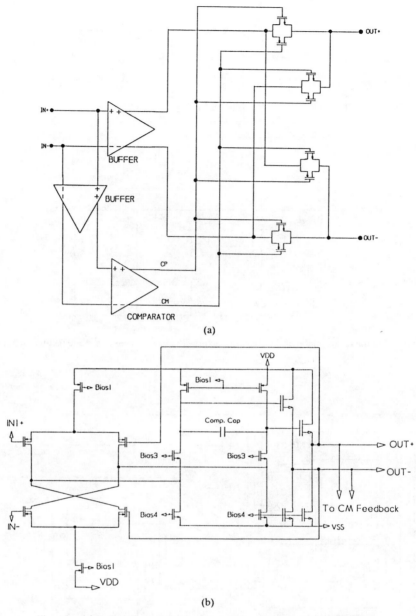

Fig. 13.   (a) Fully differential full-wave rectifier. (b) Fully differential buffer.

biquad is equal to the reference frequency. The biquad is scaled to have unity gain at its pole frequency. Any change in this gain (produced by phase errors in the integrators) is detected by the phase-control circuitry and is corrected by feedback. Note that the operation of the frequency-control loop is unaffected by the phase-control circuit. This avoids problems of convergence in vector-locked tuning loops.

For phase detection, the following method was adopted. The low-pass output signal and the incoming reference signal are converted by two balanced comparators into square waves A, $\bar{A}$, B, and $\bar{B}$, respectively. These square waves drive a pair of XNOR gates so that they can produce complementary outputs C and $\bar{C}$. To the first order, both outputs have the same nonidealities. Since these outputs are subtracted, the system is relatively insensitive to finite rise times or the exact shape of the square waves at the

output of the comparators and XNOR gates. To prevent any reverse coupling (from the output of the comparator to the filter output), both the comparators are driven by balanced buffers. The schematic of the full-wave rectifier is as shown in Fig. 13(a), and the schematic of the fully balanced buffer is as shown in Fig. 13(b). The topology of the buffer is similar to that of the fully differential folded-cascode amplifier described before. A pair of source followers is connected to the output, to reduce the output impedance.

V.   IMPLEMENTATION RESULTS

The filter with on-chip automatic tuning circuit was fabricated in a 1-μm n-well, 5-V CMOS technology. Fig. 14 shows the chip photograph. Fig. 15(a) shows the com-

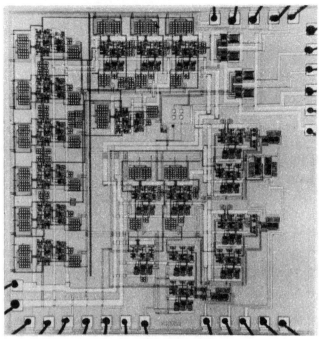

Fig. 14.   Chip photograph.

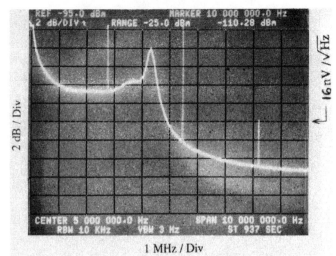

1 MHz / Div

Fig. 16.   Input-referred noise power spectral density.

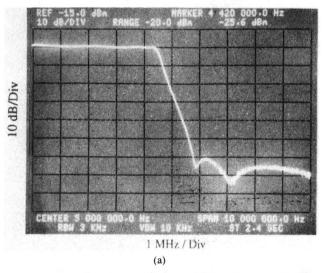

1 MHz / Div

(a)

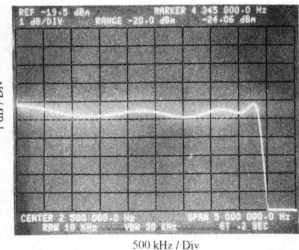

500 kHz / Div

(b)

Fig. 15.   (a) Measured frequency response. (b) Details of the passband.

TABLE I
MEASURED PERFORMANCE CHARACTERISTICS

Power supply voltage	±2.5 V
Passband edge frequency:	
Mean	4.36 MHz
Standard Deviation	0.11 MHz
Temperature variation (0 to 70 °C)	±0.08 MHz
Passband ripple:	
Mean	1.24 dB
Standard Deviation	0.26 dB
Temperature variation (0 to 70 °C)	±0.20 dB
Stop-band attenuation	Better than 60 dB
Differential input swing at 0.5% THD (Worst case over the freq. range 0 to 4.4 MHz)	0.8 Vpp
Input referred in-band random noise	210 µV rms
Reference signal feedthrough, referred to the input	130 µV rms
Dynamic range {Signal / (Noise + Feedthrough)}	61 dB
Power supply rejection ratio (at passband edge):	
VDD	49 dB
VSS	44 dB
Lock range of the tuning circuit	600 KHz to 6.8 MHz
Power dissipation	75 mW
Active area	6 mm^2

plete frequency response of the filter and Fig. 15(b) shows the details of the passband. Fig. 16 shows the input-referred noise power spectral density. The reference frequency feedthrough and its harmonics are seen as spikes in spectrum. Ninety two chips from various wafers and two different process runs were tested. Seventy-five percent of the fabricated chips were functional and 63% of them met the specifications in spite of an error in the layout which forced the phase control circuitry to perform suboptimally. Measured results are summarized in Table I.

VI. CONCLUSIONS

We have demonstrated that wide-dynamic-range continuous-time filters with on-chip automatic tuning can be designed to meet commercial grade specifications with a good yield at video frequencies. This was achieved by careful device-level design, keeping in mind the design issues that are specific to high-frequency operation. The video antialiasing filter was implemented using a standard 1-μm CMOS technology.

APPENDIX

In this section we derive an approximate expression for the frequency response of a G_m–C filter whose integrators have a parasitic pole located at a frequency ω_p. Let $H_I(s)$ be the ideal transfer function of the filter. Let one of the circuits used to implement a transconductance (say G_{m_i}) in the G_m–C filter have a parasitic pole at ω_p. Then, instead of a pure transconductance, we obtain a transadmittance given by

$$Y_{m_i} = \frac{G_{m_i}}{(1 + s/\omega_p)}.$$

When $|s| \ll \omega_p$, the above equation reduces to

$$Y_{m_i} \approx G_{m_i}(1 - s/\omega_p). \tag{A1}$$

From classical sensitivity analysis, the change in transfer function $\Delta H(s)$ due to a change ΔG_{m_i} in G_{m_i} is given by

$$\Delta H(s) = S_{G_{m_i}}^{H(s)} \left(\frac{\Delta G_{m_i}}{G_{m_i}} \right) H(s). \tag{A2}$$

From (A1), $\Delta G_{m_i}/G_{m_i} = -s/\omega_p$. Let $H_{NI_i}(s)$ be the perturbed, nonideal transfer function due to the change ΔG_{m_i} in G_{m_i}. Then using (A1) and (A2), $H_{NI_i}(s)$ is approximately given by

$$H_{NI_i}(s) = H_I(s) + \left(\frac{-s}{\omega_p} \right) H_I(s) S_{G_{m_i}}^{H_I(s)}. \tag{A3}$$

The nonideal effects of each ΔG_{m_i} can be added, and if all the transconductors have a parasitic pole at the same frequency (this is true for a G_m–C filter with an "equal G_m" restriction), the nonideal transfer function, $H_{NI}(s)$ is given by

$$H_{NI}(s) = H_I(s) + \left(-\frac{s}{\omega_p} \right) H_I(s) \sum_i S_{G_{m_i}}^{H_I(s)}. \tag{A4}$$

The summation in (A4) runs over all the transconductances of the filter and hence is a sensitivity invariant [15]:

$$\sum_i S_{G_{m_i}}^{H_I(s)} = -S_s^{H_I(s)}. \tag{A5}$$

Substituting (A5) into (A4), we get

$$H_{NI}(s) = H_I(s) + \left(\frac{s}{\omega_p} \right) H_I(s) S_s^{H_I(s)}$$

or, using the definition of sensitivity and $s = j\omega$, we get

$$H_{NI}(j\omega) = H_I(j\omega) + \left(\frac{j\omega^2}{\omega_p} \right) \left(\frac{\partial H_I(j\omega)}{\partial \omega} \right). \tag{A6}$$

Define the magnitude $M(\omega)$ and phase $\phi(\omega)$ of transfer functions such that

$$H_{NI}(j\omega) = M_{NI}(\omega) \exp\left[j\phi_{NI}(\omega) \right] \tag{A7}$$

and

$$H_I(j\omega) = M_I(\omega) \exp\left[j\phi_I(\omega) \right]. \tag{A8}$$

Substituting (A7) and (A8) in (A6), we get the nonideal magnitude transfer function to be

$$M_{NI}(\omega) = M_I(\omega)$$

$$\cdot \sqrt{ \left(1 + \frac{\omega^2}{\omega_p} \tau_I(\omega) \right)^2 + \left(\frac{\partial M_I(\omega)}{\partial \omega} \frac{1}{M_I(\omega)} \frac{\omega^2}{\omega_p} \right)^2 } \tag{A9}$$

where $\tau_I(\omega)$ is the group delay of the ideal transfer function.

Since this result is based on sensitivity analysis, it is adequate only for small variations in G_m or equivalently large values of ω_p. Also, the result becomes slightly inaccurate when second derivatives of phase and magnitude to frequency are large. This explains the slight deviation of the predicted result from the SPICE simulation results in Fig. 2. However, the result is good enough to give a sufficient measure of the passband edge deviation due to integrator phase errors.

ACKNOWLEDGMENT

The authors would like to thank the Guest Editor, Prof. B.-S. Song, for his detailed comments during the preparation of the manuscript.

REFERENCES

[1] J. R. Canning and G. Wilson, "Frequency discriminator circuit arrangement," U.K. Patent 1 421 093, Jan. 1976.
[2] K. S. Tan and P. R. Gray, "Fully integrated analog filters using bipolar-JFET technology," *IEEE J. Solid-State Circuits*, vol. SC-13, no. 6, pp. 814–821, Dec. 1978.
[3] K. W. Moulding, J. R. Quartly, P. J. Rankin, R. S. Thompson, and G. A. Wilson, "Gyrator video filter IC with automatic tuning," *IEEE J. Solid-State Circuits*, vol. SC-15, pp. 963–968, Dec. 1980.
[4] J. O. Voorman, W. H. A. Bruls, and P. J. Barth, "Integration of analog filters in a bipolar process." *IEEE J. Solid-State Circuits*, vol. SC-17, pp. 713–722, Aug. 1982.
[5] H. Khorramabadi and P. R. Gray, "High-frequency CMOS continuous-time filters," *IEEE J. Solid-State Circuits*, vol. SC-19, no. 6, pp. 939–948. Dec. 1984.
[6] M. Banu and Y. Tsividis, "An elliptic continuous-time CMOS filter with on-chip automatic tuning." *IEEE J. Solid-State Circuits*, vol. SC-20, pp. 1114–1121, Dec. 1985.

[7] C. F. Choi and R. Schaumann, "Design and performance of a fully integrated bipolar 10.7 MHz analog bandpass filter," *IEEE J. Solid-State Circuits*, vol. SC-21, pp. 6–14, Feb. 1986.

[8] F. Krummenacher and N. Joehl, "A 4 MHz CMOS continuous-time filter with on-chip automatic tuning," *IEEE J. Solid-State Circuits*, vol. 23, pp. 750–758, June 1988.

[9] C. S. Park and R. Schaumann, "Design of a 4-MHz analog integrated CMOS transconductance-C bandpass filter," *IEEE J. Solid-State Circuits*, vol. 23, pp. 987–996, Aug. 1988.

[10] Y-T. Wang, F. Lu and A. A. Abidi, "A 12.5 MHz CMOS continuous-time bandpass filter," in *ISSCC Dig. Tech. Papers* (New York), Feb. 1989, pp. 198–199.

[11] A. Kaiser, "A micropower CMOS continuous-time low-pass filter," *IEEE J. Solid-State Circuits*, vol. 24, no. 3, pp. 736–743, June 1989.

[12] F. Goodenough, "Voltage-tunable linear filters move onto a chip," *Electron. Design*, vol. 38, no. 3, pp. 43–54, Feb. 8, 1990.

[13] P. R. Gray and R. Castello, "Performance limitations in switched-capacitor filters," in *Design of MOS VLSI Circuits for Telecommunications*. Englewood Cliffs, NJ: Prentice Hall, 1985, ch. 10.

[14] D. Senderowicz, D. A. Hodges and P. R. Gray, "An NMOS integrated vector-locked loop," in *Proc. IEEE Int. Symp. CAS*, 1982, pp. 1164–1167.

[15] R. Schaumann, M. S. Ghausi, and K. R. Laker, *Design of Analog Filters, Passive, Active RC and Switched Capacitor*. Englewood Cliffs, NJ: Prentice Hall, 1990.

[16] V. Gopinathan, "High frequency transconductance-capacitance continuous-time filters," Ph.D. dissertation, Columbia Univ., New York, NY, 1990.

[17] J. O. Voorman, private communication.

[18] Y. P. Tsividis, *Operation and Modeling of the MOS Transistor*. New York: McGraw Hill, 1987.

[19] Y. Tsividis, Z. Czarnul, and S. C. Fang, "MOS transconductors and integrators with high linearity," *Electron. Lett.*, vol. 22, no. 5, pp. 245–246, Feb. 27, 1986.

[20] M. Bialko and R. W. Newcomb, "Generation of all finite linear circuits using DVCCS," *IEEE Trans. Circuit Theory*, vol. CT-18, pp. 733–736, Nov. 1971.

[21] R. L. Geiger and E. Sanchez-Sinencio, "Active filter design using operational transconductance amplifiers: A tutorial," *IEEE Circuits Syst. Mag.*, no. 1, pp. 20–32, 1985.

Paper 3-B.6

CMOS Active Filter Design at Very High Frequencies

YUN-TI WANG, STUDENT MEMBER, IEEE, AND ASAD A. ABIDI, MEMBER, IEEE

Abstract —A study of the limitations of active CMOS filters at high frequencies suggests automatic means to compensate imperfections in the filter response introduced by active devices. The effects of nonzero FET output conductance, limited frequency response and noise on the filter characteristics, and dynamic range have been analyzed, particularly for filters with high Q components, and simple equivalent circuits have been developed to describe them. These ideas have been used to demonstrate a 3-μm CMOS realization of a fourth-order bandpass filter with a 250-kHz passband centered at 12.5 MHz.

I. INTRODUCTION

ANALOG CMOS integrated circuits have revolutionized the implementation of active filters for many signal processing applications. Active voice-band filters, when analog, are almost all implemented in the sampled data domain by CMOS switched-capacitor circuits; with the greater emphasis today towards digital signal processing, the filters are more often implemented as digital circuits operating on quantized binary representations of samples of the signal, while the analog circuits are relegated mainly to building A/D converters and the antialias filters preceding them, or to smoothing filters when converting analog samples to continuous-time waveforms at the output of a D/A converter. Purely analog filtering continues to be required, however, at high frequencies typical of carrier or intermediate frequencies, or when the use of quantizers (A/D converters) is not very economical. This work describes some design techniques for these applications, which model the imperfections in high-frequency filters and automatically compensate them. A 12.5-MHz bandpass filter in a 3-μm CMOS technology has been used as a vehicle to demonstrate these techniques [1].

II. PROBLEMS IN IMPLEMENTATION OF HIGH-FREQUENCY ACTIVE FILTERS

Analog filters may be constructed in many ways using the frequency-dependent impedances of resistors, capaci-

Manuscript received April 18, 1989; revised June 25, 1990. This work was supported by Western Digital Corporation, Rockwell International, and the State of California MICRO program. This work was first presented at the 1989 International Solid-State Circuits Conference (ISSCC).

The authors are with the Integrated Circuits and Systems Laboratory, Department of Electrical Engineering, University of California, Los Angeles, CA 90024-1594.

IEEE Log Number 9038917.

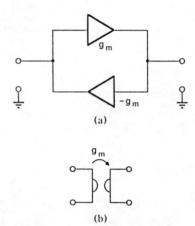

Fig. 1. (a) A gyrator implemented by an anti-parallel connection of two transconductances, and (b) the gyrator symbol.

tors, and inductors, but only a small class of these, those constructed from lossless inductors and capacitors which in the passband provide maximum power transfer from the source resistance connected at one port to the load resistance at the other, are known to possess the minimum sensitivity in their frequency response to component tolerances [2]. These are the most feasible prototypes in practice for the successful implementation of high-selectivity filters, where either a narrow passband is sought in a bandpass filter or a sharp cutoff in a low-pass filter. We will consider in the remainder of this paper the problems in implementing active filters for operation at high frequencies (which in today's CMOS technologies means between 10 and 100 MHz) based on these *LC* prototypes. Although other filter structures have been reported operating at these frequencies [3], they may not necessarily possess this low sensitivity to component tolerances.

When inductors are either too bulky or the desired values simply unavailable as on most integrated circuits, they may be simulated by active devices in combination with capacitors. A gyrator provides the most direct means of simulating an inductor in an *LC* filter prototype [4]; there are other indirect means, such as the well-known leapfrog structure, which possess the same state equations as an *LC* prototype. The quality of inductor simulation by these active circuits determines the selectivity and the maximum passband frequency of the filter. We assume in discussing the fundamental sources of imperfection in

Reprinted from *IEEE J. Solid-State Circuits*, vol. SC-25, no. 6, pp. 1562–1574, Dec. 1990.

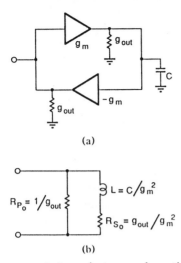

(a)

$R_{P_o} = 1/g_{out}$ $L = C/g_m^2$

$R_{S_o} = g_{out}/g_m^2$

(b)

Fig. 2. (a) Nonzero output conductances of gyration transconductances and (b) the equivalent circuit of the simulated lossy inductor.

simulated inductors that they are implemented by a gyrator and a capacitor because this is the most straightforward way to translate imperfections into equivalent circuits, but we note that the analysis may be extended to indirect methods of simulating LC filters that employ similar active building blocks.

A gyrator is most naturally realized on an integrated circuit as two equal transconductances in negative feedback (Fig. 1). A transistor used as a transconductance device also possesses a nonzero conductance at its output port, and capacitances at the input and output ports produced both by the inherent transistor action and parasitics. These two imperfections degrade the quality of inductors simulated by transistor gyrators, as is discussed below.

A. Effects of Finite dc Gain

The nonzero conductance (g_{out}) at the output of a transconductance (g_m) element sets its maximum voltage gain at dc ($A_{dc} = g_m/g_{out}$). The equivalent circuit at the input port of a gyrator constructed from this imperfect transconductance, and terminated by a capacitor at the other port, consists of an inductor L with series loss resistance R_s and shunt loss resistance R_p (Fig. 2) whose values are given by [4]

$$L = \frac{C}{g_m^2} \tag{1}$$

$$R_s = \frac{g_{out}}{g_m^2} \tag{2}$$

$$R_p = \frac{1}{g_{out}}. \tag{3}$$

Consider the special case of a simulated LC resonant circuit obtained by attaching equal capacitors C on both ports of a gyrator. The susceptance of the capacitor and simulated inductor are each g_m at the resonant frequency, $\omega_0 = g_m/C$, and the quality factor Q of the

inductor may be obtained by using a narrow-band approximation to transform R_p into a series resistor $R_s' \approx (\omega_0 L)^2/R_p = g_{out}/g_m^2$, so that

$$Q \overset{\text{def}}{=} \frac{\omega_0 L}{R_s + R_s'} = \frac{g_m}{2 g_{out}}. \tag{4}$$

The quality factor of the simulated integrator is thus one half the dc gain of the transconductors used in the gyrators, independent of the resonance frequency. Well-known techniques like the insertion of cascode transistors may be used to lower the output conductance at the gyrator ports [5], [6] when low loss inductors are required in active filters. This paper describes other, more appropriate, ways to eliminate loss when inductors are used in high-frequency filters.

B. Effects of High-Frequency Phase Shifts

A transconductance realized with compound transistor circuits will contain internal poles which produce phase shift at high frequencies, and become a serious problem when the signals in the filter passband approach the frequencies of these undesirable poles [4]; high-Q bandpass filters, for example, show an excessive peaking in the passband as a consequence of small amounts of excess phase shift [7]. If the two transconductors constituting the gyrator have a small phase lag $e^{(-j\phi)}$, the terminal admittance with a capacitor across the other gyrator port is

$$Y_{in} = \frac{g_m^2 e^{(-2j\phi)}}{j\omega C} \approx \frac{g_m^2}{j\omega C} - \frac{2 g_m^2}{\omega C} \phi. \tag{5}$$

For the special case when the gyrator has one dominant high-frequency pole (ω_1), the phase shift may be approximated by $\phi = \tan^{-1}(\omega/\omega_1) \approx \omega/\omega_1$, so

$$Y_{in} \approx \frac{1}{j\omega L} - \frac{2}{\omega_1 L}. \tag{6}$$

This corresponds to a *negative* resistance $-R_{p1}$ in paral-

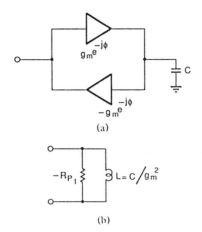

(a)

$-R_{P_1}$ $L = C/g_m^2$

(b)

Fig. 3. (a) Phase lag in the gyration transconductances produces (b) negative loss in the simulated inductor.

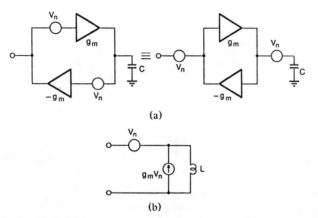

(a)

(b)

Fig. 4. (a) Noise in the gyration transconductances and (b) the noisy simulated inductance.

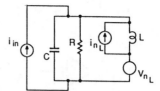

Fig. 5. Bandpass filter with a noisy simulated inductor.

lcl with the simulated inductor (Fig. 3). Suppose this inductor is used in a bandpass filter consisting of an LC resonant circuit driven by a current; the passband gain at the resonant frequency f_0 is then determined by the parallel resistance R_p in the tuned circuit. A phase lag in the gyrator transconductances produces a parasitic increase in this gain because the negative resistance will reduce the loss R_p deliberately inserted into the resonant circuit to obtain the desired bandwidth. For example, a negative resistance of magnitude $|R_{p1}| = 2R_p$ produced by a transconductance pole at $\omega_1 = 4Q\omega_0$ will result in a parasitic increase in gain of 6 dB over the designed value at resonance. To avoid this effect, the gyrator poles would have to lie well beyond $4Q$ times the resonant frequency, a condition which could only be fulfilled by the use of exceptionally high-speed active devices in a selective video-frequency bandpass filter.

C. Noise in Simulated Inductors and Resonator Dynamic Range

Noise in a resonator made from a physical inductor and capacitor arises only from dissipation in these elements. The inductor loss, capacitor leakage, and any externally applied damping resistance produce noise, but in conjunction with the reactive elements also set the noise bandwidth. It is straightforward to show that an rms broad-band noise voltage of $(kT/C)^{1/2}$ appears across the terminals of a parallel LC resonator with any positive dissipation [9].

In resonators constructed with simulated inductors, the situation is quite different, for here the active devices introduce additional noise, which as we show below may be substantially greater. Representing the noise in a CMOS transconductance stage by an equivalent voltage source in series with the input, we may associate uncorrelated noise sources of equal rms value (v_n) with each gyration transconductor (Fig. 4(a)), and when the output conductance of the transconductors is small, these noise sources may be pulled outside the feedback loop (Fig. 4(b)). This appears as an inductor with a shunt noise

current, $i_{nL} = g_m v_n$, and a series noise voltage, $v_{nL} = v_n$ (Fig. 4(c)).

The noise spectral density at resonance across the terminals of an LC resonant circuit constructed with equal capacitances across the two ports of a gyrator, and loaded with a large resistor R to obtain fractional bandwidth $1/Q$, is

$$\hat{v}_n^2 = \hat{i}_{nL}^2 R^2 + \hat{v}_{nL}^2 \left(\frac{R}{\omega_0 L}\right)^2 = 2(g_m R)^2 \hat{v}_n^2. \tag{7}$$

The gyration transconductor circuit in high-frequency filters is usually a MOS differential pair [7] or some simple extension [8], so to a reasonably good approximation, $(\hat{v}_n)^2 \approx kT/g_m$. As the noise bandwidth for a high Q resonator is approximately f_0/Q, the rms noise voltage across the resonator is

$$v_n \sim \left((g_m R)^2 \times \frac{kT}{g_m} \times \frac{\omega_0}{Q}\right)^{1/2} = \sqrt{Q}\,(kT/C)^{1/2} \tag{8}$$

where we make use of the relation $R = Q/\omega_0 C = Q/g_m$. This shows that the noise power is Q times worse in a resonant circuit employing a simulated inductor [9], because here the largest noise is produced by the simulated *reactance* ($1/g_m$ at resonance) whose value is Q times larger than the resistive dissipation, which was the only source of noise in a resonator built with a physical inductor. This leads to a fundamental limit on the attainable dynamic range of high-selectivity bandpass active filters. The maximum terminal voltage in a gyrator implementation of an LCR resonant circuit excited by a signal current is limited by considerations of distortion to some fraction α of the power supply V_{DD}. Suppose a transconductance stage converts an input voltage of a fixed maximum amplitude to the current applied to the resonator (Fig. 5); the gain of this stage must scale inversely with R to limit the maximum terminal voltage in the resonator. The equivalent noise in series with the input voltage due to noise in the resonator and in the input transconductor, whose gain we denote by A/R, is then

$$v_{eq}^2 \approx \frac{kT}{C} Q \left(\frac{1}{A}\right)^2 + \frac{kT}{(A/R)} \frac{\omega_0}{Q} = \frac{kT}{AC}\left(\frac{Q}{A}+1\right).$$

Typically A would be of the order of unity, which implies that the resonator noise, the first term in the equation above, will dominate at the input when $Q \gg 1$. The dynamic range, defined as the ratio of the maximum input signal limited by distortion to the minimum resolvable signal determined by noise, is given by

$$\text{dynamic range} = \alpha V_{DD} \sqrt{\frac{C}{kT}} \frac{1}{\sqrt{Q}}. \qquad (9)$$

We conclude then that the dynamic range worsens with increasing Q of a resonator, and may only be held constant by increasing the resonator capacitance proportional to Q. This, in turn, implies some scaling rules for chip area and power dissipation of resonators, and therefore for bandpass active filters, as a function of center frequency and fractional bandwidth. If a prescribed dynamic range must be obtained, we should scale

$$C \propto Q \qquad (10)$$

$$g_m = \omega_0 C \propto \omega_0 Q \qquad (11)$$

$$\Rightarrow \text{chip area} \propto \omega_0 Q \qquad (12)$$

and

$$\text{power dissipation} \propto \omega_0 Q \qquad (13)$$

assuming in (13) that $g_m \propto I_D$ at a fixed $V_{GS} - V_t$, as is true for short-channel MOSFET's, and that the power supply is fixed.

III. AUTOMATIC TUNING METHODS

It is common to use master–slave arrangements in the integrated circuit art for the adaptive compensation of tolerances in untrimmed components. This has been particularly exploited in continuous-time filters for the tuning, or centering, of frequency response, which due to the tolerances in quantities such as bias currents or FET transconductance, would otherwise never conform to the usually tight specifications [10]–[12]. We have extended in this work the role of adaptive tuning to remove gyrator *imperfections* which lead to either positive or negative loss in simulated inductors. This we call the tuning of dissipation, or of quality factor. The idea is to introduce a controllable phase advance in every gyration transconductance, which reduces the negative loss by overcoming phase lag; when the negative loss exactly cancels positive loss, a simulated LC resonator with no termination resistor breaks out into sustained oscillations of a constant, regulated amplitude. If other resonators on the same chip, nominally matched to this oscillator, constitute the filter path, then applying the same phase advance to those gyrators will also make them lossless, and the filter frequency response will be determined by precisely known lossless simulated inductors and capacitors, and by precisely designed termination resistors. The troublesome parasitic effects in the frequency response produced by gyrator nonidealities may in this way be completely eliminated.

A. Automatic Means to Eliminate Inductor Loss

A lossless LC resonant circuit with nonzero initial conditions produces a steady sinusoidal oscillation. If positive loss were present in the resonator, the oscillation amplitude would decay in time, or, if the loss were negative, build up until saturated by circuit nonlinearities. Nonidealities in a gyrator, as we have noted above, produce both types of loss at high frequencies. We can therefore, by controlling the magnitude of negative loss, make it exactly compensate the positive over some frequency range of interest. This we do by introducing a pole–zero pair (ω_p, ω_z) into the gyration transconductance whose frequencies may be voltage controlled, for the gyration transconductance will then be given by

$$g_m(j\omega) = g_{m0} \frac{1 + j\omega/\omega_z}{(1 + j\omega/\omega_p)(1 + j\omega/\omega_1)}$$

and the gyrator admittance with a capacitor attached to the other port (and neglecting for the moment output conductances) is

$$Y(j\omega) \approx \frac{g_m^2}{j\omega C} \left(1 - j\omega \left(\frac{2}{\omega_1} + \frac{2}{\omega_p} - \frac{2}{\omega_z} \right) \right)$$

$$\approx \frac{g_m^2}{j\omega C} - \frac{2g_m^2}{C} \left(\frac{1}{\omega_1} + \frac{1}{\omega_p} - \frac{1}{\omega_z} \right). \qquad (14)$$

By forcing $1/\omega_z = 1/\omega_p + 1/\omega_1$, negative loss due to high-frequency poles may be removed completely by the phase advance introduced by the zero at frequencies up to ω_z. An additional intentionally introduced negative loss may furthermore be made to cancel the positive loss exactly due to the gyrator output conductance we had earlier neglected. That phase shifts in gyration transconductances produce negative loss was recognized early on in the literature [13]; indeed, methods for compensation of these phase shifts based on the insertion of trim resistors were proposed [14] and used [15], [16]. The same idea was extended to indirect filter simulations by canceling a known negative dissipation due to phase lag in integrators by positive dissipation due to their finite dc gain [7], but ultimately limited in use in high-selectivity filters by the inability to exactly model the phase lags due to high-frequency poles [17]. We see, however, only one previous instance where an automatic means was used to obtain dissipation compensation in a bipolar biquad filter [12] and the extension of this idea to low Q CMOS biquad sections [18]. The latter references show the use of automatic Q tuning but do not satisfactorily explain, as we attempt in this paper, the fundamental basis and limitations of this tuning in terms of circuit equivalents. We now discuss this in greater detail.

Consider an unterminated resonant circuit in which the simulated inductance has attached to it series and parallel loss resistances, R_s and R_p, representing the nonzero output resistance R at each side of the gyrator and, in addition, a controllable negative conductance $-G$ produced by gyrator phase shift (Fig. 6). These two effects

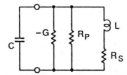

Fig. 6. Elements constituting the master resonator whose natural response is a steady sinusoidal oscillation.

may be represented independently in this way as long as their magnitudes are small. The terminal admittance of this circuit is

$$Y(s) = -G + \frac{1}{R_p} + \frac{1}{sL + R_s} + sC$$

$$= \frac{s^2 LC + s(CR_s + L/R_p - GL) + (1 + R_s/R_p)}{sL + R_s}.$$

The natural response of the circuit will be a sustained oscillation of constant amplitude at frequency ω_0 when the zeros of admittance lie on the $j\omega$ axis in the s plane. For this to occur, the negative loss conductance must attain the critical value

$$G_{crit} = \frac{CR_s}{L} + \frac{1}{R_p} = \frac{2}{R} \qquad (15)$$

after invoking the definitions of R_s, and the frequency of oscillation is then

$$\omega_0 = \left(\frac{1 + R_s/R_p}{LC} \right)^{1/2} \approx \frac{1}{\sqrt{LC}} \left(1 + \frac{1}{2A_{dc}^2} \right). \qquad (16)$$

If the negative loss in the gyrators simulating inductors in the filter path is now a slave to this value G_{crit}, the gyration admittance will become

$$Y_g = -\frac{1}{R} + \frac{1}{1/g_m^2 R + j\omega L}$$

$$= \frac{g_m^2 R - 1/R(1 + j\omega L g_m^2 R)}{1 + j\omega L g_m^2 R}$$

so

$$Z_g^{(j\omega)} = \frac{1}{Y_g} = \frac{1}{(A_{dc}^2 - 1)^2 + A_{dc}^2} R + j\omega L \frac{A_{dc}^4}{(A_{dc}^2 - 1)^2 + A_{dc}^2}$$

in the vicinity of ω_0, recalling that the dc voltage gain of a transconductor is $A_{dc} = g_m R$. A gyrator subject to this phase shift by a master simulates an inductor, $L_{eff} = L(1 + 1/A_{dc}^2)$, which equals the desired value L to a negligibly small error. At resonance, the effective series dissipation is $R_{eff} = -R/(A_{dc})^4$, an extremely small negative value. The inductor Q at resonance is then

$$Q = -\frac{\omega_0 L}{R} (A_{dc})^4 = -(A_{dc})^3 \qquad (17)$$

which is a factor of $(A_{dc})^2$ larger in magnitude than the Q obtainable from the same gyrator when no automatic means are present to balance the positive loss with nega-

tive loss. At frequencies away from resonance, the equivalent circuit of a slave gyrator consists of a small positive resistor $R/(A_{dc}^2 - 1)$ in series with inductor L, and a negative resistance $-R$ in parallel with it.

The critical value G_{crit} in the unterminated resonator may be obtained automatically by making the master resonator into a sinusoidal oscillator. We have adopted the method of sensing oscillation across the resonator, comparing the amplitude with a dc reference and deriving a feedback voltage to vary the zero frequency in the gyrator transconductances, to automatically drive the magnitude of $-G$ to G_{crit} [19].

The techniques described so far, however, ensure only that the simulated inductors are lossless; their magnitude, which depends on the gyration transconductance, is not regulated and so must be adjusted automatically by a different means.

B. Automatic Setting of Inductor Value

The electronically tunable inductance C/g_m^2 in an oscillating LC resonator may be automatically set to a predetermined value by frequency locking this oscillation to a stable externally supplied reference frequency. This may be used as a master for the usually identical reactances in the filter path [10]. Standard frequency-locked loop methods described elsewhere in detail [11] are used most often to accomplish this.

An important difference in the design of our master resonator from similar circuits described by others is that *two* decoupled electronically controllable attributes are required: a means to control the magnitude of gyration transconductance, and a separate means to control its phase. How these are obtained is described in greater detail in Section V.

IV. FILTER ARCHITECTURE

Bandpass filters using inductors and capacitors are usually realized by structures consisting of one resonator, or many resonators coupled together for greater frequency selectivity, or structures consisting of the cascade of a low-pass and a high-pass filter. We have chosen a filter of the former type, consisting of two identical resonators each with a pair of complex-conjugate poles actively coupled together [16] (Fig. 7(a)). Termination resistors appear at both ports of the gyrators and simulate a lossy inductor in parallel with a leaky capacitor to determine the filter passband. The active coupler consists of two small integrating transconductances $(sM)^{-1}$ in positive feedback (Fig. 7(b)). The input voltage is applied through a transconductance g_{mi} as a current to the filter, and the output voltage is converted to a current at the output pin by a transconductance g_{mo}.

The filter structure may be grasped more readily when it is converted to an LCR equivalent. The first gyrator presents the circuit at its left port to the coupler as a series LR connection driven by a voltage source, while

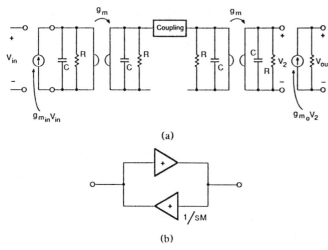

(a)

(b)

Fig. 7. (a) Architecture of our bandpass filter and (b) detail of the active coupler.

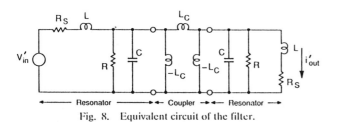

Fig. 8. Equivalent circuit of the filter.

the second gyrator presents the circuit at its right port as a series LR load. The output voltage is transformed by the gyrator into the inductor current i_{out}'. The coupler itself is equivalent to a π connection of one positive and two negative inductors of an equal large magnitude (Fig. 8). This somewhat unfamiliar circuit is nothing more than the π equivalent of the mutual inductive coupling between two resonant circuits. The transformed component values are

$$v_{in}' = \frac{g_{mi}}{g_m} v_{in}; \quad L = \frac{C}{g_m^2}; \quad R_s = \frac{1}{g_m^2 R};$$

$$L_c = M; \quad i_{out}' = g_m v_2.$$

This pair of coupled tuned circuits has two pairs of complex-conjugate poles, split apart in the s plane by the coupling to lie at

$$s = -\frac{G}{2C} \pm j \left(\frac{1}{C} \left(\frac{1}{L} \pm \frac{1}{L_c} \right) - \left(\frac{G}{2C} \right)^2 \right)^{1/2}$$

$$\approx -\frac{G}{2C} \pm \frac{j}{\sqrt{LC}} \left(1 \pm \frac{L}{2L_c} \right) \qquad (18)$$

where a narrow-band approximation has been used to lump all the loss in each resonant circuit into a shunt conductance

$$G \stackrel{\text{def}}{=} \frac{1}{R} + \frac{R_s}{(\omega_0 L)^2} = \frac{2}{R}. \qquad (19)$$

TABLE I

R_S	$70 \, \Omega$
L	0.13×10^{-3} H
R	$600 \times 10^3 \, \Omega$
C	2.1×10^{-12} F
L_C	6.7×10^{-3} H

The peak filter gain occurs at ω_0 (defined in (16)) and is

$$\frac{v_{out}}{g_{mi} v_{in}} = \frac{\omega_0 L_c}{1 + (\omega_0 L_c G)^2} \cong 1/2 \omega_0 L_c. \qquad (20)$$

We wished to design a bandpass filter centered at 12.5 MHz with a 2% fractional bandwidth, that is, a -3-dB bandwidth of 250 kHz around the center frequency, and we chose to accomplish this in a 3-μm CMOS technology so that the parasitic gyrator phase shift intended to be overcome by the automatic tuning circuit would be forced to appear in the passband frequency range. FET's of a 6-μm channel length, which make the gyrator phase lag even greater, were used in the transconductance differential pairs. The desired frequency response could now *only* be obtained if the dissipation tuning techniques described above were effective.

Table I lists the element values in the LCR equivalent circuit of the filter. In the IC implementation, the gyration transconductances were 150 μS, and the coupler was made using a cascade of an integrator with unity-gain frequency of 1.77 MHz and a transconductance of 13.3 μS. The resonator capacitors were the same value as in the LCR equivalent, as were the termination resistors which set the $Q = 50$ for the two inductors. All gyrators were further loaded by 200-kΩ resistors to deliberately lower A_{dc}, once again to force the automatic loss balancing loop to compensate for them in order to obtain the desired frequency response. The loss in these resistors is compensated by the negative gyrator dissipation in the passband, but not in the stopband where they strongly influence the filter characteristics. The simulated frequency response with Q-control in operation (Fig. 9) indicates that high selectivity may be obtained with gyrators of low dc gain (in this case, $A_{dc} \cong 16$).

V. CIRCUIT DESIGN

A. Filter Path

The balanced differential signal flow used in the filter provides immunity to interference from common-mode pickup and high-frequency noise on the power supplies, problems typical in monolithic video frequency circuits, and also affords the simple implementation of a gyrator as an antiparallel connection of differential transconductance stages [20]. The input and output pins to the chip,

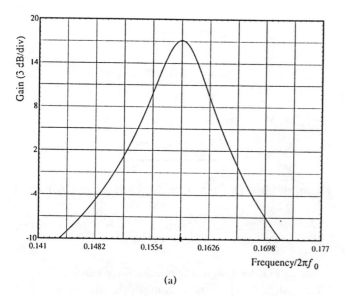

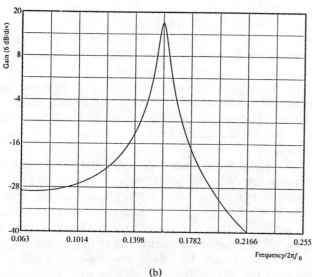

Fig. 9. Simulated frequency response of the filter on normalized axes: (a) passband and (b) stopband.

however, were single ended with respect to ground, with appropriate buffer stages converting them to balanced signals within the filter.

The gyrator transconductances were each loaded with a capacitor C_I and termination resistor R_T and therefore acted as a lossy voltage integrator. The integrator circuit (Fig. 10) consisted of a folded-cascode operational transconductance stage accompanied by a common-mode feedback loop to set the quiescent single-ended voltage at the output terminals. The filter capacitance C_I was implemented using the one layer of polysilicon available on the chip as two MOS capacitors connected back to back, with the common bottom plate to substrate remaining at virtual ground when a balanced signal is applied to the capacitance terminals. This structure occupies an area four times greater than it would if made in a double-poly structure with the same oxide thickness but zero strays at the bottom plate. The two NMOS capacitors in series were biased into inversion (or, in one case in the coupler,

in accumulation) by the FET connecting their common node to a dc bias voltage.

The termination resistor consisted of a single MOSFET with a fixed V_{GS}, which driven by a balanced source–drain voltage appears as a linear resistor in the triode region [11]. A control current sets the $V_{GS} - V_t$ of the resistor (Fig. 11) while leaving the gate free to adopt whatever common-mode voltage is imposed on it by the circuit driving its source and drain. The resistor can tolerate a maximum voltage across its terminals of $2(V_{GS} - V_t)$ before entering saturation, and becomes nonlinear for larger terminal voltages.

Another variable resistor R_Z and capacitor C_Z were used as a peaking network in the integrator differential pair, to introduce a voltage-controlled pole and zero in the gyration transconductance. The value of C_Z (2.53 pF) was chosen so that the nominal R_Z to produce the desired phase lead satisfied $2g_{m0}R_Z \sim 1$, where g_{m0} is the FET transconductance in the integrator input stage; the gyration transconductance

$$g_m = \frac{g_{m0}}{1 + g_{m0}R_Z}$$

is then not heavily degenerated, and could be varied over some reasonable range by changing the FET bias current independently of the positions of the pole and zero introduced by R_Z and C_Z. This allows the resonance frequency to be controlled by one automatic means, which we call the f-controller, and loss in the simulated inductance to be eliminated by another, called the Q-controller. SPICE simulations of the integrator frequency response showed that its phase could be swept through $-90°$ by the Q-controller without noticeably affecting the unity-gain frequency (Fig. 12).

The coupler between resonators was implemented by an integrator and a transconductance stage (Fig. 13), with the integrator input stage FET size chosen so that it imposed a small (2%) parasitic capacitive loading on the resonators. The coupling inductance L_c thus obtained was equal to the ratio of the integrator capacitance to the product of the transconductances, and its value was selected to obtain the desired ripple in the filter passband, which is controlled by the ratio L_c/L. Both transconductances in the coupler were varied by the f-controller in proportion to the gyration transconductance so as to keep the ratio L_c/L constant and thus preserve the shape of the passband across the tuning range of ω_0. The peak filter gain, however, would vary in inverse proportion to ω_0.

B. Control Loops

The transconductance and phase shift in the two identical filter gyrators were slaves to a third replica gyrator loaded with identical capacitances and simulating a lossless LC resonant circuit. In the absence of external control, the natural response of this master circuit would be a decaying oscillation if the simulated inductance has

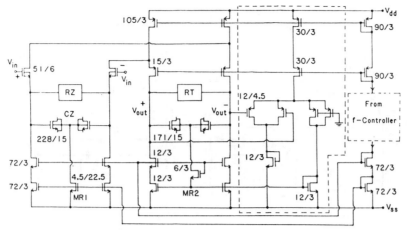

Fig. 10. Integrator circuit constituting one arm of a simulated *LC* damped resonant circuit.

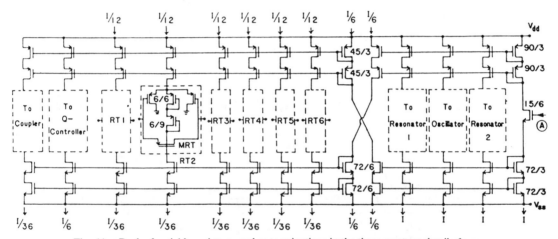

Fig. 11. Bank of variable resistors used as terminations in the three gyrators; detail of one.

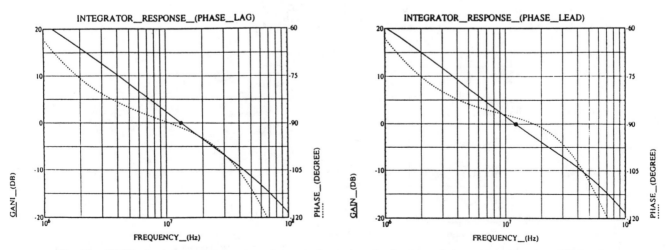

Fig. 12. SPICE simulation of integrator phase at the unity-gain frequency being swept through $-90°$ by the voltage-controlled phase advance network. The unity-gain frequency remains relatively constant.

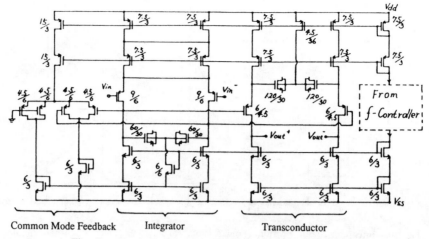

Fig. 13. One half of the active coupler between resonators.

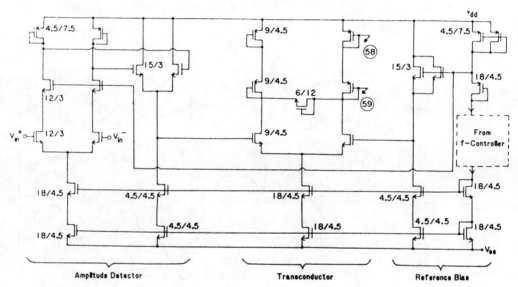

Fig. 14. The Q-control (dissipation tuning) circuit.

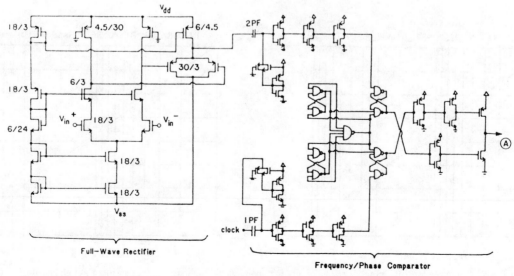

Fig. 15. The f-control (center frequency tuning) circuit.

positive loss, or if the loss is negative, an oscillation tending to grow until limited in amplitude by circuit saturation. The Q-controller senses either tendency and corrects it by feedback to produce a sustained oscillation of a predetermined amplitude; the f-controller then locks the steady-state frequency to an externally supplied reference. One may think of the Q-controller as responsible for moving the resonator poles from the left- or right-half s plane onto the $j\omega$ axis, and the f-controller then sliding these poles along the axis to some desired position.

1) Q-Control Loop: The Q-control loop consists of an oscillation peak detector which generates an error voltage to vary R_Z in all three gyrators. A balanced large-signal oscillation applied at the inputs of a differential pair is rectified at the tail because either one FET conducts or the other, so the oscillation always tends to pull up the tail voltage. This will produce a dc voltage across a large capacitance attached to the tail equal to the oscillation amplitude shifted down by V_{GS} (Fig. 14). Error currents to control R_Z are then derived by comparing this dc voltage with a reference.

2) Frequency Control Loop: The oscillation frequency of the master resonator may now be compared with a reference frequency by a conventional phase frequency detector, and an error current may be generated to control the gyration transconductance. The center frequency of the bandpass filter would be a slave to this. It is likely in this arrangement, however, for the signals of large amplitude present in the phase-locked loop to couple through the common monolithic substrate and shared power supplies into the center of the filter passband. One way to avoid this is by doubling the master resonator frequency in a nonlinear element, and then comparing it with a reference frequency set at twice the filter center frequency. The master oscillation was doubled in frequency at the tail of a differential pair acting as a full wave rectifier (Fig. 15), and then applied to the phase frequency comparator. Currents derived from the filtered output were broadcast to the three resonators, the coupler, and also to the termination resistors to maintain the fractional bandwidth ($= g_m R_T$) of the filter at a prescribed value across the tuning frequency range.

VI. EXPERIMENTAL RESULTS

The circuits described above were fabricated on a 2.3×3.4-mm chip in a 3-μm CMOS process. The roles of the different blocks on the chip determined their placement on the IC (Fig. 16). The master resonator, for instance, was placed at the geometric centroid of the two slaves to minimize the effects of mismatches caused by fabrication gradients across the chip surface. To reduce unwanted coupling of digital noise through shared lines and the substrate, the phase frequency detector was placed at the opposite end of the chip to the analog signal path. The signals derived from the f- and Q-controllers determined the conductances of FET's in the slave devices, and were therefore sent as currents across the chip to minimize

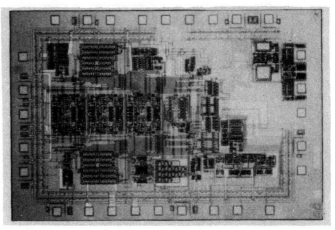

Fig. 16.   Chip photograph. Three resonators are evident on one side, the control circuits on the other.

errors introduced by global V_t mismatches. Details of the current-controlled resistor have been described above.

The frequency response of the filter was measured in a network analyzer. The absolute value of passband gain was set by an external resistor connected to the single-ended transconductance output. The measured response conformed closely to the simulations (Fig. 17), except for a deviation in the lower stopband which we could not fully account for. The master oscillation was observed on a buffered output of the master resonator to verify that the f- and Q-control circuits functioned effectively. The filter center frequency could be tuned from 12.5 to 13.5 MHz while preserving the passband shape, with a slight increase in fractional bandwidth from 2% to 2.2%, which most likely could be attributed to errors in measurement and also to imperfections in the circuit technique employed to maintain a constant passband over the tuning range. We did note, more importantly, that the master oscillation frequency was always less than the filter center frequency, by 0.3 MHz at $f_0 = 12.5$ MHz and by 1.2 MHz at $f_0 = 13.5$ MHz. This could be explained by the greater capacitive loading imposed on the master resonator by the two controllers than on the slave units by the input and output buffers. With careful modeling these loads could be more accurately absorbed into the several resonator capacitances to eliminate this undesirable discrepancy in frequency.

It was our intent to use this filter principally as a demonstration of the automatic means to eliminate dissipation in inductor simulation, and we did not go to great lengths in the design to incorporate features leading to low signal distortion, or to minimize noise. A 3-mV rms noise referred to the input was measured in a 250-kHz bandwidth. The output noise spectrum (Fig. 18) showed a peak in the filter passband; a master oscillation feedthrough signal 10 dB above the peak noise density was observed 1.2 MHz below the center frequency. The nonlinearity in the filter signal path was measured as the intermodulation distortion produced by two tones 40-kHz apart around the filter center frequency. If we regard the test tone amplitude of 211 mV at the input which pro-

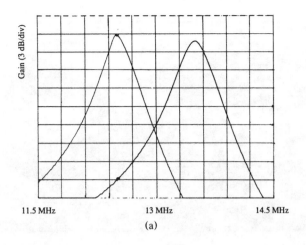

(a)

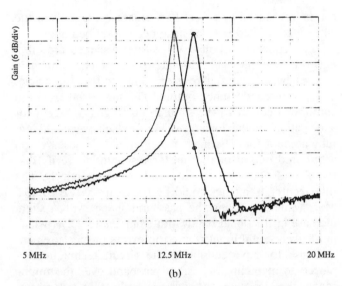

(b)

Fig. 17. (a) Measured filter passband response at center frequencies of 12.5 MHz and 13.5 MHz. (b) Measured stopband response at the same center frequencies.

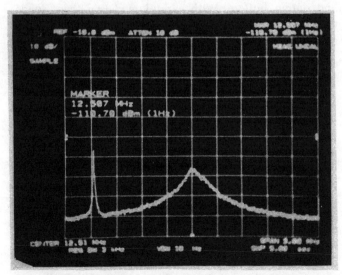

Fig. 18. Measured output noise spectrum (horizontal: 300 kHz/div; vertical: 10 dB/div).

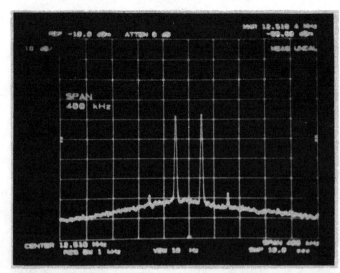

Fig. 19. Measured spectrum of two tones and their first-order intermodulation products at 1% (horizontal: 40 kHz/div; vertical: 10 dB/div).

duced 1% intermodulation products (Fig. 19) as the maximum usable input amplitude, the filter has a 37-dB dynamic range. The nonlinearity in the signal path arises mainly from the small effective gate voltage (slightly less than 0.5 V) on the FET resistors used for termination and phase advance, and could be reduced simply by scaling down the FET W/L ratio which would force the control loops to apply a larger gate voltage in order to obtain the same resistance. The measured dynamic range is within 3 dB of the prediction using (9). Distortion in the transconductance stages could be reduced by using one of the many linearized MOS transconductors described in the literature [8], [21]–[23], and further improvements in filter linearity could be obtained by eliminating the on-chip balanced-to-unbalanced conversion circuits at the input and output.

The balanced filter architecture afforded a natural immunity to fluctuations on the power supplies from corrupting the signal. The power supply rejection ratio at the filter center frequency was 40 dB from the positive power supply and 35 dB from the negative power supply.

The centering of active filter characteristics by the master–slave arrangement was verified in two different ways. First, the center frequency of a filter, once locked to a constant reference, did not change measurably with chip temperature in the range of 20 to 65°C, and second, the spread in filter center frequency in the three functional chips available to us from the MOSIS prototype run was only ±0.16% when locked to the same reference. This small spread may be taken as the estimate over a small sample of the standard deviation of master–slave mismatches on any one chip.

The filter was designed for operation at ±5 V for convenience, but operated best at ±6 V where it consumed 350 mW. The circuits could be redesigned to operate at a single 5-V power supply while retaining the same internal voltage swings.

Finally, we note from the measured frequency response that the strength of coupling between the two resonators

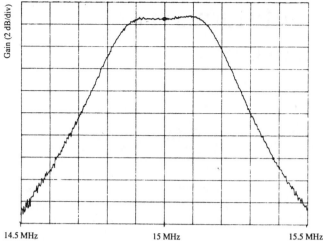

Fig. 20. Measured frequency response at 15 MHz with manual tuning to obtain an equiripple passband (horizontal: centered at 15 MHz with 100 kHz/div; vertical: 2 dB/div).

in the filter was insufficient enough to produce an equiripple response in the passband. We were able to obtain this response from the IC (Fig. 20) by a manual override of the control signals to the coupling transconductance, which suggests that it could be obtained automatically by use of appropriately larger FET's in the coupler.

VII. Conclusions

There are pressing needs for active filters operating at video speeds for use in televisions, image processing circuits, personal communication devices, and magnetic storage peripherals. The large array of techniques employed successfully to make multipole active filters in the voice-band frequency range had come to a standstill at video frequencies awaiting advances in device technology leading to orders of magnitude increases in device f_T. By demonstrating a high-selectivity filter at 12 MHz with FET's of 6-μm channel length, we have shown that the maximum frequency of filter operation is not as seriously limited by device f_T as was perhaps previously thought, but that automatic means may be employed to tune out the imperfections introduced in the filter elements by the limited voltage gain and frequency response of transistors. This technique will ultimately be limited at high frequencies when the phase advance network is no longer able to compensate for very large phase lags in the gyrator, or at low frequencies if the dc gain of the gyrator FET's approaches unity. However, as practical circuits will not approach these extremes, the ideas described in this work should spur a greater activity than witnessed to date in the successful design of high-selectivity CMOS active filters operating at tens to hundreds of megahertz.

Acknowledgment

The authors are particularly grateful to Prof. H. J. Orchard for his interest in this work and for sharing with us his many insights into the fundamentals of filter design. We also acknowledge the contributions of F. Lu to the circuit design. Testing of the filter was carried out in the UCLA Center for High Frequency Electronics.

References

[1] Y.-T. Wang, F. Lu, and A. A. Abidi, "A 12.5 MHz CMOS continuous time bandpass filter," in *ISSCC Dig. Tech. Papers* (New York), Feb. 1989, pp. 198–199.

[2] H. J. Orchard and D. F. Sheahan, "Inductorless bandpass filters," *IEEE J. Solid-State Circuits*, vol. SC-5, pp. 108–118, June 1970.

[3] Y. P. Tsividis, "Minimal transistor-only integrated VHF active filter," *Electron. Lett.*, vol. 23, pp. 777–778, July 1987.

[4] H. J. Orchard, "Gyrator circuits," in *Active Filters: Lumped, Distributed, Integrated, Digital and Parametric*, L. P. Huelsman, Ed. New York: McGraw-Hill, 1970, pp. 90–127.

[5] P. R. Gray and R. G. Meyer, *Analysis and Design of Analog Integrated Circuits*. New York: Wiley, 1984.

[6] A. A. Abidi, "On the operation of cascode gain stages," *IEEE J. Solid-State Circuits*, vol. 23, pp. 1434–1437, Dec. 1988.

[7] H. Khorramabadi and P. R. Gray, "High frequency CMOS continuous-time filters," *IEEE J. Solid-State Circuits*, vol. SC-19, pp. 939–948, Dec. 1984.

[8] F. Krummenacher and N. Joehl, "A 4 MHz CMOS continuous-time filter with on-chip automatic tuning," *IEEE J. Solid-State Circuits*, vol. 23, pp. 750–758, June 1988.

[9] D. Blom and J. O. Voorman, "Noise and dissipation of electronic gyrators," *Philips Res. Rep.*, vol. 26, pp. 103–113, Apr. 1971.

[10] K. S. Tan and P. R. Gray, "Fully integrated analog filters using bipolar-JFET technology," *IEEE J. Solid-State Circuits*, vol. SC-12, pp. 814–821, Dec. 1978.

[11] Y. Tsividis, M. Banu, and J. Khoury, "Continuous-time MOSFET-C filters in VLSI," *IEEE J. Solid-State Circuits*, vol. SC-21, pp. 15–30, Feb. 1986.

[12] C. F. Chiou and R. Schaumann, "Design and performance of a fully integrated bipolar 10.7-MHz analog bandpass filter," *IEEE J. Solid-State Circuits*, vol. SC-21, pp. 6–14, Feb. 1986.

[13] W. H. Holmes, S. Gruetzman, and W. E. Heinlein, "Direct coupled gyrators with floating ports," *Electron. Lett.*, vol. 3, pp. 46–47, Feb. 1967.

[14] H. T. van Looij and K. M. Adams, "Phase compensation in electronic gyrator circuits," *Electron. Lett.*, vol. 4, pp. 430–431, Oct. 4, 1968.

[15] K. W. Moulding and G. A. Wilson, "A fully integrated five gyrator filter at video frequencies," *IEEE J. Solid-State Circuits*, vol. SC-13, pp. 303–307, June 1978.

[16] K. W. Moulding *et al.*, "Gyrator video filter IC with automatic tuning," *IEEE J. Solid-State Circuits*, vol. SC-15, pp. 963–968, Dec. 1980.

[17] M. Koyama, H. Tanimoto, and S. Mizoguchi, "A 10.7 MHz continuous-time bandpass filter bipolar IC," in *Proc. Custom IC Conf.* (San Diego, CA), May 1989.

[18] C.-S. Park and R. Schaumann, "Design of a 4-MHz analog integrated CMOS transconductance-C bandpass filter," *IEEE J. Solid-State Circuits*, vol. 23, pp. 987–996, Aug. 1988.

[19] D. Senderowicz, D. A. Hodges, and P. R. Gray, "An NMOS integrated vector locked loop," in *Proc. ISCAS*, (Rome, Italy), May 1982, pp. 1164–1167.

[20] H. O. Voorman and A. Bishcuvel, "An electronic gyrator," *IEEE J. Solid-State Circuits*, vol. SC-7, pp. 469–474, Dec. 1972.

[21] Y. Tsividis, Z. Czarnul, and S. C. Fang, "MOS transconductors and integrators with high linearity," *Electron. Lett.*, vol. 22, pp. 245–246, 1986.

[22] K. Bult and H. Wallinga, "A class of analog CMOS circuits based on the square law characteristic of an MOS transistor in saturation," *IEEE J. Solid-State Circuits*, vol. SC-22, pp. 357–365, June 1987.

[23] E. Seevinck and R. F. Wassenaar, "A versatile CMOS linear transconductor/square-law function circuit," *IEEE J. Solid-State Circuits*, vol. SC-22, pp. 366–377, June 1987.

269

A 4-MHz CMOS Continuous-Time Filter with On-Chip Automatic Tuning

FRANÇOIS KRUMMENACHER AND NORBERT JOEHL

Abstract —This paper presents a third-order elliptic low-pass continuous-time filter with a 4-MHz cutoff frequency, integrated in a 3-μm p-well CMOS process. The design procedure is based on the direct simulation of a doubly terminated *LC* ladder filter by means of capacitors and fully balanced, current-controlled transconductance amplifiers with extended linear range. The on-chip automatic tuning circuit uses a phase-locked loop implemented with an 8.5-MHz controlled oscillator that matches a specific two-integrator loop of the filter. The complete circuit features 70-dB dynamic range (THD < − 50 dB) and consumes only 16 mW from ± 2.5-V supplies.

I. INTRODUCTION

INTEGRATED continuous-time filters are suitable solutions to perform a variety of signal processing tasks. Examples include radio and video frequency filtering applications and anti-aliasing filters in digital or switched-capacitor (SC) systems.

Two main approaches to the design of such filters that are fully compatible with current CMOS technologies have been successfully used to date. One combines MOS transistors used as voltage-controlled resistors together with capacitors and MOS operational amplifiers to realize the so-called "MOSFET-C active filters" [1], [2] whereas the other one makes use of capacitors and MOS transconductance elements only [3], [4]. In any case, an automatic tuning circuitry is necessary to maintain precise filtering characteristics against process variations, temperature drift, aging, etc.

This paper is relevant to the second approach and describes a novel class *A* transconductance element with improved linearity performance and its application to continuous-time filtering at video frequencies. The automatic tuning control and related problems are also discussed in detail.

II. BASIC DESIGN CONSIDERATIONS

As a starting point, it is worth considering the simple differential pair integrator proposed in [3] (Fig. 1). In addition to its simplicity, tunability, and area efficiency,

Manuscript received November 16, 1987; revised January 7, 1988. This work was supported by the Hasler Foundation, Bern (project AGEN 24).

The authors are with the Electronics Laboratory, Swiss Federal Institute of Technology (EPFL), DE-Ecublens, CH-1015 Lausanne, Switzerland.

IEEE Log Number 8819981.

this integrator configuration potentially achieves the best high-frequency performance because it makes use of a single source-coupled differential pair to implement the voltage-to-current converter function (as opposed to configurations with multistage operational amplifiers which suffer from large amounts of excess phase at high frequency, causing unacceptable errors in the filter response).

Although requiring additional circuitry to provide for common-mode feedback, a balanced output will improve both the dynamic range and the power supply rejection which become critical parameters in high-frequency applications for mixed analog/digital systems.

One major disadvantage of this elementary integrator, however, is that in order to maintain harmonic or intermodulation distortions at acceptable levels and to limit the unity-gain frequency shift [3] due to the nonlinear behavior of the source-coupled pair, the current modulation in the transistors must be kept low. Consequently both the signal-to-noise ratio and the efficiency (the ratio of the maximum signal power to the supply power consumption) are limited.

Several circuit techniques for improving the linearity of MOS transconductance elements have been proposed in the literature. In [5], linearization is achieved by simply adding an auxiliary cross-coupled differential pair to the source-coupled pair and by properly scaling their W/L ratios and tail currents. Another possibility is to degenerate the source-coupled pair by means of a MOS transistor operating in the triode region [6]. A combination of both techniques yields even better linearity performance [6], [7]. Other linearization methods use grounded-source triode-mode MOST's [8], cross-coupled quad configurations [9], or class *AB* operation [10]–[12].

Although offering better linearity performance and lower quiescent power dissipation, class *AB* operation leads to increasing electromagnetic compatibility problems (e.g., crosstalk via supply lines and substrate) and is therefore not to be considered for filtering applications in the megahertz range and above. Solutions involving current mirroring [9]–[12] or sophisticated cascode devices [8] must also be rejected because they suffer from significant excess phase at high frequency.

Starting from the standpoint that simplicity and good high-frequency performance are the essential features of a

Reprinted from *IEEE J. Solid-State Circuits*, vol. 23, no. 3, pp. 750–758, June 1988.

270

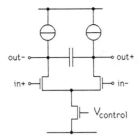

Fig. 1. Simple differential pair integrator.

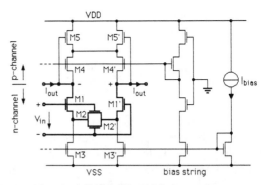

Fig. 2. Linearized CMOS differential transconductance amplifier.

linearized transconductance amplifier intended for video filtering applications, a new balanced voltage-to-current converter derived from [3] and [6] was developed. This circuit is described in the next section.

III. A New Linear CMOS Transconductor

The schematic diagram of a fully balanced transconductance amplifier with a novel four-transistor input stage (shown in thick lines) is depicted in Fig. 2. Transistors $M1$ and $M1'$, biased by current sources $M3$ and $M3'$, form the input differential pair, the transfer characteristic of which is linearized by the voltage-controlled degenerating "resistors" $M2$ and $M2'$. The common-mode output voltage is stabilized by $M5$ and $M5'$, which operate in the triode region [3].

In order to get a qualitative understanding of the behavior of this new input stage, the circuit is first analyzed using the simple square-law MOSFET model and assuming that $M1$, $M1'$, $M2$, and $M2'$ are in a common well (e.g., connected to V_{SS}). For convenience, the following parameters are introduced:

$$a = 1 + \beta_1/4\beta_2 \tag{1}$$

and

$$g_{m0} = \left.\frac{\partial I_{out}}{\partial V_{in}}\right|_{V_{in}=0} = \frac{I_{bias}}{a(V_{GS} - V_T)_{M1}}. \tag{2}$$

For low values of the input voltage V_{in}, transistors $M2$ and $M2'$ are working in the triode region and the following normalized transfer characteristic is easily obtained (here a purely differential input voltage is assumed):

$$i = v\sqrt{1 - v^2/4} \tag{3}$$

where

$$v = g_{m0}V_{in}/I_{bias} \tag{4}$$

$$i = I_{out}/I_{bias}. \tag{5}$$

From the above equations, it may be concluded that within a limited input voltage range the transfer characteristic of the input transconductance element is similar to that of a conventional source-coupled pair biased at a gate over-drive voltage equal to $a(V_{GS} - V_T)_{M1}$. Deviation from this well-known behavior occurs when either $M2'$ (for $V_{in} > 0$)

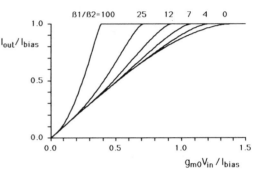

Fig. 3. Normalized i/v curves obtained from (1)–(8) for different values of the ratio β_1/β_2.

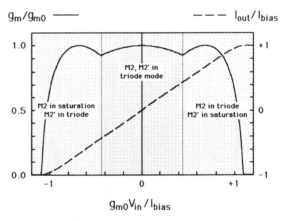

Fig. 4. Calculated i/v transfer characteristic and small-signal transconductance $g_m = \partial I_{out}/\partial V_{in}$ of the transconductor of Fig. 2 according to (1)–(8) for $\beta_1/\beta_2 = 6.7$.

or $M2$ (for $V_{in} < 0$) enters the saturation region, that is when

$$|v| = \left|\frac{g_{m0}V_{in}}{I_{bias}}\right| > v_1 = \sqrt{\frac{a^2 + a + 0.5}{a^4 + 0.25}}. \tag{6}$$

The normalized transfer characteristic then becomes

$$i = \pm \frac{\left[av\sqrt{4a - 2} \pm \sqrt{4a - 1 - a^2v^2}\right]^2}{(4a - 1)^2} \tag{7}$$

where the positive (negative) sign holds for a positive

(negative) input voltage. The maximum output current ($I_{\text{out}} = I_{\text{bias}}$ or $i = 1$) is reached for

$$|v| = \left| \frac{g_{m0} V_{\text{in}}}{I_{\text{bias}}} \right| = v_2 = \frac{\sqrt{4a - 2}}{a}. \tag{8}$$

The resulting normalized i/v curves calculated for different values of the ratio β_1/β_2 are plotted in Fig. 3. The optimum value of the latter ratio for the best linearity performance appears to be around 7. Fig. 4 is another illustration of the behavior of the four-transistor input cell showing the variations of the small-signal transconductance $g_m = \partial I_{\text{out}}/\partial V_{\text{in}}$ (for $\beta_1/\beta_2 = 6.7$) according to the above equations. The inaccuracies of the model used become evident when considering the angular shape of the g_m curve at the transition from the triode to the saturation mode for $M2$ and $M2'$ and at the points where g_m approaches zero. These angles are smoothed when the deviations from the simple square-law model in the vicinity of the threshold and at the transition from the triode to the saturation region are taken into account. More accurate simulation and experimental data confirm that the ripple in the actual g_m curve is smaller than modeled in Fig. 4 and that it may be further reduced by lowering the quiescent gate overdrive voltage $V_{GS} - V_T$ of the transistors.

For example, with $\beta_1/\beta_2 = 6.7$ and $V_{GS} - V_T > 1$ V, g_m typically varies by ± 2.5 percent over 80 percent of the output current range ($|I_{\text{out}}| \leqslant 0.8 I_{\text{bias}}$). However, the linearity is improved when the transistors are biased at reduced current densities (i.e., 0.2 V $< V_{GS} - V_T < 0.5$ V), which is often desirable for other reasons, such as to achieve higher dc voltage gain, lower bias current, or lower supply voltage. In this case, the deviations from the square-law model due to the proximity of the moderate inversion region are much more important and result in a significant reduction of the ripple in the transconductance characteristic (variations of less than ± 1 percent are achievable). On the other hand, the optimum ratio β_1/β_2 for the best linearity performance becomes slightly dependent on the quiescent gate overdrive voltages $V_{GS} - V_T$. This is a limitation of the technique since the dc bias point of the devices must be allowed to vary by a certain amount to compensate for fabrication tolerances and temperature variations. In the case of transconductor/capacitor filters the cutoff or center frequency f_c is proportional to the ratio of the transconductance g_m to the integrating capacitance C:

$$f_c \sim g_m/C \text{ with } g_m \sim \beta(V_{GS} - V_T) \sim \sqrt{\beta I_{\text{bias}}}. \tag{9}$$

Thus

$$V_{GS} - V_T \sim f_c C/\beta \tag{10}$$

and

$$I_{\text{bias}} \sim (f_c C)^2/\beta. \tag{11}$$

For a given frequency response (constant f_c), assuming that the tolerances on process parameters C and β are

± 10 and ± 20 percent, respectively, and that the circuit must operate over a 50°C temperature range with a temperature coefficient of typically 0.5 percent/°C for β (the temperature coefficient for C is usually negligible), the dc bias point of the input devices $M1$ and $M2$ may fall within the following limits:

$$\frac{(V_{GS} - V_T)_{\text{max}}}{(V_{GS} - V_T)_{\text{min}}} = \frac{C_{\text{max}}}{C_{\text{min}}} \frac{\beta_{\text{max}}}{\beta_{\text{min}}} \approx 2.4 \tag{12}$$

and

$$\frac{(I_{\text{bias}})_{\text{max}}}{(I_{\text{bias}})_{\text{min}}} = \frac{C_{\text{max}}^2}{C_{\text{min}}^2} \frac{\beta_{\text{max}}}{\beta_{\text{min}}} \approx 2.9. \tag{13}$$

Measurements made on an integrated version of the circuit of Fig. 2 will illustrate how these variations can affect the circuit performance.

If the input common-mode voltage is not constant with respect to the bulk potential, even-order terms will appear in the i/v transfer characteristic. These distortions may be minimized by increasing the bulk reverse voltage to reduce the body effect. For a purely differential mode input signal, the remaining even-order distortions would result from device mismatch, which has to be minimized by appropriate layout disposition.

In spite of the aforementioned limitations, this circuit offers an attractive combination of good high-frequency behavior, linearity, and low power dissipation for a reduced circuit complexity.

The complete transconductance circuit of Fig. 2 was fabricated in a 3-μm p-well CMOS process. The design parameter values were $g_{m0} = 150$ μA/V and $I_{\text{bias}} = 100$ μA, so that $(V_{GS} - V_T)_{M1,2} \approx 0.27$ V. With $L_1 = L_2 = 5$ μm, this corresponds to $W_1 = 396$ μm and $W_2 = 66$ μm ($\beta_1/\beta_2 = 6$). As can be seen from the experimental data shown in Fig. 5, the nonlinearity stays well below 1 percent of the full-scale output current up to 80-percent current modulation ($I_{\text{out}}/I_{\text{bias}} \leqslant 0.8$). This holds for a single (unbalanced) input (Fig. 5(b)) as well as for a differential (balanced) one (Fig. 5(a)).

In Fig. 6, the measured small-signal transconductance $g_m = \partial I_{\text{out}}/\partial V_{\text{in}}$ is also plotted as a function of the input voltage for different bias currents. With the nominal bias conditions (Fig. 6(a)), g_m does not vary by more than ± 0.8 percent for $I_{\text{out}}/I_{\text{bias}} \leqslant 0.65$. For higher bias currents, the "hump" in the middle of the g_m curve is enhanced (Fig. 6(b)) suggesting that for the transistors operating more deeply in strong inversion, the optimum ratio β_1/β_2 is slightly larger than 6. On the contrary, that "hump" tends to disappear at lower current densities (see Fig. 6(c)) where the optimum β_1/β_2 is smaller than 6. In the two latter cases the ripple in the transconductance characteristic has raised up to ± 1.6 percent for $I_{\text{out}}/I_{\text{bias}} \leqslant 0.65$.

In this implementation, input transistors $M1$, $M1'$, $M2$, and $M2'$ are in a common p-well connected to V_{SS}. Consequently, the transconductance is slightly dependent on the

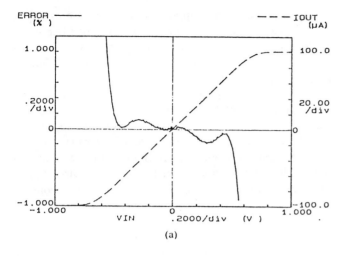

(a)

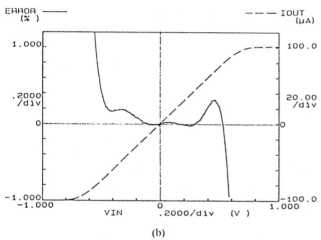

(b)

Fig. 5. Measured transfer characteristics of the transconductor of Fig. 2 for $V_{DD} = -V_{SS} = 2.5$ V, $I_{bias} = 100$ μA (a) with a differential input and (b) with a single input. The nonlinearity error is expressed here as a percentage of the full-scale current I_{bias}.

dc input common-mode voltage (body effect). This dependence, which is found to be less than 2 percent/V, may reduce the supply rejection capability but it does not degrade the linearity performance.

Other performance characteristics of the integrated transconductance amplifier are summarized in Table I. The most limiting factors for filter applications are likely to be the low dc voltage gain (37 dB) and the transductor matching accuracy of 0.7 percent (standard deviation). The latter should be compared to the typical 0.2-percent capacitor matching accuracy obtained with the same process.

IV. FILTER IMPLEMENTATION

The filter synthesis method starts from the third-order LC ladder meeting the filter specifications (Fig. 7(a)). The first step towards integration is to simulate the inductor with a gyrator–capacitor combination (Fig. 7(b)). Next, to make possible the use of fully balanced active elements, the series capacitive path C^* is transformed into two symmetric branches with twice the initial capacitor value, so as to keep the same reactance level (Fig. 7(c)).

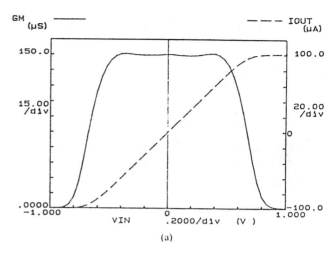

(a)

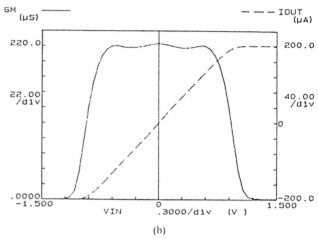

(b)

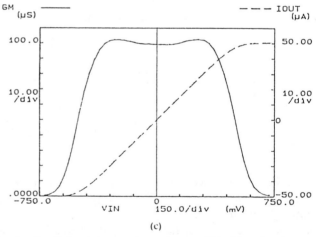

(c)

Fig. 6. Small-signal transconductance $g_m = \partial I_{out} / \partial V_{in}$ for different bias conditions: (a) $V_{DD} = -V_{SS} = 2.5$ V, $I_{bias} = 100$ μA; (b) $V_{DD} = -V_{SS} = 4$ V, $I_{bias} = 200$ μA; and (c) $V_{DD} = -V_{SS} = 2.5$ V, $I_{bias} = 50$ μA.

Each gyrator may then be implemented with a closed-loop connection of two balanced transconductors. Two more transconductance amplifiers, each connected in unity-gain configuration, are used to simulate the termination resistors. This yields the circuit depicted in Fig. 8, where the input transconductance element has been doubled to compensate for the inherent 6-dB loss of the passive LC prototype and the voltage between nodes 2

TABLE I
TYPICAL CHARACTERISTICS OF THE INTEGRATED
TRANSCONDUCTANCE AMPLIFIER OF FIG. 2
($V_{DD} = -V_{SS} = 2.5$ V, $I_{bias} = 100$ μA)

transconductance	$g_m = 150$ μA/V
output conductance	$g_0 = 2$ μA/V
DC voltage gain	$g_m/g_0 = 75$
equivalent differential input capacitance	$C_{in} = 0.42$ pF
equivalent differential output capacitance	$C_{out} = 0.22$ pF
Miller capacitance	$C_M = 0.13$ pF
input offset voltage (standard deviation)	$V_{os} = 2$ mV
transconductance matching accuracy (standard deviation)	$\Delta g_m/g_m = 0.7$ %

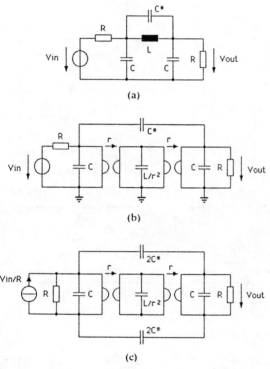

Fig. 7. Filter synthesis: (a) third-order elliptic low-pass LC ladder prototype; (b) gyrator–capacitor filter derived from (a); and (c) balanced version of (b).

and 2' has been scaled down by a factor of 2 to avoid a 5.5-dB gain peaking around 2.5 MHz (this was done by doubling both the capacitance between nodes 2 and 2' and the transconductance of the two amplifiers, the inputs of which are connected to these nodes). For a 4-MHz cutoff frequency and with unit transconductance elements of 150 μA/V, the capacitor values range from approximately 3 to 11 pF, to which the input and output stray capacitances of the transconductors contribute about 30–40 percent.

As opposed to filter synthesis methods known as indirect simulation or "voltage transfer simulation" methods where voltages and currents in the LC ladder prototype are simulated with voltages (as for most switched-capacitor filters), the approach used here is referred to as direct impedance simulation (voltages and currents in the LC ladder branches are simulated by voltages and currents,

respectively). As it may appear from the above example, this approach is not applicable to any kind of filter structure because the gyrator implementation involves transconductance amplifiers with nonzero input and output parasitic capacitances.

In the case of low-pass LC ladders, a direct substitution of inductors by gyrator–capacitor combinations (see Fig. 7) is possible since a shunt capacitor naturally appears on both the input and the output ports of each gyrator. The parasitic input and output capacitances of the transconductors then may be identified to functional capacitances in the passive prototype and they can be properly accounted for in the filter design. For most bandpass filters structures, however, a preliminary transformation of the ladder's series arms by means of additional gyrators is required before inductance simulation can be performed without introducing uncontrollable distortions in the filter response [13].

V. AUTOMATIC TUNING CONTROL CIRCUITRY

Automatic tuning is of critical importance to control the frequency response of continuous-time filters. Such a circuit is conveniently implemented by means of a phase-locked loop using either a voltage-controlled filter (Fig. 9(a)) or a voltage-controlled oscillator (Fig. 9(b)).

In the first case, an external reference signal of well-controlled frequency is applied to a second-order filter section which is similar to those used in the filter to be tuned. The frequency-dependent input–output phase characteristics of this reference filter are then exploited to tune the circuit [3]. For this reason, any offset in the phase comparator will result in a frequency tuning error. A rough calculation shows that for a typical ± 25-percent capture range (which is reasonable with respect to the variations in process parameters), the quality factor of a second-order reference filter must be less than 2 [3]. From the corresponding phase response, it becomes apparent that an offset of 2° in the phase detection will result in a tuning error of about 1 percent. This puts stringent requirements on the phase comparator accuracy and speed performance.

Another disadvantage of this first configuration is that harmonic distortion in the reference signal will, to a certain extent, introduce additional tuning errors. This is because the harmonics will not come out from the reference filter (the selectivity of which is limited for the reasons stated above) with the same phase shift as the fundamental frequency. When multiplied with the incoming signal, these residual out-of-phase harmonics will alter the result of the phase comparison. A quantitative analysis [14] has shown that for a second-order bandpass reference filter with a quality factor of 2, the harmonics of a square-wave reference signal would introduce a systematic tuning error of approximately 0.5 percent.

In the conventional approach (Fig. 9(b)), the multiplier or phase comparator has to compare the *frequency* of the signal coming out from the voltage-controlled oscillator with that of the reference signal. As opposed to the preced-

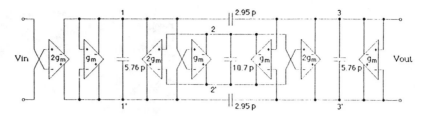

Fig. 8. Balanced transconductor-C active filter obtained from the circuit of Fig. 7(c) ($g_m = 150 \ \mu$A/V for 4-MHz cutoff frequency).

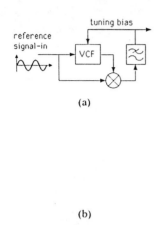

(a)

(b)

Fig. 9. Automatic tuning control methods using phase-locked loops: (a) PLL with an auxiliary voltage-controlled filter (VCF), and (b) conventional PLL using a voltage-controlled oscillator (VCO).

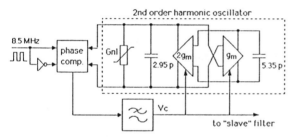

Fig. 10. Automatic tuning circuit for the filter of Fig. 8. The nonlinear conductance G_{NL} used in the second-order harmonic oscillator is intended for amplitude regulation.

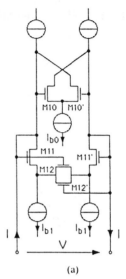

(a)

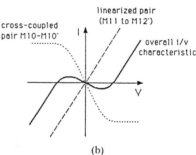

(b)

Fig. 11. (a) MOS implementation of the nonlinear amplitude limiting conductance G_{NL}, and (b) i/v characteristics of the circuit elements involved in (a).

ing PLL configuration, *absolute* phase accuracy is not necessary since only the phase *variations* of one signal with respect to the other must be detected. The requirements on the phase comparator are thus relaxed. The main problem then is the implementation of a voltage-controlled oscillator that is well-matched to the filter to be tuned. The best candidate is usually a second-order harmonic oscillator [1], the amplitude regulation of which must be carefully considered since harmonic distortion and nonlinearities in the transconductors would shift the effective oscillation frequency, thus introducing a tuning error.

For the above reasons, the automatic tuning circuit for the 4-MHz filter uses the latter PLL arrangement. The key design issues were the following (Fig. 10):

1) considering unavoidable capacitive coupling and limited power supply rejection, the reference frequency has been set to 8.5 MHz, close to the transmission zero within the filter stopband. In this way

the feedthrough from the oscillator to the filter is expected to be minimized;

2) as good matching properties between the filter and the oscillator are required, the latter was built around a specific two-integrator loop which has been implemented using the same unit transconductance elements and with approximately the same parasitic-to-functional capacitor ratio and layout disposition; and

3) finally, to avoid systematic tuning errors, the oscillation amplitude has been limited to 70 percent of the linear portion of the i/v characteristic of the transconductors by means of a simple nonlinear circuit, the function of which is explained hereafter.

Fig. 11(a) shows the actual implementation of the nonlinear conductance G_{NL} used for amplitude regulation in the

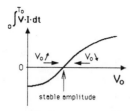

Fig. 12. Typical equivalent "energy" dissipated into the amplitude limiting network G_{NL} of Fig. 11 over one oscillation period T_0, as a function of the peak oscillation amplitude V_0.

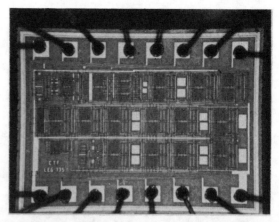

Fig. 13. Photomicrograph of the integrated 4-MHz filter.

two-integrator oscillator of Fig. 10. To obtain the desired nonlinear characteristic (Fig. 11(b)), the cross-coupled MOS differential pair $M10$, $M10'$, is added to a linearized transconductance stage ($M11$ to $M12'$) connected in unity gain.

For small signals, this circuit is equivalent to a negative conductance: it will therefore ensure oscillations build up when connected to the two-integrator loop which behaves like a passive LC resonant circuit. The amplitude of the oscillations will increase until the current I flowing through the nonlinear conductance G_{NL} has no more components at the resonant frequency f_0 of the two-integrator loop. Considering that thanks to the filtering action of the latter the voltage V across G_{NL} is purely sinusoidal regardless of the waveform of the current I, a stable oscillation amplitude is obtained when [15]

$$\int_0^{T_0} V \cdot I \cdot dt = 0$$

with

$$V = V_0 \cdot \sin(2\pi f_0 t)$$

and

$$T_0 = 1/f_0. \tag{14}$$

The above integral, which represents the equivalent "energy" dissipated into the nonlinear conductance G_{NL} over one oscillation period T_0, is plotted in Fig. 12 as a function of the peak oscillation amplitude V_0 for a typical implementation.

Considering our application, the design objectives for the circuit of Fig. 11 will be to ensure a well-controlled oscillation amplitude (within the linear range of the transconductors used in the two-integrator loop) while keeping the harmonic distortion at an acceptable level (e.g., a third-order harmonic distortion of 2 percent will lower the oscillation frequency by 0.16 percent [15, ch. 3]).

To achieve the same linearity performance, transistors $M11$ to $M12'$ must operate at the same gate overdrive voltage as the input stage (transistors $M1$ to $M2'$ in Fig. 2) of the other linearized transconductance elements used in the oscillator and in the filter. Low harmonic distortion is then obtained by limiting the bias current I_{b1} to a small fraction (between 10 and 20 percent) of the bias current of the other transconductors.

In order to keep a good control of the oscillation amplitude, the bias current and device sizes of the auxiliary

cross-coupled pair $M10$ and $M10'$ must be chosen in such a way that the resulting "energy" function (see Fig. 12) presents a maximum slope around zero (i.e., at stable oscillation amplitude). Simple analysis shows that this is achieved when the small-signal transconductance of differential pair $M10$ and $M10'$ is about 1.4 times as large as the equivalent conductance of the linearized network $M11$, $M11'$, $M12$, and $M12'$. The stable peak oscillation amplitude, which must be set within the linear range of the transconductors, is then approximately equal to $1.6 (V_{GS} - V_T)_{M10}$.

The limited quality factor of the two-integrator resonator is adequately described by a parallel parasitic conductance and may thus be properly accounted for by consequently correcting the equivalent conductance of the linearized network $M11$, $M11'$, $M12$, and $M12'$.

VI. EXPERIMENTAL RESULTS

The above-described filter, including automatic tuning control, has been designed for 4-MHz cutoff frequency and fabricated in a 3-μm single-poly single-metal p-well CMOS process. Fig. 13 is a photomicrograph of the complete circuit: the filter itself occupies the lower two-thirds of the 0.9×1.2-mm^2 chip whereas the automatic tuning circuitry is located in the upper third. Buffers using the available n-p-n vertical bipolar transistor have been added on the chip for measurement purposes.

A typical frequency response of the filter (including the on-chip voltage followers) for three different temperatures is reported in Fig. 14. Computer simulation showed that the deviations from the ideal response (like the average 0.3- to 0.7-dB loss in the passband) are due to the limited dc gain of the transconductance amplifiers ($A_{dc} \approx 70$ at 25°C) and to the variations thereof with bias current and temperature. The mean frequency of the transmission zero is found to be within 1.5 percent of its designed value; the spread around that value is about 1 percent (standard deviation).

The performance characteristics of the filter are summarized in Table II. The total harmonic distortion, measured for a balanced-driven input, is shown in Fig. 15 for

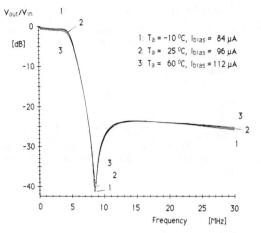

Fig. 14. Measured frequency response of the integrated filter ($V_{DD} = -V_{SS} = 2.5$ V, reference signal frequency = 8.5 MHz).

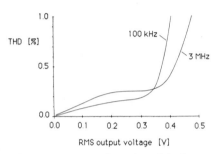

Fig. 15. Measured harmonic distortion of the integrated filter.

TABLE II
TYPICAL PERFORMANCE CHARACTERISTICS OF THE INTEGRATED
4-MHz FILTER
($V_{DD} = -V_{SS} = 2.5$ V, $f_{ref} = 8.5$ MHz, $T_a = 25°C$)

passband ripple (0 - 4 MHz)		0.6 dB
stopband rejection (f ≥ 8 MHz)		> 23 dB
max. output voltage (THD < -50 dB)		350 mV$_{RMS}$
RMS output noise (400 Hz - 40 MHz)		100 μV
reference signal feedthrough (f = 8.5 MHz)		60 μV
dynamic range		70 dB
supply rejection at 4 MHz	for V$_{DD}$	37 dB
	for V$_{SS}$	34 dB
total power dissipation		16 mW
chip area		1.1 mm^2

The total output noise power in the 400-Hz to 40-MHz band is 100 μV. This value does not include feedthrough from the automatic tuning circuit which is responsible for an additional 60-μV signal at 8.5 MHz. The resulting dynamic range is then evaluated to 70 dB.

The power supply rejection at 4 MHz is better than 34 dB for both supplies and the complete circuit dissipates only 16 mW from ± 2.5-V supplies.

VII. CONCLUSIONS

A new differential voltage-to-current converter has been proposed and experimented. The circuit is built around a simple four-transistor core cell and represents a significant improvement over previous realizations in terms of maximum signal-to-noise ratio, minimum supply voltage, and power consumption while preserving simplicity and good high-frequency performance. It has been used for the realization of a video frequency continuous-time filter but it might also find application in other types of continuous-time signal processing circuits where simple but reasonably accurate V-to-I converters are required.

The expectable performance of MOS continuous-time filters in the megahertz range has been illustrated by a specific example. In the circuit presented, the accuracy of the filter response is limited by the low dc gain of the transconductance amplifiers used; it is believed that for filtering applications requiring a higher selectivity some kind of automatic loss compensation circuitry will be necessary. In any case, filter accuracy is ultimately limited by transconductor matching.

Good dynamic range, low power dissipation, and reduced chip area indicate that such filters may be incorporated into a VLSI chip. With present MOS technologies, switched-capacitor filters appear to be limited to video frequencies, whereas continuous-time filters are likely to be able to operate at still higher frequencies (see, for example, [16]). Recent digital video filters of comparable performance [17] typically consume ten times more power and ten times more silicon area.

Although the design methodologies for continuous-time filters are well-known and exact, one must be aware that for high-frequency applications accurate device-level modeling is essential for first time success.

100 kHz, which is practically dc, and for 3 MHz. The latter frequency corresponds to a peak gain of about 3 dB at internal nodes 1 and 1' (see Fig. 8); in this case, however, the harmonics fall outside the passband. The distortion characteristic obtained with a 1-MHz input signal (for which most of the harmonics are still inside the passband) is situated in between the two other curves; for the sake of clearness it has not been reported on this figure. In any case the THD stays below 0.3 percent up to 1-V$_{p-p}$ (350 mV$_{rms}$) output voltage. With a single (unbalanced) input signal, the distortion for the same output voltage is found to be approximately twice as large.

REFERENCES

[1] M. Banu and Y. Tsividis, "An elliptic continuous-time CMOS filter with on-chip automatic tuning," *IEEE J. Solid-State Circuits*, vol. SC-20, pp. 1114–1121, Dec. 1985.
[2] Y. Tsividis, M. Banu, and J. Khoury, "Continuous-time MOSFET-C filters in VLSI," *IEEE J. Solid-State Circuits*, vol. SC-21, pp. 15–30, Feb. 1986.
[3] H. Khorramabadi and P. R. Gray, "High-frequency CMOS continuous-time filters," *IEEE J. Solid-State Circuits*, vol. SC-19, pp. 939–948, Dec. 1984.
[4] A. P. Nedungadi and R. L. Geiger, "High-frequency voltage controlled continuous-time low-pass filter using linearized CMOS integrators," *Electron. Lett.*, vol. 22, pp. 729–730, July 1986.
[5] H. Khorramabadi, "High-frequency CMOS continuous-time filters," Ph.D. dissertation, Univ. of Calif., Berkeley, Feb. 1985.

[6] Y. Tsividis, Z. Czarnul, and S. C. Fang, "MOS transconductors and integrators with high linearity," *Electron. Lett.*, vol. 22, pp. 245–246, Feb. 1986.

[7] Z. Czarnul, S. C. Fang, and Y. Tsividis, "Improving linearity in MOS fully-integrated continuous-time filters," in *Proc. IEEE ISCAS'86* (San Jose, CA), 1986.

[8] J. L. Pennock, "CMOS triode transconductor for continuous-time active integrated filters," *Electron. Lett.*, vol. 18, pp. 817–818, Aug. 1985.

[9] A. Nedungadi and T. R. Viswanathan, "Design of linear transconductance elements," *IEEE Trans. Circuits Syst.*, vol. CAS-31, pp. 891–894, Oct. 1984.

[10] C.-S. Park and R. Schaumann, "A high-frequency CMOS linear transconductance element," *IEEE Trans. Circuits Syst.*, vol. CAS-33, pp. 1132–1138, Nov. 1986.

[11] K. Bult and H. Wallinga, "A class of analog CMOS circuits based on the square-law characteristic of an MOS transistor in saturation," *IEEE J. Solid-State Circuits*, vol. SC-202, pp. 357–365, June 1987.

[12] E. Seevinck and R. F. Wassenaar, "A versatile CMOS linear transconductor/square-law function circuit," *IEEE J. Solid-State Circuits*, vol. SC-202, pp. 366–377, June 1987.

[13] N. Joehl and F. Krummenacher, "Filtres continus MOS intégrés à large échelle," *AGEN-Mitteilungen*, no. 43, pp. 49–55, May 1986.

[14] O. Rey, "Circuit de verrouillage en fréquence pour filtre continu," M.S. thesis, Swiss Federal Inst. of Technology, Lausanne, Switzerland, Dec. 1985.

[15] W. A. Edson, *Vacuum-Tube Oscillators.* New York: Wiley, 1953.

[16] Y. P. Tsividis, "Minimal transistor-only integrated VHF active filter," *Electron. Lett.*, vol. 23, pp. 777–778, July 1987.

[17] U. Kleine and M. Böhner, "A high-speed wave digital filter using carry-slave arithmetic," in *ESSCIRC'87 Dig. Tech. Papers*, Sept. 1987, pp. 43–46.

Design Considerations in High-Frequency CMOS Transconductance Amplifier Capacitor (TAC) Filters

F. KRUMMENACHER

ELECTRONICS LABORATORY, SWISS FEDERAL INSTITUTE OF TECHNOLOGY (EPFL),
LAUSANNE, SWITZERLAND

ABSTRACT

Design methodologies for HF and VHF TAC bandpass filters are reviewed and discussed. The factors limiting the filter performance are identified and it is shown that non-ideal effects may be minimized by adequate filter architecture, tuning method and circuit lay-out.

INTRODUCTION

Integrated CMOS continuous-time filters are suitable solutions to perform a variety of signal processing tasks. Examples include radio and video frequency filtering applications and anti-aliasing or smoothing circuits in sample-data systems.

Although very successful in voice-band applications, "MOSFET-C active" filter implementations [1] that use MOS transistors as tunable resistors become unpractical at high frequency due to the bandwidth limitations of the MOS operational amplifiers.

To achieve the required level of performance in the MHz range and above, the only viable approach for continuous-time filters remains the "transconductance amplifier - capacitor" (TAC) concept, where MOSFET's are basically considered as tunable voltage-controlled current sources [2]. But mainly because TAC filters are by nature sensitive to parasitic capacitances, their design and implementation require an in-depth knowledge of circuit performance and limitations in order to minimize non-ideal effects by appropriate filter architecture, tuning method and even circuit lay-out.

This paper will focus on the most important aspects of the design and realization of CMOS HF/VHF TAC bandpass filters.

TRANSCONDUCTANCE AMPLIFIERS AND GYRATORS

Several MOS implementations of linear transconductance amplifiers have been proposed to date [3]-[8]. For HF filters, solutions derived from the simple source-coupled MOST pair [7],[8] are preferable because they offer a true differential input: this is mandatory for implementing positive as well as negative transconductance values since both are necessary for filter realization. Moreover, with little increase in circuit complexity to provide for common-mode feedback [2], a balanced output will improve both the dynamic range and the power supply rejection which become critical parameters in HF monolithic circuits.

Linearization techniques based on class AB operation [4]-[6], although offering good linearity performance and low power consumption, lead to increasing EMC problems (e.g. crosstalk via supply lines and substrate) and should therefore be avoided. Solutions involving current mirroring (e.g. to implement positive transconductors [4]) must also be rejected as they generally suffer from significant excess phase at high frequencies.

To illustrate possible approaches, Fig. 1 compares the linearity performance of two linear MOST pairs to that of a simple source-coupled pair for a typical HF application. In the circuit of Fig. 1(b), the larger the transconductance of input devices M1A-M1B with respect to the conductance of the degenerating MOS resistor M2, the better the linearity provided that the input voltage is correctly balanced [8]. For the circuit of Fig. 1(c), linearity is primarily a function of the ratio $(W/L)_{M1}/(W/L)_{M2}$, the optimum value of which is between 6 and 7 [7]. In addition to superior linearity performance, this latter circuit is much less sensitive than the previous one to variations of the input common mode voltage.

The first-order, differential-mode equivalent circuit of the above transconductors is represented in Fig. 2: in addition to the desired controlled current source, one may identify the equivalent input, output and feedthrough stray capacitances C_{in}, C_{out} and C_f respectively and the parasitic output conductance g_o resulting from channel length modulation in the transistors.

Two identical transconductance amplifiers can be connected in a closed loop to form a gyrator (Fig. 3) and it is worth noting that, as mentioned in ref. [2], the effects of feedthrough cap's C_f are mutually cancelled if the voltage at both the input and output ports is symmetrical with respect to ground. This is another important advantage of balanced configurations since in HF applications the feedthrough capacitances (primarily due to the gate-to-drain overlap in the transconductor input pair) are expected to be large as wide transistors must be used.

LOW-SENSITIVITY FILTER ARCHITECTURES

The filter architecture must at least incorporate the stray

Reprinted from *Proc. IEEE ISCAS*, pp. 100–105, 1989.

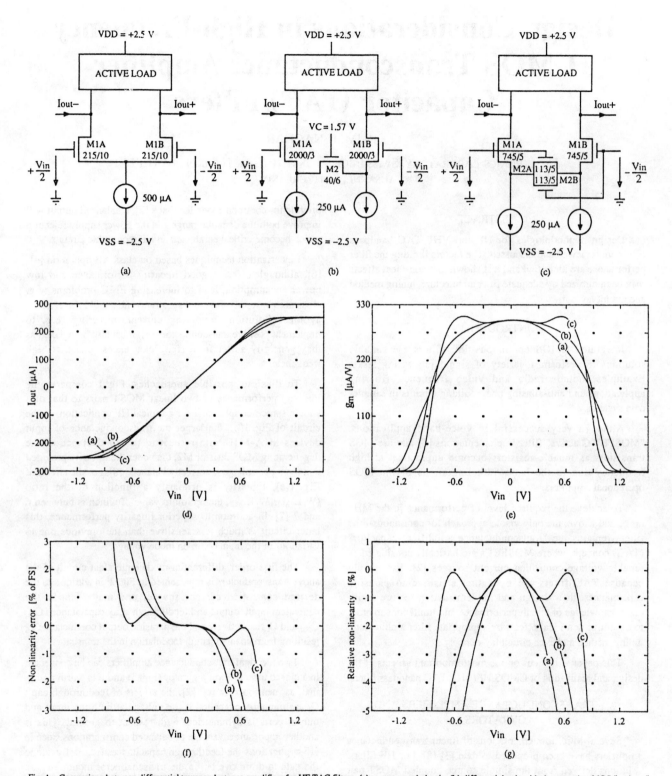

Fig. 1. Comparison between differential transconductance amplifiers for HF TAC filters: (a) source-coupled pair; (b) differential pair with degenerating MOS "resistor" [8]; (c) 4-transistor diff. pair [7]; (d) simulated transfer characteristics of the above circuits; (e) small-signal transconductance gm=∂Iout/∂Vin; (f) non-linearity error in percent of full-scale current Imax=250μA; (g) relative non-linearity in percent of the ideal value gmoVin (where gmo is the small-signal transconductance at Vin=0).

capacitances associated with each transconductance amplifier in such a way that they become functional for the filtering function to realize. This is essential for HF filters where parasitics can easily represent several ten percent of functional capacitances.

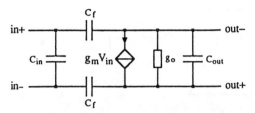

Fig. 2. Fisrt-order small-signal differential mode equivalent circuit for the transconductance amplifiers of Fig. 1.

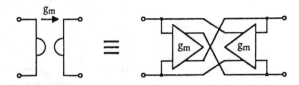

Fig. 3. Gyrator implementation using transconductance amplifiers.

Based on impedance simulation of passive LC ladders by extensive use of gyrators, a design method following this principle is described in [9]: it allows the exact synthesis of lowpass and bandpass TAC filters with or without transmission zeros. The filter structure derived by this method from a 6th order all-pole LC ladder is sketched in Fig. 4(a). It basically consists in three coupled resonators tuned on the same frequency. The bidirectional coupling (realised with gyrators) between successive resonators determines the passband shape (0.5dB equiripple in the example). The first and last resonators are damped by the termination resistors $R_d = 1/g_{md}$ simulated with transconductance amplifiers connected in unity gain.

Despite their low sensitivity to changes in component value, active filter structures derived from LC ladders remain quite sensitive to phase errors due to the finite gain and bandwidth of active elements. As it is easier to automatically control the frequency response of a resonator with limited quality factor rather than that of an ideally "lossless" circuit, filter topologies which can incorporate parasitic conductances (such as the output conductance of transconductance amplifiers) as well as stray capacitances into functional elements might be preferable.

Accordingly, an alternate realization of the 6th order bandpass transfer function of Fig. 4 can use a "Follow-the-Leader Feedback" (FLF) configuration as shown in Fig. 5(a). In this so-called "Primary Resonator Block" (PRB) design [10], all resonators have the same tuning frequency f_o and quality factor Q. The latter two parameters determine the filter center frequency and bandwidth, respectively, while the feedback coefficients determine the passband shape. However, as can be observed from the partial transfer functions shown in Fig. 5(b), the disadvantage of this structure is that the input signal is first strongly attenuated within the passband, resulting in a reduced maximum signal-to-noise ratio.

In the filter implementation of Fig. 6, this drawback is eliminated by another kind of multiple-loop feedback topology using identical 2nd order sections (same f_o and Q) for simplified tuning. This structure employs both local and global feedback; i.e. the signal is not only fed from each resonator back to the first one as in FLF configurations, but there is also a local feedback to the preceding resonator like in the circuit of Fig. 4. Such a multiple-loop feedback topology also benefits from the low-sensitivity properties of FLF or ladder-based filter implementations.

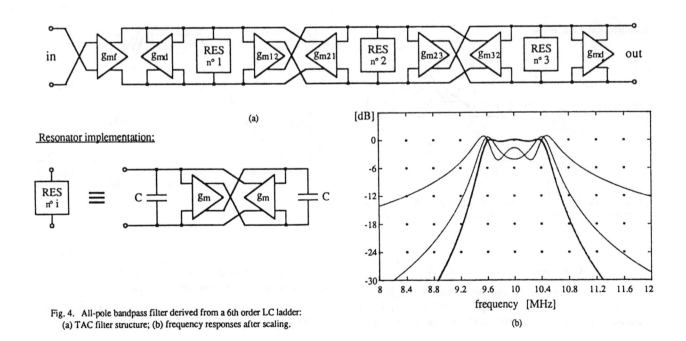

Fig. 4. All-pole bandpass filter derived from a 6th order LC ladder: (a) TAC filter structure; (b) frequency responses after scaling.

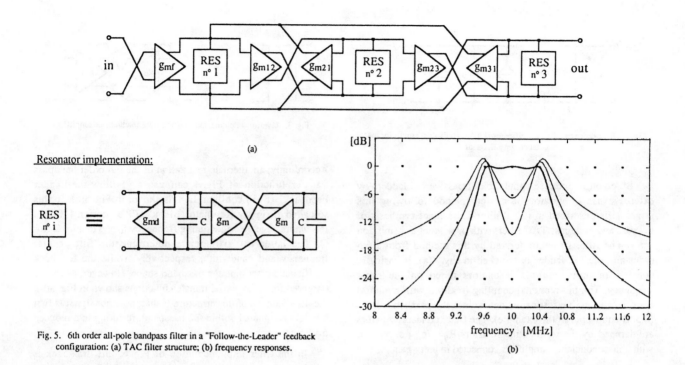

Fig. 5. 6th order all-pole bandpass filter in a "Follow-the-Leader" feedback configuration: (a) TAC filter structure; (b) frequency responses.

Resonator implementation:

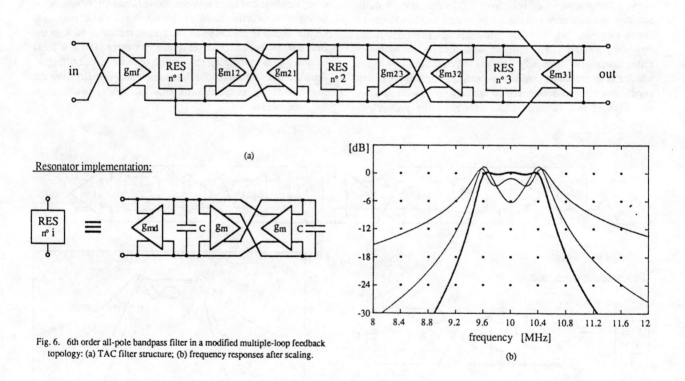

Fig. 6. 6th order all-pole bandpass filter in a modified multiple-loop feedback topology: (a) TAC filter structure; (b) frequency responses after scaling.

Resonator implementation:

AUTOMATIC TUNING AND LAYOUT

It has been shown in the previous section that high-order TAC bandpass filters may be implemented with a regular structure of coupled resonators that all have the same tuning frequency and quality factor but only differ by their respective contribution to the signal fed back to the first resonator.

In order to achieve functional matching of TAC resonators, which are intrinsically sensitive to stray capacitances, one has to

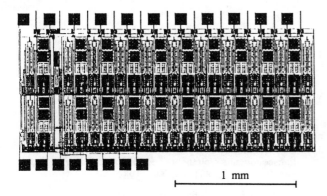

Fig. 7. Circuit lay-out of a 200kHz 18th order all-pole bandpass filter [11].

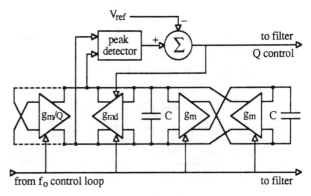

Fig. 8. Second-order harmonic oscillator for automatic fo and Q control.

insure that they are matched structurally too. This involves the use of "dummy" circuit elements so as to match the parasitics (stray cap's and, if necessary, output stray conductances) from one resonator to another. To illustrate this strategy, the lay-out of a TAC bandpass filter derived from an 18th order all-pole LC ladder [11] is reproduced in Fig. 7: in spite of important differences in the transconductance values (up to 500 %), all coupling gyrators have been laid out using the same basic structure with unit transistor elements (customization is performed mostly at the interconnexion layer). Dummy stray capacitances have been added whenever necessary. A copy of the resonator and coupling gyrator core cell for use in the automatic tuning control is visible on the left hand side of the circuit .

For several reasons which will not be detailed here (see for example [7]), automatic tuning control is best based on a phase-locked loop (PLL) arrangement employing a voltage-controlled oscillator (VCO) which is matched to the filter to be tuned. The VCO is conveniently implemented in the form of a 2nd order harmonic oscillator which provides a correct matching with the filter. Furthermore, the amplitude regulation loop of the oscillator may be configured so as to indirectly control the quality factor of the resonators used in the filter to compensate for parasitic conductances too.

A VCO based on this principle is depicted in Fig. 8. It basically consists in a 2nd order section, namely a two-integrator resonator tuned at the frequency $f_o=g_m/(2\pi C)$ with a variable damping resistor $R_d=1/g_{md}$ (nominally equal to Q/g_m) and an input transconductor $g_{mi}=g_m/Q$ (Q being the required quality factor for the resonators of the filter). The dummy elements to improve the matching with the filter are not shown on the figure. To understand the principle and advantage of the amplitude control used here, we assume that the feedback path (dotted lines) is opened and that a sinewave at frequency f_o and with peak amplitude A_{in} is applied to the input transconductor. Because of the parasitic output conductance associated with each transconductor, the resulting peak amplitude of the signal across the damping resistor is somewhat different from the ideal value $A_{out}=A_{in} \cdot g_{mi} \cdot R_d$; not too faraway, however, so that only a

small correction (within ten or twenty percent) on g_{md} is necessary to obtain the desired output amplitude. Provided that the parasitic conductances in each resonator of the filter and in the tuning VCO are matched, the corrected value for g_{md} to have $A_{out}=A_{in}$ corresponds to the value of the damping (trans)conductances in the filter resonators so that the latter have the required quality factor Q, thus compensating for errors in the filter frequency response due to parasitic conductances.

The approach used here to fulfil the condition $A_{out}=A_{in}$ at the natural frequency of the resonator is to close the input and output of the section and to maintain the circuit in the oscillating mode thanks to a feedback control employing an auxiliary non-critical amplitude detection circuit. If care is taken to make the parameters of the amplitude regulation loop as independent as possible from the parameters determining the oscillation frequency, this VCO can be incorporated into a PLL for automatic tuning of the filter center frequency.

A more detailed analysis would show that this technique indeed compensates for any phase error due to the limited gain and bandwidth of the transconductors and/or to the finite quality factor of the capacitors. Since the phase errors are likely to be frequency-dependent, this compensation must be achieved at the frequency where these errors have to be minimized. This is the reason why especially for high-Q filters, it may be unavoidable to choose the reference frequency for the automatic tuning within the filter passband, in spite of an increased feedthrough from the tuning circuit to the filter.

AN EXPLORATORY VHF TAC FILTER SECTION

The measured frequency response of an experimental 2nd order bandpass filter section is given in Fig. 9. The aim of this design was to explore the VHF domain for TAC filters implemented in the 3μm P-well CMOS process from FASELEC [12]. In this circuit, only stray capacitances are loading by about 2.2 pF fully balanced transconductance amplifiers employing the linearization technique of Fig. 1(c). Apart an extra phase shift (see Fig. 9) due to the simple on-chip voltage follower using the available vertical NPN transistor, the frequency response is very good and demonstrates that TAC filters with center frequencies of up to 100 MHz are feasible.

283

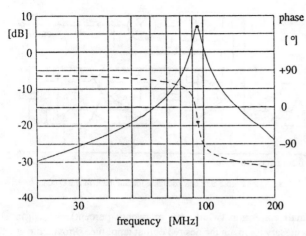

Fig. 9. Measured frequency response of a 2nd order VHF bandpass filter integrated in the 3μm SACMOS process from FASELEC AG [12].

CONCLUSIONS

The design and implementation of high-frequency CMOS TAC filters is a challenging problem for the analog circuit designer. An attempt has been made here to define a global design strategy that basically uses the parasitic capacitances and conductances associated with the active devices as functional elements. It must be emphasized that this approach relies on the tight matching between the filter and the automatic tuning circuitry to precisely control the filter center frequency and passband response.

The transconductance amplifiers for HF TAC filters are best based on simple differential/balanced circuits and must be optimized at transistor level to achieve both linearity and good high-frequency performance. An improved modeling of the high-frequency behavior of the MOS transistor accounting for the distributed nature of the channel in non-quasistatic operation will be necessary for the design of VHF TAC filters since the latter are ultimately limited by the high frequency roll-off of the transistor itself.

REFERENCES

[1] Y.Tsividis et al., "Continuous-time MOSFET-C filters in VLSI," IEEE J. Solid-State Circuits, vol. SC-21, pp. 15-30, Feb. 1986.

[2] H. Khorramabadi and P. R. Gray, "High-frequency CMOS continuous-time filters," ibid., vol SC-19, pp. 939-948, Dec. 1984.

[3] A. Nedungadi and T. R. Viswanathan, "Design of linear transconductance elements," IEEE Trans. Circuits Syst., vol. CAS-31, pp. 891-894, Oct. 1984.

[4] C.-S. Park and R. Schaumann, "A high-frequency CMOS linear transconductance element," ibid., vol. CAS-33, pp. 1132-1138, Nov. 1986.

[5] K. Bult and H. Wallinga, "A class of analog CMOS circuits based on the square-law characteristic of an MOS transistor in saturation," IEEE J. Solid-State Circuits, vol. SC-22, pp. 357-365, June 1987.

[6] E. Seevinck and R. F. Wassenaar, "A versatile CMOS linear transconductor/ square-law function circuit," ibid., vol SC-22, pp. 366-377, June 1987.

[7] F. Krummenacher and N. Joehl, "A 4-MHz CMOS continuous-time filter with on-chip automatic tuning," ibid., vol. SC-23, pp. 750-758, June 1988.

[8] Y. Tsividis et al., "MOS transconductors and integrators with high linearity," Electron. Lett., vol. 22, pp. 245-246, Feb. 1986.

[9] N. Joehl and F. Krummenacher, "Filtres continus MOS intégrés à large échelle," AGEN-Mitteilungen, no. 43, pp. 49-55, May 1986.

[10] G. Hurtig, "Voltage tunable multipole bandpass active filters," 1974 IEEE Int. Symp. Circuits and Systems, pp. 569-572, San Fransisco, Calif., 1974.

[11] G. van Ruymbeke, private communication.

[12] R. E. Luscher, "A high-density CMOS process," 1985 IEEE ISSCC Digest techn. papers, pp. 260-261, New-York, Feb. 1985.

High Performance OTA-R-C Continuous-Time Filters with Full CMOS Low Distortion Floating Resistors

MICHIEL STEYAERT, JOSE SILVA-MARTINEZ* AND WILLEY SANSEN

KATHOLIEKE UNIVERSITEIT LEUVEN, ELEKTROTECHNIEK DEPARTEMENT (ESAT-MICAS) B-3001,
HEVERLEE, BELGIUM

Abstract—Several techniques for the design of high performance fully-differential Continuous-Time Filters are introduced. The filter is based on OTA-Resistor-Capacitor (OTA-R-C) building blocks. A novel Common Mode Feedback (CMFB) system for fully-differential amplifiers is proposed. The CMFB uses only five transistors and consumes in the order of 21% of the OTA power consumption. Also, a low distortion floating resistor with low sensitivity to transistor mismatches is presented. This technique allows one to control the ripple of the filter without sacrificing the filter dynamic range. Even more, both power consumption and silicon area are lower than OTA-based resistors.

The techniques are validated by the experimental results of a fourth-order 100 kHz low-pass filter. The dynamic range of the filter is in the order of 66 dB for Total Harmonic Distortion (THD) < −60 dB. The power consumption is only 1.9 mW, with supply voltages of ±2.5 V. The chip has been fabricated in a 1.2 μm single poly N-well process. The experimental and expected results are in very good agreement.

I. INTRODUCTION

CONTINUOUS-TIME filters have gained certain maturity during the last few years. Applications from the audio frequencies up to VHF have already been reported [1–5]. In order to maximize the dynamic range and to minimize the even order non-linearities fully differential structures have been preferred. The minimization of the OTA odd order non-linearities have been carried out using linearized structures [1–6]. In this paper, several techniques for the design of high performance fully-differential continuous-time filters are proposed.

Firstly, a fully differential version of the very low distortion OTA reported in [6] is introduced. A novel technique for the common mode feedback system is proposed. The technique takes advantage of the direct connection between OTA's, avoiding the necessity of additional common mode detection. The resulting structure is quite simple (five additional transistors) and the use of resistors is avoided. Besides, the power consumption of this block is around 21% of OTA power consumption. This technique is discussed in Section II. For the control of the ripple, a linear floating resistor is introduced. This approach, instead of the unity feedback OTA resistor, presents a large tuneability range without the reduction of filter dynamic range. Furthermore, the power consumption and the silicon area are lower than for the OTA-based resistors approach. The fully-symmetrical floating resistor is presented in section III. Both the OTA and the resistor are used in the design of the 100-kHz low-pass ladder filter. The implementation of this filter is presented in Section IV. The experimental results are given in Section V. These results have shown THDs lower than −60 dB for both OTA and filter. The dynamic range of the filter is in the order of 66 dBs, with THD < −60 dB. Its power consumption is only 1.9 mW. Finally, in the last section some conclusions are given.

II. THE FULLY-DIFFERENTIAL OTA

The low-distortion fully-differential OTA used is shown in Fig 1. This topology, in a single output

---

* On leave from the Universidad Autonoma de Puebla. He is supported by CONACYT, Mexico, under grant 27585.

Reprinted from *Proc. ESSCIRC'91*, pp. 5–8, 1991.

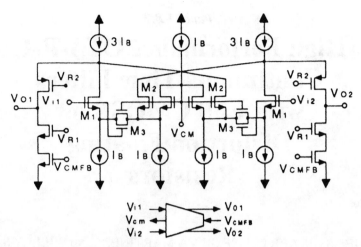

Fig. 1. Fully-differential OTA.

version, has been reported earlier [6]. In addition to the input and the output nodes, there are the common mode voltage, V_{CM}, and the common mode feedback voltage, V_{CMFB}. Because, in OTA-based filters, the output of the previous OTA is connected directly to the input of the next OTA, the common mode voltage V_{CM} of the next OTA can be used for the detection of the previous OTA common mode voltage. Thus, the additional distortion and the power consumption and the silicon area from the common mode detector are avoided. As a result, a quite simple common mode feedback system is needed. The proposed technique is shown in Fig 2. From the comparison of V_{CM} with the common mode reference, the ground in this case, the common mode feedback voltage is generated. The stability of the common mode loop can be guaranteed by splitting the integrating capacitors, into C_0 and C_1. Some of

these capacitors should be grounded, C_1 in Fig 2. There is a small penalty for this because mismatches in those capacitors introduce unbalance in the structure. Normally this is not a major problem. Experimental results have shown very small second-order harmonic distortion.

III. THE FLOATING RESISTOR

For low quality factor filters, the use of OTA-based filters is attractive because the transconductance of all the OTAs are in the same order of magnitude. When this is not the case, large capacitor ratios (sacrificing filter dynamic range and silicon area) and/or large Gm's ratios should be used. Even more, due to the parasitic effects, large adjustments in the operation point of the simulated resistors are

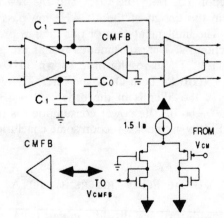

Fig. 2. CMFB system.

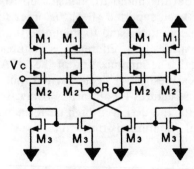

Fig. 3. Floating resistor.

286

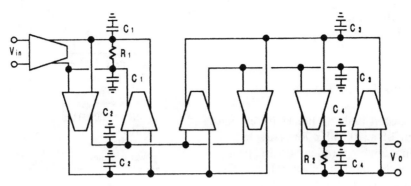

Fig. 4. Fourth-order lowpass ladder filter.

expected. A variation of 20% in the resistance value represents a 40% variation in the bias current. As the distortion in fully differential OTAs is almost proportional to the bias current, large reductions of the filter dynamic range might occur. This is not the case in some floating resistors, wherein the harmonic distortion is much less sensitive to the resistance value.

In this design the ripple of the filter is controlled by a floating resistor with low sensitivity to transistor mismatches. This new resistor structure is shown in Fig 3. In this paper, the main features of that resistor are demonstrated by experimental results. The resistance value is controlled by the voltage V_C. The THD is a direct function of the transconductance of transistor M_2. Increasing the value of this transconductance, the THD can be further reduced.

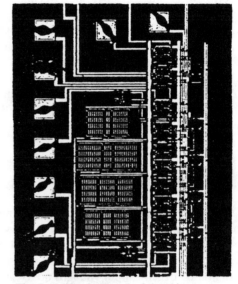

Fig. 5. Microphotograph of the chip.

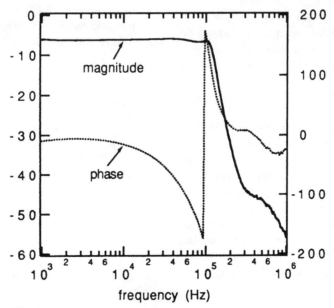

Fig. 6. Frequency response of the filter.

It has already been theoretically demonstrated that the nonlinearities of this topology have low sensitivity to the resistor value (V_C) [7].

IV. THE 100-kHz LOW PASS FILTER

The previously discussed building blocks have been used in the design of a 100 kHz low pass ladder filter. It is based on a double terminated RLC prototype. The scheme of this filter is shown in Fig 4. The filter includes seven OTAs, two floating resistors and eight grounded capacitors. The capacitors are grounded because of the singly poly technology. It should be noted that only four CMFBs are required. The current consumption of all the CMFB systems, $4(1.5I_B)$, is less than the current consumption of a single OTA, $7I_B$. The resistances are in the order of 200 kΩ and their power consumption are around 100 μW. Most of the power, 75%, is consumed by the OTAs. Also, the silicon area of the CMFB and the resistors are in the order of 25% and 20% the OTA silicon area, respectively.

V. EXPERIMENTAL RESULTS

The OTA and the filter have been fabricated in a 1.2 μm process. A microphotograph of the chip is shown in Fig 5. For the OTA, the measured second order harmonic distortion, with a 2 kΩ load resistor, is lower than -65 dBs for input voltages up to 2.6 Vpp (peak to peak differential voltage). The Third Harmonic Distortion is lower than -64 dB for Vin < 2 Vpp. The common mode offset voltage of the OTA with CMFB and measured in open loop is about 50 mV. From simulations it can be shown that a modification in the layout can reduce its value to less than 20 mV.

The experimental results of the filter are shown in table 1. An additional OTA was used to buffer out the filter outputs. So, the data of this table include the effects of the additional OTA. Its frequency response is shown in Fig 6. These results demonstrate the very low distortion predicted for the floating resistors. The ripple of the filter is easily tuneable within a decade with almost no effect on the THD. The filter dynamic range with THD < -60 dB is in the order of 66 dB. It can be increased but both the power consumption and the silicon area increase too. There is a trade off among these parameters.

TABLE 1
FOURTH-ORDER LOWPASS FILTER EXPERIMENTAL RESULTS

THD @ Vin < 2 Vpp	< -60 dB
IM3 @ Vin1 = Vin2 < 1 Vpp	< -55 dB
dynamic range	> 66 dB
CMRR @ 20 kHz	> 55 dB
PSRR @ 20 kHz VDD, VSS	> 50 dB
power consumption	1.9 mW

CONCLUSIONS

Several techniques for the design of very low distortion fully differential continuous-time filters have been proposed. A new technique for the common mode feedback of fully differential continuous-time structures is introduced. This technique takes advantage of the direct connection of the OTAs. The result is a very simple CMFB block with very low power consumption and very small silicon area. For the control of the quality factor of the filters, it is proposed to use floating resistors instead of OTA simulated resistors. The high linearity of a new fully symmetrical floating resistor has been demonstrated.

These techniques have been used in the design of a lowpass filter. Experimental results have shown THD < -60 dBs for differential input voltage up to 2 Vpp. The dynamic range, for this distortion, is in the order of 66 dB. The power consumption is 1.9 mW, with supply voltages of ±2.5 V. It is claimed that using linearized OTAs and linearized resistors, it is possible to design efficiently high performance continuous-time filters.

ACKNOWLEDGMENTS

The authors would like to thank ALCATEL-BELL (Antwerpen, Belgium) for processing the chip. The help of Didier Haspeslagh, J. Sevenhans and the advice, during the measurements, of Chris Van Grieken (ESAT-MICAS) are recognized.

REFERENCES

[1] A. Kaiser, "A Micropower CMOS Continuous-Time Low-Pass Filter," IEEE JSSC, vol. SC-24, pp. 736–743, June 1989.
[2] F. Krummenacher and N. Joehl, "A 4 MHz CMOS Continu-

ous-Time Filter with On-Chip Automatic Tuning," IEEE JSSC, vol. SC-23, pp. 750–757, June 1988.

[3] Y. T. Wang, F. Lu and A. A. Abidi, "A 12.5 MHz CMOS Continuous-Time Bandpass Filter," IEEE ISSCC-1989, pp. 198–199, February 1989.

[4] V. Gopinathan and Y. P. Tsividis, "A 5V 7th-Order Elliptic Analog Filter for Digital Video Applications," IEEE ISSCC-1990, pp. 208–209, February 1990.

[5] B. Nauta and E. Seevinck, "A Linear Transconductance Element for VHF Filters," Electronics Letters, vol. 25, pp. 448–450, March 1989.

[6] J. Silva-Martinez, M. Steyaert and W. Sansen, "A High Frequency Large Signal Very Low Distortion Transconductor," IEEE ESSCIRC-1990, pp 169–172, Sept. 1990.

[7] J. Silva-Martinez, M. Steyaert and W. Sansen, "Very Linear CMOS Floating Resistor," Electronics Letters, vol. 26, pp. 1611–1612, Sept. 1990.

A CMOS Transconductance-C Filter Technique for Very High Frequencies

Bram Nauta, *Student Member, IEEE*

Abstract—This paper presents CMOS circuits for integrated analog filters at very high frequencies, based on transconductance-C integrators. First a differential transconductance element based on CMOS inverters is described. With this circuit a linear, tunable integrator for very-high-frequency integrated filters can be made. This integrator has good linearity properties (1% relative *gm* error for 2-V_{p-p} input signals, V_{dd} = 10 V) and nondominant poles in the gigahertz range owing to the absence of internal nodes. The integrator has a tunable dc gain, resulting in a controllable integrator quality factor. Experimental results of a VHF CMOS transconductance-C low-pass filter realized in a 3-μm CMOS process are given. Both the cutoff frequency and the quality factors can be tuned. The cutoff frequency was tuned from 22 to 98 MHz and the measured filter response is very close to the ideal response of the passive prototype filter. Furthermore, a novel circuit for automatically tuning the quality factors of integrated filters built with these transconductors is described. The Q-tuning circuit itself has no signal-carrying nodes and is therefore extremely suitable for these filters at very high frequencies.

I. Introduction

SEVERAL MOS continuous-time high-frequency integrated filters have been reported in the literature [1]–[7]. Most filters are built with transconductance elements and capacitors, to take advantage of these structures for making integrators at high frequencies. The maximal cutoff frequencies were, however, limited to the lower megahertz range. Krummenacher and Joehl [1], for example, reported a 4-MHz low-pass filter and Kim and Geiger [2] reported a bandpass filter, programmable up to 16 MHz. Pu and Tsividis [3] have described another approach: minimal transistor-only VHF filters. With this technique very compact filters at very high frequencies (10–100 MHz) can be made, but these filters have restricted quality factors and accuracy. This paper describes a filter technique for accurate filters at very high frequencies. The basic building block is an integrator and general filter synthesis techniques remain applicable.

The integrator is the main building block of integrated active filters. In this paper the integrator will be implemented by a transconductance element loaded with a ca-

pacitor. One of the major problems in high-frequency active filters is the phase error of the integrators [4], [8]. The quality factors Q of the poles and zeros in the filter are highly sensitive to the phase of the integrators at the pole and zero frequencies. To avoid errors in the filter characteristic, a sufficiently high integrator dc gain is required, while the parasitic poles should be located at frequencies much higher than the cutoff frequency of the filter, in order to keep the integrator phase close to −90°. For the filter to be presented, this implies a dc gain of roughly at least 40 dB and parasitic poles located at least a factor of 100 beyond the cutoff frequency. This is a strong constraint for filters at very (up to 100 MHz) high frequencies: the transconductor should have a bandwidth of approximately 10 GHz.

Two techniques can be used to make a combination of a high integrator dc gain with a very large bandwidth possible.

1) Consider the balanced transconductance-C integrator of Fig. 1(a). If the transconductance element has *no internal nodes*,[1] then the transconductor circuit has no parasitic poles or zeros influencing the transfer function of the integrator. This is true under the condition that the capacitors C_i (or C_i') and C_L (or C_L') are functional for the filter transfer. The feedforward currents through the capacitances C_{ov} are canceled in a fully balanced gyrator structure [4].

2) Consider the balanced integrator of Fig. 1(b). The dc gain of the integrator is $gm \times r_{out}$, where r_{out} is the parasitic output resistance of the transconductor. For short-channel MOS transistors in high-frequency applications, this dc gain is normally very low (≈ 20). The dc gain can be increased by loading the transconductor—at least for differential signals—with a *negative resistance* (r_{load}) that compensates r_{out}. The dc gain is now gm times the parallel combination of r_{out} and r_{load}. For $r_{load} = -r_{out}$ the dc gain becomes, theoretically, infinite. Note that the implementation of the dc-gain enhancement technique does not require any internal node. Cascoding or cascading of stages, on the contrary, will always introduce additional internal nodes resulting in phase errors.

A combination of these two techniques for the design of a transconductance element results in an integrator with

Manuscript received January 17, 1991; revised September 6, 1991. This work was supported by The Dutch IOP (innovative research projects) program.

The author was with MESA Twente, University of Twente, 7500 AE, Enschede, The Netherlands. He is now with Philips Research Laboratories, 5600 JA, Eindhoven, The Netherlands.

IEEE Log Number 9105082.

[1]An internal node is a node in the circuit schematic that has no direct connection to either an input or an output terminal or a bias or supply terminal of the circuit.

Reprinted from *IEEE J. Solid-State Circuits,* vol. SC-27, no. 2, pp. 142–153, Feb. 1992.

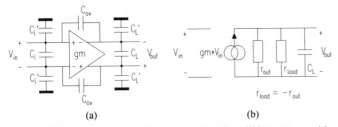

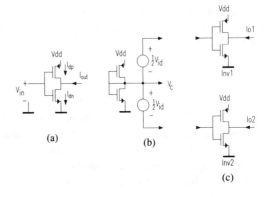

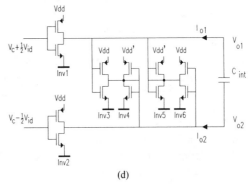

Fig. 1. (a) A transconductor without internal nodes will have no parasitic poles or zeros and will be therefore of infinite bandwidth. (b) Loading the output of an integrator with a negative load resistance makes a infinite dc gain possible, without requiring internal nodes.

Fig. 2. (a) Single inverter. (b) Generation of the common-mode voltage level V_c. (c) Two balanced inverters performing linear V-to-I conversion if driven by the circuit of Fig. 2(b). (d) The complete transconductance element.

theoretically infinite dc gain and infinite bandwidth. As a result, the integrator quality factor will also be infinite.

In this paper, first a tranconductor circuit with an excellent high-frequency behavior is described (Section II). Then, for demonstration, a third-order elliptic filter with a cutoff frequency tunable up to 98 MHz is described (Section III). For this transconductor a Q-tuning circuit with high-speed potential (Section IV) and a supply voltage buffer (Section V) are also presented. Finally, the experimental results of the circuits are discussed (Section VI).

II. TRANSCONDUCTOR

In this section, first the linear V-to-I conversion of the transconductor is described and then the common-mode control, dc-gain enhancement, bandwidth, distortion, and noise are discussed.

A. V–I Conversion

The transconductor [9] is based upon the well-known CMOS inverter. This CMOS inverter has no internal nodes and has a good linearity in V–I conversion if the β factors of the n-channel and p-channel transistors are perfectly matched. Consider first the inverter of Fig. 2(a). If the drain currents of an n- and a p-channel MOS transistor in saturation are written as

$$I_{dn} = \frac{\beta_n}{2}(V_{gsn} - V_{tn})^2, \quad \text{with } \beta_n = \frac{\mu_n C_{ox} W_n}{L_n} \quad (1a)$$

$$I_{dp} = \frac{\beta_p}{2}(V_{gsp} - V_{tp})^2, \quad \text{with } \beta_p = \frac{\mu_p C_{ox} W_p}{L_p} \quad (1b)$$

then the output current of the single inverter can be written as

$$I_{out} = I_{dn} - I_{dp} = a(V_{in} - V_{tn})^2 + b \cdot V_{in} + c \quad (2)$$

with

$$a = \tfrac{1}{2}(\beta_n - \beta_p) \quad (2a)$$

$$b = \beta_p(V_{dd} - V_{tn} + V_{tp}) \quad (2b)$$

$$c = \tfrac{1}{2}\beta_p(V_{tn}^2 - (V_{dd} + V_{tp})^2). \quad (2c)$$

All devices are assumed to operate in strong inversion and in saturation. If $\beta_n \neq \beta_p$, i.e., $a \neq 0$, the V-to-I conver-

sion will not be linear. The error is in fact a square-law term, that can be canceled if a balanced structure is used.

The output current is zero when $V_{in} = V_c$ (see Fig. 2(b)), with

$$V_c = \frac{V_{dd} - V_{tn} + V_{tp}}{1 + \sqrt{\dfrac{\beta_n}{\beta_p}}} + V_{tn}. \quad (3)$$

Note that for $\beta_p = \beta_n$ and $V_{tn} = -V_{tp}$, then $V_c = 1/2\,V_{dd}$ as can be easily verified.

Fig. 2(c) shows the balanced version of the circuit of Fig. 2(a). The two matched inverters Inv1 and Inv2 are driven by a differential input voltage V_{id}, balanced around the common-mode voltage level V_c (see (3)). The output currents I_{o1} and I_{o2} can be calculated, and subtraction results in the differential output current I_{od}:

$$I_{o1} = a(V_c - V_{tn} + \tfrac{1}{2}V_{id})^2 + b(V_c + \tfrac{1}{2}V_{id}) + c$$

$$I_{o2} = a(V_c - V_{tn} - \tfrac{1}{2}V_{id})^2 + b(V_c - \tfrac{1}{2}V_{id}) + c$$

$$I_{o1} - I_{o2} = a((V_c - V_{tn} + \tfrac{1}{2}V_{id})^2 - (V_c - V_{tn} - \tfrac{1}{2}V_{id})^2)$$
$$+ bV_{id}$$

or

$$I_{o1} - I_{o2} = V_{id}(b + 2a(V_c - V_{tn}))$$

$$= V_{id}(\beta_p(V_{dd} - V_c + V_{tp}) + \beta_n(V_c - V_{tn})). \quad (4)$$

Hence, the differential output current is linear with the differential input voltage. Using (3) for eliminating V_c, (4) can be written as

$$I_{od} = I_{o1} - I_{o2}$$

$$= V_{id}(V_{dd} - V_{tn} + V_{tp})\sqrt{\beta_n \cdot \beta_p} = V_{id} \cdot gm_d. \quad (5)$$

Equation (5) is valid as long as the transistors operate in strong inversion and saturation. The differential transconductance (gm_d) is linear, even with nonlinear inverters, i.e., if $\beta_n \neq \beta_p$. To reduce common-mode output currents, however, β_n should be chosen close to β_p. The linearity in V–I conversion is obtained by explicitly making use of the square law and matching properties of the MOS transistors. Normally the transistors have no ideal square-law behavior; these effects will be treated in the section on distortion. The transconductance can be tuned by means of the supply voltage V_{dd}. For this purpose a tunable power-supply unit needs to be implemented on chip.

The schematic of the complete transconductor is given in Fig. 2(d). It consists of six CMOS inverters, which are for the moment all assumed to be equal ($V_{dd} = V'_{dd}$). The basic V–I conversion is performed by Inv1 and Inv2. Note that the circuit of Fig. 2(d) has indeed no internal nodes, except for, of course, the supply nodes.

B. Common-Mode Control and DC-Gain Enhancement

The common-mode level of the output voltages V_{o1} and V_{o2} is controlled by the four inverters Inv3–Inv6 of Fig. 2(d). For simplicity the transconductances gm of these inverters are assumed for the moment to be linear ($\beta_n = \beta_p$). Inv4 and Inv5 are shunted as resistances connected between the output nodes and the common-mode voltage level V_c. The values of these resistances are $1/gm_4$ and $1/gm_5$. Inv3 and Inv6 inject currents $gm_3(V_c - V_{o1})$ and $gm_6(V_c - V_{o2})$, respectively, into these resistances.

The result for common-mode output signals is that the "V_{o1}" node is virtually loaded with a resistance $1/(gm_5 + gm_6)$ and the "V_{o2}" node with a virtual resistance $1/(gm_3 + gm_4)$. For differential output signals the "V_{o1}" node is loaded with a resistance $1/(gm_5 - gm_6)$ and the "V_{o2}" node is loaded with a resistance $1/(gm_4 - gm_3)$. If the four inverters have the same supply voltage and are perfectly matched, all the gm's are equal. Thus the network Inv3–Inv6 forms a low-ohmic load for common signals and a high-ohmic load for differential signals, resulting in a controlled common-mode voltage level of the outputs. The quiescent common-mode voltage will be equal to V_c of (3). The common and differential load resistances at the nodes V_{o1} and V_{o2} are recapitulated in Table I.

If the four inverters Inv3–Inv6 are not exactly linear ($\beta_n \neq \beta_p$), but still perfectly matched, it can be shown that the load resistance is nonlinear only for common-mode signals; for differential signals all even and odd nonlinear terms are cancelled [18].

The dc gain of the transconductor-C integrator can be increased by loading the differential inverters Inv1 and

TABLE I
COMMON AND DIFFERENTIAL LOAD RESISTANCES SEEN ON NODES V_{o1} AND V_{o2}, REALIZED BY THE TRANSCONDUCTANCES gm_3–gm_6 OF Inv3–Inv6

Output Node	Common Resistance	Differential Resistance
V_{o1}	$\dfrac{1}{gm_5 + gm_6}$	$\dfrac{1}{gm_5 - gm_6}$
V_{o2}	$\dfrac{1}{gm_4 + gm_3}$	$\dfrac{1}{gm_4 - gm_3}$

Inv2 with a negative resistance for differential signals as described in Section I. By choosing $gm_3 > gm_4$, $gm_5 = gm_4$, and $gm_6 = gm_3$, this negative resistance $1/\Delta gm = 1/(gm_4 - gm_3) = 1/(gm_5 - gm_6)$ is simply implemented without adding extra nodes to the circuit. The width of the transistors in Inv4 and Inv5 can be designed slightly smaller than those of Inv3 and Inv6.

To obtain a more exact filter response, the dc gain of the integrators can be fine-tuned during operation (Q-tuning) with a separate supply voltage V'_{dd} for Inv4 and Inv5 as shown in Fig. 2(d). If in a filter all inverters Inv4 and Inv5 have identical V'_{dd} and the matching of all inverters is ideal, then the dc gain of every integrator can theoretically become infinite if $\Delta gm = -3/r_{oi}$, where r_{oi} is the output resistance of one inverter. However, the maximal dc gain of an integrator will be degraded by mismatch. Assume for simplicity $gm_4 = gm_5 = gm_0$ and $gm_3 = gm_6 = gm_0 - \Delta gm - \delta gm$. Here Δgm is the desired transconductance difference and equal to $-3/r_{oi}$. For simplicity reasons it is assumed that the mismatch δgm is equal for gm_3 and gm_6. The dc gain of the transconductance-C integrator for differential output signals now becomes

$$A_o = \frac{gm_d}{g_{out}} = \frac{gm_d}{\dfrac{3}{r_{oi}} + gm_4 - gm_3}$$

$$= \frac{gm_d}{\dfrac{3}{r_{oi}} + \Delta gm + \delta gm} = \frac{gm_d}{\delta gm}. \quad (6)$$

Normally $gm_d \approx gm_3 \approx gm_4$. The dc gain is therefore equal to the reciprocal value of the relative transconductance error ($\delta gm/gm$) due to mismatch. This error is a local mismatch error and can be kept small by using proper layout techniques [19]. The measured relative transconductance error over 20 chips was less than 0.5%. Consequently, the dc gain is larger than 200 (46 dB), which is high enough for many applications. In the analysis it was assumed that the mismatch δgm is equal for gm_3 and gm_6($gm_4 = gm_5$ and $gm_3 = gm_6$). If this is not the case, the conclusion of the calculation remains valid; however, the two outputs of the integrator will be slightly asymmetrical.

If no dc-gain enhancement was applied ($\Delta gm = \delta gm = 0$), the dc gain would have been 20 (13 dB). The conclusion is that by choosing gm_3 and gm_6 larger than gm_4 and gm_5, a significant improvement of the integrator dc gain is obtained, without affecting the bandwidth.

If $\delta gm < 0$ the net load resistance will become negative. A stand-alone integrator then would become unstable due to the right-half-plane pole. However, a more detailed analysis [18] and practical experiments show that a gyrator or biquad section built with these building blocks will remain stable. This is owing to the feedback loops inherent to a filter structure constructed with gyrators or biquad sections.

C. Bandwidth

The transconductor presented here has a large bandwidth because of the absence of internal nodes, as stated in Section I. In filter structures where all the parasitic capacitances are shunted parallel to the integration capacitors, the only parasitic poles are due to the finite transit time of the carriers in the MOST channel, which are, according to [10], located in the gigahertz range. It can be shown that the series resistances in capacitors even have a compensating effect on the effects of the finite transit time in the MOS channel [18].

D. Distortion

Using the ideal square-law transistor model of (1), the V-to-I conversion will be perfectly linear. However, a more detailed analysis shows that nonlinearities due to mobility reduction occur. In first-order approximation this may be modeled as

$$\mu = \frac{\mu_o}{1 + \theta |V_{gs} - V_T|}. \tag{7}$$

In order to obtain a manageable expression, simplifications have been made. Assuming $\beta_n = \beta_p = \beta$, and therefore, $V_c - V_{tn} = V_{dd} - V_c + V_{tp} = V_o$, and also assuming $(\theta V_o)^2 \ll 1$, yields

$$I_{od} \approx \frac{\beta V_o (5 V_o (\theta_n + \theta_p) + 4)}{1 + 2 V_o (\theta_n + \theta_p)} \frac{1}{2} V_{id}$$
$$- \frac{\beta (8 V_o \theta_n \theta_p + \theta_n + \theta_p)}{1 + 4 V_o (\theta_n + \theta_p)} \frac{1}{8} V_{id}^3. \tag{8}$$

This expression can again be simplified if $\theta V_o \ll 1$:

$$I_{od} \approx 2\beta V_o V_{id} - \frac{\beta}{8} (\theta_n + \theta_p) V_{id}^3. \tag{9}$$

The mobility reduction of both the n- and p-channel devices therefore causes mainly third-order distortion. The second-order distortion due to $\beta_n \neq \beta_p$ combined with mismatch between Inv1 and Inv2 is negligibly small in practice. Normally, channel-length modulation is also a source of distortion in circuits with "square-law linearization" [11]. Owing to the compensation of the output resistances in the tranconductor (the dc-gain enhancement), channel-length modulation is no source of distortion in this circuit.

E. Noise

The thermal drain current noise of a single transistor can be written as

$$\overline{i_{dt}^2} = 4 \cdot k \cdot T \cdot c \cdot gm \cdot \Delta f, \quad \text{with} \quad 1 < c < 2. \tag{10}$$

The differential output noise of the transconductor of Fig. 2(d) can now be written as

$$\overline{i_{od}^2} = 4kTc \, \Delta f \sum gm_i \tag{11}$$

where $\sum gm_i$ is the sum of all transconductances of the six inverters and $c = c_n = c_p$ is the thermal noise coefficient of the n- and p-channel transistors $1 < c < 2$.

Note that the transconductor of Fig. 2(d) has a class-AB behavior; the supply currents will therefore also be dependent of the input signal. This makes an on-chip (low ohmic) power-supply tuning circuit more complex. In Section V of this paper a method for implementing an integrated supply voltage regulation is described.

Summarizing, we can say that we have a linear transconductor without internal nodes and with a tunable output resistance. The dc gain is only limited by mismatch: the measured transconductance mismatch of less than 0.5% gives a dc gain of at least 200, which is high enough for many filters. The parasitic poles are located in the gigahertz range and are due to the finite transit times in the MOS channels. The transconductance can be tuned by means of the supply voltage V_{dd} and the output resistance can be fine-tuned with a separate supply voltage V'_{dd}. Tuning the transconductance results in tuning of the cutoff frequency of a filter and tuning of the output resistance results in tuning of the integrator phase and thus of the quality factors of a filter built with this transconductor.

III. FILTER

A third-order elliptic filter [12], [13] has been realized with the transconductance of Fig. 2(d). The filter is derived from a passive ladder filter since ladder filters have good sensitivity and dynamic range properties. The normalized passive prototype filter [14] is given in Fig. 3. The pole quality factor is equal to 3. The active implementation is shown in Fig. 4(a). The filter is a direct implementation of the ladder filter using a gyrator ($G3$–$G6$) loaded with a capacitor (C_2, C'_2) to simulate the inductor. The resistors are also implemented with transconductance elements ($G2$ and $G7$).

The W/L ratios of the n-channel devices in the transconductors are 24 μm/3 μm for Inv1, Inv2, Inv3, and Inv6 and 21 μm/3 μm for Inv4 and Inv5. The widths of the p-channel devices are in all cases a factor of 3 ($\approx \mu_n/\mu_p$) larger. The threshold voltages are $V_{tn} = 0.75$ V and $V_{tp} = -0.80$ V.

To achieve a high cutoff frequency, the filter operates mainly on parasitic capacitances. This is possible since the parasitic capacitances are all at nodes where a capacitance is desired in the filter. The parasitic capacitances consist for roughly 70% of gate oxide capacitance C_{ox} and

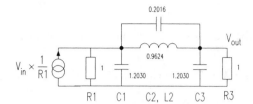

Fig. 3. Passive prototype filter [14].

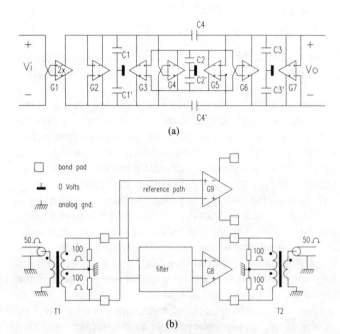

(a)

(b)

Fig. 4. (a) Active implementation of the filter of Fig. 3. (b) Test circuit that makes compensation for the parasitic elements outside the filter possible during measurements.

are consequently quite linear. C_1 and $C_{1'}$ are fully determined by parasitic capacitances. The other capacitances, C_2–C_4 are designed by adding small extra capacitors. These extra capacitors are polysilicon n-well capacitors with gate oxide dielectricum. The time constants of the filter can be written as $\tau = C/gm_d$, with C a capacitance in Fig. 4(a) and gm_d the transconductance of the transconductor. Both C and gm_d are approximately proportional to C_{ox}. The result of this is that the spread in τ due to spread in C_{ox} is small. This results in quite accurate time constants even if the filter operates mainly on its own parasitic capacitances.

No tuning circuitry has been integrated for this test chip. The tuning of both cutoff frequency (with V_{dd}) and quality factors (with V'_{dd}) is done manually with external voltage sources.

A. Experimental Setup

Measurement of the filter characteristic up to very high frequencies requires special precautions in the design of the filter IC. This is illustrated in the experimental setup of Fig. 4(b). The balanced input voltage of the filter is generated from a single-ended signal by means of an off-chip transformer ($T1$). The output voltages of the filter are converted to output currents by means of $G8$. These cur-

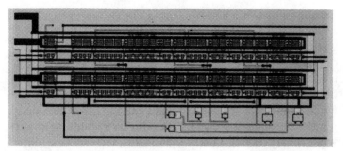

Fig. 5. Chip photograph. Area of the filter is 0.63 mm².

rents are converted to voltages by means of two off-chip 100-Ω resistors. The differential output voltage is converted to a single-ended voltage in 50 Ω by means of a transformer ($T2$). An on-chip reference path, also buffered with a matched transconductor ($G9$), is used to compensate for all parasitic elements, apart from mismatch, outside the filter during measurements. With this technique, accurate measurements up to several hundreds of megahertz can be done.

V_{dd} and V'_{dd} are applied externally. An off-chip capacitor of 4.7 μF has been connected between the V_{dd} and V'_{dd} pins and ground.

The chip was processed in a 3-μm CMOS process. A chip photograph is given in Fig. 5. The area of the filter is 0.63 mm². The experimental results obtained from this test chip are discussed in Section VI.

IV. TUNING

To correct the frequency response of an integrated filter for process and temperature variations, tuning of the cutoff frequency [15] (ƒ-tuning) is generally applied. Several filters are also provided with automatic tuning of the quality factors (Q-tuning) [16]. Combined ƒ- and Q-tuning can be applied with either a master voltage-controlled filter (VCF) [5], [16] or a master voltage-controlled oscillator (VCO) [6].

In Fig. 6 the method using a master VCO is illustrated. The VCO consists of two undamped integrators and has a controllable frequency and quality factor. Consider first the Q-tuning loop. If the Q of the VCO is infinite, then the VCO will oscillate harmonically with a constant amplitude (the poles are exactly on the $j\omega$ axis of the complex plane). The Q-loop controls the amplitude of the VCO in such a way that it will oscillate with a constant amplitude. By copying the voltage, used for tuning the Q of the two integrators in the master VCO, to the (matched) integrators in the slave filter, the quality factors of the filter will also be correct. The amplitude of the VCO signal is uncritical as long as the integrators in the VCO operate in their linear region.

The ƒ-control loop is a well-known phase-locked loop (PLL) which locks the oscillating frequency to an external reference frequency. The voltage used for tuning the frequency of the VCO is copied to the slave filter.

The combination of ƒ- and Q-tuning is possible if the ƒ- and Q-control loops are independent. This is difficult in

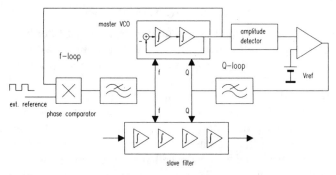

Fig. 6. Combined frequency- and Q-tuning loops.

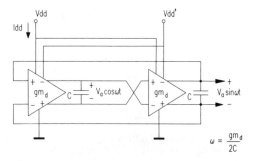

Fig. 7. Voltage-controlled oscillator for the frequency- and Q-tuning circuit.

practice. If the Q-tuning loop is much faster than the f-tuning loop, the f-tuning loop will be quasi-static and then the f- and Q-loops become practically independent. For VHF filters the Q loop must be fast enough to tune the VCO, which oscillates at least at the cutoff frequency of the filter, which can be up to 100 MHz. The Q-tuning loop must therefore be very fast.

This paper describes a Q-tuning technique without a physical loop, so that it is very fast and therefore suitable for very high frequencies [17].

A. Automatic Q-Tuning

With the transconductor described in Section II, the master VCO of Fig. 7 can be made. If the Q of the VCO is infinite, it will oscillate harmonically at a frequency determined by V_{dd}.

For every value of V_{dd} there is only one value of V'_{dd} resulting in correct Q. The inverse is also true: for each V'_{dd} there is only one value of V_{dd} so that the Q is correct. It follows that the frequency can as well be tuned with V'_{dd} if the Q loop controls V_{dd}. V_{dd} and V'_{dd} will then be related correctly. This is very important for the Q-tuning circuit described here.

Consider the VCO is oscillating harmonically with an amplitude V_a at a frequency ω. Using (1) and (3), the supply current I_{dd} is calculated (see Fig. 7). This results in

$$I_{dd} = 2\beta_p \left(2 \left(\frac{\sqrt{\beta_n/\beta_p}}{1 + \sqrt{\beta_n/\beta_p}} (V_{dd} - V_{tn} + V_{tp}) \right)^2 \right.$$
$$\left. + \frac{1}{4} V_a^2 (\sin^2 \omega t + \cos^2 \omega t) \right) \quad (12)$$

and since $\sin^2 \omega t + \cos^2 \omega t = 1$, this can be written as

$$I_{dd} = 2\beta_p \left(2 \left(\frac{\sqrt{\beta_n/\beta_p}}{1 + \sqrt{\beta_n/\beta_p}} (V_{dd} - V_{tn} + V_{tp}) \right)^2 \right.$$
$$\left. + \frac{1}{4} V_a^2 \right). \quad (13)$$

If $V_a = 0$, therefore no oscillation, then I_{dd} consists of the quiescent current of eight inverters, biased in their linear region. In the case of oscillation, $V_a \neq 0$, the current is larger but remains constant. Note that the current I_{dd} is dependent on the amplitude of the VCO output signal (V_a).

The transconductor therefore has an intrinsic wide-band amplitude detection function hidden in its supply current. This can be exploited as follows. If the node V_{dd} is supplied by means of a dc current source with a value given by (13) instead of by a voltage source with value V_{dd}, the oscillator will oscillate with a constant and well-controlled amplitude V_a. The controlling mechanism can be explained as follows.

1) Suppose the poles of the VCO are in the right complex half plane. Therefore, the amplitude V_a tends to increase. With a constant I_{dd} this implies from (13) that V_{dd} must decrease. With a (quasi-static) constant V'_{dd} this implies that gm_3 and gm_6 (Fig. 2(d)) decrease while gm_4 and gm_5 remain constant so that the oscillation is damped until the poles are forced on the imaginary axis. Hence, this ensures a feedback control for the amplitude.

2) Suppose the poles of the VCO are in the left complex half plane. The amplitude V_a tends to decrease. With a constant I_{dd} this implies that V_{dd} must increase. With a (quasi-static) constant V'_{dd} this implies that gm_3 and gm_6 increase while gm_4 and gm_5 remain constant, so that the oscillation is undamped until the poles are forced on the imaginary axis. This leads to the same conclusion about a feedback control for the amplitude.

The result of this mechanism is that, for a given V'_{dd}, V_{dd} is controlled in such a way that the poles of the VCO will always be on the imaginary axis; the Q factor of the VCO is then infinite.

If the resulting voltage V_{dd} of the master VCO is copied to the filter by means of a buffer, the quality factors of the slave filter will automatically be correct. It is concluded that the whole Q-tuning circuit can consist of only one dc current source with a current as specified by (13).

The problem now is how to realize the current source I_{dd} with the value given by (13). This can be done as follows.

Usually $V_{dd} \approx V'_{dd}$; with this in mind the current I_{dd} can be made from V'_{dd}, which in turn is determined by the frequency control loop. This is shown in Fig. 8. The current I_o is determined by V'_{dd}, V_b, and the inverter parameters.[2] The inverter in Fig. 8 is matched to those connected to V_{dd} in the VCO, all n-channel transistors have

---

[2] The sources V_b can be made on chip by driving a current through a resistorlike circuit.

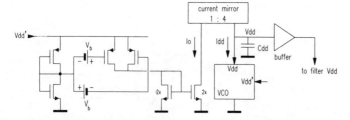

Fig. 8. Circuit that generates I_{dd} from V'_{dd} and V_b such that the amplitude of the VCO is constant and the Q is correct.

equal geometries, and all p-channel transistors have equal geometries. The current I_o can be calculated, which results in

$$I_o = \frac{1}{2} \beta_p \left(2 \left(\frac{\sqrt{\beta_n/\beta_p}}{1 + \sqrt{\beta_n/\beta_p}} (V'_{dd} - V_{tn} + V_{tp}) \right)^2 + 2V_b^2 \right). \tag{14}$$

Comparing (13) and (14) it can be seen that for

$$V_b = \frac{1}{4} \sqrt{2} V_a \tag{15}$$

the current I_o has only to be multiplied with a factor of 4 to obtain the current given by (13), as long as $V_{dd} \approx V'_{dd}$. This multiplication is simply performed with a 1:4 current mirror. The voltage buffer copies the voltage V_{dd} to the slave filter.

If V_{dd} deviates somewhat from V'_{dd} or if there is little mismatch in the circuit of Fig. 8, then only the amplitude of the oscillation will be different from the value predicted by (15). The quality factor, however, will remain correct. Normally the transistors deviate from ideal square-law behavior. This results in a current I_{dd} of the VCO which is not exactly constant. I_{dd} will contain higher harmonics of the oscillation frequency ω.

The capacitance C_{dd}, however, will drain these currents, so that the ripple in V_{dd} remains very small. The capacitance C_{dd} is the n-well-to-substrate capacitance of the p-channel transistors, which will be on chip. If necessary the buffer can in addition be preceded by a simple low-pass filter.

Note that temperature effects are compensated if the circuit of Fig. 8, the VCO, and the slave filter all have the same temperature.

This Q-tuning circuit needs no fast amplitude detectors or rectifiers, owing to the intrinsic wide-band amplitude detection provided by the transconductance element of Fig. 2(d) (see also (12)). The circuit of Fig. 8 has no signal-carrying nodes. All nodes have a (quasi-static) dc voltage during operation. For this reason the oscillating frequency of the VCO is not a limiting factor and the circuit is suitable for very high frequencies. Furthermore, the circuit is extremely simple; it only consists of one current source, two current mirrors, and a buffer. The circuit of Fig. 8 and the VCO have been realized on a breadboard. The experimental results are discussed in Section VI.

V. SUPPLY VOLTAGE BUFFER

The cutoff frequency and quality factors of a filter built with the transconductor of Fig. 2(d) are tuned with the two supply voltages V_{dd} and V'_{dd}. These two supply voltages are generated by the f- and Q-tuning loops, and need to be buffered before being applied to the filter. This section deals with the design of these supply voltage buffers.

Consider a filter built with the transconductors of Fig. 2(d). These transconductors in turn consist of three inverter pairs, all driven balanced around the common-mode voltage level V_c of (3). The inverter pairs can be either connected to the supply voltages V_{dd} or V'_{dd}. In Fig. 9 the inverter pairs connected to V_{dd} are shown schematically (ignore for the moment the dashed current sources). The supply voltage V_{dd} of the inverter pairs is applied by an on-chip supply voltage buffer, modeled with a voltage source $V_{dd,ideal}$ with series impedance Z_{dd}.

In order to obtain insight into the supply current I_{dd}, a simplification can be made by considering first only one inverter pair connected to V_{dd}. The inverter pair is driven with an input voltage V_{id} balanced around the common-mode level V_c as shown in Fig. 9. Using (1) and (3), and assuming all transistors operating in strong inversion and saturation, the supply current $I_{dd,2inv}$ of the two inverters can be calculated:

$$I_{dd,2inv} = \underbrace{\beta_p \left(\frac{\sqrt{\beta_n/\beta_p}}{1 + \sqrt{\beta_n/\beta_p}} (V_{dd} - V_{tn} + V_{tp}) \right)^2}_{\text{I}} + \underbrace{\frac{1}{4} \beta_p V_{id}^2}_{\text{II}}. \tag{16}$$

This supply current consists of a quiescent part (part I of (16)) and a signal-dependent part (part II of (16)). The sum of these signal-dependent supply currents (I_{dd}) of all inverter pairs connected to V_{dd} will cause a ripple in V_{dd} in the configuration of Fig. 9 if Z_{dd} is not low enough.

Since this occurs both for V_{dd} and V'_{dd}, the effect on complete filters will be modulation of both cutoff frequency and quality factors if the supply voltages are applied by buffers with a too high series impedance. The consequence will be distortion in the filter transfer and crosstalk causing deterioration of the stopband attenuation.

For low-frequency variations in I_{dd}, the source $V_{dd,ideal}$ with series impedance Z_{dd} can operate satisfactorily since Z_{dd} can be made low for these frequencies by using well-known feedback techniques. However, these feedback techniques are not sufficient to make Z_{dd} low for high-frequency variations in I_{dd}. For correct high-frequency operation additional current sources (Fig. 9, dashed lines) are added to the inverter pairs. The purpose of $I_{cc,2inv}$, for example, is to inject the required supply current for high-

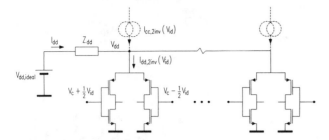

Fig. 9. A filter is built with inverter pairs which need to be supplied by a supply voltage buffer. The series impedance Z_{dd} of this buffer can be made low for low-frequency variations in I_{dd} by using feedback techniques. The high-frequency variations in the supply currents of the inverter pairs are compensated by additional (dashed) current sources. Therefore no high-frequency current flows through Z_{dd} resulting in a well-controlled V_{dd}, even for high frequencies.

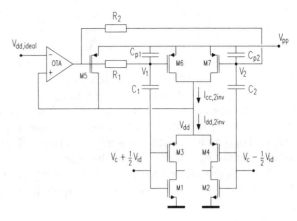

Fig. 10. Implementation of the supply current compensation technique with p-channel transistors.

frequency variations in $I_{dd,\,2\text{inv}}$. Since all inverter pairs are provided with such a compensation current source, this implies that no high-frequency current will flow through Z_{dd} and the requirements for Z_{dd} are relaxed for these frequencies. The result is a well-controlled V_{dd}, even for high-frequencies.

The basic idea is therefore the use of feedback for low frequencies and compensation for high-frequency variations in supply currents.

The compensation sources have to be implemented for each inverter pair in the filter. Since many inverter pairs will have the same input voltages and thus the same supply currents, a combination of compensation sources is possible for these inverter pairs.

In the rest of this section two possible implementations of the supply voltage buffers with high-frequency supply current compensation are given. For simplicity only circuitry for supplying one inverter pair connected to V_{dd} is discussed. Therefore, the feedback mechanism and only one compensation current source will be described.

A. Version I

Consider first the configuration of Fig. 10. $M1 = M2$ and $M3 = M4$ is the inverter pair that requires supply current compensation.

Neglecting for low frequencies all capacitors in Fig. 10, the OTA drives the gates of $M5$, and via $R1$ and $R2$ the gates of identical transistors $M6$ and $M7$. The result is a low-ohmic supply voltage buffer for low frequencies. At high frequencies the capacitive load of the OTA causes a degradation in the OTA voltage gain and thus $|Z_{dd}|$ increases.

For high frequencies the current $I_{cc,\,2\text{inv}}$, the sum of the drain currents of $M6$ and $M7$, compensates $I_{dd,\,2\text{inv}}$, the sum of the drain currents[3] of $M3$ and $M4$. The compen-

---

[3] Actually $I_{dd,\,2\text{inv}}$ is the sum of the source currents of $M3$ and $M4$. The capacitive gate and bulk currents do not contribute to $I_{dd,\,2\text{inv}}$ if the inverter inputs are driven balanced and the capacitances are assumed to be linear. The sum of the source currents is therefore equal to the sum of the drain currents of $M3$ and $M4$.

sation mechanism works as follows. The gate voltages V_1 and V_2 of $M6$ and $M7$, respectively, can be written as

$$V_1 = V_{cc} + \tfrac{1}{2} V_{cd} \qquad (17a)$$

$$V_2 = V_{cc} - \tfrac{1}{2} V_{cd} \qquad (17b)$$

where V_{cc} is the common-mode voltage and V_{cd} is the differential-mode voltage of V_1 and V_2. Using (17) and (1) $I_{cc,\,2\text{inv}}$ can be expressed as

$$I_{cc,\,2\text{inv}} = \underbrace{\beta_{p6,7}(V_{pp} - V_{cc} + V_{tp})^2}_{\text{I}} + \underbrace{\tfrac{1}{4}\beta_{p6,7}V_{cd}^2}_{\text{II}} \qquad (18)$$

where $\beta_{p6,7}$ is the β factor of $M6$ and $M7$ and V_{pp} is the "outside world" supply voltage. Comparison with (16) shows that the high-frequency ripple in $I_{dd,\,2\text{inv}}$ is compensated if for these frequencies part II of (18) is equal to part II of (16). The differential input signal of the two inverters needs therefore to be transferred to the gates of $M6$ and $M7$. This is done by the capacitive voltage dividers C_1, C_{p1} and C_2, C_{p2}. C_{p1} and C_{p2} are the equal parasitic (gate–source) capacitances of $M6$ and $M7$. $C_1 = C_2$ are added floating capacitors. The transfer from V_{id} to V_{cd} is

$$V_{cd} = V_{id} \frac{C_1}{C_1 + C_{p1}}, \qquad \text{for } \omega \gg 1/R_1 C_{p1}. \qquad (19)$$

$R_1 = R_2$ serve only for dc biasing the gates of $M6$ and $M7$ (resulting in correct V_{cc}) and are assumed to be large.

Note that the transfer of the capacitive voltage divider of (19) is frequency independent. The conversion from V_{id} of V_{cd} is of very large bandwidth. Capacitor series resistances, etc. can cause deviations from the transfer of (19) only in the gigahertz range.

The capacitors C_1 and C_2 in series with C_{p1} and C_{p2} form an extra capacitive load for the filter. The filter capacitors will need to be corrected for this.

The required voltage drop across the supply voltage buffer, that is the minimal value of $V_{pp} - V_{dd}$, is equal to $|V_{gs} - V_{tp}|$ of $M5$, $M6$, and $M7$. This value depends on the W/L ratio of these transistors. A typical value of $|V_{gs} - V_{tp}|$ ranges from 200 to 500 mV.

If the matching is perfect the ripple in $I_{dd,2\text{inv}}$ is fully compensated for the frequency range of interest. Limitations in frequency are due to capacitor nonidealities. Mismatch will cause an error in $I_{cc,2\text{inv}}$ resulting in a nonzero ripple in V_{dd}. At the end of this section simulation results are given for the case of 10% mismatch in $I_{cc,2\text{inv}}$.

In the description of the circuit of Fig. 10 it was assumed that the "outside-world" supply voltage V_{pp} is constant. This can be realized by applying a large off-chip capacitor across V_{pp}. If V_{pp} cannot be made constant, a ripple in V_{pp} is transferred to the nodes V_1 and V_2 via C_{p1} and C_{p2}. This causes an extra undesired ripple in $I_{cc,2\text{inv}}$ and thus a ripple in V_{dd} at high frequencies.

B. Version II

To circumvent this poor power supply rejection at high frequencies, an alternative solution is given in Fig. 11. The principle is the same as in Fig. 10, however, n-channel transistors instead of p-channel transistors are used for the supply voltage buffer.

The operation of the low-frequency feedback mechanism is obvious. The high-frequency compensation is similar to that of Fig. 10. First, consider that V_{dd} is constant (later it will appear that V_{dd} will be constant indeed). C_{p1} and C_{p2} are the parasitic gate-source capacitors of $M6$ and $M7$. The gate voltages of $M6$ and $M7$, V_1 and V_2, respectively, can again be written in the form of (17). V_{id} is converted to V_{cd}, by means of capacitive voltage division, as described by (19). The result is an $I_{cc,2\text{inv}}$, now generated by the n-channel transistors $M6$ and $M7$, of the form:

$$I_{cc,2\text{inv}} = \underbrace{\beta_{n6,7}(V_{cc} - V_{cd} - V_{tn})^2}_{\text{I}} + \underbrace{\tfrac{1}{4}\beta_{n6,7}V_{cd}^2}_{\text{II}}. \quad (20)$$

Compensation of the high-frequency part of $I_{dd,2\text{inv}}$ is possible if part II of (20) is equal to part II of (16).

The advantage of the n-channel compensation is that there is no significant capacitance present between the V_{pp}-node and the signal path, resulting in an improved power supply rejection. A serious disadvantage is a larger voltage drop across the supply voltage buffer. Simulation results of the circuit under 10% mismatch in $I_{cc,2\text{inv}}$ are given below.

C. Simulations

The performance of the circuits of Figs. 10 and 11 has been evaluated with SPICE (level 3) simulations.

Consider first the circuit of Fig. 10. The transistor dimensions of the two inverters are the same as Inv1 and Inv2 of the transconductors used in the filter, as described in Section III. $M5 = M6 = M7 = 2 \times M3$, $G_{OTA} = 80$ $\mu A/V$, and $R_{OTA} = 5$ MΩ. The voltages V_{pp} and V_{dd} are chosen as 5 V and 3 V, respectively. The input voltage V_{id} is a sine wave with an amplitude of 0.5 V with variable frequency. Note that the frequency of the ripple in $I_{dd,2\text{inv}}$ will be twice the frequency of V_{id}.

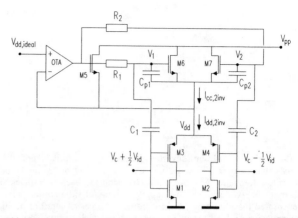

Fig. 11. Implementation of the supply current compensation technique with n-channel transistors.

To investigate the ripple in V_{dd} due to variations of V_{id}, transient simulations were carried out. For comparison, first the case of a simple feedback supply voltage buffer is analyzed by setting $R_1 = R_2 = 0$ and $C_1 = C_2 = 0$. The result can be found in curve a of Fig. 12. For low frequencies the ripple is small due to sufficient loop gain in the feedback loop. For very high frequencies the ripple is also small thanks to the capacitance present at the V_{dd} node. For the intermediate frequencies the ripple becomes much larger.

Using the supply current compensation ($C_1 = C_2 = 610$ fF and R_1 and R_2 of the same order of magnitude as R_{OTA})[4] makes zero ripple in V_{dd} possible for the case of perfect matching. Since this is not realistic in practice, an artificial error of 10% is introduced in the simulations. The result is plotted in curve b of Fig. 12. The improvement with respect to curve a is obvious. The ripple in V_{dd} is several millivolts, which is small enough [18].

Consider now the circuit of Fig. 11. $M5 = M6 = M7 = 2 \times M1$ and the rest the parameters are equal to those mentioned above.

The case of only feedback ($R_1 = R_2 = C_1 = C_2 = 0$) is plotted in curve c of Fig. 12 and a similar behavior as in curve a is found. Using the supply current compensation ($C_1 = C_2 = 200$ fF) with an artificial mismatch of 10% in $I_{cc,2\text{inv}}$ gives curve d and thus a significant improvement.

The difference in performance of the circuits of Figs. 10 and 11 becomes clear when considering the crosstalk from the "outside-world" supply voltage V_{pp} to the internally generated V_{dd}. For the circuit of Fig. 10 the transfer of variations in V_{pp}-to-V_{dd} variations has a high-pass character. For frequencies below 200 kHz the gain is -44 dB. For frequencies beyond 20 MHz the capacitances C_{p1} and C_{p2} have enabled crosstalk and the gain becomes -0.5 dB. For these frequencies[5] the power supply rejection is poor and a large off-chip capacitor across V_{pp} will be nec-

---

[4]Such a large resistor can be made actively, with a unity feedback differential pair in weak inversion.

[5]Note that a 20-MHz ripple in V_{pp} corresponds to a 10-MHz sine wave at the inputs of the inverter pairs.

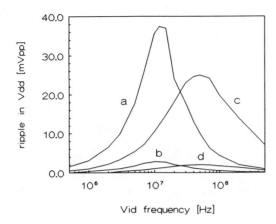

Fig. 12. Simulated ripples in V_{dd} (mV$_{\text{peak-peak}}$) versus frequency of input signal V_{id} for: (a) the circuit of Fig. 10 with feedback only ($C_1 = C_2 = R_1 = R_2 = 0$); (b) the circuit of Fig. 10 also with compensation, however, with 10% mismatch in $I_{cc,2\text{inv}}$; (c) same as curve (a) but now for the circuit of Fig. 11; (d) same as curve (b) but now for the circuit of Fig. 11.

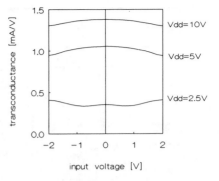

Fig. 13. Measured transconductance versus differential input voltage (V_{id}) for three values of V_{dd}.

essary. The circuit of Fig. 11 has a similar behavior, however simulations show that the transfer from V_{pp} to V_{dd} is 30 dB lower for all frequencies compared to the circuit of Fig. 10. The circuit of Fig. 11 therefore has a much better (30 dB) power-supply rejection.

VI. EXPERIMENTAL RESULTS

In this section the experimental results of the transconductor, filter, and Q-tuning circuit are discussed.

A. Transconductor

The transconductor of Fig. 2(d) has been realized on chip. The measured transconductance for different supply voltages is given in Fig. 13. The nonlinearities are mainly of the third order and due to mobility reduction as expected from (8). For $V_{dd} = 10$ V, 1% relative error in transconductance[6] occurs at a differential input voltage (V_{id}) of 1 V. If $V_{dd} = 2.5$ V, it can be seen that not all transistors operate in strong inversion for differential input voltages larger than 1 V.

B. Filter

The measured filter responses are given in Fig. 14 for three values of V_{dd}: $V_{dd} = 2.5$, 5, and 10 V. In Fig. 14(a) the corresponding responses of the ideal passive prototype of Fig. 3 (same cutoff frequency) are plotted as well. The cutoff frequency is varied from 22 MHz ($V_{dd} = 2.5$ V) to 98 MHz ($V_{dd} = 10$ V). From Fig. 14(a) a close matching with the ideal response is seen. The notch at 214 MHz is 60 dB deep and is very well positioned. Fig. 14(b) is a passband detail of Fig. 14(a). However, from this figure it can be seen that the dc filter gain is too high and the ripple in the passband is too large compared to the ideal response of the passive prototype filter, especially at

---

[6]A 1% relative transconductance error corresponds to 0.083% THD, assuming only third-order distortion.

higher values of V_{dd}. The reason appeared to be a layout error in the filter chip. In fact, the inverters Inv1 and Inv2 of $G2$ and $G7$ of Fig. 4(a) have a supply voltage V'_{dd} instead of V_{dd}. The result of this is that, especially for higher supply voltages, the transconductances of $G2$ and $G7$ become somewhat lower than their nominal values. In Fig. 14(c) the measured filter response is compared to that of the passive prototype filter with R_1 and R_3 (see Fig. 3) chosen slightly too large, corresponding to the situation caused by the layout error. From this figure it can be seen that the curves now do match very closely. Fig. 14(d) shows a passband detail of Fig. 14(c). The dc filter gain and the passband ripple of the measured responses and the responses of the passive prototype now are almost equal.

Taking the layout error into account, we may conclude that the filter response is very close to the response of the passive prototype filter. The 98-MHz filter curve matches well to that of the prototype filter up to 350 MHz. This implies that the integrator has indeed a sufficiently high dc gain and only parasitic poles far enough in the gigahertz region. The total intermodulation distortion (TIMD) of the filter for the three values of V_{dd} is plotted in Fig. 15. The TIMD was measured with a two-tone input signal with frequencies around half of the cutoff frequency of the filter.

The other experimental results are summarized in Table II. The lower limit for the dynamic range was chosen as the total passband noise and the upper limit was the 1% TIMD input rms voltage level. As can be seen from Table II the filter has a high dynamic range: 72 dB for $V_{dd} = 10$ V.

C. Q-Tuning

The circuit of Fig. 8 and the VCO have been realized on breadboard, using commercially available CA3600 CMOS arrays. The voltage V_b was chosen as 0.5 V. Using (15), the amplitude V_a of the VCO is expected to be $0.5 \cdot 2\sqrt{2} = 1.4$ V.

The VCO oscillates at frequencies up to 7 MHz. The results are plotted in Fig. 16. The voltage V_{dd} varies with V'_{dd} in such a way that the VCO oscillates with a constant amplitude of almost 1.4 V, as expected. The frequency varies almost linearly with V_{dd} as predicted by (5).

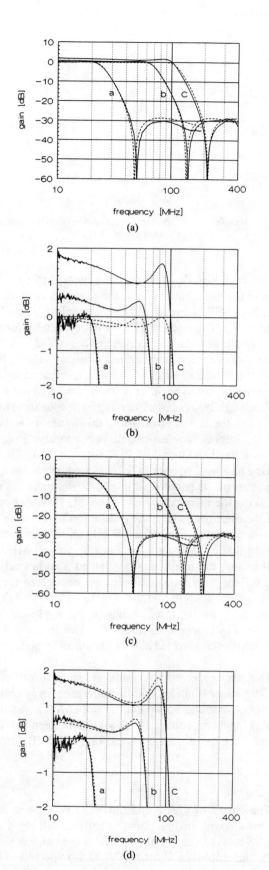

Fig. 14. (a) Measured filter response (——) and ideal response of the passive prototype filter (---): (a) $V_{dd} = 2.5$ V, (b) $V_{dd} = 5$ V, (c) $V_{dd} = 10$ V. (b) Passband detail of Fig. 14(a). (c) Measured filter response (——) and ideal response of the passive prototype filter corrected for the layout error (---): (a) $V_{dd} = 2.5$ V, (b) $V_{dd} = 5$ V, (c) $V_{dd} = 10$ V. (d) Passband detail of Fig. 14(c).

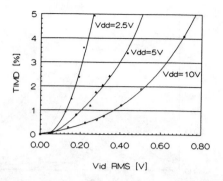

Fig. 15. Total intermodulation distortion of the filter versus rms input voltage ($f \approx \frac{1}{2} f_{cutoff}$).

TABLE II
EXPERIMENTAL RESULTS OBTAINED FROM THE FILTER TEST CHIP

Parameter	$V_{dd} = 2.5$ V	$V_{dd} = 5$ V	$V_{dd} = 10$ V
Cutoff frequency	22 MHz	63 MHz	98 MHz
Total passband input noise	?	81 μV_{rms}	96 μV_{rms}
Dynamic range*	?	68 dB	72 dB
CMRR passband	40 dB	40 dB	40 dB
Transconductance	0.35 mA/V	1.06 mA/V	1.38 mA/V
Power dissipation	4 mW	77 mW	670 mW
V'_{dd}	2.50 V	4.76 V	8.10 V

*See text.

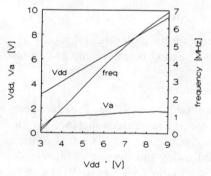

Fig. 16. Experimental results of Q-tuning circuit obtained from a breadboard realization: V_a (amplitude), V_{dd}, and frequency of the VCO versus V'_{dd}. The voltage V_b was chosen to be 0.5 V.

Simulations indicate that an on-chip realization of the circuit will be able to operate at very high frequencies (over 100 MHz). The tuning circuit is not connected to the filter because of the poor matching between breadboard components and on-chip components.

VII. CONCLUSIONS

In this paper principles and circuits for integrated filters at very high frequencies in full CMOS technology have been described.

The CMOS transconductor circuit presented has a bandwidth in the gigahertz region thanks to the absence of internal nodes. Owing to the used square-law linearization technique, the linearity is good and the transconductance can be tuned by means of the supply voltage V_{dd}. The parasitic output resistance of all the MOS transistors is compensated and the resulting net output resistance can be fine-tuned by means of a separate supply voltage V'_{dd}. Thus, Q-tuning becomes possible.

A 100-MHz CMOS continuous-time low-pass filter realized in a 3-μm process has been presented. The filter is constructed with transconductance elements and capacitors. The measured filter frequency response is close to the theoretical response for frequencies up to 350 MHz. The notch in the response is 60 dB deep and well positioned. The filter operates mainly on parasitic capacitances while the accuracy is not affected and the dynamic range is high (72 dB). The cutoff frequency and the Q factors can be tuned by means of two supply voltages.

A special Q-tuning technique for very-high-frequency filters, based on a VCO, has been presented. The Q-tuning circuit is very simple (it is, in fact, only a special dc current source) and contains no signal-carrying nodes. Therefore, no bandwidth limitations are imposed by the Q-tuning circuit, resulting in a well-controlled Q for very high frequencies. Experimental results of a breadboard realization of the Q-tuning circuit were presented, giving results that are in accordance with the theory.

A technique for making an on-chip low-ohmic supply voltage buffer for controlling V_{dd} and V'_{dd} of the transconductors has been presented. The basic idea is the use of feedback for low frequencies and compensation for high-frequency variations in supply currents. The very large bandwidth (in theory infinite) of a capacitive voltage divider is exploited for implementing ultrafast supply current compensation. Two circuit realizations have been presented and are illustrated with simulation results.

It is expected that lower supply voltages and even higher frequencies are achievable if a more advanced (smaller channel lengths) CMOS process is used. The results obtained with these transconductor, filter, and Q-tuning techniques demonstrate that accurate integrated CMOS filters at very high frequencies are possible. Applications can be found in the field of TV IF filtering [18] and other VHF filters.

ACKNOWLEDGMENT

The author wishes to thank A. Cense, J. van Lammeren, and Th. Clercx of Philips Nijmegen for making processing of the chip possible. Furthermore, I wish to thank W. J. A. de Heij, E. Klumperink, K. Hoen, and R. F. Wassenaar for fruitful discussions and H. Wallinga and R. J. Wiegerink for their useful comments on the manuscript.

REFERENCES

[1] F. Krummenacher and N. Joehl, "A 4-MHz CMOS continuous-time filter with on-chip automatic tuning," *IEEE J. Solid-State Circuits*, vol. 23, no. 3, pp. 750–758, June 1988.

[2] T. G. Kim and R. L. Geiger, "Monolithic programmable RF filter," *Electron. Lett.*, vol. 24, no. 25, pp. 1569–1571, Dec. 1988.

[3] L.-J. Pu and Y. P. Tsividis, "Transistor-only frequency-selective circuits," *IEEE J. Solid-State Circuits*, vol. 25, pp. 821–832, no. 3, June 1990.

[4] H. Khorramabadi and P. R. Gray, "High-frequency CMOS continuous-time filters," *IEEE J. Solid-State Circuits*, vol. SC-19, pp. 939–948, no. 6, Dec. 1984.

[5] C. S. Park and R. Schaumann, "Design of a 4-MHz analog integrated CMOS transconductance-C bandpass filter," *IEEE J. Solid-State Circuits*, vol. 23, no. 4, pp. 987–996, Aug. 1988.

[6] Y. Wang, F. Lu, and A. A. Abidi, "A 12.5 MHz CMOS continous time bandpass filter," in *ISSCC Dig. Tech. Papers*, Feb. 1989, pp. 198–199.

[7] V. Gopinathan, Y. P. Tsividis, K. S. Tan, and R. K. Hester, "Design considerations for high-frequency continuous-time filters and implementation of an antialiasing filter for digital video," *IEEE J. Solid-State Circuits*, vol. 25, no. 6, pp. 1368–1378, Dec. 1990.

[8] W. J. A. De Heij, E. Seevinck, and K. Hoen, "Practical formulation of the relation between filter specifications and the requirements for integrator circuits," *IEEE Trans. Circuits Syst.*, vol. 36, pp. 1124–1128, Aug. 1989.

[9] B. Nauta and E. Seevinck, "Linear CMOS transconductance element for VHF filters," *Electron. Lett.*, vol. 25, pp. 448–450, Mar. 1989.

[10] J. R. Burns, "High frequency characteristics of the insulated gate field effect transistor," *RCA Rev.*, vol. 28, pp. 385–418, Sept. 1967.

[11] K. Bult, "Analog CMOS square-law circuits," Ph.D. dissertation Univ. Twente, Enschede, The Netherlands, 1988.

[12] B. Nauta and E. Seevinck, "A 110 MHz CMOS transconductance-C low-pass filter," in *ESSCIRC Dig. Tech. Papers* (Vienna, Austria), Sept. 1989.

[13] B. Nauta, "CMOS VHF transconductance-C lowpass filter," *Electron. Lett.*, vol. 26, pp. 421–422, Mar. 1990.

[14] A. I. Zwerev, *Handbook of Filter Synthesis.* New York: Wiley, 1967.

[15] K. Tan and P. R. Gray, "Fully integrated analog filters using bipolar-JFET technology," *IEEE J. Solid-State Circuits*, vol. SC-13, pp. 814–821, Dec. 1978.

[16] C. Chiou and R. Schaumann, "Design and performance of a fully integrated bipolar 10.7 MHz analog bandpass filter," *IEEE J. Solid-State Circuits*, vol. SC-21, no. 1, pp. 6–14, Feb. 1986.

[17] B. Nauta and E. Seevinck, "Automatic tuning of quality factors for VHF CMOS filters," in *Dig. Tech. Papers ISCAS* (New Orleans), May 1990, pp. 1147–1150.

[18] B. Nauta, "Analog CMOS filters for very-high frequencies," Ph.D. dissertation, Univ. Twente, Enschede, The Netherlands, Sept. 1991.

[19] M. J. M. Pelgrom, A. C. J. Duinmaijer, and A. P. G. Welbers, "Matching properties of MOS transistors," *IEEE J. Solid-State Circuits*, vol. 24, no. 5, pp. 1433–1440, Oct. 1989.

A 10.7 MHz Continuous-Time Bandpass Filter Bipolar IC

M. KOYAMA, H. TANIMOTO and S. MIZOGUCHI*

RESEARCH & DEVELOPMENT CENTER,
TOSHIBA CORP., KAWASAKI, JAPAN

*SEMICONDUCTOR DIVISION,
TOSHIBA CORP., KAWASAKI, JAPAN

Abstract

This paper describes a transconductance-capacitor based low power integrator suitable for high frequency filters. With the integrators, a continuous-time bandpass filter IC operating from 10 MHz to 40 MHz with $Q=10$ has been fabricated by using a standard bipolar process. The measured SNR was 50 dB and the power consumption was 80 mW.

Introduction

Electric cells and ceramic IF filters are major space limiting factors in hand-carried small telecommunication electronic products like radio pagers.

To overcome these problems, it seems to be a reasonable solution to integrate the IF filters into a low power monolithic IC. Reference [1] describes an experimental 10.7 MHz bandpass filter (BPF), but it is necessary to diminish power consumption (600 mW).

This paper reports a low power (80 mW) implementation of 10-40 MHz, $Q=10$ BPFs by using a 2.5 GHz (@Ic=1 mA) bipolar IC process.

Integrator Design Considerations

The transconductance Gm of the differential amplifier for the integrator must be high or an integrating capacitance value $Cint$ must be made small to implement high frequency filters, because the center angular frequency of the filters is given by $Gm/Cint$.

The capacitance value $Cint$ must be large for high Q filters because the Q value of the BPF is proportional to the capacitance ratio $Cint/Ck$, while the lower bound of the available capacitor size of Ck is limited by a fabrication process. For Ck, refer to Fig. 5(d). Consequently, the transconductance for the high frequency and high Q filter must be high because of the lower limit for $Cint$ used.

It is desirable, considering the power consumption, to enable meeting the above high transconductance demand to form an integrator by using bipolar transistors which have higher transconductance to collector current ratio than that of MOSFETs.

Gilbert gain cell integrators using bipolar transistors shown in Fig. 1 are widely used for high frequency active filters. In Fig. 1, the RE values are chosen much larger than $1 / Gm1$ in order to linearize the input differential amplifier (Q1, Q2, RE1, RE2), where $Gm1$ is the transconductance of Q1.

The transconductance of this integrator GM is:

$$GM = \frac{1}{RE} \cdot \frac{I2}{I1} \qquad (RE \gg \frac{1}{Gm1}).$$

The input range is enlarged by the resistors RE about $(1+Gm1 \cdot RE)$ times larger, which value is set at 10-20 typically, than that of the integrator in Fig. 2 which does not have emitter degeneration resistors. However, the output noise voltage of the first stage is amplified in the expanding stage. The equivalent input noise voltage V_{n1} is:

$$\frac{V_{n1}^2}{\Delta f} \approx 4kT(2n^2 \cdot Rb + RE + \frac{n \cdot m}{2 \cdot GM}).$$

$$n = 1 + Gm1 \cdot RE, \qquad m = \frac{I2}{I1}$$

Roughly speaking, V_{n1} is about n times as large as that V_{n2} of the simple integrator shown in Fig. 2.

$$\frac{V_{n2}^2}{\Delta f} = 4kT(Rb + \frac{1}{2 \cdot Gm3})$$

Here, $Gm3$ is the transconductance of the Q7. Although the input range is enlarged, SNR remains almost unchanged owing to the amplified noise voltage. With the same current level, transconductance of this integrator is reduced to $1 / (1+Gm1 \cdot RE)$ that of the transconductance of the integrator shown in Fig. 2.

As a result, nonlinear distortion is reduced, but the power consumption becomes about n times larger and the SNR is hardly improved compared to the integrator in Fig. 2. Thus, the gain cell integrator is not suitable for the high frequency and high Q filters which need high transconductance integrators since the power consumption becomes too large.

Another linearized circuit shown in Fig. 3 was employed in audio frequency filters [2]. This differential amplifier is composed of two emitter coupled pairs. Since the transistors Q9 and Q12 have emitter areas four times larger than those of the transistors Q11 and Q10, the dc operating points of the two differential amplifiers differ from each other. The nonlinearity of the bipolar transistor is canceled by adding the output current of one differential amplifier to that of the other differential amplifier.

The linear range of the input signal (T.H.D.<1 %) is expanded three times compared to that of the integrator shown in Fig. 2 (96 mVp-p). As this differential amplifier does not amplify the noise voltage, the equivalent input noise voltage V_{n3} of this integrator is much lower than that of the gain cell integrator and is 80 % of the integrator shown in Fig. 2.

$$\frac{V_{n3}^2}{\Delta f} = 4kT \cdot 0.64(Rb + \frac{1}{2 \cdot Gm})$$

The transconductance of the integrator is 64 % of that of

Reprinted from *IEEE Proc. CICC*, pp. 25.2.1–25.2.4, 1989.

the integrator shown in Fig. 2. The input linear range and the collector current can be reduced to about $1/n$ as large as that of the gain cell integrator to realize the same SNR and the same transconductance. The power consumption of this integrator can be made $1/n$ as large as that of the gain cell integrator in forming a filter with the same center frequency, Q and SNR by using this integrator.

The base emitter capacitance Cbe of the larger transistors Q9 and Q12 lower the nondominant pole frequency since the emitter sizes of Q9 and Q12 (Fig. 3) are four times as large as those of Q10 and Q11.

To overcome this problem, we have utilized the linearization by changing the emitter size of the previous stage emitter followers so that the core differential pairs may be formed by the same minimum size transistors (Fig. 4). By this improvement, the nondominant pole frequency can be doubled that of the integrator shown in Fig. 3.

Another merit of this integrator is that temperature compensation is easily achieved by using a Vt generator circuit, because the transconductance value of the integrator is proportional to the absolute temperature.

BPF Frequency Limitation

To realize a high Q BPF, for example Q=15 BPF, the nondominant pole frequency $p2$ of the integrator must be at least one hundred times as large as the center frequency f_0 of the BPF. This fact makes it difficult to realize a high frequency BPF. To alleviate this restriction, it was possible to cancel the excess phase shift by setting the dc gain of the integrator $p2/f_0$ [3].

Using this method, the requirement on the nondominant pole frequency of the Q=15 BPF is alleviated to $15f_0$. When the f_0 is 40 MHz, the $p2$ value must be greater than 600 MHz. This value is attainable by using our fabrication process (ft=2.5 GHz, Cbe=1 pF, Rb=200 Ω). The $p2$ value of the integrator in Fig. 4 is calculated to be as follows:

$$p2 = \frac{1}{2\pi \cdot Cbe(Rb + Ro)} = 636 \text{ MHz},$$

where Ro is the output impedance of the emitter follower. Here, Ro=50 Ω is assumed. In this work, the dc gain is set by designing an appropriate value for $R1$ and $R2$. Using resistive loads makes it possible to eliminate the common-mode feedback circuit which is complicated and is necessary for a fully differential construction.

More precise compensation can be made by varying the time constant formed by the Cbe and Ro values of the emitter followers, as shown in Fig. 4.

BPF Structure

A capacitively coupled resonator type BPF was reported in reference [3]. Since this circuit is based on the classical doubly-terminated LC ladder structure, the sensitivity to component variations is retained very low. This type circuit is suitable to integrate the capacitor of the BPF in the IC chip because all the integration capacitors can be scaled to the same value.

A drawback of this circuit is that, by using narrowband approximation, the transfer function is not exactly the same as the original LC BPF. By the authors' analysis, the passband characteristic of the filter is not flat.

This problem was solved by an LC simulation based on gyrators. The transformation procedure is shown in Figs. 5(a)-5(d). The fourth order ladder structure LC

BPF is shown in Fig. 5(a). The T section, formed by three inductors, was transformed to two gyrators and the Π section, formed by three capacitors, as indicated in Fig. 5(b). The serial terminated resistor $R3$ was transformed to the parallel resistor $R4$, and the coupling capacitor $C1$ was divided into $C2$ and $C3$, as shown in Fig. 5(c). The gyrator was formed by connecting two voltage controlled current sources back to back, as shown in Fig. 5(d).

This transformation does not use any approximation at all. The transfer function is exactly the same as the original LC filter. This circuit configuration is very similar to the circuit in reference [3]. The location of the input termination resistor Ra alone was different from that of Rb in reference [3]. The fourth order BPF composed of the newly designed integrators is shown in Fig. 6. Here, $Cint$ and Ck values were designed as 32 pF and 5 pF, respectively.

Experimental Results

A photograph of the experimental IC chip of a fourth order BPF is shown in Fig. 11. The chip size was 2 x 2 mm. The frequency response and the noise spectrum of the fourth order BPF with $f_0 = 10.7$ MHz and Bw=1.1 MHz are shown in Fig. 7. The f_0 of the BPF was tuned by varying the current of differential pairs and the Q of the BPF was controlled by the emitter follower currents of the integrators.

The pass-band ripple was 0.3 dB, which indicate that the excess phase shift around the fo was small. Higher frequency BPFs can be expected. The SNR was 50 dB since the measured in-band noise was 73 μVrms. The observed center frequency shift compensated by using the Vt generator circuit was 300 ppm/°C. The power consumption per integrator was 12 mW, which can be reduced to at least 1/2 by a more careful circuit design. The intermodulation distortion at the maximum input level was -45 dB, which is shown in Fig. 9.

The detailed pass-band shape of the fourth order BPF with f_0=20 MHz and Bw=2 MHz is shown in Fig. 8. The pass-band ripple was 1.2 dB. In this filter, resistor $R1$ and $R2$ shown in Fig. 4 were designed at a smaller value than that of the 10.7 MHz BPF.

A second order BPF was designed for a higher frequency BPF. The frequency response of the second order BPF with f_0=40 MHz and Bw=3.2 MHz is shown in Fig. 10. A monotonic stop band attenuation was observed up to 200 MHz. Table 1 summarizes the experimental results.

Conclusion

High frequency 40 MHz and high Q(=12) BPFs were realized with low power consumption by the standard process. These high frequency and high Q filters became possible by using a newly designed simple integrator which made the most of the high frequency characteristics of bipolar transistors and whose noise level was low.

Acknowledgments

The authors would like to thank H. Mafune for her circuit layout design support, T. Sugawara for valuable discussions and S. Moriyama for type settings.

References

[1]C.Chiou and R. Schaumann, "Design and performance of a fully integrated bipolar 10.7 MHz analog bandpass filter," IEEE J. Solid-State Circuits, vol. SC-21, pp.6-

14,Feb.1986.

[2]Calder,D.W.H.,"Audio frequency gyrator filters for an integrated radio paging receiver," IEE Conference, Mobile Radio Systems and Techniques, No.238, 1984.

[3]H. Khorramabadi and P. R. Gray, "High frequency CMOS continuous time filters," IEEE J. Solid-State Circuits, vol. SC-19, pp.939-948, Dec. 1984.

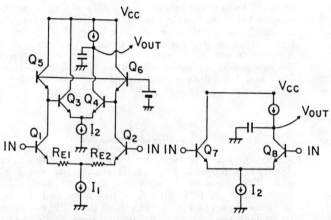

Fig. 1 Gilbert gain   Fig. 2 Basic integrator
       cell integrator

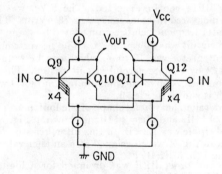

Fig. 3 Linearized integrator

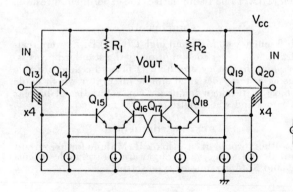

Fig. 4 Newly designed high frequency
        linearized integrator

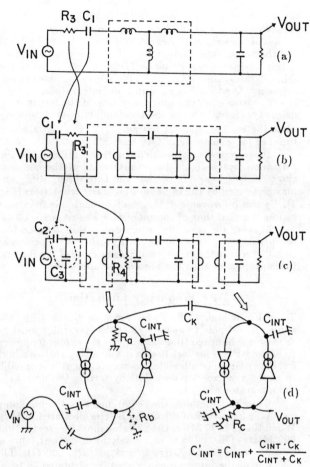

$$C'_{INT} = C_{INT} + \frac{C_{INT} \cdot C_K}{C_{INT} + C_K}$$

Figs. 5(a)-5(d) LC simulation of BPF
by new gyrator structure

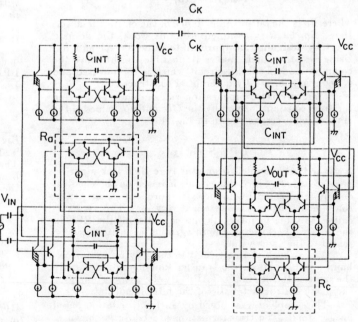

Fig. 6 Circuit diagram of fourth order BPF

304

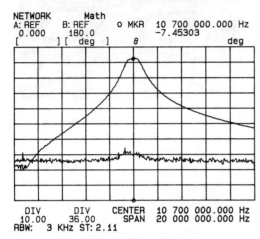

**Fig. 7 Frequency response
and noise spectrum**

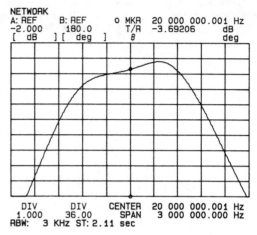

**Fig. 8 Frequency response
of 20 MHz BPF**

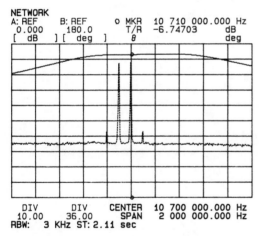

**Fig. 9 Intermodulation distortion
at maximum input level**

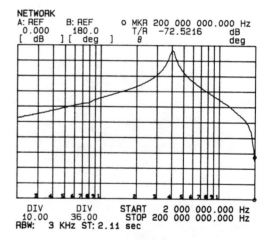

**Fig. 10 Frequency response
of 40 MHz BPF**

Table 1 Experimental results

Center frequency	10.7 MHz	20 MHz	40 MHz
Passband width	1.1 MHz	2 MHz	3.2 MHz
Order of filter	4	4	2
Passband ripple	0.3 dB	1.2 dB	—
Stopband attenuation	65 dB	65 dB	65 dB
S/N(inband, IM3=0.6%)	50 dB	46 dB	49 dB
Supply voltage	6 V	6 V	6 V
Power consumption	80 mW	105 mW	70 mW
Die size	2 x 2 mm	2 x 2 mm	1 x 2 mm

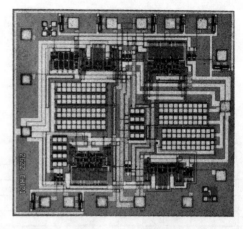

Fig. 11 Die photo of fourth order BPF

100-MHz Monolithic Low-Pass Filters with Transmission Zeros Using NIC Integrators

Shigetaka Takagi, Hajime Nitta, Jorge Koyama, Makoto Furihata, Nobuo Fujii, Minoru Nagata, and Takeshi Yanagisawa

Abstract —This paper proposes a method for monolithic implementation of VHF filters with transmission zeros, by using a modification of the well-known leapfrog simulation and negative impedance converter (NIC) integrators having good high-frequency performance. Experimental results of a monolithic 100-MHz low-pass filter with a transmission zero at 166 MHz confirm the feasibility of the proposed method.

I. INTRODUCTION

SEVERAL high-frequency fully integrated continuous-time active filters have been presented in the literature [1]–[3]. The concept used in [1] was extended to a monolithic implementation of a 100-MHz low-pass filter in [4]. Both filters used gyrators based on a balanced negative impedance converter (NIC) and operated from a single +5-V power supply. The balanced NIC used in [1] and [4] requires low internal voltage gain and can be implemented without p-n-p transistors, being therefore suitable for monolithic implementation of high-frequency filters as confirmed by the good results presented. However, filters based on NIC gyrators have two drawbacks [5]: 1) filters requiring floating capacitors, such as high-order bandpass filters and filters with transmission zeros, are not suited for monolithic implementation because voltage-controlled junction capacitors are used for tuning; and 2) the NIC gyrator requires two NIC's on the same bias line, imposing some sacrifice in parasitic resistance cancellation to obtain 5-V operation capability.

These two drawbacks can be overcome by the NIC-based integrators presented in [5].

This paper presents a monolithic implementation of a low-pass filter with cutoff frequency of 100 MHz and a transmission zero at 166 MHz. The filter uses the NIC integrator of [5] biased from a single +5-V power supply and was implemented on a 3-μm bipolar process [6]. The transmission zero was obtained using a modified leapfrog simulation [7] of a doubly terminated LC ladder. The experimental results shown confirm the feasibility of this method to obtain monolithic VHF filters with transmission zeros.

II. NIC INTEGRATOR [5]

NIC integrators can be realized by using an NIC to cancel out the loss of a passive RC integrator. Besides the distinguished features of the balanced NIC's [1] (i.e., low internal

Manuscript received September 10, 1990; revised November 21, 1990.
S. Takagi, H. Nitta, J. Koyama, N. Fujii, and T. Yanagisawa are with the Tokyo Institute of Technology, 2-12-1 O-okayama, Meguro-ku, Tokyo 152, Japan.
M. Furihata is with Takasaki Works, Hitachi Ltd., 111 Nishiyokote-machi, Takasaki-shi, Gunma-ken 370-11, Japan.
M. Nagata is with the Central Research Laboratory, Hitachi Ltd., Kokubunji, Tokyo 185, Japan.
IEEE Log Number 9042461.

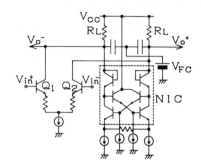

Fig. 1. NIC integrator.

gain, thus providing larger bandwidth than operational amplifiers; possibility of incorporating the parasitic capacitances at the collector side in the integrating capacitor and discounting the parasitics at the other side of the NIC [8]; and realizable without p-n-p transistors), the NIC integrators have the following main properties [5]:

a) balanced integrators that can be used as both inverting and noninverting integrators;

b) NIC integrators use only grounded capacitors, making it easy to adjust the time constants of the filters;

c) only one NIC is required for each integrator, which is suitable for low-voltage operation.

Fig. 1 shows the scheme of the NIC integrator used in this work. The load resistors R_L's of the differential amplifier are canceled by the negative resistance produced by the NIC, thus obtaining a lossless integrator. Care must be taken with the layout of these resistors, and also with careful matching of the transistors of the NIC, because incomplete cancellation of resistances will cause degradation of the quality factor of the integrator with sensitivity similar to the mismatches in the NIC gyrators (for a second-order filter the sensitivity is proportional to Q^2 of the filter [8]). The time constant of the integrator is tuned by the control voltage V_{FC} when junction capacitors are used. To compensate for the nonidealities of the NIC, a zero is introduced in the transfer function of the integrator by means of a resistor (not shown in the figure) in series with the integrating capacitor to cancel the secondary pole. This passive compensation includes the series resistance of voltage-controlled junction capacitors [4].

III. MODIFIED LEAPFROG SIMULATION [7]

Fig. 2 shows a doubly terminated third-order low-pass filter. The relationships between the nodal voltages and

Reprinted from *IEEE J. Solid-State Circuits*, vol. SC-26, no. 4, pp. 669–671, April 1991.

307

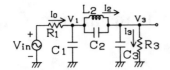

Fig. 2. Doubly terminated third-order low-pass filter.

branch currents are given by

$$I_0 = (V_{in} - V_1)/R_1 \tag{1}$$

$$V_1 = [(I_0 - I_2)/s(C_1 + C_2)] + a_{3,1}V_3 \tag{2}$$

$$I_2 = (V_1 - V_3)/sL_2 \tag{3}$$

$$V_3 = [(I_2 - I_3)/s(C_2 + C_3)] + a_{1,3}V_1 \tag{4}$$

$$I_3 = V_3/R_3 \tag{5}$$

where

$$a_{3,1} = C_2/(C_1 + C_2) \tag{6}$$

$$a_{1,3} = C_2/(C_2 + C_3). \tag{7}$$

Summing circuits at the output of the integrators are required to simulate (2) and (4). This solution not only increases the number of circuits used, but the added phase shift of these summing circuits inside the feedback loops of the leapfrog simulation severely degrades the high-frequency performance of the filters. Another solution is to bring those terms at the output of the integrators to the input by first differentiating them through floating capacitors at the input of the integrators. However, floating capacitors suffer from parasitic capacitances and are not convenient to electrically tune [1].

In order to remove the second term of (2) and (4), we consider the following transformation:

$$V_1 = V_1' + a_{3,1}V_3' \tag{8}$$

$$V_3 = a_{1,3}V_1' + V_3'. \tag{9}$$

By using (8) and (9), (1)–(5) can be transformed to

$$I_0 = [V_{in} - (V_1' + a_{3,1}V_3')]/R_1 \tag{10}$$

$$V_1' = (I_0 - I_2)/[s(C_1 + C_2)(1 - a_{3,1}a_{1,3})] \tag{11}$$

$$I_2 = [(1 - a_{1,3})V_1' - (1 - a_{3,1})V_3']/sL_2 \tag{12}$$

$$V_3' = (I_2 - I_3)/[s(C_2 + C_3)(1 - a_{3,1}a_{1,3})] \tag{13}$$

$$I_3 = (V_3' + a_{1,3}V_1')/R_3 \tag{14}$$

$$V_3 = a_{1,3}V_1' + V_3'. \tag{15}$$

Equations (10) to (15) show that summing circuits at the output of the integrators are not required, even when (10) and (14) are combined with (11) and (13), respectively. Although one additional summing circuit is necessary to realize (15), it is not inside the feedback loops.

The above modification can be applied to arbitrary-order leapfrog filters having transmission zeros as shown in detail in [7].

IV. Experimental Results

The third-order low-pass filter shown in Fig. 2 was realized using the balanced integrator shown in Fig. 1. The modified leapfrog simulation method of Section III was used resulting in the circuit shown in Fig. 3. This circuit consists of

an unbalanced-to-balanced signal converter, two lossy integrators, one NIC integrator, and the output summer. The frequency characteristics of the filter can be tuned by controlling the values of the junction capacitors with the voltage V_{FC}. Fig. 4 shows a photomicrograph of the filter implemented on a 3-μm bipolar process [6]. The filter was designed to have a cutoff frequency of 100 MHz, a transmission zero at 166 MHz, a 2.0-dB passband ripple, and a minimum attenuation of 30 dB. Fig. 5 shows the experimental results compared to the theoretical values. The passband ripple is very close to the expected results, although the frequency characteristic, especially of the transmission zero, is shifted —caused probably by parasitic capacitances and also inductances of the leads.

In the experimental IC, the cutoff frequency could be tuned from 90 to 120 MHz, although the frequency response showed a peak near the cutoff frequency and also some degradation of the attenuation depth could be observed. These problems may be the result of the passive compensation of the NIC that could not be tuned.

The power consumption was less than 40 mW from a single +5-V power supply. The maximum input signal was at least 100 mV$_{p-p}$ and the observed noise level was smaller than −50 dB.

V. Conclusions

This paper proposes a monolithic implementation method of VHF filters with transmission zeros. The transmission zeros are obtained using a modified leapfrog simulation method realized without floating capacitors that does not require summing circuits inside the feedback loops. The integrators used are balanced NIC integrators with grounded capacitors, which do not require p-n-p transistors and are suited for low-voltage applications.

A low-pass filter with cutoff frequency of 100 MHz and with a transmission zero at 166 MHz was designed and built in an integrated circuit form showing good results.

Monolithic implementation of control circuits for automatic tuning of active filters in the VHF range remains a topic for future research.

References

[1] H. Hagiwara et al., "A monolithic video frequency filter using NIC-based gyrators," IEEE J. Solid-State Circuits, vol. 23, no. 1, pp. 175–182, Feb. 1988.

[2] C.-F. Chiou and R. Schaumann, "Design and performance of a fully integrated bipolar 10.7-MHz analog bandpass filter," IEEE J. Solid-State Circuits, vol. SC-21, no. 1, pp. 6–14, Feb. 1986.

[3] H. Khorramabadi and P. R. Gray, "High-frequency CMOS continuous-time filters," IEEE J. Solid-State Circuits, vol. SC-19, no. 6, pp. 939–948, Dec. 1984.

[4] S. Akui et al., "100 MHz monolithic lowpass filter using balanced-type NIC's," in VLSI Circuits Symp., Tech. Paper Dig., 1988, pp. 95–96.

[5] J. Koyama, S. Takagi, and T. Yanagisawa, "High-frequency active filters using integrators based on negative impedance converters," Trans. IEICE, vol. E72, no. 2, pp. 124–129, Feb. 1989.

[6] K. Washio et al., "10K gate I^2L and 1K component analog compatible bipolar VLSI technology-HIT-2," IEEE J. Solid-State Circuits, vol. SC-20, no. 1, pp. 157–161, Feb. 1985.

[7] S. Takagi, N. Fujii, and T. Yanagisawa, "A synthesis of canonical MOSFET-C leapfrog filters with transmission zeros," in Proc. JTC-CSCC'88, pp. 248–253.

[8] M. Kumazawa and T. Yanagisawa, "Video frequency active filters," in Proc. of ISCAS, May 1984, pp. 638–641.

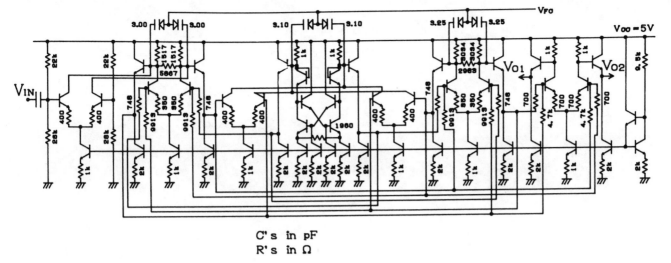

C's in pF
R's in Ω

Fig. 3.   Third-order modified leapfrog filter.

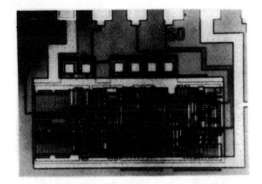

Fig. 4.   Photomicrograph of the filter of Fig. 3.

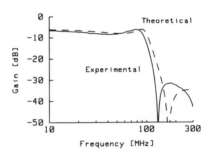

Fig. 5.   Experimental results (solid line) compared to theoretical results (broken line).

Part 4
Filters Using Capacitors, Transconductors, and Operational Amplifiers

IN Sections 2 and 3 we have included filters that use respectively operational amplifiers and transconductors as active elements. This section deals with filters that use both. The frequency characteristics are defined by transconductance and capacitance values, just as was the case with the transconductor-capacitor filters of Section 3. However, the presence of the op amps makes possible low-impedance nodes everywhere, which makes the filters less sensitive to parasitic effects, in particular parasitic capacitances and the output resistance of the transconductors. The "operational amplifier" in these filters may not be a full-fledged one, but is meant as a high-gain amplification stage.

The first paper using this approach is Paper 4-1, by Tan and Gray. A compatible JFET-bipolar technology is used for this circuit. The chip in this paper was the first in the open technical literature to include indirect automatic tuning using an external frequency reference (more on automatic tuning and its origin will be covered in Part 6). Filters and integrators akin to that of Tan and Gray, but implemented in MOS technology, are described in references [1–3]. Bipolar filters (not using junction FETs) based on the same approach are described by Fukahori in Paper 4-2, which was one of the earliest commercial stand-alone, fully integrated filters. More bipolar filters of this general type can be found in [4] and [5], and a BiCMOS implementation for a representative application can be found in Paper 7-D.3.

A Note on the Design of Suitable Transconductors

The transconductors in the above filters are of high output resistance. In principle, any of the transcon-ductors used in transconductor-C filters (Section 3) can also be used in transconductor-C–op-amp filters. However, since in the latter the transconductors feed into the virtual short-circuit of an operational amplifier, the high output resistance constraint can be relaxed and the transconductor design can be simplified. In fact, a simple interchange of the places where control bias and signal are applied in MOSFET-C integrators (Part 2) leads to corresponding transconductance-capacitance–op-amp integrators. Such an integrator, in which the transconductor part includes two MOSFETs in the triode region plus biasing, is described in [6], whereas one with four transistors in the triode region is described in [7].

References

[1] W. Kellner, "A continuous-time analog filter using MOS technology," *Frequenz*, vol. 35, no. 12, pp. 340–343, 1981.

[2] G. Tröster and W. Langheinrich, "Monolithic continuous-time analogue filters in NMOS technology," *Proc. IEEE ISCAS '84*, pp. 924–927, May 1984.

[3] A. P. Nedungadi and P. E. Allen, "A CMOS integrator for continuous-time monolithic filters," *Proc. IEEE ISCAS '84*, pp. 932–934, 1984.

[4] C. L. Perry, "An integrated continuous-time bipolar transconductance-capacitor filter," *IEEE J. Solid-State Circuits*, vol. 24, pp. 732–735, June 1989.

[5] W. J. A. de Heij, E. Seevinck, and K. Hoen, "Transconductor and integrator circuits for integrated bipolar video frequency filters," *Proc. IEEE ISCAS '89*, pp. 114–117, 1989.

[6] S. L. Wong, "Novel drain-biased transconductance building blocks for continuous-time filter applications," *Electron. Lett.*, vol. 25, pp. 100–101, Jan. 1989.

[7] P. J. Ryan and D. G. Haigh, "Novel fully differential MOS transconductor for integrated continuous-time filters," *Electron. Lett.*, vol. 23, pp. 742–743, July 2, 1987.

Fully Integrated Analog Filters Using Bipolar-JFET Technology

KHEN-SANG TAN AND PAUL R. GRAY, SENIOR MEMBER, IEEE

Abstract—A new approach for realizing high-order analog filters which can be fully integrated using a compatible bipolar and ion-implanted JFET process is described. This approach is based on the recognition that what is really needed is a long time constant monolithic integrator which can be effectively realized in a small silicon area. These integrators have been designed, fabricated, and used in a "leapfrog" or active ladder configuration to realize a fifth-order 8 kHz Chebyshev low-pass filter with 0.1 dB passband ripple. No external trimming operations and no anti-aliasing prefilter are required.

I. INTRODUCTION

FREQUENCY selective circuits are widely used in communications and control systems. In many cases, these filters must cut off sharply and must have small passband ripple. These tight specifications can only be met with precision high-order filters. Conventional *RC* active filters which use thin film or hybrid technologies often require external trimming [1], [2]. From the standpoint of cost effectiveness, it is desirable to realize a fully integrated filter system which requires small silicon area and no external trimming operations.

Two promising approaches to realizing high-order monolithic filters are the charge-coupled device (CCD) filtering technique, and the switched capacitor metal–oxide–semiconductor (MOS) filter approach [3], [4]. However, the main disadvantage of these approaches is that they are analog sampled-data systems which require a continuous-time prefilter to minimize aliasing effects.

In this paper, a new approach for realizing precision continuous-time monolithic analog filters is described. This approach is based on the recognition that what is really needed is an integrator with a long time constant which can be effectively realized in a small silicon area. Such an integrator can be used as a building block for realizing different filtering functions. The filter technique described in this paper uses ion-implanted JFET's in a new circuit technique both to achieve the required long integrator time constants and to control them precisely by reference to an external clock frequency.

Manuscript received May 10, 1978; revised August 3, 1978. This research was supported by the National Science Foundation under Grant ENG75-04986. This paper was presented in part at the International Solid-State Circuits Conference, San Francisco, CA, February 1978.

The authors are with the Department of Electrical Engineering and Computer Sciences, University of California, Berkeley, CA 94720.

Since this is a continuous-time analog filter, no anti-aliasing prefilter is required. This approach is demonstrated with a fifth-order 8 kHz Chebyshev low-pass filter with passband ripple of 0.1 dB. Excellent agreement between the experimental and designed values has been obtained.

II. INTEGRATORS AS BASIC BUILDING BLOCKS

The key element in a variety of filter configurations is an integrator which can be used to realize different filtering functions. Fig. 1 shows the circuit for a second-order "state variable" filter. It requires two resistors and two differential input integrators. Despite its simplicity, three different transfer functions are available. These transfer functions can be easily derived and are shown as follows:

$$\frac{V_{br}}{V_{in}} = \left(\frac{R_8}{R_7 + R_8}\right)\left(\frac{\omega_1 \omega_2 + s^2}{s^2 + s(\omega_1 R_7/(R_7 + R_8)) + \omega_1 \omega_2}\right) \quad (1)$$

$$\frac{V_{bp}}{V_{in}} = \left(\frac{-R_8}{R_7 + R_8}\right)\left(\frac{s\omega_1}{s^2 + s(\omega_1 R_7/(R_7 + R_8)) + \omega_1 \omega_2}\right) \quad (2)$$

$$\frac{V_{lp}}{V_{in}} = \left(\frac{R_8}{R_7 + R_8}\right)\left(\frac{\omega_1 \omega_2}{s^2 + s(\omega_1 R_7/(R_7 + R_8)) + \omega_1 \omega_2}\right). \quad (3)$$

Examining these expressions carefully, we notice that (1)–(3) correspond to the second-order bandreject, bandpass, and low-pass transfer functions, respectively. For these transfer functions, it is interesting to note that

$$\omega_o = \sqrt{\omega_1 \omega_2} \quad (4)$$

$$Q = \left(1 + \frac{R_8}{R_7}\right)\sqrt{\frac{\omega_2}{\omega_1}} \quad (5)$$

where ω_o corresponds to the resonance frequency, and Q corresponds to the quality factor of the second-order filter.

These second-order stages can be cascaded to form a higher order filter as shown in Fig. 2(a). In this example, three second-order sections are cascaded to realize a sixth-order filter. Each of the second-order sections realizes a pair of complex poles in the *s*-plane, as shown in Fig. 2(b). The main advantage of this cascading method is that it is very easy to implement for any realizable transfer function. The main disadvantage is that it typically has a higher sensitivity of network

Reprinted from *IEEE J. Solid-State Circuits*, vol. SC-2, pp. 814–821, Dec. 1978.

313

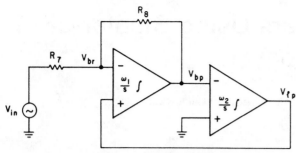

Fig. 1. Second-order filter.

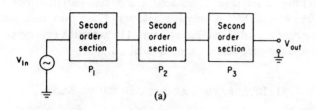

(a)

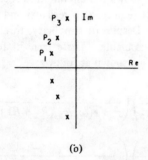

(b)

Fig. 2. (a) Sixth-order filter by cascading three second-order sections.
(b) Pole locations of the low-pass filter in the s-plane.

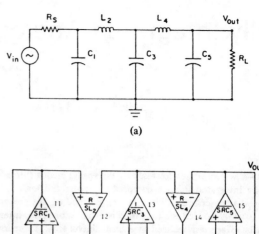

(a)

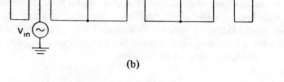

(b)

Fig. 3. (a) Doubly terminated *LC* ladder network. (b) Equivalent active ladder network.

TABLE I
THE REQUIRED UNITY-GAIN BANDWIDTHS FOR REALIZING A FIFTH-ORDER
8 kHz CHEBYSHEV LOW-PASS FILTER WITH 0.1 dB PASSBAND RIPPLE

Integrator	Unity-Gain Bandwidth
$I1$	6.9759 kHz
$I2$	5.8343 kHz
$I3$	4.0506 kHz
$I4$	5.8343 kHz
$I5$	6.9759 kHz

parameters due to component variations as compared with the direct implementation method.

One example of the direct implementation method is the fifth-order doubly terminated low-pass passive ladder network, as shown in Fig. 3(a). From classical circuit theory, it is well known that under the maximum power transfer condition, this network has an extremely low sensitivity due to component variations over the passband region [5].

By standard flowgraph techniques, this passive ladder network can be transformed into the "leapfrog" or active ladder configuration using integrators, as shown in Fig. 3(b) [6], [7]. The transfer functions of these passive and active ladder networks are identical. More importantly, there is a one-to-one correspondence between the reactive element values and the gain constants of the integrators. Because of this one-to-one correspondence, this active ladder network retains the low sensitivity properties of the passive prototype.

For instance, this active ladder network can be used to realize a fifth-order 8 kHz Chebyshev low-pass filter with passband ripple of 0.1 dB. The required unity gain bandwidths of the integrators for this example have values ranging from 4 kHz to 7 kHz, as shown in Table I. To illustrate the sensitivity of this active ladder network, the nominal magnitude response of the fifth-order low-pass filter is plotted across the frequency

band of interest, as shown by the solid line of Fig. 4. The dotted lines indicate the bounds of the worst case deviations of any combination of ±2 percent variations in the gain constants of the integrators. Notice that despite such a wide variation in component values, the maximum deviation is less than 0.1 dB. The extremely low sensitivity of this type of active ladder network enables the monolithic integration of high-order high-precision analog filters without any external trimming.

This direct implementation method is not limited to low-pass realizations. Bandpass, high-pass, and bandreject transfer functions are all realizable using integrators as basic elements [8], [9].

III. MONOLITHIC INTEGRATOR

A. Integrator Requirements

Integrators can be used in a variety of circuit configurations to realize different filtering functions. In this section, the requirements for realizing integrators with time constants in the audio frequency range are described.

A simple differential input integrator can be designed using two resistors, two capacitors, and one operational amplifier, as shown in Fig. 5. The gain constant of this integrator is

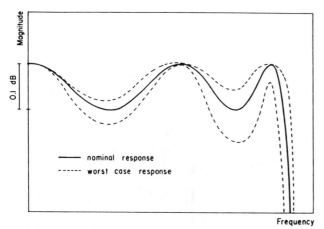

Fig. 4. Worst case deviations for a fifth-order Chebyshev low-pass filter with 0.1 dB nominal passband ripple.

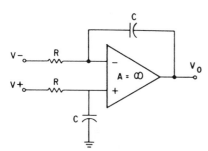

Fig. 5. Simple RC differential input integrator.

equal to $1/(RC)$. For low frequency operation, long RC time constants are required. For instance, for a frequency of 5 kHz with a monolithic capacitor of 30 pF, a resistor of 1 MΩ is required. This large value resistor is not efficiently realized in conventional monolithic approaches because it requires a large silicon area. Also, the precise value of the RC product is difficult to control due to process and temperature variations.

In order to implement integrators monolithically and efficiently, a way to realize integrators with long time constants in small silicon areas is needed. Also, a technique of stabilizing the absolute magnitude of the RC product, or equivalently, the gain constant of the integrator is required.

B. Monolithic Integrator

As described earlier, to realize an integrator with a long time constant, a large value of resistance must be realized. The circuit of Fig. 6 effectively realizes a large value resistor by employing a small value of transconductance. In this circuit, the input stage is a transconductance amplifier followed by an inverting gain stage and feedback integrating capacitor. The gain constant of this integrator is precisely defined by the ratio of G_m to C, while the transconductance G_m is given by the following expression:

$$G_m = \frac{2\sqrt{I_d I_{dss}}}{V_p} \qquad (6)$$

where I_{dss} is defined as the saturation drain current, I_d is the drain current, and V_p is the pinchoff voltage of the JFET.

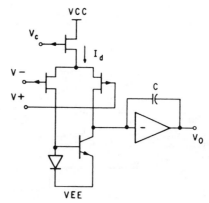

Fig. 6. Basic monolithic differential input integrator.

Again, for a frequency of 5 kHz, using a monolithic capacitor of 30 pF, a transconductance of 1 μmho is required. This small value of G_m can be easily achieved by designing JFET's with small value of Z/L, as well as by operating the input stage with low current. The required chip area for realizing such a small value transconductance (and hence large value of resistance) is small.

By varying the voltage at the controlling node at V_c, the biasing current source I_d can be varied, and by varying I_d, the G_m of the input stage is changed. Hence, by varying V_c, the G_m of the input stage, and thus the gain constant of the integrator can be varied. This feature will be used to control the absolute magnitude of the gain constant of the integrator, as described in the next section.

C. Absolute Bandwidth Control

The absolute magnitude of the gain constant of the integration is difficult to control due to process and temperature variations. This problem can be solved by utilizing the fact that while the absolute values of monolithic component parameters are not well controlled, the matching of one value to another on the same die is quite good. Using this fact, the time constants of the integrators can be locked to an externally supplied precision clock frequency using a phase-locked-loop system, as shown in Fig. 7 [10]. The three main elements of this block diagram are the phase comparator, the voltage-controlled oscillator (VCO), and the voltage-controlled filter (VCF).

The oscillating frequency of the VCO is precisely defined by the gain constants of the two integrators, and is equal to

$$\omega_{osc} = \sqrt{\omega_1 \omega_2} \qquad (7)$$

where ω_1, ω_2 are the gain constants. As previously described, the gain constant of the integrator can be controlled through V_c. Hence by controlling V_c, the frequency of oscillation can be controlled. The VCF is designed using the same type of integrators as those of the VCO. The bandwidth of the filter is designed to be exactly proportional to the frequency of the oscillator. By varying V_c, both the frequency of the oscillator and the bandwidth of the filter are varied, and the bandwidth of the filter tracks the frequency of the oscillator. The phase comparator compares the external precision clock frequency f_s to the frequency of the VCO, and generates an error voltage.

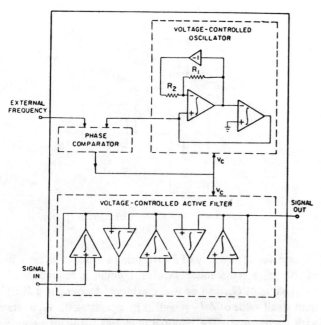

Fig. 7. Block diagram of the filter system.

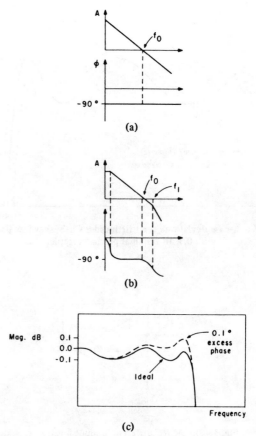

Fig. 8. (a) Frequency and phase response of an ideal integrator. (b) Frequency and phase response of a nonideal integrator. (c) Effects of excess phase.

After passing through a simple low-pass filter, the error voltage V_c is then fed back to the controlling node. In the steady state, V_c forces the gain constants of the integrators to have the desired values, such that the frequency of the oscillator is exactly equal to the external precision clock frequency. Since the bandwidth of the filter is always exactly proportional to the frequency of the oscillator, the bandwidth of the filter is always exactly proportional to the external precision clock frequency, and is independent of process and temperature variations.

The approach described above has several advantages. First, monolithic integrators with long time constants can be realized in a small area. Second, the ratio-matching of the gain constants of integrators depends only on the ratio-matching of the current sources and the ratio-matching of the capacitors. These can be accurately achieved [11], [13]. Finally, the absolute magnitude of the gain constant, and thus the bandwidth of the filter, can be precisely controlled by reference to an external precision frequency, and it is insensitive to process and temperature variations.

IV. PRACTICAL DESIGN CONSIDERATIONS

Ideally, an integrator has the $1/f$ frequency response, as shown in Fig. 8(a). The phase is exactly 90° and the gain at dc is infinite. Unfortunately, an actual monolithic integrator deviates from these ideal characteristics. For instance, the nonideal integrator has a finite dc gain. However, this is not an important consideration since for most cases, a dc gain of about 1000 is sufficient to give very accurate frequency responses.

Another nonideal effect is due to the second pole of the monolithic integrator, as shown in Fig. 8(b). In this figure, f_0 corresponds to the gain constant, and f_1 corresponds to the second pole of the nonideal integrator. Because of the presence of f_1, the phase angle at f_0 is not exactly 90°. This

excess phase will cause a slight peaking in the magnitude response, as shown in Fig. 8(c). In this case, a 0.1° phase error causes approximately a 0.1 dB peaking in the passband of the magnitude response of a fifth-order Chebyshev low-pass filter. Typically, to achieve a phase error of less than 0.1°, the ratio of f_1 to f_0 has to be greater than 50.

One important practical consideration is the nonlinearity of the monolithic integrator. Fig. 9(a) shows the basic monolithic integrator. A closer look at this circuit discloses that the input transconductance stage is linear for a limited range of input voltage. A plot of output current versus input voltage is shown in Fig. 9(b). Notice that the output current saturates at a maximum input voltage of ^+V_p, where V_p is the pinchoff voltage of the JFET transistors.

To improve the linearity of the transconductance amplifier, the maximum input voltage range can be extended by using the input stage shown in Fig. 10(a). In this circuit, four additional transistors, $Q2$ through $Q5$, are used as source degeneration JFET resistors to increase the linearity of the transconductance amplifier. A plot of output current versus input voltage is shown in Fig. 10(b). Notice that by simply adding four transistors, the maximum input voltage range has been increased by a factor of 3. Actually, we can add as many of the JFET resistors as necessary to improve the linearity of the transconductance amplifier. The only disadvantage is that when the number of transistors increases, the required chip

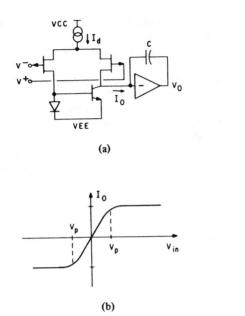

(a)

(b)

Fig. 9. (a) Basic monolithic integrator. (b) Plot of I_0 versus V_{in}.

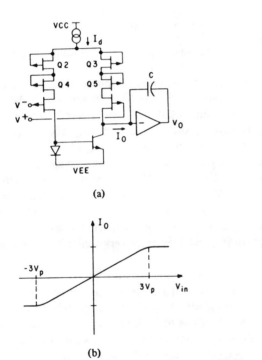

(a)

(b)

Fig. 10. (a) Monolithic integrator with a new input stage. (b) Plot of I_0 versus V_{in}.

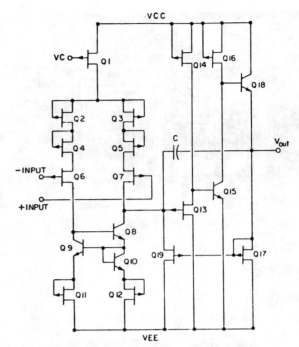

Fig. 11. Schematic of the monolithic integrator.

area also increases. This may impose a practical limit on the maximum number of transistors used.

The final design of the monolithic integrator is shown in Fig. 11. The input transconductance stage consists of transistors $Q1$ through $Q12$. Transistors $Q2$ through $Q5$ are used as source degeneration resistors as mentioned earlier. Transistors $Q8$ through $Q10$ are used as active loads. Transistors $Q11$ and $Q12$ are used as emitter degeneration resistors to improve the noise and offset of the integrator. With no emitter degeneration, the noise and offset of the bipolar devices when referred

to the input will be amplified by the ratio of the bipolar to JFET transconductances. By using JFET transistors as degeneration resistors, we can lower the noise and the offset voltage of the integrator with little increase in silicon area. Transistor $Q1$ is the biasing JFET current source. By controlling the voltage at node V_c, the biasing current, and thus the transconductance of the input stage can be varied. This feature is used to control the bandwidth of the integrator as outlined earlier.

The following stage is the source follower which consists of transistors $Q13$ and $Q14$. This is used to minimize the loading to the input transconductance stage. Transistors $Q15$ and $Q16$ constitute the common emitter inverting gain stage. Transistors $Q18$ and $Q17$ are used as emitter follower output stage to reduce the output impedance to about 10 kΩ.

The output of the integrator is clamped by transistor $Q19$, such that the output common mode range is always smaller than the input common mode range. This prevents the integrator from latching up.

Typically, to realize a given transfer function, integrators of different gain constants are required. These different gain constants are achieved by scaling the ratios of the integrating capacitors while keeping all the input transconductance stages identical. In this way, excellent matching of transconductances can be achieved. Previous work has shown that it is possible to achieve ratio-matching accuracy of a few tenths of one percent for monolithic MOS capacitors [11].

V. Experimental Results

A. Description of the Experimental IC

The photograph of the experimental IC chip is shown in Fig. 12. The overall chip size is 90 $\times$ 100 mils. A 10 μm minimum feature size and 5 μm minimum alignment tolerance were used. In this chip, there are seven ratioed MOS capacitors

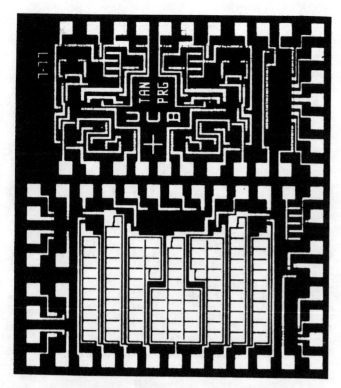

Fig. 12. Photograph of the experimental IC.

TABLE II
INTEGRATOR PERFORMANCE DATA

Power supplies	±12 V
DC open-loop gain	10 000
CMRR, PSRR (dc)	70 dB
Nominal unity-gain bandwidth (20 pF)	7 kHz
Input offset voltage (standard deviation)	16 mV
Power dissipation	4 mW
Chip area	850 mil²

of values ranging from 15 to 30 pF. There are two identical monolithic integrators with each realized in a silicon area of 850 mils². A bipolar compatible ion-implanted JFET process has been used [12], [13]. The process is similar to a standard bipolar process, with the addition of two ion-implantation steps. The first implant (boron) is used to create the channel while the second implant (phosphorus) is used to realize the top gate of the JFET transistors. The JFET pinchoff voltage is designed to be 4 V.

B. Performance of the Integrator

The measured performance of the monolithic integrator agrees very well with the design values. With power supplies of ±12 V, the dc open loop gain is 10 000. Both the power supply rejection ratio (PSRR) and the common mode rejection ratio (CMRR) are 70 dB. The nominal unity gain bandwidth using a 20 pF integrating capacitor is 7 kHz. The slew rate using a 20 pF integrating capacitor is 0.5 V/μs. The total power dissipation for each integrator is only 4 mW. Table II summarizes the performance of the monolithic integrator.

Realization of high-order high-precision filters requires precision ratio-matched integrators. As described earlier, the ratio-matching of integrators depends on the ratio matching of G_m/C. Experimental data on the matching of G_m and C are tabulated and shown in Fig. 13. Based on a sample size of 43, the standard deviation of the matching of MOS capacitors is 0.24 percent for this process, and the standard deviation of G_m based on 94 samples, is found to be 0.75 percent. Since these two parameters are uncorrelated, the standard deviation of the ratio matching of monolithic integrators is $(0.75^2 + 0.24^2)^{1/2} = 0.79$ percent. This will introduce a worst case deviation of less than 0.05 dB in the passband magnitude response of the fifth-order low-pass filter mentioned earlier.

C. Performance of the Fifth-Order Low-Pass Filter Using Leapfrog Structure

The monolithic integrators described earlier have been used in a "leapfrog" or active ladder configuration to construct a fifth-order 8 kHz Chebyshev low-pass filter with 0.1 dB passband ripple. To realize such a fifth-order low-pass filter, a total of seven integrators are required. Two integrators are used in the VCO and five integrators are used in the filter section. The estimated area to integrate this complete fifth-order low-pass filter using the process previously described would be 10 000 mils², and the total power dissipation would be approximately 50 mW.

The measured frequency response of the fifth-order low-pass filter is shown in Fig. 14(a). The measured passband ripple is 0.1 dB to within 0.05 dB, with a cutoff frequency of 8 kHz. By controlling the external frequency, the cutoff frequency of the filter was tunable over a range of 6 kHz to 10 kHz. The measured frequency response over a wider frequency range is shown in Fig. 14(b). Notice that the filter is performing well into the 200 kHz range without any aliasing problem. The stopband rolloff is approximately 100 dB/decade. These measured data were obtained without any external trimming operations, and they agree very well with the expected design values.

The filter is relatively insensitive to power supply variations. A 20 percent variation in the power supply introduced less than a 0.02 dB change in the passband of the magnitude response. A change of 50°C in ambient temperature resulted in a passband deviation of 0.05 dB and a cutoff frequency variation of 1 percent. These results were obtained on a bread-boarded filter system which consists of several packages of monolithic integrators. It is believed that, for a fully monolithic filter system, the sensitivity due to temperature variation will be very much reduced.

The filter has a wide dynamic range of operation. The measured output noise in the frequency band of 100 Hz to 10 kHz is 200 μV rms. At a signal frequency of 1 kHz, the measured total harmonic distortion (THD) for an output voltage of 7.5 V peak-to-peak is only 0.3 percent. When the output voltage is increased to 10 V peak-to-peak, the measured THD is increased to 1 percent. Based on the 1 percent THD output voltage and the 200 μV rms noise level, the dynamic range is 85 dB. Table III summarizes the performance of this fifth-order low-pass filter.

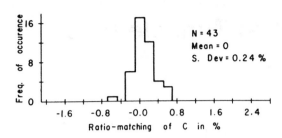

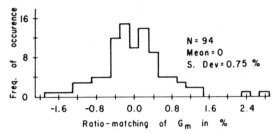

Fig. 13. Distributions of the matching of G_m and C.

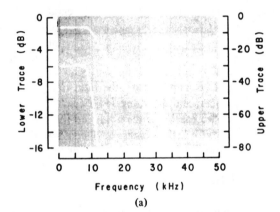

(a)

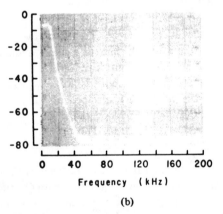

(b)

Fig. 14. (a) Measured frequency response of the fifth-order Chebyshev low-pass filter over a narrow frequency range. (b) Measured frequency response of the low-pass filter over a wide frequency range.

VI. Conclusions and Future Developments

The design techniques for realizing fully integrated analog filters using a compatible bipolar and ion-implanted JFET technology have been described. This approach is applicable to a wide variety of filters. Monolithic integrators with long time constants have been designed and fabricated. These

TABLE III
FIFTH-ORDER FILTER PERFORMANCE DATA

Ripple bandwidth	8 kHz
Passband ripple	0.1 dB
Output THD (1 kHz, 10 V peak to peak)	1 percent
Output noise (100 Hz–10 kHz)	200 μV rms
Dynamic range	85 dB

integrators have been used in a "leapfrog" or active ladder configuration to realize a fifth-order 8 kHz Chebyshev low-pass filter with 0.1 dB passband ripple. The low sensitivity properties of the active ladder structure enables the realization of this high order filter without any external trimming operations. A dynamic range of 85 dB has been obtained. Since this is a continuous time approach, no anti-aliasing prefilter is required.

Because of this nonsampled-data approach, this technique may be able to achieve a higher frequency of operation. Also, for this active ladder low-pass network, transmission zeros can be easily achieved without any additional integrators. Only two additional capacitors are needed for each pair of transmission zeros [14].

Acknowledgment

The authors want to thank S. K. Lui, who developed the bipolar compatible ion-implanted JFET process used in the experimental devices, and D. J. Allstot for useful discussions and assistance.

References

[1] J. J. Friend et al., "Star: An active biquadratic filter section," IEEE Trans. Circuits and Systems, vol. CAS-22, pp. 115–121, Feb. 1975.
[2] R. A. Friedenson et al., "RC active filters for the D3 channel bank," Bell Syst. Tech. J., vol. 54, pp. 507–529, Mar. 1975.
[3] R. D. Baertsch et al., "The design and operation of practical charge transfer transversal filters," IEEE Trans. Electron Devices, vol. ED-23, pp. 133–141, Feb. 1976.
[4] D. J. Allstot, R. W. Brodersen, and P. R. Gray, "MOS switched capacitor ladder filters," this issue, pp. 806–814.
[5] H. J. Orchard, "Inductorless filters," Electron. Lett., vol. 2, pp. 224–225, Sept. 1966.
[6] O. Wing, "Ladder network analysis by signal flow graph—Application to analog computer programming," IRE Trans. Circuit Theory, vol. CT-3, pp. 289–297, 1956.
[7] W. E. Heinlein and W. H. Holmes, Active Filters for Integrated Circuits. Englewood Cliffs, NJ: Prentice-Hall, 1974.
[8] F. E. J. Girling and E. F. Good, "Active filters, Part 12: The leapfrog or active-ladder synthesis," Wireless World, pp. 341–345, July 1970.
[9] F. E. J. Girling and E. F. Good, "Active filters, Part 13: Applications of the active-ladder synthesis," Wireless World, pp. 445–450, Sept. 1970.
[10] F. M. Gardner, Phase Lock Techniques. New York: Wiley, 1966.
[11] J. L. McCreary and P. R. Gray, "All MOS charge-redistribution A-D conversion techniques, Part I," IEEE J. Solid-State Circuits, vol. SC-10, pp. 371–379, Dec. 1975.
[12] R. W. Russell and D. D. Culmer, "Ion implanted JFET-bipolar monolithic analog circuits," in ISSCC Dig. Tech. Papers, pp. 140–141, 1974.
[13] S. K. Lui et al., "Process related characterization of bipolar compatible ion-implanted JFETs," to be published.
[14] K. S. Tan, "High-order continuous-time monolithic analog filters," Ph.D dissertation, Univ. California, Berkeley, 1978.

Paper 4-2

A Bipolar Voltage-Controlled Tunable Filter

KIYOSHI FUKAHORI

Abstract—A complete monolithic state variable filter is described which has been fabricated with bipolar technology. Two-quadrant multipliers are used in a novel fashion to achieve integration time constant large enough for audio purposes. Voltage control of frequency response from 20 Hz to above 20 kHz has been achieved without sacrifice of accuracy (notch depth >50 dB, low-pass and bandpass responses accurate to better than 0.1 dB), dynamic range (>90 dB), power supply rejection (PSRR > 40 dB) or frequency drift (<200 ppm/°C). The design has been shown to be generally useful in the design of self-contained bipolar filters.

I. INTRODUCTION

HISTORICALLY precision filters have been realized using passive inductor/capacitor (*LC*) networks, despite the physical and electrical limitations of available inductors. The current ubiquity of low cost monolithic op amps has, however, brought about a gradual change to *RC* active filters. In both cases, though, frequency response can only be adjusted by altering the absolute values of the respective component values; the procedure is very complex for high-order filters.

The MOS switched-capacitor filtering technique [1], [2] has emerged in the last four years that has alleviated this problem and monolithic realization of the filters has been made possible. However, such MOS filters require a clock input, generally tend to be noisy, and suffer from poor PSRR. In addition, they tend to suffer from the clock noise that may feed through to the filter output.

This paper describes an alternate filtering technique that makes possible the monolithic realization of filters in bipolar technology [3]. More specifically, it allows the construction of high-performance stand-alone filters that are continuously tunable; exhibit accurate frequency response; require no external precision components or clock input; have a large dynamic range, excellent PSRR, and low temperature drift. Furthermore, its absolute bandwidth can be trimmed at wafer sort to a desired value.

It was decided to use a state variable approach because of the low sensitivity to component variations, but one of the major difficulties imposed by monolithic implementation—that of obtaining suitably large time constants—had to be overcome. This time constant must be large enough to do filtering in the law audio frequency range (<100 Hz) which is not a trivial task considering the fact that the total amount of resistance and capacitance that can be integrated on a chip is extremely limited. This is the main reason that *RC* active filters usually require large off-chip passive components. The crux of this paper is to present a circuit technique to resolve this problem while maintaining the attractive features of *RC* active filters.

Manuscript received April 14, 1981; revised July 22, 1981.
The author is with Precision Monolithics, Inc., 1500 Space Park Drive, Santa Clara, CA 95050.

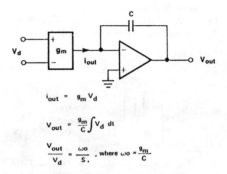

$$i_{out} = g_m V_d$$

$$V_{out} = \frac{g_m}{C} \int V_d \, dt$$

$$\frac{V_{out}}{V_d} = \frac{\omega_o}{S}, \quad \text{where } \omega_o = \frac{g_m}{C}$$

Integration Time Constant, $T = 1/\omega_o = C/g_m$

Fig. 1. Block diagram of differential integrator.

II. INTEGRATOR DESIGN

A conceptual realization of a differential integrator is shown in Fig. 1. It is nothing more than a simple transconductance amplifier followed by an integrating capacitor placed across an inverting amplifier. The current output I_{out} of the transconductance amplifier (with its transconductance equal to g_m) is given by

$$I_{out} = g_m \cdot V_d$$

where V_d is the differential voltage applied across the input terminals. The integrator output V_{out} is thus given by

$$V_{out} = \frac{g_m}{C} \int V_d \cdot dt$$

where C is the value of the integrating capacitor. In terms of the Laplace variable s,

$$\frac{V_{out}}{V_d} = \frac{\omega_o}{s}, \quad \text{where } \omega_o = \frac{g_m}{C} \equiv \text{unity gain frequency.}$$

The integration time constant T is given by the inverse of the unity gain frequency ω_o. That is,

$$T = \frac{1}{\omega_o} = \frac{C}{g_m}. \tag{1}$$

The transconductance amplifier can be realized as shown in Fig. 2. Amplifiers U_1 and U_2, in conjunction with Q_2 and Q_3, respectively, form unity gain buffers and are used to transfer the differential voltage V_d across the resistor R through which the signal current i_s flows. The signal current (V_d/R) is added to and subtraced from I_o (the magnitude of the two dc current sources) at the collectors of Q_2 and Q_3 yielding collector currents of $(I_o + i_s)$ and $(I_o - i_s)$, respectively. When they are fed to the p-n-p current mirror Q_9 and Q_{10} the current output I_{out} is equal to

$$I_{out} = \frac{2}{R} \cdot V_d.$$

Reprinted from *IEEE J. Solid-State Circuits*, vol. SC-16, no. 6, pp. 729–737, Dec. 1981.

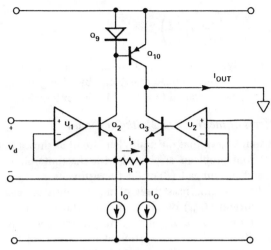

Fig. 2. Simple realization of transconductance amplifier.

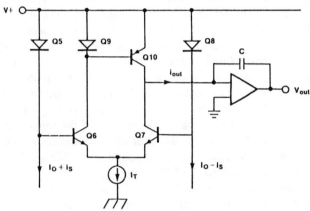

Fig. 3. Two-quadrant multiplier used to reduce transconductance or to increase integration time constant.

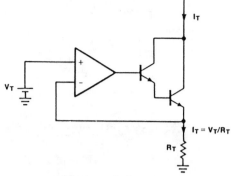

Fig. 4. V_T/I_T converter.

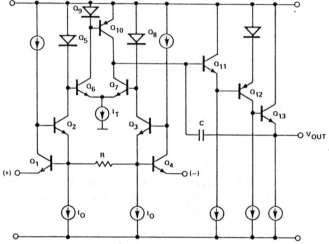

Fig. 5. Complete integrator.

That is, the transconductance g_m is given by

$$g_m = \frac{2}{R}.$$

This in conjunction with the integrating capacitor (C) will produce an integration time constant of $RC/2$. With a practically integrable amount of R and C the magnitude of the time constant realizable with this design is rather small. For example, if

$R = 40 \text{ k}\Omega$

$C = 400 \text{ pF}$,

then

$T = 8 \mu\text{s}$.

This is certainly not large enough to do filtering in sub 100 Hz region. Another drawback of this design is that it does not lend itself to convenient tuning.

III. New Integrator Design

The above problems are eliminated by the use of a two-quadrant multiplier [4] as shown in Fig. 3. The collector currents of Q_2 and Q_3 in Fig. 2 are first fed to the two quadrant multiplier consisting of Q_5-Q_8 and its outputs are then fed to the p-n-p current mirror Q_9, Q_{10}. The effective transconductance $g_{m\text{eff}}$ is now reduced from $2/R$ by a factor equal to $I_T/2I_o$, where I_T is the magnitude of the tail current of the Q_6-Q_7 differential pair. That is,

$$g_{m\text{eff}} = \frac{1}{R} \frac{I_T}{I_o}. \tag{2}$$

The integration time constant T and the unity gain frequency ω_o are changed by the same factor and given as

$$T = \frac{C}{g_{m\text{eff}}} = RC \frac{I_o}{I_T}, \tag{3}$$

$$\omega_o = \frac{1}{T} = \frac{1}{RC} \frac{I_T}{I_o}. \tag{4}$$

With the same R and C values used earlier, 16 ms of time constant is obtained when the ratio of the two dc currents I_o and I_T is made equal to 1000. The integration time constant can be varied to any value by changing this ratio.

I_o and I_T are generated from two external dc voltage sources through a pair of voltage to current converters, shown in Fig. 4 for the case of I_T. The external dc voltage V_T is converted to I_T through an on-chip resistor R_T. A Darlington pair connection is used to minimize the base current loss. I_o is similarly developed from another external dc voltage V_o through another on-chip resistor R_o.

Fig. 5 shows the complete integrator. The two unity gain buffers in Fig. 2 are replaced by Q_1-Q_2 and Q_3-Q_4 [5]. Q_{12} is a common emitter p-n-p amplifier that provides inverting gain for the integrating capacitor. In terms of the two external dc voltages V_o and V_T, (3) and (4) can be rewritten as

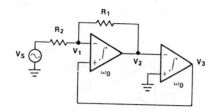

Notch :

$$\frac{V_1}{V_s} = \frac{(1 - 1/Q)(S^2 + \omega o^2)}{S^2 + 1/Q \,\omega o S + \omega o^2}$$

Band Pass :

$$\frac{V_2}{V_s} = \frac{-(1 - 1/Q)\,\omega o\, S}{S^2 + 1/Q \,\omega o + \omega o^2}$$

Low Pass :

$$\frac{V_3}{V_s} = \frac{(1 - 1/Q)\,\omega o^2}{S^2 + 1/Q \,\omega o S + \omega o^2}$$

$$Q = 1 + R_1 / R_2$$

$$f_{notch} = \frac{\omega o}{2\pi} = \frac{I_T}{2\pi RC\, Io} = \frac{1}{2\pi RC}(Ro/R_T)(V_T/Vo)$$

Fig. 6. Second-order state variable filter.

$$T = RC\left(\frac{R_T}{R_o}\right)\left(\frac{V_o}{V_T}\right), \tag{5}$$

$$\omega_o = \frac{1}{RC}\left(\frac{R_o}{R_T}\right)\left(\frac{V_T}{V_o}\right). \tag{6}$$

Notice that the product of the terms I_o and R dictates how large a differential signal can be applied across the input terminals. The maximum differential signal V_{dmax} that the integrator can take on is limited by

$$V_{dmax} = I_o R = \left(\frac{V_o}{R_o}\right) R. \tag{7}$$

In the actual circuit, R_o is matched to R so that $V_{dmax} = V_o$. V_o must be greater than the largest peak voltage that the integrator is expected to handle.

Although this technique does eliminate the problems mentioned earlier, it possesses several drawbacks that might have adverse effects on several key filter parameters. In general, circuits that employ low transconductance input stages tend to suffer from high noise, large offset voltage, and poor PSRR. This integrator design is no exception to these problems. In the following sections, these problems and ways to alleviate them are discussed in more detail.

IV. FILTER DESIGN AND PRACTICAL DESIGN CONSIDERATIONS

A. Second-Order State Variable Filter

A second-order state variable filter can be made by using two of these integrators as shown in Fig. 6. This particular configuration was chosen because it provides three functions—notch, bandpass, and low-pass responses—despite its simplicity. By making the two integrator time constants identical, the notch frequency at V_1, the center frequency of the bandpass response at V_2 and the bandwidth of the low-pass response at V_3 are all given by the inverse of integration time constant, or ω_o. This critical frequency ω_o was given by (6) and rewritten for convenience:

$$\omega_o = \frac{1}{RC}\left(\frac{R_o}{R_T}\right)\left(\frac{V_T}{V_o}\right). \tag{6}$$

Consequently, it can be said that the frequency response of the filter is made voltage tunable. By changing the ratio V_T/V_o, ω_o can be varied to a desired value externally.

B. Effects of the Nonideal Multiplier Circuit

It is well known that the multiplier circuit as shown in Fig. 3 suffers from problems associated with the finite ohmic resistances and current gain (β) of the transistors used.

The finite ohmic resistances of n-p-n transistors cause the output current (I_{out}) of the transconductance stage to be a nonlinear function of signal current (i_s) and consequently it will manifest itself as a distortion at the output of the filter. For a special purpose filter in which the ratio of two currents I_o and I_T is fixed, the problem can be easily overcome by scaling the emitter areas of the transistors in proportion to the drive currents [4]. However, for a general purpose design this ratio is arbitrarily set by the user anywhere within the tuning range. For this reason these ohmic resistances must be minimized. In the actual filter circuit this is done by making the emitter contacts large and interdigitizing them with the base contacts. Also the emitter areas of $Q_5 - Q_8$ are scaled in such a way that at the middle of the tuning range (i.e., $V_T/V_o = \frac{1}{2}$) current densities of these devices are identical giving zero distortion at that point.

The effect of finite β of the n-p-n and p-n-p transistors is to impair the otherwise linear relationship between ω_o and V_T/V_o. While the lower β of p-n-p transistors has a more adverse effect on the linear relationship, the β error of n-p-n transistors is more important because of its dependence on temperature. Therefore, its effect will be fully analyzed in the following discussion.

The exact expression for I_{out} involving finite β of n-p-n transistors β_N is

$$I_{out} = \frac{(1 - 2X) - \dfrac{2G_o}{1 + \beta_N}}{1 + \dfrac{1 + 2G_o}{\beta_N}} I_T \tag{8}$$

where

$$G_o = I_T/2I_o = \frac{1}{2}\left(\frac{R_o}{R_T}\right)\left(\frac{V_T}{V_o}\right)$$

$$X = \frac{1}{2}\left(1 + \frac{i_s}{I_o}\right) \tag{9}$$

and the p-n-p β is assumed infinite.

Thus the effective transconductance g_{meff} also becomes dependent upon β_N:

$$g_{meff} = \frac{dI_{out}}{dV_d} = \frac{I_T}{I_o R}\left(1 - \frac{1 + 2G_o}{\beta_N}\right) \tag{10}$$

$$= \underbrace{\frac{R_o}{R_T}\frac{1}{R}\left(\frac{V_T}{V_o}\right)}_{\text{Ideal}}\underbrace{\left(1 - \frac{1 + 2G_o}{\beta_N}\right)}_{\text{Error}}. \tag{11}$$

TABLE I
ERROR IN g_{meff} VERSUS CHANGES IN G_o AT VARIOUS VALUES OF β

$G_o = I_T/2I_o$	Error (%)				
	$\beta = 50$	100	200	400	800
0.001	−2.0	−1.0	−0.50	−0.25	−0.125
0.01	−2.0	−1.0	−0.51	−0.26	−0.128
0.1	−2.4	−1.2	−0.60	−0.30	−0.150
1.0	−6.0	−3.0	−1.50	−0.75	−0.375

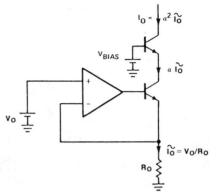

Fig. 8. V_o/I_o converter that compensates for linearity error caused by β variation.

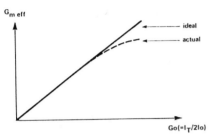

Fig. 7. Variation in g_{meff} versus G_o.

Since the error term in (10) or (11) is also dependent upon $G_o(\propto V_T/V_o)$, g_{meff} will deviate from its ideal case by a different amount depending upon where the ratio V_T/V_o is set [see (9)]. Table I summarizes the amount of deviation for different values of β_N as G_o is changed by three orders of magnitude. At any value of β_N, g_{meff} will typically lag the ideal case progressively more as G_o is increased as shown in Fig. 7. For good tuning linearity between ω_o and (V_T/V_o), higher β_N is required.

The lower β of p-n-p transistors as mentioned previously also causes nonlinear characteristics between ω_o and (V_T/V_o). The effective transconductance is, assuming $\beta_N = \infty$, given by

$$g_{meff} = -\frac{I_T}{I_o}\left(1 - \frac{3}{\beta_P}\right)$$
$$= -\underbrace{\frac{R_o}{R_T}\frac{1}{R}\left(\frac{V_T}{V_o}\right)}_{\text{Ideal}}\underbrace{\left(1 - \frac{3}{\beta_P}\right)}_{\text{Error}}. \tag{12}$$

Although the error term does not explicitly involve G_o, β_P is a function of collector current and as such the effective transconductance shows a strong dependence on G_o (i.e., V_T/V_o or I_T/I_o). Care must be taken to achieve high β_P as well as β_N. In reality, however, both β_N and β_P will be finite and will show dependence on current level, and a certain amount of nonlinearity can not be avoided. While this can be tolerated in most applications a rather strong dependence of β_N on temperature does affect another very important filter parameter and this will be discussed in the next section.

C. Drift of the Filter Response

One of the most important parameters of a stand-alone filter is the stability of its frequency response with temperature. It is far more important than the linearity between ω_o and V_T/V_o discussed in the previous section. Its first-order

dependence on temperature is clear from (6). Since the temperature coefficients (TC's) of on-chip resistors will track with each other, the temperature drift of ω_o is the inverse of the sum of the TC's of the resistor and the capacitor. The TC of the silicon chrome thin film resistor used to form the resistors is about +100 ppm/°C and that of silicon nitride capacitor is about +20 ppm/°C. Consequently, the filter drift can be expected to be about −120 ppm/°C due to R and C.

There are other second-order effects that contribute to the drift. One of the significant contributions could come from the temperature dependence of β_N as mentioned earlier. When this effect is taken into account, from (10) and (11),

$$\omega_o = \frac{g_{meff}}{C} = \left(\frac{I_T}{I_o}\right)\left(\frac{1}{RC}\right)\left(1 - \frac{1 + 2G_o}{\beta_N}\right) \tag{13}$$
$$= \underbrace{\frac{R_o}{R_T RC}\left(\frac{V_T}{V_o}\right)}_{\text{Ideal}}\underbrace{\left(1 - \frac{1 + 2G_o}{\beta_N}\right)}_{\text{Error}}. \tag{14}$$

A quick look at Table I reveals that the error varies with β_N. At any G_o the amount of deviation from ideal (which is in a direction to reduce ω_o) decreases as β_N increases. Since β_N increases with temperature, the actual ω_o approximates the ideal case more closely as temperature rises. The temperature drift due to β_N variation will be most pronounced when $G_o = 1$ as is obvious from (13) (error $= -3/\beta_N$). This problem can be easily alleviated by designing I_o to have a positive TC as shown in Fig. 8. In this case,

$$I_o = \left(\frac{V_o}{R_o}\right)\alpha^2. \tag{15}$$

where α is the common base current gain of n-p-n transistors. Substituting (15) in (13) yields

$$\omega_o = \frac{R_o}{R_T}\frac{1}{RC}\frac{V_T}{V_o}\frac{1}{\alpha^2}\left(1 - \frac{1 + 2G_o}{\beta_N}\right). \tag{16}$$

In terms of β_N, (16) simplifies to

$$\omega_o \simeq \underbrace{\frac{R_o}{R_T}\frac{1}{RC}\frac{V_T}{V_o}}_{\text{Ideal}}\underbrace{\left(1 + \frac{1 - 2G_o}{\beta_N}\right)}_{\text{Error}}. \tag{17}$$

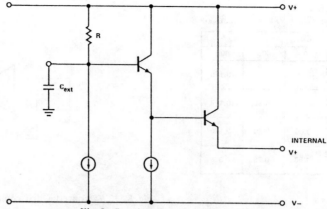

Fig. 9. Supply noise rejection circuit.

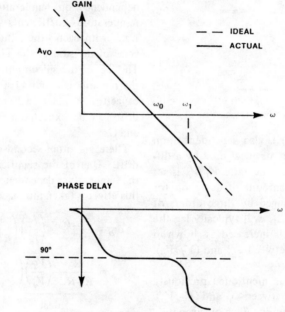

Fig. 10. Frequency response of integrator.

At $G_o = 0.001$, the error term $\simeq 1/\beta_N$ and at $G_o = 1$, $-1/\beta_N$. Thus, it is clear that the temperature dependence is reduced to less than $\pm 1/\beta_N$ at any G_o. For a typical β_N of 200 and its drift of 0.5 percent/°C, one may expect this contribution to the filter to be 25 ppm/°C.

The drift of the offset voltages of the op amps used to do V_T/I_T and V_o/I_o conversions will also contribute to the drift of ω_o which is most pronounced at low values of V_T and V_o. A careful layout of these op amps is very important to minimize these effects.

To summarize, the drift of the filter is dominated by the TC's of R and C. Due to the good design and careful layout secondary effects are minimized to an insignificant level.

D. Dynamic Range of the Filter

In order to maximize the dynamic range of the filter the noise of the integrators must be minimized. Of the transistors used in the transconductance amplifier (see Fig. 5) Q_6, Q_7, Q_9, Q_{10} are the main contributors of noise. This is due to the fact that the transconductance from input to the collectors of Q_2 and $Q_3 (\simeq 1/R)$ is further reduced to the outputs of the amplifier by the ratio equal to I_o/I_T. Thus it is obvious that the

current noise in Q_6, Q_7, Q_9, Q_{10} reflects to the input as a large voltage noise. The current noise density $\tilde{i}$ in each one of these devices is given by

$$\tilde{i} = \sqrt{2q(I_T/2)} = \sqrt{qI_T} \tag{18}$$

where q is the electronic charge.

So the total contribution from the four devices $\tilde{i}_T$ is

$$\tilde{i}_T = \sqrt{4} \times \sqrt{qI_T} = 2\sqrt{qI_T}. \tag{19}$$

The input referred voltage noise density $\tilde{V}_T$ is given by

$$\tilde{V}_T = \frac{\tilde{i}_T}{g_{m\,\text{eff}}} = \frac{2\sqrt{qI_T}}{\frac{1}{R}\frac{I_T}{I_o}} = 2RI_o\sqrt{q/I_T}. \tag{20}$$

From (7),

$$\tilde{V}_T = 2V_{d\,\text{max}}\sqrt{q/I_T}$$

or

$$\frac{V_{d\,\text{max}}}{\tilde{V}_T} = \frac{1}{2}\sqrt{I_T/q}. \tag{21}$$

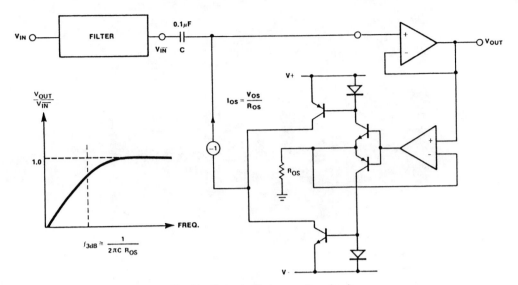

Fig. 11. Output offset correction circuit.

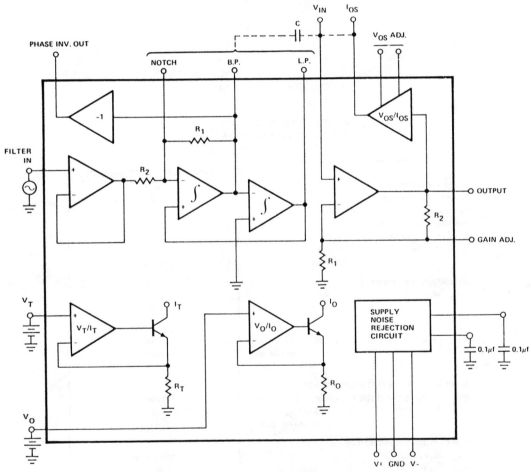

Fig. 12. Block diagram of the tunable filter.

Equation (21) is a measure of the dynamic range that can be achieved by the filter. It shows that the dynamic range will increase as a square root of I_T. Obviously, the increase in I_T must be accompanied by the proportional increase in the size of the integrating capacitor in order to maintain the same time constant of the integrator. In other words, the dynamic range will increase as a square root of the capacitor size. The high dielectric constant of silicon nitride is taken advantage of in forming a pair of large capacitors in the actual filter.

Another important factor in obtaining large dynamic range is to utilize the full rail-to-rail voltage available. That is, V_{dmax} should always be set as high as possible for a given set of power supply voltages. Since the increases in V_{dmax} $(=I_o R_o)$ must be accompanied by the increases in I_T to maintain the same

325

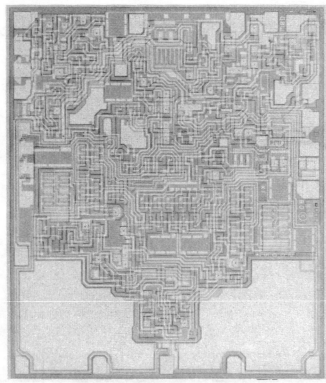

Fig. 13. Die photo of the tunable filter.

TABLE II
TYPICAL FILTER PERFORMANCE
@ $T = 25°C$, $V_S = \pm 15$ V, $Q = 2$

PARAMETER			TYPICAL PERFORMANCE
POWER CONSUMPTION			200mW
ABSOLUTE ACCURACY			±3%
TUNING LINEARITY (IN ANY OCTAVE)			±1%
MAXIMUM INPUT SIGNAL @ V_O = 10V.			10Vp
NOISE (10Hz - 100kHz):	NOTCH		220μV
@ V_O = 10V, V_T = 2V	BANDPASS		150μV
	LOWPASS		150μV
DISTORTION @ BANDPASS OUTPUT:			
@V_O = 5V, V_T = 1V	V_{IN} = 8Vp		0.3%
	V_{IN} = 1Vp		0.1%
NOTCH DEPTH:			
@V_O = 5V, INPUT FREQUENCY = ω_O = 200Hz ($V_T \simeq$ 50mV)			50dB
= 2KHz ($V_T \simeq$ 500mW)			60dB
= 10KHz ($V_T \simeq$ 2.5V)			42dB
BANDPASS AND LOWPASS RESPONSE ACCURACY:			
@V_O = 5V, INPUT FREQUENCY = ω_O = 200Hz ($V_T \simeq$ 50mV)			−0.05dB
= 2KHz ($V_T \simeq$ 500mW)			−0.02dB
= 10KHz ($V_T \simeq$ 2.5V)			+0.08dB
TEMPERATURE COEFFICIENT OF ω_O:			
@V_O = 5V, V_T = 1V			−200ppm/°C
PSSR$^{+,-}$ at dc			40dB
PSSR$^{+,-}$ at 2KHz			50dB

time constant, this results, according to (21), in an increase of dynamic range.

Noise on the supply lines also couples into the filter rather easily, again due to low transconductance of the input stage. A simple low-pass filter is employed to reject noise on the supply line as shown in Fig. 9. The noise on the positive supply line is attenuated by the RC time constant. The negative supply line is designed similarly.

E. Accuracy of Frequency Response

The accuracy of the filter response is limited by the nonidealities of the integrators used in the filter. An ideal inte-

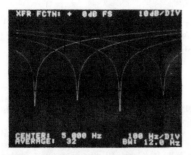

Fig. 14. Example of the filter being used as a notch filter as V_T/V_o is varied.

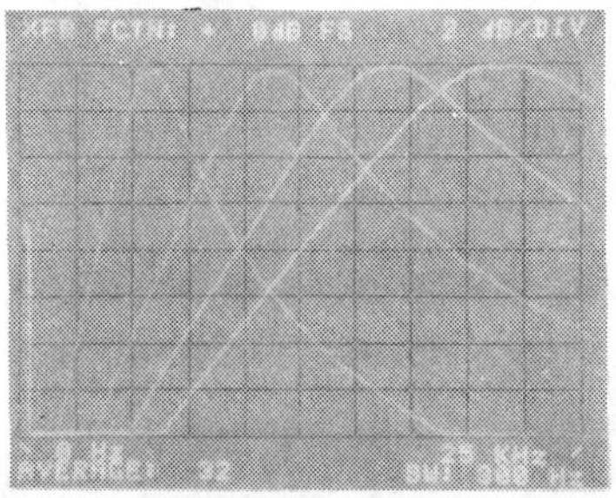

Fig. 15. Example of the filter being used as a bandpass filter V_T/V_o is varied.

grator would have a constant 90° phase lag at all frequencies. The actual integrator would approximate this fairly well in the middle of the frequency range that it is designed to handle, but at the lower end of the frequency range this phase lag is less than 90° due to finite dc gain. At the higher end, the lag is greater than 90° due to nondominant poles that unavoidably exist (see Fig. 10). A simple calculation reveals that at the lower frequency edge, the notch depth is limited by the finite dc gain A_v to $2Q/A_v$. For $Q = 2$, $A_v > 400$ is required for 40 dB of notch depth. Both bandpass and low-pass responses tend to flatten at ω_o by roughly $2Q/A_v$. For these reasons bias currents must be carefully designed to achieve sufficient dc gain. As for the effects of the secondary poles, excessive phase delay that they introduce tends to reduce notch depth as well as to cause peaking in the bandpass and low-pass responses. In this case the calculations are somewhat more involved. If we simply model the integrator response $H(s)$ by

$$H(s) = \frac{\omega_o}{s} \frac{1}{1 + \left(\dfrac{s}{\omega_1}\right)},$$

where ω_o is the ideal unity gain frequency and ω_1 is the location of the parasitic pole, then it can be shown for the filter with $Q = 2$ that in order to achieve the notch depth >40 dB and the peaking in the bandpass and low-pass responses <0.1 dB we must have $\omega_1/\omega_o > 400$. It is very important, therefore, to optimize the frequency response of the integrator. In particular, the p-n-p transistor (Q_{12} in Fig. 5) which limits the frequency response must be operated at the collector current where f_T is high. The p-n-p transistors Q_9-Q_{10} in Fig. 5 have their base width reduced to the minimum for better frequency response.

The absolute accuracy of the filter response can be adjusted by trimming either R_o or R_T [see (6)]. Since R_o is matched to R to set $V_{d\max}$ R_o should be left alone. R_T therefore is the best candidate for trimming. R_T is nominally made large enough to accommodate process variations in thin film resistors and capacitors and then Zener-trimmed [6] at wafer sort. An interesting possibility would be to make R_T external. By doing so, the filter response can be made user-programmable. Furthermore, if its TC is very small ($\ll 100$ ppm/$^\circ$C) the dominant contribution term to the filter drift can be mostly removed.

F. Output Offset Voltage

The low transconductance input amplifier used in the design of integrators introduces high offset voltage. For example, 1 mV of offset voltage between Q_5 and Q_8 would reflect to the input as 200 mV of offset voltage at room temperature if RI_o is set to 10 V. To alleviate this problem, the filter output is, through an external capacitor, ac-coupled to the output buffer (see Fig. 11). In order to provide a necessary dc bias to the buffer input, its dc offset voltage is converted to an offset correction current I_{os} by a voltage to current converter (V_{os}/I_{os} converter) and fed to the buffer input. At dc this feedback loop helps maintain low output voltage. For all relevant ac frequencies, I_{os} is shunted into the filter output by the coupling capacitor C. The 3 dB point $f_{3\,dB}$ of this ac coupling is given by

$$f_{3\,dB} = \frac{1}{2\pi R_{os}C}$$

where R_{os} is an on-chip resistor used to convert V_{os} to I_{os} and C is the external capacitor used. With $C = 0.1$ μF it is around 10 Hz and in most applications this should not be a problem.

G. Complete Filter Design

Fig. 12 is a block diagram of the complete filter showing the interconnection of the various blocks so far discussed. A phase inverter is also included to enable the filter to be used as a voltage controlled oscillator. The frequency of oscillation is identical to the ω_o of the integrators.

V. Experimental Results

A die photo of the complete filter is shown in Fig. 13. Six op amps and two integrators including about 1000 pF of capacitance are integrated in 11.4K mils^2 of silicon area. Table II summarizes the performance of the filter configured for $Q = 2$. The dynamic range of over 90 dB is obtained for the notch response, 94 dB for the low-pass and bandpass responses. The temperature drift of the filter is less than 200 ppm/$^\circ$C, most of which is due to the thin film (silicon chrome) used. In the middle of the tuning range (20 Hz-20 kHz) notch depth >60 dB is achieved and the bandpass and low-pass responses are within 0.02 dB of theoretical value. At 200 Hz, both the bandpass and the low-pass responses deviate (flatten) from theoretical value by about 0.05 dB while at 10 kHz, they show roughly 0.08 dB peaking above theoretical value.

Figs. 14 and 15 are examples of the filter being used as a notch and bandpass filter, respectively, as the ratio $(= V_T/V_o)$ is varied.

VI. Conclusion

It has been shown that it is possible to design complete integrated precision filters using only bipolar technology. The concepts discussed have been applied to a voltage tunable state variable filter requiring no external precision components, but should also prove useful in many other filter designs.

Acknowledgment

The author wishes to thank Y. Nishikawa who has made significant contribution to the design of the integrator, D. Bowers, V. Condito, and J. Flink who have reviewed the manuscript, and R. Lee who has bread-boarded this filter and helped me debug the IC version. Also my thanks to P. Scales who did the typing.

References

[1] D. J. Allstot, R. W. Broderson, and P. R. Gray, "Fully-integrated high-order NMOS sampled-data ladder filters," in *ISSCC Dig. Tech. Papers*, Feb. 1978, pp. 82–83.

[2] R. W. Broderson, P. R. Gray, and D. A. Hodges, "MOS switched-capacitor filters," *Proc. IEEE*, vol. 67, pp. 61–74, Jan. 1979.

[3] K. S. Tan and P. R. Gray, "Fully integrated analog filters using bipolar-JFET technology," *IEEE J. Solid-State Circuits*, vol. SC-13, pp. 814–821, Dec. 1978.

[4] B. Gilbert, "A precise four-quadrant multiplier with sub-nanosecond response," *IEEE J. Solid-State Circuits*, vol. SC-3, pp. 365–373, Dec. 1968.

[5] B. Blesser, "Ultralinear transistor configuration under conditions of minimal power-supply drain current," *IEEE J. Solid-State Circuits*, vol. SC-5, pp. 125–126, June 1970.

[6] G. Erdi, "A precision trim technique for monolithic analog circuits," *IEEE J. Solid-State Circuits*, vol. SC-10, pp. 412–416, Dec. 1975.

Part 5
Other Approaches

Section 5-A   Active RC Filters

IN the sections of this part, we have included filters based on principles different from those of the main integrated filter classes described in Parts 2, 3, and 4. The paper in this section returns to classical active *RC* filters with nontunable resistors for low distortion. All automatically tunable filters in the previous papers use some sort of voltage- or current-tunable element in order to make possible the elimination of tolerances and the effects of temperature and aging. Such tunable elements (transistors or junction capacitors) are nonlinear, and although nonlinearity cancellation techniques have been developed they do not allow extremely low distortion operation such as is required, for example, for high-fidelity audio. The following paper by Durham, Redman-White, and Hughes presents a filter using fixed, linear resistors and capacitors. The filter is tuned in discrete steps by switching into it an appropriate number of such elements from an array. In cases where a "quantized" tuning range is not a problem and where the resulting tuning jumps can be avoided during signal handling, such a solution can be attractive. Earlier related discussions can be found in [1] and Paper 6-6.

References

[1] J. Fincher and R. Geiger, "Monolithic frequency referenced digitally self-tuned filters," *Proc. 25th Midwest Symposium on Circuits and Systems,* pp. 1–4, 1983.

Low Distortion VLSI Compatible Self-Tuned Continuous-Time Monolithic Filters

A. M. DURHAM, SOUTHAMPTON UNIVERSITY

W. REDMAN-WHITE, SOUTHAMPTON UNIVERSITY

J. B. HUGHES, PHILIPS RESEARCH LABS., REDHILL

Abstract

The design and implementation of three highly linear monolithic continuous-time filters is described. The filters operate from a single 5V supply and are integrated in a standard double-polysilicon CMOS process. Each filter is automatically tuned to a corner frequency of 78kHz ± 5% using on-chip circuitry and an external reference clock. All filters are single-ended and have a lowpass response. The THD achieved by one type of filter is <-85dB.

Introduction

Monolithic continuous-time filters are frequently needed for anti-aliasing and reconstruction in switched-capacitor circuits or in A/D conversion for digital signal processors. As monolithic A/D converters progress to >16 bits (96dB) dynamic range, filters are required with comparable performance. These filters should ideally be VLSI process compatible and should operate from a single 5V rail.

Since the frequency determining components of monolithic continuous-time filters are both process and temperature dependent, self-tuning filter implementations are desirable.

Tunable elements

The two main approaches to such self-tuned filters involve either MOSFET-C or transconductor-capacitor (OTA-C) structures e.g.[1] [2] [3]. Both use MOS transistors as variable circuit elements to facilitate the self-tuning process. Unfortunately this results in filter signal linearity being directly affected by MOS characteristics. The lowest total harmonic distortion (THD) reported in such a filter using only a single 5V supply, is no better than -65dB [3].

As an alternative, passive frequency-determining components can be used. Structures which do not involve significant depletion regions (e.g. Polysilicon resistors, poly-metal capacitors, poly-poly capacitors) exhibit high linearity. A passive filter component can be formed using a programmable weighted array of such components. The

component value can then be fixed by applying a digital code [4]. An example of a programmable binary-weighted capacitor array, with a nominal value of 40pF, is shown in fig.1. Arrays would replace all capacitors in the original active-RC structure.

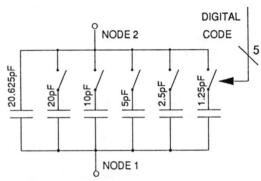

Fig.1 5-bit capacitor array

This type of scheme will display poor accuracy compared with that using continuously variable tuning techniques (±5% to ±10%, as opposed to the ±0.5% achieved in [5]) However, for the given range of applications, accuracy of this order is often acceptable. Without tuning, variations of >±50% in the RC product are possible.

Tuning scheme

A tuning scheme which derives the digital word required to programme each capacitor array, the 'dual-slope calibrator', has been described by Hughes [4]. It is shown schematically in fig.2, together with basic timing in fig.3.

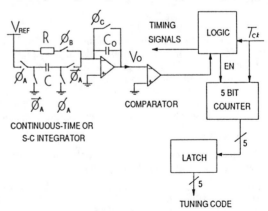

Fig.2 Dual-slope calibrator

Reprinted from *Proc. IEEE ISCAS*, pp. 1448–1451, 1991.

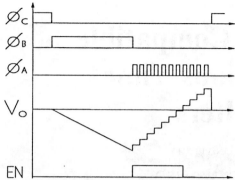

Fig.3 Simplified calibrator timing and voltage outputs

In operation, a nominal fixed time-constant, set by the period of the external clock, T_{ck}, is compared with an integrated RC time-constant (which is process and temperature dependent). A related digital code is produced which, given good on-chip matching, will correct the RC time-constants of each filter by programming each capacitor array. Thus the frequency response of each filter is adjusted to around its nominal design value.

Filter designs for integration.

A number of filters incorporating capacitor arrays for digital tuning were integrated. In their design, possible sources of distortion were identified in terms of components and architecture.

Filter architecture

Filter topologies can be roughly divided into those that are parasitic-insensitive and those that are not.

Most single-amplifier filter structures belong to the latter group. One such filter is the Sallen and Key filter. Non-linear parasitic capacitors associated with the integrated capacitors, resistors and array switches (if arrays are used) load these nodes, introducing distortion into the signal path. The filter also contains a non-inverting op amp, the inputs of which experience a high common-mode voltage. This not only limits the input signal amplitude, but produces signal distortion at the op amp output due to common-mode to differential-mode gain.

In the case of parasitic-insensitive architectures nonlinear parasitics are effectively removed from the circuit. Additionally, the op amps experience virtually zero common-mode input swing, reducing internally generated distortion.

Both types of topology were integrated for the purpose of comparison.

Op amps

For high linearity, the op amps used had high differential-mode gain, high output voltage range and low common-mode gain. Their design is similar to that described in [6]. The output stage was class A. These design considerations ensured optimum linearity. Low output resistance is required for good stopband rejection: this was obtained using short channel, high current output transistors.

Passive components

Polysilicon resistors and double-polysilicon capacitor arrays were used because of their low signal-dependence.

Two types of capacitor structure were tried, to observe the effect on filter linearity. The first was a normal poly-oxide-poly structure, shown schematically in fig.4a. The second used two such normal capacitors with the top plate of one coupled to the bottom plate of the other and vice versa. It was hoped that such a cross-coupled structure would help to cancel the weak square-law dependency of the normal double-polysilicon capacitor structure. The disadvantage of this structure is that the bottom-plate-to-substrate parasitic capacitor, C_p, associated with the normal structure is now divided equally between the two capacitor terminals. In a non parasitic-insensitive filter realisation, the presence of these parasitics could alter the shape of the filters frequency response as well as increase distortion in the signal path. This problem was overcome in the Sallen and Key filter by 'bootstrapping', whereby one of the two cross-coupled capacitors was integrated over an n-well and the parasitic is effectively removed from the circuit by driving the n-well with the same ac potential as the bottom-plate, using a source follower. This is shown in fig.4b.

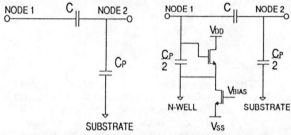

Fig.4a Normal capacitor structure   Fig.4b Bootstrapped cross-coupled capacitor structure

Test Chip Architecture

Three single-ended filters were integrated in a standard double polysilicon 5V CMOS process. Two active-RC architectures were used to illustrate differences between filter topologies.

SKN: third-order Sallen and Key filter, normal structure capacitors.

SKB: third-order Sallen and Key filter, bootstrapped cross-coupled capacitors.

BIQ: Tow-Thomas biquad filter, cross-coupled capacitors (not bootstrapped).

One dual-slope calibrator was included on chip to tune all three filters. A system diagram is given in fig.5.

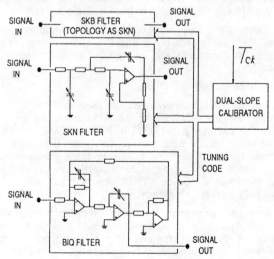

Fig.5 Schematic of integrated test device

Fig.6 Microphotograph of integrated test device

A microphotograph of the test device is shown in fig.6. Each filter had a passband gain of 2V/V, nominal corner frequency of 78kHz and a maximally-flat passband response. Each used programmable binary-weighted capacitor arrays for tuning. The Sallen and Key filters were designed with a third-order roll-off. Specified corner frequency accuracy was ±5%.

Results

Measurements were performed on 18 devices randomly chosen from two wafers of the same batch.

THD measurements were taken at varying signal amplitudes up to 1.0Vrms output, fig.7(i), at different passband frequencies up to 30kHz, fig.7(ii), and at V_{DD} values of 5V ±10%, fig.7(iii). It can be seen that THD is greatest in the SKB filter, lower in the SKN filter and very small in the BIQ filter (worst cases -64dB, -76dB and <-85dB respectively). In all cases, the second harmonic is predominant.

The THD dependency on V_{DD} for the SKB filter but not for the SKN filter suggests that SKB signal linearity is limited by the performance of the capacitor bootstrapping circuit. This has been further verified by simulation.

The inferiority of the SKN filter in comparison with the BIQ filter is explained by nonlinear switch and capacitor parasitics attached to parasitic-sensitive nodes in the SKN filter.

It is not possible to ascertain the major cause of signal distortion in the BIQ filter since the measurements were limited by the linearity of the signal source.

Dynamic range was calculated for each filter type, with and without the reference clock operating. Maximum output voltage was taken as 1.0Vrms and noise was integrated over the entire passband. The results are shown in fig.8.

The parasitic-insensitive BIQ filter has much higher dynamic range than the Sallen and Key filters (91.4dB BIQ compared with 84.2dB SKB and 81.4dB SKN, with the clock operating). The difference is due to filter topology. Parasitic-insensitive topologies tend to suppress noise injected via the substrate. Noise entering the signal path at a floating node is amplified along with the signal.

Across the entire output spectrum up to 1MHz, the only significant clock feedthrough is at the fundamental reference frequency of 624kHz. The noise amplitudes at this frequency are -88.9dB (BIQ), -63.7dB (SKB) and -59.0dB (SKN).

Frequency response shape is shown in fig.9 for the three filter types. In each case passband gain is 2V/V ±1%, passband ripple is <0.02dB and stopband rejection is limited to around 55dB (this is due to crosstalk between the input and output signal paths - a result of poor layout).

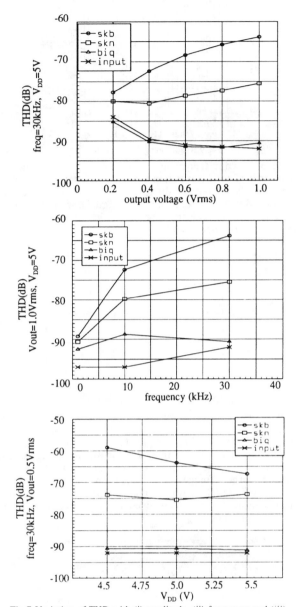

Fig.7 Variation of THD with (i) amplitude, (ii) frequency and (iii) supply voltage V_{DD}.

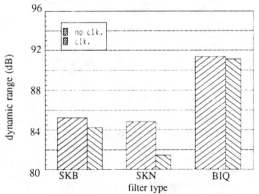

Fig.8 Measured dynamic range with and without a reference clock.

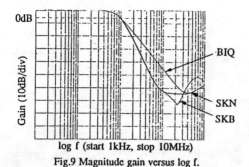

Fig.9 Magnitude gain versus log f.

Mean corner frequency (f_c) error is shown in fig.10 - the error bars span 3 standard deviations. A small proportion of device f_c's fall outside the specified ±5% error range. The errors are due to device mismatches, digital code quantisation error, f_c code-dependency (for the Sallen and Key filters), nominal setting offsets and calibrator inaccuracy.

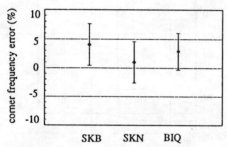

Fig.10 Mean f_c error for each type of filter.

It is not possible to test the functionality of the tuning circuitry over all process spreads. However, altering the reference clock period T_{ck} is equivalent to varying the on-chip RC time-constant. By changing T_{ck}, the digital tuning code is varied from 0 to 31. This results in the filter being tuned to 32 separate corner frequencies. Fig.11 shows the passband response of one BIQ filter for codes 0..31 *on a linear scale*. The response shape is maintained for all codes and for all types of filter (not shown).

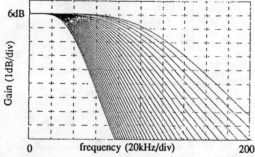

Fig.11 Typical passband response for tuning codes n=0..31

The functionality of the tuning circuitry for changes in temperature T is tested by monitering f_c as T is increased from 0 to 70°C and then decreased back to 0°C. Fig.12 displays the measured results for one SKN device. The negative temperature coefficients of the resistive and capacitive components cause f_c to increase with T in a continuous manner. When the RC product in the calibrator has changed sufficiently, the digital code decrements and the filter f_c jumps to a lower value. The discrete jumps occur at different temperatures for T increasing than for T decreasing because the calibrator has built-in hysteresis to allay the effects of code-change noise. For this device, fc error spans -1.5 to +3.8%, staying within the ±5% margins specified.

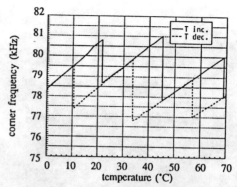

Fig.12 Measured variation of f_c with T.

Power consumption for each filter (27mW per op amp) is high compared with that of other continuous-time filters because of the high performance op amps used. These are necessary for low distortion. **Area occupation** is also high (1.4mm²:BIQ, 1.0mm²:SKB,SKN) due to the large valued passive components used.

Conclusions

Three VLSI-compatible self-tuned continuous-time filters using passive components have been integrated.

It has been shown that the parasitic-insensitive realisation (BIQ) yields low distortion (<-85dB), high dynamic range (92.4dB) and minimal clock feedthrough in the stopband (-88.9dB), making it suitable for high performance DSP applications The drawbacks include comparatively high power consumption and area occupation.

A single-amplifier filter (SKN), which is smaller and consumes less power, has reasonably high linearity (<-76dB THD) but worse noise rejection.

A similar single-amplifier filter (SKB) which uses bootstrapped capacitors displays poor linearity, the distortion originating in the bootstrapping circuitry.

It is expected that fully-balanced filter topologies will yield even better passband linearity, due to the partial cancellation of the predominant second-harmonic distortion components.

References

(1) Y.Tsividis, M.Banu, J.Khoury, "Continuous-time MOSFET-C filters in VLSI", *IEEE Trans. Circuits Syst.*, vol.CAS-33, no.2, Feb.1986, pp125-39.

(2) H.Khorramabadi, P.R.Gray, "High frequency CMOS continuous-time filters", *IEEE Jnl. Solid State Circuits*, vol.SC-19, no.6, Dec.1984, pp939-48.

(3) J.L.Pennock, "CMOS triode transconductor for continuous-time active integrated filters", *Electron Lett.*, vol.21, no.18, Aug.1985, pp817-8.

(4) J.B.Hughes, "Self-tuned RC-active filters for VLSI", *Electron Lett.*, 11th Sept.1986, vol.22, no.19, pp993-4.

(5) M.Banu, Y.Tsividis, "An Elliptic continuous-time CMOS filter with on-chip automatic tuning", *IEEE Jnl. Solid State Circuits*, vol.SC-20,no.6, Dec.1985, pp1114-21.

(6) D.B.Ribner, M.A.Copeland, "Design techniques for cascoded CMOS op amps with improved PSRR and common-mode input range", *IEEE Jnl. Solid State Circuits*, vol.SC-19, pp919-25, Dec. 1984.

Section 5-B   Distributed RC Filters

Distributed filters were investigated at length in the 1960s and 1970s, and found use in hybrid circuits [1, 2]. Papers 5-B.1 by Ahuja and 5-B.2 by Ramet describe distributed, fully integrated filters for antialiasing and/or smoothing purposes. These functions are indispensable in many sampled-data circuit applications, being employed at the input of analog-to-digital converters, sample-and-hold circuits and switched-capacitor circuits, as well as at the outputs of the latter and of digital-to-analog converters. The above filters are composed of nontunable elements and, thus, their cutoff frequencies have large tolerances and cannot be adjusted automatically. Related design considerations are described in [3]. Paper 5-B.3 presents a tunable filter in which a MOS transistor is used as the distributed element [4]. The filter consists of only four transistors. The concept is expanded and systematized in Paper 5-B.4. Another such filter can be found elsewhere [5].

It should be noted that all of the above filters have transfer functions that are not rational functions of the complex frequency. They share this drawback with their hybrid cousins [1, 2]. A technique that allows the synthesis of rational transfer functions using distributed elements, which in fact appears to be amenable to integration using only MOS transistors, is described in [6].

References

[1] M. Ghausi and J. Kelly, *Introduction to Distributed-Parameter Networks*, New York: Holt, Rinehart and Winston, 1968.

[2] W. E. Heinlein and W. H. Holmes, *Active Filters for Integrated Circuits*: *Fundamentals and Design Methods*, New York: Springer-Verlag, 1974.

[3] Z. Tomaszewski and G. Tröster, "Design considerations on monolithic distributed RC filters," *Proc. IEEE ISCAS '87,* pp. 750–753, 1987.

[4] J. Khoury, Y. Tsividis, and M. Banu, "Use of MOS transistor as a tunable distributed RC filter element," *Electron. Lett.*, vol. 20, no. 4, pp. 187–188, February 16, 1984.

[5] R. P. Jindal, "Low-pass distributed RC filter using an MOS transistor with near zero phase shift at high frequencies," *IEEE Trans. Circuits Syst.*, vol. 36, no. 8, pp. 1119–1123, August 89.

[6] J. M. Khoury and Y. P. Tsividis, "Synthesis of arbitrary rational transfer functions in *s* using uniform distributed *RC* active circuits," *IEEE Trans. Circuits Systems*, vol. 37, pp. 464–472, April 1990.

Paper 5-B.1

Implementation of Active Distributed *RC* Anti-Aliasing/Smoothing Filters

BHUPENDRA K. AHUJA

Abstract—The design of an active distributed *RC* filter is described for use as an anti-aliasing/smoothing filter in a PCM channel bank filter. A new filter configuration (known as a Rauch filter) has been chosen which uses the op amp in inverting configuration with a zero common mode signal and thus results in improved high-frequency attenuation characteristics along with good power supply rejection. A conventional configuration, Sallen and Key, with distributed *RC* elements is also discussed.

I. INTRODUCTION

THE need for a continuous prefilter exists in sampled data systems where the input contains frequency components which can be aliased. It must band limit the input signal before sampling and also smoothen the reconstructed staircase waveform at the output. PCM channel bank filters [1], [2] are one good example where the voiceband filters are implemented using switched-capacitor techniques. The requirements for the anti-aliasing/smoothing filters are to provide about −32 dB of attenuation at sampling frequency and less than 0.1 dB droop/peaking up to 3.4 kHz under worst-case process variation of *R* and *C* values. In the past, these filters have been implemented in Sallen and Key configurations with second-order Butterworth low-pass characteristics, using either the discrete *R* and *C* elements or the distributed *RC* elements [1], [2]. In this paper, a new configuration known as a Rauch filter [3] has been implemented and applied to an earlier design [1] in a distributed *RC* manner to give better high-frequency attenuation and power supply rejection from the substrate, which has parasitic coupling with the *R* and *C* elements.

II. DISTRIBUTED *RC* VERSUS DISCRETE *RC* NETWORK

In a double layer polysilicon gate MOS process, where the resistor is made using the second polysilicon layer (top layer) and the capacitor is formed between the two polysilicon layers, the choice of a distributed *RC* network over a discrete *RC* network in a continuous low-pass filter realization has the following primary advantages.

1) The passband response of the distributed *RC* network is flatter compared to a first-order equivalent discrete *RC* network (having the same −3 dB corner frequency), while at the same time, the stopband rolloff is much steeper for the distributed *RC* network.

Manuscript received July 9, 1982; revised July 20, 1982.
The author is with the Intel Corporation, Chandler, AZ 85224.

2) Coupling of substrate power supply is eliminated in the distributed *RC* network while this potential problem exists for the discrete *RC* network where *R* is being realized as a polysilicon resistor over field oxide.

3) There is a definite area saving using the distributed *RC* network due to available capacitance under the resistor which ends up reducing the discrete capacitance values.

The above three points are illustrated in Fig. 1, which shows frequency responses of two *RC* networks having the same −3 dB corner frequency of 6.3 kHz. The only disadvantage of the distributed *RC* network is the excess phase shift introduced in the circuit beyond its corner frequency. In most applications, this excess phase shift in the stopband is inconsequential.

Fig. 2 shows a cross section of a distributed *RC* element in a double layer polysilicon gate MOS process. Also shown in this figure is the mathematical model of a distributed *RC* line of *d* units of length with resistance of *r* Ω/unit, and a capacitance of *c* F/unit. The equivalent lumped π network for the distributed *RC* line can be shown to be [4] given by frequency dependent series admittance

$$Y = \frac{\sqrt{sc/r}}{\sinh\sqrt{srcd^2}} \tag{1}$$

and a shunt admittance of $(P - 1)Y$, where

$$P = \cosh\sqrt{srcd^2} \tag{2}$$

and

$$s = jw, \quad j = \sqrt{-1}, \quad w = \text{angular frequency.}$$

Using the model, the transfer function of the distributed *RC* network in Fig. 1 is given by

$$H(s) = \frac{Y}{PY + sC_0}$$

$$= \frac{\sqrt{sC/R}}{\sqrt{sC/R}\cosh(\sqrt{sRC}) + sC_0\sinh(\sqrt{sRC})}. \tag{3}$$

One can either use the above mathematical model to compute the response or a multiple-section lumped model of the *RC* line in a SPICE-like network simulator to get the approximate response.

III. SALLEN AND KEY ANTI-ALIASING FILTER DESIGN

The commonly used Sallen and Key configuration [1], [2] for a second-order low-pass filter is shown in Fig. 3(a). Its

Reprinted from *IEEE J. Solid-State Circuits*, vol. SC-17, no. 6, pp. 1076–1080, Dec. 1982.

339

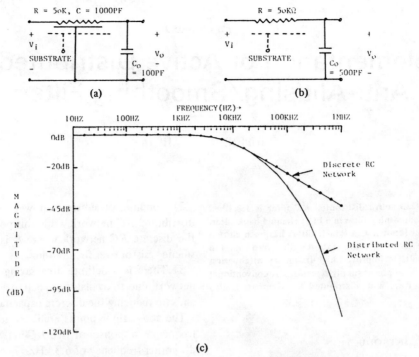

Fig. 1. Distributed *RC* versus discrete *RC* network characteristics. (a) A simple low-pass distributed *RC* network. (b) An equivalent discrete *RC* network. (c) Computed magnitude frequency responses of (a) and (b).

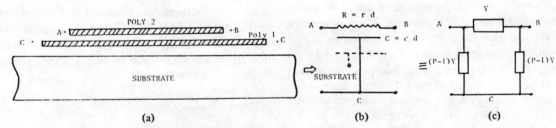

Fig. 2. (a) A distributed *RC* section in a double layer polysilicon gate MOS process. (b) Distributed *RC* representation. (c) An equivalent lumped π network.

distributed *RC* design is also shown in Fig. 3(b). Although the distributed *RC* design helps solve the power supply rejection problem from the substrate, the configuration has the drawback of using the op amp as a unity gain buffer. First, the unity gain buffer has a large common mode signal which makes the op amp design difficult. Second, at higher frequencies (near the unity gain frequency of the op amp), the output impedance of the buffer becomes significant and the high-frequency poles/zeros of the op amp result in an undesirable bump in the filter stopband characteristics. This is verified by measurements on an early version of an integrated PCM channel bank filter chip which uses a Sallen and Key type distributed *RC* anti-aliasing filter. The filter has been designed in a double polysilicon NMOS process. The top polysilicon layer, used as a 6 μm wide resistor, has a resistivity of 40 to 90 $\Omega/\square$, while the capacitor-oxide thickness is about 1750 ± 150 Å. Fig. 3(c) shows the measured frequency response of this filter, having a typical −3 dB point at 20 kHz. Also shown is the power supply re-

jection from the negative (V_{BB}) rail which is also tied to the substrate.

It should be noted in Fig. 3(b) that the parasitic capacitance (under the first polyresistor and $C1$) to substrate, $C_{sub\,1}$ and $C_{sub\,2}$, directly couple the substrate to the filter output at high frequencies. It is also noted that the discrete *RC* Sallen and Key would have required 29 pF more capacitance area than the distributed *RC* network along with severe coupling from the substrate just beyond the corner frequency of the filter. Using the mathematical model of the distributed *RC* line, the frequency response of the distributed *RC* Sallen and Key in Fig. 3(b) is given by

$$H(s) = \frac{Y^2}{s^2 C_1 C_2 + s\{P(C_1 + 2C_2) - C_1\}\,Y + P(2P - 1)\,Y^2}$$

(4)

where Y and P are the same as given in (1) and (2) and where d is the number of unit squares for the polysilicon resistors.

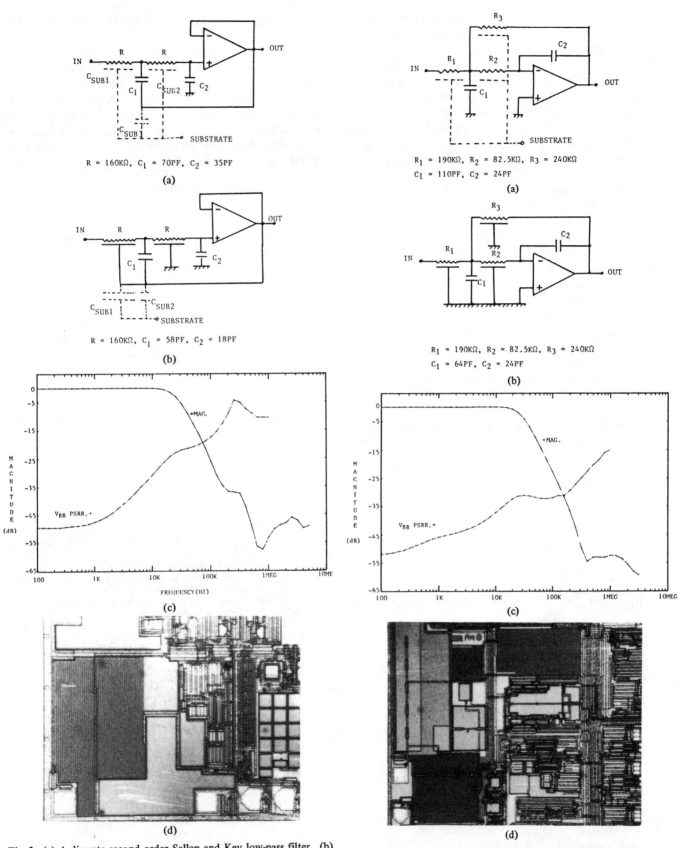

Fig. 3. (a) A discrete second-order Sallen and Key low-pass filter. (b) Distributed *RC* version. (c) Measured magnitude frequency response of (b) and its V_{BB} (and substrate) power supply rejection characteristics. (d) Photomicrograph of the Sallen and Key distributed *RC* anti-aliasing filter.

Fig. 4. (a) A discrete second-order Rauch low-pass filter. (b) Distributed *RC* version. (c) Measured magnitude frequency response of (b) and its V_{BB} (and substrate) power supply rejection characteristics. (d) Photomicrograph of the Rauch distributed *RC* smoothing filter.

341

Due to process variations in polysilicon sheet resistivity and oxide thickness, the corner frequency varies from 12 to 40 kHz; however, the passband droop is maintained less than 0.008 dB for 12 kHz corner frequency and the stopband attenuation at 256 kHz is maintained more than -32 dB for 40 kHz corner frequency. This is possible primarily due to the distributed *RC* network realization. However, if a discrete *RC* filter configuration had been chosen for these performance requirements with the given process variations in *R* and *C* element values, one would have to design at least a third-order Butterworth filter.

The photomicrograph of the Sallen and Key distributed *RC* filter section of the chip is shown in Fig. 3(d).

IV. RAUCH SMOOTHING DISTRIBUTED *RC* FILTER DESIGN

The discrete *RC* Rauch configuration (3) for a second-order low-pass filter is shown in Fig. 4(a), while the distributed *RC* version is shown in Fig. 4(b). The *R* and *C* values shown on the figures correspond to a 2 dB dc gain and Butterworth characteristics with a -3 dB point at 20 kHz. The primary advantage of this configuration over the Sallen and Key configuration is the use of the op amp in inverting mode with zero common mode input signal. This allows a relatively simple design of the op amp in applications where the output is required to swing close to the power supply rails with resistive loads. The distributed *RC* filter has been implemented as the smoothing filter at the transmit side output in the PCM channel filter chip [1]. The frequency response of the filter in Fig. 4(b) is given by

$$H(s) = \frac{-Y_1 Y_2}{s^2 C_1 C_2 + s C_2 (P_1 Y_1 + P_2 Y_2 + P_3 Y_3) + Y_2 Y_3} \quad (5)$$

where

$$P_i = \cosh \sqrt{srcd_i^2}$$

$$Y_i = \frac{\sqrt{sc/r}}{\sinh \sqrt{srcd_i^2}}$$

$d_i = d_1, d_2, d_3$ being the numbers of units squares for R_1, R_2, and R_3, respectively.

The measured frequency response and power supply rejection from the negative rail V_{BB} (also tied to the substrate) are shown in Fig. 4(c).

It is noted that the high-frequency performance of this configuration is better than the Sallen and Key filter by about 12 dB up to 3 MHz. This helps in the reducing the wide-band high-frequency output noise due to sample data system by about 8 to 10 dB. The power supply rejection from V_{BB} and the substrate is also better than Sallen and Key distributed anti-aliasing filter.

Fig. 4(d) shows the photomicrograph of the chip section containing this distributed *RC* smoothing filter.

V. DISCUSSION

Implementation of distributed *RC* filters has been discussed and shown to be quite efficient in area saving, along with better performance over discrete *RC* filters for a double layer silicon gate MOS process where a distributed *RC* structure is available. Design considerations for Sallen and Key as well as Rauch filters have been presented with measured data. Although the Rauch filter, in general, requires more *R* and *C* values (and thus chip area), it has an advantage of using the op amp in the inverting mode with zero common mode input voltage. This allows for a simpler design of the op amp which can swing resistive loads close to the power supply rails.

ACKNOWLEDGMENT

The author would like to thank T. Barnes for providing the measured data and W. Baxter for his contributions in the chip layout. Previous work done by H. Ohara on the anti-aliasing filter for this chip is also acknowledged.

REFERENCES

[1] H. Ohara, W. M. Baxter, P. R. Gray, J. L. McCreary, and C. F. Rahim, "A precision low power PCM filter with on-chip power supply regulation," *IEEE J. Solid-State Circuits*, pp. 1005–1013, Dec. 1980.

[2] B. K. Ahuja, M. R. Dwarkanath, T. Seidel, and D. G. Marsh, "A single chip CMOS codec with filters," in *Proc. Int. Solid-State Circuits Conf.*, Feb. 1981, pp. 242–243.

[3] W. E. Heinlen and W. H. Holmes, *Active Filters for Integrated Circuits*. Englewood Cliffs, NJ: Prentice-Hall, 1974, pp. 353–355.

[4] G. C. Temes and J. W. LaPatra, *Introduction to Circuit Synthesis and Design*. New York: McGraw-Hill, 1977, pp. 348–355.

A Low-Distortion Anti-Aliasing/Smoothing Filter for Sampled Data Integrated Circuits

SERGE RAMET

Abstract —This paper describes a low-distortion continuous-time low-pass filter for echo-cancelling MODEM's. Based on the Sallen and Key structure, the new configuration achieves a second-order Butterworth low-pass transfer function with a minimum silicon area and a low parametric sensitivity.

I. Introduction

The principle of echo-cancelling MODEM's is commonly based on the assumption that the echo path is linear. When harmonic distortion is generated in the echo path it cannot be cancelled by the echo canceller. Then it becomes part of the channel noise and finally it reduces the signal-to-noise ratio. In order to avoid this effect, the elements of the echo path must be carefully designed to meet the -72-dB harmonic-distortion specification needed for echo-cancelling MODEM's [1].

Because the harmonic distortion is critical, it is not possible to choose a standard Sallen and Key configuration with p-well resistors (Fig. 1(a)) for the design of the receive anti-aliasing filter and the transmit smoothing filter. The reason why is the high p-resistor voltage coefficient which is not consistent with the harmonic-distortion specification. The choice of a more linear material-like polysilicon for the resistors solves the problem of distortion but leads to a dramatic increase of the die area due to the low sheet resistance (20 Ω/sq) of the polysilicon layer.

With a double-polysilicon technology this increase of the die area can be limited by replacing the discrete resistors with a distributed RC network (DRCN) (Fig. 1(b)). The advantages of this technique, particularly the steep stopband roll-off it achieves, have been demonstrated [2]. Yet the configuration of Fig. 1(b) can be improved in terms of parametric sensitivity simply by suppressing capacitor C_2 and putting the DRCN's tap at one-third of its length from the input[1] (Fig. 2).

II. Theoretical Model for Distributed RC Network

The basic differential equations that describe the behavior of the DRCN are obtained by expressing the Kirchhoff laws for an elementary portion of the DRCN whose length is dx (Fig. 3(c)):

$$\frac{\partial i}{\partial x} = -C\frac{\partial v}{\partial t}$$

where C is the capacitance per unit of length, and

$$\frac{\partial v}{\partial x} = -Ri$$

where R is the resistance per unit of length.

The solutions of these equations have been extensively described [3] and many mathematical representations have been proposed. For my purpose, I would use the hybrid matrix representation. Considering the DRCN of Fig. 3(b), the hybrid matrix representation establishes the relationship between the Laplace transform of the output voltage and current vector and the input

[1]Patent pending.

Manuscript received January 20, 1988; revised May 10, 1988.
The author is with SGS-Thomson Microelectronics, 38019 Grenoble Cedex, France.
IEEE Log Number 8822734.

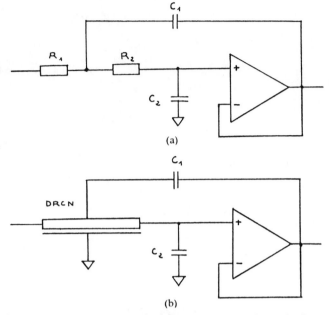

Fig. 1. (a) Sallen and Key low-pass filter with discrete resistors. (b) Conventional Sallen and Key low-pass filter with a distributed RC network.

voltage and current vector:

$$\begin{bmatrix} V(l,s) \\ I(l,s) \end{bmatrix} = \begin{bmatrix} \cosh(rl) & \dfrac{-R}{r}\sinh(rl) \\ \dfrac{-r}{R}\sinh(rl) & \cosh(rl) \end{bmatrix} \begin{bmatrix} V(0,s) \\ I(0,s) \end{bmatrix} \quad (1)$$

where $j^2 = -1$, $s = j2\pi f$, and $r^2 = RCs$.

III. Application to Sallen and Key Low-Pass Filter with Second-Order Butterworth Transfer Function

The transfer function characteristics of the second-order Butterworth low-pass filter can be obtained from the configuration in Fig. 2, although capacitor C_2 has been suppressed; the position of the tap on the DRCN top plate is then considered as a new parameter. By changing the position of the tap if C_1 is kept constant, the amount of feedforward current is modified; therefore the transfer function Q is changed. The consequence of this remark is that the presence of capacitor C_2 is not necessary to achieve any second-order low-pass transfer function. The computation of the exact transfer function of the filter (Fig. 2) confirms the latter qualitative analysis. Using the hybrid matrix representation for DRCN, the basic equations that allow the computation of the transfer function are as follows.

Equation (1) applies to the first DRCN section, and (2) applies to the second DRCN section:

$$\begin{bmatrix} V(l+d,s) \\ 0 \end{bmatrix} = \begin{bmatrix} \cosh(rd) & \dfrac{-R}{r}\sinh(rd) \\ \dfrac{-r}{R}\sinh(rd) & \cosh(rd) \end{bmatrix} \begin{bmatrix} V(l,s) \\ J(l,s) \end{bmatrix}$$

$$(2)$$

Reprinted from *IEEE J. Solid-State Circuits*, vol. SC-23, no. 5, pp. 1267–1270, Oct. 1988.

343

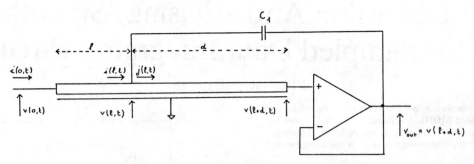

Fig. 2. Improved Sallen and Key low-pass filter with a distributed RC network.

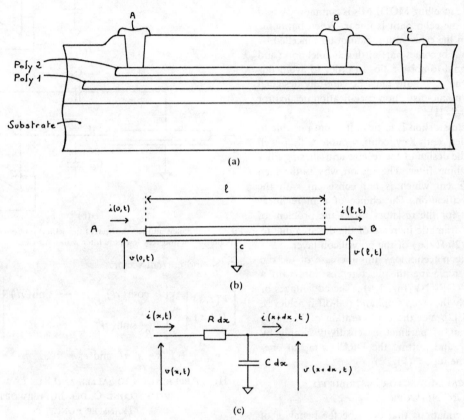

Fig. 3. (a) Distributed RC network cross section. (b) Electrical representation of a distributed RC network. (c) Electrical equivalent of an elementary portion of a distributed RC network.

$$C_2 s [V(l+d,s) - V(l,s)] + I(l,s) = J(l,s).$$

After solving this system the transfer function can be written

$$T(s) = \frac{1}{\cosh[r(l+d)] + \dfrac{RC_1 s}{r} \sinh(rl)[\cosh(rd) - 1]}. \quad (3)$$

This expression is not very easy to compare with the second-order Butterworth low-pass transfer function because it is not a polynomial fraction. Introducing the following variable changes:

$$\theta = (R_T C_T \pi f)^{1/2}$$

$$k = \frac{l}{d}$$

where $R_T = R(l+d)$ is the total capacitance of the DRCN and

$C_T = C(l+d)$ is the total resistance of the DRCN, (3) becomes

$$\tau(\theta) =$$

$$\frac{1}{\cosh[\theta(1+j)] + \theta(1+j)\dfrac{C_1}{C_T}\sinh\left[\dfrac{1+j}{1+k}\theta k\right]\left[\cosh\left[\dfrac{1+j}{1+k}\theta\right] - 1\right]}. \quad (4)$$

Assuming $\theta \ll 1$ and $k\theta \ll 1$, the Taylor expansion (limited to the fourth order) of the denominator of (4) gives a more familiar aspect to the filter transfer function:

$$\tau(\theta) = \frac{1}{1 + j\theta^2 + (j\theta^2)^2\left[\dfrac{1}{6} + \dfrac{2C_1 k}{C_T(1+k)^3}\right]}. \quad (5)$$

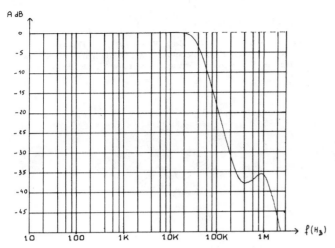

Fig. 4. Plot of the transfer function magnitude versus frequency.

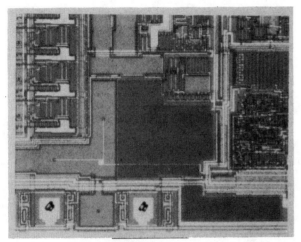

Fig. 5. Microphotograph of the R_x anti-aliasing filter.

Identifying the transfer function (5) to the second-order Butterworth transfer function gives

$$f_0 = \frac{\sqrt{2}}{\pi R_T C_T} = \frac{\sqrt{2}}{\pi R_0 C_0 (l+d)^2} \qquad (6)$$

$$\delta = \frac{1}{\sqrt{2}} = \frac{1}{2\left[\dfrac{2kC_1}{C_T(1+k)^3} + \dfrac{1}{6}\right]^{1/2}} \qquad (7)$$

where R_0 is the sheet resistance of poly 2 layer, C_0 is the poly 2/poly 1 capacitance per unit of surface, f_0 is the resonance frequency, and δ is the damping coefficient.

The first remarkable fact is that the resonance frequency depends only on the total length $(l+d)$ of the DRCN for a given technology (R_0 and C_0 are regarded as technology constants). The second remarkable fact is the existence of an optimum position of the top-plate tap which minimizes the surface of the whole filter. It comes to evidence when rewriting (7):

$$\frac{C_1}{C_T} = \frac{(1+k)^3}{6k}. \qquad (8)$$

TABLE I

Cutoff frequency $f_{-3\,dB}$:	38.9 kHz
Attenuation at 288 kHz:	36.4 dB
DRCN characteristics:	
R_T =	190 kΩ
C_T =	60.75 pF
$l+d$ =	4.5 cm
l/d =	1/2
w =	4.5 μm
C_1 =	68.34 pF
Filter area: 0.9 mm² (1400 mils²)	
Output offset voltage: 2 mV	
Signal/total harmonic distortion at 1 kHz:	
V_{out} peak to peak = 5 V:	> 80 dB
V_{out} peak to peak = 6 V:	74 dB

The surface is minimum when C_1 is minimum, i.e., when $k = 1/2$, which results in

$$C_1 = \frac{9}{8} C_T. \qquad (9)$$

IV. PRACTICAL DESIGN AND EXPERIMENTAL RESULTS

The circuit was designed in a conventional 4-μm p-well double-poly CMOS technology. The design goals were to achieve a low harmonic distortion (−80 dB) and a minimum attenuation (35 dB) at 288 kHz (the sampling frequency of the switched-capacitor filter). Equation (6) shows a dependence of the resonance frequency f_0 only on the total length of the DRCN (but not on its width); the DRCN top plate which is made of poly 2 is drawn at 4.5 μm. The process etching dispersion only affects the Q value because of its dependence on the C_1/C_T ratio.

The core amplifier is a conventional two-stage differential amplifier with a class A output [4]. The design cares to take are:

a) to minimize the output impedance of the second stage in order to reduce the undesirable bump in the transfer function magnitude plot (Fig. 4) [2]; and

b) to make the second-stage bias current one order of magnitude larger than the maximum feedforward current in order to guarantee the amplifier linearity.

The performance of the filter is summarized in Table I. A plot of the transfer function magnitude is shown in Fig. 4 and a microphotograph of the anti-aliasing R_x filter is shown in Fig. 5.

V. CONCLUSION

The theory, the practical design, and the measurement results of a simple low-distortion continuous-time filter have been discussed. The filter harmonic distortion and attenuation performances comply with the echo-cancelling MODEM specification. These features have been achieved on a smaller silicon area than the conventional Sallen and Key filter.

ACKNOWLEDGMENT

The author would like to thank L. Tallaron for providing encouragement and design advice; E. Baudouin, C. Giller, and J. Lebrun for their contribution to the layout of the chip; and J. C. Bertails for his careful review of this paper.

REFERENCES

[1] J. C. Bertails, C. Perrin, L. Tallaron, L. Mary, and C. DeLange, "A full-duplex analog front-end chip set for split-band and echo-cancelling MODEM's," in *ISSCC Dig. Tech. Papers*, Feb. 1986, pp. 174–175.

[2] B. K. Ahuja, "Implementation of active distributed RC anti-aliasing/smoothing filters," *IEEE J. Solid-State Circuits*, vol. SC-17, no. 6, pp. 1076–1080, Dec. 1982.

[3] R. W. Wyndrum Jr., in *Modern Filter Theory and Design*, G. C. Temes and S. K. Mitra, Eds. New York: Wiley, 1973, pp. 375–410.

[4] P. R. Gray, "Basic MOS operational amplifier design—An overview," in *Analog MOS Integrated Circuit*. New York: IEEE Press, 1980, pp. 28–49.

Minimal Transistor-Only Micropower Integrated VHF Active Filter

Y. P. TSIVIDIS

Indexing terms: Filters, Active filters, Continuous-time filters, Integrated filters, VHF filters, Minimal circuits

A minimal integrated filter containing four MOS transistors as the only circuit elements is presented. Voltage tuning is used to set the cutoff frequency and band-edge peaking. A filter test chip occupies an active area of 0·006 mm², has a cutoff frequency of 40 MHz and dissipates 580 μW.

Introduction: In integrated continuous-time filters, parasitic capacitances have been viewed as an obstacle to high-frequency operation.[1] It has been proposed that one of the parasitics, namely the gate-channel capacitance, can be used for filtering, albeit with the gate at AC ground and thus with serious topological restrictions.[2] Here we explore the possibility of using all parasitics as filter elements, bypass the above restrictions, and demonstrate a minimal transistor-only active filter operating at very high frequencies.

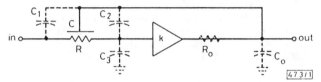

Fig. 1 *Lowpass RC filter including parasitics*

Principle: The key feature of integrated continuous-time filters, which can make possible the use of parasitics for filtering, is on-chip automatic tuning.[1] For such use of parasitics to be feasible, one must find a topology such that any unpredictability in their values can be 'tuned out' using control voltages or currents generated by the automatic tuning system. Consider the circuit shown by the solid lines in Fig. 1. In this well known lowpass filter,[3] the distributed RC element controls the cutoff frequency and k controls the peaking near the band-edge; for maximum flatness the required k is less than 0·8, and thus can be realised using a source-follower as in Fig. 2. The 'RC' element is realised by transistor M_1 operating in nonsaturation. Because of the use of complementary transistors for M_1 and then follower M_2, the latter can simultaneously provide both signal and DC bias to M_1. Thus, unlike in Reference 2, the gate of the 'RC' element does not have to be at AC ground. M_3 operates in saturation as a current source, with V_{G3} controlling its current and thus V_C, which in turn controls

$$R = [(W/L)\mu C_{ox}(V_C - V_{T1})]^{-1}$$

M_4 operates in nonsaturation with small current and large $|V_{GS}|$, acting as a conductance g_{d4} to adjust the gain

$$k = g_{m2}/(g_{m2} + g_{d2} + g_{d3} + g_{d4})$$

Consider now the parasitics shown by the broken lines in Fig. 1 in relation to Fig. 2. The nonzero output resistance $R_o = (g_{m2} + g_{d2} + g_{d3} + g_{d4})$ tends to reduce the stopband rejection;[3] this effect can be greatly suppressed[4] by using a capac-

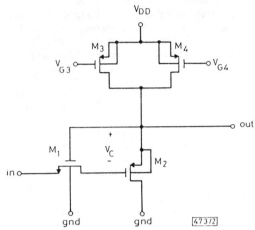

Fig. 2 *Transistor-only minimal implementation of filter in Fig. 1*

itor C_o, which is present anyway due to junctions, overlaps and loading. Parasitics C_1, C_2 and C_3 result in lumped/distributed operation and can greatly reduce the cutoff frequency below that calculated in Reference 3, but the reduction is predictable, and V_{G3} can be used to tune out processing and temperature variations. The DC gain is obviously independent of parasitic capacitances, and the peaking cannot significantly increase because of the inherently low gain k. V_{G4} can be used to adjust the peaking. Both V_{G3} and V_{G4} are envisioned as being generated automatically by an on-chip tuning circuit, as has already been done for low-frequency filters.[1] Such a tuning circuit is currently under study.

Experimental results: The circuit of Fig. 2 was integrated at AT&T Bell Laboratories in a 1·5 μm CMOS fabrication process, using the following W/L values (in micrometres): M_1: 3·75/10, M_2: 36/6, M_3: 36/6, M_4: 6/6. These dimensions are not small, but the use of the 1·5 μm process ensured small

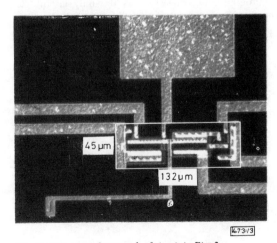

Fig. 3 *Chip microphotograph of circuit in Fig. 2*

Reprinted with permission from *El. Letters*, vol. 23, no. 15, pp. 777–778, July 1987.

extrinsic parasitics. The above values were arrived at through an iterative design procedure, using computer simulation as a guide. To simulate MOSFET distributed effects, the transistors were divided into several sections, with short-channel effects and extrinsic parasitics eliminated at intermediate, fictitious points. In the final design, however, the lumped capacitances were so dominant that the circuit could be simulated rather adequately even using common, lumped transistor models for the four devices. A chip microphotograph is shown in Fig. 3. The active area is less than $0.006\,mm^2$ ($9.2\,mil^2$). The circuit was tested on a probe station to avoid packaging parasitics. The output pad was made very small (lower left in Fig. 3), and was contacted through a special, very small probe with an input capacitance of $0.1\,pF$. Two separate ground lines were used (see Fig. 2) to avoid undesired coupling. For a single 5 V supply and a 1 V input bias, the measured frequency response for three values of V_{G3} is shown in Fig. 4 (M_4 was turned off for this measurement). The transition band rolloff reaches 18 dB/octave, and the stopband attenuation was better than 20 dB, maintained throughout the VHF range. The droop in the passband and the kinks in the response are due to the measurement set-up. The 10 MHz kink has not been adequately explained, but is not thought to be due to the filter itself since it is not movable through V_{G3}. The peaking at the band-edge could be eliminated through V_{G4}, although this made necessary the iterative adjustment of V_{G3} and V_{G4}. This problem can be reduced by modifying the operating point and the W/L ratios. With the cutoff frequency at 40 MHz (for which the design had been optimised for linearity) and a 10 MHz, $0.92\,V_{pp}$ input, the total harmonic distortion was $-40\,dB$. The equipment used did not allow measurements for input frequencies near the band-edge, but simulation shows that for a 40 MHz signal the distortion should increase to about $-25\,dB$ for the same input level. Most of this is second-order, and should be largely eliminated if two filters are used in a balanced fashion, resulting in better than $-50\,dB$ harmonic distortion for a $1\,V_{pp}$ input throughout the passband. The noise was not measured; simulation predicts $2.8\,mV_{rms}$ from 1 Hz to 300 MHz at the output. The power dissipation was $580\,\mu W$ for a 40 MHz cutoff frequency. This corresponds to a power per band-edge frequency per pole of less than 10 pJ, which is far lower than for any other integrated active filter known to me.

Conclusions: A minimal integrated filter has been demonstrated, containing four transistors as the only circuit elements. The filter includes cutoff and flatness control inputs, occupies an active chip area equal to a fraction of a typical

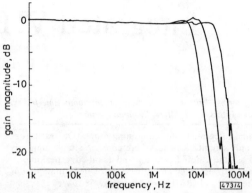

Fig. 4 *Measured frequency response (normalised to DC gain) of chip in Fig. 3*

$V_{DD} - V_{G3} = 0.73$, 1.43 and $2.23\,V$ (M_4 was turned off for this measurement)

contact pad, and operates at 40 MHz with extremely low power. Simulations show that similar filters are possible with cutoff frequencies of at least 100–200 MHz with $0.75\,\mu m$ processes. Important problems remain to be solved; these include on-chip automatic tuning, circuitry to make the output DC level and DC gain independent of V_{G3} and V_{G4}, nonlinearity reduction, a systematic design process and extension to other topologies. However, the experimental results obtained are certainly encouraging, and point to the potential of device-level, minimal circuit design.

Acknowledgments: The author thanks J. Khoury for useful discussions and his help in testing, and H. Khorramabadi and T. R. Viswanathan for providing space on their wafer for the test chip. This work was supported by National Science Foundation grant MIP-86-16394.

References

1   TSIVIDIS, Y., BANU, M., and KHOURY, J.: 'Continuous-time MOSFET-C filters in VLSI', *IEEE Trans.*, 1986, **CAS-33**, pp. 125–140; Erratum: *ibid.*, 1986, **CAS-33**, p. 1039
2   KHOURY, J., TSIVIDIS, Y., and BANU, M.: 'Use of MOS transistor as a tunable distributed *RC* filter element', *Electron. Lett.*, 1984, **20**, pp. 187–188
3   WYNDRUM, R. M. JR.: 'Active distributed *RC* networks', *IEEE J. Solid-State Circuits*, 1968, **SC-3**, pp. 308–310
4   DUTTA ROY, S. C., and SAH, R. P.: 'Active distributed *RC* low-pass filters', *Microelectron. & Reliab.*, **11**, pp. 293–295

Transistor-Only Frequency-Selective Circuits

LIH-JIUAN PU AND YANNIS P. TSIVIDIS, FELLOW, IEEE

Abstract —The possibility of implementing frequency-selective circuits using only MOS transistors is considered. Potential advantages and disadvantages of such circuits are discussed. Two approaches for the realization of such circuits are proposed, and measurement results from test chips are reported.

I. INTRODUCTION

TRADITIONAL active *RC* filters are composed of resistors, capacitors, and transistors (the latter being part of the active elements). In MOSFET-C integrated filters [1], the role of resistors is played by MOS transistors. Thus, such filters consist of only two types of elements: transistors and capacitors. The same is true of integrated transconductor–capacitor filters [2]–[7]. One is led to wonder whether it would be possible to eliminate the capacitors as well, and to make integrated filters using only transistors; and, most importantly, what advantages such an approach might have, if any. We have taken a look at this question. An initial attempt to make a MOS transistor-only filter has already been reported [8]; it yielded very encouraging results, including cutoff-frequency tunability in the 10–40-MHz range, extremely small "power dissipation per band-edge frequency per pole" (< 10 pJ), and total chip area equal to a fraction of that occupied by a common bonding pad. The entire filter consisted of only four transistors. That initial attempt was an *ad-hoc* one, producing one specific circuit derived from a well-known uniform distributed *RC* ($\overline{URC}$) topology, in which the $\overline{URC}$ element was replaced by a transistor. In this paper we offer a generalization, which allows one to derive transistor-only filters from a variety of known $\overline{URC}$ structures, using a systematic procedure. Results from a related experimental chip are also reported. In addition, we present results from a different approach, in which one begins with lumped prototypes

Manuscript received June 13, 1989; revised December 6, 1989. This work was supported in part by NSF Grant MIP-86-16394. Part of this work was presented at the International Symposium on Circuits and Systems, Espoo, Finland, 1988.

L.-J. Pu was with the Department of Electrical Engineering and Center for Telecommunications Research, Columbia University, New York, NY 10027. She is now with IBM Corporation, East Fishkill, NY 12533.

Y. P. Tsividis is with the Department of Electrical Engineering and Center for Telecommunications Research, Columbia University, New York, NY 10027.

IEEE Log Number 9034582.

(transconductance-C in our case) and replaces capacitors by MOS transistors; second-order corrections are then carried out to cancel the effect of the inherent imperfections in such "capacitors" as well as in the active elements.

II. ADVANTAGES AND DISADVANTAGES OF TRANSISTOR-ONLY FILTERS

The establishment of advantages for a new technique is an iterative process. Some advantages may be apparent in the beginning of an effort, whereas others will only become apparent after experimental structures have been designed, constructed, and evaluated. At this stage, the potential advantages we see in transistor-only filters are as follows.

1) If the MOS transistor is used as a $\overline{URC}$ element, the capacitance and resistance become physically co-located (one above the other). This, in a planar integrated-circuit fabrication process, can result in reduced chip area. For certain topologies, a transistor-only approach can result in a truly minimal implementation—cf. the first attempt mentioned above [8], in which only four transistors yielded a tunable filter with a roll-off characteristic sharper than second-order. This can become a significant advantage in cases where a large number of noncritical filters must be implemented on-chip. An example may be an electronic approximation to the human cochlea (inner ear) [9], which can contain hundreds or even thousands of filter elements.

2) The fact that a transistor-only implementation does not require separate capacitor structures may come in handy in cases where the fabrication process available does not provide such structures. Processes without good capacitors are less expensive, and are widely used for digital VLSI applications (e.g., microprocessor and logic chips). If it is needed to place a simple analog frequency-selective circuit (e.g., an oscillator or a filter for interfacing with the analog world, before an A/D or after a D/A converter) on a chip to be made using such a process, transistor-only circuits can be used, whereas conventional continuous-time or switched-capacitor techniques cannot.

3) Transistor-only filters rely on internal transistor capacitances. Provided that reliable design techniques can be developed, this could lead to operating frequencies higher than those possible with conventional approaches,

Reprinted from *IEEE J. Solid-State Circuits*, vol. SC-25, no. 3, pp. 821–832, June 1990.

in which the separate capacitors used are of values large enough to make internal transistor capacitances negligible in comparison.

4) In MOS transistors used as $\overline{URC}$ elements, the total resistance–total capacitance product can match well in spite of mismatches in their physical width, and to a large extent in spite of mismatches in their insulator thickness; these facts will be shown in the main body of the paper.

Along with the above potential advantages, though, one faces several disadvantages or currently unsolved problems, such as those that follow.

1) Since transistor-only filters rely on internal transistor capacitances, reliable design techniques would have to be developed for taking such capacitances into account. One must make sure that the variability of such capacitances in a given fabrication process is either not excessive or can be tuned out through appropriate voltage or current control. Adequate automatic tuning circuits must be developed for this purpose, just as they have for lumped continuous-time filters [1]–[7].

2) The inherently distributed nature of the MOS transistor channel is not modeled in common CAD models. This is usually not a problem for conventional circuits, because in most circuit work transistors are used at frequencies where their operation is basically "quasi-static" [10]. As the frequency of operation approaches the intrinsic device cutoff frequency, though, such models fail. It is at such frequencies that the transistors must be used in order to take advantage of the techniques presented in this paper. This means that common simulation techniques will not work.

3) Transistors are inherently nonlinear. Many linearization techniques have already been proposed for integrated filters (for example, see [1]–[7]), but all are based on quasi-static transistor operation and will not work at frequencies where the distributed nature of transistors becomes dominant. Thus, new linearization schemes need to be developed.

We have only partial answers to the above problems. With respect to problem no. 1, we can note that it is only the extrinsic-device parasitics that can be a real problem (where "extrinsic" refers to the part of the device outside the "intrinsic" area, defined to be the device's channel and the structure immediately above and below it; extrinsic parasitics include overlap and junction capacitances). The intrinsic capacitances should be viewed differently. For example, the main intrinsic capacitance is that between the gate and the channel. This capacitance is *not* a parasitic one; we *rely* on this capacitance to induce transistor action. Were it not for this capacitance, there would be no MOS transistors. This is manifested in the presence of the "oxide capacitance per unit area" as a proportionality constant in the transistor $I–V$ relations. As far as the extrinsic capacitances are concerned, one must indeed make sure that the effect of their unpredictability and variation is fully "covered" by the voltage- or current-tuning range.

Problem no. 2 points to the need for better device models in circuit simulation. It is encouraging to know that this is largely a matter of implementation; sound non-quasi-static models already exist (see [10] and the many references therein). Until these are implemented in popular simulators, an interim, albeit inconvenient, solution does exist. One can split the transistor into many small ones, with their channels in series and with common gates and substrates, ensuring that no extrinsic parasitics at intermediate nodes or artificial short-channel effects are introduced (a tricky step, not possible with some simulation models). One can also specify a high-frequency small-signal model "by hand" as part of the input file, but then distortion cannot be predicted.

With respect to problem no. 3, the only obvious partial solution is to operate filters in a balanced fashion. This will eliminate even-order, but not odd-order, distortion. This approach may be useful if a single-ended filter's even-order distortion is dominant, in which case two such filters can be used and driven in a balanced fashion. This may not be objectionable in terms of chip area, if each filter occupies a small area to begin with (see advantage no. 1 above). Admittedly, though, this is a less-than-satisfactory solution, and more "detailed" linearization schemes are needed.

We will report below on how we have attempted to use some of the above advantages, and access some of the above-mentioned problems. We will not address the problems of automatic tuning and nonlinearity cancellation in this paper. Our work to date has dealt mostly with topology development, small-area implementation, voltage or current manual tuning, and very high-frequency operation.

III. Small-Signal Modeling for the Distributed MOSFET

In the circuits to be described, a key role is played by the distributed nature of the gate–channel structure. Unfortunately, common models used in CAD programs do not take this nature properly into account. Users of such programs may have to use a many-segment lumped approximation for each transistor, or at least the crucial ones in the circuit. This can be done as described in the previous section. To provide a feeling for the distributed nature of the MOSFET, we consider the special case of zero drain–source bias below (which is of special interest for the purposes of this paper). All transistors in this paper will be assumed to be operating in strong inversion.

Consider an n-channel MOSFET, shown in Fig. 1(a). With $V_{DS} = 0$, the channel and the depletion region underneath it are practically uniform. In fact, that depletion region can be considered to be practically an extension of the depletion regions under the source and drain, with practically the same dependence on the reverse bias $V_{SB} = V_{DB}$. A small-signal model for the complete structure is shown in Fig. 1(b). The channel resistance is given

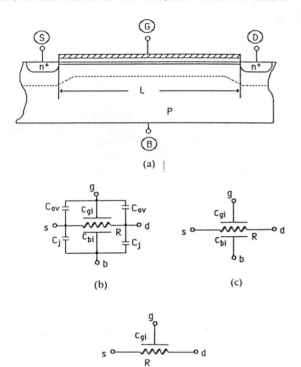

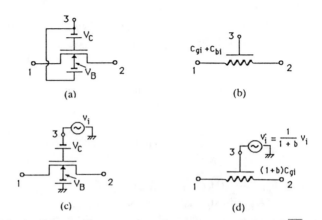

Fig. 2. Ways to bias a transistor for use as a small-signal $\overline{URC}$ element. Terminals 1, 2, and 3 are assumed to be at 0 bias. (a) Floating gate and substrate. (b) Small-signal equivalent circuit of (a). (c) Fixed-bias substrate and voltage-driven gate. (d) Small-signal equivalent of (c), valid at terminals 1 and 2 only.

Fig. 1. (a) Four-terminal MOS structure with $V_{DS} = 0$. (b) Small-signal model. (c) Small-signal model in the case of negligible extrinsic parasitics. (d) The model in (c) in the case of negligible substrate capacitance.

by

$$R = R_s \frac{L}{W} \qquad (1)$$

where L and W are the length and width of the channel, respectively, and R_s is the sheet resistance of the channel, given by

$$R_s = \left[\mu C'_{ox}(V_{GS} - V_T) \right]^{-1} \qquad (2)$$

where μ is the effective carrier mobility, C'_{ox} is the oxide capacitance per unit area, and V_T is the threshold voltage. For a modern process, $\mu C'_{ox}$ can typically be 10^{-4} S/V, and $V_T = 0.8$ V. C_{gi} is the intrinsic gate–channel distributed capacitance and is given by

$$C_{gi} = WLC'_{ox}. \qquad (3)$$

In Fig. 1(b) C_{bi} is the intrinsic channel–substrate distributed capacitance, C_{ov} are the (lumped) gate–source and gate–drain overlap capacitances, and C_j are the (lumped) source–substrate and drain–substrate junction capacitances.[1] The above capacitances are easily calculated [10]. For a modern fabrication process, assuming a couple of volts of reverse bias $V_{SB} = V_{DB}$, typical values

can be $C_{ov} = (0.2 \text{ fF}/\mu\text{m}) \times W$, $C_j = (0.6 \text{ fF}/\mu\text{m}) \times W$, $C_{gi} = [1.5 \text{ fF}/(\mu\text{m})^2] \times WL$, and $C_{bi} = [0.15 \text{ fF}/(\mu\text{m})^2] \times WL$, where W and L are the width and length of the channel, respectively.

If the channel is very long, $C_{gi} \gg C_{ov}$ and $C_{bi} \gg C_j$; then we have the simplified model shown in Fig. 1(c).[2] This long-channel simplification will be assumed to be valid until further notice. Finally, if C_{bi} can be neglected, the model reduces to that shown in Fig. 1(d).

Two cases of interest are shown in Fig. 2. In Fig. 2(a), the voltage sources are assumed to have been chosen so that, with zero potential difference between terminals 1, 2, and 3, the transistor is on and operating in the strong inversion region (always with $V_{DS} = 0$). From Fig. 1(c) it is seen that the circuit of Fig. 2(a) has the small-signal equivalent circuit shown in Fig. 2(b).

The second case of interest is shown in Fig. 2(c). Here only the gate is signal driven; the substrate is kept at a dc potential. Now the gate–channel and channel–substrate elemental capacitances form capacitive voltage dividers. Using a Thevenin equivalent of such dividers, the model of Fig. 1(c) reduces in this case to that inh Fig. 2(d), where

$$b = \frac{C_{bi}}{C_{gi}}. \qquad (4)$$

The value of b depends on $V_{SB} = V_{DB}$ and the process parameters, and can typically be 0.1. The model in Fig. 2(d) is valid as far as looking into the source and drain is concerned; the capacitance $(1 + b)C_{gi}$ is the total (gate plus depletion region) capacitance across the channel in Fig. 2(c); however, this is not the correct value for the capacitance seen from the gate in Fig. 2(c), so Fig. 2(d) can be considered a small-signal equivalent of Fig. 2(c)

---

[1]Strictly speaking, C_{ov} and C_j are also distributed over the resistive n^+ material of the source and drain; the sheet resistance of this material is, however, much smaller than that of the channel, so such effects are neglected here. Also, in a more complete model the substrate and source/drain resistances would have to be included; they are neglected here for simplicity.

[2]Similarly, if W is made large, the parasitic capacitances of the wiring external to the transistor can be made negligible in comparison.

only if the gate is voltage driven, in which case the capacitance seen from the gate is not an issue.

The case of general drain–source bias is complicated in that *uniform* distributed *RC* concepts do not apply. Nevertheless, small-signal equivalent circuits can be derived (see [10] and references therein).

IV. Matching of Distributed MOSFET Elements

The distributed *RC* element of Fig. 1(d) can be characterized by well-established theory [11], [12]. The frequency-dependent factor of its (trans)admittances depends on the product RC_{gi} which, from (2) and (3), is given by

$$RC_{gi} = \frac{L^2}{\mu(V_{GS} - V_T)}. \tag{5}$$

It is thus seen that RC_{gi} is independent of W and C'_{ox}. Thus a mismatch in these two quantities will not produce a corresponding mismatch in RC_{gi}, even if the devices are narrow, which can be a considerable advantage in integrated filters, and should be contrasted to the sensitivity of lumped filters to W mismatches [1]. If C_{bi} is taken into account, it can be found that the dependence on C'_{ox} is not eliminated totally [13]; however, the one on W still is. The sensitivity to L exhibited by (5) can be made negligible by ensuring that L is large (much larger than typical uncertainties in the relative error $\Delta L / L$), which would be needed anyway to make the models in Fig. 1(c) and (d) valid.

The above insensitivity to W and C'_{ox} mismatches is not exhibited by the frequency-independent part of the (trans)admittances, all of which are proportional to $1/R$.

V. $U\overline{RC}$-to-Transistor-Only Circuit Conversion

The floating bias sources in Fig. 2(a) and (c) can be implemented with source followers. For simplicity, only the case of Fig. 2(c) will be considered. The implementation of the structure shown in that figure is given in Fig. 3(a). Terminals 1, 2, and 3 are nominally at *ground* potential. The p-channel source follower provides both dc bias and a buffered input for applying the signal to the gate, and is assumed to have very low output impedance. The channel resistance of M_1 is controlled by the gate bias V_C, which in turn is controlled by the bias current of the follower, through V; this feature will be used for tuning. Therefore, the circuit shown in Fig. 3(a) is equivalent to a tunable $U\overline{RC}$ element as shown in Fig. 3(b) as far as terminals 1 and 2 are concerned. The control voltage V can be shared by different "MOSFET $\overline{RC}$'s" in a circuit such as a filter, as shown in Fig. 3(c). If identical source followers are used, the gate bias voltages of all MOSFET $\overline{RC}$ devices are ideally equal to each other for all values of

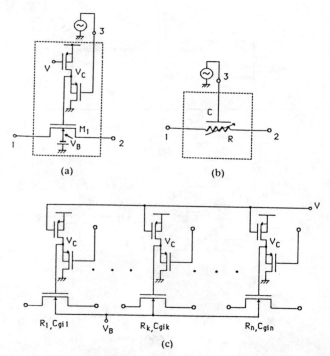

Fig. 3. (a) A MOS transistor in strong inversion with the gate biased by a source follower. Terminals 1, 2, and 3 are assumed to be at zero bias; terminal 3 is assumed to be voltage-driven. (b) Small-signal model of (a), valid at terminals 1 and 2 only. (c) n "MOSFET $\overline{RC}$" devices biased by n identical source followers.

V. Since the channel resistance of all MOSFET $\overline{RC}$ devices is expressed by (1) and (2), when V is tuned each R_k is changed by the same factor, $(V_{C_{old}} - V_T)/(V_{C_{new}} - V_T)$ for $k = 1, 2, \cdots, n$. The ratio of the distributed resistances of the MOSFET $\overline{RC}$ elements remains unchanged and equal to the ratio of their L/W's. Therefore, by tuning V the characteristic frequency of the filter which contains these MOSFET $\overline{RC}$'s can be tuned while the Q factor of the filter's poles remains unchanged. This corresponds to frequency scaling.

The procedure outlined above poses one restriction: that the capacitor terminal of the $U\overline{RC}$ element in the original distributed RC network has to be connected to ground or a voltage source, since the impedance of terminal 3 is not preserved when going from Fig. 2(c) to Fig. 3(a). Under this restriction, previously developed active distributed RC network synthesis techniques [11], [12] can be used to realize transistor-only circuits based on the procedure outlined above. The simplest example is Wyndrum's low-pass filter, shown in Fig. 4(a) [14], where the K element is a voltage buffer with negligible output impedance. Using the above procedure, one can obtain a transistor-only filter as shown in Fig. 4(b), assuming for now that the source follower has very large input impedance and very low output impedance. Since the values required for K are less than 0.9 [14], the K element can be deleted and its function taken over by the source follower. This results in the three-transistor filter shown in Fig. 4(c) [8] in which the output terminal is the output of the source follower. Two factors influencing the

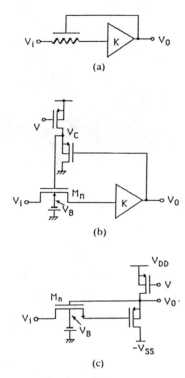

Fig. 4. (a) Wyndrum's active low-pass filter. (b) Replacing the $\overline{URC}$ element by the circuit of Fig. 3(a). (c) Simplified circuit.

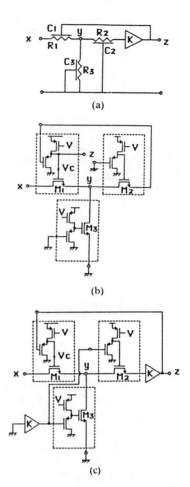

Fig. 5. (a) Renz's active low-pass distributed RC filter. (b) Transistor-only circuit. (c) More flexible transistor-only circuit.

effective value of K for this circuit will be discussed shortly. This three-transistor circuit can also be used as an oscillator by grounding its input, if the effective gain of the source follower is 0.9206 or higher, just as is the case with its $\overline{URC}$ prototype [14]. This is due to the fact that the passive $\overline{URC}$ element M_n has a gain *larger* than 1 from gate to drain in a range of frequencies (provided the extrinsic parasitics are negligible), which includes the frequency at which the total phase shift is 360°. This larger-than-unity voltage gain of a single zero-current unloaded transistor can be predicted theoretically, and has been verified experimentally [15]. The design of such an oscillator is, however, tricky, since the "gain" of the source follower is limited by the body effect and nonzero drain small-signal conductances; also, the substrate capacitance of M_n further reduces the effective gain by the factor $1/(1 + b)$, as depicted in Fig. 2(d). Finally, the loading effect of the source-follower input must be taken into account. The effective gain can be increased above the critical value only if the body effect is made small. This has been verified by computer simulation. While this simple circuit is of questionable practical value as an oscillator, it is a demonstration of the minimality achievable by transistor-only circuits, as well as of some interesting properties of distributed-parameter circuits.

Another example is shown in Fig. 5. Fig. 5(a) shows a low-pass $\overline{URC}$ filter proposed by Renz [16]. For $K = 1$, using the procedure outlined above, and assuming the source followers are "ideal," the corresponding transistor-only circuit is given in Fig. 5(b). The MOS circuit topology proposed aims at using a minimum number of

transistors. With reference to (5) the required gate bias and channel length for each transistor among M_1, M_2, and M_3 are related by $L_k = \sqrt{\mu(V_{GS} - V_T)R_k C_{gik}}$, $k = 1,2,3$. For certain desired pole locations, the required length ratios may become too large or too small and cause practical problems in implementing transistors M_1–M_3, if the gain of the voltage amplifier is restricted to be close to 1. To obtain one more degree of freedom in the synthesis, the voltage amplifier of Fig. 5(a) can be retained and allowed to have a nonunity gain. This may be needed anyway to correct for the fact that the source followers are not ideal. However, the dc level shift due to the gain stage may interfere with the frequency scaling technique mentioned previously in relation with Fig. 3(c). To solve this problem, another matched voltage amplifier with grounded input has to be added to the circuit as shown in Fig. 5(c). Needless to say, the output impedance of the K elements must be very small, to avoid alterations in the frequency response.

As a final example, Fig. 6 shows a bandpass circuit [16] and its corresponding transistor-only version; the comments above concerning the value of K apply here as well.

The above results are based on the assumption that the channel lengths are very long, so that the extrinsic para-

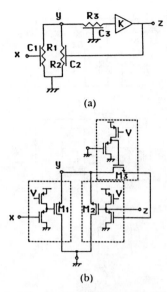

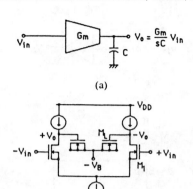

Fig. 7. (a) An ideal integrator. (b) Simplified circuit diagram of a transistor-only integrator.

Fig. 6. (a) Renz's active bandpass distributed *RC* filter. (b) Transistor-only circuit.

sitic capacitances (C_{ov} and C_j) can be neglected. However, as seen from (5), this limits operation to low frequencies. For high-frequency operation, C_{ov} and C_j cannot be neglected and neither can the finite input impedance and nonzero output impedance of the source follower. In this case one must modify the design using CAD as a guide. The distributed-parameter synthesis can be used as a starting point. Experimental results for such cases are reported in this paper in Section VIII, as well as elsewhere by other groups [20], [21].

VI. IMPLEMENTATION OF LUMPED FILTERS USING TRANSISTOR-ONLY CIRCUITS

We now discuss a different approach, namely the implementation of lumped filters in which capacitors are replaced by MOS transistors. We will use an integrator—a basic building block—to illustrate this approach. An integrator can be realized by using a transconductance amplifier loaded with a capacitor as shown in Fig. 7(a). The transconductance amplifier typically is implemented with a differential pair (nonlinearity cancellation schemes are not considered in the present context). Replacing the capacitor in Fig. 7(a) by a MOS transistor with zero drain–source bias gives the differential integrator shown in Fig. 7(b), where the capacitive load for the simple differential pair is the distributed gate capacitance of the two loading MOS transistors [17]. Due to the distributed nature of the MOS transistors, the exact transfer function of the circuit is a complicated function determined by the *y* parameters of each MOS transistor. To reduce the complexity of the analysis but still keep an insight about the distributed effects, first-order approximations of *y* parameters will be used. Assume for the present that the channels are long, so that extrinsic parasitics can be neglected. The first-order approximation of the trans-

admittance, y_{m1}, of the input transistors M_1 is [10]

$$y_{m1} \approx \frac{g_{m1}}{1 + s\tau_1} \qquad (6)$$

where

$$\tau_1 = \frac{4}{15} \frac{L_1^2(1+\delta)}{\mu(V_{GS_1} - V_{T_1})} \qquad (7)$$

with δ a factor related to the body effect. The first-order approximation of the gate input admittance of the load transistor M_L is [10]

$$y_L = \frac{sC_{gi_L}}{1 + s\tau_L} \qquad (8)$$

where

$$\tau_L = \frac{1}{12} \frac{L_L^2(1 + b_L)}{\mu(V_{GS_L} - V_{T_L})} \qquad (9)$$

where b_L is the ratio defined in (4), for the load transistors. Equations (6) and (8) are good approximations for

$$|s\tau_1| \ll 1 \qquad (10)$$

and

$$|s\tau_L| \ll 1. \qquad (11)$$

Thus the transfer function of the circuit in Fig. 7(b) is

$$H(s) = \frac{g_{m1}/(1 + s\tau_1)}{sC_{gi_L}/(1 + s\tau_L)}. \qquad (12)$$

From the above expression it can be seen that the distributed behavior of input transistor M_1 causes an extra phase lag; however, the distributed behavior of the load device M_L causes a phase lead. This suggests that by properly choosing the channel length (or the substrate bias V_B) of the load transistor M_L in such a way that

$$\tau_1 = \tau_L \qquad (13)$$

the phase lead and phase lag (or, equivalently the extra pole and zero) can be eliminated and the integrator can have a 90° phase shift, in the frequency range where the above approximations are valid ($\omega\tau_1, \omega\tau_L \ll 1$). Using (7) and (9) in (13), one can easily determine the required ratio of channel lengths. A related analysis was used in [2], but only for a pure capacitive load. In practice, it may be necessary to choose $\tau_1 \neq \tau_2$ in order to compensate for other causes of phase error, such as the finite dc gain of the transconductor.

The procedure outlined above works when the channels are very long. For higher frequency operation, as channel lengths are made shorter, C_{ov} and C_j (Fig. 1(b)) can no longer be neglected. Computer-aided design can be used to predict how much the parasitics affect the circuit operation, and to guide the choice of the optimal device sizes to use.

VII. Width Scaling

A simple technique presents itself for modifying certain circuit specifications without long redesign. This technique will be called "width scaling," and is actually not limited to the circuits under discussion. It consists simply of multiplying the channel width W of *all* devices in a circuit (including those in the active elements) by the same common factor, which we will denote by α. In this discussion we assume that the widths never become so small as to cause "narrow-channel effects" [10]. If the width of all transistors is scaled by α, the bias voltages remain the same, while their current, capacitances,[3] and transconductances are scaled by α, and resistances are scaled by $1/\alpha$. Thus, the relative variation of all (trans)admittances with frequency remains unchanged; this is also obvious from (5), which is independent of W. All voltage (or current) transfer functions remain unchanged. Of course, all (trans)admittances will be scaled by α in magnitude, but since all active elements are scaled by the same factor as well, internal driving capabilities are not affected. A summary of width scaling results is given in Table I. This technique may be found convenient in a variety of situations, for example, when it is desired to improve noise performance. The noise of distributed circuits is difficult to calculate [17]; it can be estimated by representing distributed elements as many-segment lumped approximations during simulation, as suggested in Section II.[4] We have not developed low-noise design techniques. Nevertheless, if the noise output voltage of a given transistor-only circuit is predicted to be too high by, say, a factor η, it is clear that the noise can be reduced to the desired level by multiplying all widths by η^2. This is of course accompanied by a proportional penalty in power dissipation and "active" area. Given that these parameters are likely to be small in transistor-only circuits, this penalty may be tolerable. "From scratch"

---

[3]We assume that junction capacitances scale by the same factor; whether this is true or not depends on layout details.
[4]The reader is warned [10], however, that the models found in some simulators falsely predict that MOS transistors are noiseless at $V_{DS} = 0$!

TABLE I
Effect of Scaling All Transistor Widths by α

Parameter	Resulting scaling factor
Bias currents	α
Bias voltages	1
Power dissipation	α
Active area	α
Capacitances	α
Resistances	$1/\alpha$
Bias currents	α
(Trans)admittances	α
Noise voltage spectral density	$1/\sqrt{\alpha}$
Noise voltage	$1/\sqrt{\alpha}$
Speed, characteristic frequencies	1
Load driving capability	α

low-noise design may of course be preferable; however, once the circuit is optimized, it is easy to "parameterize" it through width scaling.

VIII. Experimental Results

The techniques described above have been checked by implementing three test chips. The first one [8] implemented the simple filter of Fig. 4(c), with the only difference being that a fourth transistor, operated in nonsaturation as a variable resistor, was added in parallel with the current source to control the attenuation of the source follower, and thus the quality factor [14]. The chip microphotograph is shown in Fig. 8(a). The entire circuit fits in an area of only 0.006 mm², i.e., a fraction of the area occupied by a common bonding pad (part of such a pad is seen near the top of the photograph). The frequency responses normalized to their dc values, for three values of the control voltage V, are shown in Fig. 8(b). It can be seen that the transition-band slope approaches 15 dB/octave, corresponding to more than two "effective" poles. The output spectrum for a 10-MHz input signal of 1.2 V_{p-p} is shown in Fig. 8(c). As can be seen, the second-order harmonic distortion is dominant. Two matched filters of this type, operated in balanced fashion, could handle a signal of 1 V_{p-p} at the input with harmonic distortion better than -50 dB. The total dissipation of the filter is 580 μW for a 40-MHz cutoff frequency, corresponding to a power per band-edge frequency per pole of less than 10 pJ. Other details about the design and performance of this chip can be found in [8]. This chip demonstrates the "minimality" possible with transistor-only circuits. However, for most applications a filter *that* simple would not be adequate since it has no provision for keeping the dc gain and dc output level constant, independent of the tuning voltage. Also, noise can be coupled from the substrate of the n-channel device, through its capacitance

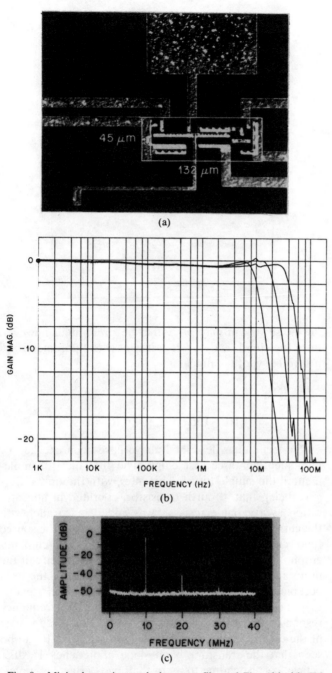

Fig. 8. Minimal transistor-only low-pass filter of Fig. 4(c). (a) Chip microphotograph. (b) Frequency responses for $V_{DD} - V = 0.73, 1.43,$ and 2.23 V. (c) Output frequency spectrum for a 1.2-V_{p-p}, 10-MHz input signal (filter −3-dB frequency set at 40 MHz).

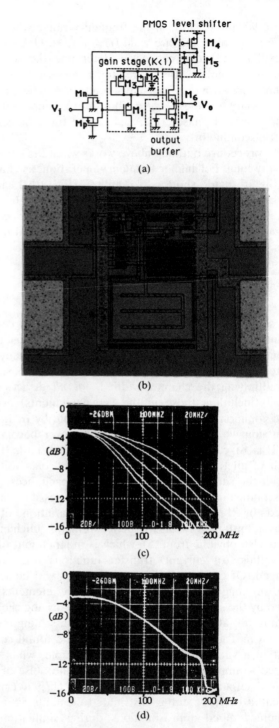

Fig. 9. A 100-MHz low-pass filter. (a) Circuit diagram. (b) Chip microphotograph. (c) Frequency responses of the filter–setup combination for $V = 2.34, 2.95, 3.24, 3.45,$ and 3.54 V. (d) Frequency responses of four filters on different chips (including setup response) with V for each tuned separately ($V = 2.95, 3.07, 3.02,$ and 3.19 V).

C_{bi}. Balanced operation would reduce this problem but not completely since C_{bi} is nonlinear.

The second chip implements the filter of Fig. 4(b) with a cutoff frequency of 100 MHz. The chip uses one "gain" stage (with gain less than one) and two cascaded source followers as shown in Fig. 9(a) to ensure that controlling the cutoff frequency of the filter does not change the output dc level. M_2 and M_3 form a linearized resistive load for M_1. The NMOS source follower is used as an output buffer to drive an external capacitive load. The PMOS source follower M_4, M_5 is used to provide the ac feedback signal and to control the gate bias voltage of the

MOSFET $\overline{RC}$, M_n. A noncritical compensation capacitor was connected between the input and output of the PMOS source follower for pole–zero cancellation. This means that, strictly speaking, this is not a pure "transistor-only" circuit. The capacitor helps to achieve the required buffer performance at high frequencies, without requiring too much power dissipation. For low-frequency applications this capacitor is not necessary. A low-frequency linearization technique has been used in the circuit [1] where a small p-channel device M_p is connected in parallel with the n-channel device M_n. We chose $(W/L)_{M_p} \mu_p C_{gi_p}$ close to $(W/L)_{M_n} \mu_n C_{gi_n}$. To turn M_p on, the input is biased at 1.2 V. This voltage is chosen low enough to make the channel resistance of M_p much higher than that of M_n, such that the response of the filter is determined by M_n. M_p only serves for nonlinearity cancellation, at least at low frequencies. The gate area of M_p is chosen small compared with M_n, in order to avoid attenuating the feedback signal coming from the PMOS source follower by the gate and the substrate capacitances of M_n and M_p. A chip microphotograph is shown in Fig. 9(b).

Unfortunately, the frequency response of this chip could not be measured adequately due to direct signal feedthrough in the measurement setup. Thus, we include here frequency response plots *only* to show tunability and to point to some results with respect to matching. For a 5-V power supply, the measured frequency response of the filter–setup combination for five different values of V is shown in Fig. 9(c). Each packaged chip contained two filters that were laid out identically for nominal matching (no special matching techniques were used, however). The cutoff-frequency matching achieved between the two, for the same control voltage V, was 10–15%. This can perhaps be attributed to the use of short channels and the fact that no special layout techniques (such as cross-coupling) were used. Nevertheless, by tuning V separately for each filter to achieve the same -3-dB frequency, the responses became practically indistinguishable. This, in fact, was the case even for filters on different chips (of the same wafer), as shown in Fig. 9(d). This result shows that the performance deviation due to mismatches can be tuned back if a high-frequency automatic direct-tuning circuit [1] (as opposed to indirect, or "master/slave") can be used on-chip.

The harmonic distortion of the circuit for a 1-V_{p-p} input was of the order of -46 to -40 dB for frequencies up to 100 MHz, for a 100-MHz cutoff frequency. Lower distortion is expected if two filters are driven by balanced voltages. The power dissipation was 12 mW.

We have also conducted an experiment to check the ability of the circuit of Fig. 4(a), with the $\overline{URC}$ element replaced by a transistor, to oscillate. This experiment was conducted on a breadboard. For reasons explained in Section V, we did not use a source follower, but rather a gain element (constructed from discrete components) with a gain of 1.047, along with dc bias as shown in Fig. 10(a). To allow us to swamp the large parasitics associated with the breadboard, we used a specifically designed p-channel transistor from a test chip, with channel dimensions of 1000 μm $\times$ 1000 μm. The circuit did indeed oscillate, and the oscillation frequency was tunable through V_G; by changing V_G from -1.6 to -3.4 V, the oscillation frequency changed from 7 to 64 kHz. The substrate bias V_B could be used as an amplitude control, since it varies the (nonlinear) substrate capacitance C_{bi}, which influences

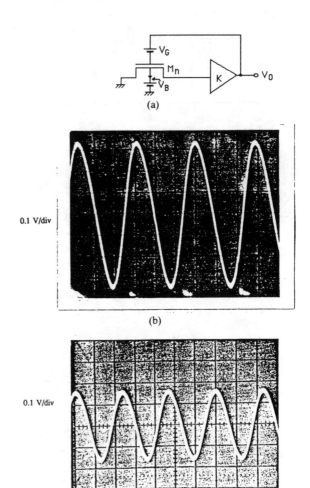

Fig. 10. Voltage-controlled oscillator. (a) Circuit diagram. (b) Output waveform for $V_G = -1.85$ V, $V_B = 2.83$ V. (c) Output for $V_G = -1.85$ V, $V_B = 2.1$ V.

the effective gain, as depicted in Fig. 2(d). A set of outpt waveforms is shown in Fig. 10(b) and (c). As expected, V_B affects the oscillation frequency also; this frequency could be corrected by a small change in V_G.

The approach described in Section VI was also verified through an experimental sixth-order bandpass filter based on the doubly terminated LC-ladder structure of Fig. 11(a).[5] The corresponding signal flow graph is shown in Fig. 11(b). The integrators were implemented based on the principle discussed in Section VI. However, the analysis given there is for circuits with long-channel devices. The frequency range of applicability is limited by the intrinsic cutoff frequency of the transistors, which is inversely proportional to the square of the channel length. Therefore in lumped-parameter MOS circuits, use of short-channel devices is unavoidable for operation at high frequencies.

---

[5]Simulation results from a similar approach have recently been reported [22].

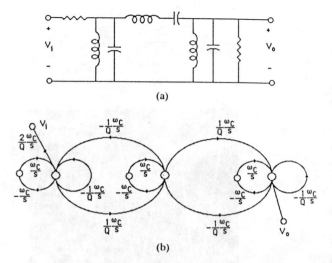

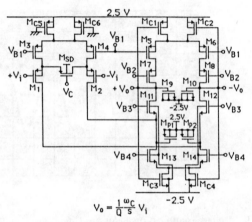

Fig. 11. (a) Doubly terminated bandpass ladder filter. (b) Signal-flow graph.

Fig. 12. Transistor-only integrator.

$$V_o = \frac{1}{Q}\frac{\omega_C}{s} V_i$$

TABLE II
TRANSISTOR SIZES FOR THE INTEGRATOR OF FIG. 12

Transistor	width (μm)	length (μm)
$M_{C1}, M_{C2}, M_{C5}, M_{C6}$	5	3
M_3, M_4, M_5, M_6	30	3
M_1, M_2, M_7, M_8	30	2.25
M_{SD}	3	10
M_9, M_{10}	94	15
M_{11}, M_{12}	20	2.25
M_{p1}, M_{p2}	38	15
M_{13}, M_{14}	30	3
M_{C3}, M_{C4}	6	7

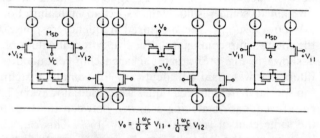

$$V_o = \frac{1}{Q}\frac{\omega_C}{s} v_{i1} + \frac{1}{Q}\frac{\omega_C}{s} v_{i2}$$

Fig. 13. Simplified circuit diagram of the summing integrator.

The complete schematic of the integrator used in the bandpass filter is shown in Fig. 12. The voltages V_{Bi} are bias voltages produced by a bias generator. Through replica biasing techniques, the bias currents of the entire filter can be changed simultaneously through a single external resistor. The integrator consists of a folded-cascode structure to achieve high dc gain so that the phase lead due to finite dc gain can be minimized. The common-mode voltage is stabilized by M_{C1}, M_{C2}, M_{C3}, and M_{C4}, with the latter devices partially cancelling the nonlinearities of the former. These four transistors are operated in the triode region [2]. M_{SD} is operated with zero drain–source bias and is used for both tuning the unity-gain frequency of the integrators and linearizing their performance [18]. The unity-gain frequency of the integrator is approximated by

$$\omega_c = \frac{g_{m1}}{(1 + g_{m1}/2g_{ds_{SD}})C_{gi_{9,10}}} \quad (14)$$

where $g_{ds_{SD}}$ is the low-frequency channel conductance of M_{SD}, which is equal to $\mu C'_{ox}(W/L)_{SD}(|V_C - V_{S_1} - V_{T_1}|)$.

Due to the distributed gate capacitance of M_{SD}, a zero is generated corresponding to a frequency of approximately

$$\omega_Z = \frac{4g_{ds_{SD}}}{C_{gi_{SD}}}. \quad (15)$$

If the frequency of the zero is too low to be neglected, M_{p1} and M_{p2} have to be used as shown to lower the second pole and compensate the zero. M_{p1} and M_{p2} may not be needed if a short-channel M_{SD} is used to push the zero to high frequencies; however, in that case linearity and tunability would be reduced. The trade-off is between signal swing range and unity-gain frequency-tuning range.

All integrators used on the chip were identical. In implementing the signal flow graph of Fig. 11(b), the integrators labeled ω_C/s were implemented by using several integrators with a transfer function of $(1/Q)\omega_C/s$ in parallel; in our case $Q = 4$, so four such integrators were used in parallel. With $\omega_C = 2\pi \times 1$ MHz, the device sizes for each transistor in Fig. 12 are listed in Table II. The summation of two integrations in Fig. 11(b) was achieved as shown in Fig. 13. An automatic tuning circuit similar to the one discussed in [2] was used, employing a master and a slave filter tuned by the same control voltage. The bandpass filter and its on-chip tuning circuit were fabricated on a chip with 1.75-μm CMOS technology. Fig. 14 is the chip microphotograph. Fig. 15(a) and (b) shows the frequency response of the filter with auto-

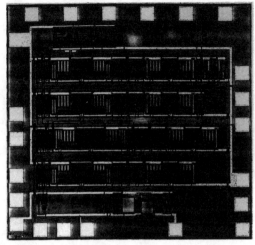

Fig. 14. Chip microphotograph of the integrated bandpass filter and its tuning circuit.

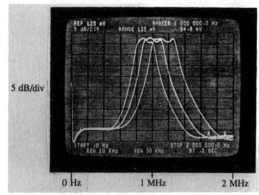

Fig. 16. Frequency responses of the bandpass filter with three different reference frequencies (1.7, 1.9, and 2 MHz).

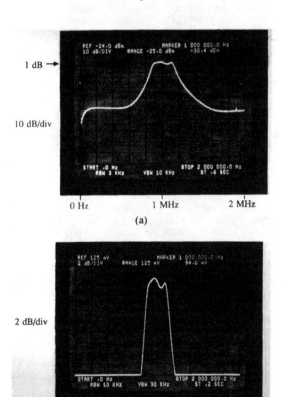

Fig. 15. (a) Frequency response of the bandpass filter. (b) Detailed view of upper portion in (a).

matic tuning when the reference frequency is 1.9 MHz (as opposed to 2 MHz in simulation). The passband ripple of the filter is 1.8 dB and the reference signal feedthrough is 630 μV_{rms}. The low reference signal feedthrough is due to the separation of the tuning circuit and the bandpass filter output path on the chip; they are placed at two opposite ends of the layout (this, however, reduces matching). Fig. 16 is the frequency response of the filter with three different reference frequencies (1.7, 1.9, and 2.1 MHz). Due to certain design errors, the performance

of the automatic tuning was not adequate, though, so we do not report more details here.

The dynamic range of the filter was determined by the signal level for 1% two-tone third-order intermodulation (IM) distortion and the total in-band noise. The differential input signal for such a measurement was 264 mV_{p-p}.[6] The equivalent differential input in-band noise of the filter was 534 μV_{rms}. The dynamic range of the filter is thus obtained as 45 dB. The low dynamic range is suspected to be due to the nonlinearities of the source degeneration transistor M_{SD} and the common-mode feedback transistors M_{C1}–M_{C4} in Fig. 12. It should be noted that similarly limited voltage swings are encountered in integrated filters using lumped capacitors (for similar frequency response specifications), if the maximum signal is defined using IM measurements as above. The power dissipation for the complete chip was 25 mW, using a single 5-V supply.

IX. CONCLUSIONS

We have reported the initial results of an effort to make transistor-only frequency-selective circuits. Such circuits may have certain advantages, among which are small chip area, good matching properties for individual elements, a potential for very high frequency of operation, and suitability for fabrication using standard digital VLSI processes. Disadvantages, or yet unsolved problems, include the implementation of automatic tuning schemes that reliably eliminate unpredictabilities and variations (notably those of the transistor extrinsic parasitics), device modeling difficulties of common simulators, and nonlinearity cancellation. We have presented a procedure for the topology development of filters in which transistors are used as $U\overline{RC}$ elements, and a technique which uses transistors as capacitors, along with first-order correction for the nonidealities of such "capacitors" and of the active elements. Measured results from three experimen-

---

[6] The input amplitude for 1% harmonic distortion was much larger (1.7 V_{p-p}), but this is not very relevant since the harmonics fall in the stopband of the filter. For a bandpass filter of this type, a much more relevant way to establish the signal handling ability is through IM distortion.

tal chips have been reported in the 1–100-MHz range. Future work would need to address the problems of automatic tuning and nonlinearity cancellation. Also, a possibility that can be investigated is the use of frequency-dependent active elements, i.e., using the frequency-dependent transadmittance of transistors to advantage. Another interesting alternative is to use MOS transistors to implement building blocks, which have driving-point admittances or transadmittances equal to those of lumped elements, using a recently reported synthesis technique [19]; such blocks include integrators.

Clearly, the status of this project is far from having demonstrated anything approaching manufacturability. As has been seen, transistor-only frequency-selective circuits come with a mixture of potential advantages and disadvantages/yet unsolved problems. We felt that the potential advantages are significant enough, and the unsolved problems challenging enough, to warrant a look at transistor-only implementations. Some of the problems were solved, but tougher ones remain. Although initial results are encouraging, the ultimate success of such circuits will depend on the results of a lot of future work.

ACKNOWLEDGMENT

The authors thank AT&T Bell Laboratories for the use of their research facilities during the period of this project. Special thanks go to T. R. Viswanathan, R. Beale, and J. Khoury at AT&T for valuable discussions and for their support in the processing of test chips, G. Venugopal for valuable discussions, and J. Vomero for arranging the printed-circuit board layout for chip testing.

REFERENCES

[1] Y. Tsividis, M. Banu, and J. Khoury, "Continuous-time MOSFET-C filters in VLSI," *IEEE Trans. Circuits Syst.*, vol. CAS-33, no. 2, pp. 125–140, Feb. 1986.

[2] H. Khorramabadi and P. Gray, "High-frequency CMOS continuous-time filters," *IEEE J. Solid-State Circuits*, vol. SC-19, pp. 939–948, Dec. 1984.

[3] J. Pennock, P. Frith, and P. G. Barker, "CMOS triode transconductor continuous-time filters," in *Proc. 1986 IEEE Custom Integrated Circuits Conf.*, pp. 378–381.

[4] A. P. Nedungadi and R. L. Geiger, "High-frequency voltage-controlled continuous-time lowpass filter using linearized CMOS integrators," *Electron. Lett.*, vol. 22, pp. 729–731, June 1986.

[5] F. Krummenacher and N. Joehl, "A 4-MHz CMOS continuous-time filter with on-chip automatic tuning," *IEEE J. Solid-State Circuits*, vol. 23, no. 3, pp. 750–758, June 1988.

[6] C. S. Park and R. Schaumann, "Design of a 4-MHz analog integrated CMOS transconductance-C bandpass filter," *IEEE J. Solid-State Circuits*, vol. 23, pp. 987–996, Aug. 1988.

[7] A. Kaiser, "A micropower CMOS continuous-time lowpass filter," *IEEE J. Solid-State Circuits*, vol. 24, pp. 736–743, June 1989.

[8] Y. Tsividis, "Minimal transistor-only micropower integrated VHF active filter," *Electron. Lett.*, vol. 23, no. 15, pp. 777–778, 1987.

[9] C. Mead, *Analog VLSI and Neural Systems*. Reading, MA: Addison-Wesley, 1989.

[10] Y. Tsividis, *Operation and Modeling of the MOS Transistor*. New York: McGraw Hill, 1987.

[11] M. Ghausi and J. Kelly, *Introduction to Distributed-Parameter Networks*. New York: Holt, Reinhart, and Winston, 1968.

[12] W. Heinlein and H. Holmes, *Active Filters for Integrated Circuits*. London: Prentice-Hall International, 1974.

[13] J. Khoury, Y. Tsividis, and M. Banu, "Use of MOS transistor as a tunable distributed RC filter element," *Electron. Lett.*, vol. 20, no. 4, pp. 187–188, Feb. 1984.

[14] R. W. Wyndrum Jr., "The realization of monomorphic thin film distributed RC networks," *IEE Conv. Rec.*, vol. 13, Part 10, pp. 90–95, 1965.

[15] Y. Tsividis, "The transistor in a box puzzle," *IEEE Circuits and Devices Mag.*, vol. 4, p. 62, Jan. 1988 and pp. 24–25, May 1988.

[16] H. W. Renz, "Synthesis and thin film implementation of distributed RC active filters," in *Proc. IEEE ISCAS*, 1976, pp. 224–227.

[17] L. J. Pu, Ph.D. dissertation, Columbia Univ., New York, NY, May 1989.

[18] Y. Tsividis, Z. Czarnul, and S. C. Fang, "MOS transconductors and integrators with high linearity," *Electron. Lett.*, vol. 22, no. 5, pp. 245–246, Feb. 1986.

[19] J. Khoury and Y. Tsividis, "Active $\overline{URC}$ circuit realization of arbitrary rational transfer functions in s," in *Proc. IEEE ISCAS* (Portland) 1989, pp. 1071–1074.

[20] M. Banu, "MOS oscillators with multi-decade tuning range and gigahertz maximum speed," *IEEE J. Solid-State Circuits*, vol. 23, no. 6, pp. 1386–1393, Dec. 1988.

[21] F. Krummenacher, "Design considerations in high-frequency CMOS transconductance amplifier capacitor (TAC) filter," in *Proc. IEEE ISCAS* (Portland), 1989, pp. 100–105.

[22] S. T. Dupuie, S. Bibyk, and M. Ismail, "A novel all-MOS high-speed continuous-time filter," in *Proc. IEEE ISCAS* (Portland), 1989, pp. 675–680.

Section 5-C   Filters Using Negative Immittance Converters

This section contains a paper by Hagiwara et al. on filters using negative immitance converters (NICs). NIC-based *RC*-active filters were among the earliest candidates (in the 1950s and 1960s) in the discrete-component, *RC*-active filter field (for a survey see [1]). They usually suffered from large sensitivities. The authors of the paper in this section and other authors [2, 3] take advantage of the possibilities opened by full integration (accurate matching of filter elements), to arrive at all-NPN filters operating in the video range.

The use of NICs (for a different purpose) can also be seen elsewhere in this volume. In Paper 3-B.12 and also in [4–6], bias currents are fed by resistors (instead of PNP-type bias current sources) to transconductor integrators, causing high losses. Negative resistances, which are implemented using NICs, compensate for the losses.

Certainly not all applications of NICs are sensitive to tolerances; another example is shown in [7], where it is proposed to combine Czarnul's four-transistor circuit (see Papers 2-B.7, 2-C.1, and 2-C.2) with a NIC, instead of an operational amplifier.

References

[1] W. E. Heinlein and W. H. Holmes, *Active Filters for Integrated Circuits*: *Fundamentals and Design Methods*, New York: Springer-Verlag, 1974.

[2] M. Kumazawa and T. Yaganisawa, "Video frequency active filters," *Proc. IEEE ISCAS '84*, pp. 638–641, 1984.

[3] S. Akui, S. Tagaki, M. Furihata, M. Nagata and T. Yaganisawa, "100 MHz monolithic low-pass filter using balanced-type NIC's," *Digest Symp. VLSI Circuits*, pp. 95–96, 1988.

[4] S. Takagi, T. Anzai and T. Yaganisawa, "A differential input/output integrator without PNP transistors and its application to leapfrog filter synthesis," *Proc. IEEE ISCAS '88*, pp. 2855–2858, 1988.

[5] S. Takagi, T. Anzai and T. Yaganisawa, "An NIC-improved balanced integrator and its application to filters," *Electronics and Communications in Japan 3*, vol. 72, no. 3, pp. 106–115, 1989.

[6] S. Takagi, N. Fujii and T. Yanagisawa, "High-frequency monolithic differential input/output integrator," *Electronics and Communications in Japan 2*, vol. 72, no. 8. pp. 87–95, 1989.

[7] S. I. Liu, H. W. Tsao, J. Wu, M. O. Yang, and J. H. Tsay, "New CMOS NIC-based MOSFET-C filters," *Electron. Lett.*, vol. 27, pp. 772–774, April 25, 1991.

A Monolithic Video Frequency Filter Using NIC-Based Gyrators

HISATOSHI HAGIWARA, MASAZUMI KUMAZAWA, SHIGETAKA TAKAGI,

MAKOTO FURIHATA, MINORU NAGATA, FELLOW, IEEE,

AND TAKESHI YANAGISAWA

Abstract —This paper proposes a filter system for analog video signal processing. This system is composed of a variable time-constant active *RC* filter part with balanced-type negative impedance converters (NIC's) and an automatic tuning circuit part using a PLL. This is different from other existing filter systems in the sense that: 1) it is implemented by a conventional junction-isolated 15-μm bipolar process with n-p-n transistors of $f_T = 400$ MHz; 2) it thereby reduces the production cost; and 3) it uses a new automatic tuning scheme with better accuracy in response.

The filter system with a passband from 3.7 to 5.2 MHz, which operates at a single 5-V supply, is implemented by the above bipolar process. Experiments showed the following excellent results: 1) the error from the center frequency chosen as 4.4 MHz is only 180 kHz; 2) the second harmonic is less by −35 dB than the input signal in spite of the use of junction capacitors; 3) a wide tunable range from 3.9 to 5.1 MHz was obtained; and 4) the center frequency was not affected by the change of temperature. The feasibility of the proposed video system has been confirmed by the experiments.

I. INTRODUCTION

FULLY integrated analog video frequency filters are strongly desired in consumer electronic video products. Filters on a monolithic chip are designed by using digital techniques [1] or switched-capacitor techniques [2]. These techniques, however, are not suitable for analog video frequency filters, because of 1) the necessity of anti-aliasing filters, 2) the high cost of producing video digital filters, and 3) the limitation of high-frequency characteristics of switched-capacitor filters due to gain-bandwidth products of operational amplifiers.

To overcome those disadvantages, this paper presents a new approach derived from active *RC* filter techniques. Recently, techniques for implementing active *RC* filters on a monolithic chip have been reported [3]–[5]. Their pro-

duction cost is relatively low, because active *RC* filters need no A/D nor D/A converters. Excellent frequency characteristics for active *RC* filters can be obtained by replacing conventionally used operational amplifiers with balanced-type negative impedance converters (NIC's) [6]. They require only n-p-n transistors and easily cancel parasitic elements. An *LC* simulation method using NIC-based gyrators is readily available to obtain low-sensitivity active *RC* filters. It is also important to note that an active filter with the NIC-based gyrators works at a single 5-V supply.

This paper describes a variable time-constant active *RC* filter structure with grounded junction capacitors and NIC-based gyrators for automatic tuning. Monolithic active *RC* filters require automatic tuning for response accuracy. A new automatic tuning circuit suitable for a balanced-type filter is also described for high accuracy in response compared with the conventional methods.

The experimental results are shown for a new automatically tunable filter system with a passband from 3.7 to 5.2 MHz implemented by a conventional junction-isolated 15-μm bipolar process with n-p-n transistors of $f_T = 400$ MHz.

II. BALANCED-TYPE NIC

Fig. 1 shows a balanced-type NIC which is composed of six n-p-n transistors. Its symbol includes an arrow which represents the direction from a short-circuit stable port to an open-circuit stable port. This NIC has better performance at high frequencies than other active elements, because it is composed of only n-p-n transistors while all other active elements need p-n-p transistors for dc biasing. Realization of high-performance n-p-n transistors is much easier, and is less costly than high-performance p-n-p transistors in a conventional bipolar process.

In Fig. 1, pairs of Q_1's, Q_2's, and Q_3's act as a voltage inversion-type NIC, level shifts, and cancellation of the emitter resistances of Q_1's, respectively. In terms of high-frequency parameters of each transistor (common-base current gain α, emitter resistance r_e, base resistance r_b, emitter diffusion capacitance C_e, collector–substrate capacitance C_{sub}), the transmission matrix $[F]$ of the NIC in

Manuscript received July 2, 1987; revised September 10, 1987.

H. Hagiwara is with Mitsubishi Corporation, 6-3, Marunouchi 2-chome, Chiyoda-ku, Tokyo 100-91, Japan.

M. Kumazawa is with the Japan Defense Agency, 5-1, Honmura-chou Ichigaya, Chinjuku-ku, Tokyo 162, Japan.

S. Takagi is with the Tokyo Institute of Technology, 2-12-1, O-okayama, Meguro-ku, Tokyo 152, Japan.

M. Furihata is with Takasaki Works, Hitachi Ltd., 111, Nishiyokote-machi, Takasaki-shi, Gunma-ken 370-11, Japan.

M. Nagata is with the Central Research Laboratory, Hitachi Ltd., Kokubunji, Tokyo 185, Japan.

T. Yanagisawa is with the Tokyo Institute of Technology, 2-12-1, O-okayama, Meguro-ku Tokyo 152, Japan.

IEEE Log Number 8718228.

Reprinted from *IEEE J. Solid-State Circuits*, vol. SC-23, no. 1, pp. 175–182, Feb. 1988.

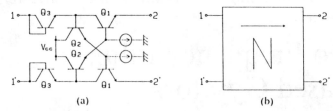

Fig. 1. Balanced-type NIC and its symbol: (a) NIC, and (b) symbol.

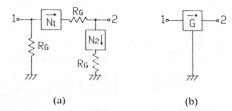

Fig. 2. NIC-based gyrator and its symbol: (a) gyrator, and (b) symbol.

Fig. 1 is given by

$$[F] = \begin{bmatrix} -(1+sT_a) & -r_p \\ -sC_p & \alpha_1(1+sT_d) \end{bmatrix} \tag{1}$$

where

$$r_p = 2(1-\alpha_1)(r_{e2}+(1-\alpha_2)r_b)$$
$$C_p = C_{c1} + C_{c2}/2 + C_{sub}$$
$$T_a = 2C_{c1}(r_b+r_{e2}+r_{e3}) + C_{c2}(r_b+r_{e3}) + C_{sub}r_{e3}$$
$$T_d = -(C_{c1}+2C_{c1}+C_{c2}+C_{sub})r_{e1}. \tag{2}$$

Provided that $|sT_a| \ll 1$, $|sT_d| \ll 1$, and $|sC_p \cdot r_p| \ll 1$, (1) is rewritten as

$$[F] = \begin{bmatrix} 1 & 0 \\ sC_p & 1 \end{bmatrix} \begin{bmatrix} -1 & 0 \\ 0 & \alpha_1/(1+sT_{ad}) \end{bmatrix} \begin{bmatrix} 1 & r_p \\ 0 & 1 \end{bmatrix} \tag{3}$$

where T_{ad} is the difference between T_a and T_d. Equation (3) shows that parasitic component r_p is considered as a series resistor at port 2 and C_p as a parallel capacitor at port 1. Although the effect of r_p can be compensated by adding a resistor $\alpha_1 \cdot r_p$ at port 1, it is negligibly small and there is no need for this compensation except for the cases of high-Q filter realizations. To avoid the effect of C_p, C_p should be included in capacitances connected at NIC ports. Since T_{ad} is also negligible even with those transistor parameter values given by a conventional bipolar process, this type of NIC shows excellent characteristics at frequencies up to 10 MHz [7].

III. New NIC-Based Gyrator Structure

It is well known that a two-port gyrator can be easily obtained by using two NIC's and three equal-value resistors as shown in Fig. 2(a). This circuit and the circuits in the following discussions are expressed as unbalanced-type ones for convenience. In this figure, it should be noted that each NIC is positioned so as to satisfy its stability condition, and that short-circuit stable ports of NIC must correspond to ports of the gyrator. Fig. 2(b) shows a symbol of the gyrator. The direction of the arrow in this symbol is herein defined as that from the short-circuit stable port to the open-circuit stable port of N_1 as shown in Fig. 2(a).

Simulation of an inductance multiport network requires an n-port gyrator ($n > 2$). It can be realized by connecting two-port gyrators in cascade. An example of the conven-

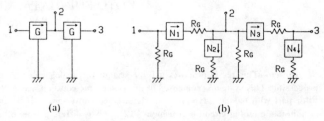

Fig. 3. Conventional three-port gyrator realization: (a) three-port gyrator realization scheme, and (b) NIC-based three-port gyrator realization.

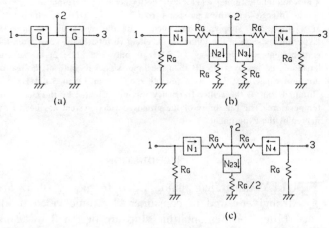

Fig. 4. New three-port gyrator realization: (a) new three-port gyrator realization scheme, (b) NIC-based three-port gyrator realization, and (c) three-port gyrator with a reduced number of NIC's.

tional method for the realization of a three-port gyrator is shown in Fig. 3(a). Fig. 3(b) shows its realization using NIC's. In this case, N_2 and the two resistors connected between each port of N_2 and the ground can be removed, because $-R_G$ produced by N_2 cancels R_G. Consequently, a three-port gyrator can be realized by three NIC's and four resistors.

This realization method has a freedom of direction indicated by the arrows in Fig. 3(a), because the direction does not influence stability of a gyrator. Two gyrators may be connected in such a way that the direction of each gyrator is opposite to the other as shown in Fig. 4(a). Fig. 4(b) shows an NIC-based realization of Fig. 4(a). In this figure, open-circuit stable ports of N_2 and N_3 have the same potential, because NIC's are of voltage-inversion type and the short-circuit stable ports of the two NIC's are connected at the same node. Therefore, N_2 and N_3 can be combined into one NIC, and resistors R_G's into $R_G/2$ as shown in Fig. 4(c). This gyrator realization method only requires the same number of elements as that of a conventional method. In addition to that, the method makes it possible to feed dc biasing to a circuit with a small supply voltage, such as a single 5-V supply which is convenient for an LSI including digital circuits. On the other hand, the supply voltage of a conventional method becomes larger as the number of *n* increases. Consequently, a gyrator realization method as shown in Fig. 4 is more suitable for a monolithic circuit implementation.

IV. FILTER DESIGN

The design of a chroma filter for video signal processing is discussed below. Fig. 5 shows an *M*-coupled bandpass filter excited by a current source instead of a voltage source. In order to treat usual voltage signals, a differential amplifier as shown in Fig. 6(a) is used as an input circuit for converting unbalanced-type voltage signals to balanced-type current signals. A differential amplifier as shown in Fig. 6(b) is used as an output circuit for converting balanced-to-unbalanced voltage signals.

To automatically tune the frequency responses of filters based on an *LC* simulation using gyrators, the use of junction capacitors is an effective method. Although the capacitors cause a signal distortion, balanced-type circuits cancel the even-order harmonics. This cancellation significantly reduces the signal distortion. The experimental results on the distortion will be shown later.

In order to feed a control voltage to junction capacitors, prototype filters without floating capacitors are necessary. A conventional method using two gyrators, however, requires two floating capacitors as shown in Fig. 7. This problem can be overcome by using four gyrators as shown in Fig. 8(a). Fig. 8(b) shows a realization of Fig. 8(a) using NIC-based gyrators. This circuit adopts a new three-port gyrator structure. Each pair of N_1 and N_3, N_4 and N_5, and N_6 and N_7 can be combined into one NIC as explained in the three-port gyrator realization. The resultant filter is shown in Fig. 9. The required number of active elements is only five in spite of using four gyrators.

Because of the four gyrators used in this configuration, R_G values can be selected in a range wide enough to allow all the capacitances to be equal, so that equal-value capacitors may have high relative accuracy in integrated-circuit implementations. A method to determine R_G is explained as follows.

An inductance L_i realized by an NIC-based gyrator is

$$L_i = C_{L,i} R_G^2. \tag{4}$$

From (4), $C_{L,i}$ becomes

$$C_{L,i} = L_i / R_G^2. \tag{5}$$

To make $C_{L,i}$ equal to C_c, R_G must be

$$R_G = \sqrt{L_i / C_c}. \tag{6}$$

Each gyrator conductance which satisfies (6) makes capacitances equal.

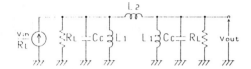

Fig. 5. Fourth-order *M*-coupled bandpass filter.

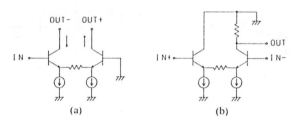

Fig. 6. Input and output circuits: (a) input circuit, and (b) output circuit.

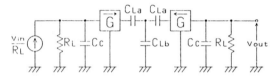

Fig. 7. Conventional *LC* simulation of Fig. 5 using two gyrators.

V. AUTOMATICALLY TUNABLE FILTER SYSTEM

A PLL can control the frequency response of an active *RC* filter [3]. In this section, an automatically tunable circuit built by a PLL will be discussed.

The new automatic tuning method to be proposed below employs a PLL with a voltage-controlled filter (VCF). A voltage-controlled oscillator (VCO) or a VCF could be used in a PLL. However, a PLL using a VCO has some difficulties, such as locking with harmonics, poor stability of oscillation, and insufficient locking and capture ranges. The use of a VCF instead of a VCO can overcome such difficulties. In particular, it allows locking and capture ranges as extensive as variable ranges correlated with junction capacitances.

Fig. 10 shows a PLL block diagram using a VCF and a signal processing filter. The input and output circuits are unbalanced-to-balanced and balanced-to-unbalanced signal converters, respectively, realized by differential amplifiers as explained in Section IV. The PLL uses Gilbert's current multiplier [8] as a phase comparator. A differential amplifier is employed as the loop filter and dc amplifier block in Fig. 10.

Assuming that the VCF is a second-order low-pass filter and its cutoff frequency is the same as a reference frequency, it gives a 90° difference between V_1 and V_2 at the cutoff frequency. When the cutoff frequency differs from the reference frequency, the phase comparator detects the phase difference from 90° and excites the loop filter and dc amplifier block with the voltage proportional to the phase difference. The loop filter and dc amplifier block applies a control voltage V_c to junction capacitors in the VCF so as to make the cutoff frequency the same as the reference frequency. It is also assumed that the signal

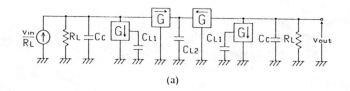

(a)

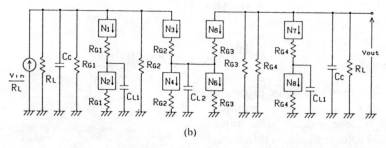

(b)

Fig. 8. *LC* simulation using a new gyrator structure: (a) gyrator-based simulation, and (b) NIC-based simulation.

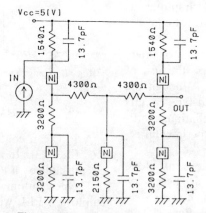

Fig. 9. Video frequency active *RC* filter.

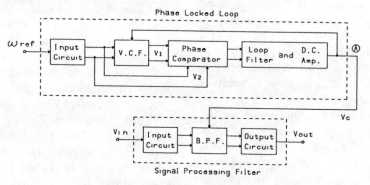

Fig. 10. Automatically tunable filter system.

processing filter has the same time constant as that of the VCF; if it is implemented on the same chip with the VCF. V_c can control the response of the signal processing filter.

The input circuit in the PLL does not affect the performance of the automatic tuning, since a reference signal out of the input circuit is compared with an output signal of the VCF. The characteristics of the loop filter determine the tracking speed. Most applications do not require a fast tracking speed. Only enough attenuation of harmonics is necessary for the loop filter. The Miller effect achieves it, even if a small capacitance is used.

The phase comparator in Fig. 10 is switched by V_1 and V_2. These two voltages are assumed to be square waves when they are much larger than the thermal voltages $V_T (V_T = kT/q)$ of transistors. Based on the phase difference between the two waves, the output dc component V_{DC} of the phase comparator through the loop filter and dc amplifier block becomes [9]

$$V_{DC} = A \cdot V_{PC}(2\theta/\pi - 1) \qquad (7)$$

where A is the gain of the dc amplifier, and V_{PC} is the product of the total current and the load resistance of the phase comparator.

The dependence of a junction capacitance $C(V_c)$ on a control voltage V_c is

$$C(V_c) = C_0[1 + (V_0 - V_c)/\phi]^{-n} + C_p \qquad (8)$$

where C_0, V_0, ϕ, n, and C_p are the zero potential capacitance, the initial dc voltage bias, the built-in potential of the junction, the gradient factor of the junction capacitor, and the parasitic capacitance, respectively. It is assumed that the cutoff angular frequency ω_0 of the VCF moves to ω_c when the PLL is closed. In this case, the following equation holds:

$$C(0)/C(V_c) = \omega_0/\omega_c. \qquad (9)$$

From (8) and (9) we can obtain

$$V_c = -\phi\left[\frac{\omega_0}{\omega_c}\left(1 + \frac{V_0}{\phi}\right)^{-n} + \frac{\omega_0 - \omega_c}{\omega_c}\frac{C_p}{C_0}\right]^{-1/n} + \phi + V_0. \qquad (10)$$

In (10), ω_c is still an unknown parameter. Since ω_c is approximately equal to the reference angular frequency ω_{ref}, it is possible to calculate V_c (ω_{ref} can be used for ω_c in (10)). By substituting V_c instead of V_{DC} into (7), the required phase difference θ_L for producing V_c is

$$\theta_L = \pi(V_c/(A \cdot V_{PC}) + 1)/2. \qquad (11)$$

This θ_L is produced by the VCF. When the control voltage V_c of (10) is applied to the VCF, the transfer function $T(s)$ of the VCF becomes

$$T(s) = \frac{\omega_c^2}{s^2 + (\omega_c/Q)s + \omega_c^2}. \qquad (12)$$

By using (12) and the phase difference θ_L, ω_{ref} can be expressed as

$$\omega_{\mathrm{ref}} = \omega_c \frac{1 \mp \sqrt{1 + 4Q^2 \tan^2\theta_L}}{2Q\tan\theta_L} \quad \left(\begin{array}{l} + \text{ for } \theta_L < \pi/2 \\ - \text{ for } \theta_L > \pi/2 \end{array}\right). \qquad (13)$$

Consequently, from (13), the difference $\Delta\omega$ between ω_{ref} and ω_c of the VCF becomes

$$\Delta\omega = \left(1 - \frac{1 \mp \sqrt{1 + 4Q^2\tan^2\theta_L}}{2Q\tan\theta_L}\right)\omega_c. \qquad (14)$$

From (11) and (14), it is clear that a PLL with the higher value Q of the VCF and the larger dc loop gain can control a filter system more accurately. The high value of Q, however, decreases the dynamic range, and the large loop gain increases the offset voltage. In this case, the appropriate values of Q and dc loop gain must be chosen. An example of the values will be given in the following section.

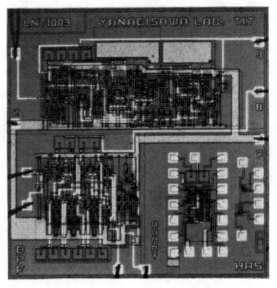

Fig. 11.   Photomicrograph of the filter system.

VI. EXPERIMENTAL RESULTS

The video filter system which uses the automatic scheme as explained in the previous chapter is implemented by a conventional junction-isolated 15-μm bipolar process with n-p-n transistors of $f_T = 400$ MHz. The circuit shown in Fig. 9 is used as the signal processing filter in this system. The VCF in the system is designed in the same way as the signal processing filter for achieving better tracking. The specifications of the video filter system are described as follows.

1) Signal Processing Filter
    Passband: 3.7–5.2 MHz
    Passband Ripple: 0.3 dB.
2) VCF
    Cutoff Frequency $f_0 = \omega_0/2\pi$: 3.9 MHz
    (when the PLL is open)
    Q: 2.0
    Initial Bias Voltage V_0: 1.0 V.
3) V_{PC}: 1.0 V.
4) Loop-Filter Cutoff Frequency: 100 kHz.
5) DC Loop Gain: 10.0.

From the experiments and the process data, the following values have been obtained: $C_C = 9.3$ pF; $C_P = 1.5$ pF; $n = 0.3$; and $\phi = 0.7$ V. It is noted that the obtained C_C value deviates from the designed value in Fig. 9.

Fig. 11 shows a photomicrograph of the chip including the system and other circuits. This chip area is 3.5×3.5 mm^2. The system occupies about three-quarters of the area and consumes 75 mW with a single 5-V supply.

Fig. 12 shows the experimental results. The broken line (a) is the theoretical values. The dashed line (b) and the solid line (c) are the gain characteristics when the loop is open and closed, respectively. ω_{ref} is chosen as 4.4 MHz. When the PLL is closed, the difference between the reference frequency and the center frequency is adjusted only to 180 kHz or less. The value is very close to 168 kHz,

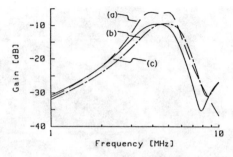

Fig. 12. Frequency responses: (*a*) theoretical, (*b*) PLL open, and (*c*) PLL closed.

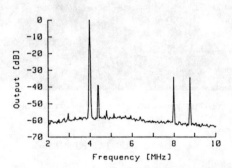

Fig. 13. Filter output spectrum.

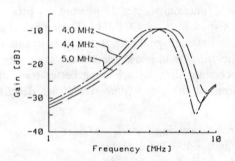

Fig. 14. Tunability performance.

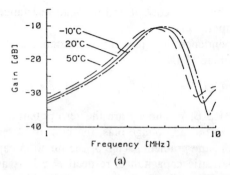

(a)

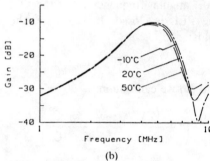

(b)

Fig. 15. Temperature characteristics: (a) PLL open, and (b) PLL closed.

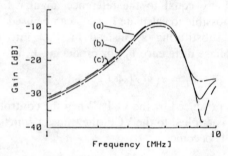

Fig. 16. Dependence of the filter responses on supply voltages: (*a*) 5.5 V, (*b*) 5.0 V, and (*c*) 4.5 V.

which is predicted by (14). This slight difference between the theoretical and the measured values is thought to be caused by factors such as a mismatching between the signal processing filter and the reference filter, and the effects of input and output circuits. The center gain of the monolithic system is slightly different from the theoretical values. This difference does not, however, affect the validity of the experimental results. It is thought to be caused mainly by the parasitic series resistances of junction capacitors produced by too small contacts. They can be easily avoided by careful layout work.

Also, a small feedthrough of a reference signal has been observed as an additional problem. The addition of a capacitor between the terminal Ⓐ of the PLL in Fig. 10 and the ground avoids this feedthrough.

The harmonic distortion including the feedthrough as shown in Fig. 13 is measured under the following conditions: 1) the input voltage of the signal processing filter is 50 mV$_{p-p}$ at 4.0 MHz; 2) the input voltage of VCF is 100 mV$_{p-p}$ at 4.4 MHz; and 3) a 100-nF capacitor is added between the terminal Ⓐ and ground. These harmonics are normalized by the input voltage level of the signal processing filter. The feedthrough at 4.4 MHz and its second harmonic are about −40 and −35 dB, respectively. The second harmonic is only −35 dB and the third harmonic has not been observed in spite of the nonlinearity of junction capacitors due to the signal processing filter being a balanced-type one.

Fig. 14 shows the tunability of this system. The responses have similar shapes to each other while the center frequency tracks the changes of the reference signal as was predicted by the theory. The obtained maximum tunable range of the center frequency is from 3.9 to 5.1 MHz. The tunable range is sufficient to overcome the difficulties of controlling the absolute values of the passive elements on the monolithic integrated circuits.

The temperature characteristics are shown in Fig. 15. Without the PLL, the center frequency changes from about 5.0 to 4.0 MHz when the temperature changes from −10 to 50°C. On the other hand, when the PLL is closed, the frequency response is not affected by the changes in temperatures.

The broken line (*a*), the solid line (*b*), and the dotted line (*c*) of Fig. 16 show the frequency responses with supply voltages of 5.5, 5.0, and 4.5 V, respectively. The change of the gain is mainly caused by that of the emitter resistances of the differential amplifiers used as the input and output circuits.

VII. Conclusion

A fully integrated video frequency active *RC* filter system has been proposed. This system is composed of a signal processing filter realized by NIC-based gyrators and a new automatic tuning circuit using a PLL. Features of each part of the system have been discussed. The system has been fully integrated by a conventional junction-isolated 15-μm bipolar process with n-p-n transistors of $f_T = 400$ MHz. This is the first attempt using transistors of such a low-value f_T. The experimental results show satisfactory agreement with the theory and show the excellent tunability against the changes in temperature. The distortion due to nonlinearity of junction capacitors is small, because the signal processing filter used in the proposed system is of a balanced type.

One of the problems encountered in the implementation of the system is the feedthrough of the reference signal. To avoid this, a capacitor was added to the chip. A more careful layout work can solve the problem.

Acknowledgment

The authors would like to thank Associate Professors N. Fujii and A. Nishihara of the Tokyo Institute of Technology for the fruitful discussions and useful suggestions. The authors also appreciate the staff in Takasaki Works of Hitachi Ltd. for their support in implementing the proposed system, and T. Sakata for performing the experimental works and drawing the figures.

References

[1] A. V. Oppenheim and R. W. Schafer, *Digital Signal Processing*. Englewood Cliffs, NJ: Prentice-Hall, 1975.
[2] G. S. Moschytz, *MOS Switched-Capacitor Filters: Analysis and Design*. New York: IEEE Press, 1984.
[3] K. S. Tan and P. R. Gray, "Fully integrated analog filters using bipolar-JFET technology," *IEEE J. Solid-State Circuits*, vol. SC-13, no. 6, pp. 814–821, Dec. 1978.
[4] R. Geiger, P. Allen, and D. Taingo, "Switched-resistor filters—A continuous time approach to monolithic MOS filter design," *IEEE Trans. Circuits Syst.*, vol. CAS-29, no. 5, pp. 306–315, May 1982.
[5] H. Khorrambadi and P. R. Gray, "High-frequency CMOS continuous-time filters," *IEEE J. Solid-State Circuits*, vol. SC-19, no. 6, pp. 939–948, Dec. 1984.
[6] M. Kumazawa and T. Yanagisawa, "Video frequency active filters," in *Proc. ISCAS '84*, May 1984, pp. 638–641.
[7] M. Kumazawa and T. Yanagisawa, "Video frequency active filters using balanced-type NIC's," *Electron. Commun. Japan (Scripta Technica, Inc.)*, vol. 69, no. 2, pp. 41–50, 1986.
[8] B. Gilbert, "A precise four-quadrant multiplier with subnanosecond response," *IEEE J. Solid-State Circuits*, vol. SC-3, no. 4, pp. 365–373, Dec. 1968.
[9] P. R. Gray and R. G. Meyer, *Analysis and Design of Analog Integrated Circuits*, 2nd ed. New York: Wiley 1983, ch. 10.

Section 5-D   *Active R Filters*

The paper by Chiou and Schaumann in this section is based on the "active-*R*" idea, which had been investigated in the 1970s for implementation in discrete filters composed only of resistors and frequency-compensated op amps; the latter were used as integrators. To avoid the excess phase shift near their unity gain frequency, the op amps had to be used at frequencies well below that, at which their gain was high. This made necessary the use of internal resistive attenuators and resulted in rather poor dynamic range in most cases. By taking advantage of the flexibility of full integration, the authors considered the design of the entire integrator as a whole and were able to achieve better performance. The paper contains a rather extensive discussion of the several problems that had to be faced. Another active-*R* filter implementation, used in conjunction with a programmable array, is described in [1].

REFERENCE

[1] M. Sartori, M. Mazzucco and R. Gaidano, "ALBA: A bipolar technology structured array for the design of high-order continuous-time filters," *IEEE J. Solid-State Circuits*, vol. 24, pp. 723–731, June 1989.

Design and Performance of a Fully Integrated Bipolar 10.7-MHz Analog Bandpass Filter

CHII-FA CHIOU AND ROLF SCHAUMANN, FELLOW, IEEE

Abstract —Design and experimental evaluation of a sixth-order fully integrated continuous-time 10.7-MHz bandpass filter are presented. Circuit performance is stabilized through on-chip tuning by a dual-loop master–slave control scheme that locks center frequency and bandwidth to an external reference signal. Difficulties in design and performance are discussed and corrections suggested where appropriate.

I. INTRODUCTION

FULLY INTEGRATED analog filters have previously been designed for low-frequency (< 50 kHz) applications both by using switched-capacitor techniques and by the continuous-time filtering method [1]–[4]. However, the extension of both techniques to higher frequencies is hindered by a number of problems and, so far, has not been consistently successful, although a few impressive results have been reported [5]–[7].

In the design of monolithic filters using the continuous-time approach, it has generally been recognized that the accurate and stable RC time constants necessary for setting the filters' frequency parameters can be implemented reliably only through the use of on-chip automatic tuning systems [1]–[4], [6]–[9]. Since other critical filter parameters, such as gains and quality factors, are dimensionless, they are set in principle by *ratios* of like components (resistors or capacitors) and thus can be realized accurately in integrated circuit form by use of suitable filter topologies and careful circuit designs. This concept works well for low frequencies, however, as application frequencies increase, the nonideal nondominant circuit parasitics become more important and difficult to predict. Some of the filter parameters, e.g., quality factors, are usually so sensitive to unpredictable parasitics that the desired filter functions can no longer be realized reliably and economically. As a result continuous-time high-frequency integrated filters, with few exceptions [6], [7], [10], have not been implemented successfully.

It was suggested in [9] that automatic tuning using a single (frequency-stabilizing) control loop would not be sufficient for obtaining reliable analog[1] high-frequency

integrated filters. Rather, in the face of unpredictable parasitic effects on important filter parameters, a tuning scheme with multiple control loops [9], [10] would have to be devised so that parameters such as bandwidth and gain could be stabilized in addition to pole–frequency.

In this context, a difficult problem which has to be faced in each individual case is that of measuring automatically, reliably, and with reasonably simple circuitry the deviations of filter parameters in order to provide the inputs to the control system. One such approach is described in this paper where the design and experimental evaluation of a fully integrated sixth-order analog bandpass filter for operation above 10 MHz will be discussed. The circuit uses the "master–slave" approach to control filter parameters automatically. In addition to the usual control loop for tuning the RC time constants that set the pole–frequencies of the filters, a second loop for monitoring and tuning the filters' quality factors is also included in the control circuitry to improve the predictability of high-frequency filter performance.

II. DESIGN OF THE 10.7-MHz ANALOG FILTER

The block diagram of a sixth-order bandpass slave filter together with the master filter and its control functions is shown in Fig. 1 The slave filter is composed of three second-order sections in cascade because multiple-loop feedback topoloiges were found to be too sensitive to high-frequency phase errors [11]. The first and last sections are bandpass filters with center-frequency f_0, gain H, and quality-factor Q as indicated in Fig. 1. The second filter section is a low Q notch filter that is derived simply by taking the voltage difference between a flat gain and a second-order bandpass stage. The master is also a second-order bandpass *filter*, in contrast to the master *oscillator* used in low-frequency implementations [1], [2]. This choice was made [9] because an oscillator, essentially a bandpass filter with infinite pole-Q is far more sensitive than a finite-Q filter to parasitic phase-shifts causing Q-enhancement. Consequently, tracking and matching of master *oscillator* and slave *filter* upon which the operation of the control scheme critically depends, can be expected to be less predictable than tracking and matching between two essentially identical master and slave filter sections [6], [9].

Manuscript received January 4, 1985; revised September 30, 1985. This work was supported by the National Science Foundation under Grant ENG 78-25577 and under Grant ECS 82-15001.

The authors are with the Department of Electrical Engineering, University of Minnesota, Minneapolis, MN 55455.

IEEE Log Number 8406491.

[1]"Analog" in the remainder of this paper is to be understood to mean "continuous-time."

Reprinted from *IEEE Trans. Circuits Syst.*, vol. CAS-33, no. 2, pp. 116–124, Feb. 1986.

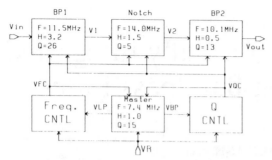

Fig. 1. Functional block diagram of sixth-order master–slave filter.

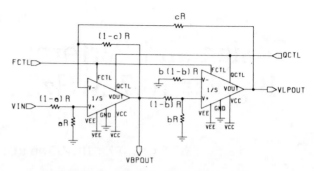

Fig. 2. Second-order active R bandpass filter.

Each second-order section, including the master filter, is based on a two-integrator-loop (active R) topology as shown in Fig. 2. The design and behavior of active R filters has been thoroughly documented in the literature [12] and is well understood. It has also been demonstrated that such circuits are useful for operation over a wide frequency range and have the further advantage of convenient electronic tuning of pole–frequency and quality factor.

On the other hand, it is also well known that most filter topologies using integrators as basic active elements suffer from Q-enhancement problems due to even very small excess-phase in the integrator. Specifically, the circuit in Fig. 2 realizes the bandpass and low-pass transfer functions

$$T_B = V_{BP}/V_{IN} = aA^{-1}/\left[A^{-2} + cA^{-1} + b(1-c)\right] \quad (1a)$$

$$T_L = V_{LP}/V_{IN} = ab/\left[A^{-2} + cA^{-1} + b(1-c)\right] \quad (1b)$$

where A denotes the gain of the integrator that can be modeled, for $\omega\tau(\omega) \ll 1$, as

$$A(j\omega) = \frac{\omega_t}{j\omega}\exp\left[-j\omega\tau(\omega)\right] \simeq \frac{\omega_t}{j\omega}\left[1 - j\omega\tau(\omega)\right] \quad (2)$$

where ω_t is the gain–bandwidth product and $\exp(-j\omega\tau)$ models the excess phase $\Delta\psi = \omega\tau(\omega)$ via a in general frequency-dependent delay $\tau(\omega)$. Inserting (2) into (1) leads, after some algebra, to the expressions for the realized *actual* values of pole–frequency and pole-Q:

$$\omega_a \simeq \omega_0; \quad Q_a \simeq Q_0/(1 - 2Q_0\omega_o\tau)$$
$$= Q_0/(1 - 2Q_0\Delta\psi) \quad (3)$$

where

$$\omega_0 \simeq \omega_t\sqrt{b(1-c)}; \quad Q_0 \simeq c^{-1}\sqrt{b(1-c)} \quad (4)$$

are the *designed* values. Similarly, the actual bandpass gain at $\omega = \omega_0$ can be derived as

$$H_a \simeq H_0/(1 - 2Q_0\omega_0\tau) = H_0/(1 - 2Q_0\Delta\psi) \quad (5a)$$

where

$$H_0 = a/c \quad (5b)$$

is the designed midband gain. Observe that the excess phase $\Delta\psi(\omega_0) \simeq \omega_0\tau(\omega_0)$ has negligible effect on ω_0 but causes severe gain- and Q-enhancement. Note that the filter sections will oscillate if $\Delta\psi(\omega_0) > 1/(2Q_0)$, which corresponds to only $\Delta\psi \simeq 1°$ for bandpass BP1. Since such small values of excess-phase in the face of parasitics in the

megahertz range are clearly undesignable, the need for special Q-control measures becomes apparent.

Fig. 3 contains a circuit diagram of the integrator. Apart from the bias circuitry, it consists of a differential input stage (Q_1–Q_4), a level shifter (Q_7, R_9), the integrator stage (Q_9, R_{11}, C_{D1}), a second level shifter (Q_{10}, Q_{11}, Q_{14}–Q_{16}), a gain stage ($Q_{12}, R_{15}, R_{16}, C_{D2}$) and an emitter follower output (Q_{13}). The integrator time constant that determines the filter's pole–frequency ω_0 is set ty $R_{11}C_{D1}$; the time constant $\tau_2 = R_{16}C_{D2}$ creates a high-frequency zero at $1/\tau_2$, so that (2) is multiplied by $(1 + j\omega\tau_2)$ and the remaining excess phase becomes

$$\Delta\psi_r \simeq \omega\left[\tau(\omega) - \tau_2\right]. \quad (6)$$

Clearly, adjusting τ_2 will allow $\Delta\psi_r(\omega_0)$ to be reduced to zero so that Q_a and H_a are realized correctly. C_{D1} and C_{D2} are junction capacitors of two reverse-biased diodes whose bias voltages are set from the frequency-control (FCTL) and Q-control (QCTL) terminals through emitter follower transistors Q_{18} and Q_{19}, respectively. All resistors were simulated as four-section RC-lines to account for capacitive effects; the various capacitors in Fig. 3 were selected by careful SPICE-optimization to achieve the best nominal integrator phase (i.e., constant 90° phase shift) in the frequency range of interest.

The frequency and Q-control voltages, V_{FC} and V_{QC}, are obtained in the control scheme in Fig. 1 that slaves the pole–frequency and quality factor of each filter section to the performance of the master filter through the "frequency-control" circuit, Freq. −CNTL, and the "Q-control" circuit, Q-CNTL, respectively. The dc frequency-control voltage V_{FC} is derived from phase-locking the low-pass output of the master filter, V_{LP} from (1b), to an external reference signal V_R based on the quadrature phase-locked-loop principle.

The problem of measuring and correcting excess phase $\Delta\psi$ and quality factor Q, that would normally require two or three frequency and signal-level measurements, is avoided by utilizing that, as shown in (3) and (5a), Q and gain in this two-integrator-loop filter have the same dependence on $\Delta\psi$. Thus if the master is designed for a nominal gain of, say, unity, a value determined according to (5b) by only the resistor ratio a/c, then any deviation from unity is caused by $\Delta\psi$ and can be detected by comparing the peak value of the master filter bandpass output V_{BP} with the amplitude of the reference signal V_R. As a result, the

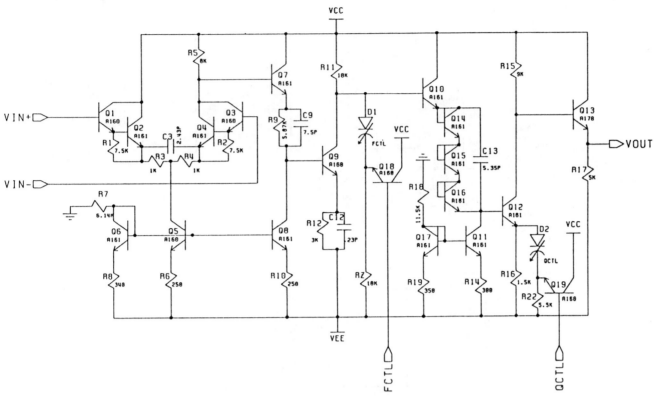

Fig. 3.   Circuit diagram of the integrator.

Q-control voltage V_{QC}, which simultaneously controls both the master and slave filters, is generated by amplitude-locking the master bandpass output V_{BP} to V_R.

The frequency-control circuitry is shown in Fig. 4(a). It consist of input buffer emitter followers (Q_{IN1}, Q_{IN2}) for minimizing any input phase errors due to layout parasitics and loading, and of the phase detector (Q_1-Q_7) and its bias circuitry (Q_8, R_1-R_6, R_9-R_{11}). The phase detector output (Q_9, R_7) is followed by a low-pass gain stage ($Q_{12}-Q_{14}$, $R_{12}-R_{15}$) with a Miller-capacitor (C_p). Since the output FCTL, i.e., V_{FC}, is to reverse bias base-emitter junction diodes (D_1 in the integrators), limiting circuitry is included to prevent forward bias or junction breakdown on D_1: $Q_{15}-Q_{17}$, $R_{16}-R_{18}$ set the lower limit of the output voltage for forward bias protection, and Q_{11}, R_{12} limit the current into the composite p-n-p transistor $Q_{12}-Q_{13}$ and thus impose an upper output voltage level for breakdown protection.

Analysis of the circuit leads to a residual master-filter frequency-error $\Delta\omega_M = \omega_{aM} - \omega_R$ obtained from [9]

$$\frac{\Delta\omega_M}{\omega_R} \simeq \frac{V_0 + \phi}{2mQ_M K_p} \frac{\Delta\omega_i}{\omega_{0M}} \qquad (7)$$

where Q_M is the quality factor and ω_{aM} the actual pole–frequency of the master, K_p the gain of the phase comparator, ω_R the reference frequency, $\Delta\omega_i = \omega_{AM} = \omega_{0M}$ the initial master pose–frequency error, and where the remaining parameters describe the capacitor C_{D1},

$$C_{D1}(V) = C_{j0}/(1 + V/\phi)^m. \qquad (8)$$

C_{j0} is the zero–bias junction capacitor ($\simeq 60$ pF), ϕ is the contact potential ($\simeq 0.8$ V) and m is the gradient factor ($\simeq 0.4$). V_0 is the nominal value to give $C_{D1} = 40$ pF. This design, assuming $\Delta\omega_i/\omega_{0M} \simeq 20$ percent leads to $\Delta\omega_M/\omega_R \simeq 0.8$ percent.

The Q-control circuit diagram is shown in Fig. 4(b). It consists of a buffer (Q_{IN1}) for the input V_{BP}, a gain stage ($Q_{14}-Q_{16}$), followed by a full-wave rectifier (Q_{12}, Q_{13}, Q_{18}) and a peak-detector (Q_{11}, R_{13}, C_{13}). An identical circuit operates on V_{REF}. Q_8-Q_{10}, Q_4-Q_5 perform amplitude comparison and amplification, with the desirable high common-mode rejection achieved by common-mode negative feedback in the current sources $Q_{10}-R_8$ and R_4-R_5. Finally, Q_1-Q_2, R_1-R_3 and the Miller capacitor C_p provide further gain, low-pass filtering and output buffering, and forward bias protection for D_2 in Fig. 3 is implemented by Q_3-R_3. Since C_{D2} is relatively small ($\simeq 2.6$ pF) only the base-collector junction ($BV_{C0} > 20$ V) is used so that breakdown protection is not needed.

Considerations similar to the ones above lead to [9]

$$\Delta Q_M/Q_R \simeq (\Delta Q_i/Q_{0M})/K_Q \qquad (9)$$

where Q_R is the designed value and Q_{0M} the open-loop value of Q of the master filter, $\Delta Q_M = Q_{aM} - Q_R$ and $Q_i = Q_{aM} - Q_{0M}$ are the remaining and initial Q-errors of the master filter, and K_Q is the Q-control loop gain (> 350 in this design).

It should be noted that the slave filters do not have to operate at the same pole-frequency as the master, and that this frequency need not be equal to ω_R (see Fig. 1). The

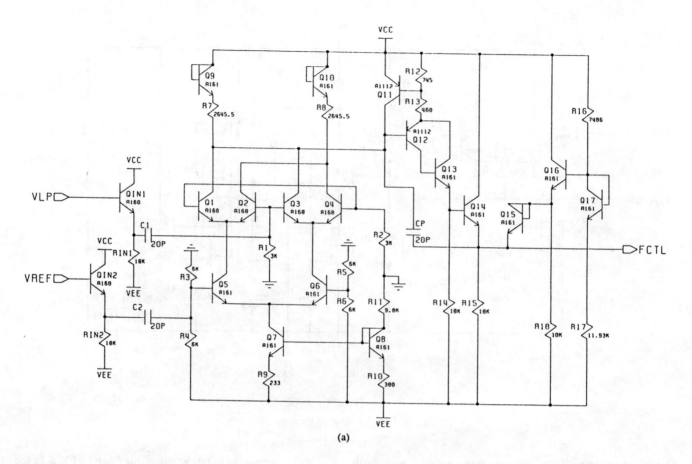

(a)

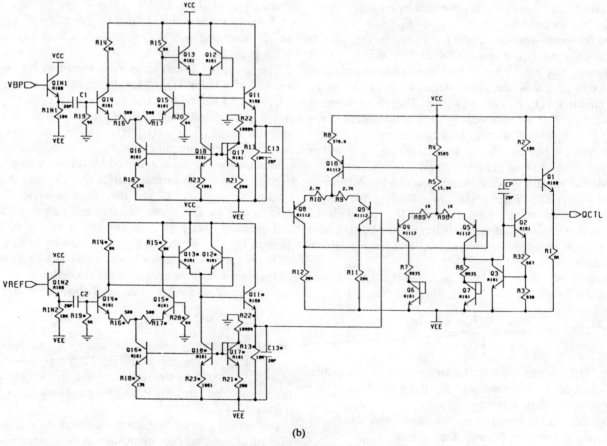

(b)

Fig. 4. Circuit diagram of: (a) The frequency-control loop. (b) The
Q-control loop.

Fig. 5. Photomicrograph of the filter chip.

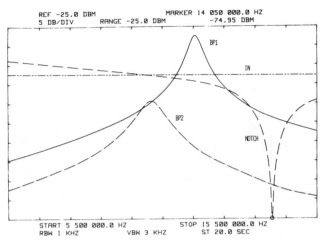

Fig. 6. Experimental frequency response of the three slave filter sections.

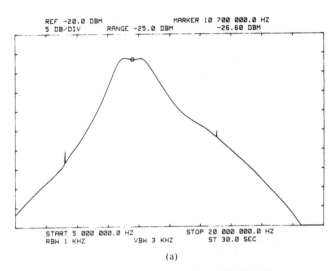

(a)

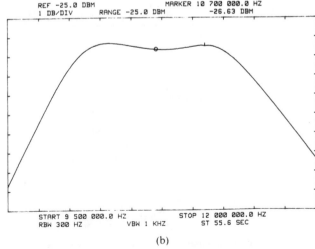

(b)

Fig. 7. (a) Experimental performance of total filter. (b) Bandpass detail.

frequency-control loop only adjusts ω_t of all (identical) integrators to the value $\omega_R/\sqrt{b_M}$, where b_M is the value of b in the master and $c \ll 1$. The pole-frequencies of all sections are then equal to ω_t times that section's $\sqrt{b}$, i.e., different pole-frequencies are derived from ω_t by designable resistor ratios. Observe that the circuit is a tracking filter, see Fig. 12, where all pole-frequencies follow any variation in ω_R over a range that is limited by the reverse-biased junction capacitor C_{D1} in (8).

Similarly, the Q-control loop simply adjusts the actual midband gain H_{Ma} of the *master* to unity thereby reducing its $\Delta\psi_r(\omega_R)$ to zero. This same adjustment will also result in $\Delta\psi_r(\omega_{s0}) = 0$, where ω_{s0} are the pole-frequencies of the slave filters, provided that, by (6), $\tau(\omega_{s0}) = \tau_2$, i.e., provided that $\Delta\psi(\omega) = \omega\tau(\omega) = \omega\tau_0$ is a linear function of ω, with $\tau(\omega) = \tau_0$ a constant delay over the frequency-range of interest, and that this linear relationship holds with variations in power supply, temperature, etc. Note from Fig. 1 that in our case the pole-frequencies of the slave filters differ by almost a factor 2, i.e., 7 MHz, from that of the master filter, $\omega_M = \omega_R$, so that this choice of widely different pole-frequencies for master and slave filters may serve as a critical test of the limits of this approach. As will be discussed later, the very different pole-frequencies in our master and slave filters do indeed cause problems in making the slave filter track properly with the master filter.

III. EXPERIMENTAL RESULTS

The complete filter circuit is implemented in Honeywell Inc.'s Advanced Linear Bipolar process. The process, employing conventional junction isolation and one-metal-layer technology, produces n-p-n transistors with a minimum size of $40 \times 67 \ \mu\mathrm{m}^2$ and $f_T = 1.5$ GHz. Ion-implanted base-layer resistors with nominal width of $9 \ \mu\mathrm{m}$ (for better resistor matching) and sheet resistance of either $50 \ \Omega/\square$ or $500 \ \Omega/\square$ are standard in this process. Fig. 5 shows a photomicrograph of the experimental chip. The total chip area is $160 \times 160 \ \mathrm{mil}^2$ and consumes 650 mW for a ± 5.5-V power supply.

The frequency response of the three individual filter sections including the 14.0-MHz notch is shown in Fig. 6. The signal level reading at filter input corresponds to an amplitude of about $0.1 \ V_{p-p}$. In Fig. 7 the overall frequency-

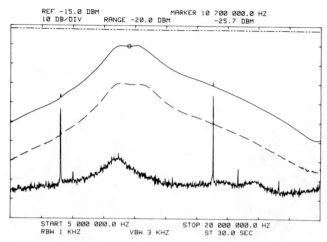

REF -15.0 DBM   MARKER 10 700 000.0 HZ
10 DB/DIV   RANGE -20.0 DBM   -25.7 DBM

START 5 000 000.0 HZ   STOP 20 000 000.0 HZ
RBW 1 KHZ   VBW 3 KHZ   ST 30.0 SEC

Fig. 8.   Maximum output signal and output noise level.

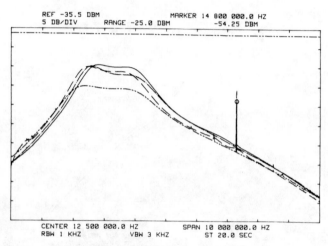

REF -35.5 DBM   MARKER 14 800 000.0 HZ
5 DB/DIV   RANGE -25.0 DBM   -54.25 DBM

CENTER 12 500 000.0 HZ   SPAN 10 000 000.0 HZ
RBW 1 KHZ   VBW 3 KHZ   ST 20.0 SEC

Fig. 9.   Performance of ensemble of four chips.

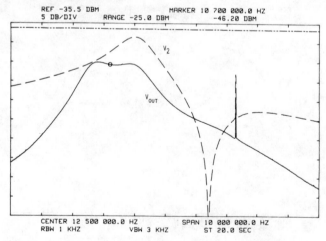

REF -35.5 DBM   MARKER 10 700 000.0 HZ
5 DB/DIV   RANGE -25.0 DBM   -46.20 DBM

V_2

V_{OUT}

CENTER 12 500 000.0 HZ   SPAN 10 000 000.0 HZ
RBW 1 KHZ   VBW 3 KHZ   ST 20.0 SEC

Fig. 10.   Frequency responses V_{out}/V_{in} and V_2/V_{in} showing the position of the 14-MHz notch.

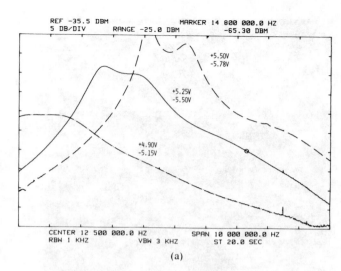

REF -35.5 DBM   MARKER 14 800 000.0 HZ
5 DB/DIV   RANGE -25.0 DBM   -65.30 DBM

+5.50V
-5.78V

+5.25V
-5.50V

+4.90V
-5.15V

CENTER 12 500 000.0 HZ   SPAN 10 000 000.0 HZ
RBW 1 KHZ   VBW 3 KHZ   ST 20.0 SEC

(a)

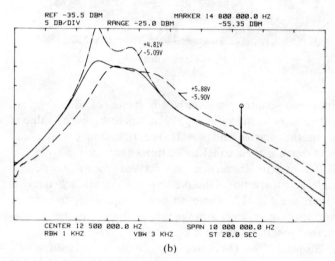

REF -35.5 DBM   MARKER 14 800 000.0 HZ
5 DB/DIV   RANGE -25.0 DBM   -55.35 DBM

+4.81V
-5.09V

+5.88V
-5.90V

CENTER 12 500 000.0 HZ   SPAN 10 000 000.0 HZ
RBW 1 KHZ   VBW 3 KHZ   ST 20.0 SEC

(b)

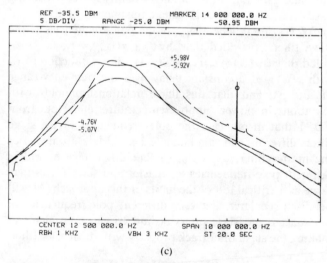

REF -35.5 DBM   MARKER 14 800 000.0 HZ
5 DB/DIV   RANGE -25.0 DBM   -50.95 DBM

+5.98V
-5.92V

-4.76V
-5.07V

CENTER 12 500 000.0 HZ   SPAN 10 000 000.0 HZ
RBW 1 KHZ   VBW 3 KHZ   ST 20.0 SEC

(c)

Fig. 11.   Filter performance with varying supply voltage: (a) Both control loops open. (b) f-control loop closed. (c) f- and Q-control loops close.

and detailed passband response of th sixth-order band-pass filter which is slaved to a 7.4 MHz 0.2 V_{p-p} reference signal is shown and Fig. 8 contains the transfer characteristic for maximum input signal (0.54 V_{p-p}), nominal signal input (dashed line, 0.1 V_{p-p}), and the filter output noise. The curves show a signal-to-noise ratio for maximum filter output voltage of 60 dB. Total harmonic distortion for this

situation is 35 dB. An ensemble of the performance of four chips is shown in Fig. 9, the lowest of these curves was obtained for an input signal reduced by 6 dB to avoid oscillations. Figs. 7–9 indicate a noticeable reference signal feedthrough at 7.4 MHz and its second harmonic to the filter output.

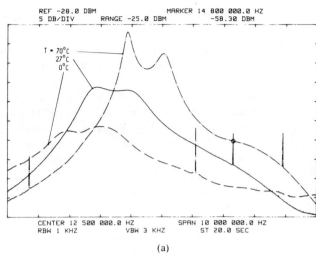

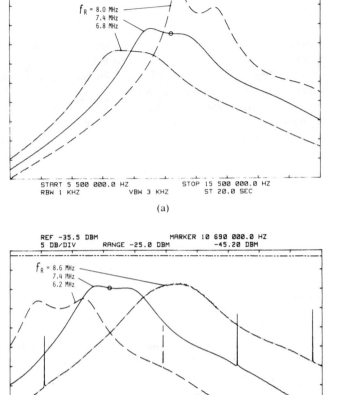

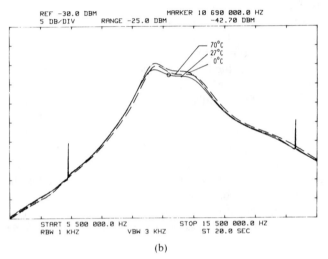

Fig. 12. Filter performance ("tracking filter") with varying reference frequency: (a) Both control loops open (b) Both loops closed.

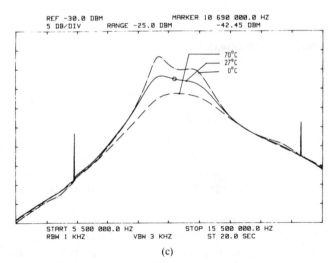

Fig. 13. Filter performance with varying temperature. (a) Both loops open. (b) f-loop closed. (c) f- and Q-loops closed.

Note from Figs. 7–9 that the 14 MHz transmission zero disappears after the cascade of three filter sections, although the notch filter functions correctly (Fig. 6) and the notch is present at the output of the second section, V_2/V_{in} (dashed line, in Fig. 10). From this figure it is apparent that some additional signal feedthrough path from filter input directly to filter output must exist that completely bypasses and thereby eliminates the effect of the notch filter. This feedthrough problem is believed to be the caused mainly by the poor power supply rejection (PSR) of the single-ended system at high frequencies. In addition, the layout limitations of the one-metal-layer technology also contribute more series resistance (from unavoidable cross-unders) in power supply lines and thus degrades PSR even further.

To demonstrate the need for both frequency and Q controls for high-frequency integrated filters, the frequency response of the filter as a function of different supply voltages is shown in Fig. 11. In Fig. 11(a) both the frequency and Q control loops are opened and V_{FC} and V_{QC} for the slave filter are fixed at a constant voltages. As supply voltage changes, not only the center-frequency but also

bandwidth (Q) change drastically. In Fig. 11(b) only the frequency-control loop is closed with V_{QC} still fixed at a constant voltage. In this case the filter center-frequency remains largely independent of voltage variations, but Q still varies widely. The filter response with both loops closed is shown in Fig. 11(c). It is apparent that the overall filter response is much less sensitive to power supply variations.

The capability and range of the slave filter response to follow the frequency variations of the reference signal V_R is indicated in Fig. 12. Again, in Fig. 12(a) with only the frequency-control loop closed, Q changes by more than one order of magnitude (i.e., greater than 20 dB of gain changes) for variations of just ± 8 percent in reference frequency. In Fig. 12(b) with both control loops active, reasonable filter performance can still be maintained with reference frequency changes of up to ± 16 percent.

The filter responses at different temperatures with a) both control loops opened, b) only the frequency-control loop closed, and c) both loops closed are shown in Fig. 13(a), (b), and (c) respectively. Note that the best filter response for temperature variations is achieved with only the frequency-control loop functioning.

An explanation for this behavior is as follows: Having established that the performance of the master filter itself with control-loops active is independent of temperature T, the reason for the temperature-dependence of the slave filter must be due to imperfect tracking between master and slaves. Specifically, since the problems are evidently caused by Q-variations it can be concluded that the difference between ω_R and the pole–frequencies ω_{s0} of the slaves, i.e., $(\omega_{s0} - \omega_R)_{\max} \simeq 2\pi \cdot 7$ MHz (Fig. 1), was chosen too large. Thus the difference between the Q-control voltage generated by the master, V_{QCM}, and that needed by the slave, V_{QCS}, becomes significant because the assumption $\tau(\omega) = \tau_0 = \text{const}$ is not valid.

The master filter Q-control loop, according to (6) sets the Q-control voltage V_{QCM} such that

$$R_{16} C_{D2}(V_{QCM}) = \tau(\omega_R) \qquad (10)$$

where C_{D2} is given by an expression similar to (8). Experimentally it was observed that $\tau(\omega_{s0})$ was larger than $\tau(\omega_R)$ so that a larger value of C_{D2} in the slave filters is needed to obtain $\Delta\psi r = 0$. The relationship that leads to an operational filter was found to be, approximately,

$$V_{QCS} = 0.33 V_{QCM} - 2.5 \text{ V} \qquad (11)$$

and was implemented by an external discrete circuit. It indicates that the nominal value of V_{QCS} is smaller than V_{QCM} leading to a larger value of C_{D2} on the $C-V$ curve (8) with a larger slope that, in turn, is compensated by the scaling factor 0.33 in (11).

Finally, the temperature variation that is still observed in Fig. 13(b), (c) can be accounted for as follows: Expanding (6) into a Taylor series around the nominal point τ_0 and τ_{20}, where the subscript "0" means "room temperature and $V_{QS, \text{nominal}}$", yields

$$\Delta\psi_r \simeq \omega_{s0} \left[\tau_0 - \tau_{20} + \left(\left. \frac{\partial\tau}{\partial T} \right|_0 - \left. \frac{\partial\tau_2}{\partial T} \right|_0 \right) \Delta T - \left. \frac{\partial\tau_2}{\partial V_{QC}} \right|_0 \Delta V_{QC} \right]. \qquad (12)$$

With V_{QCM} and V_{QCS} determined by (10) and (11), the circuit operates at the nominal point where $\Delta\psi_r$, with

$\tau_0 = \tau_{20}$, room temperature ($\Delta T = 0$), and Q-control loop open ($\Delta V_{QC} = 0$) is zero.

If T varies ($\Delta T \neq 0$) the temperature coefficient of the resistor R_{16}, $T_{CR} \simeq 2000$ ppm/°C, and that of the junction capacitor C_{D2}, $T_{CC} \simeq 100$ ppm/°C, cause the RC product τ_2 to increase with T. If the Q-control loop is open, the delay τ, determined in principle by a similar RC product, varies with T in the same manner as τ_2 so that $\Delta\psi_r$ remains approximately zero, independent of T (Fig. 13b!). If the Q-control loop is closed ($\Delta V_{QC} \simeq 0$), it performs its intended function of eliminating any remaining Q and H deviation in the master. The slaves, however, are over-compensated (Fig. 13(c)) because the scale factor 0.33 in (11), derived for the $R_{16} C_{D2}(V)$ curve at room temperature, is incorrect for $T = 0$°C and $T = 70$°C.

IV. PROBLEMS AND DISCUSSIONS

Although the experimental evaluation of the 10.7-MHz sixth-order bandpass filter shows very encouraging results, several problems encountered in the design and implementation of the circuit are apparent.

The feedthrough path that eliminates the transmission zero can be avoided by more careful layout. In addition, as also noted in [6], for high-frequency highly selective filters power supply rejection is a critical problem, especially with singled-ended systems. Poor power supply rejection together with cross-coupling introduced by parasitics and layout may cause significant feedthrough in the circuit and result in degradation of the filter performance. To minimize this problem, circuit and layout parasitics should be modeled and simulated as thoroughly as possible before actual integrated circuit fabrication and the use of fully differential circuit architecture may prove to be preferable.

The more serious problem of imperfect phase-tracking between master and slave, as discussed in the previous section, must be reduced by more careful modeling and simulation than was possible at the time of the design [9] and, especially, by reducing significantly the difference between reference frequency and slave filter pole–frequencies. Of course, this step will necessitate that attention is paid to avoid reference signal feedthrough (see, e.g., Fig. 7).

Another problem encountered with our high-frequency filter chip is potential instability/latch-up during the power-on transient. Since at power-on the control circuitry may start from any initial state, it is possible that high-Q filters can go into oscillation before the control circuit begins to function. If the oscillation becomes large enough and nonlinear, it may eventually cause the circuit to latch-up and not function at all. Indeed, SPICE simulations of the filter circuit demonstrate the existence of two stable dc operating points: one at $V_{\text{out}} = 0$ and one where V_{out} equals the positive power supply voltage, i.e., latch-up. Therefore, every effort should be made to ensure that enough latch-up protection (e.g., input clamping diodes, etc.) is included in the filter and the control circuitry. As long as the circuit does not stay in latch-up, the properly designed control circuitry will guide the slave filter into the final stable state.

Finally, it should be emphasized that for improved tracking and matching, master and slave filters should be as identical in all respects as possible, including orientation on the chip. Furthermore, corresponding amplifiers in different filter sections should be designed to see the same loads so that output impedance effects, if any [13], are identical.

V. CONCLUSIONS

This paper demonstrates that monolithic analog filters at video frequencies are indeed feasible. Stability and designability are obtained by slaving filter performance to an externally supplied reference signal of fixed frequency and arbitrary amplitude. The problems encountered in the design and implementation of these high-frequency integrated filters are discussed and possible ways to avoid the difficulties are suggested.

ACKNOWLEDGMENT

Processing of the circuits by Honeywell SSED is gratefully acknowledged, with special thanks to D. Gipp and J. Havilland for their support.

REFERENCES

[1] K. S. Tan and P. R. Gray, "Fully integrated analog filters using bipolar-JFET technology," *IEEE J. Solid-State Circuits*, vol. SC-12, pp. 814–821, Dec. 1978.

[2] K. Fukahori, "A bipolar voltage-controlled tunable filter," *IEEE J. Solid-State Circuits*, vol. SC-16, pp. 729–737, Dec. 1981.

[3] J. O. Voorman, W. H. A. Brüls, and J. P. Barth, "Integration of analog filters in a bipolar process," *IEEE J. Solid-State Circuits*, vol. SC-17, pp. 713–722, Aug. 1982.

[4] M. Banu and Y. Tsividis, "Fully integrated active *RC* filters in MOS technology," *IEEE J. Solid-State Circuits*, vol. SC-18, pp. 644–651, Dec. 1983.

[5] T. C. Choi *et al.*, "High-frequency CMOS switched-capacitor filters for communication applications," *IEEE J. Solid-State Circuits*, vol. SC-18, pp. 652–664, Dec. 1983.

[6] H. Khorramabadi and P. R. Gray, "High-frequency CMOS continuous-time filters," *IEEE J. Solid-State Circuits*, vol. SC-19, pp. 939–948, Dec. 1984.

[7] K. W. Moulding *et al.*, "Gyrator video filter IC with automatic tuning," *IEEE J. Solid-State Circuits* vol. SC-15, pp. 963–968, Dec. 1980.

[8] J. R. Brand, R. Schaumann, and E. M. Skei, "Temperature stabilized active *R* bandpass filters," in *Proc. Midwest Symp. Circuits and Systems*, pp. 295–300, 1977.

[9] R. Schaumann and C. -F. Chiou, "Design of Integrated Analog Filters," in *Proc. European Conf. Circuit Theory and Design*, pp. 407–411, 1981.

[10] D. Senderowicz, D. A. Hodges, and P. R. Gray, "An NMOS integrated vector-locked loop," *IEEE Int. Symp. Circuits and Systems*, pp. 1164–1167, 1982.

[11] R. Schaumann, J. R. Brand, and K. R. Laker, "Effects of excess phase in multiple feedback active filter," *IEEE Trans. Circuits Sys.*, vol. CAS-27, pp. 967–970, Oct. 1980.

[12] J. R. Brand and R. Schaumann, "Active *R* filters: Review of theory and practice," *IEE J. Electron. Circuits and Systems*, vol. 2, pp. 89–101, 1978.

[13] J. R. Brand and R. Schaumann, "The effects of non-zero output resistance and common-mode rejection-ratio of operational amplifiers on the performance of active *R* filters," *Proc. Midwest Symp. Circ. and Syst.*, pp. 196–201, 1976.

Section 5-E   Filters Using Inductors

High-frequency discrete-component filters use inductors routinely. Yet on integrated circuits inductors are seldom found, owing to both limited inductance range possible and low quality factor (see Paper 1-2). The following paper by Nguyen and Meyer shows that, with careful considerations, inductors can be used to advantage in high-frequency integrated filters. The reader is also referred to other work by the same authors [1]. Passive lossless filters have the advantage of lower noise than their

RC-active counterparts. This very advantage is also exploited in [2], where integrated surface acoustic wave (SAW) filters are described.

References

[1] N. M. Nguyen and R. G. Meyer, "A Si bipolar monolithic RF bandpass amplifier," *IEEE J. Solid-State Circuits*, vol. 27, no. 1, pp. 123–127, January 1992.

[2] P. T. M. van Zeijl, J. H. Visser and L. K. Nanver, "FM radio receiver front-end circuitry with on-chip SAW filters," *IEEE Trans. Consumer Electron.*, vol. 35, pp. 512–518, August 1989.

Paper 5-E.1

Si IC-Compatible Inductors and *LC* Passive Filters

NHAT M. NGUYGEN, STUDENT MEMBER, IEEE, AND ROBERT G. MEYER, FELLOW, IEEE

Abstract —Passive inductors and *LC* filters fabricated in standard Si IC technology are demonstrated. *Q* factors from 3 to 8 and inductors up to 10 nH in the gigahertz range have been realized. Measurements on a five-pole maximally flat low-pass filter give midband insertion loss and −3-dB bandwidth close to the nominal design values of 2.25 dB and 880 MHz.

I. Introduction

Planar inductors and *LC* passive filters have been implemented in practical systems for many years using a variety of substrates. These include standard PC boards, ceramic and sapphire hybrids, and more recently GaAs IC's [1], [2]. In the early development of Si IC's, planar inductors were investigated [3] but the prevailing lithographic limitations and relatively low frequencies of operation (less than several hundred megahertz) led to their abandonment as impractical due to excessive chip-area requirement and low *Q*. Reflected losses from the conductive Si substrate were a major contributor to low inductor *Q*.

Recent advances in Si IC processing technology have prompted another look at this situation. In particular, metal width and pitch in the low micrometer range allow many more inductor turns per unit area than in the past. Also, modern oxide-isolated processes with multilayer metal options allow thick oxides to help isolate the inductor from the Si substrate. In addition, interest is growing in applications at much higher frequencies with the advent of 900-MHz communications and gigahertz-range satellite reception such as Global Positioning Satellite (GPS) and Direct Broadcast Satellite (DBS).

In this paper we describe inductors and *LC* filters fabricated in a production Si bipolar process featuring oxide isolation and active device peak f_T of 8 GHz. In the frequency range of interest (above about 1 GHz) the *Q* of the filter elements is quite usable (3–8) and appears to be almost totally limited by metal and contact resistance, with little effect from the Si substrate. In this regard, there is little difference between these inductors and filters and those implemented in GaAs.

Two square-spiral inductors were fabricated, measured, and characterized. A die photo of the test layout is shown in Fig. 1. Metal width was 6.5 μm with 5.5-μm spacing of 1.8-μm-thick second-metal Al. The sheet resistance of Al was 20 mΩ/□ over 1.7 μm of oxide, and the parasitic capacitance from Al to the substrate was 0.016 fF/μm². The substrate resistivity was 14 Ω·cm and 500-μm-thick p-type Si. The larger inductor had nine turns with an outer dimension of about 230 μm. The smaller one had four turns with an outer dimension of about 115 μm. Measured S_{11} plots from 0.3 MHz to 3 GHz for these inductors

Manuscript received October 10, 1989; revised February 13, 1990. This work was supported by the U.S. Army Research Office under Grant DAAL03-87-K0079.

The authors are with the Department of Electrical Engineering and Computer Sciences and the Electronics Research Laboratory, University of California, Berkeley, CA 94720.

IEEE Log Number 9036489.

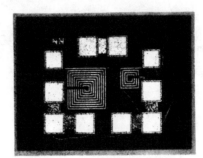

Fig. 1.   Die photograph of the inductors.

II. Inductor Characterization

in a 50-Ω system are shown in Fig. 2. The large inductor is self resonant at 2.47 GHz while the small one has an estimated resonant frequency of 9.7 GHz. Pad capacitance was zeroed out of the on-chip measurement. The large inductor had a measured value of 9.7 nH while the smaller was 1.9 nH. The theoretical values are, respectively, 9.3 and 1.3 nH [4]. The differences are attributed to lead inductances and possible minor imprecision in calibration of the test equipment. The series loss in the inductors deduced from RF measurements agreed very closely with measured and predicted dc series resistance, indicating that coupled loss from the Si substrate was negligible. While metal shrinkage due to photolithography and etching tolerances can affect the series-loss value, it theoretically has negligible effect on the inductance value. In fact , with a typical ±0.2-μm metal shrinkage, the inductance value in the large inductor has been calculated to vary less than 1%.

An equivalent circuit for the square-spiral inductor is shown in Fig. 3. In this circuit, L_s models the self and mutual inductances in the second-metal segments, R_s is the accumulated sheet resistance, C_p models the parasitic capacitance from the second-metal layer to the substrate, and R_p represents the resistance of the conductive Si substrate. Coupling capacitance between metal segments due to fringing fields in both the dielectric region and the air region is neglected in this model. Such an approximation is valid because the relative dielectric constant of the oxide is small and the inductor is used at frequencies well below its self-resonant frequency. Since the structure of the square-spiral inductor is not symmetrical, the parasitic capacitance values at the inductor terminals should be different from one another. This difference, however, is only small [5] and the two capacitors are assumed the same. If the spiral inductor is treated as a lossless transmission line with a total length much smaller than the wavelength, it can be shown that C_p is approximately equal to one half the input capacitance of the open-circuited line. This gives a first-order estimate of C_p. More accurate analytical expressions for C_p can be found in [6]. The substrate resistance R_p can be derived from measured *S* parameters. It is interesting to note that in a GaAs inductor using microstrip lines, substrate resistance R_p is not present

Reprinted from *IEEE J. Solid-State Circuits*, vol. SC-25, no. 4, pp. 1028–1031, Aug. 1990.

385

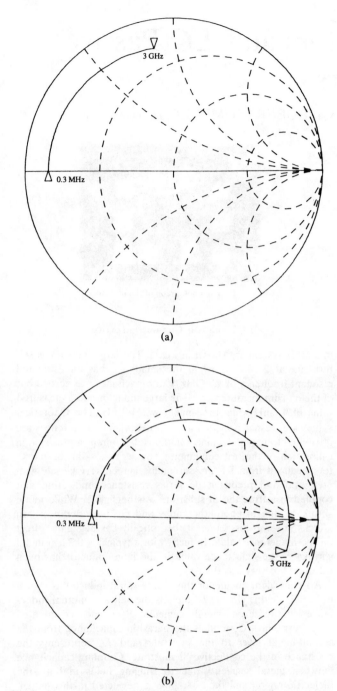

(a)

(b)

Fig. 2. Measured S_{11} plots from 0.3 MHz to 3 GHz: (a) small inductor and (b) large inductor.

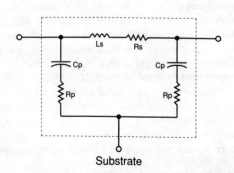

Fig. 3. Equivalent circuit of the square-spiral inductor.

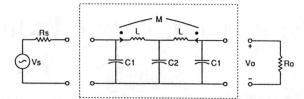

Fig. 4. Simplified circuit diagram of the five-pole maximally flat low-pass LC filter.

because the GaAs substrate acts as the dielectric layer which is in direct contact with the conductive ground plane.

If one side of the inductor is grounded, the self-resonant frequency of the spiral inductor can be derived from the equivalent circuit. It is approximately equal to

$$\omega_R = \frac{1}{\sqrt{L_s C_p}} \left[\frac{1 - R_s^2 \left(\dfrac{C_p}{L_s} \right)}{1 - R_p^2 \left(\dfrac{C_p}{L_s} \right)} \right]^{1/2} . \qquad (1)$$

Beyond the resonant frequency, the inductor becomes capacitive. Frequency ω_R is limited mainly by C_p which is inversely proportional to the oxide thickness between the second-metal layer and the substrate. The frequency at which the inductor Q is maximum can also be derived. It is

$$\omega_Q = \frac{1}{\sqrt{L_s C_p}} \left\{ \frac{R_s}{2R_p} \left[\left(1 + \frac{4}{3} \frac{R_p}{R_s} \right)^{1/2} - 1 \right] \right\}^{1/2} . \qquad (2)$$

The large inductor has a measured maximum Q of 3 at 0.9 GHz and the small one has an estimated maximum Q of 8 at 4.1 GHz. If the inductor is used as a floating inductor, the shunt branches in the equivalent circuit are effectively in series with one another. Equations (1) and (2) hence still hold provided that C_p and R_p are replaced by $C_p/2$ and $2R_p$, respectively. Circuit elements in the equivalent circuit for the large inductor were derived from both theory and measured S parameters. The set $\{ L_s, R_s, C_p, R_p \}$ is equal to $\{9.7 \text{ nH}, 15.4 \ \Omega, 590 \text{ fF}, 70 \ \Omega\}$.

III. LC FILTERS

As a test vehicle, a five-pole maximally flat low-pass filter with nominal designed -3-dB frequency of 880 MHz and midband insertion loss of 2.25 dB was fabricated. The circuit is shown in Fig. 4 where R_s and R_o are 50-Ω off-chip resistors. Element

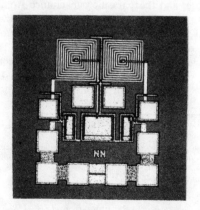

Fig. 5. Die photograph of the filter.

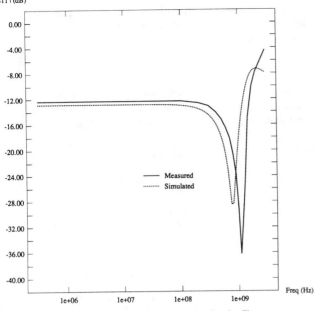

Fig. 6.   Measured and simulated $|S_{11}|$ for the filter.

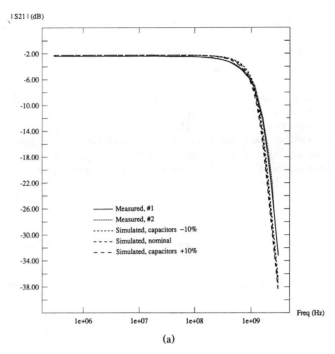

(a)

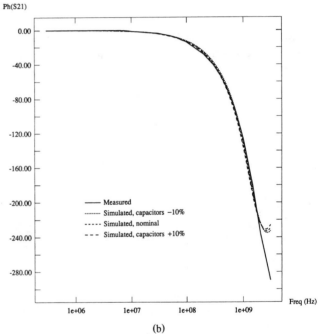

(b)

Fig. 7.   Measured and simulated S_{21} characteristics of the filter: (a) magnitude and (b) phase.

values are $L \approx 9.7$ nH, $M \approx 0.4$ nH, $C_1 \approx 1.3$ pF, and $C_2 \approx 4.3$ pF where parasitic capacitance associated with the inductors is included in the capacitor values. Mutual inductor M exists between the inductors due to layout proximity. The capacitors were fabricated in standard form using metal over 1500 Å of oxide with an n^+ bottom plate. Since the sheet resistance of n^+ is high $(20\ \Omega/\square)$, the series loss in the capacitor must be minimized by reducing the ratio L/W, where L and W are, respectively, the length and width that define the capacitor area. Pads were included with the filter to allow testing but were not included in the design and were zeroed out of the on-chip measurements. This would correspond to use of such a filter in an on-chip environment where pads are not present. If a packaged stand-alone filter was required, pads and bond wires would have to be included in the design.

The transfer function can be derived from the simplified circuit in Fig. 4 and is given by

$$\frac{V_o(S)}{V_s(S)} = \frac{a_2 s^2 + a_0}{b_5 s^5 + b_4 s^4 + b_3 s^3 + b_2 s^2 + b_1 s + b_0} \quad (3)$$

where

$$a_2 = MC_2$$

$$a_0 = 1$$

$$b_5 = (L-M)C_1(L+M)C_2 R_s C_1$$

$$b_4 = (L-M)C_1(L+M)C_2\left(1+\frac{R_s}{R_o}\right)$$

$$b_3 = (L+M)C_2\frac{(L-M)}{R_o} + [2(L-M)C_1 + 2LC_2]R_s C_1$$

$$b_2 = 2(L-M)C_1 + LC_2 + \frac{R_s}{R_o}[2(L-M)C_1 + LC_2]$$

$$b_1 = 2\frac{(L-M)}{R_o} + R_s(2C_1 + C_2)$$

$$b_0 = \left(1+\frac{R_s}{R_o}\right).$$

As seen from (3), the mutual inductance M creates two high-frequency zeros on the $j\omega$ axis. Since M is relatively small compared to the inductance value L, its effect on the filter attenuation is significant only in the stopband. Let f_Z $(= 1/[2\pi\sqrt{MC_2}])$ denote the magnitude of the complex-conjugate zeros. It can be shown that the zeros increase the stopband loss at frequencies below f_Z but decrease the loss at

IEEE JOURNAL OF SOLID-STATE CIRCUITS, VOL. 25, NO. 4, AUGUST 1990

frequencies above. If maximum high-frequency attenuation is desired, the value of M should be minimized by separating the two inductors far apart in the layout. If $M = 0$, (3) reduces to a simple five-pole transfer function.

A die photo of the filter is shown in Fig. 5. In order to minimize the electrical coupling through the substrate, a buried p-type layer was placed around the I/O pads and around the periphery of each device. Measured $|S_{11}|$ is shown in Fig. 6 and is close to the simulated values. The filter was simulated using the 3σ limits of capacitance of $\pm 10\%$ due to process variations but assuming all capacitors tracked closely. The resulting spread of S_{21} characteristics is shown in Fig. 7 together with two measured characteristics from opposite sides of a 4-in wafer. The filter has a measured midband insertion loss of 2.4 dB and measured -3-dB frequencies of 845 and 860 MHz. Simulation with capacitor tolerances predicted the -3-dB frequencies at 830, 880, and 930 MHz with 880 MHz being the nominal design value.

Since MOS capacitors display small but finite voltage coefficients [7], the filter was checked for nonlinearity by a third-order intermodulation measurement at 500 MHz. Measurements at signal levels of $+15$ dBm indicated that the third-order intercept was better than the measurement resolution of $+42$ dBm.

IV. Conclusion

Passive inductors and LC filters useful in the gigahertz range have been demonstrated in standard Si IC processing. These elements can be used for high-frequency on-chip filtering, inductive peaking of high-frequency amplifiers, and impedance matching for low-noise amplifiers.

Acknowledgment

The authors wish to acknowledge the contributions of Bill Mack of Signetics Corporation for layout assistance and characterization, and of Signetics for HS3 fabrication.

References

[1] E. Pettenpaul et al., "CAD models of lumped elements on GaAs up to 18 GHz," IEEE Trans. Microwave Theory Tech., vol. 36, no. 2, pp. 294–304, Feb. 1988.

[2] E. Frian, S. Meszaros, M. Cuhaci, and J. Wight, "Computer-aided design of square spiral transformers and inductors," in 1989 IEEE MTT-S Dig., pp. 661–664.

[3] R. M. Warner, Jr., and J. N. Fordemwalt, Integrated Circuits. New York: McGraw-Hill, p. 267.

[4] H. M. Greenhouse, "Design of planar rectangular microelectronic inductor," IEEE Trans. Parts, Hybrids, Packag., vol. PHP-10, no. 2, pp. 101–109, June 1974.

[5] M. Parisot, Y. Archambault, D. Pavlidis, and J. Magarshack, "Highly accurate design of spiral inductors for MMIC's with small size and high cut-off frequency characteristics," in 1984 IEEE MTT-S Dig., pp. 106–110.

[6] R. Garg and I. J. Bahl, "Characteristics of coupled microstrip lines," IEEE Trans. Microwave Theory Tech., vol. MTT-27, no. 7, pp. 700–705, July 1979.

[7] J. L. McCreary, "Matching properties, and voltage and temperature dependence of MOS capacitors," IEEE J. Solid-State Circuits, vol. SC-16, no. 6, pp. 608–616, Dec. 1981.

Part 6
More About Automatic Tuning
and Adaptivity

THE most important cause of inaccuracies in the frequency response of integrated continuous-time filters is the error in (trans)conductance-to-capacitance ratios due to tolerances, environmental factors such as temperature changes, and aging. This error causes mainly a frequency scaling of the intended response (e.g., a 20% shift in the critical frequencies). In a significant number of applications, such a shift can be accommodated in the system specifications. This is the case, for example, in anti-aliasing and smoothing filters used in conjunction with sampled-data signal processors, when the ratio of sampling frequency to signal frequency is high. In other applications, though (in fact, in almost all of the applications mentioned in this book), such shifts cannot be tolerated. Thus, tuning is required, which, of course, must be implemented by automatic means. Most of the systems use an external reference and an auxiliary on-chip circuit, tune the latter, and apply the same correction to the main filter; the on-chip circuit then becomes tuned indirectly, to within the degree of matching between the two filters (for early work on this concept see [1–3] and Paper 4-1 in this volume). In this way, (trans)conductance-to-capacitance ratios are corrected and critical frequencies attain the desired value.

Filter poles have different quality factors. All these quality factors are, in principle, dependent only on ratios of like filter elements, that is, ratios of transconductances and/or of capacitances. These ratios can be very accurately implemented on chip (and are usually not tuned). In critical cases, though, second-order effects, such as excess-phase in integrators, can influence quality factors and sometimes it is also attempted to tune those (see [4], Paper 5-D.1, and Paper 3-B.10 and [5]). Although in some oscillators the Q-factor of the poles is tuned (to infinity) to stabilize the signal amplitude, it is our opinion that the systems used so far for Q tuning in filters are large and tricky and that none has been demonstrated to operate satisfactorily enough to be used in commercial filters. One should try to start from a design robust enough to make the tuning of quality factors unnecessary. If it appears that such tuning is needed, one will probably be better off changing the filter topology to a more robust (less sensitive) one, or investigating the causes of quality factor inaccuracies and eliminating them at the source (e.g., redesigning the integrators to reduce their excess phase, changing the layout to reduce the effect of parasitics, etc.).

The subject of automatic tuning has already been briefly introduced in the tutorial Papers 1-1, 1-2, and 2-A.1 in this book, and has been discussed in relation to particular implementations in several papers in this volume and elsewhere [6–12]. Additional material on automatic tuning is included in this part. We also chose to include in the same part material on tracking and adaptive filters, which use techiques akin to those used in automatic tuning; after all, an automatic tuning system tracks an external reference and adapts the filter response to it.

Paper 6-1, by Schaumann and Tan, gives an introduction and overview of automatic tuning. Both frequency tuning and quality factor tuning are discussed in a general way that is not tied to particular implementations (another tutorial presentation can be found in [10]). Paper 6-2 by vanPeteghem and Song considers tuning strategies and proposes a system with two tuning frequencies instead of the usual single frequency. Paper 6-3 by Silva-Martinez, Steyaert, and Sansen investigates a different approach to automatic tuning, in which advantage is taken of the relation between frequency-domain properties and time-domain properties. In this paper, switched-capacitor techniques are used as part of the tuning system. Time-domain techniques are also used in [6, 9, 11, 12], as well as in Papers 2-B.6, 5-A.1, and 7-A.2 in this volume.

The accuracy of indirect tuning is no better than the degree of matching between the main filter and the filter locked to the reference. A way to bypass this limitation is direct tuning, as is suggested in Paper 6-4, and consists of tuning the very filter that does the processing. In some applications filters are used in burst mode and tuning can be corrected between bursts. For example, in the case of video filters, tuning can be performed in the field fly-back interval; see Paper 7-C.3 and [13]. A further example of a commercial chip employing direct tuning, this one for telephony, can be found in Paper 7-A.1. If uninterrupted service is needed, two filters could be used along with an appropriate switching sequence, as discussed in Paper 6-4; this technique, though, has not been proven so far in integrated form.

An approach to direct tuning is proposed by Plett, Copeland, and Hadaway in Paper 6-5; the tuning is performed before the filter is put into use and the required information is stored in analog form in an EPROM; see also [14]. Yet another approach is proposed by Hughes, Bird, and Soin in Paper 6-6; here element arrays are used and the tuning system switches in or out elements as required by tuning. The resulting quantization of the tuning range [15] is adequate for some applications. Related schemes are discussed in [16-18] and in Paper 5-A.1.

It should be mentioned that the subject of filter tuning has, in the past, received significant attention in the context of hybrid and discrete-component filters. Such tuning, using equipment external to the filter (sometimes automated), was performed to tune out the effects of manufacturing tolerances. References and a comparison of several techniques can be found elsewhere [19]. In that context, the tuning algorithms used have reached a remarkable degree of sophistication. These algorithms have not found their way into integrated filters, though, in part because the area overhead involved in placing the tuning circuits on-chip would be excessive. Still, there may be some ideas within such work that could indirectly be of benefit in the context of integrated filters.

Many of the integrated filters reported use tuning systems based on a voltage-controlled oscillator (VCO) or a voltage-controlled filter (VCF). In a VCO-based system, an oscillator signal is compared with a reference frequency signal. Any phase error causes a tuning signal. In a VCF-based system, the output signal of a filter (possibly 90 degrees phase-shifted) is compared with the input signal. In this case a phase error reflects a frequency difference, which activates the tuning. Paper 6-7 by Kwan and Martin reports the integration of a continuous-time CMOS biquadratic filter with VCF-type frequency tracking. A generalization of the VCF-based scheme, which tunes the filter even without affecting the signal processing in the filter, is discussed in [20] and in Paper 6-8. Correlation techniques are also used for adaptive filters. Tuning and adaptivity are strongly related. In Paper 6-9, Kozma, Johns, and Sedra propose to adapt all (or many) parameters of a filter to the parameters of an ideal reference filter

using the response error signal. The method permits accurate filter adaptation.

Probably the first fully continuous-time integrated adaptive filter was an equalizer for Teletext data—see Paper 7-C.4. It used a video frequency Laguerre filter with continuously adapted tap-weights. It has been applied in a transversal as well as in a recursive mode. Paper 6-10 by Johns, Snelgrove, and Sedra contains a recent study on the feasibility of analog recursive adaptive state space filters, and [21] considers adaptive lattice filters.

In all cases the signal processing (filtering) is analog. The updating of the coefficients is slower and may be performed digitally. Implementation of the many multipliers in the adaptive control is less complex in analog form but imperfections like DC offset in the control loops can degrade the adaptation accuracy.

References

[1] J. R. Canning and G. A. Wilson, "Frequency discriminator circuit arrangement," U.K. Patent 1 421 093, January 14, 1976.

[2] J. R. Brand, R. Schaumann, and E. M. Skei, "Temperature stabilized active-R filter," *Proc. 20th Midwest Symposium on Circuits and Systems,* pp. 295-300, April 1977.

[3] K. Radhakrishna Rao, V. Setharaman and P. K. Neelakantan, "Novel follow-the-master filter," *Proc. IEEE,* vol. 63, pp. 1725-1726, December 1977.

[4] D. Senderowicz, D. A. Hodges and P. R. Gray, "An NMOS integrated vector-locked loop," *Proc. IEEE ISCAS '82,* pp. 1164-1167, 1982.

[5] B. Nauta and E. Seevinck, "Automatic tuning of quality factors for VHF CMOS filters," *Proc. IEEE ISCAS,* pp. 1147-1150, 1990.

[6] R. L. Geiger, P. E. Allen, and D. T. Ngo, "Switched resistor filters—a continuous time approach to monolithic MOS filter design," *IEEE Trans. Circuits and Syst.,* vol. CAS-29, pp. 306-315, May 1982.

[7] K. Radhakrishna Rao and G. Venupopal, "A novel technique for the on-chip tuning of monolithic filters," *Proc. IEEE,* vol. 75, pp. 257-258, February 1987.

[8] K. Radhakrishna Rao and P. Ashar, "Magnitude locked loop," *Proc. IEEE,* vol. 76, no. 2, pp. 201-203, February 1988.

[9] W. J. A. de Heij, K. Hoen, and E. Seevinck, "Accurate automatic tuning circuit for bipolar integrated filters," *Proc. IEEE ISCAS '90,* pp. 1159-1162, 1990.

[10] R. R. Schaumann, M. Ghausi, and K. R. Laker, *Design of Analog Filters,* Englewood Cliffs, NJ: Prentice-Hall, 1990.

[11] S. Takagi, N. Fujii, T. Yanagisawa, and K. Tabei, "Automatic tuning circuit for continuous-time filters using MRCs," *Electronics and Communications in Japan, 3,* vol. 74, no. 2, pp. 97-105, 1991.

[12] M. Sartori, M. Mazzucco and R. Gaidano, "ALBA: a bipolar technology structured array for the design of high-order continuous-time filters," *IEEE J. Solid-State Circuits,* vol. 24, pp. 723-731, June 1989.

[13] J. P. M. van Lammeren and B. Motté, "Multi-standard video front end," *IEEE Trans. Consumer Electronics*, vol. CE-37, pp. 190–196, August 1991.

[14] E. Sakinger and W. Guggenbühl, "An analog trimming circuit based on a floating-gate device," *IEEE J. Solid-State Circuits*, vol. 23, pp. 1437–1440, December 1988.

[15] J. Ramirez-Angulo, R. L. Geiger, and E. Sánchez-Sinencio, "Components quantization effects on continuous-time filters," *IEEE Trans. Circuits Syst.*, vol. CAS-33, pp. 651–659, July 1986.

[16] M. A. Rubicki and R. L. Geiger, "A high frequency temperature invariant active NMOS filter," *Proc. 1982 Midwest Symposium on Circuits and Systems,* pp. 321–324, 1982.

[17] J. Fincher and R. Geiger, "Monolithic frequency referenced digitally self-tuned filters," *Proc. Midwest Symposium on Circuits and Systems,* pp. 1–4, 1983.

[18] J. E. Franca and F. Nunes, "Successive approximation tuning of monolithic continuous-time filters," *Electron. Lett.*, vol. 28, pp. 1696–1697, August 27, 1992.

[19] D. E. Hocevar and T. N. Trick, "Automatic tuning algorithms for active filters," *IEEE Trans. Circuits and Syst.*, vol. CAS-29, pp. 448–458, July 1982.

[20] T. L. Brooks and P. M. VanPeteghem, "Simultaneous tuning and signal processing in integrated continuous-time filters: the correlated tuning loop," *Proc. IEEE ISCAS '89*, pp. 651–654, 1989.

[21] H. Lev-Ari, T. Kailath and J. M. Cioffi, "Adaptive recursive-least-squares lattice and transversal filters for continuous-time signal processing," *IEEE Trans. Circuits Syst.*, vol. 39, pp. 81–89, February 1992.

The Problem of On-Chip Automatic Tuning in Continuous-Time Integrated Filters

ROLF SCHAUMANN
DEPARTMENT OF ELECTRICAL ENGINEERING
PORTLAND STATE UNIVERSITY
P.O. BOX 751, PORTLAND, OR 97207-0751, USA

MEHMET ALI TAN
DEPARTMENT OF ELECTFICAL ENGINEERING
BILKENT UNIVERSITY
P.O. BOX 8, MALTEPE, ANKARA, 0672, TURKEY

Abstract: This paper discusses the most important and difficult aspect of the design of fully integrated continuous-time (ct) filters: Continuous, real time, on-chip tuning of filter parameters against errors caused by such factors as fabrication tolerances, changes in operating conditions, parasitic effects and aging. The origins of the errors in filter parameters are pointed out and the generally adopted methods for automatic error correction are discussed: A phase-locked loop for tuning of frequency parameters, and a magnitude-locking loop for maintaining the transfer characteristic's shape. Guidelines are given to aid the designer in avoiding the most prevalent pitfalls and an illustrative example is presented which incorporates the ideas and concepts discussed in the paper.

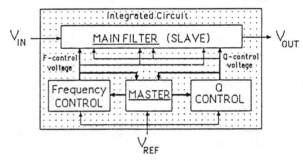

Fig. 1 Block diagram of MASTER-SLAVE control system for integrated continuous-time filters

1.Introduction

To guarantee accurate performance of fully integrated continuous-time *(ct)* filters, precise *absolute* element values must be realized *and maintained* during circuit operation. Since these are not normally available because of fabrication tolerances or varying operating conditions, the generally adopted solution is to design onto the IC an *automatic tuning scheme* as part of the total *ct* filter circuitry. A review of the literature [1]-[8] shows that an accurate *reference frequency*, e.g. a system clock, has been agreed upon among designers as the most reliable standard. From the filter's response to the reference signal at this known frequency, the tuning circuitry must then *detect* and *identify* any errors, *compute* the appropriate *corrections* and *apply* them via a suitable control circuit to the filter. All these operations must be performed *continuously*, in *real time* and with *reasonably simple on-chip circuitry*. However, in using this approach it is to be remembered that the *reference signal* must not be allowed to interfere with the filter's *main information signal* in order to avoid undesirable cross-talk or intermodulation. The problems are avoided or at least minimized by constructing on the IC a so-called *MASTER* which *models with adequate accuracy* all relevant performance criteria of the main filter, coined the *SLAVE*. The proposed tuning strategy then applies the reference signal to the MASTER and *relies on matching and tracking* between this MASTER and the sufficiently identical SLAVE on the same chip to tune the SLAVE. Tuning is accomplished by applying the correction voltage simultaneously to both MASTER and SLAVE. A block diagram of this scheme, as it is implemented in almost all cases (with few exceptions [2]) that have appeared in the literature to date, is shown in Fig. 1.

The MASTER's circuitry is designed to be *of sufficient complexity to model* the Main Filter's (SLAVE's) behavior that is relevant for tuning. The system contains a *Frequency-Control* block that detects any errors in the MASTER's frequency parameters and generates a control voltage which is applied to the MASTER *and the matched* SLAVE such that any detected errors are minimized.

The analogous function of adjusting the "quality factors" Q_i is performed by the '*Q-Control*' block in Fig. 1. Its purpose is to permit automatic tuning of the *shape* of a filter's transmission

characteristic. *Q*, a ratio of frequencies, is determined by a *ratio* of like components, the *forte* of IC processing. Consequently, it is often assumed that *Q* need not be tuned [1]-[7]. However, *Q* is known to be extremely sensitive to small parasitic phase shifts so that in high-frequency communications circuits, the primary applications of integrated *ct* filters, large performance errors must be expected. Thus, *Q*-tuning is generaly unavoidable.

Details of the control methods will be described below, along with a discussion of possible implementations of the frequency- and the *Q*-control blocks and some examples.

At this point, a number of observations are first presented that the designer of such systems should keep in mind:

1) For correct operation of the control scheme, MASTER and SLAVE *must* be well matched in their behavior and track. Frequency-parameters are not very sensitive to parasitic effects so that matching does not appear to be a problem; but, because of the *extreme* sensitivity of *Q* to parasitics and small phase errors, great care must be taken when 'modelling' the SLAVE's behavior by a MASTER circuit.

2) The designer of an IC filter chip must consider at the outset *whether the contemplated filter structure is tunable*, that is, whether an observed error can be corrected by varying the value of a dominant tunable component. Easy tunability may dictate e.g. cascade designs in spite of the superiority, in principal, of ladder simulations [8].

3) The *utmost care* must be taken to *shield* the main filtering path from the reference and extraneous digital signals on the IC which are likely to interfere with the signal processing job or at least cause the signal-to-"noise" ratio to deteriorate.

4) The designer should derive the best possible *nominal* design by use of careful modelling, statistical yield analysis, or design centering. Electronic tuning is almost always realized by changing the dc bias conditions; if very wide tuning ranges are required, often other important filter aspects, such as linearity and dynamic range, are affected. Also, wide tuning requirements tend to result in more complicated filter and control circuitry.

Reprinted from *IEEE Proc. ISCAS,* pp. 106–109, 1989.

2. The Mathematics of Tuning

Assume a transfer function $H(s,t,u)$ is to be realized where t and u are the *vectors* of tuned and untuned circuit parameters, respectively. Both t and u are subject to errors and tolerances, $t = t_o + \Delta t$ and $u = u_o + \Delta u$ where t_o and u_o are the nominal values. The goal is then to design a control system which adjusts the values of Δt such that

$$H(s,t,u) = \frac{N_m(s,t)}{D_n(s,t)} = H(s,t_o+\Delta t,u_o+\Delta u) \longrightarrow H(s,t_o,u_o) \quad (1)$$

i.e., by varying Δt, the inaccurate transfer function $H(s,t_o+\Delta t,u_o+\Delta u)$ is to be tuned to its nominal value $H(s,t_o,u_o)$. Note that Δt may consist of 'tuning changes' Δt_t and of 'errors' Δt_ε: $\Delta t = \Delta t_t + \Delta t_\varepsilon$, i.e., tuning the components in the vector t will not only compensate for the errors in u but also for errors in t itself. We have indicated in (1) that $H(s)$ is a ratio of polynomials $N_m(s)$ of order m and $D_n(s)$ of order n, that is, it is determined by $n+m+1$ coefficients. Therefore, complete tuning, in general, requires application of at least $n+m+1$ test frequencies with two possible measurements each (magnitude and phase). In practice, however, only very few reference signals, customarily just one, are applied to the filter chip!

A simple example will illustrate some important points: Disregarding for now the *dashed* components, consider the first-order RC filter in Fig. 2 and assume that the resistor is untuned (belonging to u) and the capacitor is the tunable element $C(V_c)$ (out of the set t) where V_c is the control voltage. The transfer function of this circuit equals

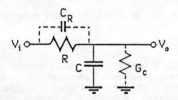

Fig. 2 First-order RC lowpass filter

$$V_o / V_i = H(s, C(V_c), R) = 1 / [sC(V_c)R + 1] \quad (2)$$

In this simple example, any errors in R or C can be corrected by adjusting V_c such that the RC product remains unchanged: $[C_o+\Delta C(V_c)][R_o+\Delta R] = C_o R_o$. Among the various possibilities for accomplishing this adjustment, a particularly simple *magnitude-locking loop* approach was proposed in [6] which equates $|H|$ of (2) with an accurate voltage divider ratio $R_2/(R_1+R_2)$. As a result, the RC-product in steady state can be shown to be set by

$$CR = \frac{1}{\omega_{ref}} \sqrt{\left(1 + \frac{R_1}{R_2}\right)^2 - 1} \quad (3)$$

This equation points out a result that is typical for *all* automatic tuning schemes:

The accuracy and long-term stability of the RC product, which sets the frequency parameter of the filter, are now as good as those of the applied reference frequency ω_{ref} and of a ratio of like components on the IC.

The tuning strategy until now has ignored the effects of the always present parasitic components. For instance, an IC implementation may have, among others, a *lossy* capacitor and a *parasitic* shunt capacitor across the resistor as is shown in dashed form in Fig. 2. In that case the transfer function equals, with $G = 1/R$,

$$V_o / V_i = [sC_R + G]/[s(C+C_R) + G+G_c] \quad (4)$$

and we can observe two effects that again are true in general:

1) *Parasitic components change the* values *of the critical frequencies.* For the case of this example, the nominal pole

value has moved from $1/(RC)$ to the new position

$$\omega_p = [G + G_c]/[C + C_R] = [1/RC]\cdot[1 + R/R_c]/[1 + C_R/C] \quad (5)$$

2) *Parasitic components* may *cause* new *critical frequencies to appear.* In the example, the parasitic capacitor C_R gave rise to a new zero at $\omega_z = 1/(C_R R)$.

The first of these two effects leads to the same result as changes in the nominal component values, that is, parasitics look like tolerances. [C_R appears as an error in the value of C: $\Delta C = C_R$, and G_c looks like an error in the conductor value: $\Delta G = G_c$]. Such errors can always be corrected by tuning.

The second effect, the creation of new poles and/or zeros, is more serious since no tuning method can reduce the "expanded" transfer function (4) to the ideal one (2). Thus, if parasitic effects are of concern — as they always are — then there exists no choice Δt of t such that the tuning operation defined in (1) can be satisfied *exactly*. Rather, if there exists a vector of parasitic components, p, the transfer function $H(s,t,u)$ becomes

$$H_p(s,t,u,p) = N_p(s,t,u,p)/D_p(s,t,u,p) \quad (6)$$

where the degrees of the new numerator N_p and denominator D_p are in general higher than those of the ideal N_m and D_n introduced in (1). Since H_p cannot be equated to $H(s,t_o,u_o)$ exactly, we have to be content with an approximate tuning solution which minimizes a remaining tuning error ε defined via a suitably chosen *norm*, $||\cdot||$, as

$$\varepsilon(\Delta t) = || H_p(s,t_o+\Delta t,u_o+\Delta u,p) - H(s,t_o,u_o) || => \min \quad (7)$$

For example, by choice of Δt one may wish to minimize the maximum difference between the magnitudes of H_p and H at a given frequency or over a frequency range of interest.

Although conceptually the tuning operation described in (7) is easy to understand, in practice it is generally very difficult to perform *automatically, on-chip, and with reasonably simple control system circuitry*. Obviously then, simplifications of the process are desirable. They may be achieved via a reduction in the complexity of the function $H_p(s,t,u,p)$, an approach referred to as "*partitioning*" [9]. It is obtained, e.g., through a *cascade* design where any effects within a second-order section are isolated and where the influence of section errors on the total transfer function is easy to identify and to correct.

A second important simplification of the tuning scheme is obtained from topologies in which *parasitics are absorbed* in the main circuit components, as is G_c in the example of Fig. 2. In that case the parasitics look like element tolerances, do not increase the order of the system, and therefore do not generate new poles and/or zeros.

The third property to look for in a system for automatic tuning is *good matching* of like components across the chip: fortunately a strong point of IC implementations. Better matching is generally obtained as the components get closer in value and characteristic, with the best match found for identical components [10].

To help evaluate the operation of the functional block diagram of the *MASTER-SLAVE* tuning system in Fig. 1, the next section will consider the typical tuning schemes adopted for IC ct filters.

3. The Control Blocks

a) The Frequency-Control Block

In almost all reported cases, the frequency-control block identified in Fig. 1 is realized via a phase-locked loop (PLL) with a general scheme as shown in Fig. 3a where the cleaned error signal $y(t)$ is applied to the MASTER *and* the matched and tracking SLAVEs in a way that corrects the detected errors. The practical performance of all schemes found in the literature is quite similar; operational details depend on the particulars of the phase detection and the MASTER circuitry. The most frequently found methods are:

- The phase detector is an analog multiplier or, usually simpler, an EXOR gate.

• The MASTER is either a voltage-controlled oscillator (VCO) or a suitable filter (if the dashed connection in Fig. 3a is used). The main difference is that a system with a MASTER *filter* results in a residual frequency error that is inversely proportional to the control loop gain whereas operation with a MASTER *VCO* yields ideally $\Delta\omega = 0$.

b) The Q-Control Block

The purpose of the "Q-control" block in Fig. 1 is to provide a suitable strategy that results in automatic control of the "shape of the transfer characteristic". A workable Q-control scheme measures ΔH at one frequency via a simple peak detector and deduces the error ΔQ, regardless of its cause. A diagram of this method is shown in Fig. 3b: The MASTER is built to model all relevant Q-errors of the SLAVE; K and A are dc amplifiers of gains K and A, respectively. It is assumed, as indeed is *necessary* for this method to function, that all frequencies of MASTER and SLAVE

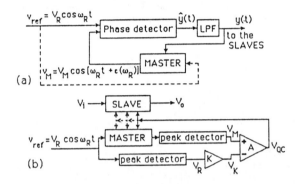

(a)

(b)

Fig. 3 a) Phase-locked loop frequency tuning scheme
b) Magnitude locking loop for Q- control

are tuned correctly. V_{QC} is returned at one or more points to both MASTER and SLAVE in a way that is appropriate for adjusting the quality factors.

The outputs of the two peak detectors are $V_M = |H(j\omega_R)|V_R$ and $V_K = KV_R$, so that the dc Q-control voltage V_{QC} equals

$$V_{QC} = A (V_M - V_K) = A (|H(j\omega_R)| - K) V_R, \qquad (8)$$

and

$$|H(j\omega_R)| - K = \frac{1}{A}\left[\frac{V_{QC}}{V_R}\right]\Big|_{A \longrightarrow \infty} = 0. \qquad (9)$$

Thus, $|H(j\omega_R)|/V_R \approx KV_R$, i.e., the two amplitudes are locked together. Assuming further that

$$|H(j\omega_R)| = |H(j\omega_R)|_0 + \Delta H = H_0 (Q_0 + \Delta Q)$$

and that K equals the nominal value $|H(j\omega_R)|_0 = H_0 Q_0$, but with a design or processing error ε_K yields $H_0 (Q_0 + \Delta Q) = K + \varepsilon_K$, i.e.,

$$\Delta Q = \varepsilon_K / H_0 \qquad (10)$$

For precise dc amplifier gain K, one would normally have $\varepsilon_K \rightarrow 0$ and consequently, obtain ideally a zero Q-error.

A little thought will convince the reader that this Q-control strategy can be made to work not only for second-order sections in cascade filters, but also for other types of topologies, such as ladder simulations; only the "tuning algorithm" that identifies *which* component to vary to achieve the correction will generally be less obvious. Careful pre-design simulations, however, will usually indicate the most appropriate tuning elements.

In the next section, an example will be presented which incorporates most of the concepts discussed in this paper [8].

4. An Example

To be implemented is an integrated CMOS all-pole ct bandpass

filter to meet the following specifications: center frequency: 4MHz; width of passband: 800kHz with $A_p \leq 0.5$dB and gain 20dB; stopbands in $f < 2.3$MHz and $f > 6.8$ MHz with $A_s \geq 70$dB; $V_{in,max} = 100$mV.

The high-frequency requirements point to *transconductance-C* techniques and the relatively large pole-Q factors of ≈ 9.8 and ≈ 23.9 make Q-tuning unavoidable. To ease tuning, *partitioning* (a cascade design) suggests itself. Design and performance of the experimental circuit can be found in [8]; here, in keeping with the topic of this paper, only the aspects of tuning will be discussed. A block diagram of the complete filter-tuning system is shown in Fig. 4. It indicates an EXOR-based PLL for frequency control which locks the frequency of the MASTER VCO (an ∞-Q copy of one SLAVE section) to f_{ref}; a lowpass filter 2 (LPF2) is inserted into the dc f-control line (y) to reduce the remaining high-frequency noise before applying $\overline{y}$ to all frequency-determining transconductors on the chip. Hence, all frequency parameters can be assumed to be correct. It remains to decide how the four fairly high Q-factors can be guaranteed, regardless of processing tolerances, temperature drifts and the large parasitic

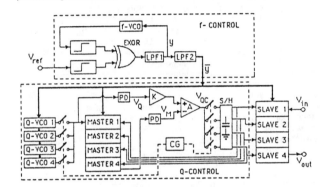

Fig. 4 Four-point tuning system

phase shifts to be expected at video frequencies. With very careful layout and modelling, the designer may attempt to rely on tracking, and tune all four Q-factors from the same control voltage. Taking a more conservative approach, the four Q- factors can be controlled *separately* with the system shown in Fig. 4:

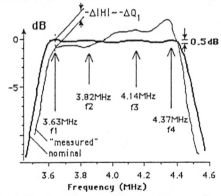

Fig. 5 Sketch of the nominal and a "measured" transfer function passband with 'support' frequencies at the reflection zeros.

The four MASTER and Q-VCO sections are *copies* of the corresponding SLAVE circuitry, of course, with the Q-VCOs'

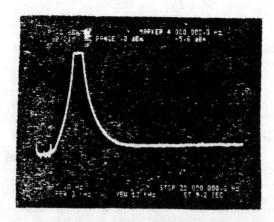

Fig. 6 Experimental performance of the circuit

identical process takes place during the remaining three phases of the tuning cycle, which is repeated with a chosen clock frequency of a few kilohertz, well outside the desired passband but fast enough to reach the final Q-values in milliseconds and, especially, fast enough to prevent drooping of the control voltages stored on $C_{S/Hi}$, $i=1,...,4$. Note that the *amplitude* of the VCOs is unimportant because it is "compared to itself" [see (8)]. The method can be shown to converge after a few (four or five) iterations [8]. Since it tunes the four pole frequencies, the four section gain constants and, implicitly, the four section Q-factors, we have now tuned *all* available parameters of the cascade realization. It follows, therefore, that such a conservative control system theoretically results in a filter that is *precisely* and *continuously* tuned against all deviations, *regardless of their origin*. The main error sources in this tuning scheme are inaccurate Q-VCO frequencies which result in Q and gain errors in the biquads.

The experimental performance of the filter, implemented in a 3μm-CMOS process was found to be within the prescribed specifications (Fig. 6) over the range 0°C ≤ T ≤ 65°C [8].

inputs grounded and their quality factors increased to ∞. For tuning Q_i of *each section individually*, the Q-control circuitry works exactly as described in connection with Fig. 3b; a difficulty arises because the *four* errors of the *four* quality factors cannot be separated by looking at the response of the eighth-order MASTER filter to *one* stimulus. By the same token, we cannot apply signals at several frequencies *simultaneously* to the filter and hope to be able to interpret the response for convenient error correction.

A possible solution is found in applying the required Q-control signals *consecutively*. To this end we construct a digital clock generator (CG) with four non-overlapping clock phases and a bank of four sample-and-hold capacitors (S/H). During Phase 1, the switches connecting Q-VCO1 and the first of the S/H-capacitors, $C_{S/H1}$, are closed, thereby completing the Q-control loop. The remaining switches stay open. Q-VCO1 is set to 3.63MHz (see Fig. 5), the frequency where the passband response has a maximum, nominally 1V, a gain of 20dB. With K set equal to 10 (20dB !), we compare the MASTER's response at 3.63MHz to $K \cdot V_{Q\text{-}VCO1}$ and generate a Q-control voltage V_{QC} that is sent to $C_{S/H1}$ and held there until the next update. If the response level at 3.63MHz is incorrect as indicated in Fig. 5, the error $\Delta|H|$ can be attributed *dominantly* to an error in the quality factor ΔQ_1 of Section 1 and corrected by applying V_{QC} from $C_{S/H1}$ to the appropriate control gates in Sections 1 of the MASTER and the matched SLAVE. The

References

[1] Moulding,K.W., et al., "Gyrator Video Filter IC with Automatic Tuning", *IEEE J.* , SC-15 , 963-968, Dec. 1980.

[2] Tsividis, Y., "Self-Tuned Filters" *Electron. Lett.*, 17, 406-407, June 1981.

[3] Fukahori,K. "A Bipolar Voltage-Controlled Tunable Filter" *IEEE J.* , SC-16, 729-737, Dec. 1981.

[4] Khorramabadi,H. and P.R.Gray, "High-Frequ. CMOS Cont.-Time Filters ", *IEEE J.* , SC-19, 963-967, Dec. 1984.

[5] Tsividis,Y., et al., "Continuous-Time MOSFET-C Filters in VLSI", *IEEE J.*., SC-21, 15-30, Febr. 1986.

[6] Miura,K., et al., "VCR Signal Processing LSIs with Self-Adjusted Integrated Filters", *Proc. 1986 BCTM*, 85-86.

[7] Krummenacher,F. and N.Joehl, "A 4-MHz CMOS Cont.-Time Filter with On-Chip Automatic Tuning", *IEEE J.*, SC-23, 750-758, June 1988.

[8] Park,C.S. and R.Schaumann, "Design of a 4 MHz Analog Integrated CMOS Transconductance-C Bandpass Filter", *IEEE J.*., SC-23, 987-996, Aug. 1988.

[9] Tan,M.A., "Design and Automatic Tuning of Fully Integrated Transconductance-Grounded Capacitor Filters", Ph. D. Thesis, U of M, 1988.

[10] McCreary,J.L., "Matching Properties and Voltage and Temperature Dependence of MOS Capacitors" *IEEE J.*, SC-16, 608-616, Dec. 1981.

Tuning Strategies in High-Frequency Integrated Continuous-Time Filters

Peter M. VanPeteghem and Rujiang Song

Abstract —In this paper, three approaches for tuning integrated continuous-time filters are discussed and compared. The presented results refer, but are not limited to, second-order bandpass filters implemented with transconductance amplifiers and capacitors (OTA-C filters). It is shown that tuning with two frequencies has superior performance over single-frequency tuning: in this first case, center frequency, bandwidth, and midband gain of a biquad can be tuned exactly; in the second case only center frequency and midband gain.

I. Introduction

Continuous-time filters can be fully integrated in MOS technologies. One way to achieve this is by modeling resistors by MOS transistors in the linear range [1]. Another strategy is to combine transconductance elements and capacitors in integrator stages [2]. A major problem, which will be addressed in this paper, is the significant discrepancy that can be observed between the desired and measured filter characteristics due to the variability of the technological parameters of the used IC process.

Practical realizations have indicated that the systematic error on a realized pole can go as high as 30–40 percent, while the random errors can be made smaller than 1 percent. It is common practice to tune the poles in a separate "master" filter, which is typically a second-order section [1]–[4]; it is then assumed that all filter parameters in the "slave" filter track the tuned parameter sufficiently close [5]. No simple automatic algorithm exists that is abel to tune a high-order filter directly. Since there is one single reference frequency, and one single objective (position of one pole resonance frequency), we will call this the T11 tuning process.

For high-Q filters, this procedure is not useful any more, since parasitic effects and mismatching errors produce significant shifts in the effective quality factor and the gain at resonance of that filter section. Therefore, additional tuning objectives have to be added. In the next paragraphs it will be shown that it is very easy to control the gain at resonance of a high-Q filter section while tuning only with a single frequency. It is further shown that tuning of all three major filter parameters of a second-order filter section can be achieved by using two frequencies. These tuning processes will be called the T12 (single frequency, two objectives) and the T23 (double frequency, three objectives) tuning processes. In all of these, we will focus mostly on what criterion is met after the tuning process has converged. This allows designers to evaluate the principal benefits of a given tuning process without being obscured by practical implementation problems. Practical circuit configurations can be found in [1], [3].

Manuscript received February 19, 1988; revised May 11, 1988. This work was supported in part by Texas Instruments Inc., Dallas TX. This paper was recommended by Associate Editor T. R. Viswanathan.

P. M. VanPeteghem is with the Department of Electrical Engineering, Texas A&M University, College Station, TX 77843.

R. Song is with the Department of Electrical Engineering, Texas A&M University, College Station, TX 77843, on leave from Beijing Institute of Radio Measurements, Beijing, China.

IEEE Log Number 8824587.

The tuning algorithms are discussed here for the case of a second-order bandpass filter. The results can be extended without lack of generality to other generic filters like low-pass and high-pass sections. A general description of a second-order bandpass filter is

$$H(s) = \frac{\dfrac{A\omega_0 S}{Q}}{S^2 + \dfrac{\omega_0 S}{Q} + \omega_0^2} \tag{1}$$

in which ω_0 is the resonant frequency (in rad/sec), Q is the quality factor, and A is the gain at resonance. A circuit that implements this bandpass filter using an OTA-C realization is given in Fig. 1. In this circuit, A, Q, and ω_0 can be controlled by tuning four transconductances, according to the following equations:

$$\omega_0 = 2\pi F_0 = \frac{g_m}{2\pi C} \tag{2}$$

$$Q = \frac{g_m}{g_{m4}} \tag{3}$$

$$A = \frac{g_{m1}}{g_{m4}} \tag{4}$$

with

$$g_{m2} = g_{m3} = g_m$$
$$C_1 = C_2 = C.$$

g_{m2} and g_{m3} effectively act as one single parameter, tuned by the same control voltage; therefore, there are only three degrees of freedom. The circuit in Fig. 1 will be used to clarify the concepts, with the following parameters: $F_0 = 1$ MHz, $Q = 10$, $A = 1$. An OTA-C filter is chosen here for its simplicity, and known good high-frequency performance.

II. Tuning Strategies

In this paper, a tuning strategy is defined by its set of tuning objectives. All of these take the form:

$$L(F_{ex}, F_0, Q, A) = K \tag{5}$$

in which the left-hand side function $L(\ )$ is a function of the input frequency F_{ex} and of the filter parameters F_0, Q, A. In general, this function L is a linear combination of imaginary and real parts of the transfer function $H(s)$ at some frequency F_{ex}. This implies that these functions $L(\ )$ can be evaluated very easily by a simple multiplication of input and output of the filter (input eventually shifted over 90°). The right-hand side of (5) is always a constant. Practical tuning proceeds by calculating the difference between $L(\ )$ and K and using the integrated difference as a control voltage to tune the appropriate parameter in the filter. For an ideal negative-feedback tuning loop, tuning will converge to a situation for which the equality in (5) holds exactly.

Reprinted from *IEEE Trans. Circuits Syst.*, vol. CAS-36, no. 1, pp. 136–139, Jan. 1989.

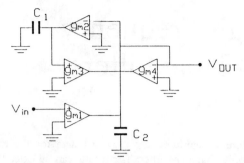

Fig. 1. Bandpass filter, built with transconductance amplifiers and capacitors.

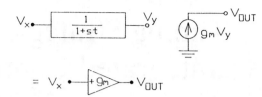

Fig. 2. Tuned filter characteristics; T11 tuning process. Objective: $F_0 = 1$ MHz.

Other tuning criteria may exist that result in convergence to the same filter parameter values, but the presented strategies have been selected for their ease of implementation using standard IC building blocks, or with simple software algorithms. As a matter of fact, efficient integrated circuit implementations have been reported before [1], [3] for two of the three tuning strategies that we discuss here.

In the well-known T11 tuning procedure [1], [4], the filter is stimulated with a signal with frequency F_{ex}. All four transconductances are tuned by one single control voltage. The tuning process adapts the value of these transconductances (see Appendix) until the following criterion is met:

$$\mathrm{Im}\big[\,H(2\pi jF_{ex})\,\big] = 0 \qquad (6)$$

in which the operator Im takes the imaginary part of a complex transfer function. A practical way to tune a bandpass filter according to (6) consists in multiplying the filter output voltage with a 90° shifted version of the input signal, followed by low-pass filtering (or integration). The resulting voltage (or current) can be used to tune all four transconductances in Fig. 1. For an ideal second-order bandpass filter (ideal meaning: no higher order poles), (6) is equivalent to

$$F_0 = F_{ex} \qquad (7)$$

This means that the tuning process forces F_0 to become equal to the excitation frequency F_{ex}. Low-pass and high-pass filters can be tuned by taking the real part instead of the imaginary part in (6), since they have an extra 90° phase shift at the resonance frequency. Even for a bandpass filter that is higher than second-order due to parasitic effects, we can use (1) in the vicinity of the resonance frequency, since the added parasitic poles are typically at much higher frequencies than the resonance frequency. Therefore (7) stays valid. Of course, any error in the tuning loop will generate tuning errors. This depends however on the actual implementation of the filter and the tuning circuitry, and can not be addressed in general. In Fig. 2, the filter characteristics are shown if the transconductors have a parasitic internal pole. The circuit model for the transconductors is given in Fig. 3. τ is the parasitic internal time-constant which can model the effect of many poles and zeros. It is seen that the T11 tuning process is able to fix the resonant frequency exactly, while a significant deviation of the gain at resonance and Q-factor is observed.

The tuning objective in (6) depends only on the imaginary part of the tuned transfer function. This suggests that more tuning information can be obtained by monitoring also the real part of the transfer function. This constitutes the T12 tuning process. A tuning process that comes close to the T12 process as it is described here has been presented before in [3]. The T12 tuning process tunes the bandpass circuit with two objectives, i.e., the

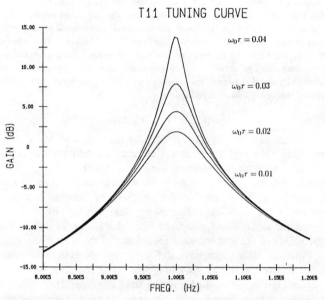

Fig. 3. Equivalent circuit of transconductance amplifier with internal pole τ.

objective stated in (6), and also (see also Appendix):

$$\mathrm{Re}\big[\,H(2\pi jF_{ex})\,\big] = 1 \qquad (8)$$

For low-pass and high-pass filters, interchange "Re" and "Im" in (6) and (8). Multiplying the filter output with its input and applying low-pass filtering (or integration) to the result is an efficient way to monitor the real part of $H(s)$ in an analog integrated circuit. For a pure second-order bandpass filter, (8) is equivalent to

$$A = 1 \qquad (9)$$

when (7) is true. The two-objective T12 tuning process can be compared to a vector-locked-loop (VLL), while the one-objective T11 tuning process is essentially a PLL system. Again, for a second-order filter, degenerated to a higher order filter by parasitic effects, (7) and (9) hold. In particular, simulation results show (see Fig. 4) that the T12 tuning process is able to tune the bandpass filter of Fig. 1 to exact gain specifications (0 dB), for the same values of the parasitic pole in the transconductance elements. Fig. 4 refers to a VLL tuning loop in which g_{m2}, g_{m3} and g_{m4} are all tuned by the primary F_0 control loop (like in T11 tuning); g_{m1} is controlled by the A control loop. For $\omega_0\tau = 0.04$ tuning performance starts to degrade, and for $\omega_0\tau$ equal or larger than 0.05 (not shown in Fig. 4), the tuning process diverges. High values of $\omega_0\tau$ lead to severe Q enhancement. This problem can not be solved by a single-frequency tuning process, since these processes only fix one point in the transfer function (i.e., the resonance point).

It is principally feasible to tune the phase margin (or excess phase shift) in an OTA using the same VLL approach [6]. In this

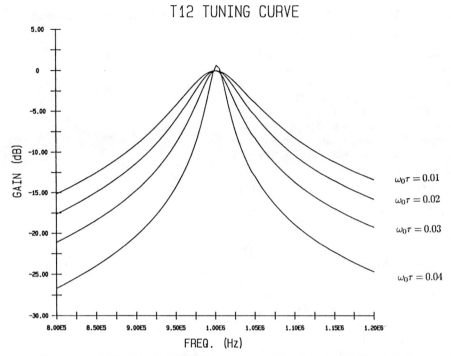

Fig. 4.   Tuned filter characteristics, T12 tuning process. Objectives: $F_0 = 1$ MHz, $A = 0$ dB.

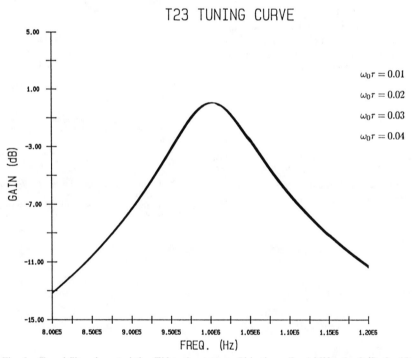

Fig. 5.   Tuned filter characteristics, T23 tuning process. Objectives: $F_0 = 1$ MHz, $A = 0$ dB, $Q = 10$.

way both A and Q errors can be annihilated at the same time since they are correlated. It should be noted however that mismatch errors also can lead to significant errors in high-Q filters. In this case, A and Q errors are definitely not correlated, and so T12 tuning will be unable to correct for any Q errors due to mismatching.

Exact tuning of the bandwidth of a high-Q filter, together with resonance frequency and gain at resonance, whatever the origin of the errors is, can only be performed if information is acquired on the value of the transfer function for at least two frequencies. If the two frequencies are chosen fairly close to the resonance frequency, effectively two frequencies are sufficient, even in the presence of high-frequency parasitic poles in the transfer function. This new tuning process is called the T23 tuning process since it has three objectives. If the lower and higher 3-dB cut-off frequencies, F_L and F_H, respectively, are chosen as the tuning frequencies, tuning proceeds until the following very simple set of objectives is fulfilled (see Appendix):

$$\text{Re}\left[H(2\pi j F_L) \right] = 0.5 \tag{10}$$

$$\text{Re}\left[H(2\pi j F_H) \right] = 0.5 \tag{11}$$

$$\mathrm{Im}\big[\,H(2\pi jF_L)\big] - \mathrm{Im}\big[\,H(2\pi jF_H)\big] = 1. \qquad (12)$$

It can be argued that principally four parameters can be tuned with two frequencies since two real and two imaginary ports can be calculated. First of all, it is not so clear what parameters, other than the three in (1) could be chosen. It does not make sense to choose a parameter that controls stopband performance (which is desirable for high-order filters), since $H(s)$ is only monitored at the edge of the passband. Overall, the presented set of objectives (10)–(12) leads to a computationally simple (and convergent!) set of tuning equations. It can be shown that (10)–(12) together with (1) is equivalent to:

$$A = 1 \qquad (13)$$

$$|H(2\pi jF_L)| = |H(2\pi jF_H)| = 1/\sqrt{2} \qquad (14)$$

for an ideal second-order bandpass filter ((1)), or for a second-order filter with high-frequency parasitic poles. Equations (13) and (14) guarantee that the filter has the right gain at resonance, and the right-3 dB frequencies; this leads indirectly to the right values for F_0 and Q. Again transfer functions are shown in Fig. 5 for tuning the circuit in Fig. 1, in the presence of an extra pole with parasitic delay τ in the transconductors. The tuned filter is now almost exactly equal to the desired filter for all values of $\omega_0\tau$; this shows the superior performance of the T23 tuning strategy. It is however clear that T23 tuning leads to a considerably more complex tuning circuit (or algorithm). Hence, this strategy is suitable for the case where tuning is performed using digital signal processing concepts, or in those cases where many different errors add together (e.g., mismatching errors). In this last case, A and Q errors do not necessarily track, and the transfer function has to be tuned in at least two frequencies, as is presented here.

APPENDIX 1

Here we describe how exactly the control parameters of the filter have to be adapted, to yield a stable and converging tuning process. In this section, we will use the symbols $V_{\omega0}$, V_A, and V_Q for the control variables that control the corresponding filter parameter. K is an integration constant, which can be chosen independently in any of the following sets of equations.

T11: Single-frequency, single-objective tuning process:
Control of $g_{m1}, g_{m2}, g_{m3}, g_{m4}$:

$$V_{\omega0} = - K \int \mathrm{Im}\big[\,H(2\pi jF_{\mathrm{ex}})\big] \cdot dt. \qquad (A1)$$

T12: Single-frequency, double-objective tuning process:
Control of g_{m2}, g_{m3}, g_{m4}:

$$V_{\omega0} = - K \int \mathrm{Im}\big[\,H(2\pi jF_{\mathrm{ex}})\big] \cdot dt. \qquad (A2)$$

Control of g_{m1}:

$$V_A = - K \int \big\{ \mathrm{Re}\big[\,H(2\pi jF_{\mathrm{ex}})\big] - 1\big\} \cdot dt. \qquad (A3)$$

T23: Double-frequency, triple-objective tuning process:
Control of g_{m2}, g_{m3}:

$$V_{\omega0} = - K \int \big\{ \mathrm{Im}\big[\,H(2\pi jF_L)\big] - \mathrm{Im}\big[\,H(2\pi jF_H)\big] - 1\big\} \cdot dt. \quad (A4)$$

Control of g_{m1}:

$$V_A = - K \int \big\{ \mathrm{Re}\big[\,H(2\pi jF_L)\big] - 0.5\big\} \cdot dt. \qquad (A5)$$

Control of g_{m4}:

$$V_Q = K \int \big\{ \mathrm{Re}\big[\,H(2\pi jF_H)\big] - 0.5\big\} \cdot dt. \qquad (A6)$$

REFERENCES

[1] Y. Tsividis, M. Banu, and J. Khoury, "Continuous-time MOSFET-C filters in VLSI," *IEEE J. Solid-State Circuits*, vol. SC-21, pp. 15–30, Feb. 1986.

[2] H. Khorramabadi and P. R. Gray, "High-frequency CMOS continuous-time filters," *IEEE J. Solid-State Circuits*, vol. SC-19, pp. 939–948, Dec. 1984.

[3] C. Chiou and R. Schaumann, "Design and performance of a fully integrated bipolar 10.7 MHz analog bandpass filter," *IEEE Trans. Circuits Syst.*, vol. CAS-33, pp. 116–124, Feb. 1986.

[4] K. S. Tan and P. R. Gray, "Fully integrated analog filters using bipolar-JFET technology," *IEEE J. Solid-State Circuits*, vol. SC-13, pp. 814–821, Dec. 1978.

[5] Y. Tsividis, "Self-tuned filters," *Electron. Lett.*, vol. 17, no. 2, pp. 206–207, June 1981.

[6] A. Nedungadi, "Design of linear transconductance elements in CMOS technology," Ph.D. dissertation, Texas A&M Univ., Dallas, 1987.

A NOVEL APPROACH FOR THE AUTOMATIC TUNING OF
CONTINUOUS TIME FILTERS

José Silva-Martinez[*], Michiel Steyaert and Willy Sansen

Katholieke Universiteit Leuven
Elektrotechniek departement ESAT-MICAS
Kardinaal Mercierlaan 94, B-3030 Heverlee, Belgium.

ABSTRACT: A novel approach for the automatic tuning of Continuous-Time Filters (CTF) is introduced. This approach uses a charge comparison principle for the tuning of the pole frequency (ω_0) and the pulse response of a biquadratic filter for tuning the filter quality factor (Q). Both frequency and Q tuning are performed at lower frequency than the pole frequencies. Thus, these techniques reduce the tuning signal feedthrough in bandpass filters. The Q tuning include the filter high frequency effects. This Q tuning technique is well situated for narrow band filters. Simulated results and breadboard experimental results are presented and discussed.

I. INTRODUCTION

Recently, several fully-integrated continuous-time filters have been reported. Most of them uses Operational Transconductance Amplifiers (OTA) and Capacitors (C) as the main components. Due to the lack of virtual grounds and low impedance nodes, CTF are sensitive to the parasitic capacitors. The time constant depends of C/g_m ratios, with g_m been the OTA transconductance. This time constant is not well controlled because is affected by the process parameter tolerances. This can be more than 30% including temperature variations, parasitic capacitors and other effects. In addition to these effects, the active filters are very sensitive to the OTA excess phase shift and its finite DC gain.

In a first approximation, the magnitude of g_m/C determines the frequency of the poles (ω_0). Usually, the variations of this ratio are corrected with a Phase Locked Loop (PLL). A replica of a two integrator loop is included in this PLL in order to match g_m/C with an external clock frequency. Typically, it is not necessary to tune all the loops of the main filter because ω_0 is not very sensitive to the OTA excess phase shift and the matching of time constants, of the same value, can be very well controlled in CMOS technologies. Because the phase comparison, the lock range of this approach is limited. Unfortunately, the Q of the filter is quite sensitive to the OTA excess phase shift and to its finite DC gain. These errors can be partially corrected using magnitude detection [2,3] and/or phase detection [4] techniques. The frequency of both tuning loops is preferred to be in the passband frequency range. This last fact increases the tuning signal feedthrough, mainly in high frequency applications.

In this paper it is proposed to tune ω_0 and Q using a different frequency range than this of the filter passband. For bandpass filters the tuning signals feedthrough is further reduced. Furthermore, because phase comparison is not used, the

[*]On leave from the Universidad Autonoma de Puebla.
 He is supported by CONACYT, Mexico.

tuning range of the proposed techniques is larger than the phase locked based tuning techniques. The proposed ω_0 tuning technique is based in the bias current, or charge comparison, principle. In this technique it is tried to match ω_0 with an external clock reference times a ratio of DC current sources. For the Q tuning, the pulse response of the filter is exploited. In biquadratic filters, for Q>0.5, the envelope of its pulse response is an exponential function of the filter bandwidth. This envelope corresponds to the pulse response of a first order filter with a pole frequency equal to a half of the bandwidth of the biquadratic filter. In this proposed technique the envelope of a lower frequency first order filter is matched with the envelope of a biquadratic filter with higher pole frequency, equal to ω_0, and with bandwidth equal to BW.

The proposed techniques for ω_0 and Q tuning are introduced in sections II and III, respectively. The limitations of these techniques are discussed in section IV. Simulated and experimental results are presented in section V. In the final section some conclusions are given.

II FREQUENCY TUNING.

The typical biquadratic loop is shown in fig 1. ω_0 and Q can be determined using circuits analysis as (see fig 1)

$$\omega_0 \cong \sqrt{\frac{g_{m1} g_{m2}}{C_1 C_2}} \sqrt{1 + \left[\frac{g_1 + g_{01}}{g_{m1}}\right]\left[\frac{g_2 + g_{02}}{g_{m2}}\right] - \frac{g_{m1} g_{m2}}{C_1 C_2}\theta^2} \quad (1)$$

$$BW = \frac{\omega_0}{Q} \cong \frac{g_1}{C_1} + \frac{g_2}{C_2} + \frac{g_{01}}{C_1} + \frac{g_{02}}{C_2} + 2\theta \frac{g_{m1} g_{m2}}{C_1 C_2} \quad (2)$$

with g_1 and g_2 been the conductances to be used in the Q tuning. g_{01} and g_{02} are the finite output conductances of OTA1 and OTA2, respectively. θ is the OTA excess phase shift, it is considered $\theta=\theta_1=\theta_2$, and models the effect of the OTA parasitic poles and zeros. It can be noted, from 1, that in order to reduce the effects of g_1, g_{01}, g_2 and g_{02} on ω_0, it is very desirable to control BW with a single conductance, either g_1 or g_2. Furthermore, the use of cascode output stages is very desirable, in order to reduce g_{01} and g_{02}. Under these conditions and since ω_0 is almost insensitive to θ, eqn 1 suggests to tune the frequency of the poles with a single pole circuit. Thus, tuning a single g_{mi}/C_i the other pole frequencies can be tuned by capacitor ratios and/or g_m ratios. Because the better matching, in CMOS technologies, of capacitor ratios than transconductance ratios it is preferred the former approach. Evenmore, designing the filter with equally transconductors and large capacitors, with small spread as possible, both the matching of the pole frequencies and the filter dynamic range improve.

The block diagram, in a fully-differential version, of the

Reprinted from *IEEE Proc. ISCAS*, pp. 1452–1455, 1991.

proposed implementation is shown in fig 2. It uses a switched-capacitor integrator and two DC current sources I_B and KI_B. g_{m1} and $C_1'=C_1+C_{P1}/2$ are the transconductance and the capacitor to be tuned. The OPAMP output voltage V_{02} can be computed from

$$V_{02}(t) = \frac{2}{C_H} \int_{t_0}^{t_0+t} \left[KI_B - \left(C_1' V_{C1}(t) \right)_{\varphi 2} \right] dt + V_{02}(t_0) \qquad (3)$$

In the integral, the first term corresponds to the extracted charge by the current source KI_B. The second term is the total injected charge, during $\varphi 2$, to C_H from the capacitor C_1'. If the time constants are sufficiently large to charge and discharge C_1', the injected charge is determined by the ratio of the DC current I_B and g_{m1}, the transconductance of OTA1. The voltage V_{02} corresponds, in the control loop, to the integrated error voltage. This error voltage is averaged in the lowpass filter and fed back to control the bias current of OTA1. In steady state and in the ideal case, the average of the error voltage is zero and hence the tuned pole frequency becomes

$$\omega_{01} = \frac{g_{m1}}{C_1'} = \frac{1}{KT} \qquad (4)$$

with T and K been the clock period and the current sources ratio, respectively.

III. Q TUNING

The bandwidth of a second order filter can be detected in both domains frequency and time. The Q detection in the frequency domain has been discussed elsewhere [2-6]. It is important to point out that this detection has been carried out at the center frequency of the filter. In the time domain, the impulse or the pulse response of a biquadratic filter allows also the Q detection. The unity impulse response of a biquadratic lowpass filter with unity DC gain and Q>0.5 is characterized by

$$h(t) = \frac{1}{\sqrt{1 - \frac{1}{4Q^2}}} \exp^{-\frac{BW\,t}{2}} \sin\left(\sqrt{1 - \frac{1}{4Q^2}} \, \omega_O t + \phi \right) \qquad (5)$$

where ϕ is a function of Q. For large Q, the first factor can be approximated as unity. Hence h(t) equals a sinusoidal function whose amplitude decays exponentially. Under this condition, the positive envelope of h(t) corresponds to the unity impulse response of a first order filter with pole frequency equal to BW/2. Thus, the error voltage of the Q tuning loop can be generated by comparing the impulse or pulse response of both the first order "reference filter" and the master, second order, filter. The pole of the reference filter can be tuned from the frequency loop. Its pole frequency will depend of both transconductance and capacitor ratios.

The proposed implementation of this technique uses the pulse response instead of the impulse response. The block diagram is depicted in fig 3. The envelopes are detected and compared only in a single clock phase, in this case during the negative transition. This is because in the envelope detector the positive exponential is always detected, and, in the positive transition the comparison must be done with the negative exponential of eqn 5. The error voltage V_{02} is averaged by the lowpass filter and fed back to the active resistor. The lowpass filter has been implemented as a switched capacitor integrator. So, The sample and hold operation is implied in the integrator. The active resistor can be implemented with an OTA simulated resistor [4,8,9] or with a triode biased transistor based resistor [10] or with a current source based resistor [11].

IV. LIMITATIONS OF THE TECHNIQUES

There are several practical limitations in the proposed

techniques. Some of these are discussed in this section.

FREQUENCY LOOP: It has been demonstrated before that the errors in current ratios are almost proportional to the reciprocal of the gate area of the transistors. The error can be as small as 0.4 % (8 bits) and sometimes better [12]. So, if properly designed, the precision of factor K (DC current sources ratio) can be quite good. The major design problem of this loop is the mismatch between the capacitors in the filter and this associated with the tuning loop. In the filter, there are several parasitic capacitors due to the additional devices connected to the output of the OTA's, represented by C_{01} and C_{02} in fig 1. These parasitic capacitors, in every node, are the parallel of all the parasitics coming from the input and output stages connected to that node. Their value is not very well controlled. It is necessary a carefully modelling, from the layout, and simulation of these capacitors in order to include their effect in C_1'. There is a tradeoff between the value of the polysilicon capacitors, C_1 and C_2 in fig 1, and the power consumption. The higher the value of these capacitors the better the matching, but, the higher the transconductance, increasing both the power consumption and the silicon area.

Q TUNING LOOP: There are also several practical problems in the Q tuning loop. The pole of the first order reference filter must be equal to half the bandwidth frequency, that is equal to $\omega_0/2Q$. If the value of the capacitor associated with the reference filter is twice the value of the capacitor in the frequency control loop, the transconductance associated with the reference filter, g_{mr}, should be equal to g_{m1}/Q. Then, for high Q filters large transconductance ratios are required.

Unfortunately, large transconductance ratios are not very well controlled in current CMOS processes. These large ratios very often depend of both effective transistor width ratios and effective transistor length ratios. The uncertainty of both effective lengths and effective widths (due to lateral diffusion, birds beak, depletion regions, etc.) are two of the most limiting factors in the accuracy of these ratios. Simulated results have shown errors in the order of 1 to 4%, depending of the minimum dimensions, g_m's ratio and the technology. This is the main limitation of this approach.

The peak gain of the biquadratic filter can be very well controlled because it depends of the input transconductance and the reference transconductance. Both transconductances are in the same order of magnitude.

THE TRANSFER FUNCTION: It has been already demonstrated that the transfer function of the biquadratic filters is more sensitive to ω_0 variations than to Q variations [13]. Evenmore, the maximum of these sensitivities are in the order of Q and 1, respectively. In biquadratic filters, these maximum sensitivities occur at the -3 dB's frequencies, for ω_0, and at $\omega=\omega_0$, for Q. Thus, the most important effects of these errors are reflected in the filter passband. It can be demonstrated that the high order bandpass transfer functions are almost insensitive to Q variations when the error in every biquadratic section is of the same sign (either Q's increasing or Q's decreasing). In this case the major effect is a non very critical increment of the passband ripple. The transfer function is much more sensitive to ω_0 errors. Fortunately, this is the case in the proposed technique. The absolute value of the Q's is not very well controlled, but, because the Q of the sections are in the same order, can be designed equals, the mismatches between them can be further reduced. So, seems to be more important to control very accurately the frequency of the poles than the exact value of Q, providing that the Q mismatches between the structures are small; e.g. less than 1%.

V. SIMULATED AND EXPERIMENTAL RESULTS

Both tuning loops have been simulated. The OTA used is a fully differential version of this reported in [11]. The supply voltages are $\pm$ 2.5 V. For the frequency tuning loop, the lowpass filter has been implemented with a differential to single signal converter and with the typical RC first order filter, the resistor was implemented with the switched capacitor technique. The simulated results are shown in fig 4. The voltage V_{02} has a sawtooth waveform. The jump is due to the injected (extracted in the other OPAMP input) charge from C_1' and the ramp is due to the extracted (injected) DC current KI_B. The voltage V_{FREQ}, which controls the bias current of OTA1, is shown in the bottom trace. The clock frequency is 15,000 cycles/sec and the frequency of the poles is 100.2 KHz. The ideal value of factor K is 1/42. Simulated results, including 1% transistor mismatches, have shown an error in the poles frequency in the order of 1 %. Similar results have been obtained for the design of a 10.7 MHz bandpass filter.

The implementation of the automatic BW control involves several building blocks. The input signals V_1 and V_2 are pulse trains with pulsed values of 0V, 0.5V and 0V, -0.5V, respectively. The master filter is just a replica of a main filter second order section. The reference filter has been implemented with two OTAs, with the same transconductance, and a capacitor. Both filters, the master and the reference, are fully-differential. The envelope detector involves a rectifier and the detector [10]. The lowpass filter is similar to this used in the frequency tuning loop. The active resistor has been simulated with a floating resistor based in a triode biased P transistor. The simulated results are shown in fig 5. In the middle trace the outputs of the master and the reference filters are shown. The quality factor of the filter is 4. The output of the envelope detectors are shown in the bottom of this figure. The BW control voltage V_{BW} is shown in the top trace. Typically, the system converges to its final value after 7 or 8 periods. The error in the absolute value of the tuned Q, with 1% transistor mismatches, is in the order 2 to 3 %.

A single ended breadboard has been implemented with Discrete OPAMPs, discrete OTAs, 1% tolerance resistors, 5% tolerance capacitors and a CMOS transistor, used as voltage controlled resistor. The experimental results for two cases are shown in fig 6. In the top traces, the envelope output voltages for Q=15 are depicted. The bottom traces correspond to Q=2.5. The experimental Q errors, for several cases, were in the order of 3 to 7 %. It was not attempted neither to adjust the capacitor values nor to cancel offsets of the OTA and OPAMS. The intention of this breadboard was to demonstrate that the technique works indeed. Two chips have been already submitted to fabrication and the experimental results will be published in a near future.

CONCLUSIONS

A novel techniques for the automatic tuning of continuous-time filters have been introduced. The proposed techniques carry out the automatic tuning at different frequency range than the filter passband frequency range. This fact reduces the tuning signal feedthrough and as result increases the dynamic range of the filter.

The precision of the frequency tuning loop, if properly designed, is as good as this obtained with PLL based techniques. Furthermore, the tuning range of the proposed technique is higher. This is due to the absence of phase lock. The topology is a classical second order system and its stability can be easily guarantied for a wide tuning range.

In general, the precision in the control of the absolute value of Q of the proposed Q tuning system is in the order of 1 to 4%. Designing the filter with small Q spread in the biquadratic sections, the effect of the mismatches is almost cancelled. The proposed techniques are well situated for narrow band applications.

REFERENCES

[1] H. Khorramabadi and P. R. Gray," High Frequency CMOS Continuous-Time Filters," IEEE J. of Solid-State Circuits, vol. SC-19, pp 939-948, Dec. 1984.

[2] C. S. Park and R. Schauman," Design of a 4 MHz Analog Integrated CMOS Transconductance-C Bandpass Filter," IEEE J of Solid-State Circuits, vol SC-23, pp 750-758, Aug. 1988.

[3] R. Schauman and M. A. Tan," The problem of On-Chip Automatic Tuning in Continuous-Time Integrated Filters," IEEE ISCAS-89, Portland Oregon, pp. 106-109, May 1989.

[4] V. Gopinathan, Y. P. Tsividis, R. K. Hester and K. S. Tan," A 5 V, 7th Order Elliptic Analog Filter for Digital Video Applications," IEEE ISSCC-89, San Francisco Calif, pp 208-209, Feb 1990.

[5] P. M. VanPeteghem, S. Rujiang," Tuning Strategies in High Frequency Integrated Continuous-Time Filters," IEEE Trans on Circuits and Systems, vol CAS-36, pp 136-139, Jan 1989.

[6] T. L. Brooks and P. M. VanPeteghem," Simultaneous Tuning and Signal Processing in Integrated Continuous-Time Filters: The Correlated Tuning Loop," IEEE ISCAS-89, Portland Oregon, pp 651-654, May 1989.

[7] K. A. Kozma, D. A. Jones and A. S. Sedra," An Adaptive Tuning for Integrated Continuous-Time Filters," IEEE ISCAS-90, New Orleans NO, pp. 1163-1166, June 1990.

[8] E. Sanchez-Sinencio, R. L. Geiger and H. Nevarez-Lozano," Generation of Continuous-Time Two Integrator Loop OTA Filter Structures," IEEE Trans. on Circuits and Systems, vol. CAS-35, pp. 936-946, August 1988.

[9] H. Nevarez-Lozano, A. Hill and E. Sanchez-Sinencio," Frequency Limitations of Continuous-Time OTA-C Filters," IEEE ISCAS-88, Espoo Finland, pp. 2169-2172, June 1988.

[10] Y. T. Wang, F. Lu and A. A. Abidi," A 12.5 MHz CMOS Continuous-Time Bandpass Filter," IEEE ISSCC-89, New York NY, pp. 198-199, Feb 1989.

[11] J. Silva-Martinez, M. Steyaert and W. Sansen," A High Frequency Large Signal Very Low Distortion Transconductor," IEEE ESSCIRC-90, Grenoble France, pp 169-172, Sept 1990.

[12] J. B. Shyu, G. C. Temes and F. Krummenacher," Random Error Effects in Matched MOS Capacitors and Current Sources," IEEE J. of Solid-State Circuits, vol. SC-19, pp 948-955, Dec 1984.

[13] A. S. Sedra and P. O. Brackett, "Filter Theory and Design: Active and Passive," Matrix publishers, Inc., Champaign Illinois, 1978.

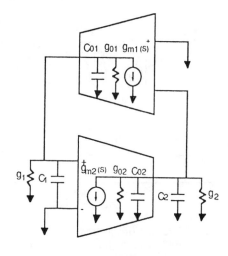

fig. 1. Typical loop of biquadratic filters.

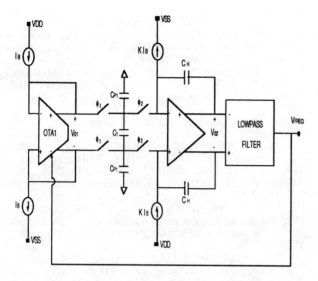

fig. 2. proposed frequency tuning system for fully-differential structures.

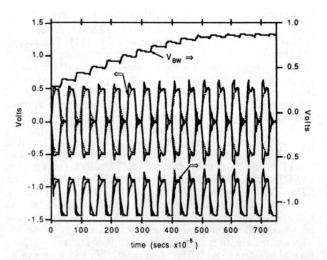

fig. 5. Simulated results of the Q tuning loop. The outputs of the master and the reference filters are shown in the middle trace. The output of the envelope detectors and the bandwidth control voltage VBW are shown in the bottom and top trace, respectively.

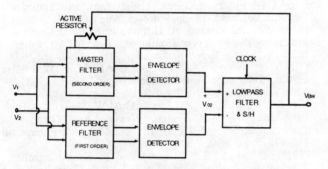

fig. 3. Block diagram of the proposed Q tuning system for fully-differential filters.

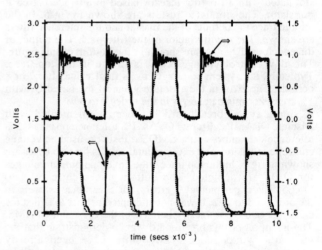

fig. 6. Breadboard experimental results. The top trace corresponds to Q=15 and the bottom trace to Q=2.5.

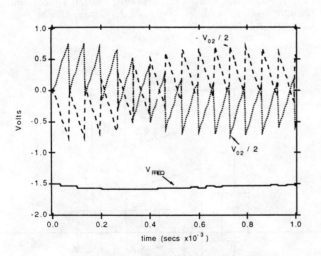

fig. 4. Simulated results of the frequency tuning loop.The outputs of the OPAM and the frequency control voltage are shown in the top and bottom trace, respectively.

Paper 6-4

Self-Tuned Filters

Y. TSIVIDIS

DEPARTMENT OF ELECTRICAL ENGINEERING

COLUMBIA, UNIVERSITY

NEW YORK, NY 10027, USA

Indexing terms: Filters, Self-tuning

A scheme for the tuning of filters is proposed. In it, filters are time-shared between a signal path and a tuning path, so that each filter in a system is individually tuned. An accurate system frequency response can thus be achieved which does not rely on tight matching between filters.

The characteristics of analogue filters are often sensitive to parameters which are not accurately predictable, and which vary with temperature, power supply voltages, and age (such a parameter is, for example, the gain-bandwidth product of an op amp). Several techniques have been reported for stabilising the characteristics of such filters, with the help of control circuitry and an external stable frequency reference;[1-4] the basic idea in these techniques is as follows. Both the filter to be used for processing of a signal of interest (the 'slave' filter) and an additional filter (the 'master' filter) are made tunable by a control bias. A control circuit adjusts that bias until the master filter is tuned, using the external stable frequency source as a reference. If the control bias is also connected to the slave filter, the latter will also be tuned, if the two filters are matched. The slave filter can therefore be used for processing of signals, whereas the master filter is devoted to keeping the system tuned. The accuracy of the above technique is limited by the accuracy of matching between the characteristics of the two filters; in the case of op amp gain-bandwidth products, for example, such matching is about 1% to 2% at best, even if the op amps are integrated on one chip.

A scheme which avoids the tight-matching accuracy of the above technique is illustrated in Fig. 1; the switches shown represent electronic switches or analogue gates. With the switch positions as shown, filter B is being tuned while filter A processes the input signal. Next, the role of A and B is to be interchanged; however, one cannot move all four switches down simultaneously, as then the build-up transients of B would appear at the output. Accordingly, switch 3 is first moved to the input. After the transients in filter B diminish, switches 1, 2 and 4 are moved down. Filter A is now tuned while B processes the input signal, with the proper control voltage V_{CB} being held by the bottom 'hold' circuit at the value established during the previous tuning halfcycle. Following the tuning of filter A, switch 1 is moved to the input; after the transients in A die out, switches 2, 3 and 4 are moved up, with the proper value of the control voltage V_{CA} held by the top 'hold' circuit. The process is then repeated periodically. Since each filter is individually tuned, accurate frequency responses can be implemented without having to rely on tight matching between filters. The procedure described can, of course, be extended to running more than one parameter in each filter, for example, centre frequency and gain magnitude.

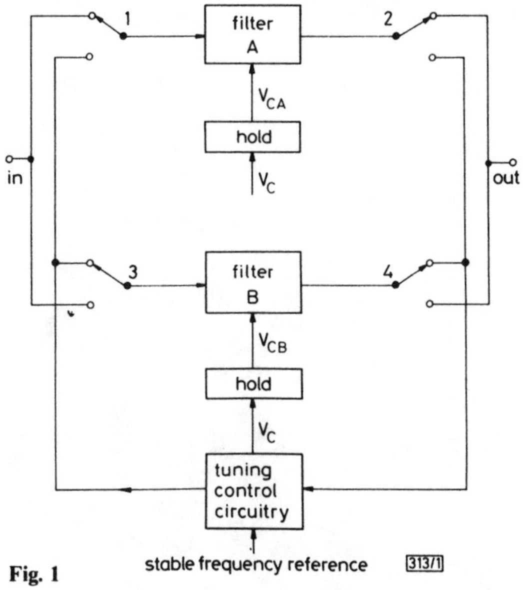

An example of a case where the above-proposed scheme can offer advantages is that of a cascade of n low-order high-Q bandpass filters, used, say, in the IF stage of a receiver. One would have to implement $n + 1$ such filters; at any given time, n of these would be in cascade processing the signal, and one would be under tuning. All filters would take turns in the tuning path, one at a time. Let us assume that the tuning system adjusts the centre frequency within an error Δf. This error will be the same for all filters in the cascade, resulting in a frequency shift in their response. Thus, the overall frequency response of the cascade will also be shifted, but its shape will not be distorted; a high-Q overall response will be achieved, which is necessary for adjacent channel rejection. The small frequency shift of the response will correspond to a small 'dial error' in the receiver, which will be insignificant for most applications.

Consider now using the 'master–slave' approach in the above application. Again $n + 1$ filters would have to be implemented. One of these would be the master; the remaining n filters would be connected in cascade and would be locked to the master. The element value mismatching between these filters will result in mismatches between their responses; their centre frequencies will be off by various amounts. This will result in a distortion of the shape of the overall frequency response for the cascade, and a potential serious degradation of the quality factor.

In the scheme proposed the output switching must be done carefully to ensure a smooth transition. What constitutes a 'smooth transition' depends on the application; for example, in the case of an AM receiver IF stage followed by an envelope demodulator, nonperfect transitions are not likely to be of serious consequence.

Fig. 1

stable frequency reference   313/1

Acknowledgment: The author would like to thank R. Schaumann for a useful discussion.

Reprinted with permission from *El. Letters,* vol. 17, no. 12, pp. 406–407, June 1981.

References

1 BRAND, J. R., SCHAUMANN, R., and SKEI, E. M.: 'Temperature-stabilized active R bandpass filters'. Proceedings 21st midwest symposium on circuits and systems, 1977, pp. 295–300

2 RAO, K. R., SETHURAMAN, V., and NEELAKANTAN, P. K.: 'A novel "follow the master" filter', *Proc. IEEE*, 1977, **65**, pp. 1725–1726

3 TAN, K. S., and GRAY, P. R.: 'Fully-integrated analog filter using bipolar-JFET technology', *IEEE J. Solid-State Circuits*, 1978, **SC-13**, pp. 303–307

4 SCHAUMANN, R., and BRAND, J. R.: 'Integrable analogue active filters for implementation in MOS technology', *IEE Proc. G, Electron. Circ. & Syst.*, 1981, **128**, (1), pp. 19–24

Continuous Time Filters Using Open Loop Tuneable Transconductance Amplifiers

C. PLETT, M. A. COPELAND, R. A. HADAWAY

DEPARTMENT OF ELECTRONICS, CARLETON UNIVERSITY, OTTAWA, ONTARIO, CANADA. K1S 5B6
NORTHERN TELECOM ELECTRONICS, LTD., OTTAWA, ONTARIO, CANADA. K1Y 4H7

ABSTRACT

This paper will report work on high-frequency continuous-time filters which use tuned transconductance amplifiers, in particular the folded cascode OP amp, as open-loop transconductance integrators. This allows for high output impedance and easy interconnection of integrators. A biquad filter has been fabricated in CMOS which features close relative position of poles and zeros to achieve fast passband roll-off.

A second important feature of the work is the use of monolithically integrated EPROM's as a means of macroscopically pre-tuning filter parameters. A method of tuning the biquad filter using EPROM's in a novel analog sense will be suggested.

INTRODUCTION

There has been considerable recent interest in continuous time monolithic MOS filters as an alternative at high frequencies to sampled data (switched capacitor) filters. The opportunity here is to be able to avoid the problem of the aliasing of signals and noise that occurs with sampled data approaches; the difficulty is in achieving equivalent tuning precision, stability and linearity. This paper will report our work on two specific aspects: (i) tuneable biquads based on the folded cascode operational amplifier (1) used open loop as a transconductance integrator, and (ii) the use of eraseable programmable read-only memory (EPROM) in various ways as a means of pre-tuning the filter.

CONTINUOUS TIME FILTERING

Our work on transconductance filtering is primarily focussed on tuneable folded cascode operational amplifiers (1). Figure 1 shows such an amplifier. The rationale for using this amplifier rather than simpler earlier approaches (2) is that it solves level matching problems readily, and allows good dc performance including high output impedance and DC coupling. The problem of design of the transconductance integrator can now be related clearly to known OP amp design. The input transistors M1 and M2 are reduced in size and the unity gain bandwidth of the integrator is

g_{M1}/C, where C is the output load. Higher order poles and finite dc gain of the OP amp are seen to directly relate to spurious phase shift from 90° which modifies the effective Qs of the transconductance filter.

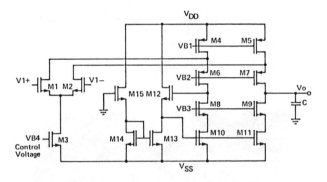

Figure 1 The Operational Transconductance Amplifier (OTA).

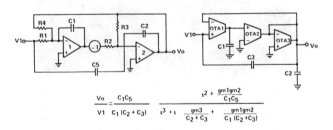

$$\frac{V_o}{V_1} = \frac{C_1 C_5}{C_1 (C_2 + C_3)} \cdot \frac{s^2 + \frac{g_{m1}g_{m2}}{C_1 C_5}}{s^3 + s \frac{g_{m3}}{C_2 + C_3} + \frac{g_{m1}g_{m2}}{C_1 (C_2 + C_3)}}$$

Figure 2 Biquad and OTA based equivalent.

In a single ended configuration such as Figure 1, the wide tuning current variations in M3 could cause offset problems. However, the offset stabilizing loop, M12-M13, has been found to keep the offset within reasonable levels. This offset will vary as a result of the tuning process.

Both single ended and fully differential filters are achievable. Figure 2 shows a circuit diagram of a single ended biquad and its OTA based equivalent (3), while Figure 3 shows a photomicrograph of its realization in a 5μ CMOS double-poly silicon gate process. We have paid particular attention to the feasibility of obtaining zeros as

Reprinted from *IEEE Proc. ISCAS*, pp. 1173–1176, 1986.

well as poles to allow precision tuning; for example in IF filters. The transfer function of Figure 2 shows that the pole and zero frequencies are precisely related by a capacitance ratio even-though their absolute position is tuneable by current in the transconductance filter. Figure 4 compares some theoretical and experimental frequency responses. Figure 5 shows a polaroid of one experimental response at 20 μA. Although the theoretical/experimental match is not precise, due to variability of component absolute values (parti-cularly g_M of the input transistors), the trends and general behaviour with tuning are correct. At low current, spurious phase delays are minimal and high-Q zeros are obtained. This suppresses the peak of the poles to give a sharp corner to the low pass response. At higher currents, spurious phase delays degrade the performance. Figure 6 shows the frequency of the zeros and the attenuation at the zeros versus tuning current. The anomalous behaviour at very low or very high currents is due to loss of favourable bias environment. This has been overcome in later designs by a more sophisti-cated design of the bias circuit; e.g., changing bias currents in the cascoded output stages in proportion to the tuning current. The offset of the amplifier is then much less dependent on the tuning current.

Buffering of the filter is critical for accurate frequency performance. The output requires a voltage follower buffer so that succeed-ing stages or measurement devices do not modify frequency parameters. The experimental response in Figure 5 reflects increased parasitic capacitance due to an error in layout. As well, the notch at −30 dB to 35 dB attenuation is modified due to background noise.

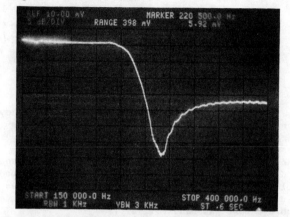

Figure 5 Frequency response of biquad at a bias current of 20 μA. Zero frequency is 290 kHz, notch depth is 34 dB.

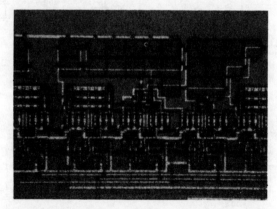

Figure 3 Photomicrograph of OTA based biquad.

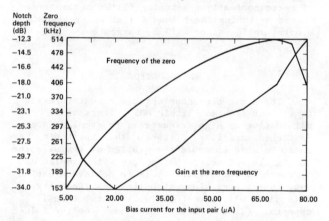

Figure 6 Frequency of the zero and attenuation at the zero frequency versus tuning current.

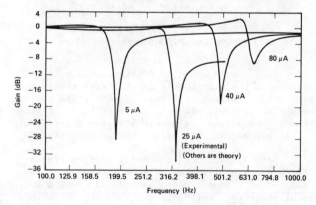

Figure 4 Frequency of biquad filter. Theoretical response at bias currents of 5 μA, 40 μA and 80 μA. Experimental response at 25 μA.

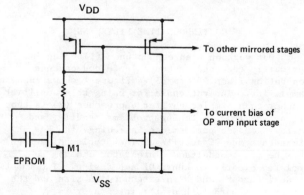

Figure 7 Basic circuit for mirroring EPROM analog tuning circuit.

408

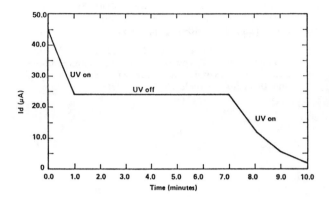

Figure 8   Typical time behaviour of EPROM current
with UV light.

FILTER TUNING

We now proceed to the second main topic of the
work which is an investigation of using EPROM's
programmed in an analog sense to provide the
current bias which tunes the filter. Figure 7
shows one possible basic circuit. Transistor M1
symbolizes an EPROM. The current in this EPROM
transistor is mirrored to all transconductance-
amplifier tuning transistors (which are not
EPROM's). The EPROM bias current is tuned in
circuit, before the filter is put into use, with
either conventional extended-amplitude pulsing or a
novel low voltage ultra-violet light enhanced
programming.

Figure 8 shows a typical experiment for tuning
with UV light. Initially, the erased EPROM
transistor threshold is low, thus the mirrored
current in Figure 7 is high. The current drops
with time as UV light and applied bias causes the
threshold to increase. When a filter parameter,
such as the frequency of the zero in Figure 6,
reaches the desired value, the UV light is turned
off. The figure shows apparent complete short-term
current stability thereafter, until the UV light is
turned back on. Long-term stability measurements
are in progress.

OPTIMIZATION AND TRADEOFFS

The analog-tuned EPROM approach raises
critical questions regarding retention time and
temperature stability. Depending on this
stability, we are considering three different
approaches: (i) simple analog as just described,
(ii) totally binary where digitally programmed
EPROM's would select unit current sources which do
not exhibit the EPROM instabilities, and (iii) a
combination where the least significant bit (LSB)
would be tuned in a continuous way as (i) with the
range of the LSB reflecting the known temperature
and time stability. A variation of (iii) would be
to have a simplified continuous time in-loop feedback hold the last-significant bit range. This
could reduce the design complexity of the continuous in-loop feedback circuit.

Regarding temperature stability of current:
from theoretical considerations we expect two
opposing effects which may counterbalance under
some conditions. The first effect is the drop of
mobility with temperature rise ($T^{-3/2}$). The
second is a drop in threshold voltage with temperature rise. If the EPROM of Figure 7 was biased
only slightly above threshold after analog programming, the threshold shift effect would dominate so
we would expect that for low current levels,
current would increase with temperature. For high
current levels, mobility decrease would dominate
causing current to decrease with temperature. We
have confirmed this behaviour experimentally. For
example, for bias at 6.05 μA at room temperature
(25°C) the measured current rose to 6.28 μA at
125°C. For bias of 73.5 μA at 25°C, current fell
to 62.1 μA at 125°C. At 15 μA, current was level
to within 0.4% over the range 25°C to 125°C
confirming the opposing trends discussed above. Of
course these results must be considered in light of
the thermal dependence of the transconductance
amplifier and the entire filter assembly.

Regarding retention time or long-term drift:
continuous read disturb and charge leakage effects
may be instrumental in determining the useful life
of a circuit tuned using the simple analog EPROM
method. A characterization effort, presently
underway, will quantify these mechanisms and help
to choose the appropriate tuning architecture.

CONCLUSIONS

We have reported on a single-ended continuous
time filter using open loop tuneable transconductance amplifiers. The filter response has been
shown to be tuneable over a wide range and the
accompanying variation in amplifier offset can be
made reasonably small. Of course, where offset and
linearity requirements are critical, a fully
differential amplifier could be used.

The filter response can be pre-tuned using
EPROM's with either conventional extended amplitude
pulsing or a novel low voltage light enhanced
programming. Initial results are favourable,
although the practicality of using EPROM's in the
filter architecture will be strongly dependent on
the application requirements for stability of
filter parameters. Only real-time in-circuit
tuning could give maximum stability and that has
not been studied here. The best use of the EPROM
feature may well be as a gross pre-tuning to bring
filter parameters into a guaranteed range for other
techniques to take over. We will not know the most
appropriate technique until the characterization
effort has been completed, i.e. until long-term
stability is understood.

FUTURE WORK

Further work is presently in progress on
matching phase delays, use of a 3μ process, a
fully differential circuit, and study of linearity
and noise.

409

REFERENCES

(1) T.C. Choi, R.T. Kaneshiro, R.W. Brodersen, P.R. Gray, W.B. Jett and M. Wilcox, "High Frequency CMOS Switched Capacitor Filters for Communication Applications", ISSCC, February 25, 1983, pp. 246-247, 314.

(2) H. Khorramabadi, P.R. Gray, "High Frequency Continuous-Time Filters", J. Solid State Circuits, Vol. SC-19, pp. 939-955, Dec. 84.

(3) R.L. Geiger, E. Sanchez-Sinencio, "Active Filter Design Using Operational Transconductance Amplifiers: A Tutorial, IEEE Circuits and Devices, March 1985, pp. 20-32.

410

Self-Tuned *RC*-Active Filters for VLSI

J. B. HUGHES, N. C. BIRD, AND R. S. SOIN

PHILIPS RESEARCH LABORATORIES, CROSS OAK LANE, REDHILL, SURREY RH1 5HA, UNITED KINGDOM

Indexing terms: Filters, VLSI

A technique is presented for automatically tuning integrated-circuit active *RC* filters. The control circuit uses a combination of digital and switched-capacitor techniques and is suitable for implementation in MOS technology. Simulated performance for an 80 kHz third-order lowpass filter is given and indicates that the degradation of linearity due to the tuning technique is minimal.

Introduction: Active filters consisting of networks of resistors, capacitors and op-amps have been very successful where the passive components may be selected or trimmed to achieve the required filter accuracy. Monolithic integration has, however, proved difficult due to the poor control of the absolute values of integrated resistors and capacitors. For example, in CMOS these spreads may produce variations in the *RC* products as high as $\pm 50\%$. Both resistors and capacitors within an IC track very well (approximately $\pm 0.5\%$ and $\pm 0.1\%$, respectively, in CMOS) allowing the filter *RC* products to be evaluated by a separate on-chip monitor circuit. Various control arrangements have been described[1-5] which tune the monitor circuits to an external reference. The filter is simultaneously tuned by the same control and highly accurate filters have resulted. A common weakness of the tuning techniques is that they usually involve changing the working point of the filter's active devices, and consequently the linearity is degraded.

The technique proposed here retains the standard configuration of the active *RC* filter and achieves tuning without significant degradation of linearity.

Tuning technique: The method uses the fact that deviations from the nominal values of resistors and/or capacitors of an active *RC* filter due to processing spreads, aging or temperature effects, can be fully compensated by making changes to only the filter capacitors (or resistors). Fig. 1 shows a third-order lowpass configuration which, for good matching and ease of layout, is designed with equal capacitors. These capacitors are made adjustable by using programmable binary weighted capacitor arrays which are designed to have nominal centre values equal to the design values (C_f). Their range needs to be at least as great as the combined spreads of the resistors and capacitors and their resolution consistent with the desired filter accuracy. Tuning is achieved by supplying an appropriate digital code to set the arrays.

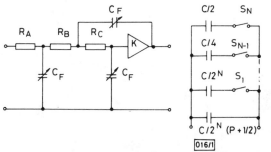

Fig. 1 *Third-order lowpass filter and binary weighted capacitor array*

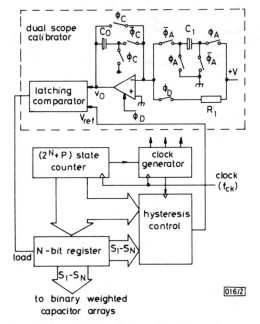

Fig. 2 *Control circuit*

The digital code for setting the arrays is generated by the control circuit shown in Fig. 2. This circuit calibrates the filter by comparing the value of the monitor *RC* product ($R_1 C_1$) with the external clock period ($1/f_c$) and then generates the appropriate code. The measurement of the $R_1 C_1$ product is performed in the dual-slope calibrator, the waveforms for which are shown in Fig. 3. During the interval $t_1 - t_2$ the integrator is reset ($v_0 = 0$). Next, the integrating capacitor C_0 is charged from R_1 ($t_2 - t_3$) with constant current producing the negative-going ramp which has a slope dependent on $R_1 C_1$. Finally, C_0 is charged by the switched capacitor C_1 to produce a positive-going staircase with constant slope ($t_3 - t_5$). It can easily be shown that the number of steps in the staircase before the waveform crosses zero is given by $n \simeq T/R_1 C_1$, where T is the time interval ($t_2 - t_3$) $= 2^N/f_c$.

Clearly the state of the counter at the zero-crossing gives a measure of the $R_1 C_1$ product which is designed with a nominal value equal to the clock period ($1/f_c$). The counter is reset at t_4 (P clock periods after t_3) and, with the binary weighted capacitor array designed according to Fig. 1, the code in the ($2^N + P$) state counter at the zero-crossing is just that required to tune the filter to its nominal frequency response. The control circuit parameters P and N are chosen according to the expected processing spreads and the required filter accuracy. It can be shown that the technique compensates processing spreads in the range $\pm 100/(1 + P/2^{N-1})\%$ and produces a filter with an accuracy (quantisation error) of $\pm 50/(P + 1)\%$. A more rigorous treatment of the technique is given elsewhere.[6]

Results: The technique has been used in the design of a third-order lowpass filter (Sallen and Key configuration, Fig. 1) with a cutoff frequency of 80 kHz using a double polysilicon CMOS process. The specification was for a filter with cutoff

Reprinted with permission from *El. Letters*, vol. 22, no. 19, pp. 993–994, Sept. 1986.

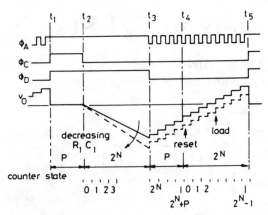

Fig. 3 *Control cycle*
$P = 4, 2^N = 8$

frequency accurate to $\pm 5\%$ with a total spread of *RC* product of $\pm 50\%$. This was achieved by setting $P = 16$ and $2^N = 32$ ($N = 5$).

The system was simulated in two steps. First, the control circuit operation was verified in a special-purpose program able to handle mixed sampled data and logic circuits.[7] Secondly, the filter performance was simulated using an in-house version of SPICE. Worst-case processing conditions added $\pm 1 \cdot 5\%$ to the $\pm 3\%$ quantisation error. The worst-case total harmonic distortion due to the finite voltage-dependent parasitics of the MOS switches of the binary weighted capacitor arrays was less than $0 \cdot 05\%$ for an output sinusoid of 3Vp-p at 40 kHz. The control circuit dissipates only 1 mW.

Conclusions: A technique has been described which enables automatic on-chip tuning of standard active *RC* filters. While the digital control can be designed to cope with any degree of processing spread and produce extremely small quantisation error, there remain finite analogue errors due to circuit parasitics, noise and offset voltages which will limit the ultimate accuracy of the technique. However, it is felt that with judicious circuit design, filter accuracy in the region of $\pm 1\%$ is feasible. The worsening of the filter's linearity due to the tuning technique is minimal ($0 \cdot 05\%$).

References

1   CANNING, J. R., and WILSON, G. A.: 'Frequency discriminator circuit arrangement'. UK patent no. 1 421 093, published Jan. 1976, and US patent no. 3 997 856, published Dec. 1976
2   BRAND, J. R., SCHAUMANN, R., and SKEI, E. M.: 'Temperature-stabilised active R bandpass filters'. Proceedings of 20th midwest symposium on circuits and systems, Aug. 1977, pp. 295–300
3   MOULDING, K. W., QUARTLY, J. R., RANKIN, P. J., THOMPSON, R. S., and WILSON, G. A.: 'Gyrator video filter IC with automatic tuning', *IEEE J. Solid-State Circuits*, 1980, **SC-15**, pp. 963–968
4   GEIGER, R. L., ALLEN, P. E., and NGO, D. T.: 'Switched-resistor filters—a continuous time approach to monolithic MOS filter design', *IEEE Trans.*, 1982, **CAS-29**, pp. 306–315
5   BANU, M., and TSIVIDIS, Y.: 'On-chip automatic tuning for a CMOS continuous-time filter'. International solid state circuits conference, Feb. 1985, pp. 286–287
6   HUGHES, J. B., BIRD, N. C., and SOIN, R. S.: 'A novel digitally self-tuned continuous-time filter technique'. Digest of 1986 IEEE international symposium on circuits and systems, pp. 1177–1180
7   SOIN, R. S., HUGHES, J. B., and BIRD, N. C.: 'A novel approach to the time domain simulation of switched capacitor systems'. European conference on circuit theory and design, Sept. 1985, pp. 713–716

An Adaptive Analog Continuous-Time CMOS Biquadratic Filter

Tom Kwan, *Member*, *IEEE*, and Kenneth Martin, *Fellow*, *IEEE*

Abstract —An adaptive analog continuous-time biquadratic filter is realized in a 2-μm digital CMOS process for operation at 300 kHz. The biquad implements the notch, bandpass, and low-pass transfer functions. The only parameter adapted is the resonant frequency of the biquad, which is identical to the notch frequency and the bandpass center frequency. The update method is based on a least-means-square (LMS) algorithm, which adapts the notch frequency to minimize the power at the notch filter output. The actual update is modified to reduce the circuit complexity to one biquad and one correlator. When the filter is tracking a sinusoid, this update generates a ripple-free gradient that decreases tracking error. Applications include phase–frequency detectors, FM demodulators (linear and FSK), clock extractors, and frequency acquisition aids for PLL's and Costas loops. Measured results from experimental prototypes are presented. Nonidealities of an all-analog implementation are discussed along with suggestions to improve performance.

I. Introduction

RESEARCH on adaptive filtering algorithms has advanced the use of signal processing in such diverse applications as line enhancement, channel equalization, speech coding, and spectral estimation [1]. Although most implementations of adaptive algorithms have been digital in nature, all-analog continuous-time realizations can result in smaller chip area, lower power dissipation, and freedom from clocking and aliasing effects [2]. Until recently, finite-impulse-response (FIR) adaptive filters have received the most attention. As a result, adaptive FIR filters have matured to the point where they are routinely applied in many commercial systems. However, there is growing interest in infinite-impulse-response (IIR) adaptive filters in some signal processing applications, due to the IIR filter's efficiency in meeting difficult frequency response specifications with relatively few multipliers [3]. Also, recently, much work has been accomplished in the area of monolithic continuous-time recursive (IIR) filters [4]–[8]. Since these filters are inherently tunable, they are prime candidates for the analog implementation of adaptive IIR filters.

In this paper, we present an analog implementation of an adaptive biquadratic filter designed to track the frequency of a sinusoid. The biquad has a notch, bandpass, and low-pass output and is characterized as constant bandwidth.[1] The only parameter adapted is the resonant frequency of the biquad, which is identical to the notch frequency and the bandpass center frequency. The update method is based on a least-means-square (LMS) algorithm, which adapts the notch frequency to minimize the power at the notch filter output. The actual update is modified to reduce the circuit complexity to one biquad and one correlator. This modification is referred to as the "one-biquad implementation" in [9]. The modified update is derived from the correlation of the notch and low-pass outputs. When the notch has converged to an input sinusoid, the notch filter will have zero output and hence the update (gradient) will have zero ripple. This lack of ripple translates directly to decreased variance in the demodulated frequency of the input sinusoid.

Applications of the adaptive biquad include frequency demodulation (both linear and FSK), frequency acquisition[2] for PLL and Costas loops, and clock extraction through the tracking bandpass output.[3]

In the following section, we describe an implementation of the constant bandwidth biquad and its update algorithm based on continuous-time transconductance-C filter topology. In Section III, experimental results of prototypes fabricated using a digital 2-μm n-well CMOS process are presented. Finally, in Section IV, problems with an all-analog implementation are discussed and suggestions to improve performance are given.

II. Adaptive Biquad and Update Algorithm

A block diagram of the biquad and the update algorithm based on fully differential operational transconductance amplifiers (OTA's) is shown in Fig. 1. The notch filter is implemented using an OTA with *multiple* outputs

Manuscript received July 30, 1990; revised January 22, 1991. This work was supported in part by the National Science Foundation under Grant MIP-8913164.

T. Kwan was with the Integrated Circuits and Systems Laboratory, Department of Electrical Engineering, University of California, Los Angeles, CA 90024. He is now with Analog Devices, Norwood, MA.

K. Martin is with the Integrated Circuits and Systems Laboratory, Department of Electrical Engineering, University of California, Los Angeles, CA 90024.

IEEE Log Number 9144582.

[1]The bandwidth of the filter remains constant when its resonant frequency is changed.
[2]The VCO should be resonator based and matched to the two-integrator loop of the biquad (see [9]).
[3]This requires a bandpass filter with quality factor of 100 or more.

Reprinted from *IEEE J. Solid-State Circuits*, vol. SC-26, no. 6, pp. 859−867, June 1991.

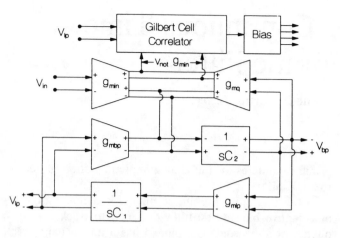

Fig. 1. Block diagram of the constant bandwidth biquad and update algorithm.

to minimize the phase shift around the loop $g_{mq}, 1/(sC_2)$. In an alternate realization using OTA's with single outputs, a transresistance amplifier would be needed to sum the currents between g_{min} and g_{mq}, and to convert the result to a voltage for the notch output. Also, an additional OTA would be needed to convert the notch output voltage to a current to be summed with the current output of the cell g_{mbp}, all contributing excess phase shift and impeding high-frequency performance. By using multiple current output OTA's, the notch output becomes current oriented. Moreover, since one input set of the correlator multiplier cell is current driven, this configuration simplifies the correlator circuitry.

The biquad structure shown is sufficient in generating the notch current ($v_{not} g_{min}$), bandpass output (v_{bp}), and low-pass output (v_{lp}). The notch current, bandpass, and low-pass transfer functions are given by

$$H_{not}(s) = g_{min}\left(s^2 + \frac{g_{mbp}g_{mlp}}{C_1C_2}\right)\bigg/ D(s) \qquad (1)$$

$$H_{bp}(s) = s\frac{-g_{min}}{C_2}\bigg/ D(s) \qquad (2)$$

$$H_{lp}(s) = \frac{g_{min}g_{mlp}}{C_1C_2}\bigg/ D(s) \qquad (3)$$

respectively, where

$$D(s) = s^- + s\frac{g_{mq}}{C_2} + \frac{g_{mbp}g_{mlp}}{C_1C_2}. \qquad (4)$$

The peak gain of the bandpass is given by g_{min}/g_{mq} with the resonant frequency ω_0 and half-power bandwidth B given by

$$\omega_0 = \sqrt{\frac{g_{mbp}g_{mlp}}{C_1C_2}} \qquad (5)$$

$$B = g_{mq}/C_2. \qquad (6)$$

In a nominal design, g_{min} and g_{mq} are matched to g_{mB}, g_{mbp} and g_{mlp} are matched to g_{mW}, and C_1 and C_2 are matched to C. This results in a peak gain of one for the

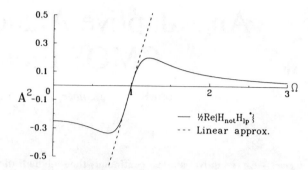

Fig. 2. Plot of the biquad gradient for a sinusoidal input with amplitude A and normalized frequency Ω, and its linear approximation.

bandpass output, a resonant frequency[4] of g_{mW}/C, and a bandwidth of $(g_{mB}/g_{mW})\omega_0$. The resonant frequency of the filter is adapted by tuning g_{mW} while g_{mB} remains fixed, thus maintaining constant bandwidth. As shown below, this constant bandwidth property gives a constant "frequency-difference gain" for the gradient which makes the design of the algorithm update simpler.

It should be noted that the realization of the bandpass and notch filter functions is not contingent on the matching of the above transconductances and capacitances. A mismatch of the first set (g_{mB}) results only in a nonunity gain for the bandpass output, while the effect on the second and third set (g_{mw}, C) affects only the resonant frequency, which is precisely the parameter being adapted.

The adaptation gradient is derived from the correlation between the low-pass and notch outputs of the biquad. For a sinusoidal input and given (1) and (3), this correlation yields

$$g(\omega) = E\big[v_{not}(t)v_{lp}(t)\big]$$

$$= -\frac{A^2}{2}\sqrt{\frac{g_{mq}^2 C_1}{g_{mbp}g_{mlp}C_2}}$$

$$\cdot \frac{1-\Omega^2}{(1-\Omega^2)^2 + \frac{C_1 g_{mq}^2}{C_2 g_{mbp}g_{mlp}}\Omega^2}. \qquad (7)$$

where $\Omega = \omega/\omega_0$ and A are the normalized frequency and the amplitude of the input, respectively. For the above nominal design with $g_{mB}/g_{mW} = 1/2$, (7) is plotted in Fig. 2.

Algorithm Update: Choosing the update size (or gain in the case of continuous-time systems) in adaptive filters is often an empirical process. The selection process generally involves simulating an algorithm's behavior for various step sizes and then selecting the one that will give the fastest convergence result while maintaining stability. Fortunately, for this particular adaptive system, one can linearize the gradient about its operating point and apply conventional feedback analysis to ensure stability, analogous to the linearized analysis of phase-locked loops.

From the gradient curve of Fig. 2, it can be seen that for an input sinusoid of sufficiently small frequency devia-

[4]Identical to the notch and bandpass center frequency.

tion from the resonant frequency ω_0, the gradient curve is well approximated by a straight line. The slope of this line represents a "frequency-difference gain" and can be found by taking the derivative of the curve with respect to ω and inserting $\omega = \omega_0$ in the final result. This gain is found to be $A^2 C_2 / g_{mq}$. Not only is this linear approximation accurate near the resonant frequency but it also represents an upper bound for the magnitude of the "frequency-difference gain." Thus, an update gain designed to be stable with a sinusoidal input at the resonant frequency will also enjoy global stability. Note that this gain is independent of the resonant frequency of the filter, which makes a linearized feedback analysis of the frequency-tracking loop more accurate. This is not the case with constant Q filters.

A. Filter Components

1) Operational Transconductance Amplifier: Unlike an op-amp-based integrator which has a large feedback gain over its operating frequencies to reduce the signal swing at its input, transconductance-C integrators typically operate near their unity-gain frequencies, which imposes a large-signal-linearity requirement for the transconductors. Numerous circuit techniques have been proposed in the implementation of large-signal linear transconductors in CMOS [6], [8], [10], [13]. The one developed here is based on the well-known source-coupled differential pair with source degeneration as shown in Fig. 3(a). Given that the transconductance of the MOSFET's (g_m) is much larger than $1/R$, only a small portion of the input voltage lies across the active devices, implying reduced signal swing and distortion. The requirement $g_m \gg 1/R$ can usually be satisfied with large transistors and/or bias currents. In many applications, this may not be desirable in terms of area and power consumption. An alternate way is to boost the g_m of the p-channel by using a compound device as shown in Fig. 3(b) [15]. This compound configuration is often used in the design of many bipolar output stages instead of a single p-n-p transistor with poor performance. In this case, $M1$ acts like a floating voltage source. Its g_m is no longer an important factor in the distortion performance of the OTA. However, any threshold voltage shift due to the body effect becomes part of the input signal. For this reason, p-channel input transistors were chosen for the n-well process, in which the body effect can be minimized by connecting the source of each input transistor to its own well.

A basic OTA with the compound devices and biasing is shown in Fig. 3(c). The p-channels serve as voltage followers buffering the input voltage across the resistor while the four constant current sources force any change in the resistor current to be directly reflected to the drain currents of $M2$ and $M2'$, which is mirrored to the output by $M3$ and $M3'$. Multiple current outputs can be obtained by adding additional transistors to the mirror.

a) Resistor implementation: In a standard CMOS technology, realization of large resistances is impractical

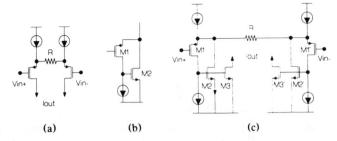

Fig. 3. (a) Differential pair with source degeneration. (b) Composite p-channel device. (c) Basic G_m cell.

because of the low sheet resistance and poor tolerances. By contrast, a MOSFET can exhibit a large linear resistance behavior while operating in the triode region for small drain-to-source bias voltages. A circuit for realizing a floating linear resistor is shown in Fig. 4(a) [14].[5] A constant floating control voltage (v_{gs}) is generated across the gate and source of $M5$ and $M5'$ operating in the linear region, which helps to cancel the nonlinear terms in the MOSFET current equation. Linearity of the circuit is dependent on this constant v_{gs} bias, a small body-effect parameter γ, and the matching of $M5$ and $M5'$. Further details can be found in [14] and [17]. This floating resistor implementation is used to replace the resistor in the basic g_m cell of Fig. 3(c). The complete OTA including various enhancements is shown in Fig. 4(b). The addition of $M4$ keeps the v_{ds} of $M1$ constant, which improves its voltage follower action[6] and minimizes the effect of C_{gd3} on the previous stage. $M9$ and C_c serve to compensate the $M1, M6, M2, M8, M4$ feedback loop, similar to the compensation of a conventional two-stage CMOS op amp in which a zero at 1.2 times the unity-gain frequency of the loop is added to the loop transfer function for increased stability [19]. The compensation capacitor C_c is realized between the layers $metal_1$ (lower plane) and $metal_2$ (upper plane). Since $metal_1$ forms a significant parasitic capacitance (shown as dashed lines in Fig. 4(b)) with the substrate (50% of the $metal_1$, $metal_2$ capacitance), it is tied to the gate of $M2$ to increase the phase margin. Finally, a diode ($M10$) is used to clamp the maximum gate voltages of $M2$ and $M3$ to prevent overdriving the load stage in the unlikely event that the common-mode input voltage swings to the negative power rail. This can cause the common-mode output of a two-integrator loop to latch up to the power rail, if the common-mode feedback stage has insufficient current drive.

The transconductance of the stage (G_m) is determined solely by the resistances of $M5$ and $M5'$, which are controlled by their gate-to-source bias voltages. These bias voltages can be varied by changing the bias currents. Given that the current through $M11$ and $M12$ is $3I$, and the current through $M1$ is I, an approximate relationship

---

[5]Unless otherwise stated, unlabeled transistors in the right half of the circuit are understood to be identical to the left half.
[6]SPICE simulations show an improvement in gain from 0.93 to 0.90.

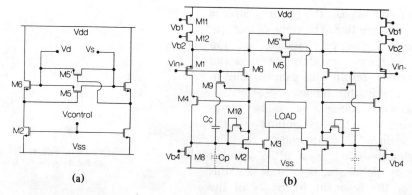

Fig. 4. (a) CMOS circuit for realizing a floating linear resistor. (b) Adaptation of a CMOS floating resistor circuit in an OTA.

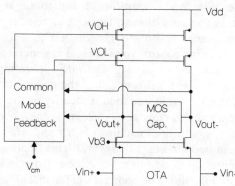

Fig. 5. OTA-based integrator.

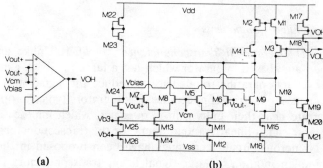

Fig. 6. (a) Differential difference amplifier. (b) Common-mode feedback circuit.

between the G_m of the OTA and the bias current I is

$$G_m = 2k_5 \left[\sqrt{I} \left(\sqrt{2/k_1} + \sqrt{4/k_6} \right) + |V_{T1}| + V_{T6} - V_{T5} \right] \quad (8)$$

where $k_i = \mu C_{ox} (W/L)_i$ and V_{Ti} is the threshold voltage of M_i.

The bandwidth of the OTA can be estimated by finding the source of the dominant time constant in the circuit. For the circuit in Fig. 4(b), it can be shown that this time constant comes from the gate node of $M2$ where the impedance is highest. The approximate resistance and capacitance seen at this node are the output resistance of $M8$ divided by the loop gain and the Miller capacitance due to C_c, respectively.

2) Integrator: The signal current from the OTA is mirrored through $M3$ of Fig. 4(b) into the cascode load of Fig. 5 to form an integrator. To save area, the integrator capacitor is realized by using a pair of back-to-back PMOS transistors biased in the saturation region [16]. In a standard digital CMOS process, the thin oxide of a MOSFET is the most area-efficient (thinnest) insulator available for realizing capacitors. For the 2-μm process, this translates to a factor of 18 less in area compared to the second most efficient implementation (thick oxide between the two metal layers).

3) Common-Mode Feedback Circuit: The common-mode feedback circuitry for the OTA-based integrator is shown in Fig. 6(b). This circuit is based on the "differential-difference amplifier" concept in [11] extended to three

sets of inputs from two (see Fig. 6(a)). Both *VOH* and *VOL* can swing to V_{dd} and near V_{ss}. This ensures that the common-mode output voltage stays near V_{cm} (which prevents latch-up problems) regardless of the OTA's common-mode input voltage. The symmetrical bias arrangement ($M22$ to $M26$) ensures there is no systematic offset in the common-mode output voltage. Compensation of the common-mode feedback loop is provided by the load capacitor.

4) Correlator: As described previously, the gradient signal for the adaptive filter can be generated by correlating the notch and low-pass filter outputs. The first stage of the proposed correlator consists of a Gilbert four-quadrant multiplier which, as mentioned earlier, can accept current as one set of its inputs. Current output from the multiplier is then integrated across a capacitor to form a correlator. This capacitor is made entirely from parasitic capacitances, but its terminals are made accessible off chip so that extra capacitance can be added if needed.[7] The complete correlator circuit is shown in Fig. 7(a). Defining the quiescent current through $M16-M19$ to be I_{D16}, the transconductance of the differential pair $M24$, $M25$ as g_{mf}, and the effective output conductance seen by C_i to be g_o, the output of the correlator can be

---

[7]With bonding pads and external wiring, the estimated parasitic capacitance is on the order of 1–2 pF.

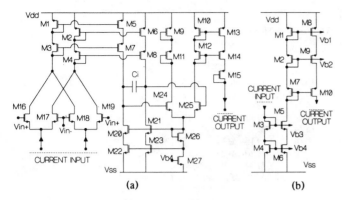

(a)   (b)

Fig. 7.   (a) Correlator. (b) Bias circuitry.

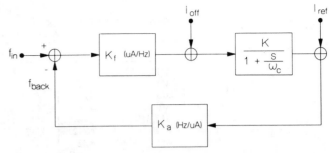

Fig. 8.   Linear frequency-signal based model of the biquad tracking loop.

described by

$$\Delta I(t) = I_{d25}(t) - I_{d26}(t)$$

$$= \left\{ \frac{k_2}{k_5} \sqrt{\frac{k_{16}}{2I_{D16}}} \, g_{\min} v_{not}(t) v_{lp}(t) \right\}$$

$$* \, \mathcal{L}^{-1} \left\{ \frac{g_{mf}}{sC_i + g_0} \right\} \qquad (9)$$

where "$*$" and $\mathcal{L}^{-1}$ denote time convolution and inverse Laplace transform, respectively. The current output of the correlator drives a number of bias circuits (shown in Fig. 7(b)), which redistributes the current to the OTA's that control the filter's resonant frequency.[8]

To model the biquad frequency tracking loop as a frequency-signal control system, a frequency-difference gain was derived earlier to approximate the gradient for input sinusoids with small frequency deviations from the resonant frequency. Using the correlator of Fig. 7, an expression for this frequency-difference gain is

$$K_f = \frac{E[\Delta I(t)]}{\Delta \omega} \bigg|_{\omega = \omega_0} = \frac{A^2}{B} \cdot \frac{k_2}{k_5} \sqrt{\frac{k_{16}}{2I_{D16}}} \, g_{\min} \quad (10)$$

where $E[\cdot]$ denotes the expectation operation over time.

5) Output Buffers: The bandpass and low-pass outputs of the biquad have very high output impedance which needs to be buffered for measurement purposes. The OTA cell described earlier is modified to serve as a buffer for the bandpass and low-pass outputs by increasing the size of its output transistors by a factor of 4. The notch output is obtained by wiring a third set of current outputs (not shown in Fig. 1) from the transconductance blocks $g_{\min}$ and g_{mq} in Fig. 1 to the pads.

B. Linear Analysis of Tracking Loop

With the circuit description of building blocks complete, we can describe a simple linear frequency-signal control system based on circuit parameters to model the tracking behavior of the adaptive filter. For a narrow-band

signal whose bandwidth is less than one-tenth of its center frequency, the transient response of the biquad can be ignored relative to the much slower closed-loop response (see [9]). Fig. 8 shows a block diagram of such a linear model of the adaptive filter. The frequency-difference gain K_f is in units of microamperes per hertz. The accumulated effect of all dc offsets in the system, including the OTA's and the multiplier, is represented by I_{off}. The gain K and the corner frequency ω_c are given by g_{mf}/g_o and g_o/C_i, respectively, where g_{mf}, g_o, and C_i are defined as in (9). In nominal operation, the actual current driving the OTA's that control the filter's resonant frequency consists of two components. One component is fixed and gives the filter an initial starting frequency. The second component is derived from the adaptation process and its magnitude defines the tracking range of the biquad. I_{ref} stands for the first component. Finally, K_a is the sensitivity of the biquad's resonant frequency with respect to the bias currents in the OTA blocks' g_{mlp} and g_{mbp} in Fig. 1. This sensitivity is simply the derivative of (8) with respect to I normalized by the integration capacitance C. K_a is in units of hertz per microampere.

The tracking performance can be estimated by simple feedback analysis. Solving for f_{back} in Fig. 8 in terms of f_{in}, I_{off}, and I_{ref} gives

$$f_{\text{back}} = \left(f_{\text{in}} \frac{K_f K K_a}{1 + K_f K K_a} + I_{\text{off}} \frac{K K_a}{1 + K_f K K_a} \right.$$

$$\left. + I_{\text{ref}} \frac{K_a}{1 + K_f K K_a} \right) \frac{1}{1 + \dfrac{s}{\omega_c (K_f K K_a)}}. \quad (11)$$

A large K_f is essential in minimizing any tracking errors introduced by the offset and reference currents

III. EXPERIMENTAL RESULTS

The constant bandwidth biquad was designed to have a resonant frequency of 360 kHz and a bandwidth of 180 kHz. The adaptive biquad was fabricated through MOSIS's 2-μm double-metal single-poly n-well CMOS process. The transistor sizes used in the components of the biquad are listed in Table I. A chip microphotograph is shown in Fig. 9. There exist significant differences in

---

[8]The actual frequency control current is routed through an off-chip jumper so that the adaptation loop can be broken to measure the filter response and gradient under a fixed bias.

TABLE I
COMPONENT SIZES FOR THE g_m CELL (OTA), COMMON-MODE FEEDBACK CIRCUIT
(CM), AND CORRELATOR CIRCUIT (COR) (W/L IN MICROMETERS)

OTA		CM		COR	
$M11, M12$	48/4	$M1-M4$	16/4	$M1-M4$	8/4
$M1, M4$	6/2	$M5-M8$	4/24	$M5-M8$	12/8
$M5$	4/16	$M9, M10$	4/12	$M9-M12$	8/4
$M6$	4/6	$M11-M14$	8/4	$M13, M14$	16/4
$M2, M8$	16/4	$M15, M16$	16/4	$M15$	8/4
$M9$	4/12	$M17-M26$	8/4	$M16-M19$	4/12
$M10$	4/2			$M20-M23$	16/4
C_c	0.15 pF			$M24, M25$	4/4
C_p	0.1 pF			$M26, M27$	32/4

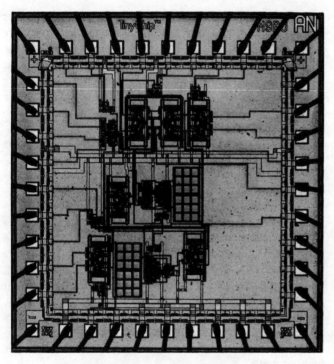

Fig. 9. Chip microphotograph.

TABLE II
TYPICAL PERFORMANCE CHARACTERISTICS OF THE TRANSCONDUCTANCE
CELL FOR A 10-V SUPPLY VOLTAGE AND 108-μA SUPPLY CURRENT

Total harmonic distortion (THD)	0.31% at $V_{in} = 1$ V_{p-p}, 100 kHz
	0.69% at $V_{in} = 2$ V_{p-p}, 100 kHz
-3-dB bandwidth	11.3 MHz
Offset voltage	10-mV typical
Transconductance	$1/10.4$ kΩ

appropriate terminal of C_i in the correlator circuit of Fig. 7(a).

Typical frequency responses of the OTA and the biquad (including off-chip differential-to-single-ended converters) are shown in Figs. 10 and 11, respectively. A scaled version of the gradient signal is measured by disconnecting the current feedback that controls the resonant frequency and biasing the filter with a fixed current. A 1-MΩ resistor is shunted across the correlator capacitance C_i and the voltage across this resistor is tabulated for a sine-wave input of varying frequency.[9] The results are plotted in Fig. 12 for an input sinusoid of amplitude 0.5 V. The measured slope of the gradient is 1.2e-6 μA/rad, which is in close agreement with value of 1.1e-6 μA/rad calculated from (10). Note that the cumulative effect of all offsets in the system results in approximately 70 mV of offset at the correlator output. The measured magnitude and phase response of the tracking bandpass output of the biquad is shown in Fig. 13. For this measurement, the current controlling the resonant frequency of the biquad has two components. One component is fixed at 40 μA while the other is allowed to vary from 0 to 40 μA to adapt the resonant frequency of the biquad to that of an input sinusoid. The range of adaptation shown is determined by the second current component. In Fig. 14, the transient response of the adaptive biquad's notch output (with offset trimming) is shown while tracking the frequency of an FSK input.

the process parameters extracted from this run and the parameters used in the original design. Most notable of these are: t_{ox} decreased by 20%, p-channel μC_{ox} increased by 35%, and n-channel γ decreased by 86%. Substituting the new process parameters in (8) and noting that the integrator capacitance is inversely proportional to t_{ox}, the combined effect of the various parameter changes is to decrease the resonant frequency of the filter by a factor of 0.85. This works out to be approximately 305 kHz. Four chips were received from MOSIS in which the measured resonant frequencies ranged from 283 to 300 kHz.

The performance characteristics of the OTA buffer and the tracking biquad filter are summarized in Tables II and III, respectively. The total harmonic distortion measurements are obtained using a balanced-driven input and an off-chip differential-to-single-ended converter. For the tracking notch depth measurement, the dc offset is trimmed using an off-chip current source attached to the

IV. NONIDEAL EFFECTS

A practical implementation of an adaptive filter is often plagued by many nonideal effects, the major outcome being deviations from ideal filter response and tracking

---

[9]The actual gradient current is twice the current through the resistor due to the common-mode feedback to the current sources $M22$ and $M23$.

TABLE III
TYPICAL PERFORMANCE CHARACTERISTICS OF THE TRANSCONDUCTANCE-C INTEGRATOR
AND TRACKING BIQUADRATIC FILTER FOR A 10-V SUPPLY VOLTAGE

Integrator:	
DC gain	55 dB
Q factor	707
Tracking Filter:	
Notch frequency	291 kHz at $I_w = 21.1~\mu$A
-3-dB bandwidth	132 kHz at $I_b = 18.4~\mu$A
	cf. 131 kHz theoretical
Notch depth	45 dB
Tracking Error	-7% without dc offset trimming
	-0.28% with trimming
Tracking Notch Depth	11 dB without dc offset trimming
	39 dB with trimming
CMRR (bandpass output)	59.5 dB at 300 kHz
CMRR (low-pass output)	59.3 dB at 300 kHz
CMRR (notch output)	59.8 dB at 100 kHz
	53.9 dB at 500 kHz
Power supply rejection ratio $(+, -)$	
Bandpass	33.4 dB, 35.1 dB at 300 kHz
Low pass	30.9 dB, 33.9 dB at 300 kHz
Notch	38.1 dB, 33.9 dB at 100 kHz
THD (notch output)	0.40% at $V_{in} = 1$ V$_{p-p}$, 30 kHz
	0.81% at $V_{in} = 2$ V$_{p-p}$, 30 kHz
THD (low-pass output)	0.44% at $V_{in} = 1$ V$_{p-p}$, 30 kHz
	0.93% at $V_{in} = 2$ V$_{p-p}$, 30 kHz
Power dissipation	6.84 mW
Chip Area	1741 μm $\times$ 1012 μm

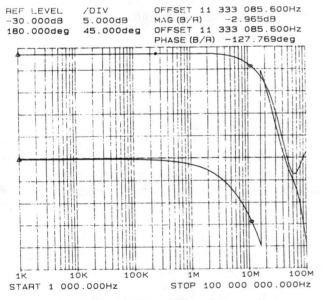

REF LEVEL   /DIV   OFFSET 11 333 085.600Hz
-30.000dB   5.000dB   MAG (B/R)   -2.965dB
180.000deg   45.000deg OFFSET 11 333 085.600Hz
                       PHASE (B/R) -127.769deg

1K   10K   100K   1M   10M   100M
START 1 000.000Hz   STOP 100 000 000.000Hz

Fig. 10. Measured OTA magnitude and phase response.

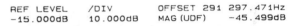

REF LEVEL   /DIV   OFFSET 291 297.471Hz
-15.000dB   10.000dB MAG (UDF)   -45.499dB

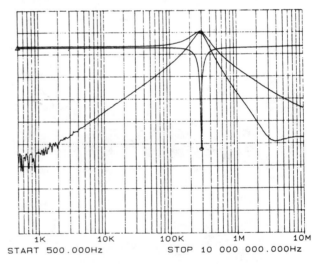

1K   10K   100K   1M   10M
START 500.000Hz   STOP 10 000 000.000Hz

Fig. 11. Measured magnitude response of the notch, bandpass, and low-pass outputs of the biquadratic filter.

accuracy. For example, parasitic capacitances and integrators with finite Q's can contribute to finite notch depths, and dc offsets can lead to biases in the filter tracking behavior. In the following, we discuss the effect of finite integrator quality factor Q on notch filter performance and several factors that can contribute to tracking inaccuracies in which dc offsets are the most dominant.

A. Finite Integrator Q Factor

One measure of an integrator's nonideal performance is its quality factor [18]. By modeling an integrator with a finite Q factor, the effects of any integrator phase-shift

error (due to high-frequency parasitic poles or finite integrator dc gain) on filter performance can be estimated. For the biquad shown in Fig. 1, it can be shown that the notch depth ϵ_{not} is

$$\epsilon_{not} = \frac{2\omega_0}{BQ_I} \qquad (12)$$

where Q_I is the quality factor of the integrators. To obtain a large notch depth at high frequencies, excess phase shift of high-frequency poles needs to be compensated. One solution is to insert a zero above the resonant

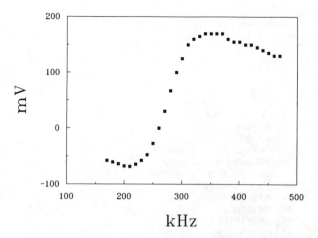

Fig. 12.   Measured gradient curve.

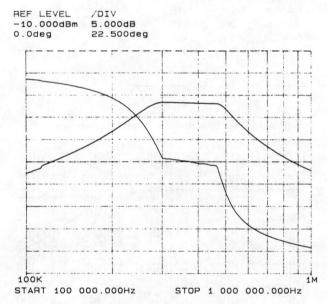

REF LEVEL   /DIV
-10.000dBm   5.000dB
0.0deg   22.500deg

100K   1M
START 100 000.000Hz   STOP 1 000 000.000Hz

Fig. 13.   Measured magnitude and phase response of the tracking bandpass output of the biquadratic filter.

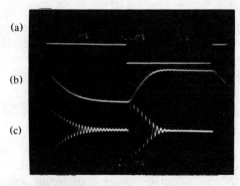

Fig. 14.   Measured waveforms while tracking an FSK input signal (f_c = 260 kHz, Δf = 47 kHz): (a) FSK modulating input, (b) filter demodulated output, and (c) notch filter output.

frequency of the biquad to introduce phase lead. To account for process and temperature variations, a master–slave tuning arrangement similar to most fixed filter tuning schemes [4], [5], [8], [16] can be used.

B. DC Offset

Of all the potential problems in an all-analog implementation of the adaptive biquad, dc offset is one of the most serious. The cumulative effect of the dc offsets in the OTA's and the Gilbert multiplier results in a dc shift of the true gradient. The biquad will converge to a frequency at which the generated gradient will exactly cancel this dc offset, resulting in a bias in the tracking frequency. If the offset is large enough such that the generate gradient is not able to cancel it, then the biquad fails to adapt.

Given the signal flow graph of the biquad in Fig. 1, we can calculate the worst-case notch and low-pass dc offsets by assuming the various sources of offsets can be lumped into an equivalent offset voltage at the input of each transconductance block. Let V_{os1}, V_{os2}, V_{os3}, and V_{os4} represent the input-referred offset voltages of the transconductance blocks g_{min}, g_{mq}, g_{mbp}, and g_{mlp}, respectively; then the worst-case offsets of the notch current and low-pass voltage outputs are

$$I_{not} = V_{os1}g_{min} + V_{os2}g_{mq} \tag{13}$$

$$Vl_p = V_{os1}\frac{g_{min}}{g_{mbp}} + V_{os2}\frac{g_{mq}}{g_{mbp}} + V_{os3} + V_{os4}\frac{g_{mq}}{g_{mbp}}. \tag{14}$$

The dominant source of dc offset in the gradient comes from the Gilbert multiplier. The multiplier was initially designed to have: 1) a large v_{gs} bias across its input devices ($M16$–$M19$) to minimize the nonlinearity of the source couple pairs, and 2) a small multiplier gain to ensure algorithm stability, which resulted in less than optimal scaling in terms of its input-referred offset voltage. Worst-case SPICE simulations show that a 1% width mismatch of the multiplier input pairs ($M16$–$M19$) coupled with a dc offset of 10 mV for each OTA results in an offset that is twice as large as measured in experiment. If the offset of the multiplier is eliminated, the worst-case offset of the gradient (due to OTA's alone) is reduced by a factor of 60. The multiplier's gain needs to be increased dramatically to reduce its input-referred offset voltage. This increase in multiplier gain can then be compensated by scaling the gain in the following differential pair ($M24$, $M25$) and current mirrors ($M10$–$M13$).

C. Finite Gain of Correlator Integrator

Since the "integrator" has only finite dc gain due to the finite impedance of the current sources surrounding C_i, a small amount of signal current is lost to leakage, which also contributes to a frequency bias in the tracking loop. This leakage current is directly proportional to the amplitude of the integrated voltage across the capacitor C_i. With a 1-V signal across C_i and an effective output impedance of 14 MΩ for the current sources, this leakage current is in the same order of magnitude as the measured dc offset current. A regulated current source that can lower the output conductance by an order of magnitude would be an ideal solution for this problem [12].

D. Harmonic Distortion

Under perfect tracking of an input sinusoid, the notch filter's output becomes dominated by its second and third harmonic components since the fundamental is "notched out." These harmonics, depending on their relative phase, can produce a gradient error signal when correlated with the low-pass output. This is an additional source of bias in frequency tracking.

For the OTA, one can improve the OTA's harmonic distortion at the expense of more circuitry and power dissipation. This can be accomplished by adding two extra source followers to bias the V_{gs} of $M5$ and $M5'$ in Fig. 4. This would eliminate $M6$'s V_{gs} fluctuation which is tied to the output current in the present circuit. SPICE simulations of the modified circuit show a THD of 0.15%, an improvement of a factor of 4 for a 2-V_{p-p} input.

ACKNOWLEDGMENT

The authors would like to thank S. Willingham for numerous discussions and the anonymous reviewers for their useful and constructive comments, which improved the presentation of this paper.

REFERENCES

[1] B. Widrow and S. Stearns, *Adaptive Signal Processing*. Englewood Cliffs, NJ: Prentice Hall, 1985.
[2] K. Bult and H. Wallinga, "A CMOS analog continuous-time delay line with adaptive delay-time control," *IEEE J. Solid-State Circuits*, vol. 23, pp. 759–766, June 1988.
[3] D. A. Johns, W. M. Snelgrove, and A. S. Sedra, "Continuous-time analog adaptive recursive filters," in *1989 IEEE ISCAS Proc.*, pp. 667–670.
[4] Y. Tsividis, M. Banu, and J. Khoury, "Continuous-time MOSFET-C filters in VLSI," *IEEE Trans. Circuits Syst.*, vol. CAS-33, pp. 125–39, Feb. 1986.
[5] C.-F. Chiou and R. Schaumann, "Design and performance of a fully integrated bipolar 10.7-MHz analog bandpass filter," *IEEE J. Solid-State Circuits*, vol. SC-21, pp. 6–14, Feb. 1986.
[6] A. P. Nedungadi and R. L. Geiger, "High-frequency voltage-controlled continuous-time lowpass filter using linearized CMOS integrators," *Electron. Lett.*, vol. 22, pp. 729–731, Dec. 1986.
[7] H. Khorramabadi and P. R. Gray, "High-frequency CMOS continuous-time filters," *IEEE J. Solid-State Circuits*, vol. SC-19, pp. 939–948, Dec. 1984.
[8] C. S. Park and R. Schaumann, "Design of a 4-MHz analog integrated CMOS transconductance-C bandpass filter," *IEEE J. Solid-State Circuits*, vol. 23, pp. 987–996, Aug. 1988.
[9] T. Kwan and K. Martin, "A notch-filter-based frequency-difference detector and its applications," in *1990 IEEE ISCAS Proc.*, pp. 1343–1346.
[10] A. P. Nedungadi and P. E. Allen, "Design of linear CMOS transconductance elements," *IEEE Trans. Circuits Syst.*, vol. CAS-31, pp. 891–894, Oct. 1984.
[11] E. Säckinger and W. Guggenbühl, "A versatile building block: The CMOS differential difference amplifier," *IEEE J. Solid-State Circuits*, vol. SC-22, pp. 287–294, Apr. 1987.
[12] E. Säckinger and W. Guggenbühl, "A high-swing, high-impedance MOS cascode circuit," *IEEE J. Solid-State Circuits*, vol. 25, pp. 289–298, Feb. 1990.
[13] Y. Tsividis, Z. Czarnul, and S. C. Fang, "MOS transconductors and integrators with high linearity," *Electron. Lett.*, vol. 22, pp. 245–246, 1986.
[14] M. Banu and Y. Tsividis, "Floating voltage-controlled resistors in CMOS technology," *Electron. Lett.*, vol. 18, pp. 678–679, 1982.
[15] S. Willingham, private communication, 1989.
[16] Y. T. Wang, "A 12.5 MHz CMOS continuous-time bandpass filter," Master thesis, Univ. of Calif., Los Angeles, 1989.
[17] R. Gregorian and G. C. Temes, *Analog MOS Integrated Circuits for Signal Processing*. New York: Wiley 1986.
[18] A. Sedra and P. O. Brackett, *Filter Theory and Design: Active and Passive*. Champaign, IL: Matrix, 1978.
[19] J. K. Roberge, *Operational Amplifiers: Theory and Practice*. New York: Wiley, 1975.

Fully-Integrated Correlated Tuning Processor For Continuous-Time Filters

by: P.M. VanPeteghem, T.L. Brooks, W.J. Adams, H.M. Fossati,
K.H. Loh, S. Narayan, G.R. Spalding, R. Yin
Texas A&M University, EE Department, College Station, TX 77843-3128

Partially supported by: Texas Instruments, by DOE, and by
NSF Research Initiation Award, Grant MIP-8809365

Abstract

Measurement results are presented on the Correlated Tuning Loop (CTL), a novel tuning loop for continuous-time filters integrated in a 2 uM CMOS process. Measured performance indicates that a 2nd-order bandpass filter at 2.5 MHz and Q-factor of 10 can be tuned with an error in resonance frequency of only 0.2% and a gain error of only 1.1 dB.

Introduction

Continuous-time filters have excellent potential for operation in frequency ranges that exceed the useful range of SC filters, or where clocked filters are not appropriate. However, such filters must be tuned, not only to compensate for variations in the device parameters, but also to correct for integrator phase errors [1,2]. Recently, the Correlated Tuning Loop (CTL), a new tuning loop configuration for integrated continuous-time filters, was proposed [3]. The CTL configuration derives tuning signals by calculating the time-averaged auto and cross correlation functions of the filter input and output signals. Hence, the CTL permits simultaneous signal processing within, and tuning of, a given filter, as long as the input signal contains sufficient energy in the filter passband. It does not require a perfectly sinusoidal test signal, unlike classical tuning schemes. This constitutes a major improvement over other published on-chip filter tuning schemes. Extensive simulations indicate that a 2nd-order bandpass filter can be tuned to its ideal performance, even when the input signal consists of broadband random noise [3].

The operation of the CTL chip while tuning a filter, as illustrated in Fig.1, corresponds to a classical feedback control loop with two variables. The internal circuitry acts as sensing elements to estimate the filter performance and obtain feedback signals, β_1 and β_2, related to the real and imaginary parts of the filter transfer function evaluated at the chopping frequency. The real and imaginary parts of the filter transfer function are equal to zero and one respectively at the filter center frequency. Thus the two feedback signals β_1(Re-1) and β_2(Im) may directly be compared with ground to obtain error signals, α_1 and α_2. These are then scaled and integrated by the loop controllers to derive the control voltages, V_A and V_{Fo} for the filter. Both the error signals and the control signals are derived within the CTL chip.

Design of Prototype Circuit

In this paper, the first fully-integrated prototype of a CTL is presented. In Fig 5 the die photograph of this circuit, which was implemented in a MOSIS 2 uM CMOS process, is shown. This prototype circuit, which measures 4.8 mm² (Fig. 5), has been designed and optimized specifically to tune a 2nd order bandpass filter at 10 MHz [2]. The CTL approach, however, may be applied to any filter structure in which the attenuation specifications can be translated to specifications of real and imaginary parts of transfer functions. In this prototype all subcircuits have been designed to be as versatile as possible so that they may be used (either directly for a 2nd order bandpass filter, or with slight modifications in other circuit configurations) to tune a wide variety of filters and filter specifications.

A high-speed PLL generates a clean, high-frequency clock signal, which serves as the reference for tuning the resonance frequencies of filter sections. This PLL has a very broad experimentally verified tuning and lock range of over two decades. This very broad tuning range was obtained using components optimized for this purpose. A simple three-stage current-controlled ring oscillator VCO (Fig.2) was designed to maximize frequency range. The phase-frequency detector is an improved version of a previously published circuit [4,5] with superior glitch suppression in order to extend the tracking and locking performance of the PLL. The PLL loop filter is driven by a charge pump. A phase splitter generates two sets of complementary clock signals, with frequency F_{ch}, from the VCO output signal. These quadrature signals have an accurate 90 degree phase difference. The output frequency F_{ch} is four times lower than the VCO output frequency.

The input and output signal of the tuned filter are synchronously demodulated by a combination of chopping (at F_{ch}, using the quadrature clocks) and low pass filtering. Both functions are merged in a single circuit (Fig.3). Linearized transconductance cells [6] yield high CMRR and high rejection of chopper clock feedthrough. They provide a novel technique for CM feedback: the transconductance cell on the right side of Fig.3 provides both DM and CM feedback, which yields a compact and highly linear fully-differential circuit. The four signals Va, Vb, Vc, and Vd are combined in an array of four-quadrant Gilbert-cell multipliers with single-ended current outputs. Multiplier distortion was reduced by implementing large voltage drops across the input transistors. The output currents are summed and inverted at the integrator inputs in order to obtain error signals α_1 and α_2. These signals are estimations of the error between the desired and actual resonance frequency of the tuned filter (α_1) and between the desired and actual gain at resonance (α_2). During tuning operation, the integrators implemented in the loop controllers force the steady-state values of α_1 and α_2 to zero as the loop settles.

Steady state accuracy of the tuned filter is only relevant if the loop remains stable during transient tuning operation as the loop settles in response to initial conditions. The high nonlinearity associated with the filter transfer function results in a system with serious stability concerns. Extensive simulations have been performed in order to determine the optimal CTL design parameters with respect to loop stability [7,3]. Fig.4 presents a behavioral simulation of the transient response of the center frequency of a 2nd order bandpass filter tuned using a CTL with parameters similar to those of the prototype circuit. An important concern in the system design of the CTL chip was the implementation of circuitry to ensure the testability of all major circuit blocks. Banks of CMOS switches and buffers were added between important internal nodes and external pads in order to make the nodes observable and controllable. This circuitry was added to the outputs of the synchronous demodulators, the inputs of the integrators, the outputs of the 90 degree phase splitter, the input of the VCO inside the PLL, and to the output of the phase detector.

Switches added at the integrator inputs serve a dual purpose. They provide the ability to both monitor the feedback signals α_1 and α_2 and to implement sample and hold functions in the integrators. This S/H function is particularly useful if the CTL is applied to tune high order filters consisting of several biquads. The outputs of a single CTL module could be switched from one pair of integrators to another, each used to tune a different biquad, while the CTL inputs are switched to monitor the corresponding filter section.

Measurements of Building Blocks

The lock range of the PLL is an important factor in determining the frequency range over which the CTL will operate. In Fig. 6, the measured VCO control voltage versus VCO output frequency is shown while the PLL was locking. The actual verified operating range is between 1 kHz and 100 MHz. Fig. 6, however, corresponds to the typical operation of OTAC filters. In Fig. 7, the linearity of the synchronous demodulators is shown as measued from a single-ended output. The DM operation will reduce the even order harmonics by another 20 dB.

Open-loop Measurement Setup

Open-loop measurements of the CTL can be used to evaluate the intrinsic accuracy of the tuning process. In particular, the values of gain and phase (or conversely gain and resonance frequency) that a tuned filter will have, after the tuning process has converged, can be evaluated. The sensitivity of the feedback signals α_1 and α_2 to variations in gain and phase around the values at convergence can also be determined. This sensitivity is an indication of the loop feedback gain, and thus has an important effect upon the loop bandwidth. Low sensitivities correspond to slow convergence times and an inversion in slope can cause

instability. For the open-loop measurement, it is necessary to synchronize the chopping signals and the input and output signals to avoid slow drifts in the values of α_1 and α_2. Hence, in order to implement this measurement, the PLL circuit on the prototype chip (which generates the chopping signals during normal operation) was bypassed. A stable 10 MHz reference clock, generated by an HP3585A spectrum analyzer, was divided by four to generate the quadrature chopping signals. The input signal for the tuning loop, V_{in}, was derived from one of these phases. The signal V_{out} was generated by an HP3325A function generator with input reference signal connected to V_{in}. Thus, V_{out} had programmable phase and amplitude which was phase-locked to V_{in}.

Open-Loop Measurements and Interpretation

The steady-state values of gain and phase of a tuned filter will be equal to the open-loop measued values of gain and phase that correspond to in α_1 and α_2 being equal to zero. The relation between center frequency and phase of a 2nd order bandpass filter is given below and is accurate for small values of phase:

$$\frac{\Delta\omega_o}{\omega_o} = \frac{\sin\phi}{2Q} \quad (1)$$

Thus, the relationship between filter center frequency error and phase can only be established for a particular value of filter Q-factor. Filters with higher Q-factors will have smaller errors in center frequency for a given phase error (we have, however, observed in simulation that the stability of the tuning loop will degrade for higher filter Q-factor and the tuning loop may become unstable).

Analytical expressions for the relation between α_1 and α_2 to parameters of input sinusoidal test signals at V_{in} and V_{out} and internal offsets in the tuning loop are given below:

$$\alpha_1 = A\frac{[V_{in}]^2}{4}\sin\varphi + E_b E_c - E_a E_d$$
$$+ \frac{[V_{in}]}{2}[A(K_c\sin(w_b t+\varphi)-E_d\cos(w_b t+\varphi))$$
$$+ (E_b\cos w_b t-E_a\sin w_b t)]$$

$$\alpha_2 = \frac{[V_{in}]^2}{4}[A\cos\varphi-1] + E_b E_d+E_a E_c-E_c^2-E_d^2$$
$$+ \frac{[V_{in}]}{2}[A(E_d\sin(w_b t+\varphi)+E_c\cos(w_b t+\varphi))$$
$$+ (E_b\sin w_b t+E_a\cos w_b t)-2(E_d\sin w_b t+E_c\cos w_b t)] \quad (2)$$

In these expressions, the magnitude of the input signal at V_{in} is denoted by $|V_{in}|$ and the gain of the input signal at V_{out} with respect to $|V_{in}|$ is denoted by A. The phase difference between these two signals is denoted by phi. The term w_b represents the beat frequency between the chopping frequency and the frequency of the input sinusoids. The terms E_a, E_b, E_c, and E_d represent internal offsets at the outputs of the four synchronous demodulators. These offsets are important sources of error in the CTL chip . Other sources include nonlinearities and noise in the multipliers and synchronous demodulators, and phase error in the quadrature chopping signals generated by the PLL.

Equation 2 indicates that the values of α_1 and α_2 consist of scaled versions of the desired imaginary and real parts of the filter transfer function plus inaccuracy terms resulting from error sources in the CTL. The scale factor, $|V_{in}|^2/2$, has an important effect on the loop performance. Open-loop measurements of the CTL indicate indeed roughly that transfer function errors are indeed inversely related to the square of the input signal amplitude. Table 1 presents open-loop measurements as a function of signal amplitude. Equation 1 has been applied in order to relate the measured data to the corresponding errors in gain and center frequency of two filters with Q-factors of 3 and 10. The measured data for α_1 and α_2, as a function of gain and phase for a 2.2 V_{pp} input test amplitude applied to V_{in}, are presented in Fig.8. The data of Fig.8 and Table 1 are consistent with Equation 2. This equation indicates that the variation of α_2 with gain should be linear and the variation of α_1 with phase should be sinusoidal. In order for the loop to remain stable, the slopes of the sensitivities of the two error signals must remain positive. The nonlinear characteristic of α_1 indicates that effective phase errors must be less than 90 degrees for the loop to converge. Hence, we can predict that decreasing signal amplitude results in decreasing sensitivity (loop bandwidth decreases and convergence time increases) and increased error in the steady-state filter transfer function.

Conclusions

A demonstration is given of the tuning accuracy achievable with a CTL tuning loop (0.2% error in F_o for a 2nd order bandpass filter). This proves that OTAC filters can be designed with very accurate frequency specifications, close to the specifications achievable in SC filters.

Reference List

[1]J.M. KHOURY, et al., "Analysis and Compensation of High-Frequency Effects in Integrated MOSFET-C Continuous-Time Filters", IEEE Trans. Circ. & Sys., Vol.CAS-34, No.8, pp.862-875, Aug. 1987

[2]P. M. VANPETEGHEM, S. RUJIANG, "Tuning Strategies in High-Frequency Integrated Continuous-Time Filters", IEEE Trans. Circ. & Sys., Vol. CAS-36, No.1, pp.136-139, January 1989

[3]T.L. BROOKS, P.M. VANPETEGHEM, "SimultaneousTuning and Signal Processing inIntegrated Continuous-Time Filters: the Correlated Tuning Loop.", Proceedings of the International Conference on Circuits and Systems (ISCAS), Vol.1, pp.651-654, Portland, OR, May 1989

[4]F.M. GARDNER, Phaselock Techniques, Wiley, 1979

[5]D.-K. Jeong, et.al., "Design of PLL-Based Clock Generation Circuits," IEEE JSSC, Vol. SC-22, No. 2, pp 255-261, Apr. 1987

[6]P.M. VANPETEGHEM, H.M. FOSSATI, G.L.RICE, S.Y.LEE, "Design of a Very-Linear CMOS Transconductance Input Stage for Continuous-Time Filters.", IEEE JSSC, Vol.SC-25, No.2, April 1990

[7]P.M. VANPETEGHEM, T.L. BROOKS, G.L. RICE, "On the Design of On-Chip Tuning Loops for High-Performance, High-Frequency Continuous-Time Filters in Standard CMOS Technology.",Proceedings of the 1989 ICCAS, Nanjing, PR China, July 1989

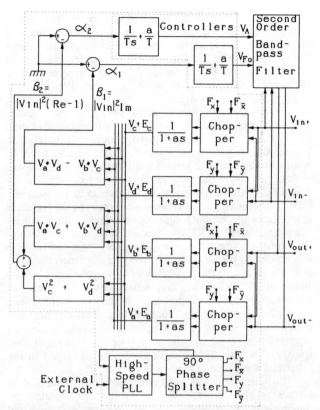

Fig.1: Block Diagram of CTL. All modules inside the dotted line are implemented in the test circuit.

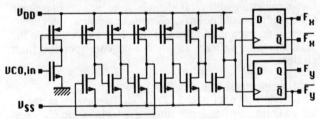

Fig.2: Circuit Schematic of high-speed VCO with quadrature clock phase generator.

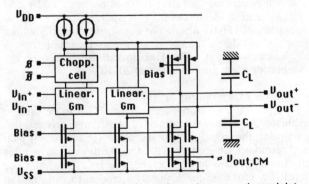

Fig.3: High-swing, fully-balanced synchronous demodulator with linearized transconductance cells and built-in CM feedback.

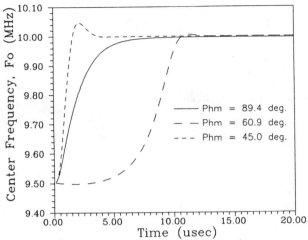

Fig.4: Convergence of 2nd order bandpass filter center frequency for three different values of phase margin of the integrators in the filter. Simulated using behavioral models for all subcircuits.

Fig.5: Die photograph of CMOS test circuit, integrated in 2 uM CMOS process of MOSIS (Tiny chip:4.8mm^2).

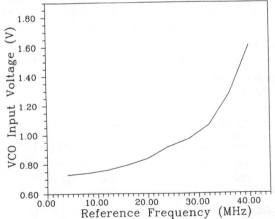

Fig.6: Measured tuning curve for high-speed VCO versus frequency at the VCO output. The 90 degree phase splitter divides this frequency by 4 to obtain chopping frequency.

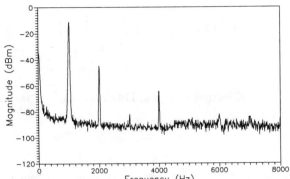

Fig.7: Linearity of synchronous demodulator measured from a single-ended test output (chopping is disabled and input signal is 1 Vpp). Even order distortion components are reduced by at least another 20 dB by internal differential-mode operation.

Signal Amplitude	ΔA(dB)	Δφ (deg)	Δωo/ωo	
			Q=3	Q=10
0.22 Vpp	11.0	−120	no locking gauranteed	no locking gauranteed
0.43 Vpp	3.0	−59.7	14.4%	4.3%
0.90 Vpp	1.9	−5.5	1.6%	0.5%
2.20 Vpp	1.1	−2.5	0.7%	0.2%

Table 1: Relation between signal amplitude in a tuned 2nd order filter and the resulting errors in gain and resonance frequency after tuning.

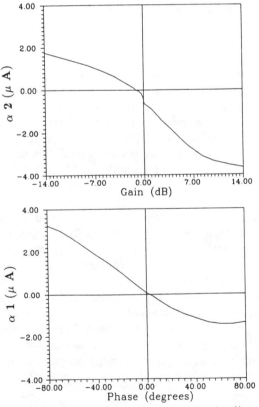

Fig.8: Measured error signals (currents) as a function of phase and amplitude of the filter at the applied test frequency (see definitions in Fig.1)
a) Gain error signal versus effective gain of a tuned filter.
b) Fo error signal versus effective phase of a tuned filter.

Automatic Tuning of Continuous-Time Integrated Filters Using an Adaptive Filter Technique

Karen A. Kozma, David A. Johns, *Member, IEEE*, and Adel S. Sedra, *Fellow, IEEE*

Abstract —An adaptive filter technique for tuning continuous-time integrated filters is presented. This adaptive technique is based on the model-matching configuration and tunes both the poles and zeros of the transfer function. Circuit details of an experimental prototype are given. The experimental prototype consists of an integrated third-order filter that is automatically tuned by off-chip circuitry realizing the adaptive tuning system. Both experimental and simulation results are presented to confirm the viability of the proposed approach.

I. Introduction

WITHOUT tuning, the transfer function of a continuous-time integrated filter will vary considerably due to fabrication tolerances, environmental changes, parasitic effects, and the finite input and output impedances of the integrators [1], [2]. In order to reduce this transfer-function variability, automatic tuning circuits have been developed. The present approach for automatic tuning (known in the literature as the master/slave tuning method) usually adjusts the pole frequencies and quality factors of a model while relying upon matching between the corresponding elements of the model and the filter to be tuned [1]–[9]. Exactly how the critical frequencies and quality factors are tuned depends upon the technology used. For example, in MOSFET-C technology, an equivalent voltage-controlled resistor can be obtained by adjusting the gate voltage of a transistor (operated in the triode region) [10], whereas, in transconductance-C technology, a variable coefficient can be obtained by altering the bias current of transconductance cells [1]–[9]. Because present schemes rely upon element matching, both the model and the filter should be physically near each other. Unfortunately, being close together encourages the feedthrough of control signals, originating in the tuning circuitry, to the filter. Thus the physical distance between the filter and the model should be a compromise between good matching properties and low noise interference. As well, since the present schemes

tune the model rather than the filter, the transfer function of the filter itself is never evaluated.

The tuning scheme proposed in this paper is based on the model-matching configuration, which is well known to adaptive filter designers. With this adaptive tuning approach, the tuned transfer-function is continually monitored since the output of the filter is used to operate the tuning circuitry. There are no critical matching dependencies between integrated filter elements thus allowing the tuning circuit and filter to be well isolated from each other. Furthermore, whereas present approaches only tune the poles, the adaptive tuning scheme tunes all the poles and *zeros*, thereby enabling a closer match to the desired transfer function. However, it is expected that the proposed scheme will use slightly more silicon area than a master/slave tuning system where each pole-pair is individually tuned. As well, this adaptive tuning scheme requires two low-resolution digital-to-analog converters (DAC's) operating at a frequency greater than the passband of the tunable filter.

An overview of this paper is as follows. The adaptive tuning approach is introduced in Section II, and many of the details on the implementation of the approach are discussed in Sections III and IV. Simulation results are given to show the validity of the proposed tuning method in Section V. Finally, circuit details and experimental results of a prototype, realizing the adaptive tuning system, are presented in Sections VI and VII, respectively. The prototype consists of an integrated CMOS filter and off-chip tuning circuitry.

II. The Adaptive Tuning Approach

As mentioned above, the adaptive tuning approach is based on the model-matching system shown in Fig. 1(a). The basic concept underlying the model-matching configuration is to adjust the transfer function of a tunable filter to be the same as that of a reference filter. This goal is accomplished by applying a spectrally rich signal (usually white noise) to the inputs of the tunable and reference filters and then utilizing an adaptive algorithm to adjust the coefficients of the tunable filter so as to minimize some measure of an error signal, $e(t)$. The error signal,

Manuscript received February 4, 1991; revised July 8, 1991. This paper was recommended by Associate Editor D. J. Allstot.

The authors are with the Department of Electrical Engineering, University of Toronto, Toronto, Ontario.

IEEE Log Number 9103419.

Reprinted from *IEEE Trans. Circuits Syst.*, vol. CAS-38, no. 11, pp. 1241–1248, Nov. 1991.

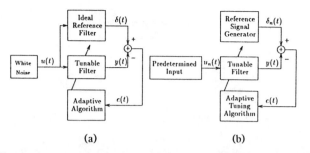

Fig. 1. Model-matching configuration. (a) Traditional configuration. (b) Adaptive tuning system (modified configuration by replacing the ideal reference filter).

$e(t)$, is simply the difference between the output of the reference filter, $\delta(t)$, and the output of the tunable filter, $y(t)$.

The model-matching configuration in Fig. 1(a) suggests that, given an ideal reference filter, the tunable filter may be tuned to a desired transfer function. However, the assumption that an "ideal" filter already exists obviously conflicts with the fundamental need for tuning. The adaptive tuning system, shown in Fig. 1(b), eliminates the need for the ideal filter as follows. The white noise input is replaced by a predetermined input, $u_n(t)$, so that the corresponding output, $\delta(t)$, can be precalculated. For implementation simplicity, the precalculated output, $\delta(t)$, is replaced by a discrete-time version, $\delta_n(t)$. We will show in the next section that the input, $u_n(t)$, and the reference signal, $\delta_n(t)$, can be efficiently realized in terms of silicon area.

Although the adaptive tuning system in Fig. 1(b) suggests the filter cannot service the system input during tuning, this need not be the case. For example, two tunable filters may be included on the same chip so that one services the system input while the other is being tuned by the adaptive loop [11]. Switching between the filter in service and the filter being tuned will then facilitate the tuning of both filters as well as servicing the input. An alternative method that does not involve interrupting the filter that produces the system output may also be implemented [12], [13]. Once again two filters are used where one filter (A) continuously services the input. The second filter (B) is first tuned by the adaptive loop so that it may be used as a "reference filter" for tuning filter A. Once filter B is tuned, the actual input signal is applied to filter B creating a reference signal, $\delta(t)$, used to tune filter A. Thus this method assumes the spectral content of the system input is sufficiently rich to fully characterize the desired transfer function. Note, however, that no critical matching is required between the integrated elements of filters A and B, and the system output is never interrupted.

Before proceeding, a few comments are worth making. First, note that the type of adaptive algorithm has not been specified. In fact, any adaptive algorithm that performs well in the model-matching configuration can be used. For practical reasons, we have chosen to use the

least-mean-squared (LMS) algorithm[1] which minimizes the mean-squared-error (MSE) value [14]. Thus, for the remainder of this paper, we assume the use of the LMS algorithm. Also note that no mention has been made of the structure of the tunable filter. Ideally, any structure can be used with the constraint that the variable elements should allow placement of the poles and zeros to their desired locations. However, it has been shown that the choice of filter structure can significantly affect the overall performance of an adaptive system [15]. Also, note the feedback in this adaptive tuning approach: The coefficients of the tunable filter are adjusted through the use of the adaptive algorithm, and the output, $y(t)$, is continually compared to the reference signal, $\delta_n(t)$, to minimize the MSE value. Thus the accuracy of the final transfer function is dependent on the accuracies of the adaptive algorithm, the input signal, and the reference signal, rather than on the matching between a model and the filter. Finally, since the method makes use of an IIR LMS algorithm in a model-matching configuration, one might have to be concerned with converging to a local minimum. Fortunately, theoretical results have been derived proving that as long as the order of the tunable filter is at least as high as that of the reference filter, and that all poles and zeros are adjusted, then local minima do not exist [16]. Thus, for the specific case of tuning filters, converging to a local minimum is not a problem since the order of the tunable filter can be chosen to be the same as that of the known reference filter.

III. GENERATION OF SUITABLE INPUT AND REFERENCE SIGNALS

For the adaptive tuning system in Fig. 1(b) to perform as well as the traditional model-matching scheme, the predetermined input, $u_n(t)$, should be spectrally rich enough to fully characterize the filter being tuned, and the reference signal, $\delta_n(t)$, should suitably replace the function of the ideal reference filter. As well, for practical purposes, the input and reference signals should be generated by circuitry that is simple yet accurate. Appropriate input and reference signals are presented here.

For a spectrally rich input signal, we propose the use of a pseudorandom noise (PN) sequence. It is well known that PN sequences can be generated through the use of shift registers and some simple logic, with the length of the PN sequence determined by $length = 2^{\#registers} - 1$ [17]. Perhaps not as well known is the fact that the length of the PN sequence influences how closely the sequence resembles white noise. Specifically, for a fixed repetition rate, an increase in the length of the PN sequence results in the sequence more closely resembling white noise for frequencies above the repetition rate. The next section will present simulation results demonstrating how the spectral richness of the input signal can affect tuning performance.

[1] The LMS algorithm will be defined in Section III.

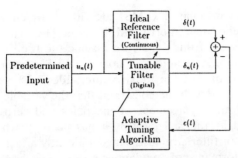

Fig. 2. Simulation setup for calculating the discrete-time reference signal, $\delta_n(t)$.

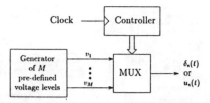

Fig. 3. Block diagram showing the generation of M discrete levels.

To generate the reference signal, we make use of the fact that at steady-state, a periodic input fed to a linear system results in a periodic output at the same repetition rate. Therefore, since the proposed input is periodic and the ideal continuous-time reference filter is linear, it is clear that the reference signal must also be a continuous-time periodic signal. However, since it is difficult to generate arbitrary continuous-time signals, we propose the use of discrete levels for the reference signal. As will be seen, exact tuning behavior can be obtained by using a relatively small number of discrete levels for both the input signal and the reference signal. Consequently, both signals can be generated by making use of area efficient circuits.

We next address the issue of determining a set of values that optimally represent the reference signal. Referring to the adaptive tuning system in Fig. 1(b), it is evident that the adaptive algorithm adjusts the coefficients of the tunable filter until the MSE value is minimized. A key point here is that an adaptive algorithm is used to vary the continuous-time signal, $y(t)$, to best match the discrete-time signal, $\delta_n(t)$, by minimizing the MSE value. An obvious approach to obtain the discrete levels, $\delta_n(t)$, would be to uniformly sample the desired continuous-time signal. However, it was found that an extremely high number of samples would be necessary to reduce the MSE value between $\delta_n(t)$ and the desired output, $\delta(t)$, to an acceptable level [13]. Thus another approach was employed to obtain a reduced number of discrete levels. Specifically, the discrete-time signal, generated by an Nth-order filter, which best minimizes the MSE value between the discrete levels and the desired continuous-time signal was calculated. A logical procedure to do this would be to simulate the reverse setup of the adaptive tuning system, as shown in Fig. 2. Using the predetermined input, $u_n(t)$, an ideal reference filter produces the desired continuous output, $\delta(t)$, while a digital filter is adapted to produce the reference samples, $\delta_n(t)$. Since the simulation scheme shown in Fig. 2 minimizes the MSE value between $\delta_n(t)$ and $\delta(t)$, upon implementation of the adaptive tuning system, shown in Fig. 1(b), $y(t)$ should be tuned to equal $\delta(t)$.

In terms of circuit implementation, if the number of discrete levels for both the input and reference signals are not large, the system shown in Fig. 3 can be used to

generate each. Having a pre-defined set of M voltage levels, a discrete-time signal is generated by clocking out one of the M possible voltage levels at the appropriate time. Note that this implementation is equivalent to using a DAC and selecting one of the M possible output values at the appropriate time. It should be emphasized here that with ideal adaptive circuitry, the transfer-function matching is determined by the accuracy of the levels rather than the number of samples, M, used. Specifically, using 4-bit DAC's ($M = 16$) accurate to 10 bits would give a coefficient accuracy of around 10 bits rather than only 4 bits.

IV. THE EFFECT OF THE LENGTH OF THE PN SEQUENCE ON THE SPEED OF TUNING

In this section, a simulation example is presented to illustrate the trade-offs between the speed of tuning and the length of, and hence the size of circuitry required to generate, the PN sequence input. For simplicity, the model-matching configuration in Fig. 1(a) was simulated. Specifically, an ideal continuous-time reference filter created the desired output, and the adjoint of the orthonormal ladder filter structure, described in [18], was used for the tunable filter. Both continuous-time filters were simulated by applying the bilinear transform to obtain digital filter equivalents that were clocked at 100 times the respective passband frequencies. As well, PN sequences were substituted for the white noise input. The repetition rates of all the PN sequences corresponded to two-thirds the passband frequency of the desired transfer function. This repetition rate was chosen as an arbitrary compromise between too low a rate, which would interfere with the low adaptation rates of the overall system, and a rate in the stopband of the filter, where the power of the output signals, $\delta_n(t)$, $y(t)$, and $e(t)$, would be too small to enable any useful adaptation.

The reference filter had a third-order low-pass transfer function with the following characteristics:

$$\text{poles} = \{ -0.43 \pm j1.25, -0.99 \}$$

$$\text{zeros} = \{ \pm j2.33, \infty \}$$

$$\text{dc gain} = 1.46. \tag{1}$$

A plot of the transfer function of this filter is shown in Fig. 4. As a starting point for the programmable filter, all the feed-forward coefficients (refer to the orthonormal structure in [18]) were set to zero while the feedback coefficients were set such that the following poles were

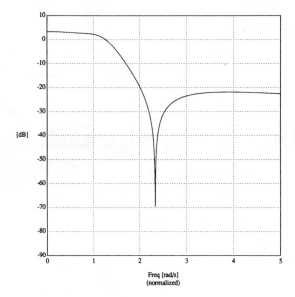

Fig. 4.   Plot of the ideal transfer function.

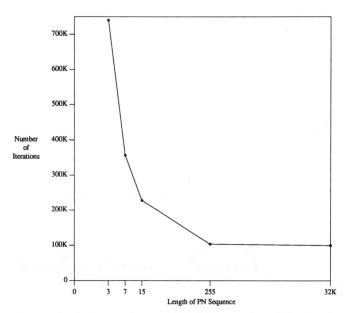

Fig. 5.   Number of iterations performed to tune a third-order filter for PN sequences of different lengths.

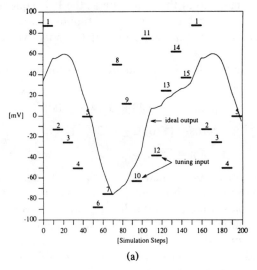

(a)

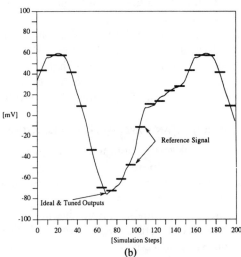

(b)

Fig. 6.   Plots illustrating the 4-bit PN sequence input, discrete-time reference signal, ideal output, and tuned output. (a) PN sequence input, $u_n(t)$, and ideal output, $\delta(t)$. (b) Discrete-time reference signal, $\delta_n t$, ideal output, $\delta(t)$, and tuned output, $y(t)$.

realized:

$$\text{poles} = \{-0.24 \pm j2.77, -0.52\}. \qquad (2)$$

For comparison purposes, the filter was considered tuned when the MSE value was reduced by 75 dB. The number of iterations performed to tune the filter for the different PN inputs are plotted in Fig. 5. As expected, the number of iterations required to tune the filter decreases as the length of the PN sequence is increased. Although only adaptation speed is compared, this measure is usually related to the conditioning of the performance surface. Specifically, a relatively long adaptation time can indicate an ill-conditioned performance surface and hence a poor overall adaptation performance in terms of coefficient matching. Thus we see from this third-order example that a trade-off must be made between the length of the PN

sequence and adaptation performance. For higher order filters, the tuning-input signal should more closely resemble white noise and correspondingly, the length of the PN sequence will increase.

V. VERIFICATION OF THE ADAPTIVE TUNING SYSTEM

Another simulation example is presented here to verify the validity of the adaptive tuning system in Fig. 1(b). Once again, the adjoint of the orthonormal ladder filter structure was used for the tunable filter and simulated by the method described in the preceding section. The desired transfer function was the same third-order filter illustrated in Fig. 4, and a four-bit PN input was employed. The 15 horizontal lines in Fig. 6(a) represent the PN samples and the solid curve is the ideal response, $\delta(t)$. Fifteen samples were also chosen to implement the reference signal and were determined by simulating the system shown in Fig. 2. Here, the output of the digital filter was sampled at the same rate as the PN sequence so that the same clock can control the tuning and reference sequences in a circuit realization of the adaptive tuning system.

After tuning, the filter had the following characteristics:

$$\text{poles} = \{-0.43 \pm j1.24, -1.00\}$$
$$\text{zeros} = \{-0.02 \pm j2.34, \infty\}$$
$$\text{dc gain} = 1.46. \tag{3}$$

Fig. 6(b) illustrates the matching between the desired and tuned outputs. The horizontal lines depict the 15 reference samples while the two solid coincident curves represent the output to which the filter was tuned, $y(t)$, and the ideal output, $\delta(t)$. This close matching between the ideal and tuned outputs was obtained for arbitrary initial starting points for the tunable filter, indicating the absence of local minima.

In summary, the ideal reference filter in the model-matching configuration can be replaced by a PN sequence and reference samples. It was shown that a third-order filter may be tuned to arbitrary precision by using two signals, each consisting of 15 discrete voltage levels.

VI. DESIGN OF AN EXPERIMENTAL PROTOTYPE

For experimental verification, a discrete prototype circuit was constructed to tune a third-order integrated CMOS filter. This section will present some of the circuit details of this prototype system.

For the integrated tunable filter, the adjoint of the orthonormal ladder structure [18] was used which is best described with state-space equations:

$$sX(s) = AX(s) + bU(s)$$
$$Y(s) = c^T X(s) + dU(s) \tag{4}$$

where $U(s)$ is the input signal; $X(s)$ is a vector of N states (for a filter of order N), which in fact are integrator outputs; $Y(s)$ is the output signal; and A, b, c, and d are coefficients relating these variables. The transfer function of this system can be easily shown to be

$$T(s) = \frac{Y(s)}{U(s)} = c^T(sI - A)^{-1}b + d. \tag{5}$$

The poles are determined by the A coefficients while the coefficients of all four matrices determine the zeros of the transfer function.

For the adjoint of a third-order orthonormal ladder filter, the coefficients, A, b, c, and d take the form:

$$A = \begin{bmatrix} 0 & -a_1 & 0 \\ a_1 & 0 & -a_2 \\ 0 & a_2 & -a_3 \end{bmatrix} \quad b = \begin{bmatrix} b_1 \\ b_2 \\ b_3 \end{bmatrix}$$

$$c^T = \begin{bmatrix} 0 & 0 & 1 \end{bmatrix} \qquad d = 0 \tag{6}$$

where d has been set to zero since we will be tuning the filter to a transfer function that has at least one zero at

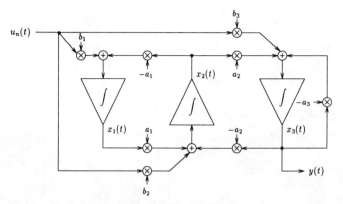

Fig. 7. Block diagram of the adjoint of a third-order orthonormal ladder filter.

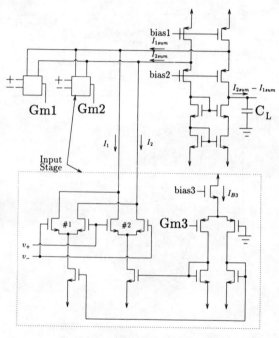

Fig. 8. Circuitry for a 3-input voltage-controlled transconductance-C integrator.

infinity. With this filter structure, it is not difficult to show that arbitrary poles and zeros (with at least one zero at infinity) can be obtained by adjusting the A and b coefficients. The structure also has a simple stability check system [19]:

$$a_3 > 0 \qquad \text{and} \qquad a_1, a_2 \neq 0. \tag{7}$$

As well, note that the c vector is simply a basis vector and therefore eliminates the need for constructing a separate output summing stage.

A block diagram for this filter structure is shown in Fig. 7. As discussed, the states of the system are defined as the outputs of the integrators, $x_i(t)$, and the output, $y(t)$, is taken directly from the third state. Each integrator/summer in Fig. 7 was realized with the three input transconductance-C circuit shown in Fig. 8, where the circuitry for each input transconductance stage is expanded in the dotted box. Here, cross-coupled differential pairs enable both positive and negative transconductance, G_m, values. Assuming small-signal operation of the differential pairs #1 and #2, one can show that if the voltage at the node labelled Gm3 is positive, the difference output current, $I_2 - I_1$, will be proportional to the input, $v_+ - v_-$. Conversely, for a negative voltage at Gm3, the output will be proportional to $-(v_+ - v_-)$. However, if the voltage at Gm3 is at ground potential, the output currents will be equal resulting in $I_2 - I_1 = 0$ for arbitrary inputs. The output currents, I_1 and I_2, of each input transconductance stage are summed and reproduced at the output of a high-output-impedance stage realized by stacked current mirrors. Finally, capacitor C_L performs the integration on the output current, $I_{2sum} - I_{1sum}$, and also acts as a compensating capacitor to maintain amplifier stability. Note that $I_1 + I_2$ equals the constant current I_{B3}, and therefore, varying individual Gm's does not affect the bias current through the output stage. Also note that all transconductance stages are identical, and thus coefficient values are determined solely by varying control voltages rather than transistor sizing. Although this transconductance approach is beneficial for arbitrary transfer functions, for a known transfer function, it would be advantageous to use transistor sizing to obtain close coefficient values. With the latter approach, the control voltages would only need to fine-tune the transfer function. As a final note, it should be mentioned here that since the integrated circuit we fabricated was mainly intended for the verification of the proposed tuning scheme, no effort was made to linearize the transconductance amplifier.

Making use of these transconductance-C integrators to realize the filter structure of Fig. 7 results in the tunable coefficients, a_i and b_i, being directly proportional to the voltages at the Gm nodes. Voltages at these Gm nodes are then varied in order to tune the filter to the desired transfer function where the set of realizable transfer functions is limited by the range over which the transconductance, G_m, values can be varied. For our prototype, the adaptive algorithm used to adjust these coefficients is the LMS algorithm [14] which attempts to minimize the mean-squared value of the error signal, $e(t)$. To describe the LMS algorithm, consider the case where coefficient b_1 is being adjusted. In this case, the coefficient b_1 is updated according to the following formula:

$$b_1(t) = \int_0^t 2\mu e(\tau)\phi_{b_1}(\tau)\,d\tau \qquad (8)$$

where μ is a positive constant that controls the rate of adaptation, and:

$$e(t) = \delta_n(t) - y(t)$$

$$\phi_{b_1}(t) = \frac{\partial y}{\partial b_1}(t). \qquad (9)$$

The purpose of using the error, $e(t)$, and gradient, $\phi_{b_1}(t)$, signals may be intuitively interpreted as follows. The error simply determines if y should be increased or decreased

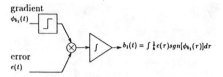

Fig. 9. Block diagram of the LMS coefficient update algorithm.

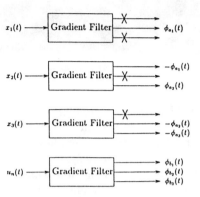

Fig. 10. Block diagram showing the generation of gradients for the third-order filter.

in order to match δ_n, while the gradient, ϕ_{b_1}, determines in which direction the coefficient b_1 should be steered. For example, a positive error, $\delta_n > y$, implies that y should be increased. Therefore, to increase y, b_1 should be increased if the gradient is positive but decreased if the gradient is negative.

Fig. 9 illustrates a block diagram of the LMS coefficient update procedure. The rate at which the coefficient b_1 is updated is controlled by the step size, μ, which is realized by the integration time constant, k. Note that in this block diagram, only the sign of the gradient signal is used in order to simplify the multiplication circuitry [20].

The error signal is simply obtained by taking the difference between the reference signal and the output of the tunable filter. However, obtaining the gradients is more involved: for the third-order case, the gradients for the coefficients of A and b can be obtained from the output states of four identical state-space filters [15]. We will refer to these extra filters as *gradient filters*. The gradient filter is the transpose or adjoint of the tunable filter and its coefficients are obtained from the coefficients of the tunable filter as follows:

$$A_{grad} = A^T$$

$$b_{grad} = c. \qquad (10)$$

Note that since the gradients are realized by the states of the gradient filter, only the A_{grad} and b_{grad} coefficients are necessary.

The gradient signals for the first column of A are the output state signals of a gradient filter whose input signal is the first state signal of the tunable filter, $x_1(t)$. This is shown in Fig. 10. Note that only the second state signal, $\phi_{a_2}(t)$, is used since the other coefficients in the first column of A are zero. Likewise, the gradients for the

Fig. 11. Integrated chip.

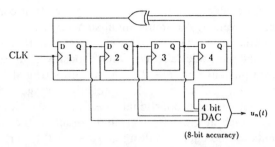

Fig. 12. Four-bit PN sequence circuit.

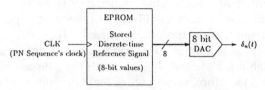

Fig. 13. Block diagram of the reference signal generator.

second and third columns of A are the output states of gradient filters with $x_2(t)$ and $x_3(t)$ as the inputs. As illustrated in Fig. 10, only the gradients for the nonzero elements of A are useful. Finally, the gradients $\phi_{b_i}(t)$ are produced by another gradient filter whose input signal is the system input, $u_n(t)$. It should be mentioned here that although the coefficients of the gradient filter are derived from the coefficients of the tunable filter, the matching between these filters is not critical. Since the LMS algorithm follows a path of steepest descent, it is clear that a small change in the path taken will still result in a downward descent to a minimum. Also, an attractive quality of the gradient filter is that it has orthonormal states (since the tunable filter is the adjoint of the orthonormal ladder structure) [18]. Thus the gradients for the coefficients of the b vector will be orthonormal when white noise is applied to the input. Having orthogonal gradients indicates that the coefficients may be updated independently and thus increases the speed of tuning. It has been proven that the adaptation rate of the adaptive linear combiner[2] increases if the gradients are orthonormal [14].

As all four gradient filters are identical, it is possible to build only one gradient filter and multiplex the input and output signals. This multiplexing approach was used in the prototype, and details on the use of multiplexing can be found in [13].

Both the tunable and gradient filters were fabricated using a 3-μm CMOS process, and a photograph of the integrated chip is shown in Fig. 11. A test transconductance cell is shown in the top right corner while the tunable and gradient filters are shown in the middle and bottom of the photograph, respectively. Although simulations indicated the integrated filter could operate up to the megahertz range, the integrating capacitors were kept off-chip in order to experiment with the prototype tuning scheme at lower frequencies. Each filter occupied 0.7 mm^2 and dissipated 3 mW with a $\pm$3-V supply.

For the input PN sequence signal, a repetition length of 15 (i.e., four-bit) was chosen as a trade-off between the complexity of the circuitry for generating the PN se-

quence and the adaptation performance. The PN sequence was generated by the setup shown in Fig. 12. As discussed previously, the reference signal, $\delta_n(t)$, could be realized by using the system in Fig. 3. However, for more generality, the discrete prototype uses 15 8-bit values stored in an EPROM and an 8-bit DAC as shown in Fig. 13.

VII. EXPERIMENTAL RESULTS

For testing, it was desired to tune the integrated filter to the poles and zeros given in (1) with the passband edge denormalized to 1 kHz. This desired transfer function is shown in Fig. 14(a). The input and reference sequences were repeated at a rate equivalent to 2/3 kHz. The gradient signals were multiplexed at a rate of 100 Hz and the time constants of the LMS integrators were set to 1 s.

Within 10 to 60 s after power-up, the integrated filter was tuned to the transfer function shown in Fig. 14(b). In order to maintain stability, the minimum time constant of the LMS algorithm integrators is related to the filter's poles. Therefore, it is expected that if the passband edge was at 1 MHz, the adaptation time would be under 60 ms. As well, in this prototype, the initial transfer function of the tunable filter is arbitrary (which accounts for the large variation in tuning speed). By having the initial transfer function closer to the desired one, the tuning speed could be further improved.

VIII. CONCLUSIONS

An adaptive technique, based on the traditional model-matching configuration, was presented for tuning integrated continuous-time filters. Whereas present approaches tune only the poles, this adaptive approach tunes all the poles and zeros, thereby allowing a closer match to the desired transfer function. Simulation and experimental results, showing the viability of the proposed approach, were presented. The experimental proto-

---

[2]The adaptive linear combiner is a common example of an adaptive FIR filter.

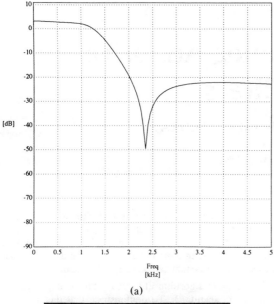

(a)

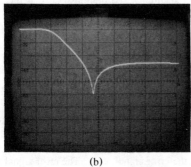

(b)

Fig. 14. Tuned transfer function with a four-bit PN sequence input and 15 reference samples. (a) Simulation results. (b) Experimental results. Vertical scale = 10 dB/div; horizontal scale = 0.5 kHz/div.

type consisted of an integrated third-order filter and off-chip circuitry realizing the adaptive tuning system.

In terms of nonideal effects, dc offsets and parasitic poles appear to be the most critical ones. It has been shown that the effects of dc offsets appearing at the LMS integrators cause a coefficient mismatch and formulas have been derived to determine the effect of these offsets [20]. We are currently developing circuit techniques to reduce the effects of dc offsets. With respect to parasitic poles in the integrators of the filter, this tuning method has the potential for partially accounting for these poles through some innovative circuit and system design.

REFERENCES

[1] R. Schaumann, M. S. Ghausi, and K. R. Laker, *Design of Analog Filters: Passive, Active RC, and Switched Capacitor*. Englewood Cliffs, NJ: Prentice-Hall, 1990.
[2] R. Schaumann and M. A. Tan, "The problem of on-chip automatic tuning in continuous-time integrated filters," in *Proc. 1989 IEEE Int. Symp. Circuits and Systems*, pp. 106–109, Feb. 1989.
[3] C. S. Park and R. Schaumann, "Design of a 4-MHz analog integrated CMOS transconductance-C bandpass filter," *IEEE J. Solid-State Circuits*, vol. 23, pp. 987–996, Aug. 1988.
[4] F. Krummenacher and N. Joehl, "A 4-MHz CMOS continuous-time filter with on-chip automatic tuning," *IEEE J. Solid-State Circuits*, vol. 23, pp. 750–758, June 1988.
[5] K. S. Tan and P. R. Gray, "Fully integrated analog filters using bipolar-JFET technology," *IEEE J. Solid-State Circuits*, vol. 17, pp. 814–821, Dec. 1978.
[6] H. Khorramabadi and P. R. Gray, "High-frequency CMOS continuous-time filters," *IEEE J. Solid-State Circuits*, vol. 19, pp. 939–948, Dec. 1984.
[7] K. W. Moulding, J. R. Quartly, P. J. Rankin, R. S. Thompson, and G. A. Wilson, "Gyrator video filter IC with automatic tuning," *IEEE J. Solid-State Circuits*, vol. 15, pp. 963–968, Dec. 1980.
[8] K. Fukahori, "A bipolar voltage-controlled tunable filter," *IEEE J. Solid-State Circuits*, vol. 16, pp. 729–737, Dec. 1981.
[9] V. Gopinathan, Y. P. Tsividis, K. S. Tan, and R. K. Hester, "Design considerations for high-frequency continuous-time filters and implementation of an antialiasing filter for digital video," *IEEE J. Solid-State Circuits*, vol. 25, pp. 1368–1378, Dec. 1990.
[10] Y. P. Tsividis, M. Banu, and J. Khoury, "Continuous-time MOSFET-C filters in VLSI," *IEEE J. Solid-State Circuits*, vol. 21, pp. 15–30, Feb. 1986.
[11] Y. Tsividis, "Self-tuned filters," *Electron. Lett.*, vol. 17, pp. 406–407, June 1981.
[12] Personal communication with W. M. Snelgrove, 1989.
[13] K. A. Kozma, "Tuning integrated continuous-time filters using an adaptive technique," M.A.Sc. Thesis, Univ. Toronto, Aug. 1990.
[14] B. Widrow and S. D. Stearns, *Adaptive Signal Processing*. Englewood Cliffs, NJ: Prentice-Hall, 1985.
[15] D. A. Johns, W. M. Snelgrove, and A. S. Sedra, "Adaptive recursive state-space filters using a gradient-based algorithm," *IEEE Trans. Circuits Syst.*, vol. 37, pp. 673–684, June 1990.
[16] H. Fan and M. Nayeri, "On error surfaces of sufficient order adaptive IIR filters: Proofs and counterexamples to a unimodality conjecture," *IEEE Trans. Acoust., Speech, Signal Processing*, vol. ASSP-37, pp. 1436–1442, Sept. 1989.
[17] H. Taub and D. Schilling, *Digital Integrated Electronics*. New York: McGraw-Hill, 1977.
[18] D. A. Johns, W. M. Snelgrove, and A. S. Sedra, "Orthonormal ladder filters," *IEEE Trans. Circuits Syst.*, vol. 36, pp. 337–343, Mar. 1989.
[19] D. A. Johns, "Analog and digital state-space adaptive IIR filters," Ph.D. dissertation, Univ. Toronto, Mar. 1989.
[20] D. A. Johns *et al.*, "Continuous-time LMS adaptive recursive filters," *IEEE Trans. Circuits Syst.*, vol. 38, pp. 769–778, July 1991.

Continuous-Time Analog Adaptive Recursive Filters

D. A. JOHNS, W. M. SNELGROVE, and A. S. SEDRA

UNIVERSITY OF TORONTO, CANADA

ABSTRACT

This paper presents an approach to implement continuous-time analog adaptive recursive filters. The building blocks used to implement such filters are all commonly used in integrated circuits and, thus, the resulting filters can be fully integrated. Circuit details and experimental results for a discrete prototype are also presented.

1. INTRODUCTION

Many papers have been published in the digital signal processing literature concerning the use and implementation of adaptive filters. However, few papers on adaptive filters appear in the analog signal processing literature. This situation is unfortunate since, in general, analog implementations often satisfy specifications that can not be met using digital realizations. In particular, specifications concerning high frequency performance or implementation size are often more easily met using analog realizations. Thus, practical implementations of analog adaptive filters should lead to new adaptive filter applications. (For a description of adaptive filter applications, see [1].) Towards this goal, this paper proposes a design technique that can be used to implement continuous-time adaptive filters. Experimental results are presented to verify some of the concepts developed.

Performing adaptive filtering with analog components is not new. In fact, analog adaptive filter implementations presently exist for high frequency applications [2,3,4] and recent publications investigate new structures [5]. However, the usual approach for analog filtering is to use analog delay lines and adapt only the zeros of the transfer function. The use of analog delay lines makes the system difficult to integrate while adapting only the zeros of the transfer function often leads to higher filter orders than that required if both the poles and zeros are adapted.

To overcome the above difficulties, a method was proposed for implementing analog adaptive recursive filters [6] where both the poles and zeros are adapted using a sequential-linear-search algorithm. However, this approach requires an accurate RMS measurement of the error signal which is difficult to obtain. This paper also presents a method for implementing analog adaptive recursive filters, however,

the method presented here does not require accurate RMS measurements. As an additional benefit, this new approach can be implemented entirely with analog components, if desired. As well, integrators rather than analog delay lines are utilized so that the system can be fully integrated.

The adaptive algorithm utilized for this analog approach is presented in section 2. To demonstrate that this approach works successfully in the analog domain, section 3 presents the circuit details and experimental results for a discrete prototype.

2. ADAPTIVE ALGORITHM

A block diagram of an adaptive filter is shown in figure 1. The system has two inputs: the filter input, $u(t)$, and the reference signal, $\delta(t)$. The programmable filter is adjusted by changing the filter coefficients, p_i. Qualitatively, the adaptive algorithm adjusts the programmable filter so as to reduce the RMS level of the error signal, $e(t)$. The error signal is simply the difference between the reference signal, $\delta(t)$, and the filter output, $y(t)$. In order to compute the necessary coefficient changes in the programmable filter, the adaptive algorithm requires the error signal as well as internal states of the filter as inputs.

The choice of adaptive algorithms can be made from one of the many algorithms presented for digital recursive filters. However, most of these algorithms require that the recursive filter structure be in direct-form or a close relation to it. Unfortunately, this type of structure results in poor performance for continuous-time filter realizations. Therefore, for purposes of investigating continuous-time adaptive filters, it was felt that the adaptive algorithm chosen should be easily adjusted to different filter structures. As well, the chosen algorithm should be of such simplicity that it can be implemented entirely in analog form. For these reasons, the Least Mean Square (LMS) algorithm [1] was chosen as the method of adapting the filter coefficients.

In the continuous-time domain, the LMS algorithm to update each of the filter coefficients, $p_i(t)$, is [7]

$$p_i(t) = 2\mu \int_0^t e(\tau) \frac{\partial y(\tau)}{\partial p_i} d\tau \qquad (1)$$

where μ is the step size that controls the speed of adaptation. Note that although the signal $e(t)$ is readily available, the gradient signal corresponding to $\dfrac{\partial y(t)}{\partial p_i}$ must somehow be

Reprinted from *IEEE Proc. ISCAS*, pp. 667–670, 1989.

obtained. To create this signal, we use the sensitivity formulae derived for state-space systems. Therefore, it will be assumed that the programmable filter is implemented in the form of a state-space system.

An N'th order state-space filter can be described by the following equations:

$$sX(s) = AX(s) + bU(s) \qquad (2)$$

$$Y(s) = c^T X(s) + dU(s)$$

where $X(s)$ is a vector of N states (which are the integrator outputs), $U(s)$ is the input, $Y(s)$ is the output and A, b, c and d are the filter coefficients relating these variables. The matrix A is NxN, the vectors b and c are Nx1 and d is a scalar.

An approach for adapting *all* the coefficients of an arbitrary state-space system is given in [8] where N extra filters are required to obtain all the necessary gradient signals. Unfortunately, these extra filters would require a large silicon area and therefore limits the practicality of this general approach. However, with this general approach, there is a great deal of redundancy since only N of the N^2 elements in the A matrix need to be adapted to define N poles. To reduce the computational load from the general case to adapting only N elements of the A matrix, a single row adaptive filter has been proposed [9]. It was shown in [9] that given an arbitrary A matrix, the poles of that matrix can be arbitrarily placed by changing the N'th row of the A matrix if at least one of the set of transfer functions from the input of the N'th integrator to the integrator outputs is N'th order. As well, if the input of the filter only appears at the input of the N'th integrator, then only one extra filter is required to obtain the gradients needed for adaptation. A block diagram of a single-row adaptive filter is shown in figure 2. The state-space system is shown as two separate blocks which correspond with the state-space describing equations. Specifically, the feedback matrix, A, and input summing vector, b, implement the first equation of a state-space system and create the state signals, $x(t)$, as the outputs of the first block. These state signals together with the system input, u, are weighted using the output summing vector, c, and the output scalar, d, to obtain the filter output, $y(t)$, at the output of the second block. The state signals, $\alpha(t)$, are the gradient signals used to adapt the coefficients in the last row of the A matrix. Each of the integrator circuits shown perform the adaptation algorithm for the system coefficients as described in equation (1).

It is thought that this single-row adaptive filter will not perform much better than a direct-form implementation if the adaptation of the row moves the poles far from their original position. However, if an estimate of the final pole locations is known, one can design a good filter structure for a set of poles close to the final set. In this case, if the poles do not move far, the adapted filter should maintain the good properties of the original filter. For this reason, this single-row adaptive filter is applicable where an estimate of the final pole locations is known.

3. DISCRETE PROTOTYPE

Using discrete parts, a single-row continuous-time adaptive filter was constructed. The experimental prototype is third-order with no d term and therefore a zero at infinity. A block diagram of the circuit is shown in figure 3 where the basic structure of the feedback systems in the programmable and gradient filters is a newly proposed orthonormal ladder structure [11]. Note that only the signs of the gradient signals, $x_{i(t)}$ and $\alpha_{i(t)}$, are used to multiply the error signal, $e(t)$. This modifies the LMS algorithm to what is sometimes referred to as the "sign-data" algorithm [3]. This considerably simplifies the multiplier circuit for this part of the circuit and therefore decreases any DC offsets introduced at this stage. The remaining multipliers are implemented using differential pairs of NMOS transistors [10]. The detailed circuit implementation of the breadboard prototype is shown in figures 4 through 8. Note that AC coupling and a large gain were used in the "Error Gen" block shown in figure 7 to reduce DC offset problems. It should be emphasized that this breadboard was constructed only to test the adaptive filter concepts and should be considerably modified in order to construct a fully integrated version.

To test the adaptive filter, a model matching application was used. In this application, the reference signal, $\delta(t)$, is obtained as the output of a fixed reference filter. White noise is then injected to both the adaptive filter and reference filter causing the adaptive filter to match the transfer function of the reference filter after adaptation. Figure 8 shows experimental results of the adaptive filter matching a third-order reference filter. In figure 8 (a), the spectrum for both the programmable filter's output signal, $y(t)$ and the reference signal, $\delta(t)$ are shown where the two lines are difficult to distinguish. In figure 8 (b), the spectrum of the error signal, $e(t)$, is shown along with the filter output, $y(t)$. Note that the passband of the error signal is approximately 40 dB down from the passband of the reference and filter output signals. The time for adaptation was typically a few seconds but could be decreased to under 1 sec.

4. CONCLUSIONS

A design approach for continuous-time adaptive recursive filters was presented. Circuit details and experimental results for a discrete prototype were presented showing that the concepts are practical. All the building blocks used in the new filter can easily be integrated and thus small adaptive filter systems could be created. Presently, work is being performed to fabricate a fully integrated version of an analog adaptive filter using the concepts in this paper. It is also believed that some of these concepts may be applied to fixed continuous-time integrated filters.

REFERENCES

[1]   B. Widrow and S.D. Stearns, *Adaptive Signal Processing,* Englewood Cliffs, New Jersey, Prentice-Hall, 1985.

[2]   S.U.H. Qureshi, "Adaptive Equalization," *Proc IEEE,* vol. 73, No. 9, pp. 1349-1387, Sept. 1985.

[3]   J.R. Treichler, C.R. Johnson, Jr. and M.G. Larimore, *Theory and Design of Adaptive Filters,* New York, New York, John Wiley & Sons, 1987.

[4]   R.T. Compton, JR., *Adaptive Antennas,* Englewood Cliffs, N.J.: Prentice-Hall, Inc., 1988.

[5] H. Lev-Ari, J.M. Cioffi and T. Kailath, "Continuous-Time Least Squares Fast Transversal Filters," *Proc. 1987 IEEE Int. Conf. Acoust. Speech and Signal Processing*, pp. 415-418, Dallas, Texas, April 1987.

[6] W.B. Mikhael and F.F. Yassa, "Stable High Order, Continuous Adaptive Filters," *IEEE Int. Symp. on Circuits & Systems Proc.*, pp. 666-669, Rome, Italy, May 1982.

[7] B. Widrow, P.E. Mantey, L.J. Griffiths, and B.B. Goode, "Adaptive Antenna Systems," *Proc IEEE*, vol. 55, No. 12, pp. 2143-2159, Dec. 1967.

[8] D.A. Johns, W.M. Snelgrove and A.S. Sedra, "State-Space Adaptive Recursive Filters," *1988 IEEE International Symposium on Circuits and Systems*, pp. 2153-2156, Espoo, Finland, June 1988.

[9] D.A. Johns, W.M. Snelgrove and A.S. Sedra, "Adaptive Recursive State-Space Filters Using a Gradient-Based Approach," submitted to *IEEE Trans. on Circuits and Systems*.

[10] M. Banu and Y. Tsividis, "Fully Integrated Active RC Filters in MOS Technology," *IEEE J. Solid-State Circuits*, vol. SC-18, pp. 664-651, Dec. 1983.

[11] D.A. Johns, W.M. Snelgrove and A.S. Sedra, "Orthonormal Ladder Filters," *IEEE Trans. on Circuits and Systems*, to be published in March, 1989.

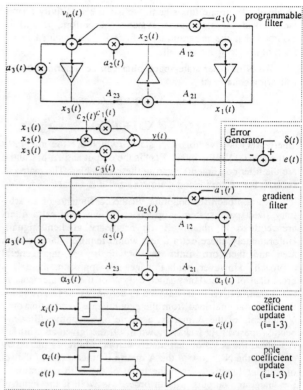

Figure 3: Block diagram of a third-order single-row analog adaptive filter

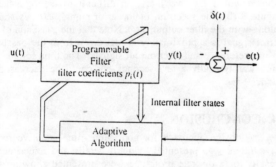

Figure 1: Adaptive filter block diagram.

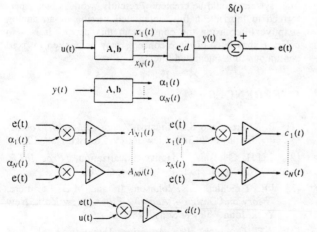

Figure 2: Single row adaptive filter when the only non-zero element of b is in the last row.

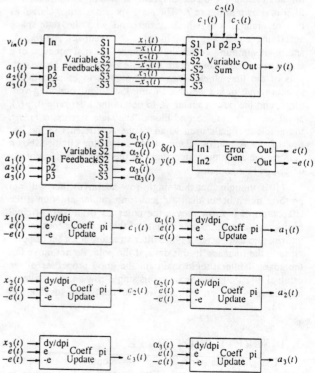

Figure 4: Circuit implementation of breadboard prototype at block level.

436

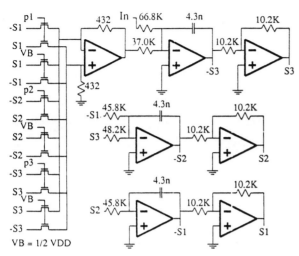

Figure 5: Circuit details of "Variable Feedback" block.

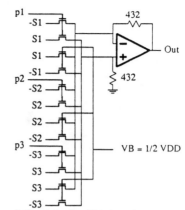

Figure 6: Circuit details of "Variable Sum" block.

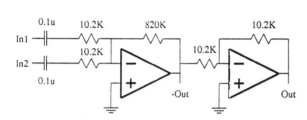

Figure 7: Circuit details for "Error Gen" block.

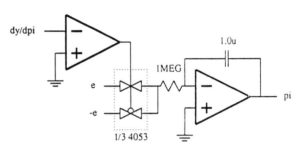

Figure 8: Circuit details of "Coeff Update" block.

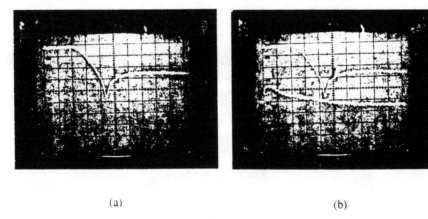

(a)   (b)

Figure 9: Experimental results for adaptive filter model matching application
Curves shown are after adaptation for white noise applied to inputs
of adaptive filter and reference filter.
Vertical scale = 10 dB/div, Horizontal scale = 500 Hz/div
(a) Spectrum for $\delta(t)$ and $y(t)$
The two curves are almost equal.
(b) Spectrum for $y(t)$ (upper curve)
Spectrum for $e(t) = \delta(t) - y(t)$ (lower curve)

437

Part 7
Applications

Section 7-A   Filters for Audio Frequencies

THE remaining papers in this book deal with representative applications in which continuous-time filters are used. We have tried to concentrate on applications in which continuous-time filters are essential or at least provide an advantage. This is in contrast to other applications for which continuous-time filters have been studied but do not so far provide competitive solutions (i.e., 455 KHz or 10.7 MHz intermediate frequency filtering).

The papers in this section cover voiceband and audio applications. Paper 7-A.1 by Smolka et al. has been written specifically for this volume and describes the use of continuous-time filters in a telephony application: the interface between an analog trunk line and a PCM codec filter. Careful noise considerations lead to a large dynamic range and direct tuning leads to high accuracy. Paper 7-A.2 by Yamamoto et al. is a typical example showing how industry improves ICs step-by-step: reducing costs while maintaining quality. This paper contains architectural discussions and presents the design of filters for FM audio with large dynamic range, as required by Hi-Fi specifications. Moreover, a simple automatic tuning system is described. Finally, Paper 7-A.3 by Wilson et al. discusses the integration of a radio paging receiver. By using a zero intermediate frequency (IF), the IF filters operate in the audio band and the performance required of them allows their full integration. Other filters in the same frequency range can be found in Papers 2-B.1, 2-B.2, 2-B.6, 3-A.5, 3-B.2, 4-2, 5-A.1, and elsewhere [1, 2].

Techniques like those used in the aforementioned papers can be used for operation at kHz frequencies and above. At lower frequencies, the very large CR or C/Gm values required make practical implementation difficult. Yet there are important applications at very low frequencies—in control loops for PLLs, FLLs, and adaptive filters, and for AC coupling or DC offset reduction. Discussions of associated problems can be found elsewhere [3–5].

Analog circuits profit less from the miniaturization of IC processes than do digital circuits. For example, capacitor sizes are determined more by signal-to-noise ratio and matching-related arguments than by minimum clearances. Moreover, there is a tendency to reduce supply voltages, necessitating lower signal voltages and correspondingly higher capacitor values to maintain sufficient dynamic range. This has made it more and more difficult for analog high-quality audio and sub-audio applications to compete with digital solutions.

References

[1] H. J. Kuehn, J. Brilka, M. Horl, K. Sanders and G. Sieboerger, "Single-chip BTSC multi-channel TV sound decoder," *IEEE Trans. Consumer Electronics*, vol. 34, pp. 620–624, August 1988.

[2] Y. Yamamoto, T. Kume, F. Hashimoto, K. Ohya, S. Miura, T. Sekino and Y. Ishii, "A new audio processor for EIAJ MTS," *IEEE Trans. Consumer Electronics*, vol. 34, pp. 625–633, August 1988.

[3] R. J. Wiegerink, E. Seevinck and W. de Jager, "Offset cancelling circuit," *IEEE J. Solid-State Circuits*, vol. 24, pp. 651–658, June 1989.

[4] W. H. G. Deguelle, "Limitations on the integration of analog filters for frequencies below 10 Hz," *Proc. ESSCIRC'88*, pp. 131–134.

[5] M. Steyaert, P. Kinget, W. Sansen and J. van der Spiegel, "Full integration of extremely large time constants in CMOS," *Electron. Lett.*, vol. 27, pp. 790–791, May 9, 1991.

Paper 7-A.1

A Low-Noise Trunk Interface Circuit
with Continuous-Time Filters and
On-Chip Tuning

G. J. SMOLKA, U. RIEDLE*, U. GREHL[+], B. JAHN[+], F. PARZEFALL[+], W. VEIT[+],
H. WERKER[+]

SIEMENS AG, PUBLIC COMMUNICATION NETWORKS
HOFMANNSTR.51, D-8000 MUNICH 70, GERMANY
PHONE: + + 49-89-722-25755
FAX: + + 49-89-722-27697
[+] SIEMENS AG, COMPONENT DIVISION,
BALANSTR.73, D-8000 MUNICH 80, GERMANY
* SIEMENS AG, PRIVATE COMMUNICATION NETWORKS,
HOFMANNSTR. 51, D-8000 MUNICH 70, GERMANY

Abstract—A fully analog trunk interface circuit with a wide dynamic range is described. It is used on an analog line card as the link between the trunk line transformer and the codec filter and various detection units in a PBX. The circuit suppresses meter pulses in the voice channel and contains feedback and feedforward loop filters for hybrid balancing and impedance matching. Furthermore, the circuit filters and detects meter and ringing signals. All the filter functions are implemented in a continuous-time MOSFET-*C* technique with automatic on-chip tuning. It has been implemented in a 2-μm CMOS double-poly silicon, double-metal process, measures 43 mm², and operates from ±5 V power supplies.

1. INTRODUCTION

IN recent years, more and more information processing is performed in the digital domain. The integrated services digital network (ISDN) makes it possible to integrate the transmission of digital data and analog speech into a single communication network providing a large spectrum of services to the customer [1]. However, as the change from the classical analog to the fully digital networks will take several years, the need arises to integrate various analog functions on the analog line card, which is the interface between the analog world and the digital processing. At present, these are built in

Note: G. J. Smolka was with Siemens AG, Component Division. He is now with Siemens AG, Public Communication Networks.

discrete form or in hybrid thin- or thick-film technology. The goal is to minimize the circuit and chip count on the line card, have more line connections on a line card and, thus, minimize the system costs.

The trunk interface circuit (TRIC) integrates various functions between an analog trunk line connecting a public exchange and the signal processing codec filter (SICOFI) and detection units in a private branch exchange (PBX). The first task of the TRIC is to support the SICOFI with various analog functions in the voice channels, such as adjustable amplifications, suppression of unwanted signals, and distortions and filtering functions for hybrid balancing and impedance matching. The second task is the filtering, detection, and digital evaluation of ringing signals (for building up and stopping a phone connection) and meter pulses (to determine what the customer has to pay for a call). Additionally, there are different digital interfaces on the chip for the adjustment of the chip itself and for the conversion of digital data.

In Section 2, the system is described showing the connections between the different blocks. The considerations that lead to the chosen continuous-time MOSFET-*C* filters [2] with a four-transistor configuration [3] are described in Section 3. To the knowledge of the authors, the fully balanced four-transistor configuration has never before been implemented in silicon. The filter implementation is considered in the following section. A three-stage tuning system is used for the on-chip tuning, described in Section 5. Because of the low noise requirements, the internal, fully differential, balanced operational amplifiers have to drive large capacitive loads together with resistive loads. Solutions are given in Section 6. Chip implementation and details of other circuits are elaborated in Section 7. Section 8 discusses the measured results from the chip, followed by the conclusions in Section 9.

2. SYSTEM DESCRIPTION AND SPECIFICATIONS

The complete system block diagram of the TRIC is shown in Fig. 1. In the transmit path, after a buffer that ensures a high input impedance, follows a second-order lowpass filter that rejects distorting signals above the voice band. The frequency response specifications to be met by this filter function are as shown in Fig. 2. The meter pulses at 12 kHz or 16 kHz ± 80 Hz, depending on the country, are attenuated by at least 20 dB through the subtraction of an output of the meter-pulse bandpass filter from the unfiltered voice channel. The amplifier K_{TX} is adjustable between four gain values from 0 dB to +6 dB. The overall accuracy of absolute and relative attenuation distortion has to be less than ± 0.05 dB for all variations of technology, power supply, and temperature. The maximum input voltage is 6 V_{pp} in the voice band and, additionally, 2.6 V_{pp} meter pulses.

In the receive path for the attenuators K_{RX} and K_{RXB}, four different values from 0 dB to −8 dB also can be chosen. The line driver has to drain a current of 30 mA, in the worst case, caused by meter signals

at frequencies of 12 kHz or 16 kHz while in the worst case a voice channel frequency, with a voltage amplitude of 6 V_{pp} and with the opposite sign to these meter signals, is sent.

The impedance matching, as a support of the programmable SICOFI function, is simply achieved by a gain factor of $KZ = 0.55$. The hybrid balancing (also as a support of the SICOFI) is achieved by three different fourth-order bandpass functions in the feedback branch (balancing filters). These three different frequency responses are needed to meet together with the SICOFI the requirements of all countries and are shown in Fig. 3. The relative and absolute accuracy has to be better than 0.2 dB for the gain and 5 degrees for the phase in the voice band from 0.3 kHz to 3.4 kHz. The balancing filter in the feedback loop is placed after the feedforward loop for impedance matching because system simulations showed stability up to frequencies greater than 16 kHz in this configuration only.

The voltages from the inputs *TXE* and *RXE* are subtracted in front of the amplifier K_{TX}, as shown in Fig. 1. So, even if the input voltages have maximum values, the remaining voltage at the input of the K_{TX} amplifier can be very small. Therefore, this amplifier has to be placed as the last block in the transmit path. The consequence is that all noise and harmonic distortion caused in the chip are amplified at the end in the K_{TX} amplifier.

The meter pulses are filtered by fourth-order bandpass filters with center frequencies at 12 kHz or 16 kHz. The frequency response templates are given in Fig. 4. The input voltage bursts are detected and digitally evaluated for additional suppression of distorting signals shorter than 12 or 16 periods. The

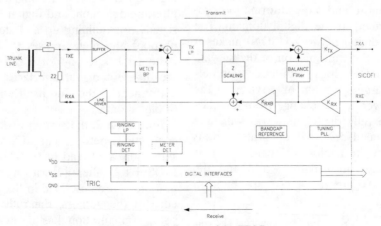

Fig. 1.   Block diagram of the TRIC.

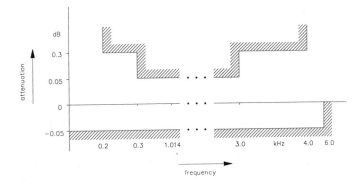

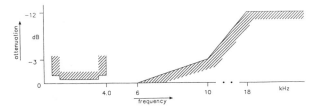

Fig. 2. Frequency response specifications for the lowpass filter.

minimum voltage values are: 6 mV$_p$ lead to a logical 0, 10 mV$_p$ lead to a logical 1. The burst behavior of the meter signals is used for direct tuning. For this reason, the bandpass is switched between the signal path and the tuning circuit, as described in Section 5.

The circuits described above do not work in the power-down state. In this state, only the ringing signals (for call build up) from 25 Hz to 50 Hz are filtered by a second-order lowpass filter with a 3-dB corner frequency of 100 Hz. After that, they are detected and digitally evaluated.

The TRIC has a μP interface for the adjustment of the various functions, a serial series line interface digital (SLD) interface with slave clock and reset function, and a parallel interface, which transmits the information of ringing, meter signals, and data from the SLD interface.

3. DESIGN CONSIDERATIONS

One of the most stringent design requirements of the TRIC is an idle channel noise of −78 dBm0p at the outputs *TXA* and *RXA* of the two channels, respectively. In the transmit channel especially, the uncorrelated noise from the lowpass filter and the balance filters is added and then amplified by the

maximum gain $K_{TX} = 6$ dB. As already mentioned, a very tight absolute and relative attenuation tolerance of ± 0.05 dB in the voice half channels and a group delay distortion of ± 1 μs in the transmit and receive directions, is required.

It should be possible, in principle, to fullfill these requirements with a switched capacitor (SC) solution. However, as SC filters are sampled-data systems, they need input antialiasing filters. Because of the group delay distortion requirement, the sampling frequency of an SC solution would have to be at least at 2 MHz. This would yield small group delay variations enough despite the large technology tolerances of an antialiasing filter. The accuracy requirements of filter attenuation and phase also need a large operational-amplifier bandwidth and a high gain. Estimations showed that the operational amplifiers would have to drive capacitive loads of more than 200 pF because of the noise requirements with a unity-gain bandwith of more than 40 MHz. At the time the project started, these requirements seemed very difficult to fulfill. In SC filters, internally generated operational amplifier noise at high frequency is aliased into the baseband because of sampling by each switch. The clock feedthrough caused by switching is difficult to predict and eliminate. Switch charge injection can depend on the signal level. This

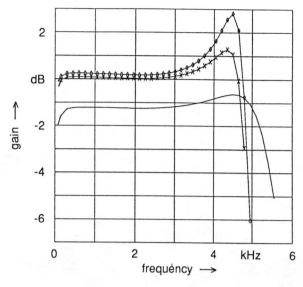

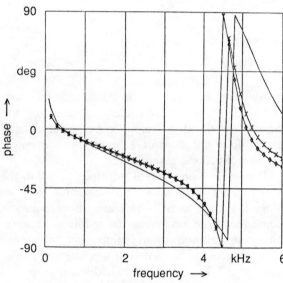

Fig. 3. Gain and phase responses of the balancing filters.

causes distortion with undesirable side effects regarding the gain-tracking requirements. Because of this, a continuous-time MOSFET-C filter technique [2] was chosen. In order to minimize distortions in the voice channels caused by clock signals, all the filters on the chip were designed with this technique.

For the integrators of the filters, the four-transistor balanced MOSFET-C integrator structure shown in Fig. 5 was implemented [3]. The reasons for this choice follow. Using balanced input voltages and tuning voltages, V_A and V_C, we obtain for the circuit [3]

$$V_{\text{out}} = -\frac{1}{RC} \int_{-\infty}^{t} V_{\text{in}}(t)\, dt \qquad (1)$$

with

$$\frac{1}{R} = \frac{1}{R_1} - \frac{1}{R_2} = \mu C_{ox}' \frac{W}{L} (V_A - V_C) \qquad (2)$$

and

$$|V_{\text{in}}| < \min \{ |V_A - V_T|, |V_C - V_T| \}. \qquad (3)$$

A major advantage of the four-transistor structure versus the two-transistor structure [4] is that a resistance value does not depend on a substrate voltage V_B and, thus, substrate parasitic signals cannot modulate the resistance value. Also, parasitic signals common to the tuning voltages V_A and V_C cancel out [3]. Because the threshold voltage V_T does not appear in Equation (2), the temperature dependence is due only to the mobility μ, thus decreasing the range of the needed automatic tuning. The sensitivity to mismatches, which is increased by the doubled number of "resistor"-transistors, was found to be neglible. The even harmonics are canceled out by the symmetric structure. Suppression of the odd harmonics depends upon the position of the tuning voltages in the triode region. This makes the four-transistor structure suitable for a high-swing application as in the TRIC.

A further important advantage of the four-transistor structure is the inherent cancelation of parasitic distributed capacitance effects of the MOSFETs [5] that model the resistors. In the transmit lowpass filter, for example, these parasitic capacitances would cause a peaking of about 0.5 dB near the cutoff frequency. In the high-quality factor meter-pulse bandpasses, these effects can cause severe stability problems. Because of the latter and the high attenuation and phase accuracy requirements, and to avoid the compensation of technology-dependent parasitic capacitances, the four-transistor structure is preferred.

For simulating noise behavior, each "resistor"-transistor is replaced by a linear resistor with the inverse value of the transistors output conductance. Because the drain-to-source voltages are zero, these transistors have no $1/f$-noise [6]. The noise power spectral density of the equivalent resistor is

$$S_R = 4kTR. \qquad (4)$$

For comparison of the noise behavior of the two- and four-transistor structures, the single-ended version of the equivalent small-signal circuit in Fig. 6 is regarded. At the integrator output, taking into account Equations (4) and (2), the following noise

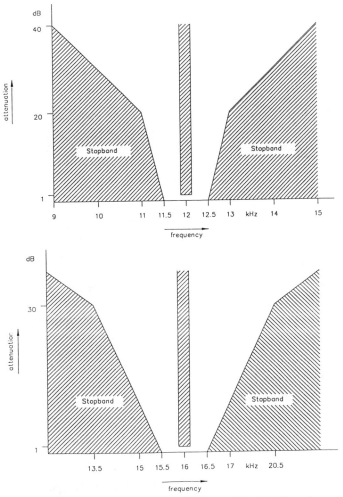

Fig. 4. Frequency response specifications of the 12-kHz and 16-kHz bandpass filters.

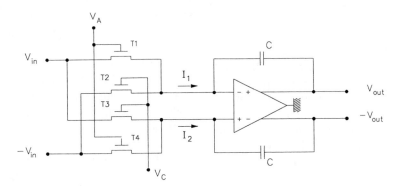

Fig. 5. Four-transistor continuous-time integrator structure.

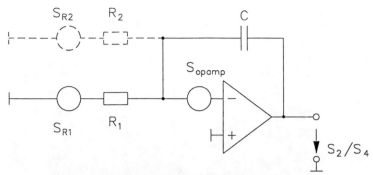

Fig. 6. Equivalent single-ended small-signal circuit of Fig. 5, including noise sources.

spectral densities are obtained

$$S_2 = \frac{4kT}{\omega^2 C^2 R} + \left(1 + \frac{1}{\omega^2 C^2 R^2}\right) S_{op\,amp} \quad (5)$$

for the two-transistor structure (solid lines in Fig. 6) and

$$S_4 = \frac{4kT}{\omega^2 C^2 R} \left(\frac{1}{R_1} + \frac{1}{R_2}\right)$$
$$+ \left[1 + \frac{1}{\omega^2 C^2} \left(\frac{1}{R_1^2} + \frac{1}{R_2^2}\right)\right] S_{op\,amp} \quad (6)$$

for the four-transistor structure (Fig. 5). With the approximation $\frac{1}{\omega^2 R^2 C^2} \gg 1$ we get for the portion of the resistor-caused noise the relation

$$\frac{S_{2R}}{S_{4R}} = \frac{1/R_1 - 1/R_2}{1/R_1 + 1/R_2} \quad (7)$$

and for the operational amplifier-caused noise,

$$\frac{S_{2op\,amp}}{S_{4op\,amp}} = \frac{(1/R_1 - 1/R_2)^2}{1/R_1^2 + 1/R_2^2}. \quad (8)$$

It can be seen that the noise of the four-transistor structure is, in principle, larger than that of the two-transistor structure. From Equation (2), it follows that $V_A - V_C$ should be as great as possible to minimize the noise. The minimum occurs, if the second transistor pair is turned off and the four-transistor structure is changed into the two-transistor structure. The increase of $V_A - V_C$ has its limit at the voltage swing requirements.

With $T_i = R_i C$,

$$S_4 = \frac{4kT}{\omega^2 C} \left(\frac{1}{T_1} + \frac{1}{T_2}\right)$$
$$+ \frac{S_{op\,amp}}{\omega^2} \left(\frac{1}{T_1^2} + \frac{1}{T_2^2}\right) \quad (9)$$

is obtained. Obviously, with an increase of the integrator capacitance C, only the part of the resistor noise is decreased, but not the operational-amplifier part[1].

Because of the requirements with respect to voltage swing and attenuation accuracy, and because of its smaller dependency to parasitic technology parameters, the four-transistor structure was chosen. To fullfill the noise and voltage swing requirements, an appropriate internal scaling had to be found.

4. Filter Implementation

For the balancing filters, the transmission function $H(s)$ was given. From this function, using a synthesis program, a classic fourth-order, doubly terminated LC ladder prototype was derived as shown in Fig. 7. This structure was chosen because of its superior sensitivity properties. The circuit of Fig. 7 can be represented by a signal-flow graph as in Fig. 8 [7, 8]. Using integrator blocks, as in Fig. 5, and coupling capacitances for the realization of the finite transmission zeros, the complete balanced filter in Fig. 9 is obtained. In the next step, the operational amplifier output voltages were scaled for optimum dynamic range at the frequencies of interest.

The gate width of the "resistor"-transistors was selected at $W = 8\ \mu$m because of the accuracy requirements. These transistors are composed of unit transistors of $W/L = 8\ \mu$m$/20\ \mu$m. The capacitors are composed of unit capacitors with values of 0.65 pF. The values of capacitors and transistor lengths are given in Table 1. As discussed in Section 3, no perturbation of element values was necessary.

---

[1] Note: the author received from a reviewer the hint that the above shown relations can be found in: J. Khoury, "Realization of lumped and distributed integrated continuous-time filters," *Doctoral Dissertation*, Columbia University, New York, 1988.

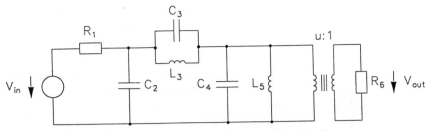

Fig. 7.   RLC ladder reference filter of the balancing filters.

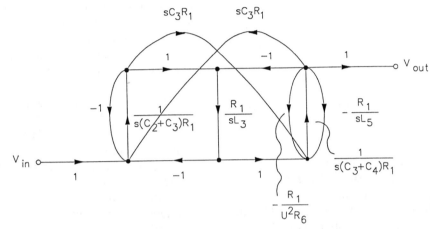

Fig. 8.   Signal-flow graph for the reference filter in Fig. 7.

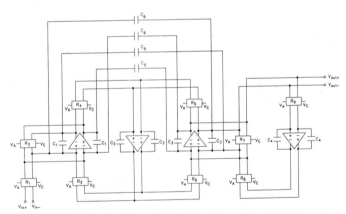

Fig. 9.   Completely balanced balancing filter with the four-
transistor structure in the boxes.

In order to fullfill the requirements depicted in Fig. 4, a fourth-order LC bandpass filter, as shown in Fig. 10(a), was synthesized. This circuit has a quality factor of $Q = 24$. The resonant circuits have been realized with biquads similar to the one presented in [5], with a modification of the coupling to a leap-frog structure as shown in Fig. 10(b) [5, 9]. First simulations showed instability of the integrator loops at the center frequency of the bandpass filter. It

could be seen that, in the four-transistor integrator, the parasitic capacitances are nearly cancelled out, as already mentioned. A small improvement of the phase margin was possible by increasing the feedback and coupling capacitances and decreasing the values of the resistors, thus also decreasing the distributed capacitances of the "resistor"-transistors. This improvement was due to the fact that the approximation, which leads to a cancelation of the

449

TABLE 1
VALUES OF CAPACITORS AND "RESISTOR"-TRANSISTOR
LENGTHS OF THE BALANCING FILTER.

Element	Value	Unit
C_1	67.3	pF
C_2	31.3	pF
C_3	57.3	pF
C_4	53.8	pF
C_5	38.7	pF
C_6	23.2	pF
1_{R1}	114	μm
1_{R2}	80	μm
1_{R3}	240	μm
1_{R4}	240	μm
1_{R5}	400	μm
1_{R6}	80	μm
1_{R7}	134	μm
1_{R8}	400	μm
1_{R9}	3200	μm

parasitic capacitances, was for the regarded frequencies no longer exactly valid. The remaining phase shift, in comparison to an ideal integrator, was caused only by the phase shift introduced by the first pole of the operational amplifiers. For a lag compensation according to [5], the compensation capacitance would have to be so large that the transmission function itself would be intolerably disturbed. The countermeasure implemented was to increase the first pole frequency up to the center frequency of the bandpass. The remaining phase margin in the integrator loops is about 25 degrees (see Fig. 11). This is enough taking into account a stable fre-

quency tuning of the filter. Worst-case simulations showed that because of the high operational-amplifier gain at the filter passband, the gain variation due to the temperature and power supply variations was less than ±1 dB, small enough for a correct detection of the meter signals.

5. TUNING SYSTEM

In continuous-time MOSFET-C filters with the four-transistor structure, the filter characteristic has to be adjusted by the tuning voltage difference $V_A - V_C$. The tuning voltages for the various filters are automatically created by the three-stage tuning system shown in Fig. 12. It consists of an analog phase-locked loop (PLL) for indirect tuning [2, 7], a digital initialization circuit to ensure a stable lock-in of the analog PLL, and a digital PLL for direct tuning.

For the analog tuning PLL, two different reference frequencies at 8.533 kHz and 10.24 kHz for the 12-kHz and 16-kHz meter-pulse case are used. This is to prevent meter signal frequencies, which are mirrored at the reference and the double reference frequency, from falling into the voice band. The mirroring at the double reference frequency is because of the EXOR gate used as a phase detector. The VCO is a second-order circuit with elements similar to those in the filters [7]. The "TRANSF.NW" block contains simply a number of current sources. Two current sources are controlled by the analog voltages created in the initialization circuit (V_{INIT}) and in the analog PLL (V_{AN}). They are added and changed into the tuning voltage difference $V_A - V_C$

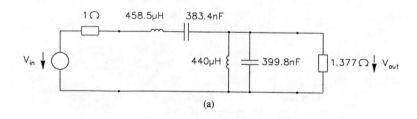

(a)

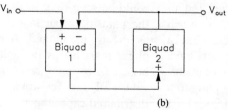

(b)

Fig. 10. (a) RLC reference filter. (b) Leap-frog bandpass filter.

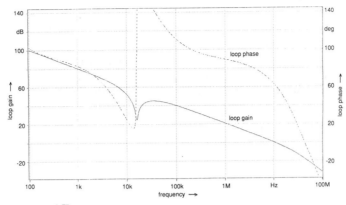

Fig. 11. Gain and phase of an integrator loop in the 16-kHz
meter bandpass filter.

across a resistance. These tuning voltages are used for all the filters and the VCO except the meter-pulse bandpass filter.

Measurements on a prototype showed insufficient tracking between the VCO and the meter-pulse bandpass filter. The frequency response variations over temperature and power-supply variation was ±300 Hz, too much to guarantee a reliable post-filter detection. Because of the burst character of the meter signal, it was possible to introduce direct tuning [2]. The bandpass has a phase shift of a multiple of π at the center frequency. For a well defined amplitude of ±0.25 V with a reference clock of 16 kHz (a fraction of the system clock) the set-

tling time of the filter is less than 5 ms. The reference clock is passed simultaneously into the bandpass and beside it into the comparators. A frequency- and phase-selective phase detector of type 4 [10] creates, according to the phase shift, up or down pulses. These pulses are counted in an up/down counter. In a decoder, the control bits are created for the following "TRANSF.NW" block. There a set of 6 binary weighted current sources from V_{DD} and V_{SS}, in each case forming a D/A converter through adding or subtracting current increments to the analog-controlled currents described above. Similar to the voltages V_A and V_C, the tuning voltages V_A' and V_C' are created across a resistance. With an accuracy

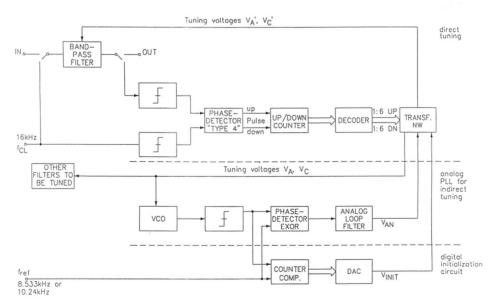

Fig. 12. Three-stage tuning system.

of the tuning voltage of $\Delta(V'_A - V'_C) = 6$ mV, the center frequency is adjusted to within 40 Hz. The correction voltage is stored in a digital manner in the up/down counter, thus avoiding the use of a relatively large capacitor, which would have to keep this voltage within sufficient accuracy for a relatively long time.

6. OPERATIONAL AMPLIFIERS

From Table 1 it can be seen that the operational amplifiers, especially in the balancing filters, have to drive large capacitive loads and simultaneously resistive loads because of sense resistances for the common-mode feedback, and stages for differential-to-single ended conversion. The fully differentially balanced operational amplifier in Fig. 13 uses a similar principle as in [11]. In order to enhance the driving capability, a parasitic NPN bipolar transistor is used in the output stage. Due to capacitive loads of up to 200 pF, special care has to be taken for a sufficiently low resistance of the stage that drives the emitter follower. For the same load and output voltage swing, CMOS transistors with 13000 μm/2 μm instead of the bipolar transistors would have to be used. Thus, the use of the bipolar transistors leads to a very compact operational amplifier of high performance. In order to minimize the operational amplifier noise, the currents in the differential input stages have to be small, a fact that is inconsistent with the requirement of a large bandwidth. The operational amplifier data are listed in Table 2.

TABLE 2
PERFORMANCE OF THE OP AMP IN THE
BALANCING FILTERS.

Power supply	±5 V
Gain	80 dB
Unity gain bandwidth	4 MHz
Phase margin	62 degrees
at C_{load}	200 pF
R_{load}	15 kOhm
Output voltage swing	6.8 V_{pp}
Power consumption	20 mW
Area	0.26 mm^2

7. CHIP IMPLEMENTATION

In front of and behind the continuous-time filters, single-to-differential (and vice versa) converters are inserted. These simultaneously perform a scaling of the voltages by a factor of 1.25 in the direction TXE − TXA and a factor of 1.5 in the direction RXE − TXA. In each case, the single ended voltages at the inputs or outputs are compared with the differential voltages in the filters.

In the meter-pulse detection, two different thresholds for each frequency are implemented. This corresponds to a change of sensitivity. For the lower threshold an amplifier with a very exact amplification of 26 dB and an integrated offset canceller are used. This increases the decision range, for example, from between 6 mV to 10 mV up to a range of between 60 mV to 100 mV, which can be easier realized by comparators and reference voltages.

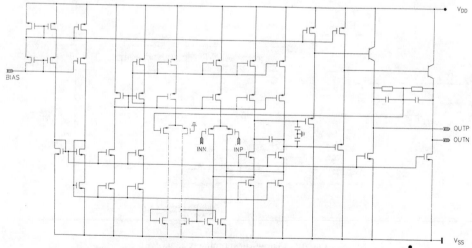

Fig. 13. Schematic of the operational amplifier of the balancing filters.

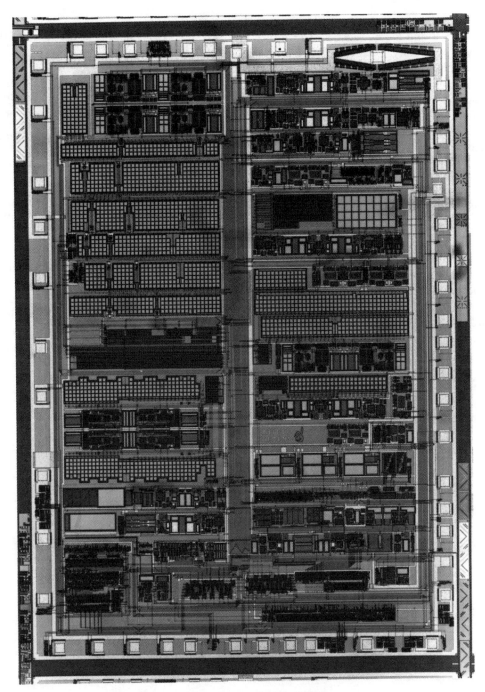

Fig. 14. Microphotograph of the TRIC.

The tuning voltages were nominally chosen as: $V_A = V_{SS} = -5$ V and $V_C = -2.91$ V. The choice of $V_A = V_{SS}$ was necessary because of the large dynamic range required. Compared with a tuning voltage V_A and an appropriately related voltage V_C derived, for example, from a bandgap reference, this has the disadvantages of a greater tuning range, a variation of noise according to Equation (2), and harmonic distortions.

For the "resistor"-transistors, PMOS transistors are used. These transistors are closely surrounded by contact rings connected to V_{DD} to minimize parasitic coupling from the substrate. Distortions out of the substrate act as common mode voltages and are cancelled out if the structures are ideally symmetrical. Careful layout tried to take this into account. All the capacitors were laid out over a grounded P-well. Special care was taken to achieve a good component matching within the various filters themselves and between the VCO and the filters, using throughout the same unit capacitors and unit transistors.

The above design was implemented in a 2-μm double-poly silicon and double-metal CMOS process. The 28-pin device has an area of 43 mm^2. Fig. 14 shows a microphotograph of the chip.

8. Experimental Results

In Table 3, some measured performance characteristics are presented. Depending on power supply volt-

TABLE 3
MEASURED PERFORMANCE CHARACTERISTICS.

Power supply voltage	± 5 V, $\pm 5\%$
Idle channel noise	
Transmit path	-78 dBm0p ± 1 dB
Receive path	-89 dBm0p ± 1 dB
Input voltage:	
Transmit path: voice, signal	$\leq 6\,V_{pp}$
+ meter pulse	$+(20\text{ mV}_{PP} \cdots 2.6\,V_{PP})$
In power down: ringing signal	$\leq 10\,V_{PP}$
Receive path	$\leq 6\,V_{PP}$
Dynamic range (input transmit path,	
harmonic distortion < -48 dB)	95 dB
PSRR (V_{DD}/V_{SS}) $(f \leq 100$ kHz$)$	< -42 dB
Power dissipation	300 mW

age and temperature, the idle channel noise varies by ± 1 dB.

Figures 15 to 19 show the frequency responses of the different filters implemented on the chip. In Fig. 15, in addition to the second-order function of the transmit lowpass, the bandstop characteristic for the 12-kHz and 16-kHz case can be seen simultaneously, which is achieved by subtracting the frequency response of the output from the meter-pulse bandpass. The three different balancing filter frequency responses are depicted in Fig. 16. The bandpass response in Fig. 17 is measured in such a way that a tuning of the digital PLL occures every 512 ms. Using a sweep time of 5 sec on the network analyzer, a bump appears every 200 Hz, indicating that

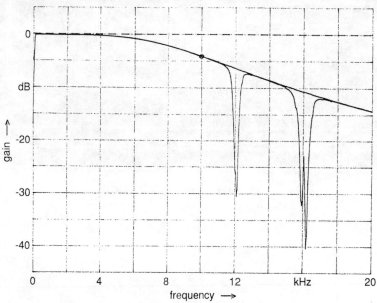

Fig. 15. Frequency responses of the transmit lowpass filter for the 12-kHz and 16-kHz cases.

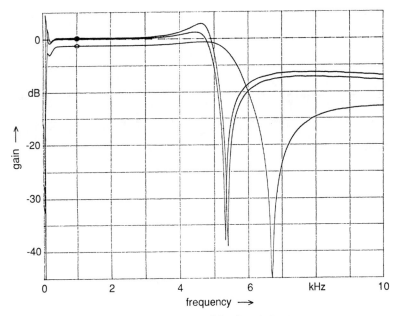

Fig. 16.   Frequency responses of the three balancing filters.

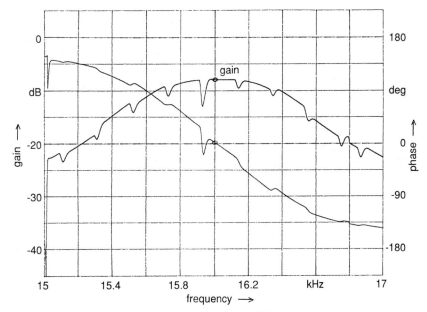

Fig. 17.   Frequency response of the 16-kHz meter bandpass
filter tuned every 512 ms and with a sweep time of 5 sec on
the network analyzer with "tuning bumps".

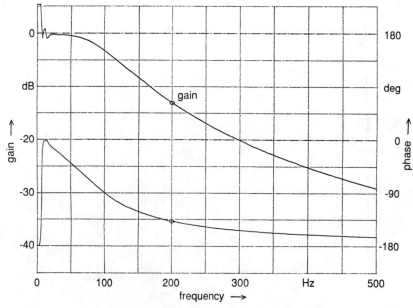

Fig. 18. Frequency response of the ringing lowpass filter.

the filter is switched off for tuning. The ringing filter lowpass response is shown in Fig. 18. In Fig. 19 the total distortion, depending on a band-limited input noise signal with the power spectrum between 350 Hz and 550 Hz according to CCITT recommendation O.131, is presented. Fig. 20 shows the excellent gain-tracking behavior of the complete transmit path.

9. CONCLUSIONS

It has been demonstrated that with continuous-time MOSFET-*C* filters, a wide dynamic range and a high accuracy of 7 different filter frequency responses with common on-chip automatic tuning can be designed on a single chip. This device illustrates the

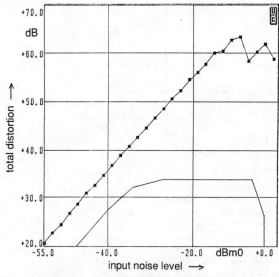

Fig. 19. Total harmonic distortion, depending on input noise, with the power spectrum betweeen 350 Hz and 450 Hz according to CCITT recommendation O.131.

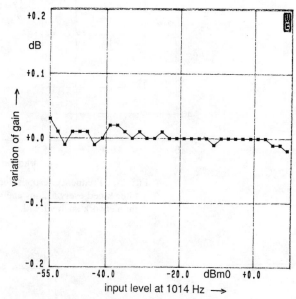

Fig. 20. Gain tracking of the transmit path.

potential of complex mixed analog–digital VLSI chips with high-performance analog circuits at the analog front end.

ACKNOWLEDGMENT

The authors wish to thank Prof. Y. Tsividis of the National Technical University of Athens, for his valuable advices and discussions, and S. Siegel and K. Guse for the CAD support.

REFERENCES

[1] G. Geiger and L. Lerach, "ISDN-oriented modular VLSI chip set for central-office and PABX applications," *IEEE J. Selected Areas Commun.*, vol. SAC-4, pp. 1268–1274, November 1986.

[2] Y. Tsividis, M. Banu, and J. Khoury, "Continuous-Time MOSFET-C filters in VLSI," *J. Solid-State Circuits*, vol. SC-21, pp. 15–20, February 1986.

[3] Z. Czarnul, "Modification of Banu-Tsividis continuous-time integrator structure," *IEEE Trans. Circuits Syst.*, vol. CAS-33, no. 7, July 1986.

[4] M. Banu and Y. Tsividis, "Fully integrated active *RC* filters in MOS technology," *IEEE J. Solid-State Circuits*, vol. SC-18, pp. 664–651, December 1983.

[5] J. M. Khoury and Y. Tsividis, "Analysis and compensation of high-frequency effects in integrated MOSFET-C continuous-time filters," *IEEE Trans. Circuits Syst.*, vol. CAS-34, no. 8, pp. 862–875, August 1987.

[6] Y. Tsividis and G. Masetti, "Problems in precision modelling of the MOS transistor for analog applications," *IEEE Trans. Computer Aided Des.*, vol. CAD-3, pp. 72–79, 1984.

[7] M. Banu and Y. Tsividis, "An elliptic continuous-time CMOS filter with on-chip automatic tuning," *IEEE J. Solid-State Circuits*, vol. SC-20, pp. 1113–1121, December 1985.

[8] G. M. Jacobs, D. J. Allstot, R. W. Brodersen, and P. R. Gray, "Design techniques for MOS switched capacitor ladder filters," *IEEE Trans. Circuits Syst.*, vol. CAS-5, pp. 1014–1021, December 1978.

[9] M. Yoshihiro, A. Nishihara, and T. Yanagisawa, "Low-sensitivity active and digital filters based on the node-voltage simulation of LC ladder structures," *IEEE Int. Symposium on Circuits and Systems*, 1977, pp. 360–361.

[10] R. Best, "Phase-locked loops," New York: McGraw Hill, 1984.

[11] M. Banu, J. Khoury, and Y. Tsividis, "Fully differential operational amplifiers with accurate output balancing," *IEEE J. Solid-State Circuits*, vol. SC-23, pp. 1410–1414, December 1988.

FM Audio IC for VHS VCR Using New Signal Processing

T. YAMAMOTO[*], I. KAMOSHIDA[*]
K. KOGA[*], T. SAKAI[**], S. SAWA[***]

[*]CONSUMER PRODUCTS ENGINEERING LAB.
[**]VIDEO PRODUCT DIVISION
[***]SEMICONDUCTOR DIVISION

TOSHIBA CORPORATION

ABSTRACT

A new VHS FM audio processing IC has been developed. By the new circuitry developed, audio filters can be fully-integrated without degrading its performance and the total dynamic range. In addition to that, the trimming points of the system are reduced from 6 to 2, which results in high cost effectiveness.

INTRODUCTION

High quality picture and sound have been essential for recent consumer use VCR. In order to reproduce Hi-Fi sound, FM audio recording format was standardized for VHS format VCR, called HiFi VHS. This type of VCR has penetrated into the markets, and now becomes very popular.

A new VHS FM audio processing IC with excellent performance has been developed. The IC contains a PNR (Peak Noise Reduction) system and a MODEM system, which were difficult for the total integration because of poor S/N ratio or poor frequency alignment of the conventional IC circuits. Setting our target to hit the most cost effectiveness, we designed a new audio processing IC so as to reduce the external parts and the trimming points, while keeping high performances.

FULLY INTEGRATED CONTINUOUS-TIME ACTIVE FILTER

In most cases, audio band filters are the most expensive external com-ponents in conventional audio IC systems. Full integration of them might bring about high cost effectiveness. But, it has been quite difficult for HiFi audio use, because integrated filters may have poor S/N ratio not enough for high quality sound processing[1].

Fully-integrated continuous-time active filters are firstly implemented. They are a 4th-order audio band limitting filter (20kHz-LPF) and a 1st-order FM de-emphasis filter. The IC is fabricated by standard bipolar process.

The detailed explanation follows:
 (1)A New PNR System
 (2)Audio Band Integrated Filters
 (3)Automatic Tuning System

(1) A New PNR System

The schematic block diagram of the new FM audio system is shown in Fig.1-a with the conventional one in Fig.1-b. In general, triangular spectrum noise is usually dominant in the FM audio recording system noise. The VHS HiFi standard requires wide dynamic range by utilizing a noise reduction system, which is a dynamic range expansion method by decibel-linear compressing of a record signal amplitude. The noise reduction circuit consists of an OP-AMP (Operational Amplifier) and a VCA (Voltage Controlled Amplifier). In recording mode, input signals are amplitude-compressed by the compressor, in which the VCA is connected in the feedback path of the OP-AMP. In playback mode, the compressed signals reproduced are amplitude-expanded by the

Reprinted from *IEEE Trans. Cons. El.,* vol. CE-35, no. 4, pp. 723–731, November 1989.

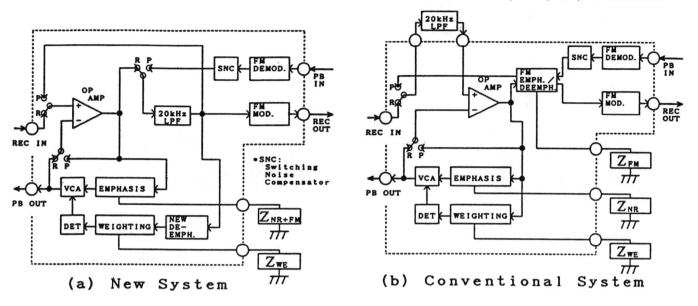

(a) New System
(b) Conventional System

Fig.1 Block Diagram of the FM Audio Systems

VCA. In this way, original sounds are reproduced, keeping its dynamic range more than 90dB. We effectively make use of the noise reduction system and integrate the filters in the IC.

1-1. The Integration of 20kHz LPF

Figures 2-a and 2-b show the simplified block diagram of the new PNR system and the conventional one in recording mode, respectively. The difference between the two systems is the location of the 20kHz-LPFs. In the new system, it is placed just after the PNR loop. VCA gain in the feedback loop is controlled so as to be proportional to the peak amplitude of the PNR output. The gain is expressed by the following equation:

$$H_{CCA} = \frac{Z_{NR} V_0}{Z_{WE} V_c} \qquad (1)$$

where V_c is a constant voltage depending on the VCA circuit. Using (1), the signal transfer equations of the PNRs in both cases are expressed by the identical expression, which is;

$$V_0 = \left(\frac{Z_{WE}}{Z_{NR}} H_{LPF} V_c \right)^{\frac{1}{2}} V_i^{\frac{1}{2}} \qquad (2)$$

This means that the output signals of the PNR circuit are compressed in decibel-linear format.

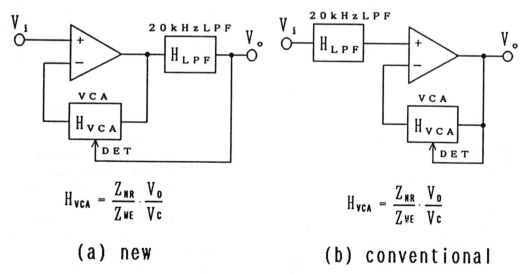

$$H_{VCA} = \frac{Z_{NR}}{Z_{WE}} \cdot \frac{V_0}{V_c}$$

$$H_{VCA} = \frac{Z_{NR}}{Z_{WE}} \cdot \frac{V_0}{V_c}$$

(a) new
(b) conventional

Fig.2 Simplified Block Diagram of the PNR Systems

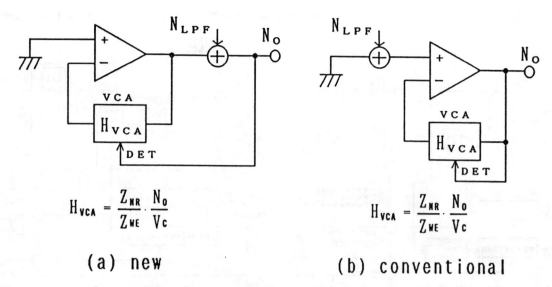

$$H_{VCA} = \frac{Z_{NR}}{Z_{WE}} \cdot \frac{N_0}{V_C}$$

(a) new

$$H_{VCA} = \frac{Z_{NR}}{Z_{WE}} \cdot \frac{N_0}{V_C}$$

(b) conventional

**Fig.3 Block Diagram
on the 20kHz-LPF Noise Estimation**

We estimate total noise character-istics of the PNR circuits. Noise in these systems is mostly generated from the 20kHz LPF. Higher noise level results in poor system dynamic range. Figures 3-a and 3-b comparatively show noise equivalent circuits of the new and conventional PNRs, respectively. In the conventional system, the filter noise is directly added to the PNR input signal. Therefore, the noise transfer equation is equal to the signal transfer equation (2), which is rewritten as follows:

$$N_0 = \left(\frac{Z_{WE}}{Z_{NR}} V_C \right)^{\frac{1}{2}} N_{LPF}^{\frac{1}{2}} \quad (3)$$

In the new system, the filter noise is added to the PNR output signal. Therefore, the output noise is equal to the LPF noise, which is expressed as follows:

$$N_0 = N_{LPF} \quad (4)$$

Comparing (3) with (4), we conclude that the direct noise in the new PNR (4) is much smaller than the compress-ed noise in the conventional one (3), because the noise in the conventional circuit is amplified by the PNR circuit. In other words, the new system can have noise reduction effect and can have wider dynamic range than that in the conventional system. An experimental measurement has shown

that total dynamic range of more than 90dB can be achievable even with the integrated 20kHz-LPF with 75dB dynamic range.

1-2. The Integrated FM Emphasis Circuit with No External Parts

The VHS HiFi system has FM empha-sis function in order to compensate the degradation caused by FM triangu-lar spectrum noise. In our conven-tional IC, the FM emphasis circuit was located after the PNR loop and had an external impedance circuit Z_{FM}. Full integration of the filter circuit was difficult, because the induced noise components from the filter might cause poor system S/N ratio. In our new system, FM emphasis circuit block is combined within the VCA circuit by rearranging the external impedance circuit of NR emphasis from Z_{NR} to Z_{NR+FM}, as shown in Fig.4-a and 4-b. This refinement becomes feasible, uti-lizing the time constant relationship in the VHS HiFi standard; the zero frequency in the NR emphasis is just equal to the pole in the FM emphasis, which is 56usec as shown in Fig.5.

Additional auxiliary filter H_{NEW} preceding to the peak detector, on the other hand, called a new deemphasis circuit, is necessary in order to keep the same frequency characteris-tics as that of the convential system. Its transfer function H_{NEW} must be re-ciprocal to the FM emphasis function

H_{FM}. We get the same signal transfer equation for both systems, which is as follows:

$$V_O = \frac{1}{Z_{FM}} \left(\frac{Z_{WE}}{Z_{NR}} V_C \right)^{\frac{1}{2}} V_i^{\frac{1}{2}} \quad (5)$$

This additional filter need not have high S/N ratio, because it relates only to peak detection and does not affect signal quality. In this way, the additional filter is easily implemented on the IC chip.

(2) Audio Band Integrated Filters

Audio IC filters, in general, must be tunable in order to compensate absolute spreads in component values (time constant variation) caused by the fabrication of the ICs. A conventional tunable filter is usually composed of several integrators with variable transconductance (variable Gm circuits), which is shown in Fig.6-b. The transfer function of this integrator is described by the following

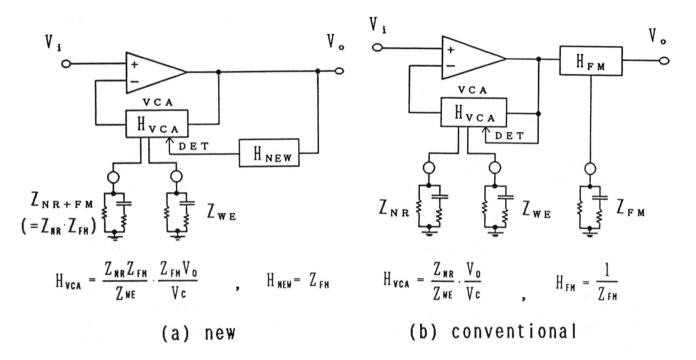

$$H_{VCA} = \frac{Z_{NR}Z_{FM}}{Z_{WE}} \cdot \frac{Z_{FM}V_O}{V_C} \quad , \quad H_{NEW} = Z_{FM}$$

(a) new

$$H_{VCA} = \frac{Z_{NR}}{Z_{WE}} \cdot \frac{V_O}{V_C} \quad , \quad H_{FM} = \frac{1}{Z_{FM}}$$

(b) conventional

Fig.4 Simplified Block Diagram
of the PNR and FM Emphasis Systems

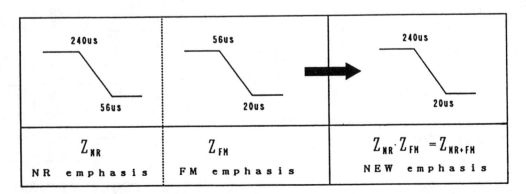

Fig.5 Degeneration in Emphasis Impedance Function

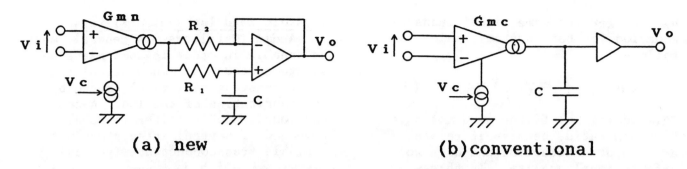

(a) new   (b)conventional

Fig.6 Integrators Used in a Building Block
of Fully-Integrated Filters

equation:

$$H(s) = \frac{Gmc}{C \cdot s} \qquad (6)$$

The serious problem associated with this circuit is that the variable Gm circuit cannot usually have high S/N ratio. And the S/N ratio gets worse as the transconductance becomes smaller. For a large time constant audio-band filter, we have to design a very low transconductance IC circuit, or we must use large capacitor, which are neither practical nor economical.

To solve this problem, we have developed a new integrator using a variable Gm circuit as shown in Fig.6-a. Two input terminals of the voltage follower of the integrator oprate as imaginally terminated. Thereby, the Gm circuit output current is divided into the ratio of $R_1:R_2$.

The current passed through R_1 is used for integrator operation. Therefore, the transfer function of this new integrator is expressed as follows:

$$H(s) = \frac{R_2}{R_1 + R_2} \cdot \frac{Gmc}{C \cdot s} \qquad (7)$$

Assume that new and conventional integrators with the same value of capacitances had the same transfer functions, we can obtain the following equation from (6) and (7):

$$\frac{Gmn}{Gmc} = \frac{R_1 + R_2}{R_2} \qquad (8)$$

In general, S/N ratio of a variable Gm circuit is approximately proportional to the square root of its transconductance. This relation is almost always valid on condition that the shot noise is dominant at the output terminal. Therefore, the S/N

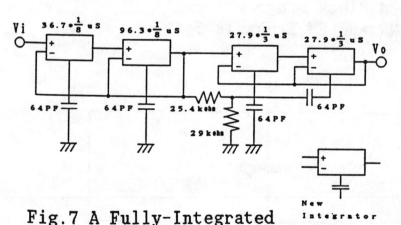

Fig.7 A Fully-Integrated
20kHz-LPF

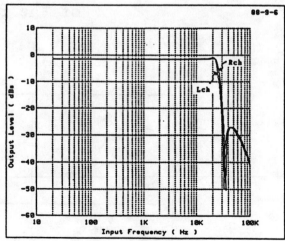

Fig.8 Frequency Characteristic
of the 20kHz-LPF

ratio of both integrators is described as follows:

$$\frac{(S/N)\,n}{(S/N)\,c} \simeq \left(\frac{R_1 + R_2}{R_2}\right)^{\frac{1}{2}} \quad (9)$$

Obviously, this equation means that the new integrator has higher S/N ratio than the conventional one by the factor determined by the resistor network. We practically apply this integrator to audio band filters in this IC, and improve their S/N ratio by about 10dB.

A schematic of the 20kHz LPF circuit is shown in Fig.7. It has about 220 elements and 256pF on-chip capacitors. Figure 8 shows an experimental frequency characteristic. This filter is designed to meet the specification listed as follows; (1)the passband should be less than 20kHz, (2)the notch frequency be 33kHz, (3)the passband-ripple be less than 0.3dB and (4)the stopband supression should be more than 25dB. We met all desirable performances of the filter.

(3)Automatic Tuning System

A frequency tuning error in an integrated filter may occur by fabrication process parameter variations. In order to tune the filter, we have developed an automatic tuning circuit which is illustrated in Fig.9. This is simpler than any other tuning systems reported before[2],[3]. This IC contains the additional integrator for highly accurate tracking, which is identical to the integartors in the main filters. The integrator output waveform at the capacitor terminal is repetitive saw tooth by integral

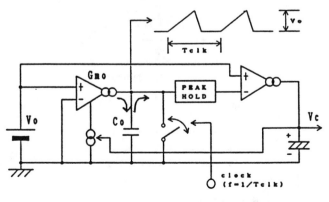

Fig.9 Automatic Tuning System

charge and instantaneously discharge of the capacitor during one accurate clock period. Controlling the integrator transconductance, the triangular output amplitude is kept to constant voltage Vo. We obtain the following equation under the stable state:

$$\frac{C_0}{Gm_0} = \frac{Tclk}{2}(\text{constant}) \quad (10)$$

This equation means that the automatic tuning loop adjusts the time constant of the integrator so as to be defined only by the precise clock period. The tuning voltage is also supplied to each main filters. In this way, frequency tuning characteristics of the filters are adjusted accurately in accordance with the tuning circuit.

TRIMMING-FREE SYSTEM

External circuit trimming points are one of the concerns of the IC circuitry. In this IC, we have reduced the number of trimming points from 6 to 2.

At first, in order to eliminate the FM deviation trimming, we developed an accurate tracking adjustment technique; a simultaneous adjustment of both the FM center and deviation frequencies. The new adjustment system of the FM modulator is shown in Fig.10. A multivibrator is controlled by two bias currents, the equations of which are expressed in the figure. The two currents are arranged so as to track fixed ratio of $n_1:n_2$. Transconductance of the variable Gm circuit is proportionally controlled by one of the bias currents of n_2Ic. Substituting the expression of Ic_1 and Ic_2 in the oscillation condition equation, we obtain the following center frequency:

$$f_0 = (f_{FM})_{vi=0} = \frac{n_1 Ic}{4 C_M V_A} \quad (11)$$

By differentiating the oscillation expression and using (11), we obtain the FM deviation as expressed in the following equation:

$$B = \frac{df_{FM}}{dVi} = \frac{n_2 Ic}{2 C_M V_A Vc} = \frac{n_2 f_0}{n_1 Vc} \quad (12)$$

This expression means that the FM deviation is trimmed indirectly. The current ratio n_2/n_1 and the constant voltage V_G can be defined accurately. FM center frequency f_0 in this circuit is adjusted manually. In other words, the accurate manual adjustment of the center frequency simultaneously adjusts the course FM deviation. Figure 11 shows experimental data of FM deviation error before and after the center frequency trimming. The horizontal coordinate shows the error before the trimming and the vertical coordinate shows the error after the trimming. This elliptical distribution means that the error is reduced statistically by the trimming. We obtained the triple standard deviation of the distributions to decrease from 5.3kHz to 2.3kHz, which well meets the requirement. Thus, we no longer need independent FM deviation trimming.

Secondly, in order to eliminate the play-back level trimming, we employ a PLL type FM demodulator in play-back mode. In the demodulator, we use the same VCO that is used as FM modulator in recording mode. Thus, the signal amplitude fluctuation at play-back mode is reduced by less than 7%, because the amplitude fluctuation of the modulator and that of the demodulator are mainly cancelled each other.

SWITCHING NOISE COMPENSATION

FM audio signal is recorded in video track area, and two rotary heads pick it up alternatively. Discontinuity in the played-back FM signal, caused by head switching, results in terrible demodulation noise.

We have developed a new head switching noise compensation system as shown in Fig.12. There were two types

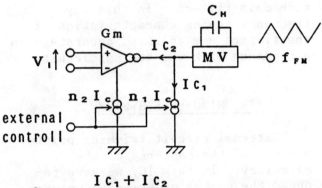

$$f_{FM} = \frac{IC_1 + IC_2}{4\,C_M\,V_A}$$

$$IC_1 = n_1 I_c \quad, \quad IC_2 = \frac{2\,n_2\,IC}{V_G}\,V_1$$

Fig.10 New Adjustment System of FM modulator

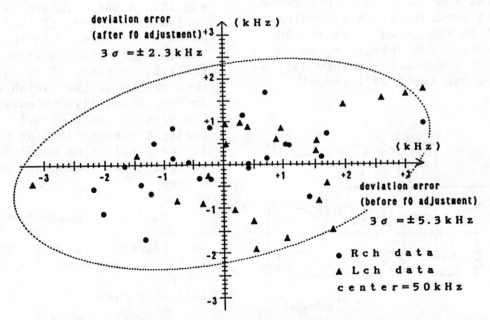

deviation error
(after f0 adjustment) $3\sigma = \pm 2.3\,kHz$

deviation error
(before f0 adjustment) $3\sigma = \pm 5.3\,kHz$

● Rch data
▲ Lch data
center = 50kHz

Fig.11 FM-Deviation Error Distribution

of compensation used in the conventional VCRs, which were (1) a sample-hold compensation and (2) a differential sloped (d/dt) compensation. As shown in Fig.14, the former has a merit of low sensitivity for noise and circuitry offset voltage. The latter can compensate the switching noise more accurately than the former one especially for high slew rate signals. However, the d/dt compensation is rather complicated.

The new method developed is an effective combination of them. This utilizes a modification of V-I characteristic in the differential sloped compensator. Figure 13 shows the new V-I conversion characteristic with insensitive band or dead zone near zero input. The circuit diagram of V-I converter with dead zone is illustrated in Fig.15. The new system operates as the sample-hold compensator for low slew rate signals, and as the differential sloped compensator for high slew rate signals.

CONCLUSION

The system specification of the new FM audio IC is summerized in the follwing Table 1. This newly developed IC has brought about the following improvements.
1) Audio band active filters are fully-integrated with keeping the system dynamic range of more than 90dB.
2) Advantageous manufacturing cost

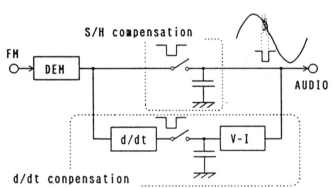

Fig.12 Swiching Noise
Compensation Circuit

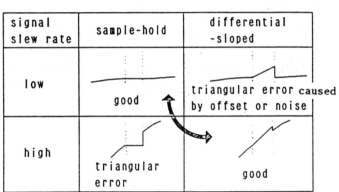

Fig.14 Comparison of Switching
Noise Compensators

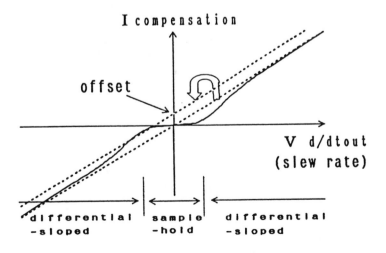

Fig.13 V-I Conversion
in New Compensator

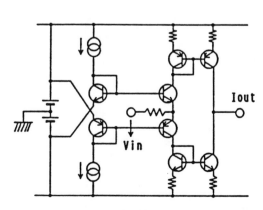

Fig.15 V-I Converter
in The New Compensator

and small mounting area are achieved by reducing the number of external components and trimming points.

The newly developed IC, as a conclusion, is the most suited for VHS HiFi audio systems.

System	Conventional		New
IC	PNR	MODEM	
External Parts	53	52	56
Adjustment Points	0	6	2
IC Pins	36	30	42
IC Elements	1000	1417	3676
Die Size (mm×mm)	4.6×3.9	3.5×3.5	5.3×4.7

Table1 Comparison of the New IC with the Conventional ICs

ACKNOWLEDGEMENT

The authors would like to express our appreciation to Mr.M.Tanabe for his helpful suggestions in designing this IC, and to Mr.S.Makino and Mr.H. Tajiri for their kind guidance in preparing this paper.

REFERENCES

[1] K.Fukahori :"A Bipolar Voltage-Controlled Tunable Filter", IEEE, J.Solid-State Circuits, vol.SC-16, No.6, Dec.1981.
[2] K.W.Moulding, J.R.Quartly, P.J.Rankin, R.S.Thompson, and G.A.Wilson :"Gyrator Video Filter IC with Automatic Tuning", IEEE, J.Solid-State Circuits, vol.SC-15, Dec.1980.
[3] H.Khorramabadi, P.R.Gray, :"High-Frequency CMOS Continuous-Time Filters", IEEE, J.Solid-State Circuits, vol.SC-19,No.6, Dec.1984

A Single-Chip VHF and UHF Receiver for Radio Paging

John F. Wilson, Richard Youell, Tony H. Richards, Gwilym Luff, and Ralf Pilaski

Abstract —We describe a single-chip radio receiver for VHF and UHF digital wide-area paging transmissions up to 500 MHz with FSK data rates up to 1200 Bd. All channel filtering is on-chip and the IC requires only 28 surface mounted external components and a quartz crystal to make a complete receiver. With −126-dBm sensitivity, 70-dB adjacent channel rejection, and 60-dB intermodulation immunity, it satisfies all known pager specifications, worldwide, using the POCSAG paging code. High-dynamic-range mixers, integrated gyrator filters, small-area high-pass filters, and an efficient FSK demodulator combine to give good performance with a current consumption of only 2.7 mA from a 2-V supply. High-density on-chip capacitors in a bipolar process designed for analog RF applications give a chip size of only 4.6×3.8 mm.

I. INTRODUCTION

THIS PAPER describes a single-chip radio receiver for VHF and UHF wide-area paging transmissions up to 500 MHz with FSK data rates up to 1200 Bd. Radio pagers are a demanding integrated circuit application on the borderline between professional and consumer products. Pagers are sold directly to end users in a fiercely competitive market, competing on cost, size, and user features. Physical space is tight, and the pagers must operate for months from small batteries. The digital parts of the pager are already subject to considerable integration, and one way of reducing the cost and physical size of a pager is to integrate the receiver function. We need to considerably reduce the total number of components including bulky and expensive parts such as crystal and ceramic filters to justify the effort of developing a custom IC. The chip described here achieves this by integrating all the channel filtering and active elements of a radio receiver onto a single IC that requires only 28 surface mounted external passive components and a quartz crystal to act as a radio receiver suitable for FSK data formats up to 1200 Bd.

Previous single-chip receivers [1]–[3] have all had various deficiencies, such as operation only up to 200 MHz, off-chip channel filtering components, operation only at low baud rates, and insufficient dynamic range, which have not allowed them to fully meet the international wide-area paging specifications.

II. ZERO IF

Most pager receivers are of a conventional super-heterodyne design, gaining selectivity from quartz crystal and ceramic filters. These are bulky and expensive components which we wish to replace with on-chip filters. These integrated filters must inevitably be continuous-time filters such as RC or transconductance-C filters with limited total capacitance. Switched-capacitor techniques are not suitable due to their high noise contribution and use of clocks, neither of which is compatible with the handling of microvolt signals in receiver IF's. The dynamic range of such filters is inversely proportional to their Q, so they must operate at a very low IF frequency to have a large dynamic range. However, a low IF frequency requires very selective filtering before the mixer to eliminate unwanted image responses. These opposing requirements are reconciled in the zero IF or direct conversion receiver [4]. Here the IF center frequency is the lowest possible (zero) and the channel filters are low-pass filters with modest Q values. The local oscillator is therefore at the channel frequency and no image filtering is required before the mixers, thus minimizing off-chip RF components. The penalty is that two identical IF channels carrying signals in phase quadrature are now needed in order to be able to distinguish between signals above and below the local oscillator frequency. With on-chip filtering this duplication is of on-chip circuit blocks and not of external components. Another way of viewing the zero IF receiver is as processing the received signal as a complex low-pass (I and Q) signal between the mixer output and the demodulator.

An unavoidable problem with this architecture is that the receiver will receive interference from its own local oscillator producing a dc component in the IF; this and circuit dc offsets must be removed by high-pass filters in the IF circuitry. However, FSK paging signals use low data rates, 512 and 1200 Bd, with frequency shifts of ±4.5 kHz, and thus have a spectrum where most of the signal energy is concentrated about the FSK tone frequencies and little at the center (Fig. 1). The high-pass filters can therefore have relatively high cutoff frequencies without affecting receiver operation. Fig. 2 shows the resulting block diagram of the paging receiver.

Manuscript received May 1, 1991; revised August 27, 1991. This work was performed at Philips Radio Communications Systems Ltd.

J. F. Wilson, R. Youell, and A. H. Richards are with Philips Radio Communications Systems Ltd., Cambridge CB4 1DP, England.

G. Luff was with Philips Radio Communications Systems Ltd., Cambridge CB4 1DP, England. He is now with the European Research Laboratory, Communications Division of Motorola Ltd., Basingstoke, Hampshire RG22 4PD, England.

R. Pilaski is with Philips Semiconductors RHW, D-2104 Hamburg 92, Germany.

IEEE Log Number 9103701.

Reprinted from *IEEE J. Solid-State Circuits*, vol. SC-26, no. 12, pp. 1944–1950, Dec. 1991.

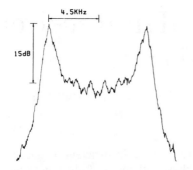

Fig. 1. Frequency spectrum of POCSAG coded FSK signal.

In a complete pager the demodulated digital output is connected to a CMOS decoder IC [5] which performs digital filtering, clock recovery, data decoding, and all the other functions required for a "bleep only" pager.

III. RF STAGES

The RF amplifier (Fig. 3) is a fully differential cascode arrangement. The tuned loop antenna, commonly used in paging, is designed to be a good match for direct connection to the bases of the input transistors. A balanced tuned circuit is used at the output with a matching network to feed the phase splitter. The 3-dB noise figure at frequencies up to 500 MHz is achieved by careful optimization of device size in a process designed for good RF analog performance.

A low-Q lumped component phase splitter generates the quadrature phase shifted signals needed for the complex baseband processing. The following common-base input tree mixers present a low input impedance to the phase splitter over a wide frequency range. The common-base input also gives a better total dynamic range performance than the usual emitter-coupled pair input for a given current drain. Fig. 4 shows the phase splitter and mixer stages.

The mixer local oscillator input comes from a conventional Colpitts crystal oscillator and frequency multiplier chain. The current through all the RF stages can be set by external resistors to suit the operating frequency.

IV. IF FILTERING AND AMPLIFICATION

These stages operate at audio frequencies and provide all the adjacent channel selectivity of the receiver. They provide a 9-kHz passband to accommodate the nominal 4.5-kHz IF frequency (produced by the ± 4.5-kHz frequency deviation of the POCSAG coded FSK signal) and the frequency drift of the local oscillator. The 85-dB stopband attenuation starts at 15 kHz to allow use in European 20-kHz channels.

A cascade of on-chip filters of increasing complexity is used, each reducing the level of the interfering signals to within the dynamic range of the following filter. The first filter is a passive RC network at the mixer output which protects the low-noise preamplifier. Together with the following fully differential Sallen and Key stage, this

forms a third-order elliptic filter with 18-dB stopband attenuation. These filters have a good dynamic range but their cutoff frequency is fixed and depends upon both the capacitance per unit area of the on-chip capacitors and the sheet resistance of the base diffusion. Between this filter and the gyrator channel filter is a high-pass filter of a similar type to those in the limiter but with a current mirror load to give a single-ended current output.

The third filter is a seventh-order gyrator–capacitor [6] elliptic filter. It implements a doubly terminated LC filter taken from standard tables [7] so as to be relatively insensitive to component value variations. Constructing each gyrator from linearized transconductance amplifiers (transconductors) with a differential input and single-ended output and then merging transconductors leads to the leapfrog-like structure of Fig. 5. This is still a gyrator filter in the sense that the capacitor configuration of the original LC filter can be seen in the lower part of the circuit, and the network of transconductors and capacitors in the upper part simulates a network of inductors. Using a gyrator filter rather than a leapfrog filter with active integrators gives many fewer components in the signal path, which simultaneously reduces noise and power consumption. Also each "top" zero forming capacitor in the prototype LC filter is represented by one capacitor in the gyrator filter. This saves chip area compared to a true leapfrog filter in which four capacitors of that value are required [8].

The gyration resistance of the filter is equal to the termination resistance of 150 kΩ, and is set by an external resistor that defines PTAT bias current to the transconductors. Changing this resistor alters the cutoff frequency of the gyrator filters, and with a 100-kΩ external resistor the chip is suitable for 12.5-kHz channel spacing.

Base current compensation is applied to every transconductor. A voltage limiting circuit restricts the voltage swing at the third pole of the filter to ± 45-mV peak to speed up recovery from overloading by large low-frequency signals. Each gyrator filter takes 3 μA from the 2-V supply.

V. LIMITING AMPLIFIER

Hard limiting can be used in each channel of the zero IF receiver because of the high modulation index of the POCSAG coded FSK transmissions. The limiting amplifiers provide 75 dB of small-signal gain between the filter output and the demodulator and contain high-pass filtering to remove accumulated dc offsets.

The high-pass filters use a new circuit [9] to provide low cutoff frequencies (150 Hz) with small on-chip capacitors (330 pF). The circuit is derived from the single-ended high-pass filter circuit in Fig. 6(a) which is used to make one-pin high-pass filters. Fig. 6(b) shows the differential version, where two of the circuits of Fig. 6(a) are connected in parallel and the two capacitors to ground are replaced by a single differentially connected capacitor of half the value needed in the single-ended circuit. There is

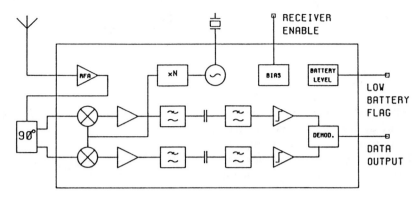

Fig. 2.   Receiver block diagram.

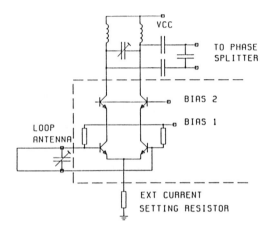

Fig. 3.   RF amplifier.

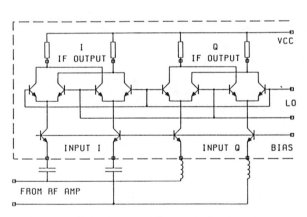

Fig. 4.   Phase splitter and mixers.

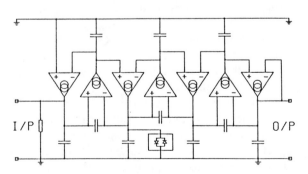

Fig. 5.   Gyrator filter structure.

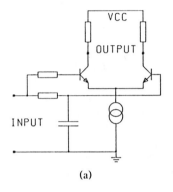

(a)

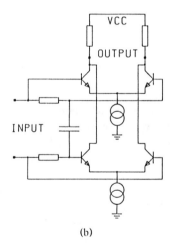

(b)

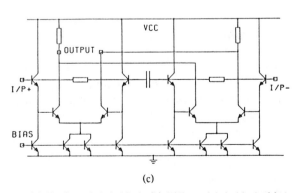

(c)

Fig. 6.   (a) Single-ended dc block. (b) Differential dc block. (c) Actual
differential dc block.

now no dc bias voltage across the capacitor, so when the circuit is turned on the capacitor can charge to its final voltage very quickly. The base-current-induced voltage drops across the resistors cancel at the filter output. This allows the use of high-value pinch resistors and small capacitors, which leads to the complete limiter circuit, using the practical dc block circuits of Fig. 6(c), occupying an area of only 1.6 mm^2. The dc blocks interface easily to the differential pairs, which provide the gain and progressive limiting required. The outputs of this amplifier are fully limiting on the receiver's own noise so a digital demodulator can be used.

The low frequency of operation allows microamp bias currents and pinch resistors to be used to give a total supply current for the limiter of only 40 μA.

VI. DEMODULATOR AND DATA OUTPUT

The information in the limiter outputs requires demodulation to recover the binary data from the FSK signal in the quadrature baseband I and Q channels. The rate of change of the phase of the received signal is represented in the limiter outputs by a sequence of zero crossings. If the I-channel signal leads the Q-channel signal in phase, the FSK tone frequency lies above the local oscillator frequency (POCSAG data "0"). If the I channel lags the Q channel, the FSK tone frequency lies below the local oscillator frequency (POCSAG data "1").

The demodulator is a micropower (2 μA/gate) current-mode logic circuit which implements the modified differentiate and multiply algorithm shown in Fig. 7(a) [10]. At each zero crossing in either channel a pulse is produced by a differentiator which is multiplied by the signal in the other channel. The combination of the two multiplier outputs is a series of short pulses (Fig. 7(b)) whose polarity indicates whether the received signal frequency is above or below the receiver center frequency. An hysteresis circuit holds the polarity of the last pulse until the next pulse occurs. This demodulator uses all the information contained in the hard-limited IF signals to give a bit error rate of 3×10^{-2} for an input signal-to-noise ratio of 0.8 dB (in the 18-kHz RF bandwidth) with a single-bit digital filter in the companion decoder IC providing post-detection filtering.

The CMOS-compatible data output buffer acts as a constant current source during data transitions to give controlled output slew rates. This minimizes interference to the microvolt level signals in the IF, which are in a similar frequency range to that of the demodulated data. The data output block also contains a battery endpoint detector that monitors the chip's supply voltage and gives a logic signal to the decoder IC if the supply voltage falls below a nominal 2.05 V. This voltage comparator uses an identical controlled slew-rate buffer to the data output.

VII. HOUSEKEEPING

A central bandgap reference and housekeeping circuit provides bias currents to all other circuit blocks. These are distributed as scaled currents to avoid errors caused

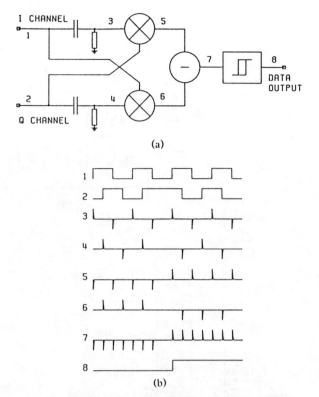

Fig. 7. (a) FSK demodulator. (b) Demodulator waveforms.

by voltage drops in the V_{EE} wiring. A V_{be}-related bias voltage is generated for the RF circuits, which allows their bias currents to be set by external resistors to ground. The comparatively large current of 40 μA is used in these bias circuits to reduce the noise in the bias supplies. The measured noise on the bandgap reference output was 168 nV/$\sqrt{\text{Hz}}$.

The POCSAG paging code allows the page receiver to be turned off for much of the time to increase the life of the pager's battery. To support this the entire IC can be powered up or down in 5 ms by enabling or disabling the main bandgap reference with a logic input.

VIII. PROCESS AND LAYOUT

The chip was processed in a 2-μm junction-isolated bipolar process with high-density (1 nF/mm^2) dielectric capacitors. RF devices with 6-GHz F_T and low noise figures at UHF are available as well as lateral p-n-p transistors with high beta and 40-MHz F_T. The well-controlled high-density capacitors are required for the on-chip filtering and the good lateral p-n-p's are needed in the gyrator filter transconductors.

Two-level aluminum interconnect and a grid-based layout style made a rapid and compact layout possible. The chip microphotograph in Fig. 8 shows the duplicated I and Q channels as well as the block floor plan. The pin-out was chosen to give a good PCB layout for the external RF components with the RF and power connections made via the short central leads of an SO28 pack

Fig. 8.   Chip microphotograph.

age. The large unbroken areas are capacitors which occupy over half of the 18-mm^2 chip area. The channel filter, limiter, demodulator, and housekeeping blocks occupy the chip core, with the RF circuits, IF preamplifiers, and logic output drivers between the pads. Each circuit block has independent power connections to the V_{CC} and V_{EE} pads, and is encircled by a substrate connection which is connected to its own "quiet" V_{EE} pin. Signal interconnections between circuit blocks are either differential or made by current transfer. There are no stability or signal breakthrough problems on the chip despite the presence of 120 dB of small-signal gain and 85 dB of stopband attenuation.

IX. Test

This chip is difficult to test as it is an analog "system on a chip": the signal enters the chip as low-level RF at the mixer inputs and next emerges as demodulated digital data at the data output pin. Buffered test points are provided at the gyrator filter outputs for chip test and receiver alignment, and test multiplexers can route the limiter outputs to the data output and battery level pins. The RF circuits are quite accessible and can be dc tested, but the IF circuits have to be functionally tested by injecting an audio signal at the mixer inputs. The filter responses are observed at the IF test points and the limiter performance observed at the digital outputs via the test multiplexer. This increases the chip test time as measurements have to be made of the filter attenuation at several frequencies, some of them low. Extra bond

pads give access to the IF preamplifier outputs and housekeeping bias voltages at wafer probe.

The first mask set also included a low-frequency test chip in which all the RF circuitry was omitted and individual IF functions were brought out to package pins and an RF test chip containing only the RF circuits. This made possible the verification of subcircuit performance against circuit-level simulations. The IF test circuits proved very difficult to measure because of their high gain and high selectivity at high impedance, which made them very susceptible to capacitive coupling between package pins.

X. Design Methodology

This IC is specified as a paging receiver by its sensitivity and its immunity to intermodulation, blocking, and adjacent channel signals. Individual stages, however, are specified by performance measures such as power gain, noise figure, third-order intermodulation intercept point, and adjacent channel attenuation. To predict the performance of the complete receiver from these figures for individual stages, a radio receiver architecture analysis program was developed. This uses equations for the noise figure and third-order intermodulation intercept point of cascaded stages to calculate the overall performance.

This type of system simulation is particularly necessary with receivers using active filters as, unlike LC, quartz, and ceramic filters, their contribution to the receiver IP3 figure is considerable. This means that it is no longer possible to provide enough gain in the RF amplifier stage to reduce the noise figure contribution of succeeding stages to negligible proportions as this would result in unacceptable IP3 performance. The program gives a complete analysis of the signal levels, noise figure, and IP3 at the input of each stage of the receiver together with the percentage contribution of each stage to the overall noise figure and IP3 performance. This allows decisions to be made about the initial specification of each stage, and design trade-offs to be made easily. Finally, the measured performance of the complete receiver can be checked against that of the individual circuit blocks on the test chips and against the simulation results.

Circuit blocks were simulated in ESPICE and PHILPAC, a Philips proprietary circuit simulator capable of Monte-Carlo statistical analysis and optimization. Fourier post processing of time-domain analyses of the RF, mixer, and filter stages was used to calculate intermodulation products. A functional breadboard was constructed which verified the receiver principles and was used to evaluate different demodulator designs.

Conventional full-custom analog layout methods were used. The complete layout was connectivity checked against a schematic capture derived netlist which had been used to simulate the power up sequence of the complete receiver. Principal node voltages at the end of the power-up sequence simulation were hand compared with those from the block-level simulations. These analyses in turn provided the input data to the architecture analysis program.

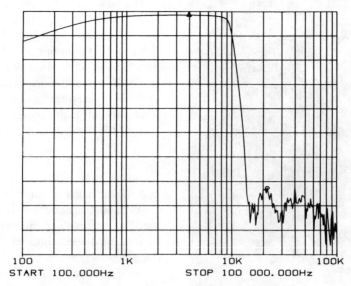

REF LEVEL	/DIV	OFFSET 17 960.772Hz
24.000dB	12.000dB	MAG(A/R) -85.364dB

START 100.000Hz   STOP 100 000.000Hz

Fig. 9.   IF filter measured frequency response.

TABLE I
TYPICAL PERFORMANCE AT 470 MHz (FROM A 50-Ω SOURCE)
MEASURED WITH 4-kHz DEVIATION 1200-Bd PRBS DATA

Operating Frequency	20–500 MHz
Data Rate	1200 Bd
Channel Spacing	20–30 kHz
Sensitivity	−126 dBm
Adjacent Channel	70 dB
Intermodulation	60 dB
Frequency Offset	± 2.5 kHz
Blocking (1 MHz off)	82 dB
Deviation Acceptance	1.5 to 8 kHz
Power Consumption	2.7 mA at 2 V
Power Down Current	< 1 μA
Chip Size	4.6 × 3.8 mm

XI. RESULTS

The first diffusion of the IC was fully functional and met all specifications except 1-MHz blocking. All the subblocks on the test chips performed as simulated. A new mask set was required for production because the original set was a multichip reticle including a complete receiver and the two test chips. In this second diffusion extra decoupling of the front-end bias was added to improve 1-MHz blocking and diodes were added to the RF amplifier input to protect it against ESD and large RF input signals. Fig. 9 shows the frequency response of the complete IF filtering as measured between the *I*-channel mixer input pins (with a 200-mV dc offset between the mixer LO inputs) and the *I*-channel IF test point. Table I shows the performance of the chip as measured on a 470-MHz test board which uses external components representative of those used in current pagers. This performance is achieved with a current drain of 2.7 mA from a 2.0- to 3.5-V supply. This voltage range gives a typical pager over three months operation from two AAA size alkaline cells. The chips operate to full specification in production 1200-Bd 470-MHz POCSAG pagers. At 930 MHz the mixer conversion gain is significantly reduced by the stray impedances of the SO28 package. Either an external RF amplifier can be added or the IC could be packaged differently for 930-MHz use.

XII. CONCLUSION

A highly integrated receiver for VHF and UHF FSK paging transmissions has been realized. It is engineered to consistently meet paging receiver specifications worldwide with a supply voltage of 2 V and minimal current drain. It represents a high state of analog system integration, with much functionality entirely on-chip.

The systematic design, large-scale analog simulation, and design verification techniques now available mean that analog LSI can have predictable and reliable performance when first fabricated. This reduces the large time risk that IC redesign cycles traditionally present to product developments dependent upon custom analog integrated circuits.

REFERENCES

[1] R. C. French, "A high technology VHF radio paging receiver", in *Proc. IEE Mobile Radio Syst. Tech. Conf.* (York, England), 1984 (IEE Conf. Publ. 238).
[2] SL6639 data sheet, Plessey Semiconductors, Swindon, U.K., 1990.
[3] UAA2033 data sheet, Philips Semiconductors, Eindhoven, The Netherlands, 1987.
[4] I. A. W. Vance, "Fully integrated radio paging receiver," *Proc. Inst. Elec. Eng. F*, vol. 129, no. 1, pp. 2–6, Feb. 1982.
[5] "PCF5001 POCSAG decoder IC," data sheet, Philips Semiconductors, Eindhoven, The Netherlands, 1991.
[6] J. O. Voorman, "The gyrator as a monolithic circuit in electronic systems," Ph.D. dissertation, Univ. Nijmegen, Nijmegen, The Netherlands, 1977.

[7] A. I. Zverev, *Handbook of Filter Synthesis*. New York: Wiley, 1967.

[8] G. M. Jacobs, D. J. Allstot, R. W. Brodersen, and P. R. Gray, "Design techniques for MOS switched capacitor ladder filters," *IEEE Trans. Circuits Syst.*, vol. CAS-25, no. 12, pp. 1014–1021, Dec. 1978.

[9] A. H. Richards, "D.C. blocking amplifier," European Patent Spec. 0397250A2, filed May 4, 1990.

[10] G. F. Luff, J. F. Wilson, and R. J. Youell, "Radio receiver," European Patent Spec. 0405676A2, filed June 25, 1990.

Section 7-B   Sub-Video Filters

In the frequency range between 10kHz and 1MHz, continuous-time filters are most easily implemented. Element values are compatible with a small chip area and in common IC processes excess phase shifts do not present serious problems.

We include here a paper by Krummenacher and Van Ruymbeke on the design of a bandpass filter at 200 kHz for use in a sophisticated FM demodulation scheme. It concerns a high-order filter with tuning control in CMOS technology. Another filter in this frequency range is described in Paper 3-B.9.

Paper 7-B.1

Integrated Selectivity for Narrow-Band FM IF Systems

F. KRUMMENACHER AND G. VAN RUYMBEKE

Abstract —An 18th-order all-pole continuous-time bandpass filter for IF filtering purposes has been designed and integrated in a 3-μm CMOS process. Implemented using nine fully balanced, transconductor–capacitor coupled resonators, the filter features 20-kHz bandwidth at 200-kHz center frequency, 54-dB dynamic range (IM3 < −40 dB), and consumes 300 μA from a single 4-V supply.

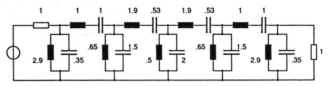

Fig. 1.   18th-order normalized *LC* bandpass filter (Butterworth approximation).

I. INTRODUCTION

The IF filter is the most critical component of a fully integrated, low-power, narrow-band FM demodulation chip that would also include a mixer/oscillator, an IF limiting amplifier, and an FM detector. Special care must be taken in order to minimize noise and intermodulation distortion, as well as to ensure the required selectivity. For several reasons, which will not be developed here, a continuous-time filter has been preferred to a switched-capacitor implementation. Power consumption was a critical parameter in the present application and the most appropriate approach was to use the "transconductor–capacitor" technique, where MOSFET's are basically considered as tunable voltage-controlled current sources [1], [2], rather than the alternate "MOSFET-C active" implementation [3], [4] using MOS transistors as voltage-controlled resistors together with MOS operational amplifiers.

II. FILTER ARCHITECTURE

The IF bandwidth must be ± 10 kHz for a channel spacing of 25 kHz. On the contrary to a passive realization, the noise of an active filter implementation is proportional to the filter quality factor Q_f (i.e., the center frequency-to-bandwidth ratio f_0/B). This is the reason why the center frequency was lowered from the usual value of 455 kHz down to 200 kHz. This also relaxes the requirements on the precision of the filter components.

The filter synthesis starts from the 18th-order, all-pole, passive *LC* ladder (Fig. 1) meeting the filter specifications. The initial steps towards integration are first to transform the four *LC* series arms into parallel resonant circuits by extensive use of gyrators (hereafter referred to as the "coupling" gyrators) and next to replace each inductor by a gyrator–capacitor combination (Fig. 2) [5]. The gyrators are then implemented with a closed-loop connection of two transconductance amplifiers. Finally, two additional transconductance amplifiers, each connected in unity gain, are used to simulate the termination resistors to end up with the circuit depicted in Fig. 3.

The circuit obtained by this method has the following properties:

a)   it is built up with nine identical coupled second-order resonators;

Manuscript received October 15, 1989.

The authors are with the Electronics Laboratory, Swiss Federal Institute of Technology (EPFL), CH 1015 Lausanne, Switzerland.

IEEE Log Number 9035015.

b)   the center frequency of the filter corresponds to that of the resonators; and

c)   the filter quality factor $Q_f = f_0/B$ depends on the relative value of the transconductors used in the resonators compared to the transconductors used for coupling and for the termination resistors (the transconductor spread is proportional to the filter quality factor and, to a certain extent, to the passband ripple).

Note that all the filter parameters are easily programmable: the bandwidth B can be changed (at constant f_0) by varying the transconductance of the coupling gyrators alone, or the center frequency can be modified (while maintaining a constant bandwidth) by varying the transconductance of the resonators alone. Increasing the value of all transconductors by the same amount (e.g., 30%) will increase the center frequency *and* the bandwidth by the same proportion.

III. TRANSCONDUCTOR IMPLEMENTATION

A simple differential, fully balanced transconductor (Fig. 4) was preferred for its versatility, HF performance, and superior supply rejection capability compared to a single-ended implementation. The input differential pair employs a simple linearization technique that has already proven to be efficient for high-frequency applications [6]. In this scheme, linearity is primarily a function of the relative size of the input transistors $M1a$ and $M1b$ compared to $M2a$ and $M2b$. As it was mandatory to minimize power dissipation, these transistors are biased at low current (6 μA) and low $V_{GS} - V_T$ (about 0.18 V); their sizes have been adjusted by computer simulation for maximum linearity.

The output common-mode voltage is stabilized by $M6a$ and $M6b$, which operate in the triode region [1]. The conductance of the p-channel current sources $M5a$ and $M5b$ is reduced thanks to the cascode transistors $M4a$ and $M4b$.

The measured dc voltage-to-current transfer characteristics of the transconductors used in the resonators are shown in Fig. 5. For input voltages up to 460 mV$_{p-p}$, the nonlinearity error is less than 0.3% and the transconductance variations stay under ± 1%. Compared to a simple source-coupled pair with the same transconductance and bias current, the linearized input $M1a$, $M1b$, $M2a$, $M2b$ yields an improvement of about 8 dB in the maximum signal handling capability.

Reprinted from *IEEE J. Solid-State Circuits*, vol. SC-25, no. 3, pp. 757–760, June 1990.

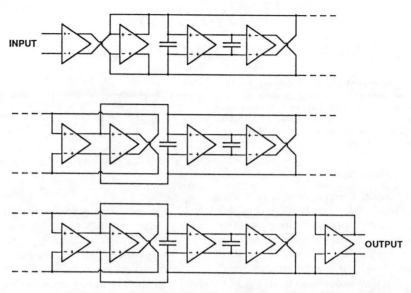

Fig. 2. Gyrator–capacitor filter derived from Fig. 1.

Fig. 3. Balanced transconductor–capacitor bandpass filter structure.

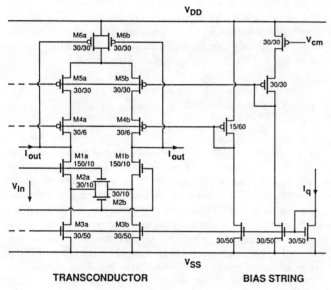

Fig. 4. Transconductor equivalent schematic.

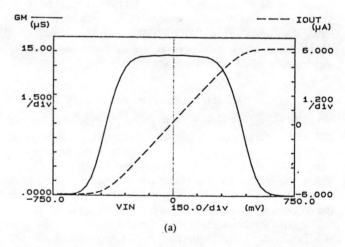

(a)

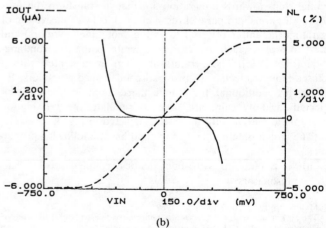

(b)

Fig. 5. Measured V/I transfer characteristic of the transconductor of Fig. 4: (a) small-signal transconductance $g_m = \partial I_{out} / \partial V_{in}$ and (b) nonlinearity error, expressed in percent of the full-scale current I_q.

IV. CIRCUIT LAYOUT

Transconductor–capacitor filter structures are by nature sensitive to stray capacitances. Consequently, in order to achieve functional matching of the resonators, one has to insure that they are matched structurally too. This involves the use of "dummy" circuit elements so as to match the parasitic capacitances (associated with the transconductors and with the routing lines) from one resonator to another. This is the reason why, in spite of important differences in the transconductance values (up to 500%), all coupling transconductors have been laid out using the same basic structure with unit transistor elements (customization is performed mostly at the interconnection layer).

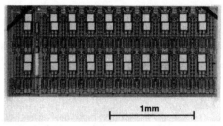

Fig. 6. Photomicrograph of the IF filter chip.

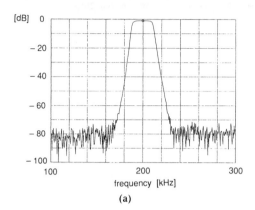

(a)

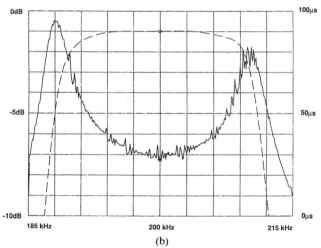

(b)

Fig. 7. (a) Measured filter frequency response. (b) Details of the passband response (dotted line) and group delay characteristics (solid line).

Dummy stray capacitances have been added whenever necessary. As a result, the layout of the circuit is highly regular and the nine resonators are clearly visible on the photomicrograph of Fig. 6. The resonator and coupling transconductor core cell has been reproduced on the left-hand side of the circuit: it is intended to be the voltage-controlled oscillator (VCO) within the automatic tuning control phase-locked loop.

V. Experimental Results

The filter was fabricated in the 3-μm single-poly p-well CMOS process from Faselec AG in Zürich [7]. The capacitance for the whole filter amounts to 200 pF and the active area is 1.0×2.4 mm². A typical frequency response is shown in Fig. 7: this measurement was carried out using the extra resonator available on chip as a VCO within an off-chip phase-locked loop operating at 200 kHz. It was observed that as long as the VCO output sine wave is kept below 200 mV$_{p-p}$ by an appropriate amplitude

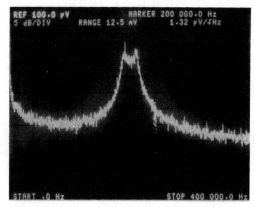

Fig. 8. Filter output noise spectral density.

TABLE I
PERFORMANCE CHARACTERISTICS OF THE IF FILTER CHIP

supply voltage	4 V to 6 V
supply current	300 µA typ.
center frequency	200 kHz ± 1 kHz
passband attenuation	< 2 dB
passband ripple	< 1 dB
stopband rejection	> 70dB
output noise (1 kHz - 1 MHz)	280 µV$_{rms}$
dynamic range (IM3 < - 40dB)	54 dB
PSRR+	> 35 dB
PSRR-	> 30 dB
chip area (filter + VCO)	2.5 mm²

regulator, the feedthrough from the VCO to the filter is overwhelmed by the noise of the filter itself, despite the fact that the VCO signal is right in the middle of the passband. The measured total output noise (1 kHz to 1 MHz) is 280 μV$_{rms}$; the noise spectral density is given in Fig. 8.

The distortion performance is another key feature of the filter. Considering the application of the circuit, the intermodulation was measured using two signals of equal amplitude A in two adjacent channels (one at 225 kHz and the other at 250 kHz) so that the third-order intermodulation products fall in the middle of the filter passband. The value of A, measured at the filter input, was increased until the intermodulation signal at the filter output was 41 dB lower (to account for the average passband attenuation of 1 dB). The obtained value A_{max} was 450 mV$_{p-p}$, which is consistent with the expected linear range of the transconductors.

Other performance characteristics of the IF filter chip are summarized in Table I.

VI. Conclusions

The feasibility of a low-power, fully integrated IF filter for narrow-band FM systems has been demonstrated. With the use of conventional PLL techniques for automatic tuning, the accuracy of the filter response is comparable to that of present ceramic filters. As expected, the fundamental limitations of such an active implementation compared to a passive realization are noise and distortion; dynamic range can only be increased at the cost of a lower filter center frequency (reduced filter quality factor f_0/B), a lower filter order (reduced selectivity), a higher power consumption, and/or a larger silicon area. It is thus likely that in order to take full advantage of integrated selectivity, one might have to reconsider some design options and trade-offs in the receiver system to take these limitations into account.

REFERENCES

[1] H. Khorramabadi and P. R. Gray, "High-frequency CMOS continuous-time filters," *IEEE J. Solid-State Circuits*, vol. SC-19, pp. 939–948, Dec. 1984.

[2] R. L. Geiger and E. Sanchez-Sinencio, "Active filter design using operational transconductance amplifiers: A tutorial," *IEEE Circuits and Devices Mag.*, pp. 20–32, Mar. 1985.

[3] Y. Tsividis, M. Banu, and J. Khoury, "Continuous-time MOSFET-C filters in VLSI," *IEEE J. Solid-State Circuits*, vol. SC-21, pp. 15–30, Feb. 1986.

[4] J. Khoury and Y. Tsividis, "Analysis and compensation of high-frequency effects in integrated MOSFET-C continuous-time filters," *IEEE Trans. Circuits Syst.*, vol. CAS-34, pp. 862–875, Aug. 1987.

[5] N. Joehl and F. Krummenacher, "Filtres continus MOS intégrés à large échelle," *AGEN-Mitteilungen*, no. 43, pp. 49–55, May 1986.

[6] F. Krummenacher and N. Joehl, "A 4-MHz CMOS continuous-time filter with on-chip automatic tuning," *IEEE J. Solid-State Circuits*, vol. 23, pp. 750–758, June 1988.

[7] R. E. Luscher, "A high-density CMOS process," in *ISSCC Dig. Tech. Papers* (New York), Feb. 1985, pp. 260–261.

Section 7-C   Filters and Systems for Video Frequencies

Integration of video filters has been a challenge to many designers. Simple video filters can be made in several ways but the more demanding filters are difficult to integrate. For the latter, typical requirements on tolerances are time constants to within $\pm 0.5\%$ and parasitic phase-shifts of electronic elements (transconductors, integrators) to within ± 0.2 degrees. Assuming that the filter elements have a first-order roll-off with frequency, the requirements on excess phase shift mean that the parasitic pole frequency must be of the order of 1 GHz for video applications. Even in modern IC processes it is not self-evident how to design accurate tunable circuits with parasitic pole frequencies above 1 GHz at supply voltages of 5 V today and 3 V tomorrow.

The very first examples from Moulding et al. (see Papers 7-C.1, 3-A.1, and 3-A.2) are part of successful bipolar chips. In Paper 7-C.1 performance boundaries, design, and measurements are discussed for two ICs with video filters and a short continuous-time video delay line. Paper 7-C.2 by Fukuda et al. and [1] describe ICs with video (and audio) filters for VCR applications. In the case of VCRs, more emphasis is put on low dissipation and, hence, simplicity of the circuits. Paper 7-C.3 by Koblitz and Rieger and [2] are recent papers on TV signal processors. Both describe the use of a BiCMOS process. In Paper 7-C.3 the filter functions needed in the video signal processor are surveyed and the best implementation for each filter function is separately chosen. For additional information, the reader is referred to Papers 2-B.5, 3-B.5, 3-B.7, and [3–5].

An adaptive Laguerre filter for echo reduction in Teletext data signals can be found in Paper 7-C.4 by Voorman et al. A Laguerre filter is a tapped delay line with first-order, all-pass sections as delay elements and taps with a first-order, low-pass characteristic. The IC, a fully analog signal processor, has been developed during the standardization discussions for Teletext and has successfully remedied multipath reception problems in mountainous areas.

References

[1] K. Miura, Y. Okada, M. Shiomi, M. Masuda, E. Funaki, Y. Okada and S. Ogura, "VCR signal processing LSIs with self-adjusted integrated filters," *Proc. Bipolar Circuits and Technology Meeting*, pp. 85–86 and 120, 1986.

[2] J. P. M. van Lammeren and B. Motté, "Multi-standard video front end," *IEEE Trans. Consumer Electronics*, vol. 37, pp. 190–196, August 1991.

[3] T. Fukuda, K. Nishitani, F. Yamaguchi, K. Abe and T. Narabu, "New video signal-processing LSI's for 8mm VCRs," *IEEE Trans. Consumer Electronics*, vol. 34, pp. 543–551, August 1988.

[4] Y. Yamamoto, T. Tamura, K. Watanabe, A. Hirabayashi, H. Murayama, Y. Okumara, T. Sekino and H. Numata, "A new video processor for color TV," *IEEE Trans. Consumer Electronics*, vol. 34, pp. 443–451, August 1988.

[5] T. Kiyofuji, M. Yoshida, M. Aso, N. Murakami and S. Miyazaki, "Video camera signal processing IC with CCD delay lines," *IEEE Trans. Consumer Electronics*, vol. 36, pp. 503–509, August 1990.

Experience with High-Frequency Gyrator Filters Including a New Video Delay-Line IC

K. W. MOULDING AND P. J. RANKIN

PHILIPS RESEARCH LABOROTORIES, REDHILL, SURREY, ENGLAND

ABSTRACT

The performance boundaries of integrated high-frequency gyrator filters are defined in terms of frequency, bandwidth and dynamic range. Two large integration projects are described to show the potential of gyrator-based filtering. The first is a six-gyrator video filter IC whose tuning frequencies are controlled by a reference input signal and the second is a video delay line, comprising a series of eleven all-pass cells, with delay switchable up to 1 us.

1. PERFORMANCE BOUNDARIES

The performance boundaries of high frequency gyrator filters can be expressed in terms of frequency precision, working Q-factor and dynamic range.

The accepted method for automatic frequency control of integrated active filters is to tune a reference filter circuit, in our case an additional gyrator resonator, to an incoming frequency reference using a frequency locking circuit. The close matching of resistors and capacitors across a chip then ensures that all filter circuits will be on frequency provided the same tuning is applied throughout. With careful layout, on-chip components can match to within a few tenths of 1% and track with temperature, giving better than 0.5% tuning accuracy; adequate precision for the majority of applications.

The maximum allowable Q is governed by the sensitivity of Q to phase-shift in the gyrator amplifiers ($S_\phi^Q = \phi Q$). A typical compensated gyrator will have spreads in phase shift of between $\pm$ 0.02 and $\pm$ 0.1 /MHz depending upon transistors f_T. The maximum permitted Q can therefore be calculated for any specified Q-spread. For example a Q-tolerance of $\pm$ 20% could be held on a Q of 114 at 5 MHz.

The excess noise power and the magnitude of intermodulation products increase in proportion to Q. However the intermodulation can be reduced in the simplest case by emitter degeneration in the long-tailed pair amplifiers forming the gyrator. Fig. 1 shows how, in simple theory, the input signal varies with Q and degeneration for constant third-order intermodulation. The figure also shows the onset of intermodulation in voltage dependent junction capacitors when these are used for the gyrator port capacitors. (The use of oxide capacitors has recently been reported with bipolar gyrators[1], which would confine capacitor distortion to that from resistor and transistor junction strays).

2. A GYRATOR VIDEO FILTER IC WITH AUTOMATIC TUNING [2]

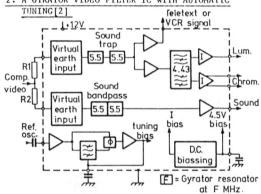

Fig.2. Gyrator video filter i.c.

This first application example is a filter designed to separate the video signal in t.v. receivers. In the single chip filter (Fig. 2), L-C resonators are simulated with gyrators terminated by junction capacitors, the voltage dependence of the latter being exploited for tuning.

The composite video signal is stripped of the intercarrier sound signal in a two-stage trap and is then applied to a single gyrator resonator to separate the luminance and chrominance signals. A bandpass pair provides the necessary selectivity in the sound while an automatic tuning system holds the five resonators accurately on tune. The chip is 11 mm^2 in area, uses standard bipolar technology (f_T = 400 MHz),and has 567 components dissipating 650 mW. Six gyrators use the same layout design (fourteen transistors each) in 1/3 of the chip area.

The gyrators are formed from two balanced amplifiers (voltage controlled current sources, Fig. 3) and are therefore floating, while the capcitors require a tuning bias and so are grounded. Q can be defined by parallel damping, R_Q, or series damping, R_d. Figs. 4(a)-(c) show the flexibility of gyrator I/0 connections which can be exploited in filter design.

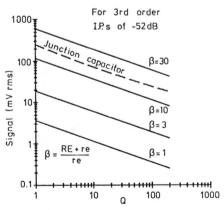

Fig.1. Signal level limitations.

Reprinted from *Proc. ECCTD'83*, Stuttgart, pp. 105–107, Sept. 1983.

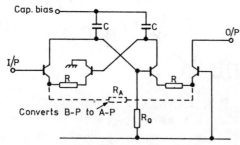

Fig.3. Modified gyrator cell

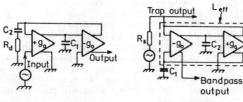

(a) Symmetrical bandpass.

(b) Series trap with band-pass output (highpass filter).

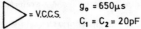

= V.C.C.S.

$g_o = 650 \mu s$
$C_1 = C_2 = 20 pF$

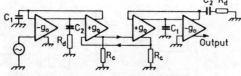

(c) Actively coupled second-order bandpass

Fig.4. Gyrator filter arrangements.

In the tuning system an auxiliary gyrator (Q = 25) is designed to resonate at colour subcarrier frequency but, owing to production spreads of resistors and capcitors, the resonant frequency could vary by up to ± 20%. The incoming reference frequency is passed through this gyrator resonator where it suffers a 90° nominal phase sift and is then compared in phase with a sample of the incoming reference. Any deviation from 90° produces a control voltage which is amplified and smoothed to give a capacitor bias potential which tunes the gyrator to the reference frequency. Thanks to the close matching of components, this bias will also be appropriate for the other gyrators on the chip.

The resonance of a gyrator resonator is given by $\omega = 1/RC$ where R defines the trans-conductances and C the load capacitors. In the filter, the sound trap must be accurate to about ± 0.5% implying component matching of similar accuracy. Resistor matching is a function of resistivity, etching and contact variations. These are minimized by placing the resistors in close proximity with the same orientation and by using generous dimensions with large contacts. The capacitors are formed by emitter and collector junctions of a transistor structure with coarse stripes to reduce series resistance.

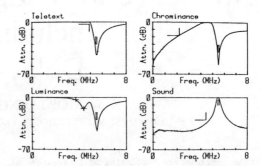

Fig.5. Measured filter responses.

Geometrically-scaled models are used throughout the CAD of the filter, all stray resistance and capacitance, plus encapsulation inductance being represented. Crosstalk between the sound channel or tuning circuit and the luminance or chrominance output must be very low. This means that any common paths must be carefully considered. Complete simulation of 3000 filter elements to investigate crosstalk (exploiting macromodelling) revealed several problem areas which were cured by re-routng power rails, etc.

Fig. 5 shows the measured responses of a filter for European TV systems B and G with the specification points marked. Samples show very consistent performance which agrees closely with design predictions. The automatic tuning operates over the capacitor bias range 0.5 to 6V and gives 10 kHz maximum error. The temperature dependence of f_o is 60 ppm/°C. Measured S/N (CCIR weighted) is better than 80 dB, 70 dB and 60 dB in the teletext luminance and chrominance channels, respectively, confirmed by good performance in a TV receiver.

3. AN INTEGRATED ANALOGUE DELAY-LINE FOR T.V.

The second application example concerns a switchable delay-line which has been designed in collaboration with Valvo Hamburg to provide delays in the range 720 to 1035 ns with bandwidth in excess of 5 MHz. The delay sections employ gyrators used in second-order all-pass circuits.

In essence, a second-order all-pass circuit comprises a transmission path including a tuned circuit, whose output is substracted from a fraction of the input signal. This function can be seen in the gyrator circuit of Fig. 3 in

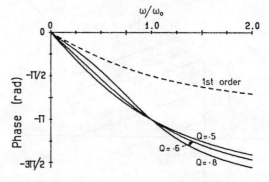

Fig.6. Phase of second-order all-pass section.

484

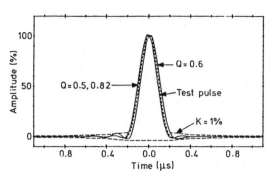

Fig.7. Response of 10 ideal A.P. filters.

which the L/C resonance is simulated at point A and the direct signal is subtracted by the addition of R_A (dotted).

The phase characteristic (Fig. 6) of a second-order all-pass circuit, for differing Q values is,

$$\tau(\omega) = \exp\{-j2 \arctan[(p/Q)/(1-p^2)]\} \text{ where}$$

$$p = \omega/\omega_0$$

Optimum phase linearity occurs at $Q \approx 0.6$ but an even better result can be obtained by using pairs of cells with staggered Q´s. Fig. 7 compares the response to a standard sine-squared test pulse for the fixed Q and the chosen staggered-Q cases.

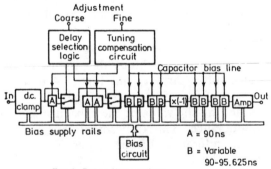

Fig. 6. Delay line system.

Fig. 8 shows the general arrangement comprising 11 cells of 90 ns. The first 3 cells can be switched in or out while the remaining 8 are always connected but their delays can be increased from 90 to 95.6 ns by a further switch. A phase inverter is interposed part way along the line so that unwanted effects such as d.c. offset errors and detuning will tend to cancel rather than accumulate. The tuning circuit controls the bias voltage of the junction capacitors in each cell in such a way as to compensate changes in the overall delay time due to I.C. spreads (especially doping and line-widths) and temperature variations. This is done by continuously monitorng the I.C. layer resistivities with on-chip resistors and using a resultant d.c. signal to regulate the capacitor bias rail. A single, central biassing circuit provides the rail voltages required elsewhere for current sources etc.

Care was taken in the I.C. layout to keep stray capacitance to a minimum in order not to dilute

the voltage-tunable capacitance too greatly. Strays totalled 1 pF with a port capacitance of 4 pF. A first-order analysis of this circuit gives

$$\tau = CR, \quad R_Q = QR \text{ and } R_A = R (2/Q-1).$$

However an accurate analysis of the full model including all strays is highly complex. The design approach adopted employed a circuit optimising routine to obtain the best fit to an ideal all-pass characteristic. The delay cells were connected directly in cascade, pairing off cells having complementary staggered-Q values.

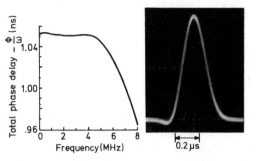

Fig.9. Computed delay.   Fig. 10. Measured pulse response.

The various modules of the complete system were each carefully modelled from geometry and process information. The ´black-box´ multiport admittance matrices were then calculated for a spread of technological parameters over a range of frequencies and put into a library file. The complete system with all bias rail resistances included could then be interactively simulated by recalling the y-matrices to check response, crosstalk and h.f. stability. Control of bandwidth despite I.C. spreads proved to be difficult as the amplitude deviations of one cell are raised to the 11th power in the complete line. The resulting nominal phase delay characteristic (Fig. 9) was found to be constant to within 8 ns over the 5 MHz bandwidth. The computed pulse response showed only slight overshoots and a small increase in pulse height. This was due to a deliberate 1.5 dB lift in the amplitude response at mid-band. Fig 10 shows the measured response to a laboratory test pulse.

The final cell design occupies 0.32 mm^2 of chip and takes 0.65 mA at 12V while the whole delay line occupies 6 mm^2. The delay accuracy is ± 5% under technology spreads, power supply and temperature variations.

4. REFERENCES

[1] VOORMAN, J.O., BRULS, W.H.A. and BARTH,P.J. "Integration of Analog. Filters in a Bipolar Process", IEEE J. Solid-State Circuits, Vol.SC-17, No.4, pp.713-722, Aug. 1982.

[2] MOULDING, K.W., QUARTLY, J.R., RANKIN, P.J., THOMPSON, R.S. and WILSON, G.A. "Gyrator Video Filter IC with Automatic Tuning", IEEE J. Solid-State Cicuits, Vol.SC-15, No.6, pp.963-968, Dec. 1980.

A Fully Integrated Filter Circuit For VCRs

TOKUYA FUKUDA, SHIGEKI ISHIZUKA, KIYOSHI NISHITANI
CONSUMER VIDEO DIVISION
SONY CORPORATION
2-13-40, KOHNAN MINATO-KU
TOKYO, 108 JAPAN

YASUO TAKATSU
SEMICONDUCTOR DIVISION
SONY CORPORATION
14-1, ASAHI-CHO 4-CHOME, ATSUGI-SHI,
KANAGAWA-KEN, 243 JAPAN

1. Introduction

In order to miniaturize VCRs, various components have been integrated with semiconductor circuits, but to date video filters such as luminance LPFs, emphasis filters, and chrominance BPFs have not been integrated. We have recently developed an integrated filter circuit for processing video signals. The new circuit was fabricated using a new bipolar process called the Hiplanar process and has been applied to a dynamic emphasis IC for VCRs. Because this filter circuit operates up to 10 MHz, any video filter can be integrated by the same means.

2. Design Concept

There are various techniques for integrating video filters. Although digital filters and SCFs are remarkable, they have a large power consumption and require a large chip, even if they have been fabricated using the extremely fine patterns of the MOS process. CCD transversal filters are being increasingly used but their signal-to-noise performance is not ideal and they also have a large power consumption. In addition, these clocked systems generate a high level of radiation.

A video signal processing circuit must have a low power consumption, small chip size, and a low level of radiation if it is to be integrated into the circuits in a consumer VCR. Ordinary bipolar active filters satisfy these requirements, but they have inherent problems such as thermal drift and the need for adjustment. Our newly developed circuit avoids these problems. Our circuit is based on biquad filters with transconductance controlled by the reference current source so there is no need for an external time constant. The circuit has precise and stable frequency characteristics.

3. The New Integrated Filter

3-1. Eliminating the need for adjustment

Although Sallen Key filters, as in Fig. 2, are often applied to ICs, they have inherent shortcomings when fabricated by the silicon process. There tend to be large variations in frequency response caused by variations in resistance due to temperature change, and there are variations in capacitors. In addition, only a small time constant is available. ($\leq 1\mu$ sec.) Therefore, these filters can be used for only limited purposes.

Figure 3 is a block diagram of the new integrated filter circuit, and Figure 4 is a equivalent circuit of the filter, whose cut-off frequency is defined by the value of the capacitor and the transconductance. The transconductance is controlled by the reference current source. The transfer function of this filter is represented as:

$$F_1(S) = \frac{1}{K} \cdot \frac{1 + sCrK}{1 + sCr} \tag{1}$$

$$\frac{1}{r} = gm = \frac{1}{2R_2} \cdot \frac{Ix}{In} = \frac{R_1}{2R_2} \cdot \frac{Ix}{Vr} \tag{2}$$

where $s = j\omega$

In Equation 2, the transfer response does not depend on the absolute value of the resistors but on the ratio between the values of the resistors and also on the values of the capacitors. Hence, to obtain accurate frequency characteristics, it is necessary to fabricate resistors, the ratio between whose values doesn't change and capacitors which are accurate and thermally stable.

Our newly developed Hiplanar process can fabricate resistors and capacitors which meet these conditions. The performance of components fabri-

Reprinted from *IEEE Trans. Cons. El.*, vol. CE-32, no. 3, pp. 644–650, Aug. 1986.

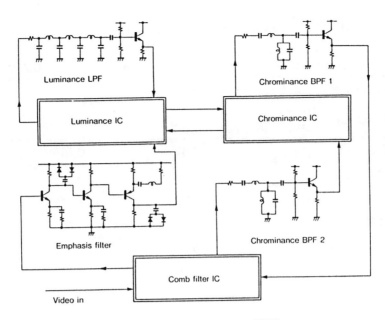

Fig. 1   The video filters in current VCR systems

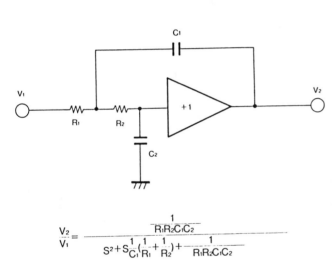

$$\frac{V_2}{V_1} = \cfrac{\cfrac{1}{R_1 R_2 C_1 C_2}}{S^2 + S\cfrac{1}{C_1}\left(\cfrac{1}{R_1} + \cfrac{1}{R_2}\right) + \cfrac{1}{R_1 R_2 C_1 C_2}}$$

Fig. 2   The sallen key filter

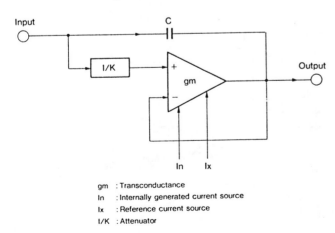

gm : Transconductance
In : Internally generated current source
Ix : Reference current source
I/K : Attenuator

Fig. 3   Block diagram of the new integrated filter

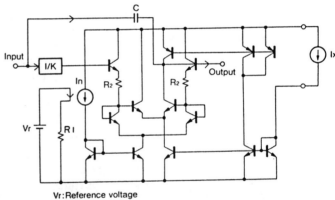

Vr : Reference voltage

Fig. 4   Equivalent circuit of the new integrated filter

cated by this process is shown in Table I. As can be seen, the parameters which are concerned with frequency response are greatly improved. Particularly, variations in the ratio between the resistor values are reduced to less than 1%.

3-2. High-order filters

Second-order filters have a biquad structure, and those of a high-order are composed of a cascaded connection of second-order filters. The biquad structure corresponds directly with the desired transfer function shown as Fig. 5. Figure 6 shows the equivalent circuit of the second-order filters. As for the r in Fig. 5, integrated resistors are replaced by the transconductance circuits in the same way as in filters of the first-order. Therefore, this filter can also be controlled by the reference current source. When a plural number of filters is

487

Table I   The performance of components fabricated by the Hiplanar process

Parameter			Hiplanar	Standard
Minimum contact size (μm)			2.4	5.0
NPN Tr	F_T(GHz) $V_{CE}=1V$ $I_c=1.5mA$		3.75	1.0~1.5
	C_{CS}(PF)		0.17	0.61
	ΔV_{BE}(mV)		1.2	3.0
R	TCR (ppm/°C)		800	2100
	ΔR (%)		1.0	5.0
C	TCC (ppm/°C)		70	70

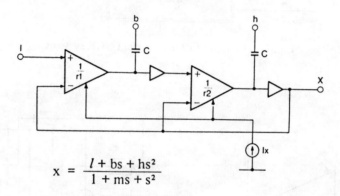

$$x = \frac{l + bs + hs^2}{1 + ms + s^2}$$

$$s = j\omega cr$$

l: Low-pass filter in
b: Band-pass filter in
h: High-pass filter in
x: Output

Fig. 5   The biquad filter

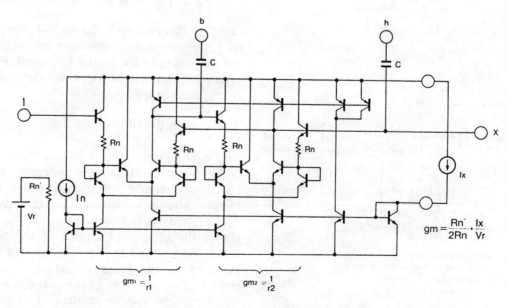

Fig. 6   Equivalent circuit of the second-order filter

employed in an IC, they can be controlled by a common reference current source. In order to achieve the smallest relative error in multiple filters, it is necessary that they are fabricated to a very precise common pattern. The Hiplanar process satisfies this requirement because of the small value of its ΔR and ΔV_{BE} performance.

3-3. Performance of the filter

Extensive computer simulation was used in the design of the filter. The performance of the filter, as obtained by the simulation, will be described. Figure 7 shows the gain vs frequency characteristics of the transconductance circuit, which defines the maximum operating frequency of the filter. We obtained the result that the filter can operate up to 10 MHz. Figure 7 also shows the gain vs frequency characteristics of a luminance LPF of the seventh-order and a chrominance BPF of the fourth-order, both of which are used in this transconductance circuit.

The luminance LPF has a −75 dB/oct. slope in the transition band. In designing such high-order filters, signal-to-noise performance must be considered. The signal-to-noise ratio (S/N) of the filters is defined by thermal-noise and shot-noise which are expressed by these well-known equations.

$$En^2 = 4KT \left(rbb' + \frac{1}{2gm}\right) \quad [V^2/Hz] \quad (3)$$

$$In^2 = 2qI \quad [A^2/Hz] \quad (4)$$

where rbb' = Base spreading resistance
q = Electron charge

We can estimate the video S/N by integrating the noise level, calculated from equation (3) and (4), in the range from 100 kHz to 4.2 MHz. The resulting video S/N of the seventh-order LPF is better than 68 dB. This value is achieved by use of the small rbb' characteristics of the new process and optimum current operation of the filter circuit. For the optimum S/N with low distortion, the video level (sync tip to white) fed to the filter is set at $\simeq 500$ mVp-p. When a signal near the cut-off frequency is fed to the filter, the third distortion ratio is 0.4%. The maximum signal level, with acceptable distortion ($\leq 2\%$), is 1Vp-p in spite of the low power supply of 5V.

Within the transconductance circuit, it is important that the p-n-p current sources accurately match the n-p-n current sinks to avoid DC shifts. DC offset voltages of the circuit are kept low (≤ 20 mV) because of the small ΔV_{BE} characteristics of the new process. Thus, the performance of the filter is adequate for processing video signals.

4. Application to Emphasis IC

4-1. Emphasis characteristics

The quality of the reproduced picture of VCRs has been much improved by the use of new circuits and new signal processing systems such as those shift in the FM carrier and a feedback comb-filter. In these systems, modification of dynamic emphasis and de-emphasis characteristics has contributed to the improvement of the S/N, resolution, and interchangeability. However, a dynamic emphasis circuit requires very strict specifications for variable gain vs frequency characteristics in the frequency range from 10 kHz to 3 MHz. For instance the tolerance of the gain is ±0.2 dB in the lower frequencies which have the most influence on the S/N and on interchangeability. Because of this, fully integrating the dynamic emphasis circuit is very difficult to achieve.

Our new IC is totally integrated with the Beta-format emphasis circuit and requires no external time constant and no adjustment. Figure 8 shows the construction of the Beta-format emphasis system. Emphasis 1 is used to improve the S/N in

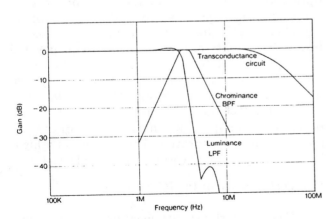

Fig. 7 Gain vs frequency characteristics of the filters

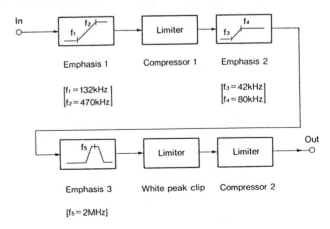

Fig. 8 Emphasis system for the Beta-format

489

the middle frequency range, emphasis 2 is for reducing the crosstalk noise caused by a playback signal from adjacent video tracks, and emphasis 3 is for reducing the high frequency noise on the edge and detail of video signals. Figure 9 shows the overall emphasis characteristics. In the recording mode, the video signal is compressed by the emphasis circuit which provides these frequency vs gain characteristics.

4-2. Configuration of the IC

Figure 10 shows the configuration of the emphasis filters. Emphasises 1 and 2 are high-pass filters with double time constants, the same type of integrated filters as shown in Figs. 3 and 4. Emphasis 3 is a band-pass filter of the second-order, and is also an integrated biquad filter as shown in Fig. 6. The transfer function is represented as:

$$F_2(S) = \frac{1}{K_3} \cdot \frac{1 + sCrK_3}{1 + sCr + (sCr)^2} \qquad (5)$$

where $\quad s = j\omega, \quad r = \dfrac{1}{gm}$

As for the r in Equation (5), integrated resistors are replaced by the transconductance circuits. The reference currents are fed to each of the transconductance circuits of Emphasises 1, 2 and 3. The reference current source ensures that the values of the operating currents are the same from one transconductance circuit to the next and do not vary too widely as temperature and processing accuracy vary.

Figure 11 is a block diagram of the IC. This IC uses the 5V ± 10% power supply, normally available in a VCR. An internally generated 4.2V reference voltage provides a suitable bias potential for the transconductance circuit. The power supply

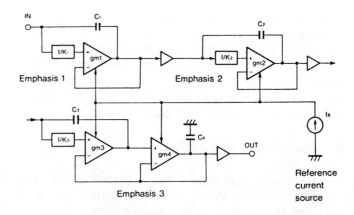

Fig. 10　Configuration of the emphasis filters

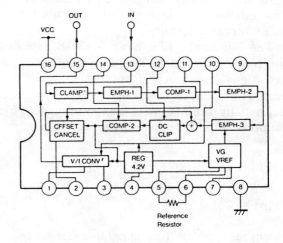

Fig. 11　Block diagram of the emphasis IC (CXA-1022)

uses a bandgap potential which gives the frequency response immunity from variations in the supply voltage.

Compressors 1 and 2 are diode limiters with circuits to compensate for thermal DC drift. The optimum bias potentials for these compressors are supplied from the bandgap voltage. The offset canceller is a feedback type clamp circuit used to insure the stability of the FM carrier frequency and the clip level. Reference DC levels of the offset canceller are also supplied from the bandgap voltage so there is no need for adjustment of the clip level. Using these techniques, variations of the frequency response and temperature characteristics of the clip level are greatly improved. This IC allows a high-band VCR to be more easily constructed.

4-3. Performance of the IC

Figure 12 shows the measured value of the emphasis characteristics obtained from an IC,

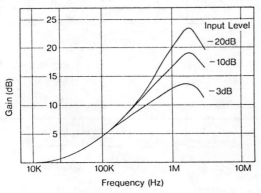

(Input 0dB is the level from sync tip to white)

Fig. 9　Emphasis characteristics

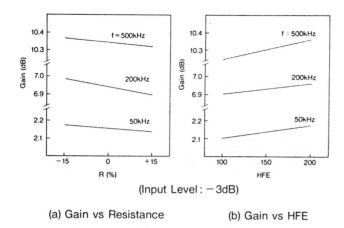

(a) Gain vs Resistance   (b) Gain vs HFE

(Input Level : −3dB)

Fig. 12   Variations of the frequency response

Table II   Specifications of the IC

Number of elements	800
Chip size	1.96 × 2.40mm
Supply voltage	+ 5V
Power consumption	100mW
Package	16pin DIP

whose process parameters such as resistor value and HFE value have been varied artificially. As can be seen, the emphasis gain characteristics have a small variation, and they do not depend on the variations in process parameters. The gain characteristics vary only ± 0.1 dB when the resistance is varied ± 15% and the HFE is varied from 100 to 200. The temperature coefficient of the cut off frequency was found to be 100 ppm/°C, which is satisfactory.

Finally, we were able to reduce the number of parts as well as the power consumption of the new IC to about 1/3 of that of the circuit in current use. Further, we were able to realize accurate frequency response without the need for adjustment. The specifications of the new IC are shown in Table II.

5.   Conclusion

We have developed a new IC by successfully integrating a new filter circuit using a newly developed process. The new IC has contributed to higher reliability, improvement of picture quality, and reduction of cost. We believe that this filter represents an important step towards larger scale integration in video signal processing circuits.

6.   Acknowledgements

The authors wish to express their sincere thanks to Mr. H. Godo, Mr. K. Yamagiwa and Mr. Y. Machida for their encouragement, and also to Mr. Y. Uno, Mr. H. Narahara, Mr. A. Ishitani, Mr. K. Abe and Mr. F. Yamaguchi for fabricating the device.

7.   References

(1) Lee C. Thomas, "The Biquad: Part I − Some Practical Design Considerations", IEEE Trans. vol. CT-18, No. 3, May 1971.

(2) Lee C. Thomas, "The Biquad: Part II − A Multipurpose Active Filtering System", IEEE Trans. vol. CT-18, No. 3, May 1971.

(3) Hans O. Voorman and Arnold Biesheuvel, "An Electronic Gyrator", IEEE J. Solid-State Circuits, vol. SC-7, No. 6, December 1972.

Paper 7-C.3

A BICMOS TV-Signal Processor

RUDOLF KOBLITZ AND MARTIN RIEGER

THOMSON CONSUMER ELECTRONICS R & D LABS, D-7730 VILLINGEN, W. GERMANY

Abstract—The paper presents the realization of an integrated television signal processor in BICMOS technology. Comparing the different possibilities in this technology, analog signal processing has been proved as the most economical way to realize the different necessary functions. Therefore, the internal integrated filters are of analogue biquad type. Switched capacitor structures will be used for the chroma delay line. The key point for the system architecture is the use of an appropriate alignment procedure to adjust the nominal values of the analogue structures.

INTRODUCTION

FIGURE 1 shows a block-diagram of a conventional television receiver. Since this kind of TV-set is produced in very high quantities, it is very interesting to integrate as many functions as possible in a VLSI-circuit to reduce the production costs. A key element for controlling the whole signal processing is the uP, which is a very cheap element today

and represents with different ROM-masks the different television sets with their different options and features. In order to be flexible, this element must be excluded from a VLSI integration. The tuner and the SAW filter as the selectivity component is today still a problem for integration. Since VLSI integration uses very small design rules, the breakdown voltage is limited (e.g., 12 V). Therefore, all power stages (audio output amplifier, vertical and horizontal deflection output stages, video output amplifiers) must also be excluded from a VLSI integration. Thus, the components enclosed by the dotted line are the functional blocks of the presented IC.

INTEGRATION ASPECTS

Figure 2 shows the more detailed functions of the IC. The input is represented by the two IF-ampli-

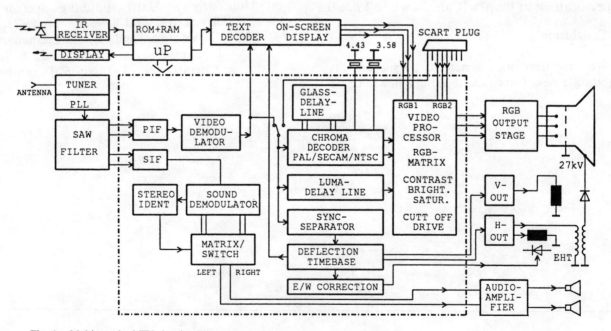

Fig. 1. Multi-standard TV-chassis.

Reprinted from *GME-Fachbericht 6: VDE Verlag*, pp. 79–85, Feb. 1990.

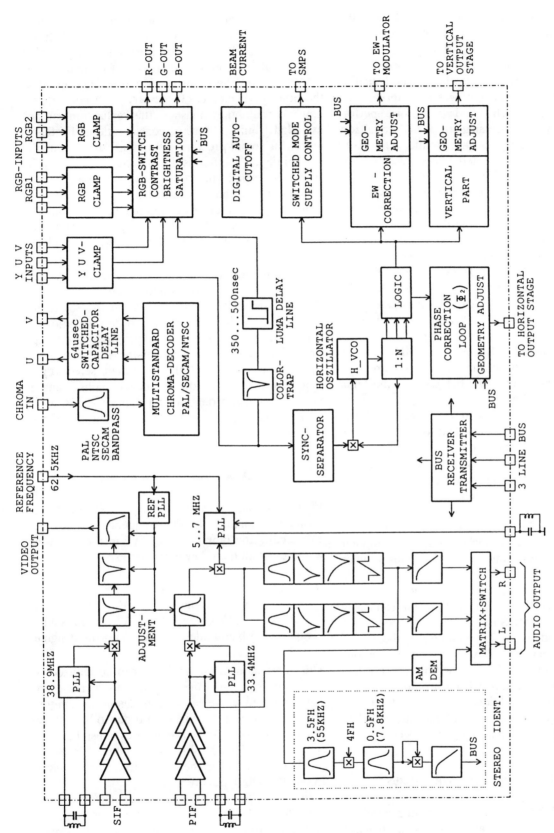

Fig. 2. BICMOS TV-signal processor.

493

fiers, one for picture and one for sound. Due to the very high requirements for S/N (60 dB), and the gain variation (60 dB), this part is purely bipolar. The video-demodulation and first sound-conversion is made with a PLL guaranteeing a good quality. Also this part is bipolar and uses an external tank circuit (L-C) to reach good jitter(noise)-performance. The sound processing (traps and equalizers in the video part, bandpass filters in the sound path) requires some fully integrated filters. Also the FM demodulator is a fully integrated type. Thus, no external ceramic filter or L-C circuits are provided. The use of the fully integrated filters allows in a very simple way the handling of the different sound and chroma standards (in conventional TV-multistandard sets, a lot of different ceramic resonators and L-C circuits are necessary). The stereo identification requires additional filters (55 kHz, 7.8 kHz). The chroma decoder needs a chroma bandpass filter (3.58/4.43 MHz) and a chroma trap is located in the luminance part. The frequency range for the integrated filters is between 10 Hz and 6.5 MHz.

Additional critical functional blocks are the switched capacitor delay line (64 μS) and the luma delay line (350–500 nS).

The whole IC is controlled via 3-line serial bus from the uP. All user defined adjustments (volume, contrast, brightness, saturation...) and all production oriented adjustments (picture width, height, geometry...) are also inside this IC. External adjustments via trimming potentiometers are completely avoided.

Integrating this wide range of different functions we see that for a lot of blocks, an analogue bipolar solution is the best way. Other functions require high impedance input opamps and "analogue switches" (SC-Structures) which can be realized in CMOS. The high variety of logic functions can easily be realized with CMOS too.

Thus, a mixed BICMOS technology is the appropriate technology for this IC. The technology in question, the "HF2CMOS-Process" of ST-Microelectronics developed from a bipolar process requires only three additional masks to extend it to BICMOS. Therefore, only slight increase in price compared to a bipolar technology is expected.

COMPARISON OF FILTER STRUCTURES

Based on a BICMOS process, we could realize the filters in a fully digital way, as switched-capacitor (SC) technique and as analogue biquad filters. In the proposed BICMOS technology "HF2CMOS" from ST, a digital filter of order 2 with let's say 8 bits requires about 1 mm^^2 chip area. Compared with 0.1 mm^^2 for the other two solutions, and besides the other disadvantages (necessary D/A converters, power consumption, aliasing), this realization can be excluded from our further consideration. (Furthermore, for sound-processing 8 bits are not enough!) A semi-digital solution is the SC-filter structure with acceptable small chip area, power dissipation and good accuracy, but the aliasing effect of such a sampled system requires additional analog antialiasing filters. The signal frequencies up to 6.5 MHz for sound could cause problems with a too high clock frequency.

Therefore, we use the analogue biquad filters type [1]. Its Q-value of max 20 allows the realization of the SECAM Bell filter (Q = 16), but the selectivity of ceramic bandpass filters (sound demodulation) is not achievable. Therefore we propose in our approach a second sound conversion from 4.5...6.5 MHz down to 500/260 kHz. The main selectivity is made in these two low frequency paths using a bandpass of 2nd order and two traps of 2nd order in each sound channel. In this case, a Q-value of 5 is sufficient.

ANALOGUE BIQUAD FILTER

Figure 3 shows the schematic diagram and the corresponding equations in the frequency domain [2]. Connecting the inputs Va, Vb, Vc in the following way, we obtain the following functions:

Lowpass:	Vb, Vc grounded;	Va = input signal
Highpass:	Va, Vb grounded;	Vc = input signal
Bandpass:	Va, Vc grounded;	Vb = input signal
Trap:	Vb grounded;	Va, Vc = input signal

The transconductance amplifiers can be realized via simple differential pair. In order to increase the signal amplitude, we can add diodes in the emitterpath as you can see in Fig. 4. In order to have larger signal amplitude, the gm-structures must be more complicated (Fig. 5). In Figs. 4 and 5, also the resulting relation for the center frequency is given. In our IC, both types are used.

In a test chip, we investigated the performance of these filters. Figure 6 shows the frequency response of a sound trap with gm amplifier typI and a capaci-

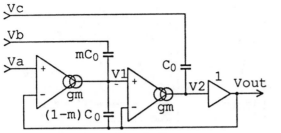

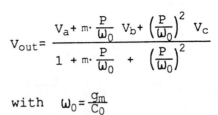

$$V_{out} = \frac{V_a + m \cdot \frac{P}{\omega_0} V_b + \left(\frac{P}{\omega_0}\right)^2 V_c}{1 + m \cdot \frac{P}{\omega_0} + \left(\frac{P}{\omega_0}\right)^2}$$

with $\omega_0 = \frac{g_m}{C_0}$

Fig. 3. Basic analogue biquad cell.

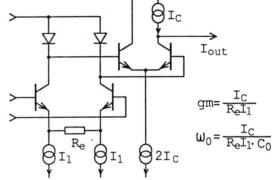

$$g_m = \frac{I_{CON}}{6V_T}$$

$$\omega_0 = \frac{F_C}{6V_T \cdot C_0}$$

Fig. 4. gm-amplifier typI.

$$g_m = \frac{I_C}{R_e I_1}$$

$$\omega_0 = \frac{I_C}{R_e I_1 \cdot C_0}$$

Fig. 5. gm-amplifier typII.

tive load of 1.5 Pf. The suppression at the center frequency 5.5 MHz is greater than 30 dB. The comparison between measured and simulated response shows very good agreement. The spectral noise density of the output voltage is for frequencies below 5 MHz less than 50 nV/Sqrt (Hz). The S/N-ratio is about 66 dB. The chip area used is 0.1 mm^^2, the power consumption is 6 mW.

A key feature of this analogue-filter is the easy adjustment of the center frequency via control current Ic. On the other hand, we are fully dependent on the production spread of the capacitor values and

(for typI) the temperature. Thus, an alignment procedure is necessary and will be described in the section "Alignment-Tree." Since this alignment tree contains other functional blocks, namely oscillators and the FM-demodulators, they will be described next.

OSCILLATORS AND FM-DEMODULATOR

Figure 7 shows the basic diagram of the oscillator circuit, used in this IC. Q6-Q8 form a Schmitt trigger controlling the differential switch Q4, Q5. Thus,

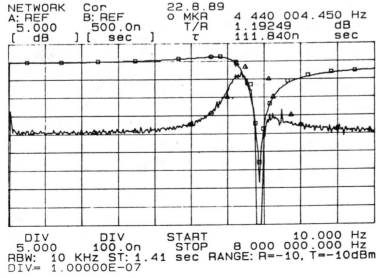

```
NETWORK    Cor        22.8.89
A: REF     B: REF     ○ MKR    4 440 004.450 Hz
   5.000      500.0n     T/R    1.19249        dB
[  dB   ] [  sec   ]     τ      111.840n       sec
```

□ simulated values for attenuation

△ simulated values for group-delay

```
    DIV        DIV        START              10.000 Hz
    5.000      100.0n     STOP      8 000 000.000 Hz
RBW:  10 KHZ ST: 1.41 sec RANGE: R=-10, T=-10dBm
DIV.= 1.00000E-07
```

Fig. 6. Sound trap—measurement and simulation.

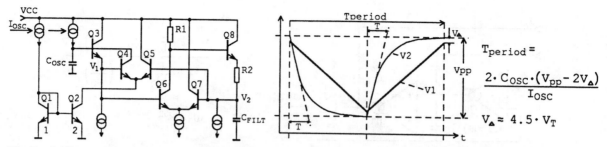

Fig. 7. Oscillator schematic- and timing diagram.

$$T_{period} = \frac{2 \cdot C_{OSC} \cdot (V_{pp} - 2V_{\Delta})}{I_{OSC}}$$

$$V_{\Delta} \approx 4.5 \cdot V_T$$

a triangular waveform is generated as shown in the timing diagram of Fig. 7. Special attention should be paid to the noise (jitter) performance of this oscillator (used as horizontal oscillator and in the FM-demodulators). To have a good noise performance it is necessary to limit the bandwidth of the Schmitt-trigger. Therefore, we have the filter capacitor C_{filt}. The time constant is as large as possible, but small enough to avoid a too large frequency deviation ($T = 0.13 \cdot T_{period}$). (Without this Filtering, the noise performance of the FM-demodulator is not sufficient.) We can use this oscillator as the kernel of the FM demodulator (Fig. 8). The controlling current (I_O) is modulated by the incoming signal. If its frequency is near the nominal frequency (fnom) of the oscillator, it will be synchronized and shows the timing behavior corresponding to Fig. 8. If the incoming signal has the same frequency as the oscillator nominal frequency, a phase shift of 90 degree is present. For deviation from the nominal frequency, we have a linear phase deviation (see Fig. 8). Giving the input signal and the oscillator signal to a Gilbert-Cell Multiplier, we have on the output directly the demodulated AF-Signal. Simulation and measuring on produced silicon shows good performance (S/N = 70 dB, distortion smaller than 0.2%,

side-channel separation, 40 dB). Since the mid-frequency (fnom) of this FM-demodulator is dependent from the capacitor spread also this block must be included in the "alignment-tree."

ALIGNMENT TREE

Figure 9 shows the alignment tree, necessary to adjust all the analogue functional blocks. The basic idea of such an adjustment procedure has been proposed in several papers, e.g., [3]. The key adjustment block is the horizontal oscillator. Its frequency can easily be measured and is adjusted to ±1% accuracy via the 5 bit D/A converter. It is a production adjustment. Considering the unavoidable disturbances in the TV-environment (high voltage flash) the latch of this D/A-converter can lose its content. A dangerous situation (horizontal frequency too low) could damage the horizontal output stage and the switch-mode power supply. In order to have more security, we add a parity check to this D/A-converter: if this check fails, the maximum current is taken, i.e., the horizontal frequency is maximum (and not critical).

If once the horizontal oscillator is adjusted, we have the current "Ic" which is "capacitor-adjusted."

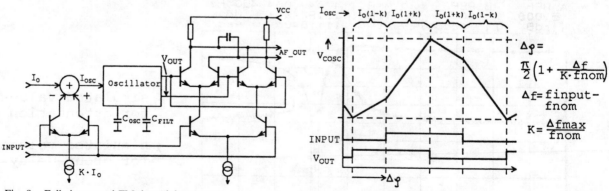

$$\Delta \varphi = \frac{\pi}{2}\left(1 + \frac{\Delta f}{K \cdot fnom}\right)$$

$$\Delta f = finput - fnom$$

$$K = \frac{\Delta fmax}{fnom}$$

Fig. 8. Fully integrated FM-demodulator.

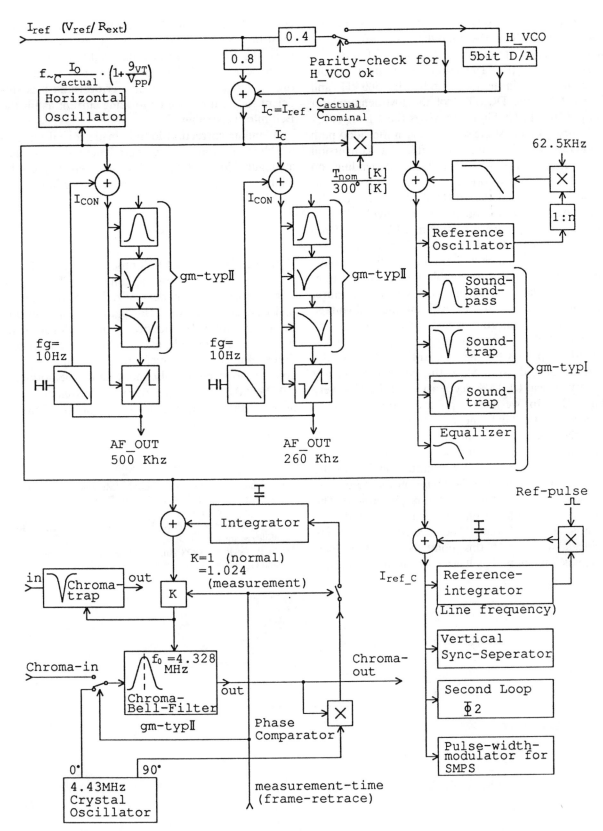

Fig. 9. Alignment tree.

This current is already a good approximation for the oscillators in the FM-demodulator (mid-frequency) and the center frequency of the biquad filters with gm-amplifier typII. The criterion to fine-tune the current "Icon" in the two sound-paths (500 kHz and 260 kHz) is the DC-offset of the FM-demodulator output (the 10 Hz filter suppresses the AF-signal).

In order to adjust the sound traps in the video-path and the sound-preselection after 1st conversion (frequency range 4.5...6.5 MHz, depending on sound standard) we use an additional reference biquad filter. It is connected (feedback) as the oscillator. Together with a programmable divider ("1:n") we put this reference oscillator in a PLL-loop. Placing these sound filters near together, we expect a sufficient good matching between the filters (tolerance $\pm 1\%$) which is acceptable for this application. To avoid a large variation range with temperature, we correct the current "Ic" with the thermal voltage (Vt). This multiplication is necessary due to the use of biquad-filters with gm-amplifiers typI. A critical situation appears for the SECAM Bell filter in the chroma demodulator. Since the nominal frequency is very critical ($\pm 0.4\%$ necessary) and the Q is very high ($Q = 16$) we must apply a different alignment procedure: In the frame retrace (cathode-beam is suppressed), we have enough time to switch this filter into an adjustment mode. We inject the PAL-Chroma carrier (4.43 MHz, Quartz-stability) to the filter input and observe the phase on the output via phase-comparator (for fin = fnom: phase = 0). The output of the phase-comparator is connected to a sample and hold-circuit. (The leakage-current is very critical: we use at this point NMOS input-pair opamps!) Its output voltage corrects the reference current Ic. Additionally, a small correction factor must be inserted (k) during the measurement time, since the PAL-carrier and the Bell-filter f0 have a slight deviation (2–3%). The chroma trap accuracy (in the luminance-part) is less critical and it is sufficient to use the same controlling current as for the Bell-filter (matching).

A similar correction loop is made for all integrator-blocks for the scanning-part. There are still other analogue blocks (luma delay line) which must be adjusted via appropriate alignment procedure.

Conclusion

With the aid of a BICMOS process, developed from a good bipolar process, a conventional analogue signal processing can be realized in a very simple and cost effective way. The parameter spread and the temperature dependence of the analogue-structures are eliminated, using self-alignment procedures. Future development of this technology enables us to integrate also nonvolatile memory-cells (EEPROM). In this case, we save safety-circuitry, we decrease the bus traffic, and we increase the reliability.

References

[1] Y. Ishigaki, K. Utsunomiya, et al., "Monolithic Filter and Its Application to TV MPX Sound Decoder IC", ICCE'83, Chicago Conf. proc.
[2] G. S. Moschytz, "Active Filter Design Handbook", John Wiley & Sons.
[3] Y. P. Tsividis, "MOS Analog IC design–New Ideas, Trends and Obstacles", ESSCIRC'86, Delft Conference proceedings.

An automatic equalizer for echo reduction in Teletext on a single chip

J. O. Voorman, P. J. Snijder, J. S. Vromans and P. J. Barth

The signal standard for broadcast television includes some unused 'space'. In the European 625-line system there are twice 25 lines that are not filled with picture information. These 'field-flyback intervals' contain the frame synchronization pulses and some test signals, but there are also a number of unused lines in which information can be accommodated. Teletext takes advantage of this: digitally coded pictures with text and figures are transmitted simultaneously with the TV programme and can be stored in a memory in the receiver. The contents may range from weather reports and sports results to traffic information and the latest news. Teletext reception can sometimes be upset by strong echoes, even though these may not seriously affect the TV picture if the delay is short. A correction circuit has been designed that equalizes the transmission path, and thus compensates for the echoes. In this circuit the signals are processed by analog rather than digital methods. This reduces the extent and dissipation of the circuit required, and the authors have been able to integrate the circuit — including the capacitors — on a single chip. Their original publication [3] received the second place in the '1981 Transactions Papers Award' of the IEEE Consumer Electronics Group.

Introduction

Teletext

Teletext is a television broadcasting service — already provided in several West European countries — in which, in addition to the regular television programme, information of general interest is transmitted, such as the latest news, the weather forecast, traffic information, sports results and so on. The Teletext information is arranged in 'pages', each taking up a full screen, and can only be displayed by a receiver with the appropriate circuits. The viewer can select the number of the page he requires from a list of contents, and key it in on a remote control unit, for example.

The Teletext information is transmitted during the field-flyback intervals and is coded in digital form. Echoes with a short delay can sometimes spoil the reception and in this article we present a circuit that effectively removes the interference caused by such echoes. The system and organization of Teletext differ from one country to another, but this makes little difference to the problems of reliable reception. For convenience, we shall confine ourselves here to the Teletext standard introduced in the United Kingdom. Some details are given in *figs 1* and *2*.

Teletext reproduces the pages by using characters stored in a memory. These include letters and digits and a number of graphic elements from which illustrations, maps etc. can be composed. The display on the screen consists of 24 lines of 40 characters. The transmitted data determines the characters from the memory that will be displayed and their position.

Interference caused by echoes

One bit of the eight-bit words containing the Teletext information is usually a parity bit. This effectively protects the word from distortion, though some im-

Dr Ir J. O. Voorman, Ing. P. J. Snijder and Ing. P. J. Barth are with Philips Research Laboratories, Eindhoven; Ing. J. S. Vromans is with the Philips Video Division, Eindhoven.

Reprinted with permission from *Philips Technical Review*, vol. 40, no. 11/12, pp. 319–328, 1982.

portant words are given better protection. The Teletext signal therefore has reasonable protection from
noise, interference from other transmitters and most
echoes. More often than not, the picture quality of
the television programme will have become unacceptable before the Teletext decoding breaks down. An

exception has to be made, however, for echoes with a
delay shorter than 1 µs. These are often strong enough
to interfere with the decoding of the Teletext signal,
although they may not seriously affect the television
picture, since they are more or less concealed by the
main signal (*fig. 3*) [1][2].

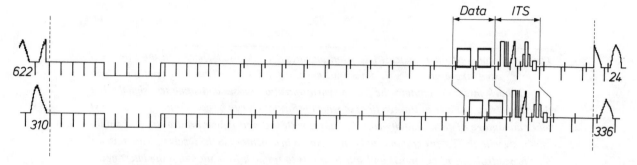

Fig. 1. The signals in the two field-flyback intervals of a television picture. Each line begins with a
line-synchronization pulse. Above, from left to right can be seen the last field line, equalizing
pulses, the frame-synchronization signal, more equalizing pulses, a number of empty lines, two
lines carrying Teletext data (*Data*), two lines carrying test signals (*ITS*), and on the far right the
first line for the next field scan. Each field line is preceded by a 'colour burst', a sample of the
colour carrier used to synchronize the colour decoding. The numbering of the lines is indicated.

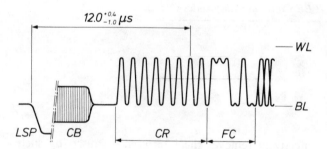

Fig. 2. Beginning of a Teletext line. *LSP* line-synchronization pulse.
CB colour burst. *CR* clock run-in signal (two words of eight bits
'10101010 10101010'). *FC* framing code for word synchronization
('11100100'). *WL* white level, *BL* black level of the TV signal.

These echoes originate in the part of the transmission path where the television signal is the modulation
on a carrier. They may be caused by multipath reception — for instance by reflections from hills or build-
ings — or they may be due to mismatched cable terminations in TV distribution systems, misalignment
of the antenna or inaccurate tuning of the receiver.

Automatic equalizer

To counteract short-delay echoes we have developed
an automatic equalizer [3]. This is a circuit that eliminates echoes by subtracting a signal of the same waveform. The equalizer operates on the television signal
in the baseband, i.e. after demodulation. It adjusts
itself automatically to give optimum reduction of the
echoes (*fig. 4*). Its operation depends on the binary
nature of a correctly transmitted Teletext signal: it has
only two levels, with fast transitions between them.
Echoes introduce additional levels; these are taken as
the starting point for the automatic equalization.

The equalizer takes the form of a transversal filter
with variable coefficients; we shall say more about this
later. It operates on the television signal in its ordinary
analog form; we decided to use analog signal processing because the circuits required for a high information flow and many multiplications are simpler and
take less current than digital circuits. We were able to
design the equalizer on a single chip, which requires
less than 500 mW of power. One special feature of the
chip is that it contains integrated capacitors of rela-

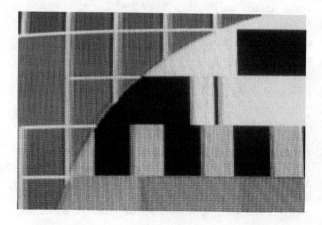

Fig. 3. Visibility in the test picture of an echo with a delay of 300 ns,
an amplitude of 45% of the main signal and a phase angle of 0°.
Such echoes are not unusual and viewers do not find them particularly annoying.

tively high capacitance (a total of over two nano-farads; see *fig. 5*).

We shall now consider the waveforms that the echoes can assume after demodulation of the television signal and the use of a transversal filter to eliminate them.

periods, i.e. when the path difference is an integral number of wavelengths (fig. 6b). An extra half-wave-length (which is only about 25 cm in the UHF band) gives a negative echo of the waveform shape (fig. 6c). A phase shift of 90° or 270° gives the echo a different waveform (fig. 6d). It is then known as a quadrature

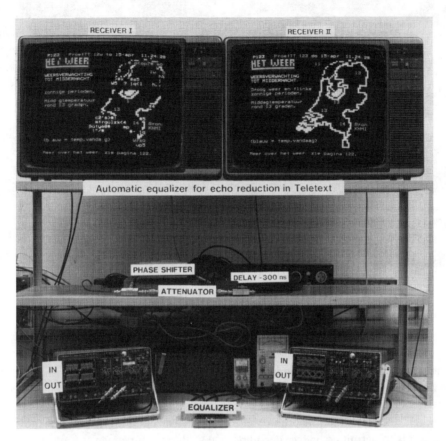

Fig. 4. Correction of the Teletext information by the equalizer. *Receiver I:* Teletext page degraded by the echo in fig. 3. Many graphic elements of the test picture have been replaced by random alphanumerical characters. *Receiver II:* The Teletext page corrected by the equalizer. The oscillograms on the left show the time signals before and after the equalizer; those on the right show the eye patterns.

Principle of echo compensation

Waveform of the echoes

Before demodulation an echo is just a delayed copy of the original signal. In the demodulation the phase of the carrier of the echo relative to that of the original signal is an important quantity. To recover the signal from the vestigial-sideband amplitude modulation used in television, it is necessary to regenerate the original carrier signal in the correct phase. Depending on the phase relative to the original carrier, the echo after demodulation can have various waveforms; see *fig. 6.*

An echo preserves the waveform of the original signal only if the delay is an integral number of carrier

echo. In case *d* the echo also changes the phase of the regenerated carrier signal in the receiver, so that the main signal also becomes distorted on demodulation.

The echo may thus have a different waveform from the original signal. We can consider it as a combination of delayed versions of the original signal, so that,

[1] R. Klingler, Influence of receivers, decoders and transmission impairments on Teletext signals (UK Teletext and French Antiope), in: G. Cantraine and J. Destiné (eds), New systems and services in telecommunications (Int. Conf. Liège 1980), North-Holland, Amsterdam 1981, pp. 37-44.

[2] Y. Ishigaki, Y. Okada, T. Hashimoto and T. Ishikawa, Television design aspects for better Teletext reception, IEEE Trans. **CE-26**, 622-628, 1980.

[3] J. O. Voorman, P. J. Snijder, P. J. Barth and J. S. Vromans, A one-chip automatic equalizer for echo reduction in Teletext, IEEE Trans. **CE-27**, 512-529, 1981.

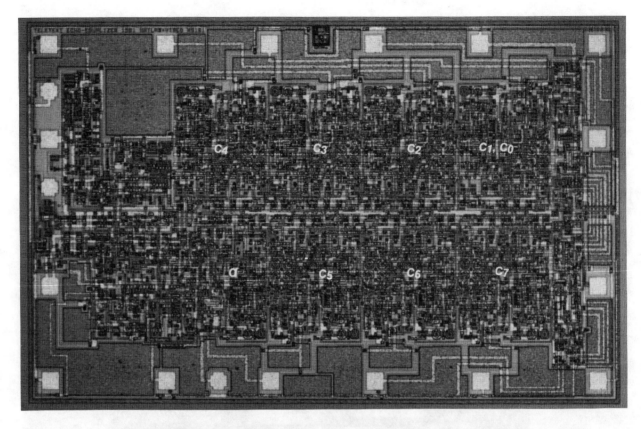

Fig. 5. Photomicrograph of the integrated equalizer (magnification 36×). The integrated capacitors (total capacitance more than 2 nF) can be seen along the edges. c_0 determination of d.c. correction. $c_1 \ldots c_7$ the seven sections of the filter. a determination of amplitude of auxiliary signal.

to a first approximation, the quadrature echo in fig. 6*d* may be regarded as a positive echo immediately followed by a negative one.

We must not forget, of course, that the primary aim of the echo reduction is to permit error-free decoding of the Teletext data. The decoding is possible when the oscillogram of the received data signal has open 'eye patterns' (see fig. 4)[4]. This does not require the echo reduction to be extremely accurate. The self-adjustment of the equalizer can therefore be made very fast, enabling it to track moving echo patterns, e.g. due to movement of an antenna in the wind.

Echo compensation by means of a transversal filter

The principle of echo compensation with a transversal filter is illustrated in *fig. 7*. It is based on the elimination of the echo by subtraction of a version of the main signal that has been delayed and given the appropriate amplitude. It can be seen that the elimination of either post- or pre-echoes leaves a higher-order and weaker echo; the more sections the filter has, the weaker is the higher-order echo and the further away it is from the main signal. Complete elimination is not possible with a transversal filter. The operation of the circuits, as represented in fig. 7, depends on the incorporated delays being equal to the time difference between main signal and echo. In practice, however, this time difference is not known, nor is it always the same. We could split up the delay line into as many sections as we expect to have echo delays. The subdivision need be no finer, however, than the value corresponding to the bandwidth of the television signal

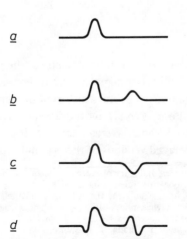

Fig. 6. Waveform of the echo after demodulation. *a*) Original signal. *b*) Echo in phase. *c*) Echo out of phase. *d*) Quadrature echo with a phase angle of 90°; this produces a pre-echo before the main signal.

(5 MHz): from the sampling theorem this is fully described by sampling at intervals of 100 ns. It is therefore unnecessary to make the delay per section shorter than 100 ns. The transversal filter then has the configuration shown in *fig. 8*. There are only seven sections, yet this is sufficient for the compensation of short echoes and the circuit need only be small. The attenuations in the branches — the 'tap coefficients' or 'tap weights' of the filter — are continuously adjusted automatically to give optimum cancellation of all echoes within the range determined by the filter length.

represents a convolution. We denote the filter coefficients by $c_1, c_2, \ldots, c_n$ and the response of the complete filter to an input signal $x(t)$ is

$$c_1 x(t) * h_1(t) + c_2 x(t) * h_2(t) + \ldots + c_n x(t) * h_n(t).$$

After the addition of a d.c. term c_0 to make the output data symmetrical with respect to zero, the output signal becomes

$$y(t) = c_0 + c_1 x(t) * h_1(t) + \ldots + c_n x(t) * h_n(t). \quad (1)$$

This expression is easily written as the scalar product of the vectors [5]

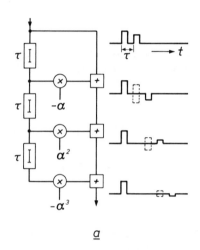

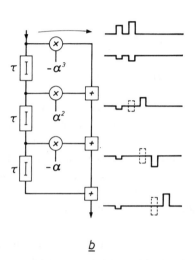

Fig. 7. Principle of echo reduction with a transversal filter. The delay τ is equal to the spacing between main signal and echo. *a*) Post-echo. Main signal and echo are delayed by a time τ, so that the delayed main signal coincides in time of arrival with the original echo. The delayed signal is multiplied by a factor α, giving the delayed main signal the same magnitude as the original echo. The delayed main signal is subtracted from this. At the same time an echo is produced at a spacing 2τ, but this is weaker than the original echo by a factor α. The process is repeated in the following sections of the filter. *b*) Pre-echo. The received signal is multiplied by a factor $-\alpha^3$. A version, delayed by a time τ, is multiplied by a factor α^2. On summation the non-delayed main signal cancels the delayed pre-echo. This process is repeated in the following sections of the filter.

Automatic control of the filter coefficients

The circuit derives the appropriate filter-coefficient values from an error signal. A required condition is that the control process should converge towards the correct solution — the set of coefficients that minimizes the residual echoes — and that the solution should be a stable end state. We shall now take a closer look at this control process.

Keeping the description general, we assume that we have a filter with n taps. Let the response at tap k to a unit impulse at the input be $h_k(t)$. The response to an input signal $x(t)$ is then $x(t) * h_k(t)$, where the asterisk

$$c = (c_0, c_1, \ldots, c_n)$$

and

$$x = (1, x(t) * h_1(t), \ldots, x(t) * h_n(t)),$$

hence as

$$y(t) = c \cdot x. \quad (2)$$

If all the coefficients have the correct value, the output signal is as free from echoes as possible; we designate this reference state as

$$y_r(t) = c_r \cdot x. \quad (3)$$

If the reference signal is available for comparison, then control towards the end state can be achieved by determining the error $y - y_r$ and varying each coefficient c_k in the direction that will minimize the square of this error:

---

[4] F. W. de Vrijer, Modulation, Philips tech. Rev. **36**, 305-362, 1976; see page 345.

[5] We do not treat these vectors as single-column matrices (as has been the usual practice in the literature). On multiplication we therefore use the notation for the scalar vector product and there is no transposition from column to row.

$$\frac{d}{dt} c_k = -f \frac{\partial}{\partial c_k} (y - y_r)^2 = -2f(y - y_r) \frac{\partial}{\partial c_k} (y - y_r),$$

where f is a positive loop gain.

Since y_r does not depend on the variable coefficients c_k, $\frac{\partial}{\partial c_k} y_r = 0$, and from (1):

$$\frac{\partial}{\partial c_k} y = x * h_k.$$

With the abbreviated notation $x * h_k = x_k$ it follows that

$$\frac{d}{dt} c_k = -2f x_k (y - y_r). \tag{4}$$

From this it can be shown that:

$$\frac{d}{dt} |c - c_r|^2 = -4f(y - y_r)^2. \tag{5}$$

As long as the output signal y differs from the reference signal y_r, the coefficient vector c converges to c_r.

A system in which a receiver generates a reference signal at the beginning of each Teletext line, for comparison with the same received signal, would certainly be feasible. However, as we noted earlier, we decided to adopt a solution based on the intrinsic binary nature of the Teletext signal, to provide us with information about the presence of echoes. This has the advantage that international agreement on a standard reference signal is not required.

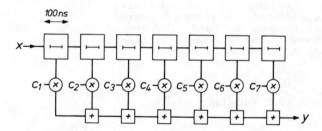

100 ns

Fig. 8. The transversal filter. x input signal. y output signal. $c_1 \ldots c_7$ the tap coefficients of the filter. Each delay element has a separate output for a tap.

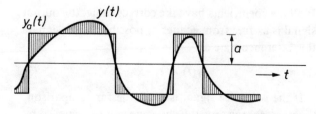

Fig. 9. The auxiliary signal $y_a(t) = a \operatorname{sgn} y(t)$, which is generated as an approximation to the correct Teletext signal. Adaptive control of the filter coefficients causes both signals y and y_a to converge towards the echo-free binary Teletext signal.

Our system does not therefore have a reference signal. Instead, we generate an auxiliary signal,

$$y_a(t) = a \operatorname{sgn} y(t), \tag{6}$$

which we may regard as a better approximation to the Teletext signal than $y(t)$ itself (see *fig. 9*). We try to make this signal and the output signal $y(t)$ converge by varying the coefficients c_k and the amplitude a. Both signals then tend towards the echo-free waveform.

This is done by starting from the error $y - y_a$, and as before we have

$$\frac{d}{dt} c_k = -f \frac{\partial}{\partial c_k} (y - y_a)^2 = -2f x_k (y - y_a). \tag{7}$$

In equation (7) it is assumed that $\partial y_a / \partial c_k$ may be neglected. This is reasonable, since y_a changes only at the zero-crossings, where the function $(y - y_a)^2$ is continuous.

In vector form this relation becomes:

$$\frac{d}{dt} c = -2f x (y - y_a). \tag{8}$$

An expression comparable with (5) cannot be derived from this vector equation. This would require dc_a/dt to be equal to zero, which is not the case, unlike dc_r/dt (c_a is the vector of the coefficients c_k, where $y = y_a$). Instead we can describe the convergence process as follows:

$$\begin{aligned} \frac{d}{dt} |c|^2 &= 2 c \cdot \frac{d}{dt} c \\ &= -4f c \cdot x(y - y_a) \\ &= -4f y (y - y_a) \\ &= -4f |y| (|y| - a). \end{aligned} \tag{9}$$

This gives three possible equilibrium states: $y = 0$, $y = a$ and $y = -a$.

In the state $y = 0$ all the coefficients c_k are zero. To avoid this trivial solution we give one of the tap coefficients a fixed value: $c_m = 1$. If y is close to zero, (9) becomes

$$\frac{d}{dt} |c|^2 \approx +4f |y| a, \tag{10}$$

where a is positive and y can no longer become zero, since $c_m = 1$. It follows that if y is small, $|c|^2$ increases, so that the equilibrium state $y = 0$ is unstable.

There are then two equilibrium states left, $y = +a$ and $y = -a$. The circuit can become locked in one of these two states or alternate between the two. This third mode is the required one. To prevent latching at a fixed value of $+a$ or $-a$, the amplitude a is set at zero if there have been no more zero-crossings of $y(t)$ (e.g. during half a line period). The d.c. correction c_0 now makes the mean value of the signal $y(t)$ equal to zero, so that zero-crossings occur again and the alternation is resumed.

Finally the coefficients c_k (including c_0) and the amplitude a are obtained by integration. Putting

$$y(t) - y_a(t) = \varepsilon(t) \tag{11}$$

to simplify, we have:

$$c_0 = -2f \int_0^t \varepsilon(\tau)\, d\tau,$$

$$c_k = -2f \int_0^t \varepsilon(\tau)\, x_k(\tau)\, d\tau, \quad \begin{array}{l} k = 1, 2, \ldots, n, \\ k \neq m, \end{array}$$

$$a = +2f \int_0^t \varepsilon(\tau)\, \mathrm{sgn}\, y(\tau)\, d\tau. \tag{12}$$

Fig. 10 shows how the filter in fig. 8 is developed to form a network that performs the required operations. It contains the delay elements $D_1, D_2, \ldots, D_7$, each with an integrator that stores charge only during

All the tap coefficients of the filter should have a value < 1 except $c_m = 1$. This forces the main signal to take tap m; the other taps reduce the echoes. This is consistent with the definition of the main signal as the 'largest echo' and improves the adaptation rate of the coefficients.

The electronic circuit

Principle of the delay line and other subcircuits

In principle, the required operations might be performed either digitally or by an analog circuit. In our case, as we saw, there are arguments against a digital approach. The data rate is high (7 Mbits/s), there are many multiplications and the ratio of the smallest time constant (the delay per section) to the largest (in the control loop) is three or four orders of magnitude. A digital circuit that gave the necessary performance would require a relatively large chip area and a high supply current.

We started from a common bipolar process with two layers of interconnection. A particular feature is the inclusion of integrated dielectric capacitors of

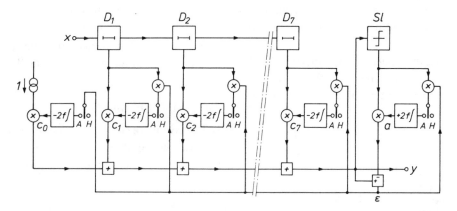

Fig. 10. Block diagram of the equalizer. x input signal. y output signal. $D_1 \ldots D_7$ delay elements. A/H adapt/hold switches, which are closed only during reception of the Teletext signals, to permit adaptation of the coefficients $c_0 \ldots c_7$ and the amplitude a. Sl slicer.

reception of a Teletext signal, because that is the only time when the switches A/H 'Adapt/Hold' are closed. While the remaining lines are being received the switches are open and the resulting values of the coefficients are preserved.

In the first section the d.c. correction c_0 is generated by integration of ε from eq. (12), and in the final section the amplitude a of the auxiliary signal $y_a(t)$ is generated. This requires the sign of the output signal, $\mathrm{sgn}\, y$, which is derived from a zero-crossing detector called a 'slicer'. The signal $\mathrm{sgn}\, y$ is also very suitable as input to a Teletext decoder.

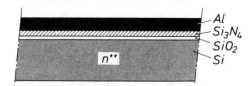

Fig. 11. Cross-section of an integrated capacitor.

relatively high value (see *fig. 11*). These are necessary because the filter coefficients are determined by the integral of a current. This integral is generated during the Teletext lines. Since the values obtained have to be held until the next Teletext lines arrive, the leakage current has to be extremely small.

Capacitors of this type are also used in the delay line. The analog delay line consists of a cascade of first-order phase shifters.

The transfer function from the filter input to tap k is:

$$H_k(p) = \frac{1}{1 + pRC} \left(\frac{1 - pRC}{1 + pRC} \right)^{k-1}, \qquad (13)$$

where $p = \sigma + j\omega$ is the complex frequency, $\omega = 2\pi$ times the frequency in hertz, R is the resistance and C the capacitance in each phase shifter. The transfer function is the Laplace transform of the Laguerre function of order k, and the filter is therefore sometimes called a Laguerre filter [6].

The basic circuit of the phase shifters is given in *fig. 12*. The low-frequency component of the input current flows through the resistor R and is tapped (i_t). The high-frequency component flows through the capacitor C to a 'current mirror', which reverses the current, so that the high-frequency component is subtracted from the output current. This output current is the input current for the next phase shifter.

To make the amplitude ratio of the input and output currents frequency-independent in the practical circuit, correct matching is necessary and compensation for parasitic effects may be required because of the large bandwidth (5 MHz). First-order compensation can be obtained by adjusting the gain of the current mirror.

The principle of a multiplier circuit is given in *fig. 13*. Multiplication depends on the logarithmic relationship between the base-emitter voltage and the collec-

tor current of a bipolar transistor; addition of base-emitter voltages corresponds to multiplication of collector currents and subtraction corresponds to division. In fig. 13, where I and J are the supply currents, and i and j are the signal currents, then for identical transistors:

$$\frac{I + i}{J + j} = \frac{I - i}{J - j}, \qquad (14)$$

so that

$$j = \frac{J}{I} i. \qquad (15)$$

The signal current i can thus be multiplied by a desired factor by giving the supply current J the appropriate value.

The sign function sgn y is generated in the 'slicer', a zero-crossing detector, shown in essentials in *fig. 14*. The output voltage y of the transversal filter is applied to the bases of the differential amplifier $T_{1,2}$. The cross-connected differential stage $T_{3,4}$ presents a negative resistance, which neutralizes most of the resistance of the base-emitter diodes of $T_{1,2}$. Consequently, when the input signal passes through zero, the differential stage $T_{1,2}$ switches very quickly from one extreme state to the other. The output transistors $T_{5,6}$ deliver a corresponding output current, whose amplitude is determined by the constant-current source a; the difference current at the output is thus a sgn y.

The complete circuit

The complete circuit of a single section of the adaptive transversal filter is shown in *fig. 15*. Fig. 15a gives the 'Laguerre filter section'; the input signal is divided

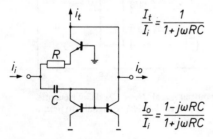

Fig. 12. Principle of the first-order phase shifter or 'Laguerre filter cell'. i_i input current, i_o output current. i_t tap current.

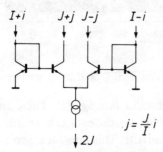

Fig. 13. Principle of the multiplier. Addition of the base-emitter voltages of bipolar transistors corresponds to multiplication of the collector currents, subtraction corresponds to division.

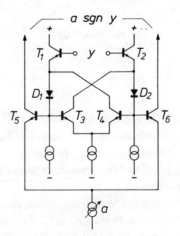

Fig. 14. Principle of the slicer. The emitter diode resistances of the differential stage $T_{1,2}$ are largely neutralized by the negative resistance presented by the cross-connected differential stage $T_{3,4}$, so that when y passes through zero the differential stage $T_{1,2}$ switches very rapidly from one extreme state to the other. $D_{1,2}$ diodes for d.c. level shift. $T_{5,6}$ output transistors.

between the resistor R and the capacitor C. The tapped signal x_k appears between the terminals A and B.

These appear again at two places in fig. 15b. The multiplication by the error signal ε (see (12)) takes place at the lower right; the current $\varepsilon(t)x_k(t)$ charges the capacitor C_{int}. The voltage across this capacitor is the integral of the product of the multiplication; in the multiplier circuit at the lower left the product c_kx_k is produced; this product, expressed in terms of a difference current, goes to the output terminals P and Q, which are summation points for all taps.

In the filter section with a fixed coefficient ($c_m = 1$) the right-hand part of the circuit is not necessary, and

Practical results

The equalizer has been tested in the laboratory and in field trials, in the Netherlands and Switzerland and recently in Australia and Norway. The laboratory tests show that the equalizer is capable of restoring the Teletext signal even when there are exceptionally strong echoes. This is verified by the field trials, which showed that multiple echoes are also reduced effectively and that the Teletext reception only fails when the ordinary television reception has become unacceptable.

Our example of a laboratory test has already been shown in fig. 4. An artificial echo is added with a variable delay, phase and amplitude. The input and

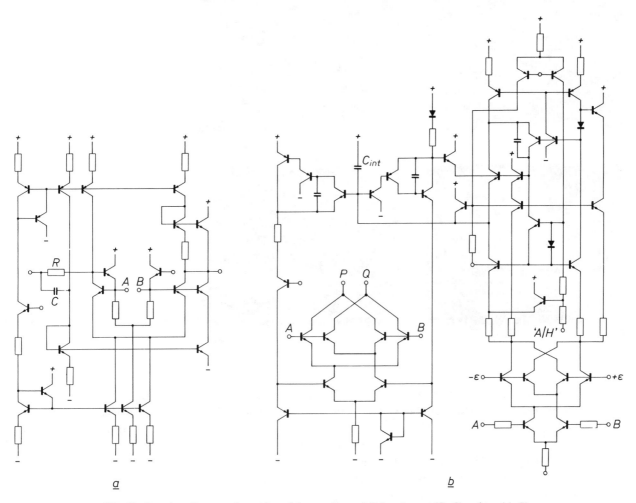

Fig. 15. Complete diagram of a section of the equalizer. *a*) Delay element (R, C) and tap (A, B). *b*) *Right:* Multiplication by the error signal $\varepsilon(t)$. 'A/H' adapt/hold control (see fig. 10). *Left:* Integration of the product in C_{int} and multiplication of the tap signal by the filter coefficient. P, Q difference-current summation points for all taps.

for calculating the d.c. correction term c_0 the left-hand part is redundant. The locations of the various circuits on the chip are indicated in fig. 5. The first section (c_1) of the transversal filter has a fixed setting; the other six ($c_2 \ldots c_7$) are adaptive, as are c_0 and a. The integrated capacitors are located along the edge of the chip.

output signals of the equalizer after addition of an echo with a delay of 300 ns, an amplitude of 45% of the main signal and phase differences of 0°, 90° and 180° are given in *fig. 16 a, b, c.* In each picture the upper trace gives the input signal — part of a Teletext

[6] Y. W. Lee, Statistical theory of communication, Wiley, New York 1960.

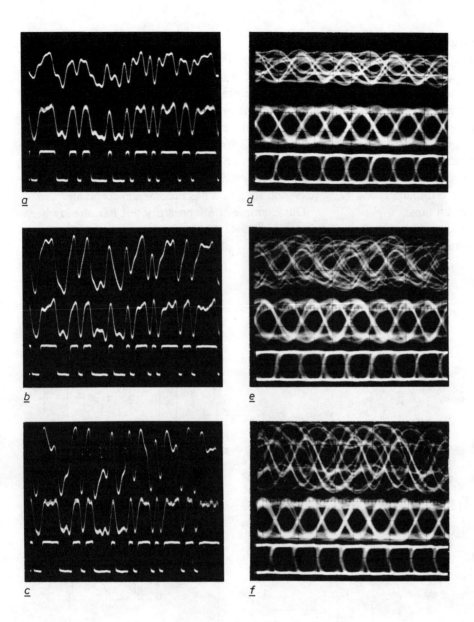

Fig. 16. Input and output signals of the equalizer. *a*, *b*, *c*) Waveforms. *d*, *e*, *f*) Eye patterns. The traces show, from top to bottom, the input signal, the direct output signal (*y*) and the output signal from the slicer (sgn *y*) for an echo with a delay of 300 ns, an amplitude of 45% and a phase angle of 0° (*a*, *d*), 90° (*b*, *e*) and 180° (*c*, *f*). It can be seen that in all cases the equalizer restores the binary nature of the Teletext signal and opens the eye patterns.

data signal chosen at random, with the echo added. It can clearly be seen that plateaus at about half height appear in the signal, making it difficult to decide whether a '1' or a '0' is intended. The centre trace gives the output signal *y* from the equalizer, showing that the binary nature of the signal has been restored. The lower trace gives the same output signal after it has passed through the slicer, which generates the function sgn *y* from the function *y* and accentuates the binary nature of the signal, which is passed in this form to the Teletext decoder.

By way of further illustration, the eye patterns obtained under the conditions described are shown in fig. 16 *d*, *e* and *f*. These show that even with such a strong echo as this the conditions can be created for reliable Teletext reception.

These experimental results have been confirmed by the field trials. Tests on equalizers designed with dif-ferent numbers of filter sections have shown that, even with multiple echoes, seven sections were sufficient to ensure reliable Teletext reception when an acceptable television picture was received.

Summary. The decoding of the digital Teletext signal can be seriously impaired by echoes. In particular, echoes that reach the receiver less than 1 µs after the main signal are often strong and occur quite frequently. They are accepted because they do not generally seriously degrade the quality of the television picture. The echoes can be compensated by subtraction of delayed and attenuated versions of the main signal. An equalizer has been developed that performs this function; it consists mainly of a transversal filter of seven sections, in which the filter coefficients are continuously and automatically controlled so as to produce a binary Teletext signal. The equalizer is integrated on a single chip, including a few capacitors with a total capacitance of more than 2 nF. Experiments and field trials have shown that the equalizer can ensure error-free Teletext reception in all conditions in which acceptable television reception is possible.

Section 7-D   Filters for Data Retrieval

These last three papers are a fitting conclusion to this volume. As they well demonstrate, the capabilities and flexibility of integrated continuous-time filters are such that these filters have even moved into digital computer hardware. All three papers describe filters for the read channel of disk drives. This large-volume application is uniquely well-suited to the use of integrated continuous-time filters and was key in their industrial acceptance and visibility. Paper 7-D.1 by Khoury describes the disk drive application and presents the detailed design of a transconductor-capacitor filter for it using CMOS technology. Paper 7-D.2 by De Veirman and Yamasaki presents a filter for the same application using bipolar technology and Paper 7-D.3 by Laber and Gray presents a BiCMOS solution.

Design of a 15-MHz CMOS Continuous-Time Filter with On-Chip Tuning

John M. Khoury, *Member, IEEE*

Abstract —A fifth-order CMOS continuous-time Bessel filter with a tunable 6- to 15-MHz cutoff frequency is described. This fully balanced transconductance–capacitor (G_m-C) leapfrog filter achieves a dynamic range of 55 dB while dissipating 96 mW in a 5-V 0.9-μm CMOS process. The on-chip master–slave tuning system uses a voltage-controlled oscillator (VCO).

I. Introduction

THE REALIZATION of more complex and better performing fully integrated signal processors is needed to improve the performance and reduce the cost of many electronic systems. Filtering implementations in complementary metal–oxide–semiconductors (CMOS), the dominant IC technology, can be achieved with analog or digital signal processors. Filters with passbands well below 1 MHz are typically realized with switched-capacitor analog signal processing or with digital signal processing techniques. However, passbands above 1 MHz usually require the use of continuous-time analog signal processors in today's CMOS technologies. This paper presents the design of a 15-MHz transconductance–capacitor (G_m-C) continuous-time filter for the read channel in hard-disk drive systems. Although the presentation will be application specific, the methods can be applied generally.

The paper is organized into seven sections. Section II reviews the disk-drive application and filtering requirements, and explains why the G_m-C continuous-time filtering approach was used. Section III describes the chip's architecture. The design of the main filter is presented in Section IV while Section V describes the tuning circuitry with particular concentration on the oscillator implementation. Experimental results are presented in Section VI, and conclusions are given in Section VII.

II. The Disk-Drive Application

A block diagram of the read channel of a disk drive is shown in Fig. 1. The preamplifier and automatic gain control amplify the signal developed at the magnetic read head from the flux reversals on the disk to about 1 V_{p-p}.

Manuscript received April 30, 1991; revised August 8, 1991.
The author is with AT&T Bell Laboratories, Murray Hill, NJ 07974.
IEEE Log Number 9103324.

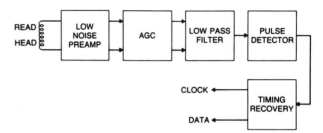

Fig. 1.   Block diagram of a disk-drive read channel.

The filter band-limits the wide-band noise of the amplified signal. Following the filter, the pulse detector circuit determines the position in time of the pulse peaks (i.e., flux reversals) and generates a digital output from which the data and clock are extracted.

In many applications, the filter also provides equalization. Since equalization is dependent on the particular disk-drive system design, the filter presented here assumes that if equalization is necessary, it is performed elsewhere. To minimize pulse-shape distortion or shifting in the time of the pulse peaks, a Bessel response is chosen because it maintains maximally flat group delay in the passband. A fifth-order Bessel filter with a 15-MHz corner frequency is adequate to accommodate 24-Mb/s systems. Since many new disk drives use variable data rates to achieve constant density recording, the filter's corner frequency is designed to be tuned over a wide range, 6–15 MHz.

The read channel application is ideally handled with continuous-time signal processors for several reasons. First, attempting to implement the 15-MHz bandwidth with a switched-capacitor filter would not be feasible because the sampling rate in a practical design would be several times the Nyquist rate (i.e., over 100 MHz). Secondly, tuning the filter's corner frequency for constant density recording is easily performed with the automatic tuning circuit, which is always included in the design of continuous-time filters. Finally, since the filter is preceded by an AGC circuit, the linearity and dynamic range requirements for this application are modest; both are in the range of 30 to 40 dB.

Several successful continuous-time filtering techniques have been published [1]–[7]. The MOSFET-C approach

Reprinted from *IEEE J. Solid-State Circuits*, vol. SC-26, no. 12, pp. 1988–1997, Dec. 1991.

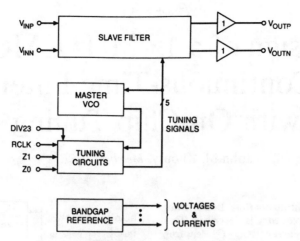

Fig. 2.   Block diagram of the filter chip.

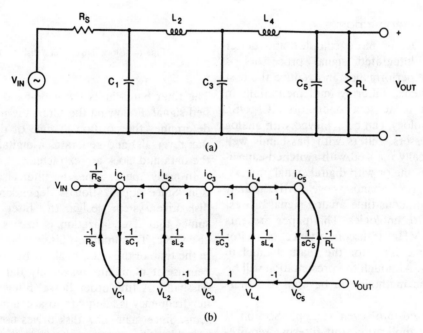

(a)

(b)

Fig. 3.   Synthesis process for the active filter. (a) Fifth-order *LC* low-pass prototype. (b) Signal flow graph of the *LC* filter.

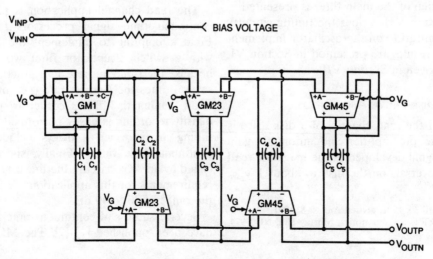

Fig. 4.   Slave filter leapfrog implementation based on Fig. 3.

[1], [8] would work well in this application; however, balanced op amps with gain–bandwidth products over 150 MHz would be necessary. Such op amps would dissipate considerable power. To minimize power the transconductance–capacitance approach [2]–[5] was chosen. Unlike MOSFET-C filters, the G_m–C filter's frequency response is sensitive to parasitic capacitances, requiring extremely careful layout. To save power in this application, some performance parameters were not optimized.

III. High-Level Design of the Filter Chip

A block diagram of the filter is shown in Fig. 2. It consists of three major blocks: the slave, master, and tuning circuits. Since the slave filter is implemented with continuous-time circuits, it must be tuned; otherwise, the corner frequency could vary by up to $\pm 50\%$ due to processing, temperature, and aging. The master and tuning circuit work together to tune the slave. In this application, the master is a voltage-controlled oscillator (VCO) that is constructed from the same type of transconductance amplifiers and capacitors that are in the slave. If the signal that controls the VCO's frequency is applied also to the slave filter, then the corner frequency of the slave Bessel filter will track the VCO. The tuning circuits and master form a phase-lock loop (PLL) that locks to an external digital clock source. A Q-control loop [2], [3], [9] was unnecessary for this application because the Bessel response has low-Q poles and is therefore tolerant of integrator phase errors [10]. See Section IV for more discussion.

The filter corner frequency is locked to the desired value by using the zone bits, Z_1 and Z_0 in conjunction with the external reference frequency source. The zone bits provide coarse filter tuning while the on-chip PLL fine-tunes the filter to either $1/2$ or $1/3$ of the reference clock frequency. The filter's wide tuning range, 6–15 MHz, is achieved with the zone bits as will be described later.

IV. The Slave Filter Design

The design of the slave filter topology begins with the normalized LC low-pass prototype shown in Fig. 3(a). With proper component value selection, this LC ladder can realize a fifth-order Bessel response. The signal flow graph (SFG) shown in Fig. 3(b) is a pictorial representation of all the equations governing the ladder's operation and is derived as in [11]. The SFG can be converted to a leapfrog filter, as in Fig. 4. The resulting structure simulates the operation of the passive LC ladder in Fig. 3.

The integrators in Fig. 4 are implemented as transconductance amplifiers loaded by a capacitor and weighted summation is performed in the current domain with multiple-input transconductors. Frequency tuning the filter is accomplished by varying the G_m of the transconductance amplifiers via the voltage applied on the V_G terminal. The capacitors shown in Fig. 4 serve two functions. They capacitively load the transconductors to perform integra-

TABLE I
Component Values for Fig. 4

Nominal Values for 15-MHz Bessel Response

Component	Value
$G_{M1(A, B, \&C)}$	500 μA/V
$G_{M23(A \& B)}$	200 μA/V
$G_{M45(A)}$	100 μA/V
$G_{M45(B)}$	50 μA/V
C_1	1.90 pF
C_2	2.21 pF
C_3	3.50 pF
C_4	2.42 pF
C_5	2.46 pF

tion and additionally they stabilize the common-mode feedback loop of the amplifiers at high frequencies. The filter's differential inputs are biased on-chip to permit ac coupling from an off-chip signal source.

In the design of a leapfrog filter, the resulting passband gain will be -6 dB as in the LC prototype unless gain scaling changes are made. The gain of 6 dB can be placed at the input of the filter by doubling the value of $G_{M1(B)}$; however, power dissipation is increased with this solution. An alternative that saves power but sacrifices noise and output dc offset is to place 6 dB of gain at the output of the filter. This is done by reducing the value of C_5 by a factor of 2 as well as halving the value of $G_{M45(B)}$. Table I shows the transconductor and capacitor values used for the 15-MHz Bessel response. To further save power, the capacitor values were scaled as small as possible while still achieving acceptable matching and insensitivity to parasitics.

The two-input transconductance amplifier with capacitive loading, shown in Fig. 5(a), uses a folded-cascode structure to obtain the high output impedance needed for a high-quality integrator. The amplifier's transconductance is determined by the source degeneration provided by transistors M_{AA} through M_{EA} for the A input and by M_{AB} through M_{EB} for the B input. These devices are identical in size with $W = 6$ μm and $L = 5$ μm. Earlier work [12] has shown that when driven by a balanced signal, the even nonlinearities of the current flowing through the source degeneration transistors are eliminated. Cross-coupling to eliminate odd nonlinearities [12] was not used because the superior linearity could not justify the additional power. The gate voltages of the five "MOS resistors" are varied to tune the filter. Typically, two or more of these transistors are controlled with one gate voltage while the remaining unused devices have their gates tied to V_{DDA}. The zone bits determine how many of the "MOS resistors" are connected to V_G. Other transconductance schemes are possible [2], [4], [5]; however, they tune the transconductance of the amplifier by varying the current in the differential pair making a wide tuning range impractical in contrast to that presented here.

The capacitors in Fig. 5(a) perform integration and additionally provide high-frequency common-mode feedback via the $BN2$ bias line. Note that each integrator

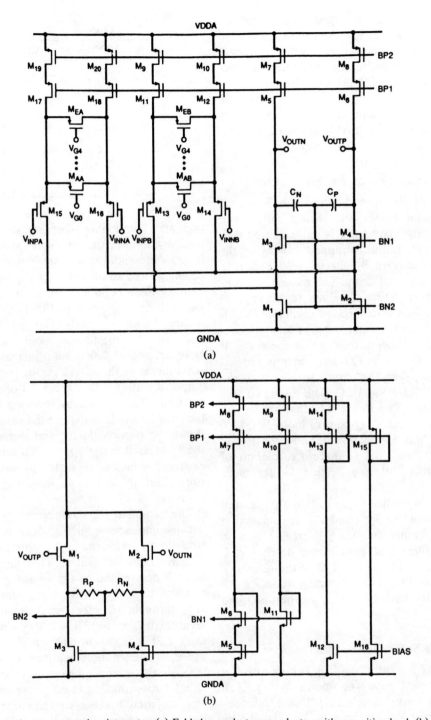

Fig. 5. Transconductance–capacitor integrator. (a) Folded-cascode transconductor with capacitive load. (b) Biasing and common-mode feedback for the transconductor.

must have a separate $BN2$ bias line, but the $BN1$, $BP1$, and $BP2$ bias lines could be shared among amplifiers, if desired.

To save power, the bias current in transistors M_3-M_8 is determined solely by the load capacitance and the maximum signal swing expected at the amplifier output and is independent of the number of inputs to the transconductor [3]. This method takes advantage of the fact that the A and B inputs are forced by the filter topology to be out of phase causing partial cancellation of the differential signal currents.

Biasing and low-frequency common-mode feedback for the folded-cascode transconductance amplifier are shown in Fig. 5(b). The biasing scheme maximizes output swing by biasing the cascoded current sources a few tenths of a volt above the triode region. $M_{13}-M_{15}$, all biased with the same currents, are used to generate the $BP1$ and $BP2$ bias lines for the p-channel cascode current sources. M_{14} provides the basic current mirroring while M_{15} provides biasing for the cascode devices. The aspect ratio of M_{15} is made sufficiently smaller than M_{14} to ensure that M_8 and M_9 are biased above the triode region. M_{13} forces M_{14} to

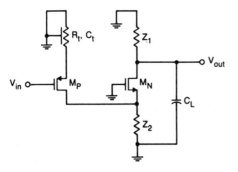

Fig. 6.   Small-signal half-circuit model of the G_m–C integrator.

have the same drain-to-source voltage as M_8 and M_9 to achieve accurate current mirroring. The biasing method is described in more detail in [13]. The $BN1$ and $BN2$ bias lines are generated in the same way. Common-mode feedback is provided with the source followers M_1 and M_2 along with resistors R_p and R_n. The output common-mode voltage of the transconductance amplifier is set two n-channel gate-to-source voltages above ground and is in the range of 1.6 to 2.1 V for all processing and temperature variation. Such variation is acceptable for this application since the maximum differential voltage swing is 1 V$_{p-p}$. Common-mode feedback schemes that use an error amplifier with negative feedback to force the output common-mode level to equal a dc reference voltage level are more precise; however, the error amplifier stage complicates common-mode frequency compensation and increases power dissipation.

All biasing in the slave filter, as well as the remainder of the chip, originates from a bandgap voltage and current reference circuit [14]. The reference circuit operates from an internally regulated supply to maximize power supply noise suppression.

A. High-Frequency Effects on Slave Filter Performance

The nonideality effects on the filter will be examined in terms of the integrator performance. For ideal transconductance–capacitor integrators, the unity-gain frequency is $\omega_0 = G_m / C$ and the phase response is $-\pi / 2$ rad for all frequencies. In practice, however, parasitic poles, zeros, and finite integrator gain at dc cause errors in ω_0 and more importantly cause errors in the phase response.

Fig. 6 shows a simplified small-signal half-circuit model of a G_m–C integrator. z_1 and z_2 model the impedance of the current sources in the transconductor's output stage and the uniform $\overline{RC}$ transmission line models the triode-operated transistor that sets the transconductance of the amplifier. R_t is half the channel resistance of the triode-operated device and C_t is half the distributed gate and depletion layer capacitance. Other transistors in the amplifier are modeled as lumped devices since their channel lengths are much less than the triode-operated device. The integrator transfer function $H(s)$ can be placed in the following form:

$$H(s) = Y_m Z_{\text{out}} \tag{1}$$

where Y_m is the transadmittance of the amplifier and Z_{out} is the output impedance of the integrator. Neglecting the output conductance of M_p and assuming that $1/g_{mn} \ll |z_2|$ for all frequencies, then

$$Y_m = \frac{g_{mp}}{1 + g_{mp}/y} \tag{2}$$

where y is the driving point admittance of a uniformly distributed $\overline{RC}$ line. From [15] y can be approximated by:

$$y = \frac{1 + \dfrac{sR_t C_t}{2}}{R_t\left(1 + \dfrac{sR_t C_t}{6}\right)}. \tag{3}$$

If $g_{mp} \gg 1/R_t$ and $sR_t C_t \ll 1$, Y_m can be approximated by

$$Y_m \approx \frac{1}{R_t}\left[1 + \frac{sR_t C_t}{3}\right]. \tag{4}$$

The transfer function of the G_m–C integrator is then approximated as

$$H(s) = \left(\frac{1}{R_t}\right)\left(\frac{r_o}{sr_o C_L + 1}\right)\left(1 + \frac{sR_t C_t}{3}\right)\left(\frac{1}{1 + s/\omega_p}\right). \tag{5}$$

ω_p is the frequency of the equivalent nondominant pole resulting from parasitic capacitances in the amplifier. From the above equation we see that the distributed capacitance of the triode device creates a zero in the transfer function that provides phase lead that can partially cancel phase lag due to parasitic poles. The output resistance of the amplifier, r_o, also provides additional phase lead. Based on the assumptions given above, r_o can be approximated by

$$r_o = z_1(\omega = 0)\|[g_{mn}r_{\text{on}}z_2(\omega = 0)] \tag{6}$$

where r_{on} is the output resistance of M_n.

Simulation of the slave filter with nonideal integrators having distributed capacitance effects showed that integrators with up to $\pm2°$ of phase error at the filter corner frequency would not adversely degrade the frequency response. Without lead-lag cancellation the phase error requirement of 2° would mean that only a single parasitic pole at or above 450 MHz could be tolerated for a 15-MHz filter. Since such a requirement on the parasitic pole is not practical, the filter design took advantage of the inherent lead-lag compensation shown in (5) by using a large value of C_t.

V. The Tuning Circuit

A. Review of Tuning Circuit Approaches

Several tuning circuit approaches for continuous-time filters exist [1]–[9], [16], [17]. For slave filters implemented with state-variable topologies, the function of frequency tuning the circuit is equivalent to accurately setting the unity-gain frequency of all integrators. Tuning circuits have been devised that also tune the phase response of

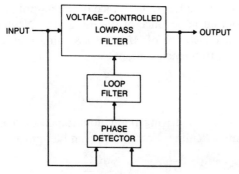

Fig. 7. Frequency tuning loop utilizing a voltage-controlled filter (VCF).

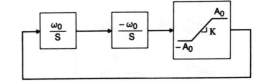

Fig. 8. An oscillator constructed with a loop of two integrators.

the integrators [2], [3], [9]. For this application, a Q-control loop to tune the integrator phase error was unnecessary so the following discussion is restricted to the frequency control loop.

Of the several approaches to frequency tune a filter, we will discuss the two basic configurations that use a master cell within a PLL. The first method uses a voltage-controlled filter (VCF) [2]-[4] as depicted in Fig. 7. The PLL circuitry will frequency tune the master filter until the relative phase shift of the input and output signals settles to a predetermined level. If the VCF is a second-order low-pass filter, the $\pi/2$-rad phase shift that occurs at the corner frequency is typically used.

The main advantage of this technique is that the master VCF is easier to design than the VCO presented in the following technique. The most serious weakness of the VCF technique is that the reference signal should be a sinusoid to make meaningful relative phase measurements between input and output. If the reference signal is rich in harmonics, such as a square wave, the phase (and amplitude) relation of the harmonics at the input of the VCF is well defined, but not at the output causing tuning errors. As found in [3], filter tuning worked well with sinusoids or even triangular reference signals, but worked poorly with square waves. The other weakness in the VCF approach is that the frequency accuracy and hence master-slave tracking can be degraded by low PLL loop gain, dc offsets within the loop, or mismatches in the delays at the phase detector inputs.

Use of a master VCO cell was employed in this chip design principally because the reference frequency signal was a digital clock that was not easily converted to a sine or triangular wave over the wide tuning range of 6-15 MHz. The VCO approach does not suffer frequency errors from low dc PLL loop gain, dc offsets within the loop, or mismatches in the delays at the phase detector inputs. These nonidealities simply cause an inconsequential phase error between the VCO and the reference.

B. VCO Design

The design of a high-frequency sinusoidal oscillator is complex because nonlinearities can cause the frequency of oscillation to deviate from that expected based on linear operation if the amplitude becomes excessive. Al-

though a VCO having significant nonlinearities can be locked to the external clock with a PLL, the control voltage developed for the VCO will have the incorrect value to tune properly the slave filter. Poor master-slave tracking results. Consequently, VCO linearity is critical and is maintained by controlling the amplitude of the oscillations. Amplitude control can be achieved with an automatic gain control circuit (AGC) or more simply with a carefully designed clamp circuit. For continuous-time filter applications, the VCO topology must be designed so that the controls for frequency and amplitude of oscillation are orthogonal.

As is well known, if unity-gain feedback is provided around a linear network, sinusoidal oscillations will occur at a frequency ω_0 provided that the loop gain $T(j\omega)$ of the network has $|T(j\omega_0)| = 1$ and $\Phi[T(j\omega_0)] = 0$. Under these conditions, the poles of the closed-loop system will be on the $j\omega$ axis; however, if the magnitude response is less than one, the oscillations will not be sustained. Consequently, in practice the oscillator must be designed with $|T(j\omega_0)| > 1$, causing the oscillations to increase exponentially with time, until nonlinearities alter the effective value of $|T(j\omega_0)|$ such that it is equal to one. There are three tasks at hand: 1) determine a suitable $T(s)$ function; 2) guarantee that $|T(j\omega_0)| > 1$; and 3) control the amplitude of the oscillations to minimize the effect of circuit nonlinearities on the oscillation frequency.

Consider an oscillator constructed with a loop of two integrators as shown in Fig. 8. For the moment, if the gain element is modeled as a linear circuit with gain K, the loop gain is

$$T(j\omega) = K[\omega_0/\omega]^2 e^{j0}. \tag{7}$$

Notice that the phase of the loop gain is zero for all frequencies, so the phase response does not determine the oscillation frequency. The oscillation frequency is set when the loop gain reaches unity as governed by ω_0 *and* K. If a describing function analysis [18] is performed, the effective gain of the nonlinear element is not K, but is signal and clamp-level dependent. The effective gain is the ratio of the amplitude of the fundamental frequency component at the output of the nonlinear block to the amplitude of the sinusoid at the input. Consequently, as the oscillation amplitude is modified via the clamp levels, the frequency of oscillation is also changed making tight tracking of the master-slave tuning scheme difficult. An even more fundamental problem with this oscillator is that under ideal conditions the poles are exactly on the $j\omega$ axis so oscillations are not guaranteed to occur.

The loop gain of the oscillator must be chosen so that the oscillation frequency is determined by the loop-gain phase rather than magnitude, so that the amplitude and frequency controls of the oscillator are decoupled. This decoupling can be achieved with a second-order band-pass-filter-based oscillator [19], [20] because there is only a single frequency at which the loop has a zero phase condition. Consider a second-order bandpass filter with the following transfer function:

$$H(j\omega) = \frac{\frac{\omega}{Q}e^{j\theta}}{\left[\left(\omega_0^2 - \omega^2\right)^2 + \left(\omega\omega_0/Q\right)^2\right]^{1/2}} \quad (8)$$

where the phase response θ is given by

$$\theta(\omega) = \pi - \arctan\left[\frac{\omega\omega_0}{Q\left(\omega_0^2 - \omega^2\right)}\right]. \quad (9)$$

From (8) and (9), the phase response is zero only at $\omega = \omega_0$, and the magnitude response at that frequency is unity. The design of the oscillator uses a bandpass filter with its input and output connected with an amplifier as shown in Fig. 9. The $H(s)$ transfer function that implements the bandpass filter is constructed with a loop of two integrators, a $-1/Q$ amplifier for damping and a $1/Q$ gain element for input signal amplification. The feedback network nominally provides a gain of unity with clamping at $\pm A_0$. The clamping levels indirectly control the amplitude of the oscillations. If the gain in the feedback loop is made much larger than unity (before clamping), the feedback loop can be viewed as a sine-to-square-wave converter. Since a high-Q bandpass filter only passes the frequencies around ω_0, the harmonics of the square wave do not appear at the output of the filter. Describing function analysis can then model the oscillator operation [18].

We have shown that the nonlinear circuit element controls the amplitude, but does not affect the frequency of oscillation. This is only true if the input sinusoid and output fundamental frequency component are in phase. In practice, a phase shift does occur causing an error in the frequency of oscillation. This error can be approximated by examining the derivative of the bandpass filter's phase response given in (9):

$$\frac{d\theta}{d\omega} = -\frac{2Q}{\omega_0} \quad \text{for } \omega = \omega_0. \quad (10)$$

If the effective phase through the nonlinear circuit is ϕ, then the fractional error in the frequency of oscillation is

$$\frac{\Delta\omega}{\omega_0} = \frac{-\phi}{2Q}. \quad (11)$$

Clearly, use of a high-Q bandpass filter eases the bandwidth requirements of the amplifier shown.

The oscillator schematic is given in Fig. 10. The first transconductance amplifier shown has three sets of in-

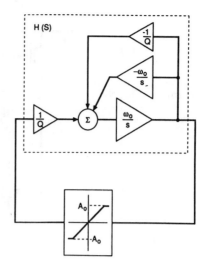

Fig. 9. Bandpass-filter-based oscillator.

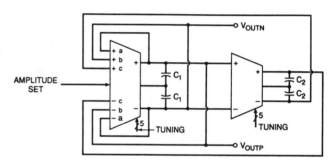

Fig. 10. Implementation of the oscillator.

puts. The A and B inputs provide positive and negative feedback, respectively, from the oscillator output. When the output is near its zero crossings, the overall feedback to the input of the first transconductor is positive; however, when the output amplitude reaches a specified level the positive feedback is clamped so the overall feedback becomes negative.

The VCO uses essentially the same transconductance amplifiers as in the slave except for a small modification in the three-input design, shown in Fig. 11. The B and C inputs are designed to be linear and are the same as for the slave design. The A input, however, uses no source degeneration for two reasons. First, when the A input is in its linear region, the transconductance is much higher than that of the B input, ensuring that the feedback path of the oscillator will have a gain greater than unity. The second reason to eliminate degeneration in the A inputs is to clamp the signal at low levels. Essentially a sine wave applied to the A inputs is converted to a square wave, in the current domain. The clamping level of the feedback signal is controlled with the tail current provided by M_{23}, indirectly setting the oscillation amplitude. An auxiliary circuit, not shown, programs the tail current as a function of the resistance value chosen for the transconductors by using the zone bits and the V_G signal generated in the tuning circuits.

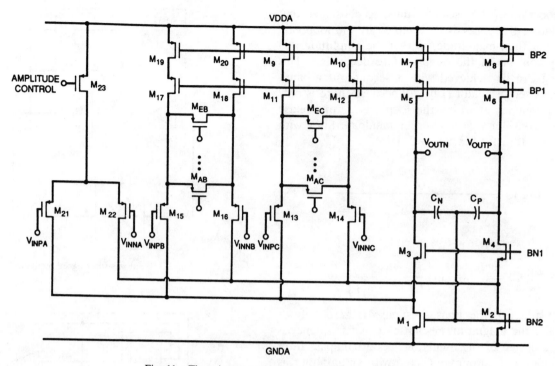

Fig. 11. Three-input transconductor used in the oscillator.

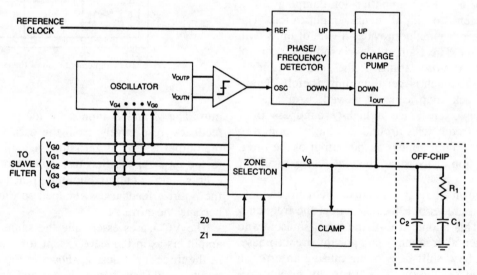

Fig. 12. Tuning system block diagram.

C. Tuning Scheme Implemented

The overall tuning scheme, shown in Fig. 12, has three major components: the VCO, phase/frequency detector, and charge pump. Since the output of the master is a sine wave and the phase/frequency detector is a logic circuit, a high-speed comparator [21] was designed to convert the output of the master to a square wave. A phase/frequency detector was chosen, rather than a simple phase detector, to eliminate the possibility of harmonic locking or not achieving lock. The tuning range is large, approximately 6–15 MHz, but only one external loop filter is permitted. Therefore, the phase/frequency approach permits the

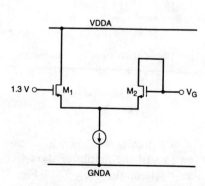

Fig. 13. Circuit to clamp V_G to 1.3 V.

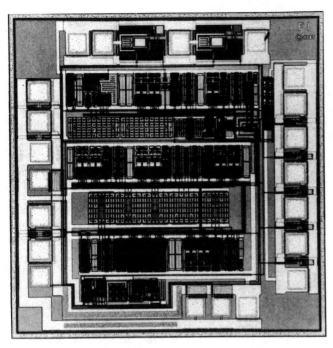

Fig. 14. Photomicrograph of the continuous-time filter chip.

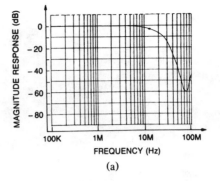

(a)

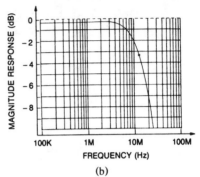

(b)

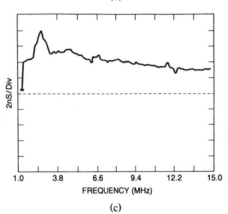

(c)

Fig. 15. Frequency response of the filter with a 30-MHz clock input and divide-by-2 mode selected: (a) magnitude response, (b) passband magnitude response, and (c) passband group delay response.

TABLE II
EXPERIMENTAL RESULTS

Typical Device Measurements	
−3-dB Bandwidth (mean)	12.78 MHz
−3-dB Bandwidth (std. dev.)	0.45 MHz
Maximum tuning range	1.0–16.6 MHz
Passband gain (mean)	−0.2 dB
Passband gain (std. dev.)	0.1 dB
Passband group delay deviation (2–13 MHz)	±2 ns
Differential output offset (mean)	32.3 mV
Differential output offset (std. dev.)	56.0 mV
THD at 1-V_{p-p} differential swing	41.0 dB
Integrated output noise	392 μV_{rms}
30-MHz feedthrough at output	500 μV_{rms}
Dynamic range	55 dB
Dynamic range (neglecting feedthrough)	59 dB
V_{DD} rejection at 100 kHz	68 dB
V_{DD} rejection at 1 MHz	63 dB
V_{DD} rejection at 12.8 MHz	45 dB
Power dissipation	96 mW
Active area	2.6 mm^2

use of a low-bandwidth loop filter while still achieving lock.

The zone selection block provides coarse tuning of both the VCO and the slave. Depending on the setting of Z_1 and Z_0, the individual tuning voltages V_{G0}–V_{G4} will either be connected to the V_G tuning signal or to V_{DDA} as determined by the transmission gates and decoding logic in the zone selection circuit. The range of the V_G tuning signal is limited from 0 to 1.3 V with the clamp circuit shown to ensure that the "MOS resistors" in the VCO and filter are biased with adequate gate-to-source voltage to prevent filter linearity degradation with 1-V_{p-p} signals. Clamping V_G at 1.3 V has the additional function of preventing the tuning circuit from disabling the filter and oscillator by placing too high a voltage on the gates of the "MOS resistors," resulting in zero transconductance for

all amplifiers. If V_G is clamped at either end of the range, the zone selected should be changed. The clamp circuit shown in Fig. 13 is biased with a tail current that is 50% larger than the charge pump current output to enable clamping at 1.3 V.

VI. EXPERIMENTAL RESULTS

The photomicrograph of the chip is shown in Fig. 14. The tuning circuit occupies the top third of the chip while the slave filter is in the section immediately below. The bandgap reference is in the lower left-hand corner.

The experimental results from several first silicon devices are summarized in Table II. For these measurements the input reference frequency was 30 MHz and the VCO was locked to 15 MHz (i.e., with the divide-by-2 mode selected). The maximum zone selection, $Z_1 Z_0 = 11$, was used, except for the measurement specifying the maximum tuning range. The frequency response is given

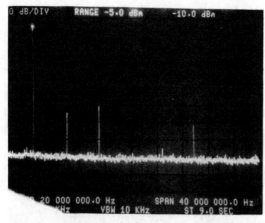

Fig. 16. Spectral response at output of the filter depicting the noise floor, filter linearity, and clock feedthrough at 30 MHz. Notice digital clock feedthrough at 30 MHz but no oscillator feedthrough at 15 MHz.

in Fig. 15. The magnitude response is shown in Fig. 15(a) with the passband expanded in Fig. 15(b). Fig. 15(c) shows the group delay response. It has a deviation of approximately ± 2 ns from 2 to 15 MHz, the frequency range of interest.

Finally, a spectrum depicting the linearity, noise floor and clock feedthrough is given in Fig. 16 for a 1-V_{p-p} differential output signal. Digital clock feedthrough at 30 MHz is visible at the 500-μV_{rms} level. Notice that there is no detectable oscillator feedthrough at 15 MHz. Physically separating the master and slave circuits in the layout helped to minimize clock feedthrough. Additionally, the master and slave used separate power supply rails to eliminate common impedance coupling.

VII. CONCLUSIONS

A fifth-order 15-MHz transconductance–capacitance continuous-time filter chip with on-chip tuning system has been demonstrated. The performance of this self-contained device exceeds the requirements for many of today's hard disk-drive read channels. Considerably higher frequency of operation can be achieved if power dissipation is increased and if a Q-control loop is used to control the effect of high-order nondominant poles.

ACKNOWLEDGMENT

The author thanks J. Sonntag, V. Gopinathan, K. Nagaraj, W. M. Snelgrove, and Y. Tsividis for useful discussions. The layout work of J. Barner, J. Clemente, and M. Tarsia is greatly appreciated.

REFERENCES

[1] M. Banu and Y. Tsividis, "An elliptic continuous-time CMOS filter with on-chip automatic tuning," *IEEE J. Solid-State Circuits*, vol. SC-20, no. 6, pp. 1114–1121, Dec. 1985.
[2] C. Chiou and R. Schaumann, "Design and performance of a fully integrated bipolar 10.7 MHz analog bandpass filter," *IEEE Trans. Circuits Syst.*, vol. CAS-33, no. 2, pp. 116–124, Feb. 1986.
[3] V. Gopinathan, Y. Tsividis, K.-S. Tan, and R. Hester, "Design considerations for high-frequency continuous-time filters and implementation of an anti-aliasing filter for digital video," *IEEE J. Solid-State Circuits*, vol. 25, no. 6, pp. 1368–1378, Dec. 1990.
[4] H. Khorramabadi and P. R. Gray, "High-frequency CMOS continuous-time filters," *IEEE J. Solid-State Circuits*, vol. SC-19, no. 6, pp. 939–948, Dec. 1984.
[5] F. Krummenacher and N. Joehl, "A 4-MHz CMOS continuous-time filter with on-chip automatic tuning," *IEEE J. Solid-State Circuits*, vol. 23, no. 3, pp. 750–758, June 1988.
[6] K. W. Moulding, J. R. Quartly, P. J. Rankin, R. S. Thompson, and G. A. Wilson, "Gyrator video filter IC with automatic tuning," *IEEE J. Solid-State Circuits*, vol. SC-15, no. 6, pp. 963–968, Dec. 1980.
[7] K. S. Tan and P. R. Gray, "Fully integrated analog filters using bipolar FET technology," *IEEE J. Solid-State Circuits*, vol. SC-13, no. 6, pp. 814–821, Dec. 1978.
[8] Y. Tsividis, M. Banu, and J. Khoury, "Continuous-time MOSFET-C filters in VLSI," *IEEE J. Solid-State Circuits*, vol. SC-21, no. 1, pp. 15–30, Feb. 1986; also *IEEE Trans. Circuits Syst.*, vol. CAS-33, no. 2, pp. 125–140, Feb. 1986.
[9] D. Senderowicz, D. Hodges, and P. Gray, "An NMOS integrated vector-locked loop," in *Proc. IEEE Int. Symp. Circuits Syst.*, May 1982, pp. 1164–1167.
[10] G. A. De Veirman and R. G. Yamasaki, "Fully-integrated 5 to 15 MHz programmable bipolar Bessel lowpass filter," in *Proc. IEEE Int. Symp. Circuits Syst.*, May 1–3, 1990, pp. 1155–1158.
[11] O. Wing, "Ladder network analysis by signal flow graph application to analog computer programming," *IRE Trans. Circuit Theory*, vol. CT-3, pp. 289–294, Dec. 1956.
[12] Y. Tsividis, Z. Czarnul, and S-C Fang, "MOS transconductors and integrators with high linearity," *Electron. Lett.*, vol. 22, pp. 245–246, Feb. 1986.
[13] J. N. Babanezhad and R. Gregorian, "A programmable gain/loss circuit," *IEEE J. Solid-State Circuits*, vol. SC-22, no. 6, pp. 1082–1090, Dec. 1987.
[14] J. L. Sonntag and T. R. Viswanathan, "CMOS bandgap voltage reference apparatus and method," U.S. Patent 4 848 684, July 18, 1989.
[15] J. Khoury and Y. Tsividis, "Analysis and compensation of high frequency effects in integrated MOSFET-C continuous-time filters," *IEEE Trans. Circuits Syst.*, vol. CAS-34, no. 8, pp. 862–875, Aug. 1987.
[16] Y. Tsividis, "Self-tuned filters," *Electron. Lett.*, vol. 17, no. 12, pp. 406–407, June 1981.
[17] T. R. Viswanathan, S. Murtuza, V. Syed, J. Berry, and M. Staszel, "Switched-capacitor-frequency control loop," *IEEE J. Solid-State Circuits*, vol. SC-17, no. 4, pp. 775–778, Aug. 1982.
[18] A. Gelb and W. Vander Velde, *Multiple-Input Describing Functions and Nonlinear System Design*. New York: McGraw-Hill, 1968.
[19] A. Rodgriguez-Vazquez, B. Linares-Barrance, J. Huertas, and E. Sanchez-Sinencio, "On the design of voltage-controlled sinusoidal oscillators using OTA's," *IEEE Trans. Circuits Syst.*, vol. 37, no. 2, pp. 198–211, Feb. 1990.
[20] B. Linares-Barrance, A. Rodriguez-Vazquez, E. Sanchez-Sinencio, and J. Huertas, "CMOS OTA-C high-frequency sinusoidal oscillators," *IEEE J. Solid-State Circuits*, vol. 26, no. 2, pp. 160–165, Feb. 1991.
[21] J. Scott et al., "A 16 Mb/s data detector and timing recovery circuit for token ring LAN," in *ISSCC Dig. Tech. Papers* (New York), Feb. 1989, pp. 150–151.

Monolithic 10 - 30 MHz Tunable Bipolar Bessel Lowpass Filter

Geert A. De Veirman and Richard G. Yamasaki

Silicon Systems Inc.
14351 Myford Road
Tustin, CA 92680

Abstract

This paper describes a fully-differential bipolar monolithic 7th-order Bessel transconductance-capacitor (g_m-C) lowpass filter with a cut-off frequency (f_c) tunable between 10 and 30 MHz. The filter has matched normal and differentiated outputs. Programmable equalization up to 15 dB at f_c is also provided. Total harmonic distortion at 1.5 V_{pp} output signal is less than 1%. Nominal power consumption from a single 5 V supply is 200 mW.

Introduction

Disk drive and video applications require MHz frequency filters with accurately controllable and often tunable magnitude response as well as constant group delay characteristics. At these high frequencies, the continuous-time filtering approach is the only alternative. It is well known that monolithic continuous-time filters suffer severely from poor absolute component tolerances and high sensitivities to excess phase effects caused by unavoidable parasitics. Transconductance-capacitor (g_m-C) filters have emerged as the generally preferred synthesis method. Until very recently [1], however, reliable industrial application has been very limited. This paper describes a commercial 10 - 30 MHz 7th-order g_m-C Bessel filter optimized for use in the read channel of disk drives utilizing constant density recording techniques and data rates up to 48 MBit/s. Both normal and differentiated lowpass outputs are provided. Pulse slimming can be achieved through user programmable equalization up to 15 dB at f_c. The filter was implemented in an advanced oxide isolated bipolar process.

Transconductance Element

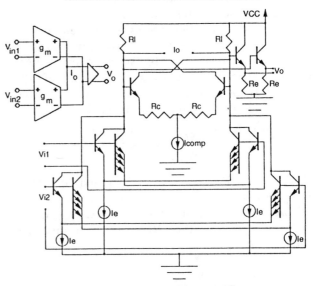

Figure 1: Dual Input Transconductance
a) Circuit Symbol b)Transistor Schematic

Figure 1 shows a simplified transistor schematic and circuit symbol for the dual input transconductance element which is the primary filter building block. The hyperbolic I-V transfer characteristics of the bipolar transistors in both input stages can be linearized by parallel connecting two emitter-coupled pairs with respective 1:4 and 4:1 transistor emitter ratios, and adding their output currents [2-4]. Compared to a single matched differential pair, the linear input range for 1% THD is increased threefold (96 mV$_{pp}$). The current i_0 can be expressed as

$$i_o = 0.64 \frac{I_e}{V_T} (V_{i1} + V_{i2}) \qquad (1)$$

where $V_T = kT/q$ is the thermal voltage. Hence,

Reprinted from *IEEE Proc. ISCAS*, pp. 1444–1447, 1991.

$$g_m = \frac{i_o}{V_{i1}} = \frac{i_o}{V_{i2}} = 0.64 \frac{I_e}{V_T} \qquad (2)$$

which is 64% of the transconductance of a single matched pair with equal power dissipation (i.e. tail current $2I_e$).

Contrary to the common practice of using PNP current sources as active loads, we have chosen to use a simple resistive load. As such, the need for a common-mode stabilization circuit in this fully-differential realization is avoided. DC bias constraints, however, allow only load resistors of the order of a few kΩ, which would result in a far from ideal transconductance element. The solution relies in the inclusion of an output conductance cancellation circuit (or negative resistor) to boost the transconductance's AC output resistance. Elementary analysis of the differential AC conductance at the current output node of the circuit in figure 1 yields

$$G_o = \frac{1}{R_o} \approx -\frac{1}{2}\frac{g_{mc}G_c}{g_{mc} + G_c} + \frac{1}{2}G_l + \frac{1}{2}G_b + \frac{I_e}{V_A} \quad (3)$$

where $G_c = 1/R_c$, $g_{mc} = I_{comp}/2V_T$, and $G_l = 1/R_l$. $G_b = 1/R_b$, the input conductance of the emitter follower buffers is negligibly small. V_A is the Early voltage of the NPN input transistors. Consequently,

$$R_{pos} = 2 R_l \| (\frac{V_A}{I_e}) \qquad (4)$$

while

$$R_{neg} = -2\{R_c + (\frac{2V_T}{I_{comp}})\} \qquad (5)$$

i.e. the negative series combination of $2R_c$ and $2/g_{mc}$. By nominally choosing $R_c = R_l - 2V_T/I_{comp}$, the differential AC output resistance equals

$$R_o = \frac{V_A}{I_e} \qquad (6)$$

which, although process dependent, is typically of the order of several hundred kΩ. G_o is therefore about two orders of magnitude smaller than the g_m values used in this design. Combined with the excellent transconductance phase behavior thanks to the absence of internal high-impedance nodes, this suffices to maintain the accuracy of the (relatively low) biquad pole quality factors within the boundaries set by the tight group delay spec.

On-chip Q control can thus be avoided.

First- and Second-Order Building Blocks

Figures 2 and 3 respectively show the first-order g_m-C lowpass and highpass circuits. Each circuit uses one dual input transconductance cell.

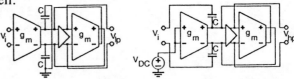

Figure 2: First-Order Lowpass   Figure 3: First-Order Highpass

The transfer functions are given by

$$\frac{V_{lp}}{V_i} = \frac{g_m}{g_m + sC} \qquad \frac{V_{hp}}{V_i} = \frac{sC}{g_m + sC} \qquad (7)$$

The group delay of both sections is identical and can be expressed as

$$GDL(\omega) = -\frac{d\varphi(\omega)}{d\omega} = \frac{g_m C}{g_m^2 + \omega^2 C^2} \qquad (8)$$

The fully-differential transconductance-C state-variable biquad building block is given in figure 4. The circuit consists of two capacitively loaded dual input transconductances, resulting in complete symmetry.

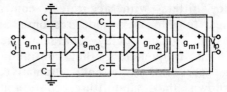

Figure 4: Transconductance-C State-Variable Biquad

Its lowpass transfer function is readily found to be

$$\frac{V_{lp}}{V_i} = \frac{\dfrac{g_{m1}g_{m2}}{C^2}}{s^2 + s\dfrac{g_{m2}}{C} + \dfrac{g_{m1}g_{m2}}{C^2}} \qquad (9)$$

Consequently, the biquad's pole frequency and pole quality factor are

$$\omega_o = \frac{\sqrt{g_{m1}g_{m2}}}{C} \qquad Q_o = \sqrt{\frac{g_{m1}}{g_{m2}}} \qquad (10)$$

Pulse slimming equalization is achieved by lifting the two right most capacitors from ground and feeding the input signal forward through an inverting variable gain amplifier, thus realizing two programmable magnitude, opposite sign zeros on the real axis. The biquad/equalizer circuit is shown in figure 5.

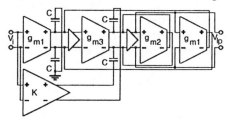

Figure 5: Lowpass Biquad and Programmable Equalizer

Elementary circuit analysis yields

$$\frac{V_{lp}}{V_i} = \frac{-Ks^2 + \frac{g_{m1}g_{m2}}{C^2}}{s^2 + s\frac{g_{m2}}{C} + \frac{g_{m1}g_{m2}}{C^2}} \quad (11)$$

Since with $s = j\omega$ in Eq. (11), the numerator remains real, the biquad's group delay is only a function of the denominator polynomial and therefore independent of the amount of equalization. The group delay can be expressed as

$$GDL(\omega) = \frac{\frac{g_{m2}}{C}[\omega^2 + \frac{g_{m1}g_{m2}}{C^2}]}{[-\omega^2 + \frac{g_{m1}g_{m2}}{C^2}]^2 + [\omega\frac{g_{m2}}{C}]^2} \quad (12)$$

7th-Order Filter

Figure 6 shows a block diagram of the 7th-order Bessel filter. An input attenuator and output amplifiers are included so that output signals up to 1.5 V_{pp} can be processed. The complete normal transfer function has a DC gain of 2 (6 dB). Normal and differentiated gains are equal at 2/3 f_c. The normalized pole frequencies (i.e. for $\omega_c = 2\pi f_c = 1$) and Q's of the filter sections are listed in Table 1.

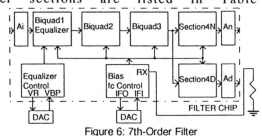

Figure 6: 7th-Order Filter

	Pole Frequency	Pole Q
Biquad1	1.71736	0.53236
Biquad2	1.82348	0.66083
Biquad3	2.05069	1.12625
Section4	1.68536	

Table 1: 7th-Order Bessel Filter

The filter pole frequency f_c is a function of g_m/C. From Eq. (2), transconductance temperature stability can be achieved by making the bias current I_e proportional to absolute temperature (PTAT). A precision V_T-based reference circuit is included on chip. By connecting a single accurate external resistor from this reference output to ground, a PTAT current IFO is generated. This current can either be fed back into the chip directly (i.e. IFO = IFI), or be used as reference current for a current output DAC as shown in figure 6. Even with the resulting accurate and temperature stable transconductances, f_c would still be subject to uncontrollable process variations in absolute capacitor values. The latter are accounted for by an initial frequency trim during wafer probe. The desired amount of equalization is programmed by a voltage input VBP. A fixed amount of boost can be set by a resistor divider network from an on-chip bandgap reference VR to VBP and ground. Alternatively, VBP can be supplied from a voltage output DAC as shown in figure 6.

Experimental Results

Figures 7 and 8 show the normal lowpass magnitude responses for cut-off frequencies between 10 and 30 MHz, both without and with maximum boost. Corresponding plots for the differentiated lowpass output are found in figures 9 and 10. f_c accuracy is ± 5% over temperature (0 - 70 °C) and ± 10% supply variation. The filter's group delay response for three different pole frequencies is illustrated in figures 11 - 13. Over the tuning range, less than 2% group delay variation up to f_c was observed over temperature and supply as well as different wafer lots. Apart from a small difference in absolute value, group delay is practically independent of the programmable equalization. The approximately 1 ns delay difference between normal and differentiated outputs is intentional and results from a different amplifier design in both paths. Key measurement results are summarized in table 2.

Conclusions

A monolithic 10 - 30 MHz g_m-C Bessel filter was presented. A very close match between the filter response and its ideal prototype over temperature, supply, and process variations was demonstrated. This makes the design a viable candidate for reliable, wide-scale commercial application.

Temperature Range	0 - 70 °C
Supply Voltage	5V ± 10%
Filter Cutoff Frequency	10 - 30 MHz
Cutoff Frequency Accuracy	± 5 %
Output Voltage with 1 % THD	≥ 1.5 V_{PP} (530 mV RMS)
Normal Output Noise BW = 100 MHz, R_S = 50 Ω	2.5 mV RMS
Differentiated Output Noise BW = 100 MHz, R_S = 50 Ω	5.5 mV RMS
Dynamic Range with ≤ 1% THD Normal Output	46.5 dB
Dynamic Range with ≤ 1% THD Differentiated Output	40 dB
Maximum Equalization at f_c	15 dB
Equalization Boost Accuracy at Maximum Boost	± 1 dB
Delay Variation up to f_c f_c = 10 - 30 MHz	< 2 %
Nominal Power Dissipation	200 mW

Table 2: Key Measurement Results

Acknowledgements

The contributions of mask designers Gary Thomas, Steve Coughlin and Dennis Garcia, and engineering associates Tom Gibson and Ronald Morris are gratefully acknowledged.

References

[1] G. A. De Veirman and R. G. Yamasaki, "Fully-Integrated 5 to 15 MHz Programmable Bipolar Bessel Lowpass Filter," in Proceedings ISCAS, pp. 1155-1158, 1990.

[2] D. W. H. Calder, "Audio Frequency Gyrator Filters for an Integrated Radio Paging Receiver," IEE Conference, Mobile Radio Systems and Techniques, No. 238, 1984.

[3] M. Koyama, H. Tanimoto, and S. Mizoguchi, "A 10.7 MHz Continuous-Time Bandpass Filter Bipolar IC," in Proceedings CICC, 1989.

[4] G. A. De Veirman and R. G. Yamasaki, "2 - 10 MHz Programmable Continuous-Time .05° Equiripple Linear Phase Filter," in Proceedings CICC, 1991.

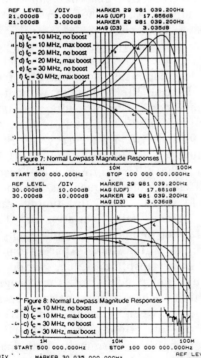

Figure 7: Normal Lowpass Magnitude Responses

Figure 8: Normal Lowpass Magnitude Responses

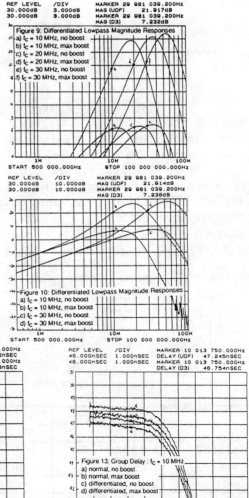

Figure 9: Differentiated Lowpass Magnitude Responses

Figure 10: Differentiated Lowpass Magnitude Responses

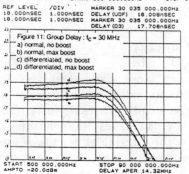

Figure 11: Group Delay : f_c = 30 MHz
a) normal, no boost
b) normal, max boost
c) differentiated, no boost
d) differentiated, max boost

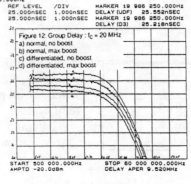

Figure 12: Group Delay : f_c = 20 MHz
a) normal, no boost
b) normal, max boost
c) differentiated, no boost
d) differentiated, max boost

Figure 13: Group Delay : f_c = 10 MHz
a) normal, no boost
b) normal, max boost
c) differentiated, no boost
d) differentiated, max boost

Paper 7-D.3

A 20MHz 6th Order BiCMOS Programmable Filter Using Parasitic-Insensitive Integrators

C. A. Laber

Micro Linear Corporation,
2092 Concourse Drive
San Jose, California, 95131

P. R. Gray

Department of EECS
University of California
Berkeley, California, 94720

Abstract- **A fast parasitic-insensitive continuous-time filter that uses an active integrating-capacitor is described. Techniques for excess-phase nulling and Gm-setting independent of supply and temperature are also described. This 20MHz, 5V equalizer has 0.24% of THD with 2Vp-p signals and is built in 1.5m/4GHz BiCMOS.**

I. INTRODUCTION

Previous high-frequency continuous-time filters have principally utilized a basic integrator consisting of a transconductance stage driving a passive integrating capacitor[1,3]. These approaches are susceptible to frequency response variations due to the parasitic capacitances associated with the parasitic-sensitive output nodes of the integrator. This type of transconductance stage also often has low open-circuit voltage gain, resulting in limited practical Q range in the filter. The use of an active parasitic-insensitive integrator, has generally been avoided in these filters because of the additional excess phase that the amplifier contributes.

This paper describes a continuous-time filter based on a transconductor[1,2] and a high-speed parasitic-free active integrator, allowing complete independence of the filter response from interconnect parasitics and a very wide range of realizable filter Q. A unique approach to canceling the excess phase contributed by the high-speed BiCMOS amplifier allows this filter to achieve reproducible responses at 20Mhz filter bandwidth in a 1.5μ/4GHz BiCMOS process. This contrasts with the fastest passive integrating-capacitor filter yet reported at 27MHz using a 13GHz bipolar technology[3]. This active integrator incorporates a novel technique for setting the transconductor Gm value as a function of an external precision resistor, independent of temperature, supply, in conjunction with a wafer-sort trim technique to adjust capacitor process tolerances. This eliminates the need for an on-chip PLL for tuning. Finally, experimental results are presented from a disk-drive equalizer integrated circuit.

II. DESCRIPTION

A. Transconductor and integrator: Fig.1 shows the simplified schematic of the BiCMOS differential transconductor and integrator. Transistors M1 and M2 operate in the triode region with a drain voltage equal to V_{DS}. This is set by the cascode bipolar devices Q1 and Q2 whose base bias V_{BB} is determined by the Gm setting circuit described below. Thus, M1, Q1, M2 and Q2 define the value of $Gm = \mu C_{ox}(W/L)V_{DS}$[1]. The values of V_{GS}-V_{TH} and V_{DS} are chosen to satisfy a set of constraints such as signal swing, the amplifier output range, power consumption and operating frequency. A feedback loop, not shown, sets the common-mode voltage at A and B.

B. Phase-shift cancellation: The key problem in making the parasitic-insensitive active-integrator approach practical is the design of the pole-cancellation circuitry. In principle, the location of the higher-order poles of the integrator are a known function of the active element values, and the goal of the cancellation circuitry is to generate a control voltage V_{BC} that tracks the process, temperature and supply variations using replica concepts so that first-order cancellation is achieved. In Fig.1, M7 and M8 operating in the triode region produce a zero at $\tau_Z = (C_I/gds_{M7})[1-(gds_{M7}/gm_2)]$, where gm_2 is the transconductance of the amplifier in Fig.2. This zero is adjusted to cancel the non-dominant pole associated with amplifier gm_2 at $\tau_2 = [C_1 + C_2 + (C_1 C_2/C_I)]/gm_2$, where C_1 and C_2 are the capacitances at nodes A, B and the amplifier outputs. Thus, after the initial process trim is performed, the remaining problem is that of supply and temperature tracking between gds_{M7} and gm_2. This is done by connecting M7 and M8 to the V_{GS} of a diode connected transistor with a current $I_{MB} = A\mu C_{ox}T^2$[4]. Then, if A, B, C, and D are constants, V_{GS}-$V_{TH} = BT$, and $gds = C\mu C_{ox}T$. Also, since this current is used to bias the amplifier then, $gm_2 = qI_C/kT = Dgds$.

C. Gm setting: The value of Gm is set by forcing a known current $k_T \Delta i$ to flow through the transconductor, when a known voltage Δv is forced at its inputs. This is shown in Fig. 3. The current $k_T \Delta i$ is generated on-chip, and the voltage by an external resistor biased by Δi. Thus,

Reprinted from *Digest of Technical Papers, Int. Symp. on VLSI Circuits*, Seattle, pp. 104–105, 1992.

$Gm=k_T\Delta i/\Delta v=k_T\Delta i/(R_{ext}\Delta i)=k_T/R_{ext}.$ The process tolerance on capacitance value is removed by an initial trim to adjust k_T. In Fig. 3, M1, Q1, M2, and Q2 make up the transconductor. $\Delta i/2$ is forced to flow from A to B. A1 forces voltage V_{CM} at A and B while producing I_{CM} through M3 and M4, and A2 keeps A and B at the same potential while finding the V_{DS} that satisfies the given Δi and Δv.

III. FILTER/EQUALIZER

A. Description: The filter IC shown in Fig. 4 consists of a 6th order Bessel lowpass and a 2nd order cosine-equalizer stage. It is made up of 3 biquads with lowpass and bandpass outputs. Both outputs of the last stage are available with matched group-delay characteristics. The corner frequency is digitally programmable through the digital serial interface to 64 values over a 4 to 1 range. This is done by changing the integrating capacitor. Also, slimming equalization is done by programming two real symmetric-zeros. This boosts the high-frequency response in 32 steps from 0 to 10dB.

B. Experimental results: The die-photo is shown in Fig. 5. Fig. 6 shows measured slimming and corner-frequency equalization. The temperature and supply responses show a very small deviation from Fig. 6. Table I summarizes the performance of the filter.

REFERENCES

[1] R. Castello, et. al., "A Very Linear BiCMOS Transconductor for High-Frequency Filtering Applications" Proc. of ISCAS 1990, pp. 1364-1367.

[2] S. L. Wong, "Novel Drain-Biased Transconductance Building Blocks for Continuous-Time Filter Applications" Electronics Letters, VOL. 25 No. 2 Jan 1989, pp. 100-101.

[3] G. A. De Veirman, et. al., "A 27 MHz Programmable Bipolar 0.05° Equiripple Linear-Phase Lowpass Filter", ISSCC Dig. of Technical Papers, Feb. 1992.

[4] C. Laber, et. al., "Design Considerations for a High-Performance 3μ CMOS Analog Standard Cell Library", IEEE JSSC, VOL. SC-22, No.2 pp. 181,189 April 1987.

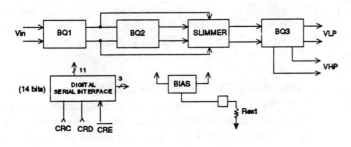

Fig. 4. Filter/Equalizer Block Diagram

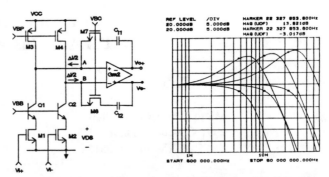

Fig. 1. Transconductor & Integrator   Fig. 6. Measured Amplitude Response

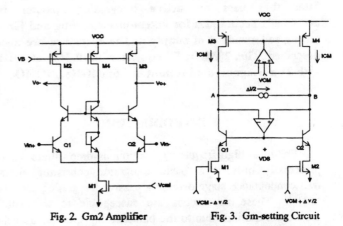

Fig. 2. Gm2 Amplifier   Fig. 3. Gm-setting Circuit

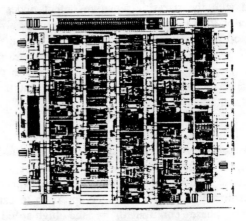

Fig. 5. Filter/Equalizer Die Photo

Filter Cutoff Frequency	4.7 to 20.3MHz
Accuracy	+5%
Equalization Range	0 to 10dB
Accuracy	+0.5dB
THD with 2Vp-p	0.24%
Noise (BW=100MHz; R_s=50Ω)	2.0mV$_{RMS}$
Power Supply	+5V
Temperature Range	0 - 70°C
Power Dissipation	350mW
Standby Power	7.5mW
Technology	1.5μ/4GHz BiCMOS

TABLE I: TYPICAL PERFORMANCE PARAMETERS

Author Index

Subject Index

Editors' Biographies

Yannis P. Tsividis was born in Greece in 1946. He received the B.S. degree from the University of Minnesota, Minneapolis, in 1972, and the M.S. and Ph.D. degrees from the University of California, Berkeley, in 1973 and 1976 respectively.

He was an engineer with Motorola Semiconductor in 1974, and a Member of the Technical Staff at AT & T Bell Laboratories, Murray Hill, in 1977, where he remained part-time as a resident visitor until 1987. In 1976, he joined the Department of Electrical Engineering at Columbia University, New York, where he became a Full Professor in 1984. He has been a Professor in the Division of Computer Science at the National Technical University of Athens, Greece, since 1990. His research interests include integrated circuits, circuit theory, signal processing, and solid-state device modeling.

Dr. Tsividis is the author of *Operation and Modeling of the MOS Transistor* (McGraw-Hill Book Company, 1987), and co-editor and co-author of *Design of MOS VLSI Circuits for Telecommunications* (Prentice-Hall, Inc., 1985). He is a member of the Administrative Committee of the IEEE Circuits and Systems Society, and was a member of the United Nations Advisory Committee on Science and Technology for Development from 1985 to 1987. He is the recipient of the 1984 IEEE W. R. G. Baker Best Paper Award and the 1986 European Solid-State Circuits Conference Best Paper Award, as well as co-recipient of the 1987 IEEE Circuits and Systems Society Darlington Best Paper Award. He has also received the Great Teacher Award at Columbia University.

J. O. Voorman was born in The Netherlands in 1941. He received the M.S. degree in electrical engineering from the Delft University of Technology, Delft, The Netherlands, in 1964. In 1965, he joined the Philips Research Laboratories, Eindhoven, The Netherlands, where he became engaged in research on network theory and filters (RC-active filters, ceramic resonator filters, optical interference filters, gyrator integration, and applications). He received the Ph.D. degree in mathematics and physics from the University of Nijmegen, Nijmegen, The Netherlands, in 1977 on a thesis, "The gyrator as a monolithic circuit in electronic systems."

Later he was involved in the integration of a one-chip viewdata modem and an all-analog adaptive echo canceller for short echoes in teletext. Via activities on ghost-cancelling for TV, 3-level exponential modulation and transparent transmitters, his activities were shifted to contribute to the development of new biCMOS processes, having the potential to be the best for the implementation of complex high-performance mixed analog-digital systems. As an example, the design of a 10–14 bit video analog-to-digital converter based on sigma-delta modulation was studied (in the context of ESPRIT PROJECT 412, biCMOS).

As chief scientist, he is now involved in the design of many analog filters, circuits, and filter applications in bipolar, biCMOS and CMOS IC processes, for low and high frequencies, and together with many different product groups within Philips.